THE MINIATURE SCORE SERIES

THE SYMPHONIES OF HAYDN SCHUBERT AND MOZART IN SCORE

Edited and devised by

ALBERT E. WIER

Malaspina College
DEPARTMENT OF MUSIC

The system of arrow signals and special typographical markings, employed in this work to enable those unacquainted with the art of score reading to follow the instrumental outline and to identify the various themes as they appear and recur, is the subject of a pending application for Letters Patent of the United States owned by Harcourt, Brace and Company, Inc.

HARCOURT, BRACE AND COMPANY
NEW YORK

PREFACE

For the comprehension of orchestral scores, even with the assistance of the system of arrow signals employed in this volume, ability to read instrumental music in both treble and bass clefs is necessary.

It must also be borne in mind that certain wind instruments, such as the clarinet (except the clarinet in C), the French horn (except the horn in C) and the trumpets (except the trumpet in C) are transposing instruments; also that viola and Tenor trombone parts are written in the Alto and Tenor clefs, therefore some knowledge of transposition and of these clefs will be useful.

Four separate pages of miniature score are printed on each large page of this volume. The large page is bisected by horizontal and vertical lines, the miniature pages located numerically as follows:

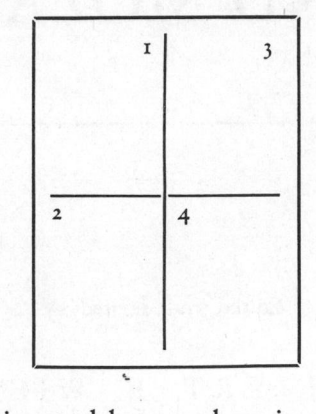

The large pages of this volume are designated by numbers in parentheses at the bottom of the pages; the miniature score pages of each symphony are numbered separately (starting with Page 1) in the upper right and left hand corners.

The opposite page contains a miniature reproduction of two pages from the score of a Haydn symphony. It will be noted that the top page comprises five bars of music with a separate line provided for each instrument, its name being noted before the line. The lower page contains two sections of scoring; this is known as score condensation because all instruments that have no notes to play during the six measures of the first section on the page are omitted, and all instruments that have no notes to play in the seven measures of the second section are omitted. The presence of two or more sections of scoring on one page is always indicated by the mark **//** between each section, and these marks must be carefully observed when reading score.

The system of arrow signals used in this volume will be easily comprehended if its purpose is fully understood before attempting to make use of them. The purpose, starting with the first measure of each symphony, is to indicate the main melodic line as it progresses from instrument to instrument in the wood-wind, brass, string and percussion sections of the orchestra. A practical example of this method of score-reading is given on the opposite page (Page 3).

In addition to the arrow signal system, the various divisions of each symphonic movement, such as **Introduction, Exposition, Development, Recapitulation, Coda, etc.,** are indicated *over* the score; the names and lengths of the various themes, such as **Principal Theme, Subordinate Theme, Concluding Theme, etc.,** are printed *under* the score with a wavy black line to indicate their length.

EXPLANATION OF ARROW SIGNAL SYSTEM

The pages used here for explanatory purposes are taken from the *Allegretto* of the "Military" Symphony by Josef Haydn.

The circled numbers near the arrows are used *only on this page* to aid in clarifying the explanation; they are *not* used elsewhere in the volume.

Arrows Nos. 1 & 2 indicate the appearance of the Principal Theme, Part I in the 1st violins and flute. At the bottom of the page is the name of the theme, the wavy black line indicating its length.

Arrow No. 3 indicates an ascending figure in the violas.

Arrows Nos. 4 & 5 indicate the continuance of the theme in the 1st violins and flute.

Arrows Nos. 6 & 7 indicate the repetition of the Principal Theme in the oboe and clarinet.

The Mark ∥ indicates the separation of the page into two sections of score.

Arrows Nos. 8 & 9 indicate the continuance of the Principal Theme in the oboe and clarinet.

Arrow No. 11 points out a figure in the French horns.

Arrows Nos. 10, 12, & 13 indicate the continuance of the melodic line in the flute, 1st violins and 2nd violins.

SPECIAL NOTE

When two or more arrows are marked in the same measure, it means that the passage is to be found in other instruments at the same time, or that an important counter-theme or special musical figure is being developed. The eye can follow any one of these arrows.

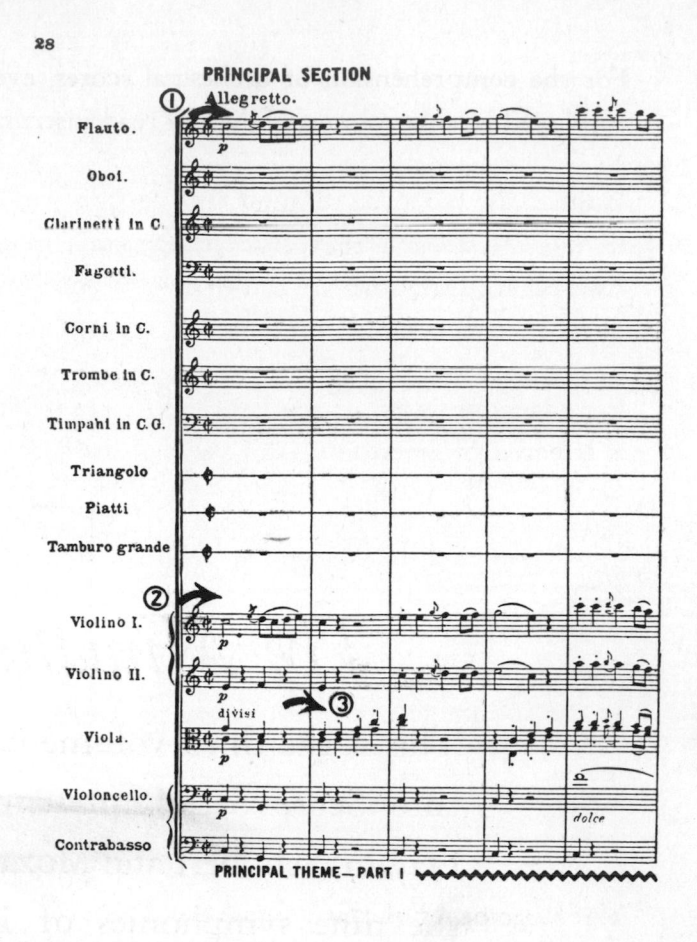

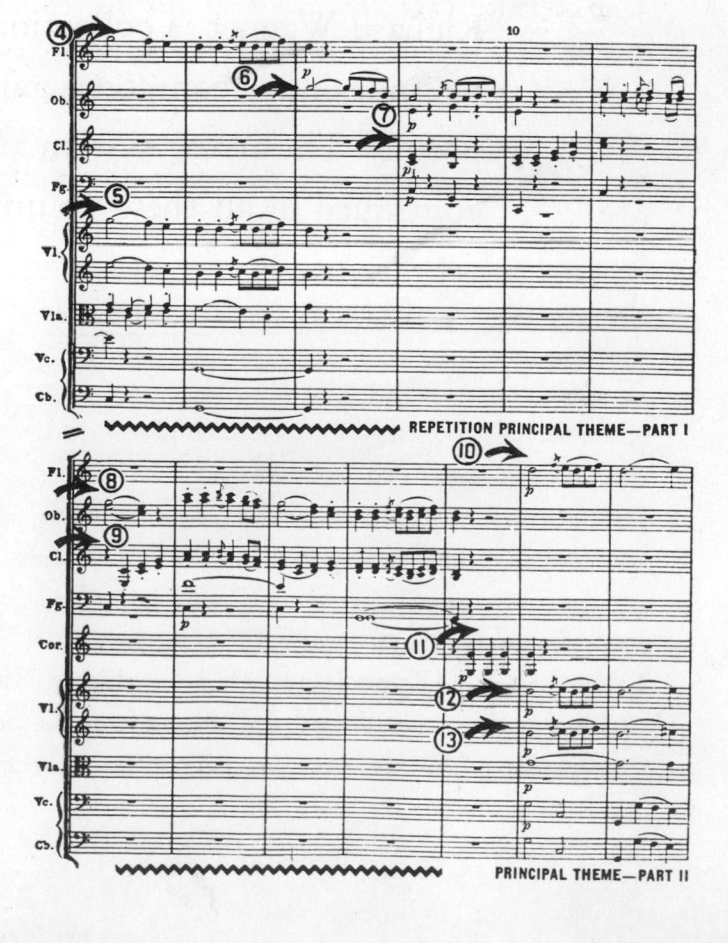

The Miniature Score Series

This is the third volume in the Harcourt, Brace Miniature Score Series, presenting sixteen symphonies by Haydn, Schubert and Mozart. The first volume contains the nine symphonies of Beethoven, the second, four Brahms and three Tschaikowsky symphonies. Future volumes include a book of orchestral excerpts from Richard Wagner, a collection of ten famous symphonies by individual composers, also a volume of symphonic poems. The arrow system (in course of patent) will be continued in all these volumes.

THE EDITOR

INDEX

(5)

HISTORICAL AND CRITICAL COMMENT ON
HAYDN SYMPHONIES

The symphonies of Josef Haydn were scored for the following instruments:.

Flauto (Flute)	*Fl.*	Timpani	*Timp.*
Oboi (Oboes)	*Ob.*	Violini (Violins)	*Vl.*
Clarinetti (Clarinets)	*Cl.*	Viola	*Vla.*
Fagotti (Bassoons)	*Fg.*	Violoncello	*Vc.*
Corni (Horns)	*Cor.*	Contrabasso (Basso)	*Cb. or B.*
Trombe (Trumpets)	*Tbe.*		

These are the names under which the instruments are listed on the first page of each score; the abbreviation used on succeeding pages follows. It will be noted that Haydn did not use trombones and employed clarinets only in the "Clock" and "London" Symphonies.

THE "FAREWELL" SYMPHONY   Page 8

Haydn wrote this symphony in 1772 during the period in which he was conductor of Prince Esterhazy's orchestra. Shortly before conceiving this work, Haydn had asked the Prince for an extended leave of absence, but His Royal Highness, anticipating the arrival of several distinguished guests for whom he wished the orchestra to perform, urged the Maestro to defer what was really a greatly needed vacation. Haydn, not to be put off, elected to reiterate his request in musical form by arranging the instrumentation of the last movement in this symphony so that one by one the players stop, pick up their instruments, turn out the lights on their desks, and walk out of the room, leaving only two violinists to play the last few bars of the movement. History has it that the "Farewell" Symphony accomplished its purpose in gaining the desired leave of absence.

This symphony is recorded by Sir Henry Wood and the London Symphony Orchestra.

THE "OXFORD" SYMPHONY   Page 19

In the period from 1787 to 1790 Haydn composed some of his greatest works, including the six "Russian" string quartets, fifteen piano trios and twelve symphonies for which he received a commission from the "Concert Spirituel", an institution founded in 1725 by Philidor. These symphonies were divided into two sets of six each; one in the second set became known as the "Oxford" Symphony because it was performed in the Sheldonian Theatre on July 8, 1791, when Haydn was awarded the degree of Doctor of Music by Oxford University.

This symphony is recorded by Hans Weisbach and the London Symphony Orchestra.

THE "SURPRISE" SYMPHONY   Page 35

Haydn's first visit to London began on New Year's Day 1791, and was crowned with such success that he remained there until June, 1792. He visited the English metropolis to fulfill a contract with Johann Salomon, an orchestra conductor, to compose six symphonies and conduct them at the piano. The success of the first six was so great that Haydn wrote another series, one of which was the "Surprise" Symphony presented here. It was first played in London on March 23, 1792, and its nickname "Surprise" is derived from the fact that the *Andante* contains an extraordinarily loud drum beat at the conclusion of the first *pianissimo* presentation of the principal theme.

This symphony is recorded by Serge Koussevitzky and the Boston Symphony Orchestra.

THE "SALOMON" SYMPHONY Page 51

This is another of the symphonies composed by Haydn during the visits made to London from 1791 to 1795. The remuneration for these symphonies was as follows: he received $1500 for six symphonies and $1000 for the copyright; $1000 for twenty new compositions to be produced at the same number of concerts, and $1000 guaranteed as the proceeds of a benefit concert. In comparison to the amounts received by Franz Schubert, these figures are apparently very substantial, but it must be remembered that Haydn had to pay all his own traveling expenses and his living expenses while in London.

This symphony is recorded by Hans Weisbach and the London Symphony Orchestra.

THE "MILITARY" SYMPHONY Page 68

Haydn's second visit to London began on February 4, 1794, and ended on August 15, 1795; it is said that on the two visits he made a net profit of about $12,000, sufficient to relieve him of all anxiety of a financial character. The "Military" symphony was one of six written for the second English visit. It was performed in the Spring of 1794, and the nickname is derived from certain characteristics of its second movement such as the employment of several percussion instruments, and the use of an Austrian bugle call in the Coda. It is said that this symphony pleased the King so greatly, in spite of his previously expressed preference for the works of Handel, that Haydn was specially presented to his Majesty by the Prince of Wales.

This symphony is recorded by Hans Knappertsbusch and Symphony Orchestra.

THE "CLOCK" SYMPHONY Page 90

Sir George Grove reports that Haydn himself made the statement that it was not until after his visits to England that he became famous in Germany and Austria. Although this may not be strictly true, it is an undisputed fact that the English people were the first to give him not only recognition of the most flattering character, but also really substantial remuneration. The "Clock" symphony was one of twelve composed for the Salomon concerts in London, and was first performed at the Haymarket Theatre on May 4, 1795. It owes the nickname to the accompaniment figure used in the *Andante* movement, resembling the rhythmic tick-tack of a clock.

This symphony is recorded by Arturo Toscanini and the New York Philharmonic Symphony Orchestra.

THE "LONDON" SYMPHONY Page 106

This symphony is one of the series written by Haydn during his second sojourn in England in 1795; it was first performed at one of the Opera Concerts in London, its nickname being derived naturally in remembrance of this occasion. J. Cuthbert Hadden, in his biography of Haydn, has this to say of the Salomon symphonies: "These, so far as his instrumental music is concerned, are the crowning glory of his life work. They are the ripe fruits of his long experience working upon the example of Mozart, and mark to the full all those qualities of natural geniality, humour, vigor and simple good-heartedness which are the leading characteristics of his style".

This symphony is recorded by John Barbirolli's Orchestra.

"Farewell" Symphony

Allegro assai **EXPOSITION**

Joseph Haydn
1732-1809

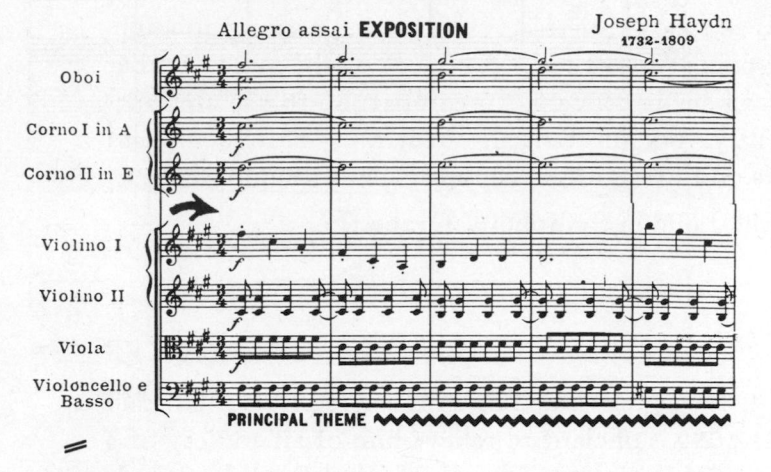

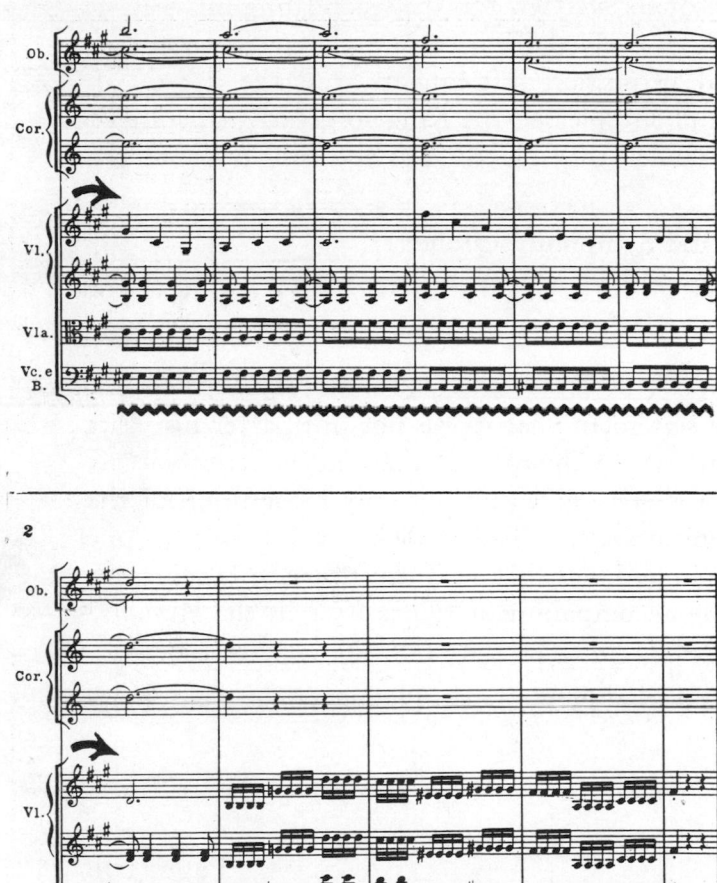

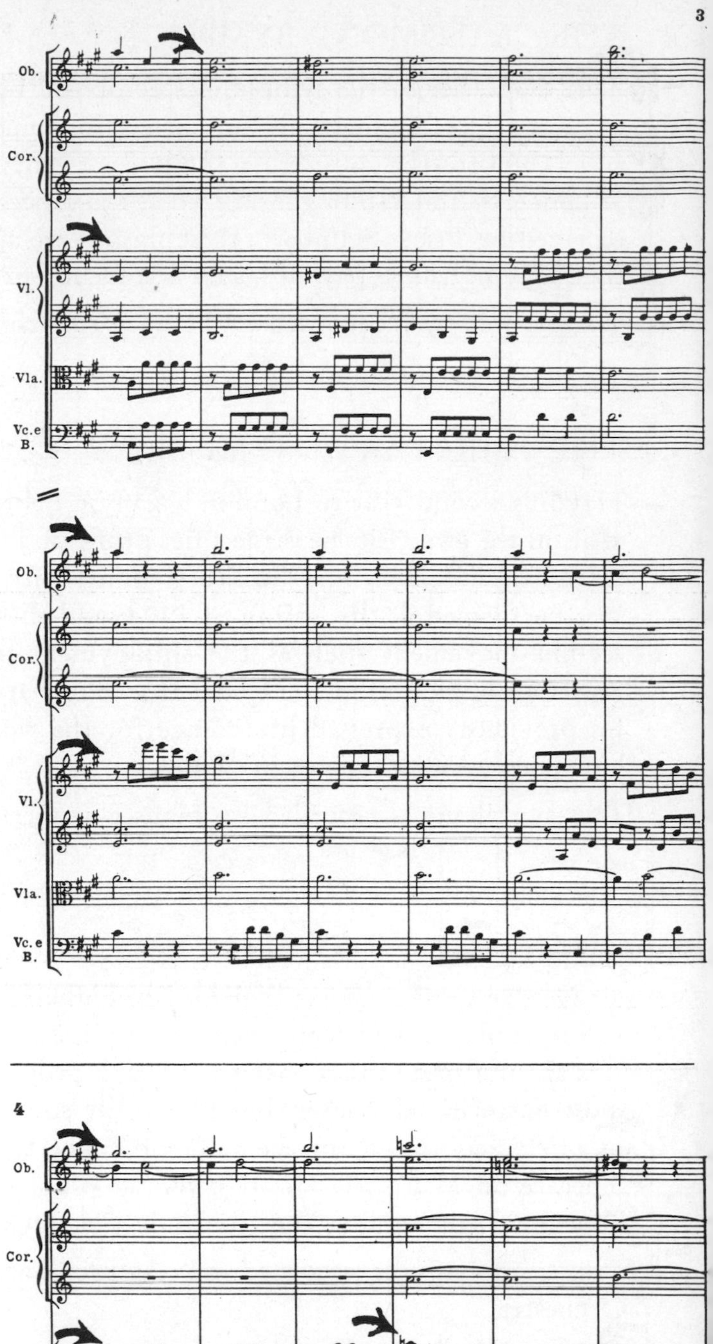

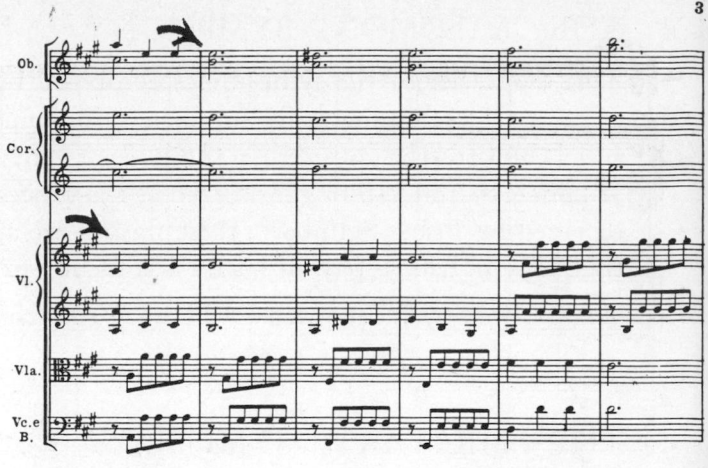

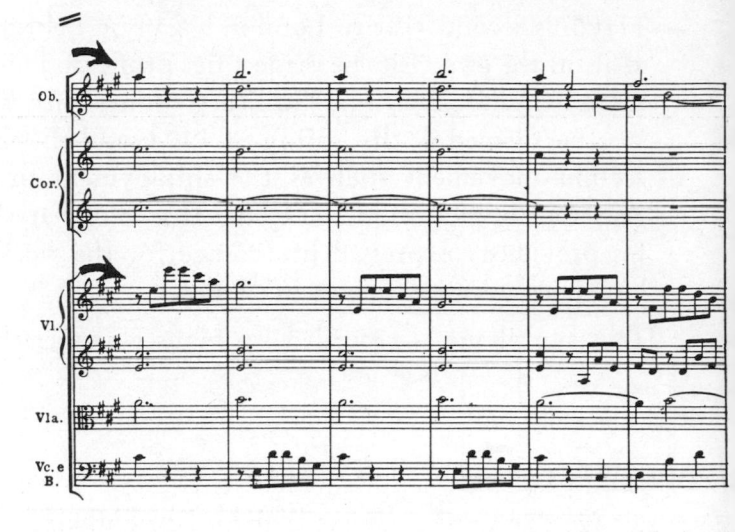

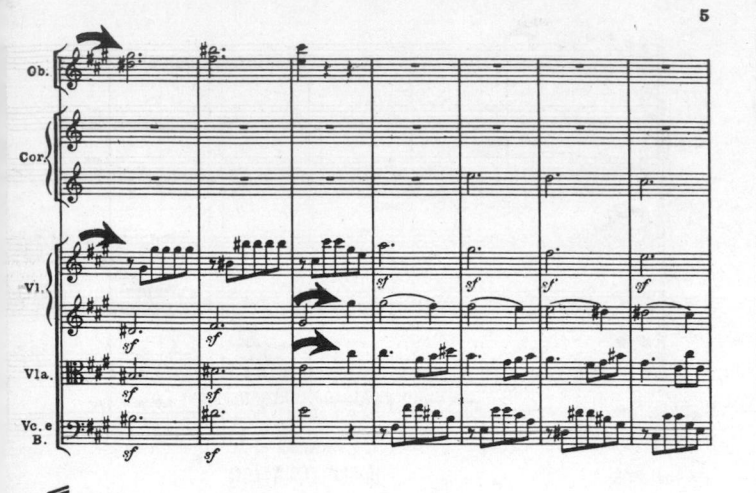

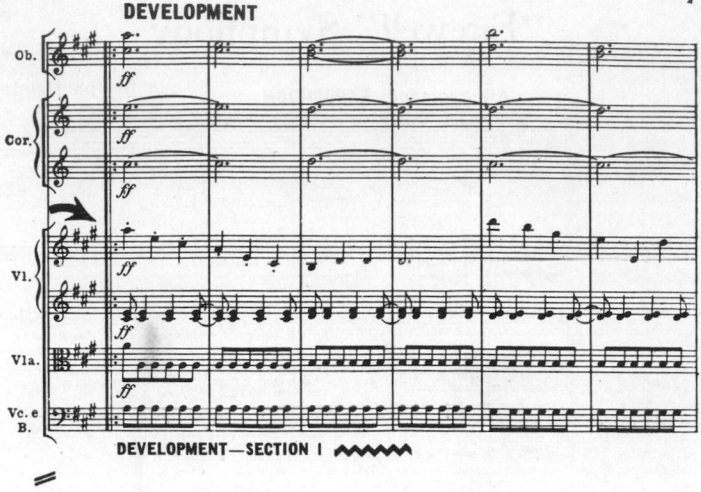

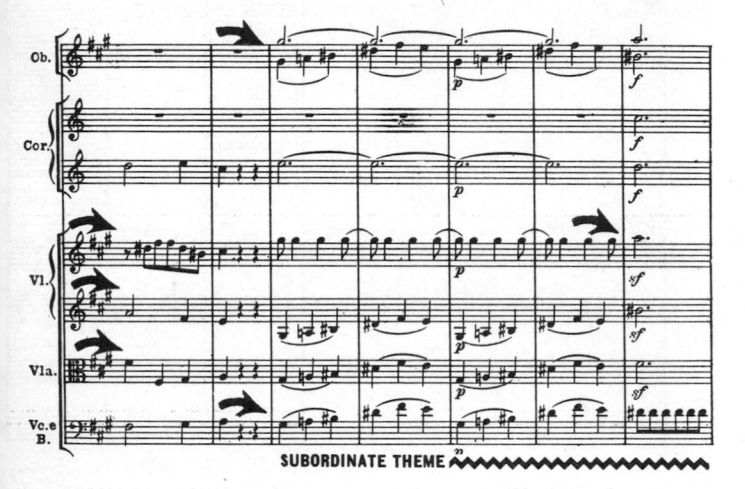

DEVELOPMENT—SECTION I 〰〰

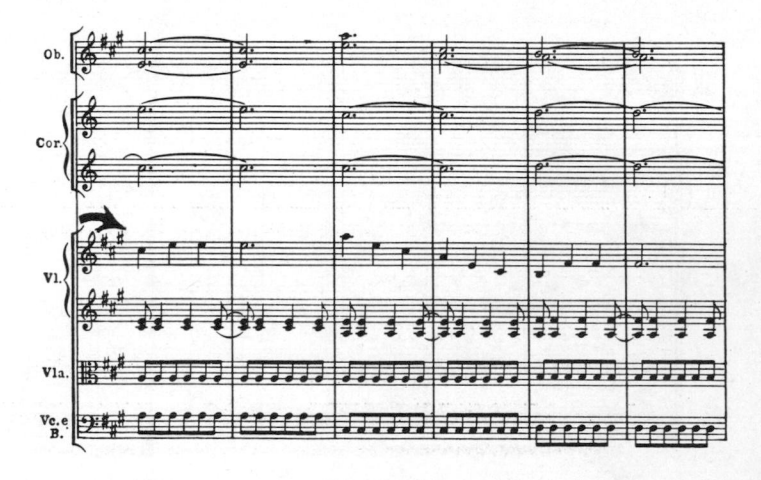

SUBORDINATE THEME 〰〰〰〰〰〰〰〰

8

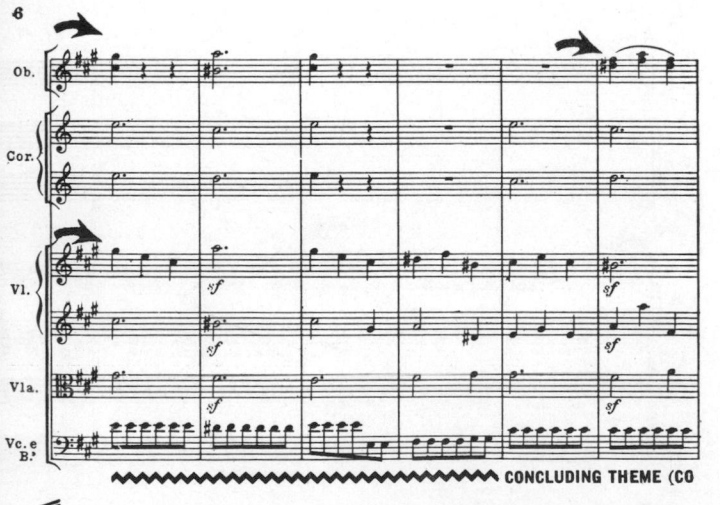

CONCLUDING THEME (CO

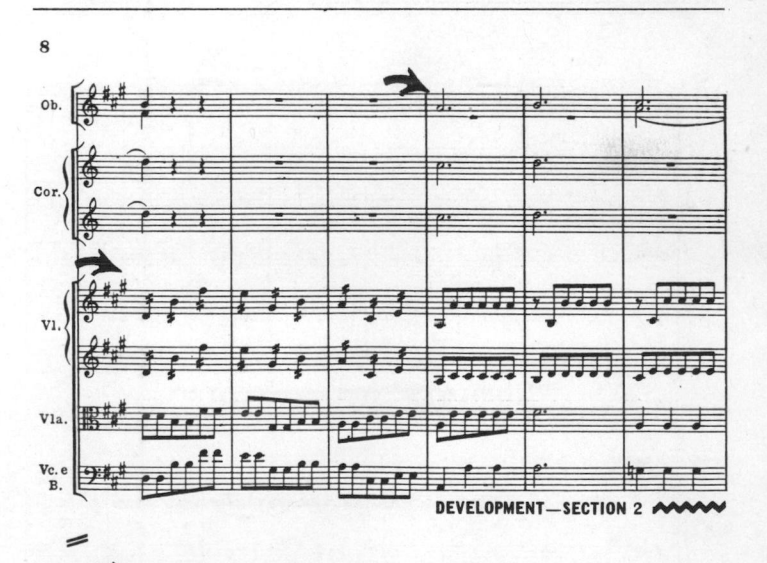

DEVELOPMENT—SECTION 2 〰〰〰

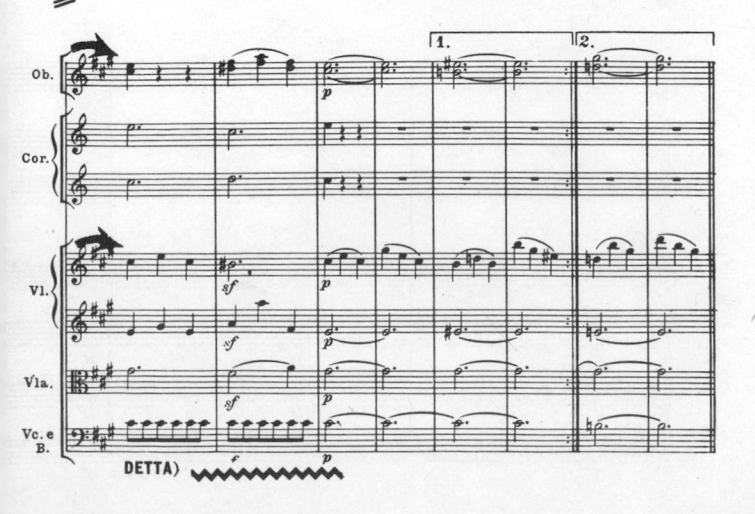

DETTA) 〰〰〰〰〰〰〰

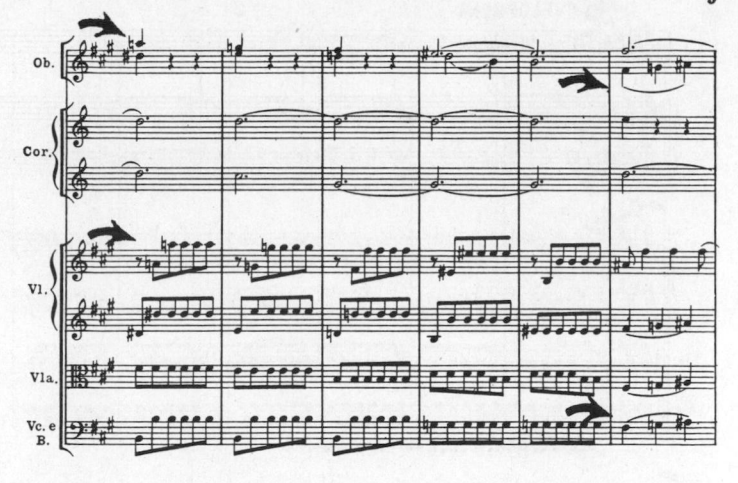

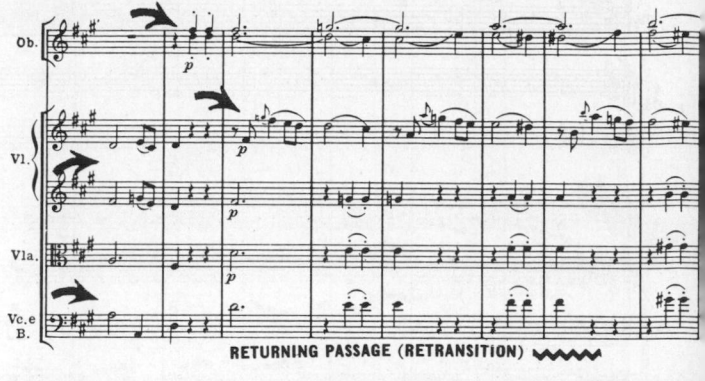

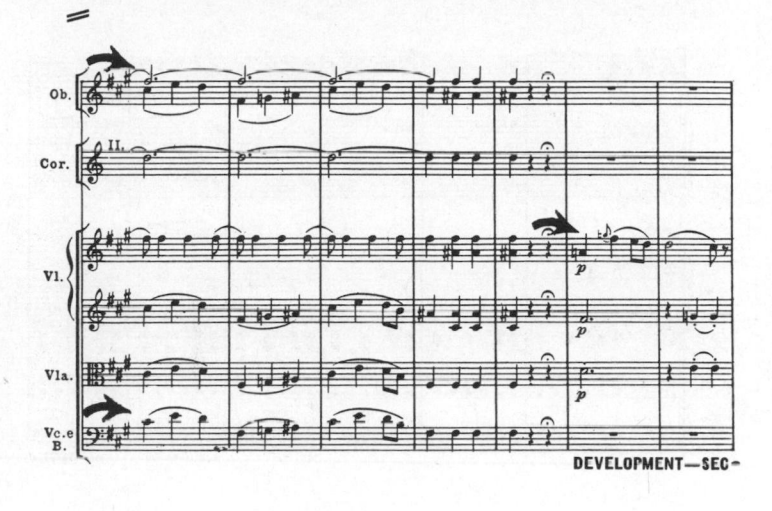

DEVELOPMENT—SEC-

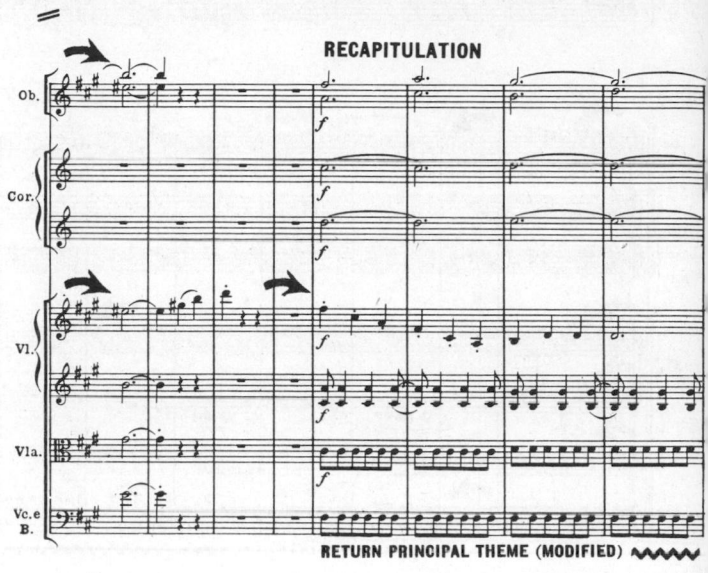

RETURNING PASSAGE (RETRANSITION) 〰〰〰

RECAPITULATION

RETURN PRINCIPAL THEME (MODIFIED) 〰〰〰

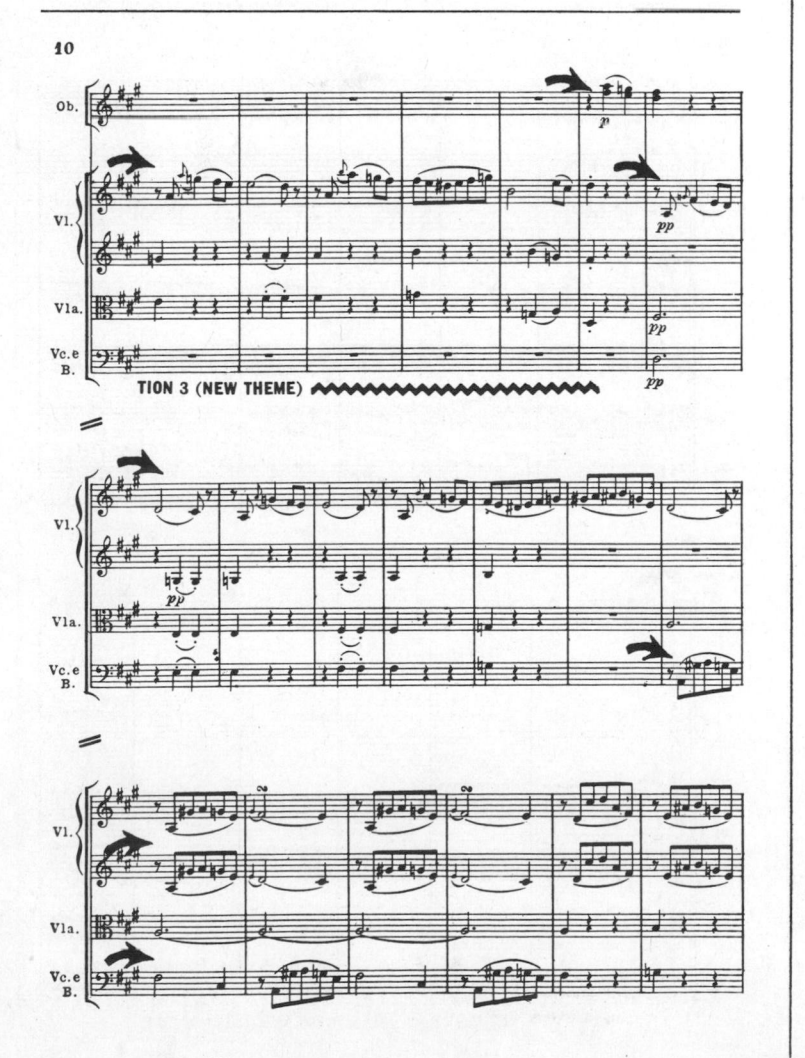

TION 3 (NEW THEME) 〰〰〰〰〰〰〰〰〰〰

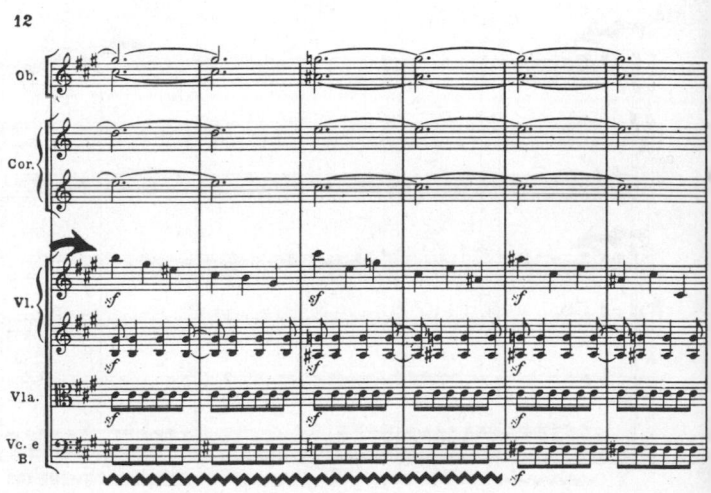

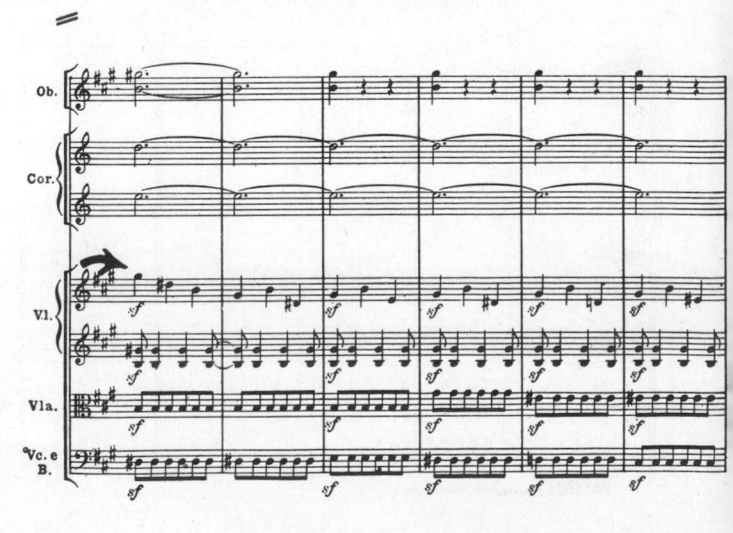

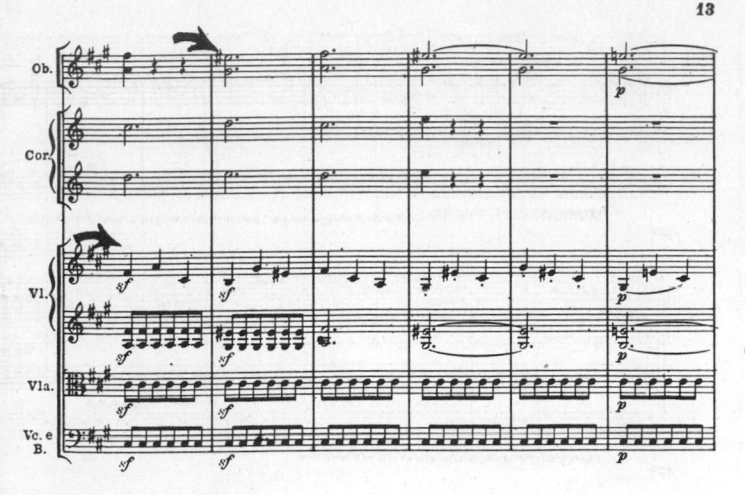

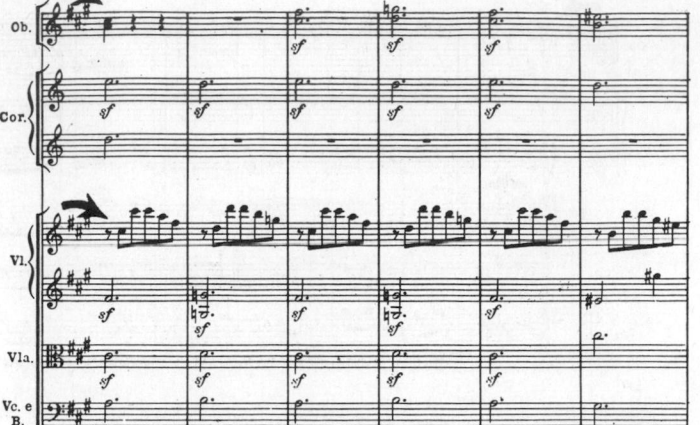

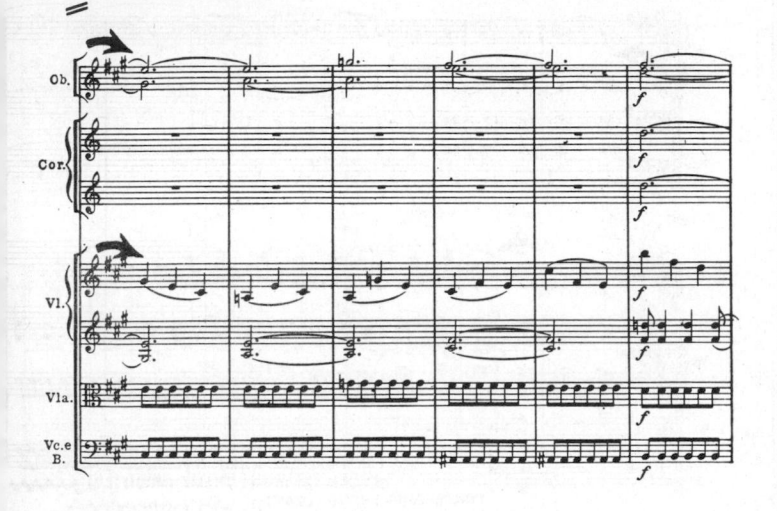

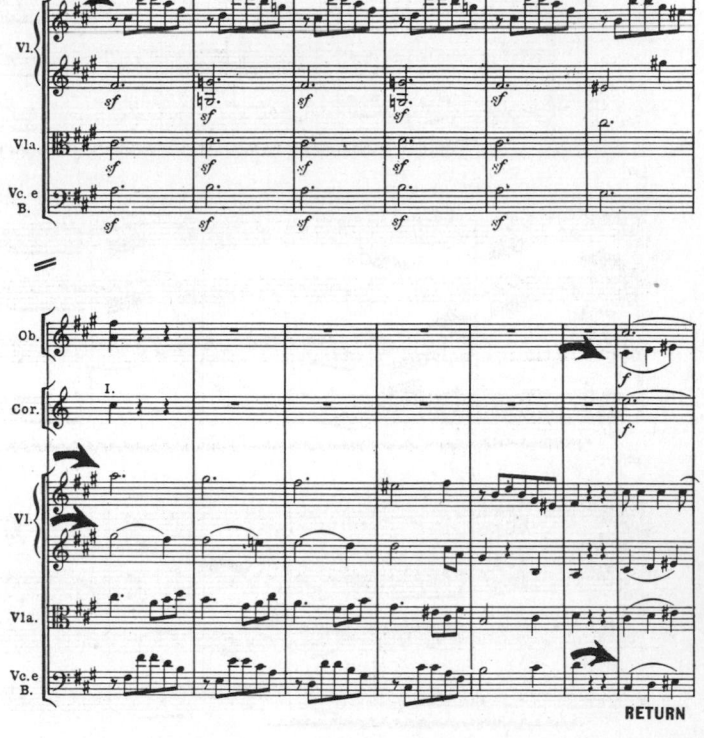

RETURN

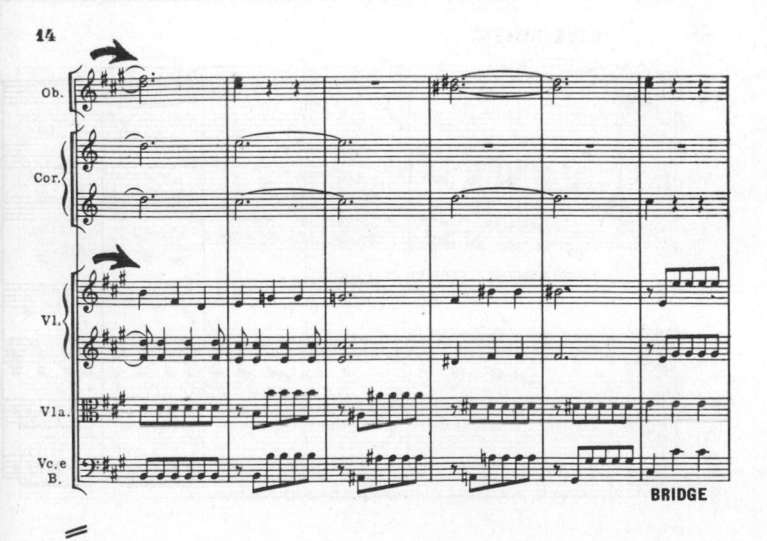

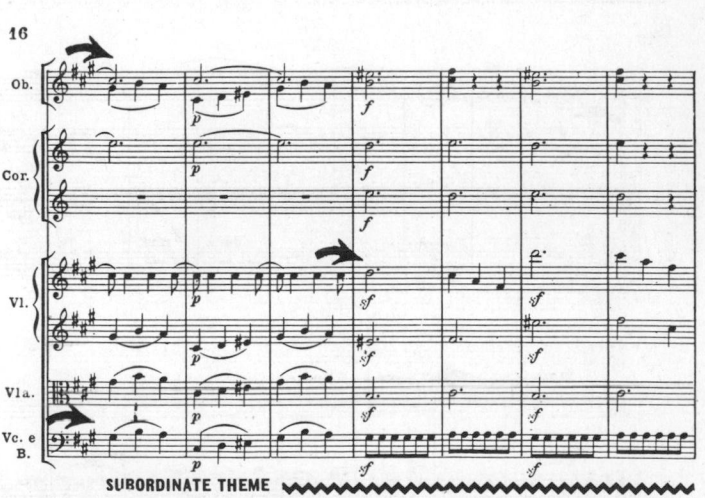

BRIDGE

SUBORDINATE THEME ∿∿∿∿∿∿∿∿∿∿∿∿∿∿∿∿

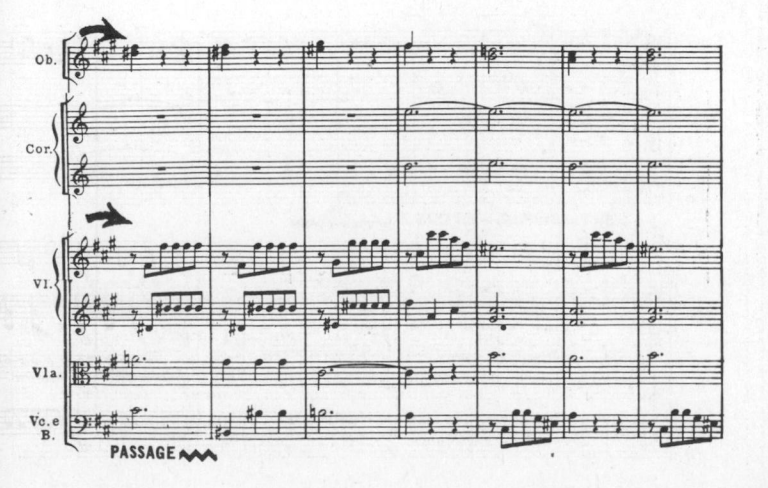

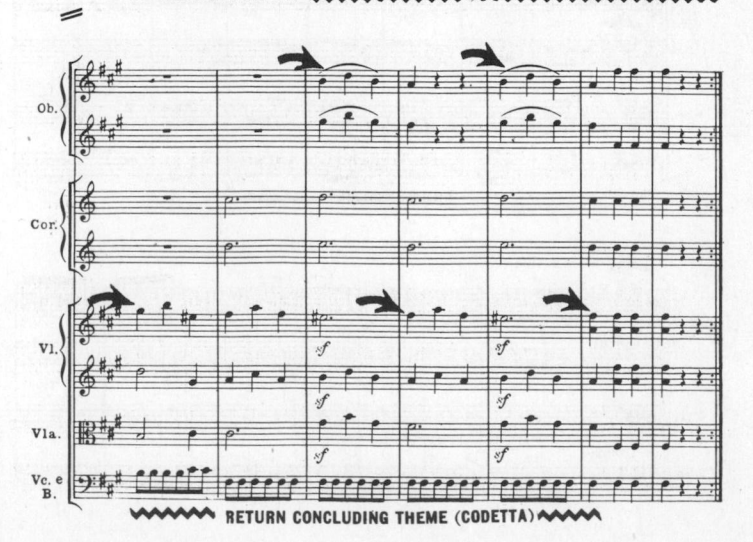

PASSAGE ∿∿∿

∿∿∿∿ **RETURN CONCLUDING THEME (CODETTA)** ∿∿∿∿

17

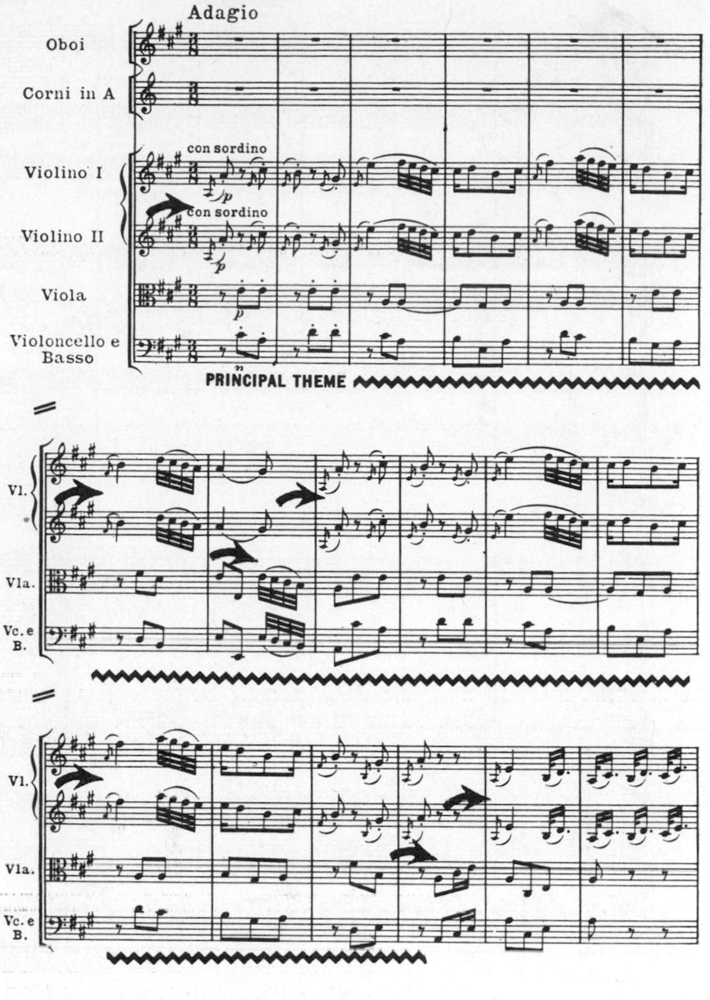
EXPOSITION
Adagio
Oboi
Corni in A
Violino I
con sordino
Violino II
con sordino
Viola
Violoncello e Basso
PRINCIPAL THEME
Vl.
Vla.
Vc. e B.

18

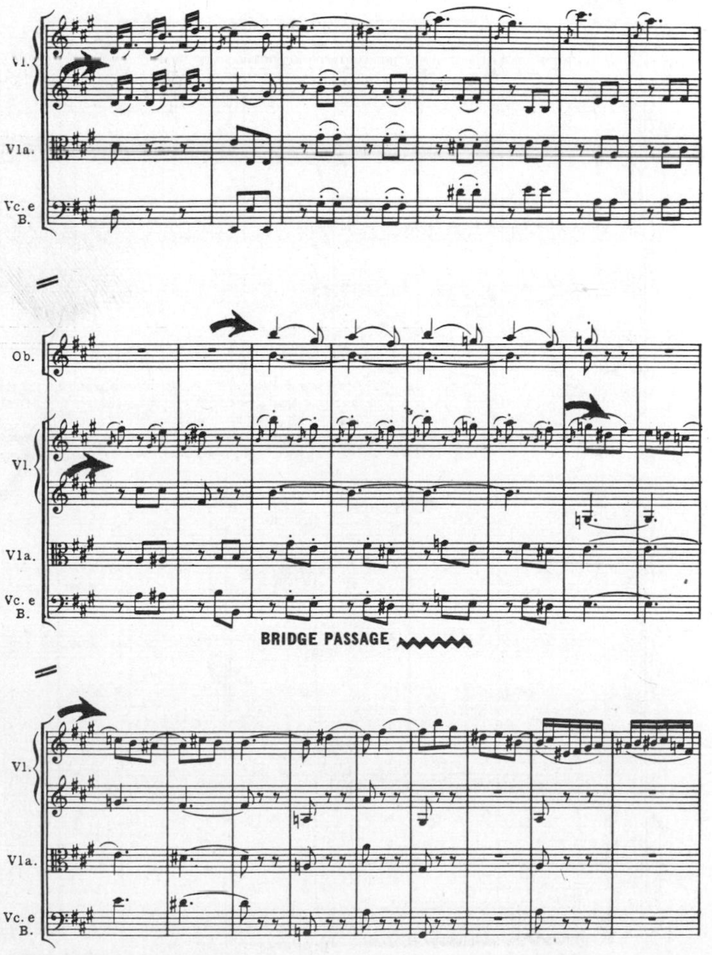
Vl.
Vla.
Vc. e B.
Ob.
BRIDGE PASSAGE

19

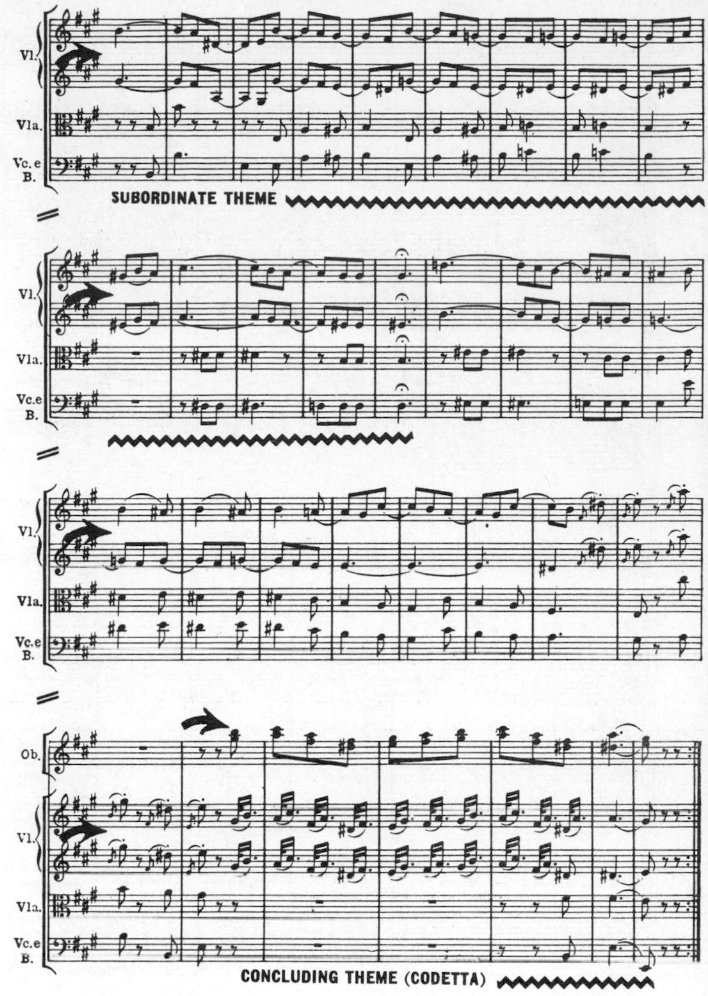
Vl.
Vla.
Vc. e B.
SUBORDINATE THEME
Ob.
CONCLUDING THEME (CODETTA)

20

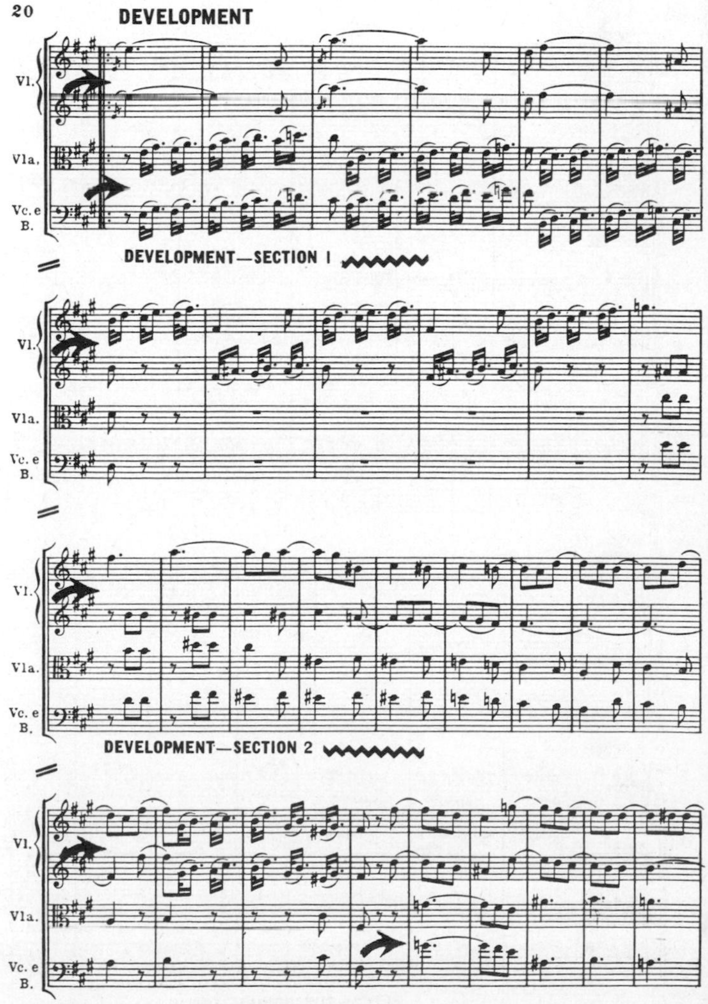
DEVELOPMENT
Vl.
Vla.
Vc. e B.
DEVELOPMENT—SECTION I
DEVELOPMENT—SECTION 2

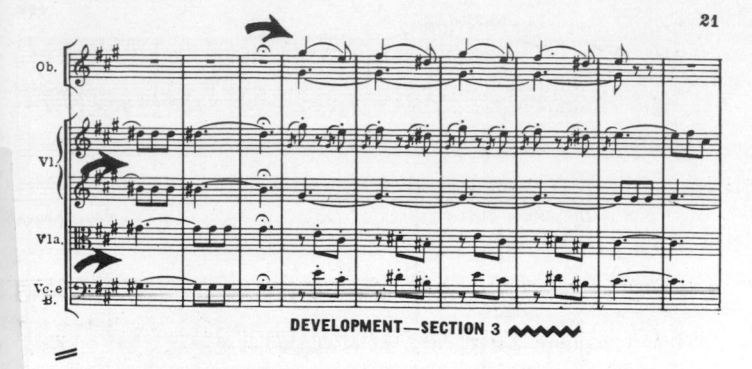

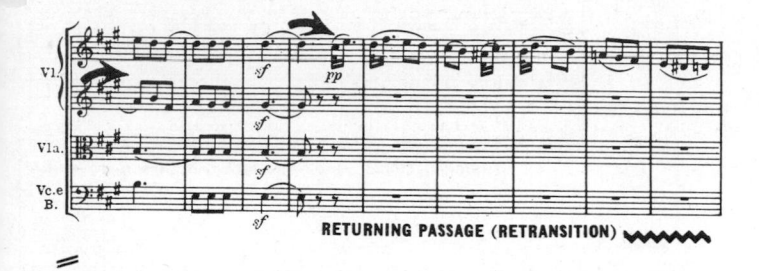

DEVELOPMENT—SECTION 3

RETURNING PASSAGE (RETRANSITION)

RECAPITULATION

RETURN PRINCIPAL THEME

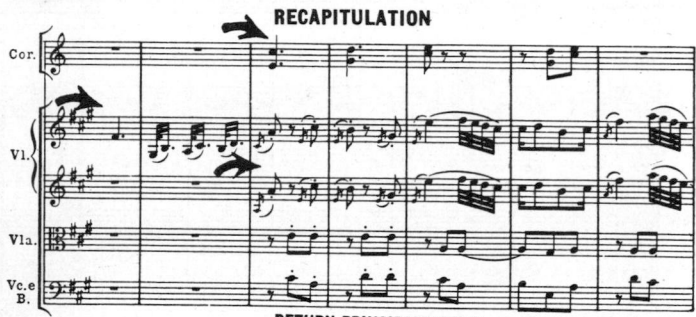

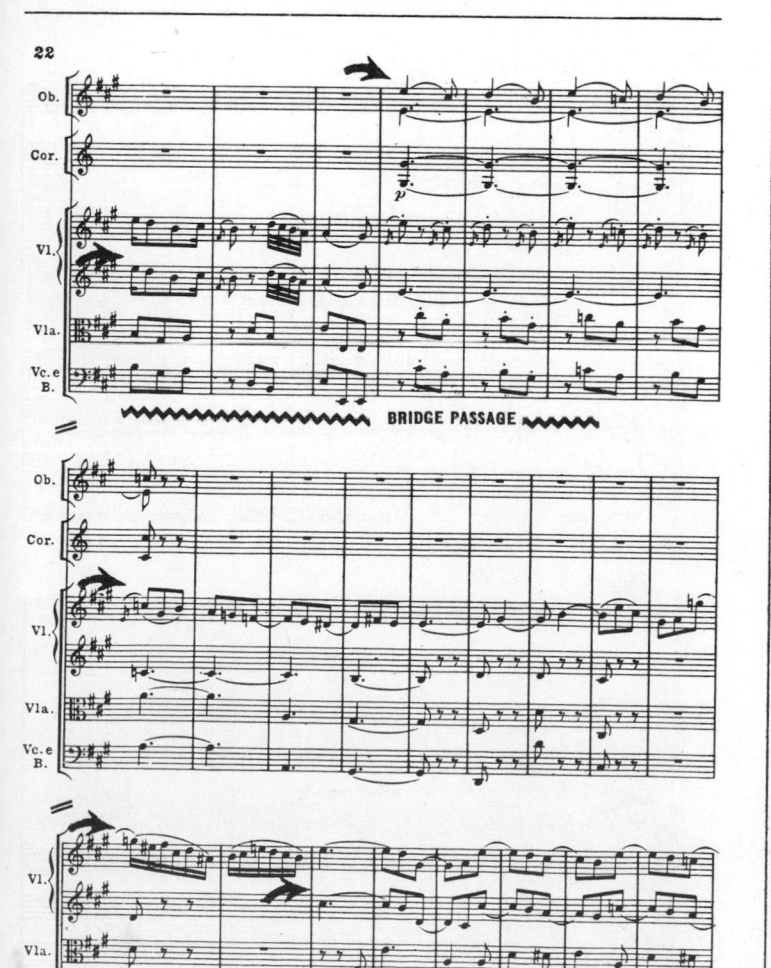

BRIDGE PASSAGE

RETURN SUBORDINATE THEME

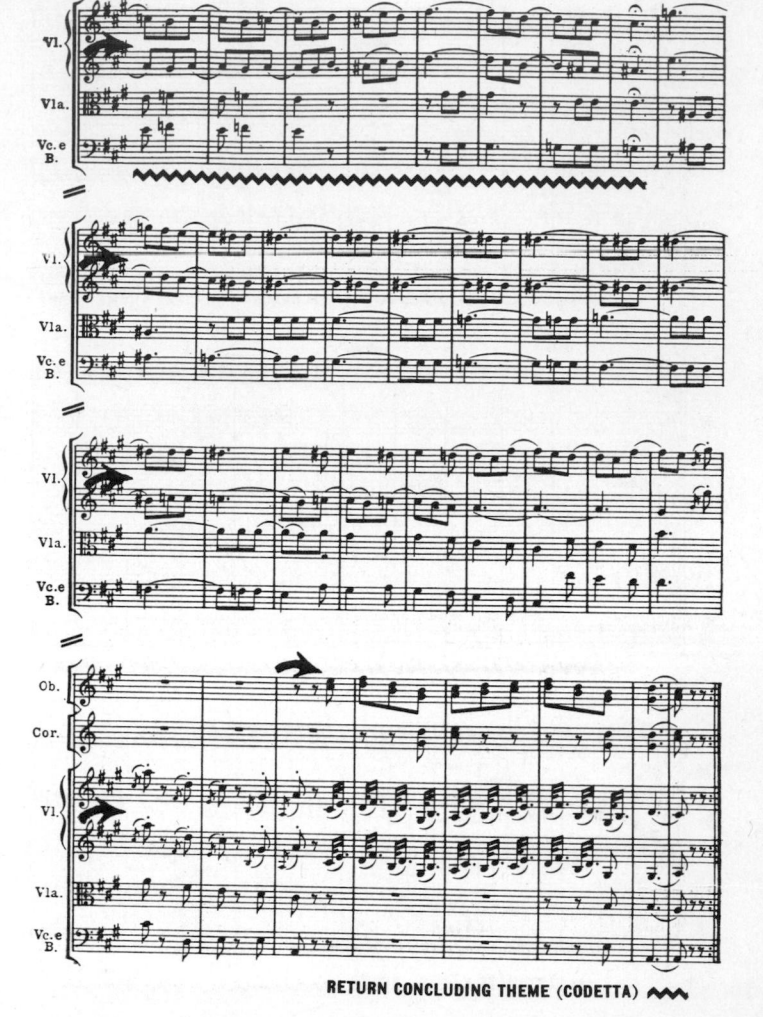

RETURN CONCLUDING THEME (CODETTA)

PRINCIPAL SECTION

Menuetto
Allegretto

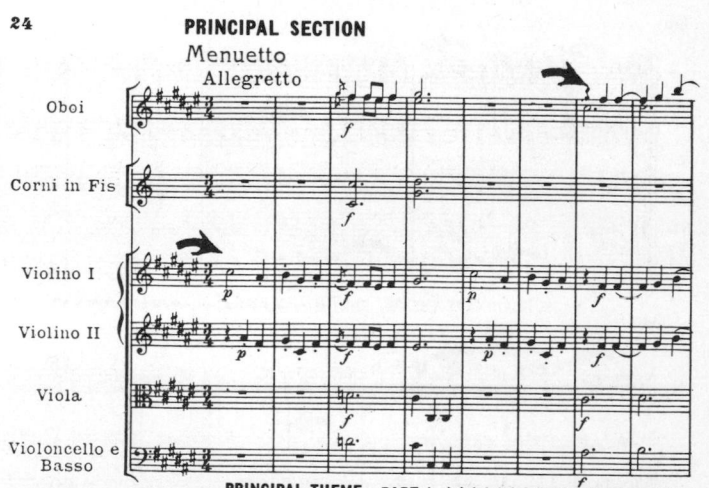

Oboi

Corni in Fis

Violino I

Violino II

Viola

Violoncello e Basso

PRINCIPAL THEME—PART I

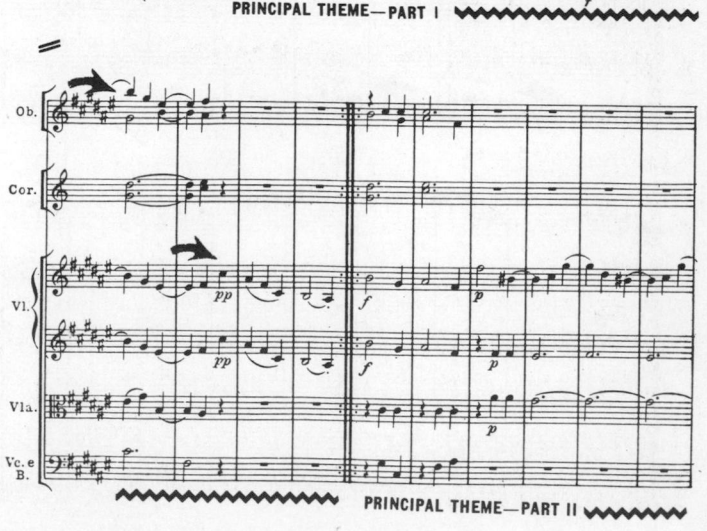

PRINCIPAL THEME—PART II

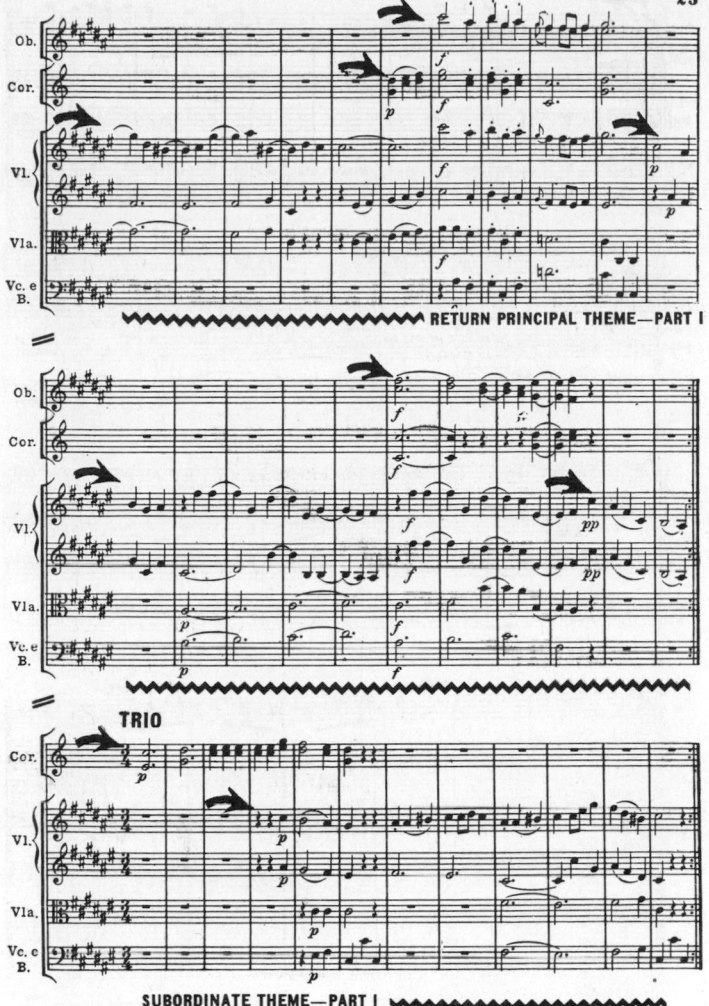

RETURN PRINCIPAL THEME—PART I

TRIO

SUBORDINATE THEME—PART I

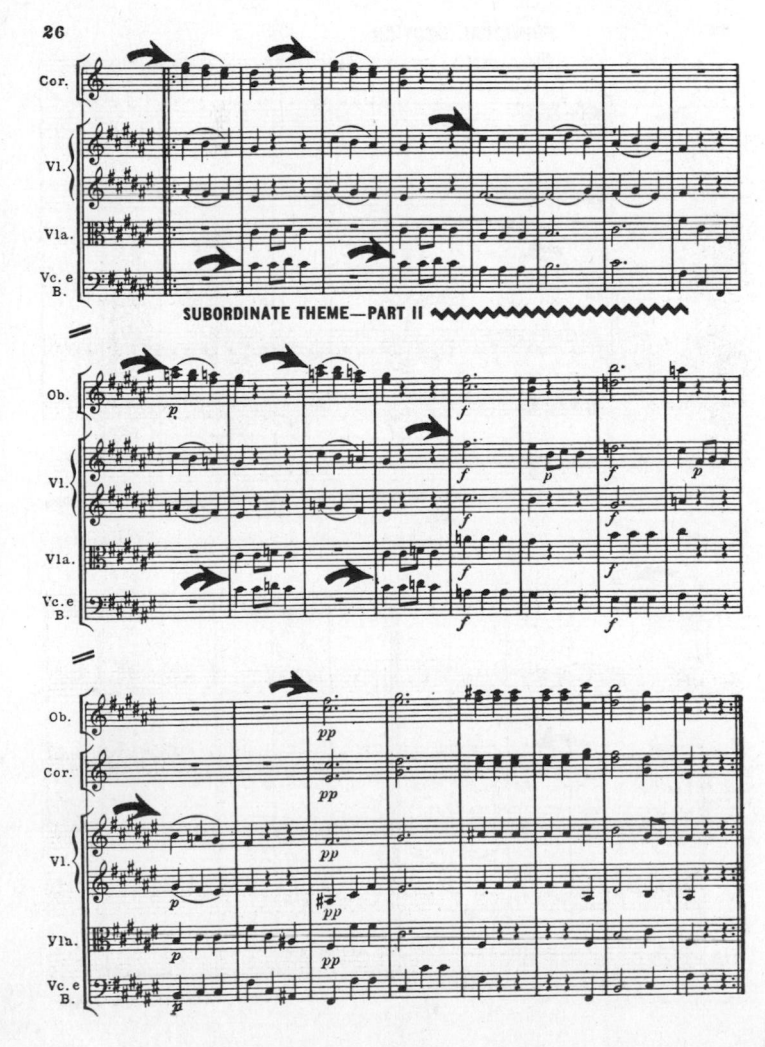

SUBORDINATE THEME—PART II

EXPOSITION
Finale
Presto

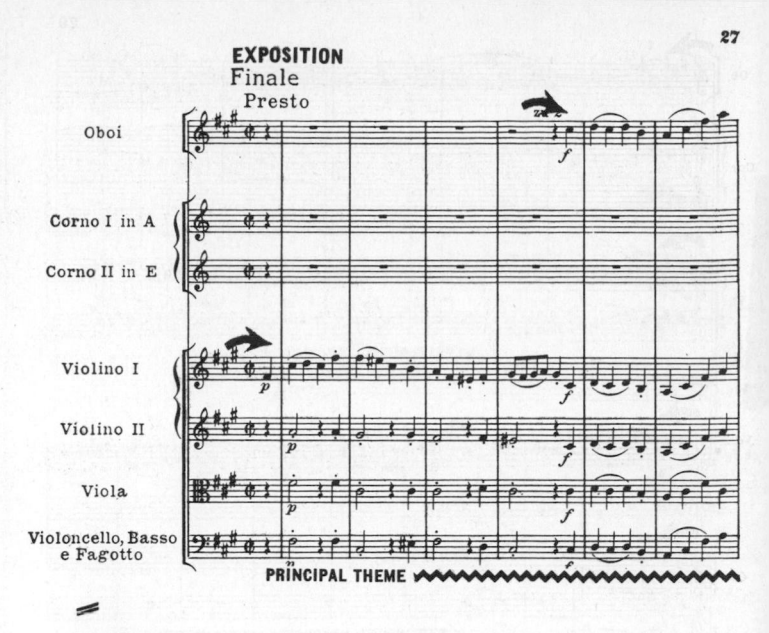

Oboi

Corno I in A

Corno II in E

Violino I

Violino II

Viola

Violoncello, Basso
e Fagotto

PRINCIPAL THEME

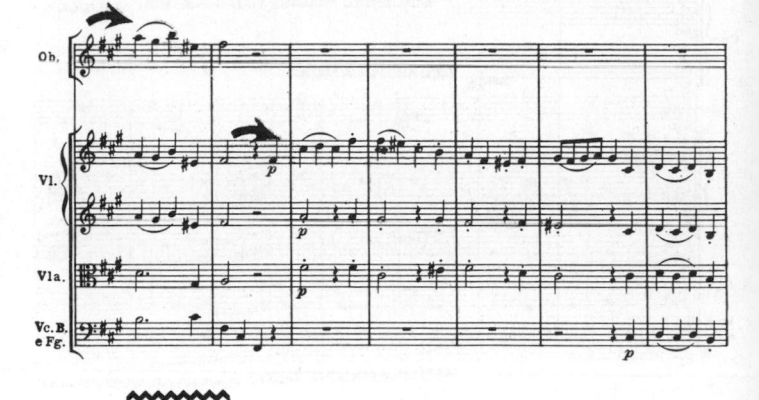

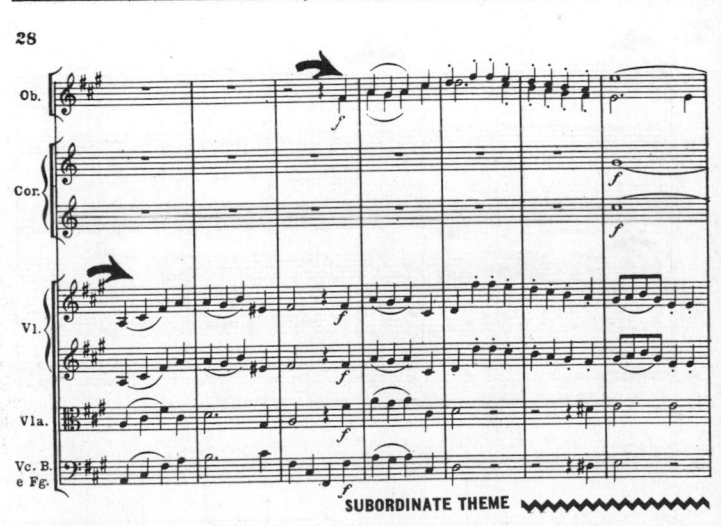

SUBORDINATE THEME

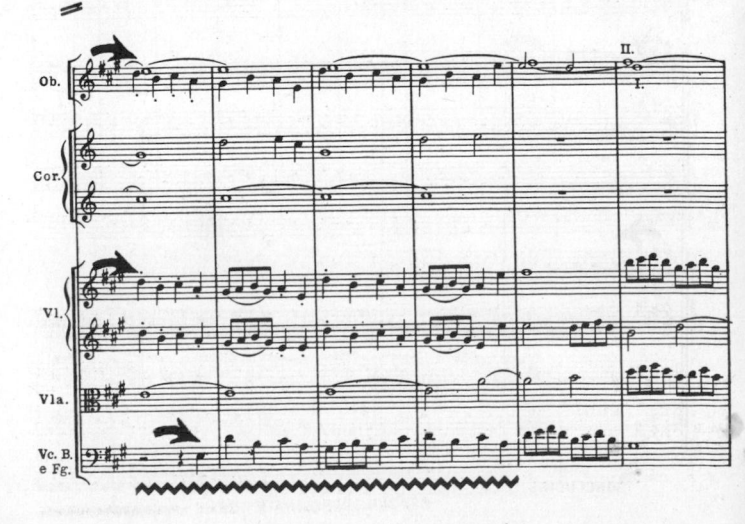

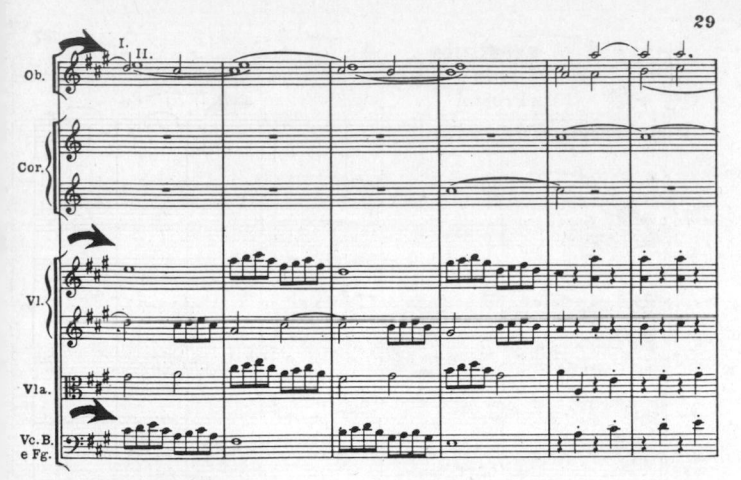

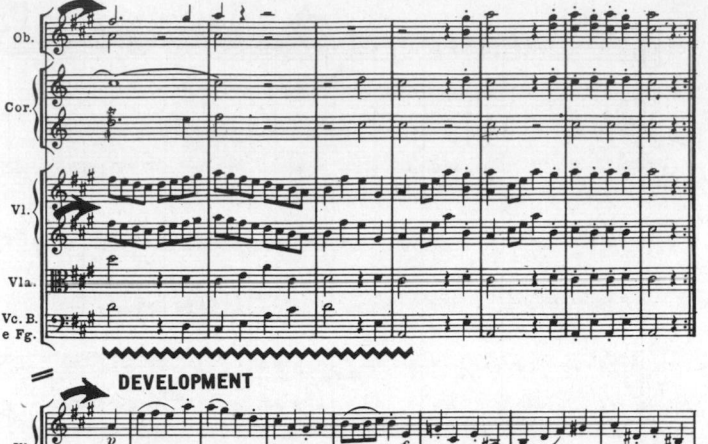

DEVELOPMENT

DEVELOPMENT—SECTION I 〰〰〰 *f*

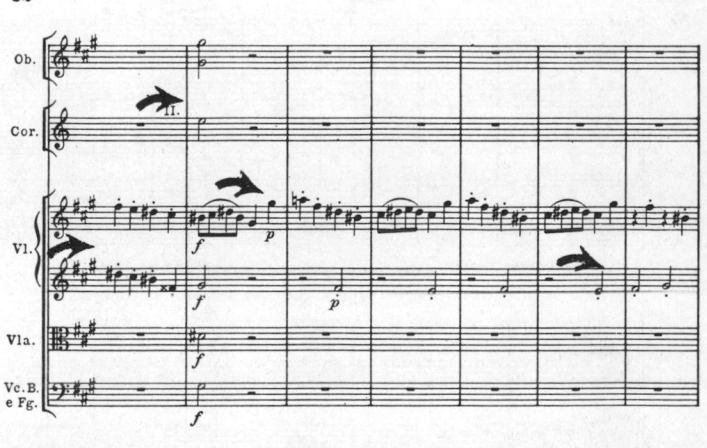

DEVELOPMENT—SECTION 2 〰〰〰

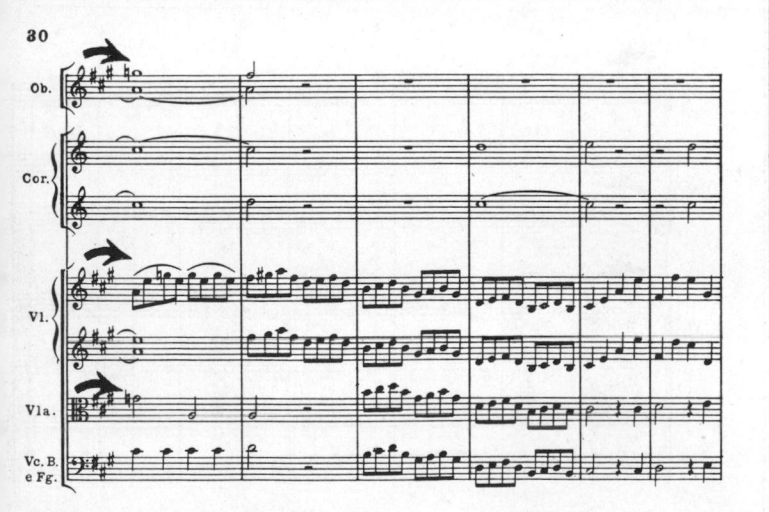

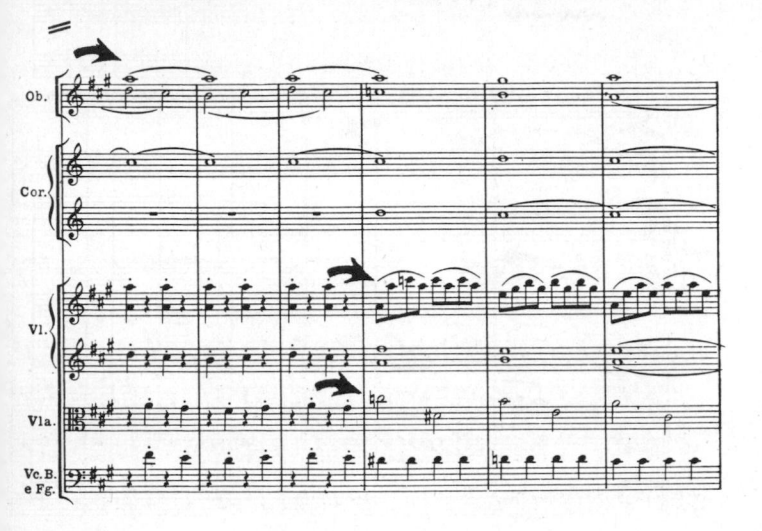

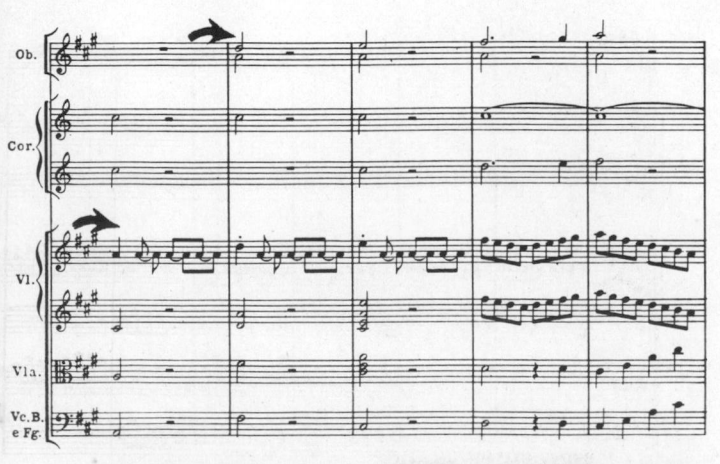

CONCLUDING THEME (CODETTA) 〰〰〰〰〰〰〰

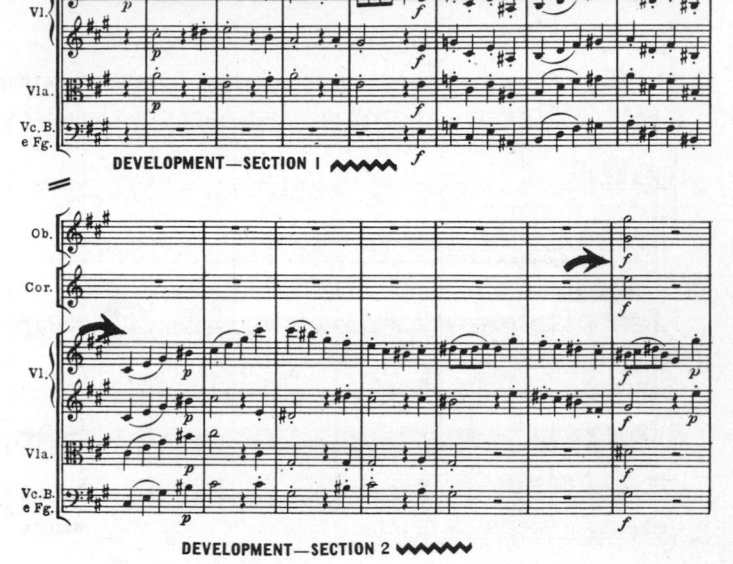

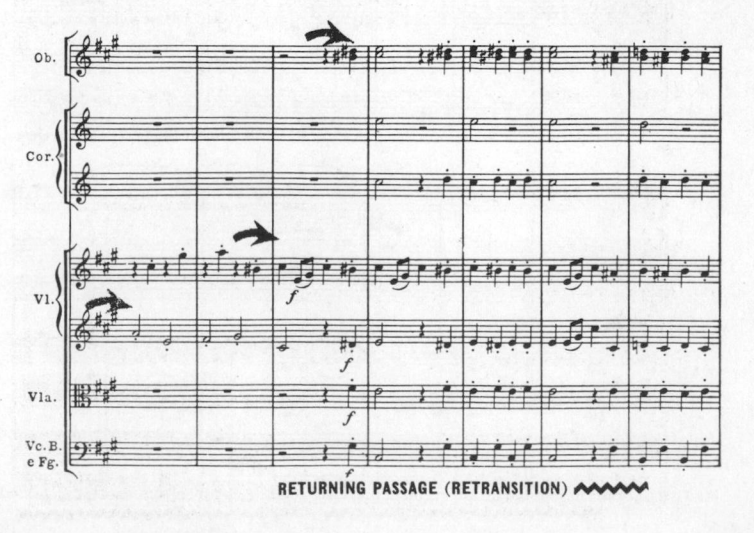

RETURNING PASSAGE (RETRANSITION) 〰〰〰

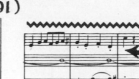

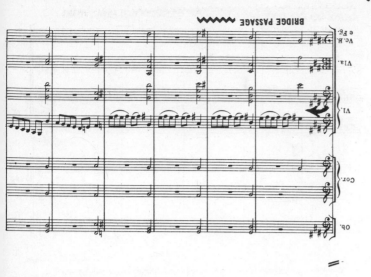

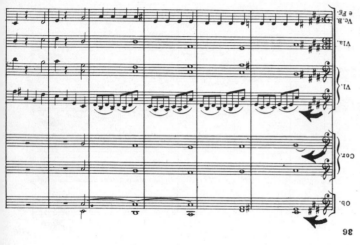

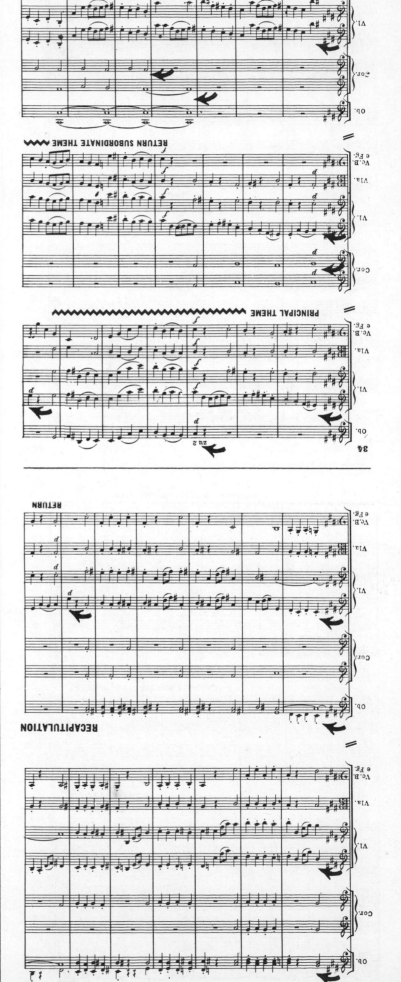

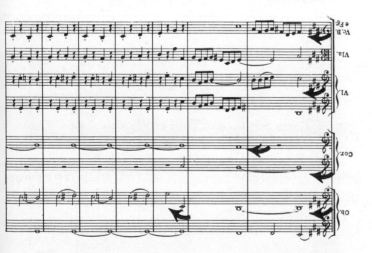

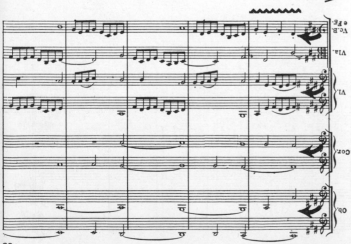

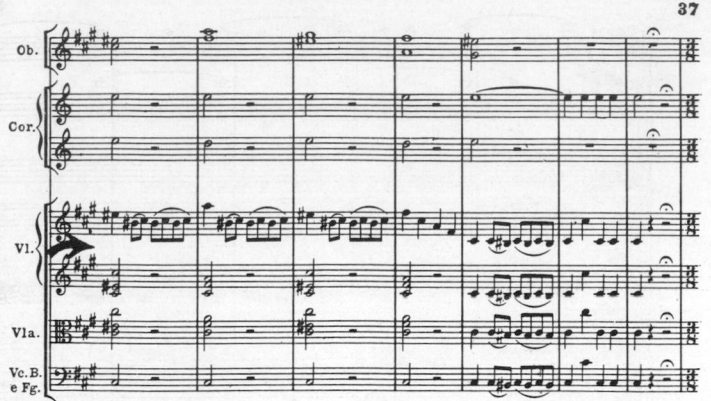

37

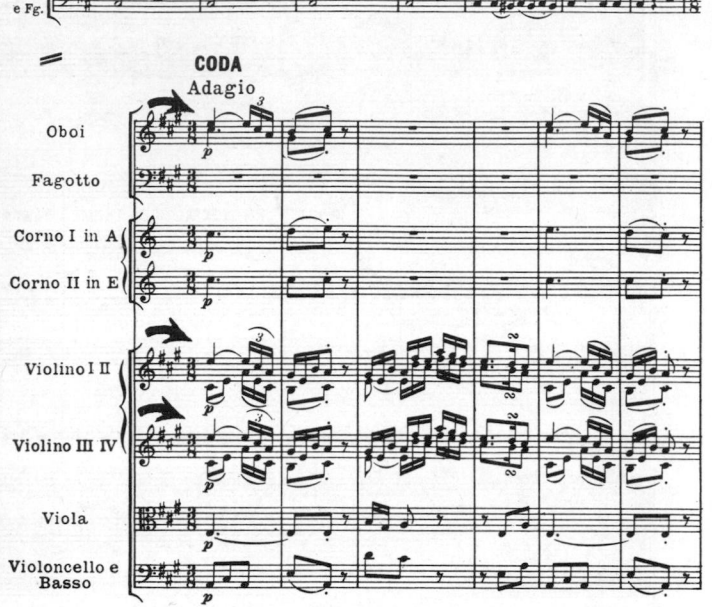

CODA
Adagio

Oboi
Fagotto
Corno I in A
Corno II in E
Violino I II
Violino III IV
Viola
Violoncello e Basso

SPECIAL CODA THEME—PART I 〜〜〜〜〜〜〜

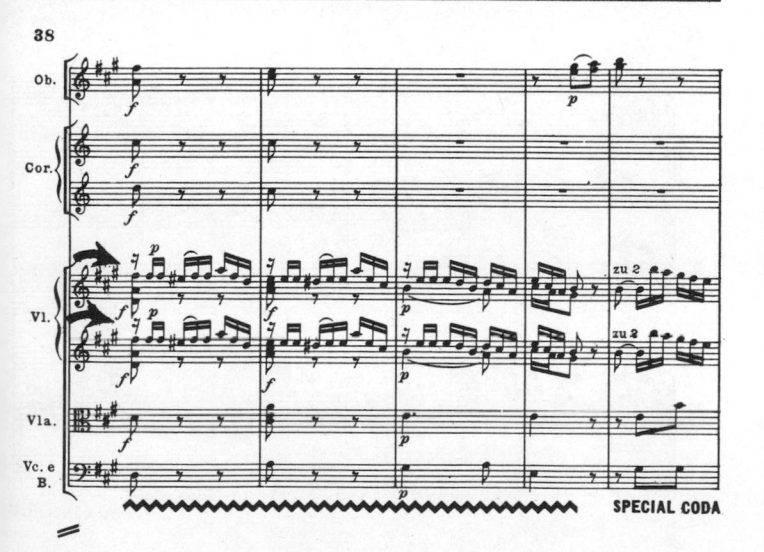

38

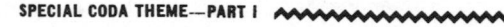

SPECIAL CODA

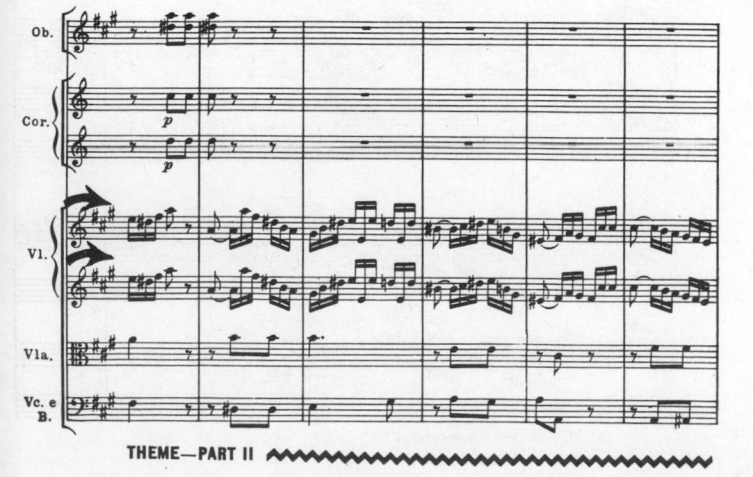

THEME—PART II 〜〜〜〜〜〜〜〜〜〜〜〜

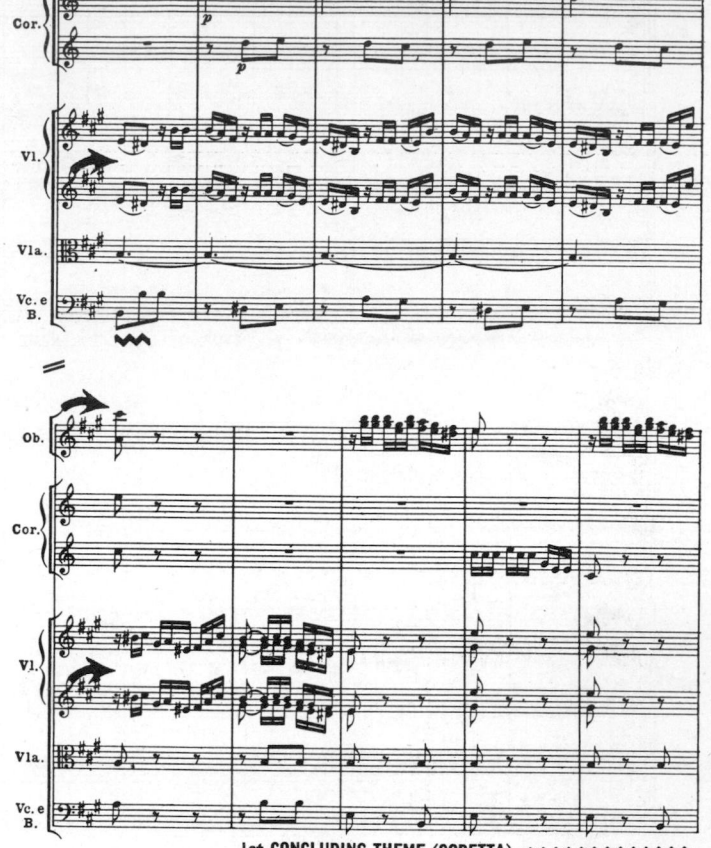

39

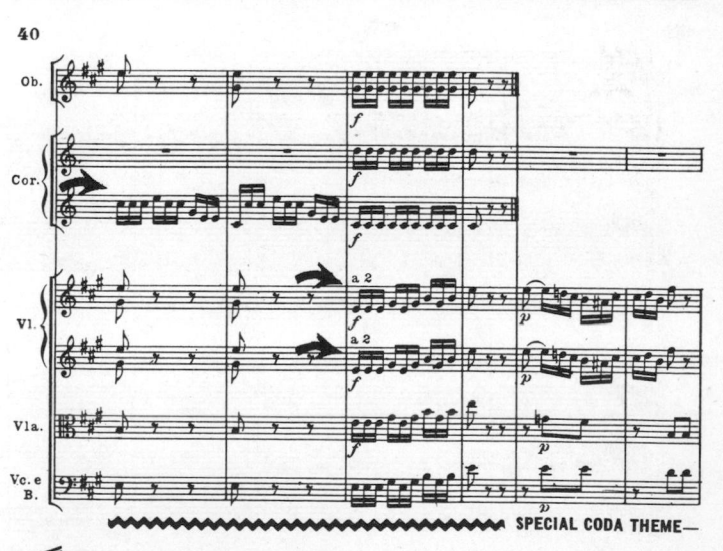

1st CONCLUDING THEME (CODETTA) 〜〜〜〜〜

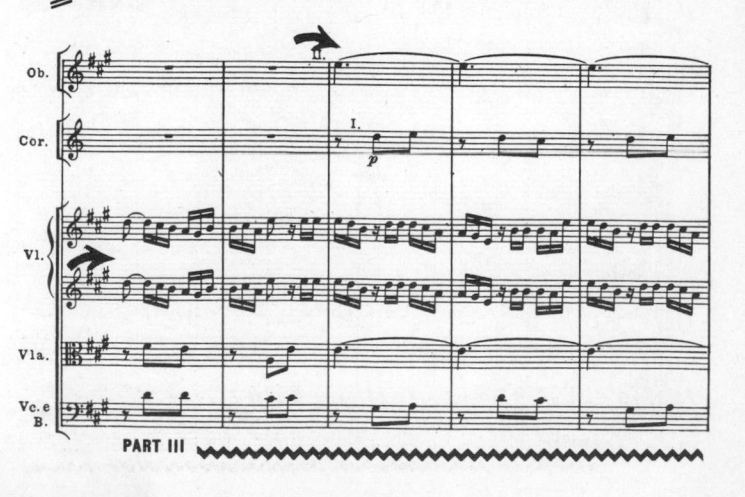

40

SPECIAL CODA THEME—

PART III 〜〜〜〜〜〜〜〜

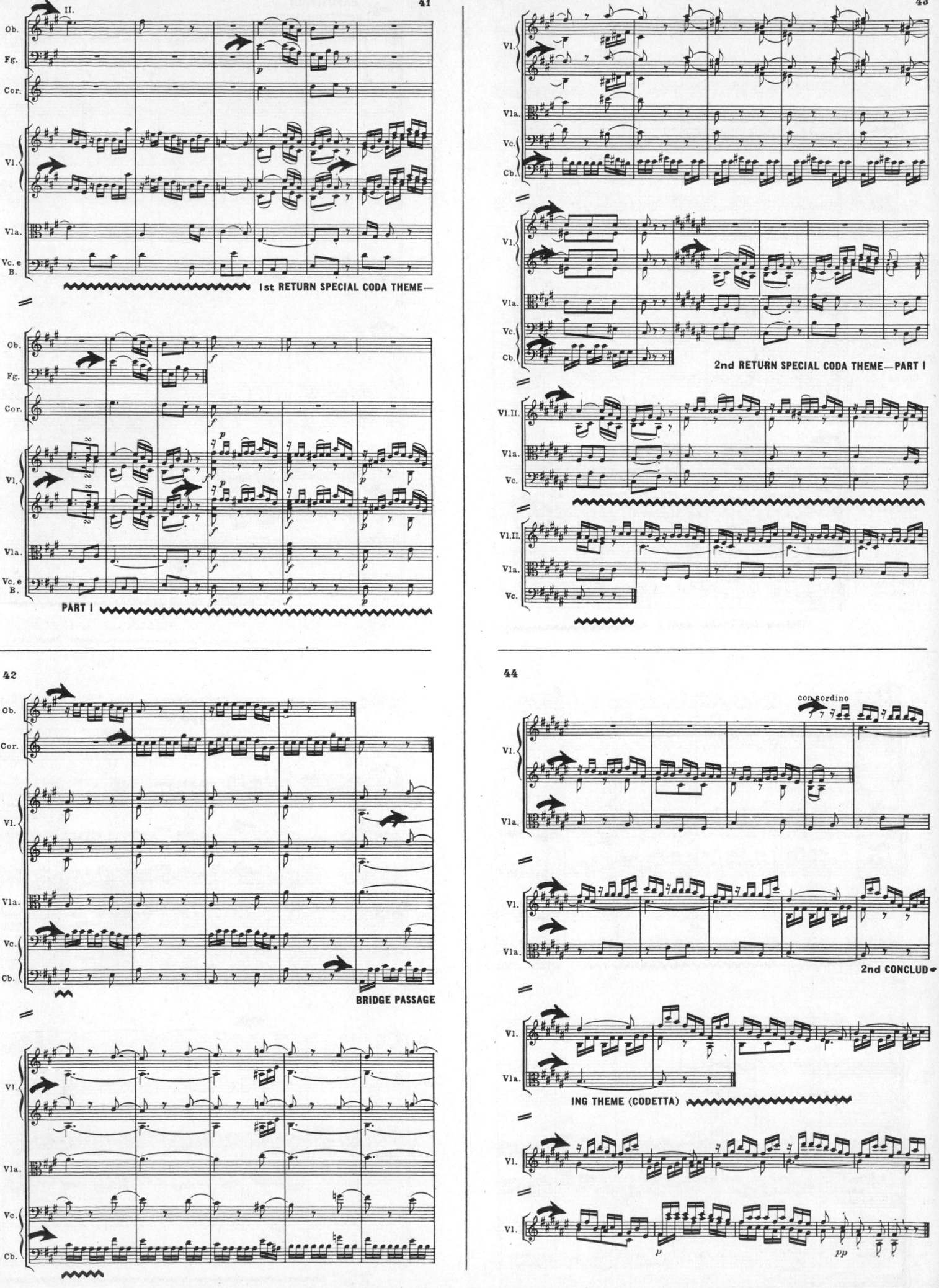

"Oxford" Symphony

Joseph Haydn
(1732 – 1809)

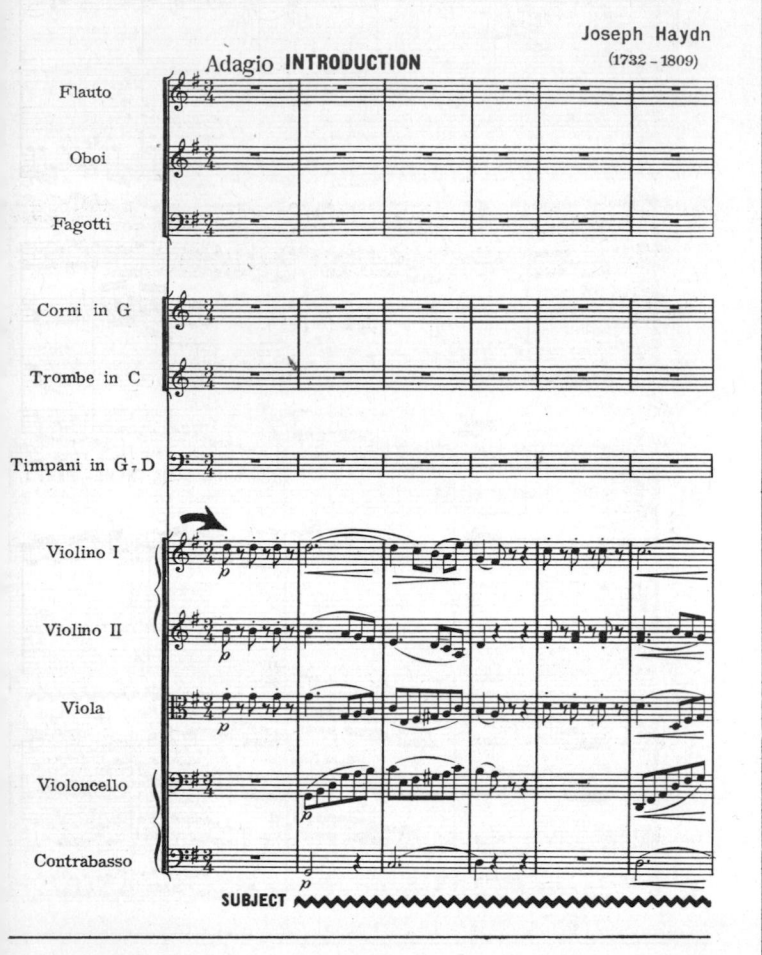

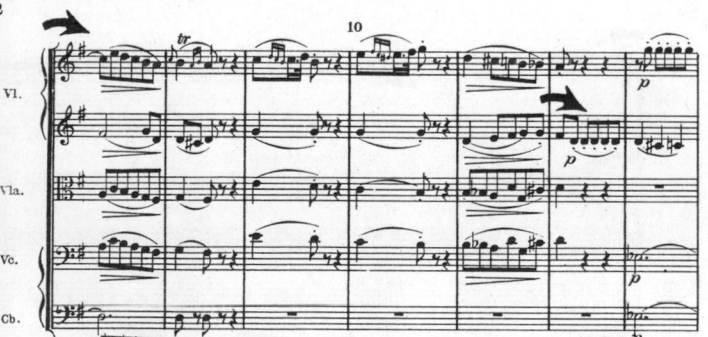

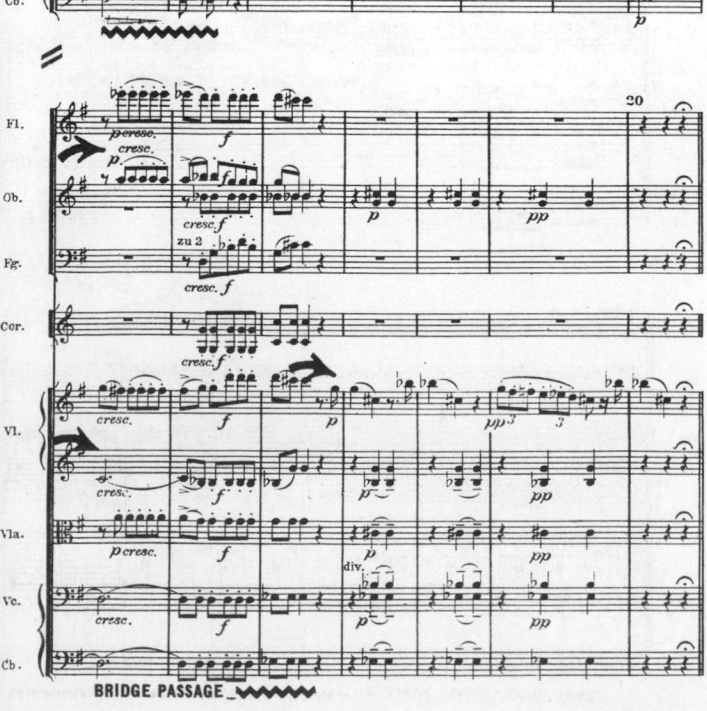

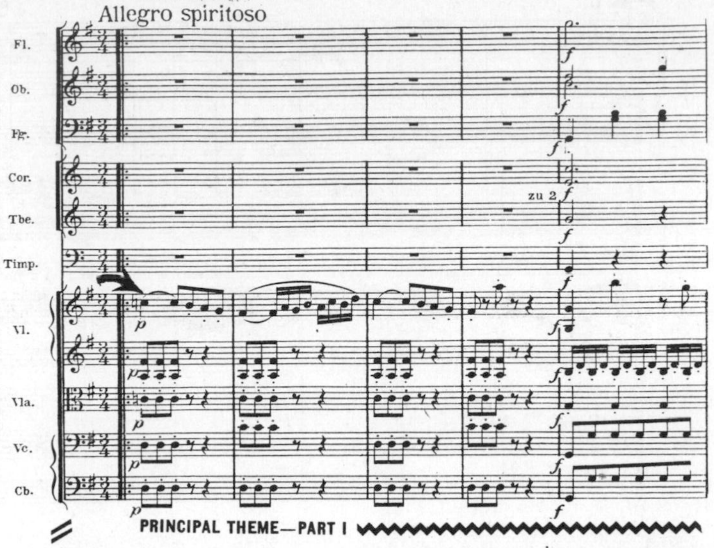

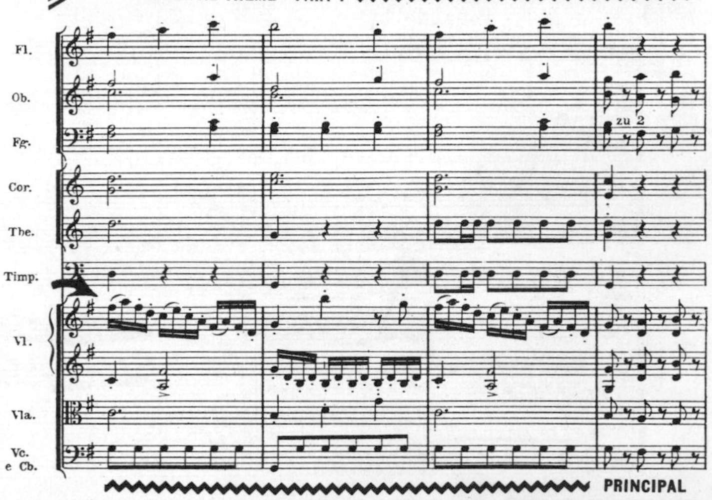

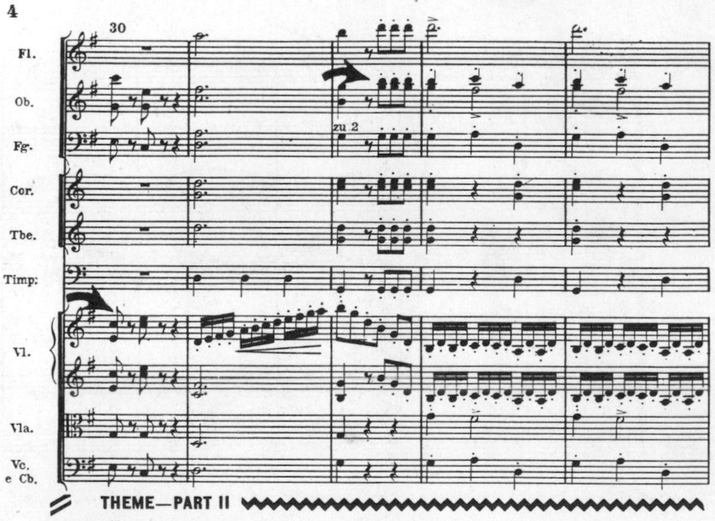

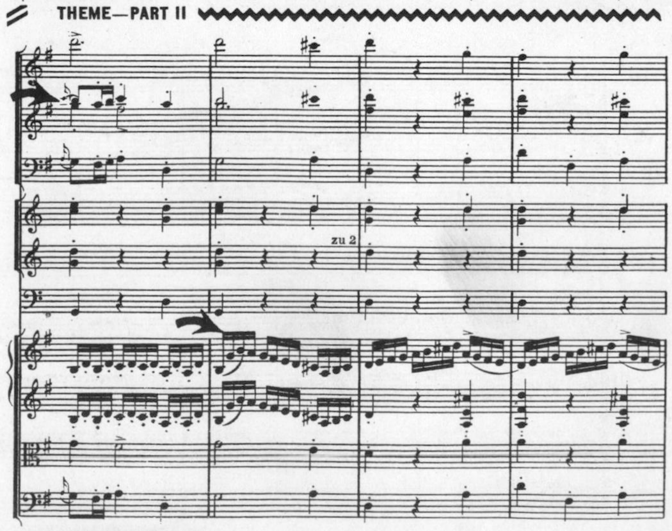

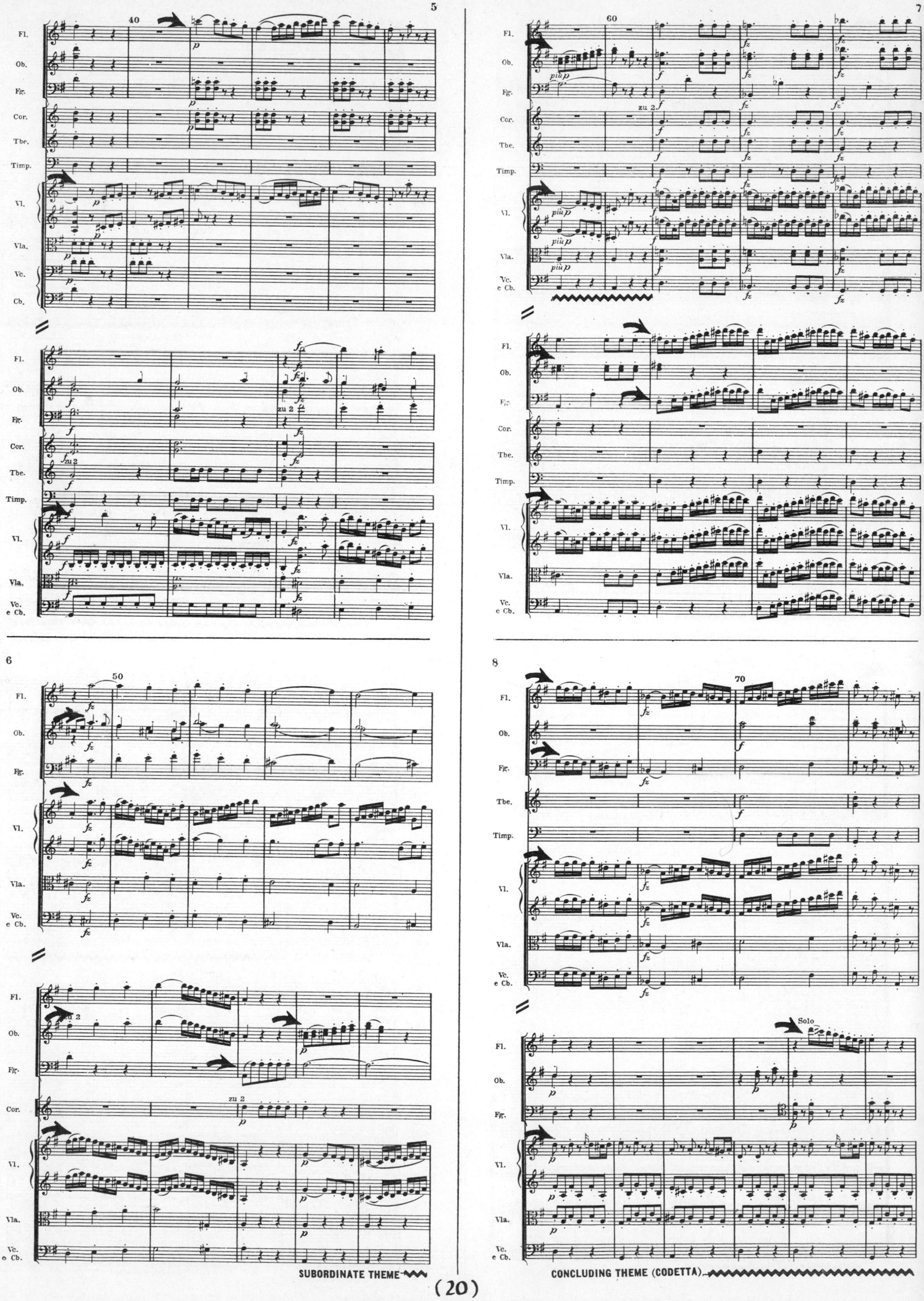
5
40
Fl.
Ob.
Fg.
Cor.
Tbe.
Timp.
Vl.
Vla.
Vc.
Cb.
e Cb.
zu 2
piu p
Solo
6
50
7
60
8
70
SUBORDINATE THEME
CONCLUDING THEME (CODETTA)

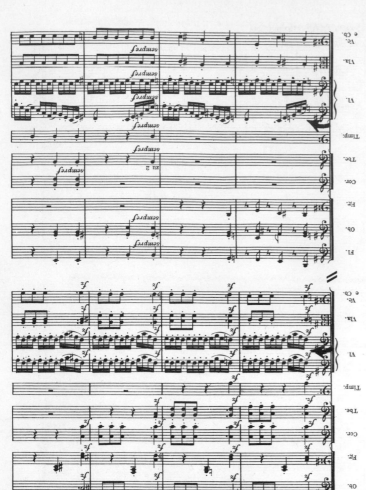
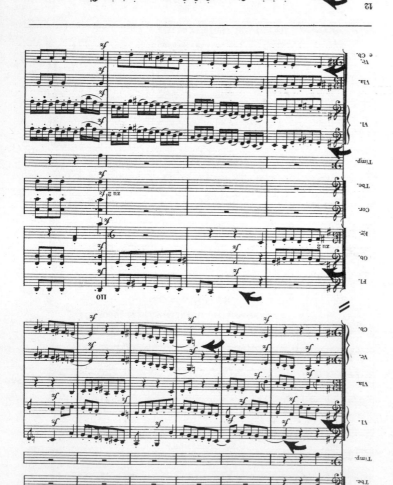
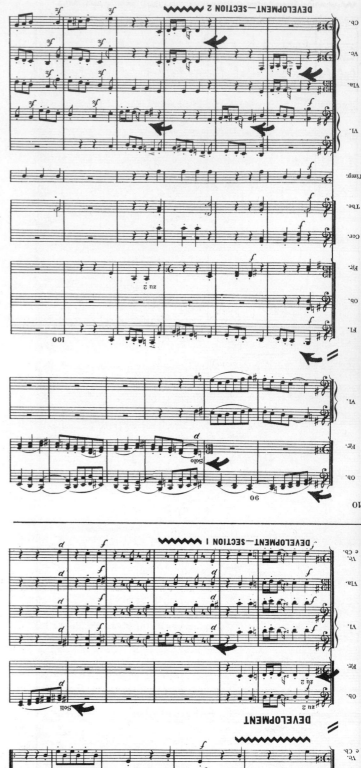

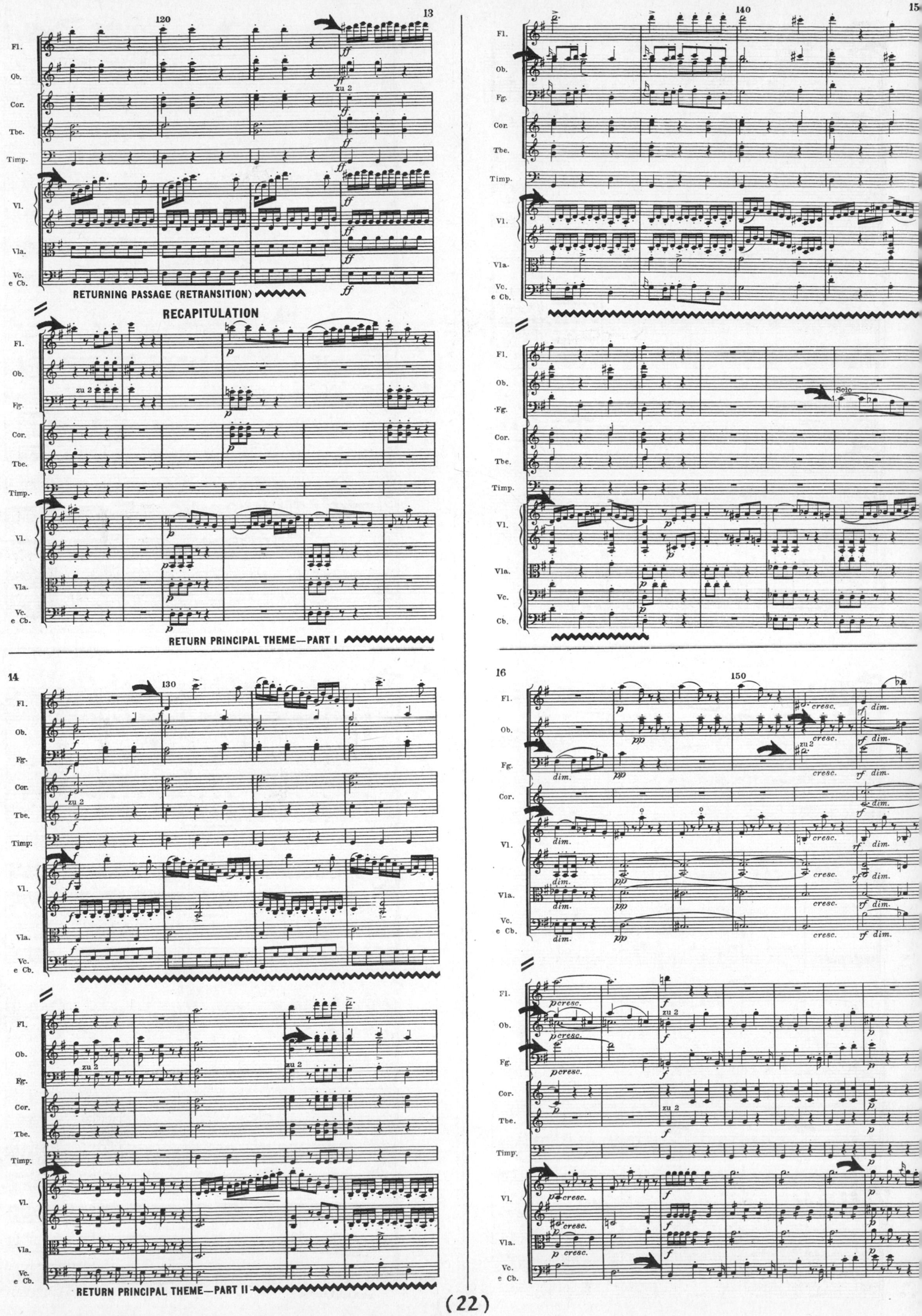

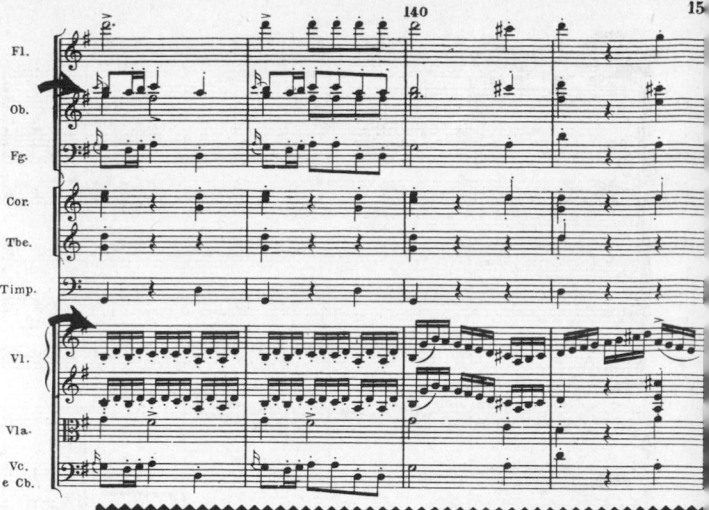

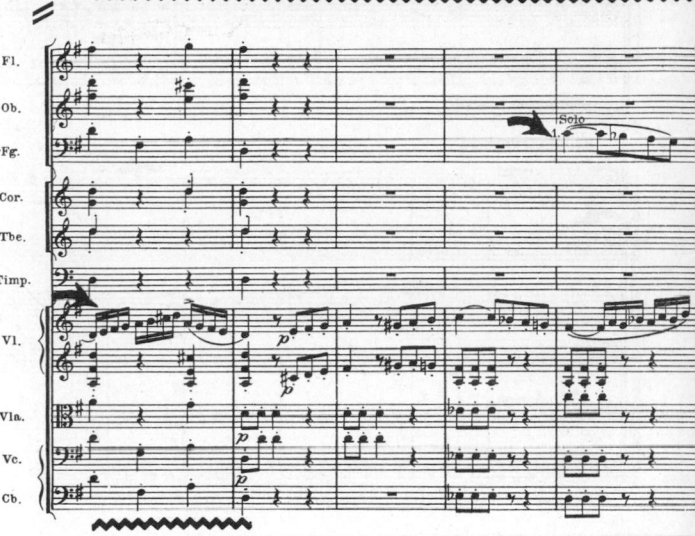

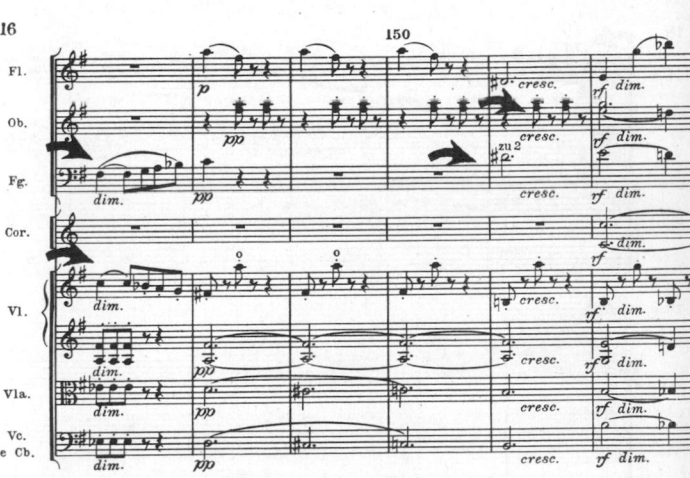

RETURNING PASSAGE (RETRANSITION)

RECAPITULATION

RETURN PRINCIPAL THEME—PART I

RETURN PRINCIPAL THEME—PART II

(22)

17

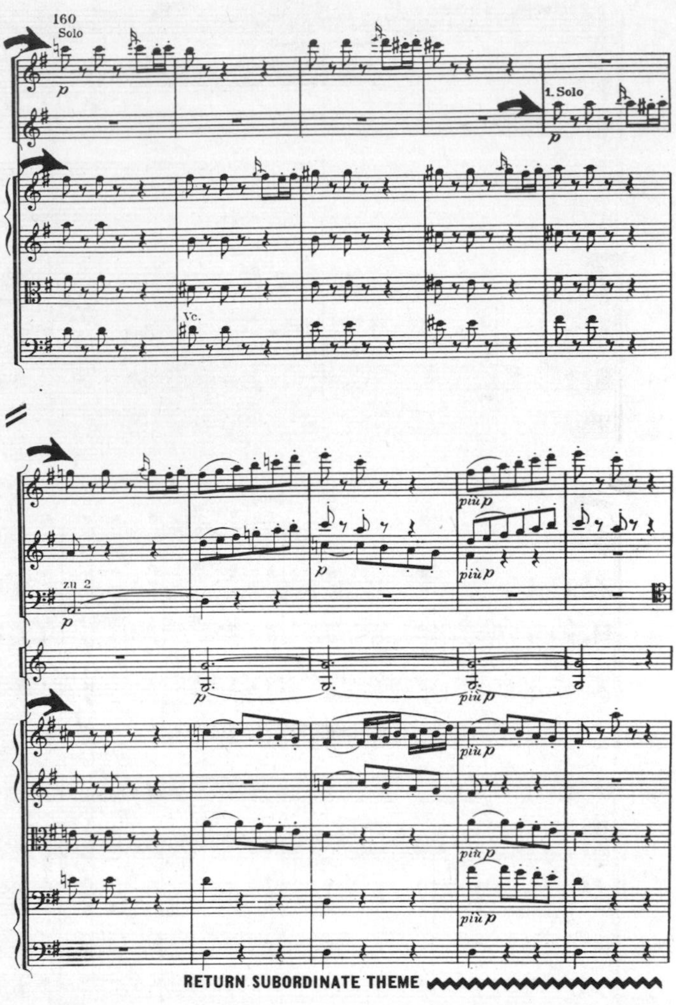
160
Solo
1. Solo
Fl.
Ob.
Vl.
Vla.
Vc.
Vc.
e Cb.
Fg.
Cor.
Cb.
zu 2
più p
RETURN SUBORDINATE THEME

18

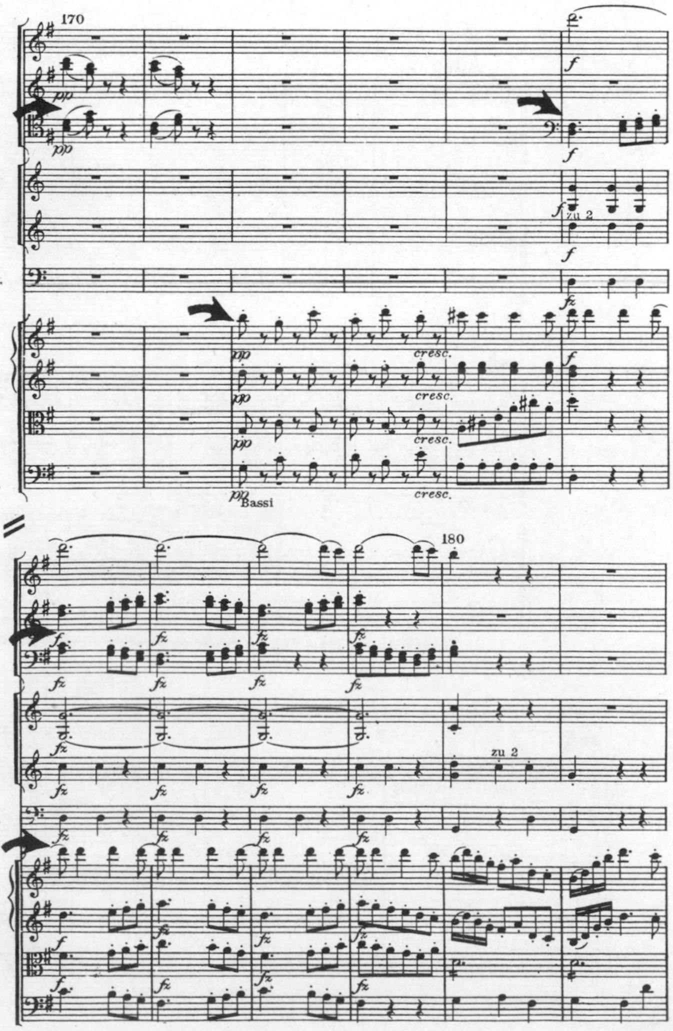
170
Fl.
Ob.
Fg.
Cor.
Tbe.
Timp.
Vl.
Vla.
Vc.
e Cb.
zu 2
cresc.
Bassi
180

19

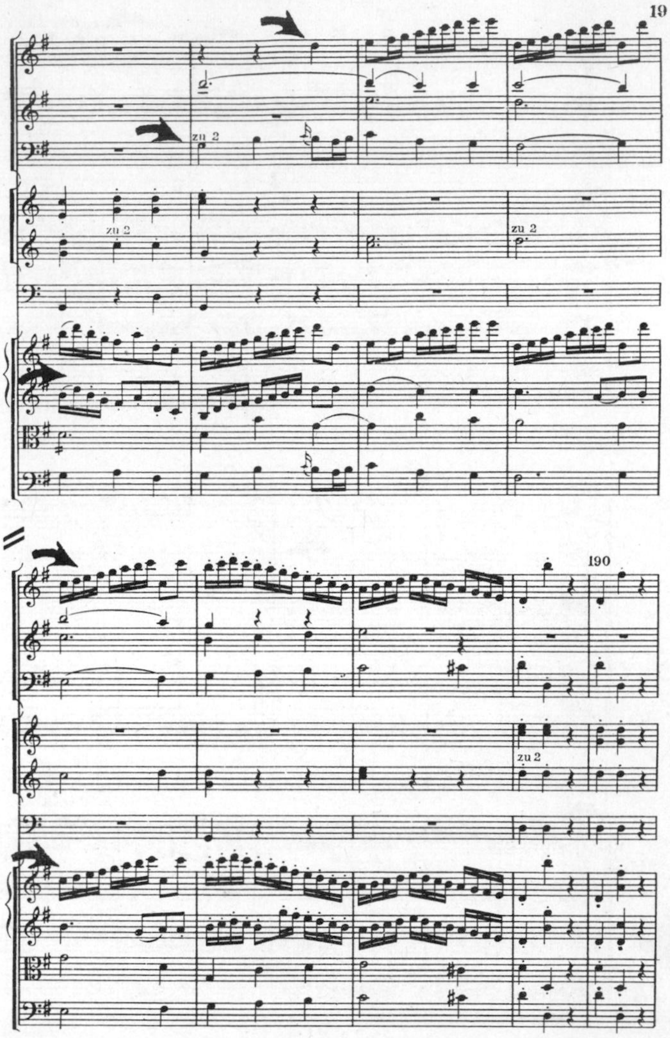
Fl.
Ob.
Fg.
Cor.
Tbe.
Timp.
Vl.
Vla.
Vc.
e Cb.
zu 2
190

20

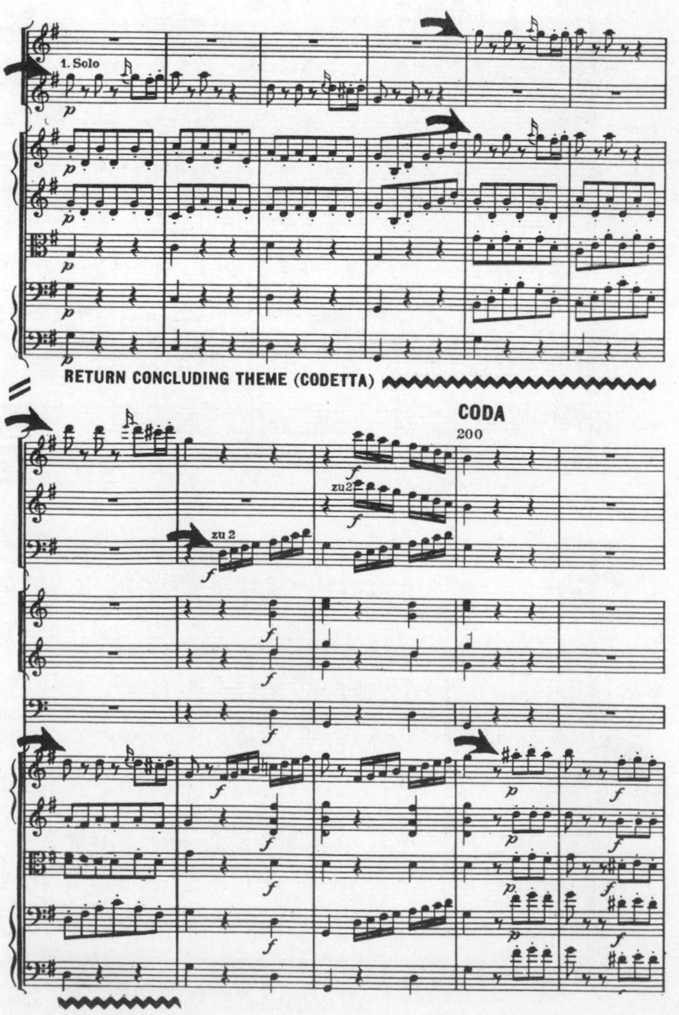
Fl.
Ob.
1. Solo
Vl.
Vla.
Vc.
Cb.
RETURN CONCLUDING THEME (CODETTA)
CODA
200
Fg.
Cor.
Tbe.
Timp.
zu 2

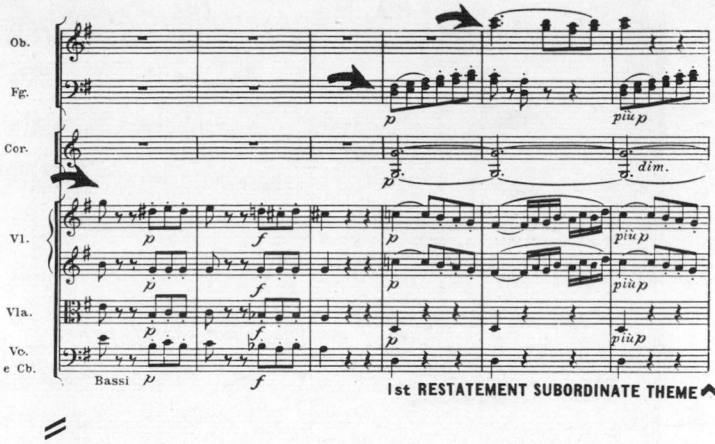

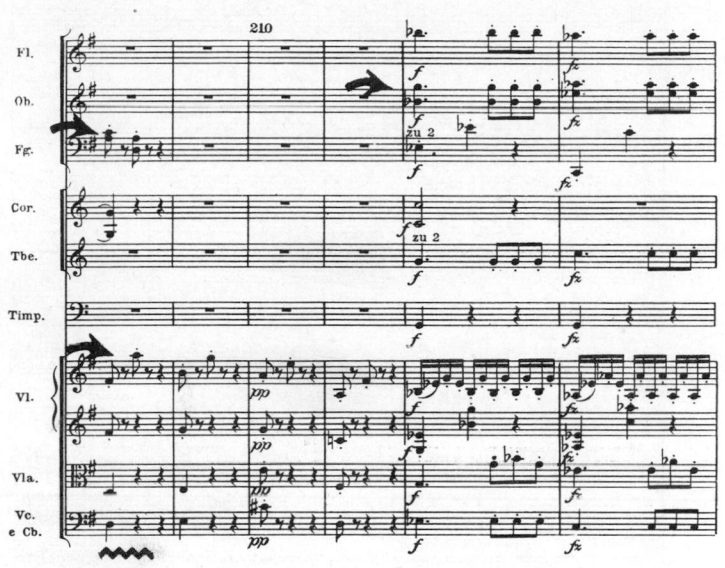

1st RESTATEMENT SUBORDINATE THEME

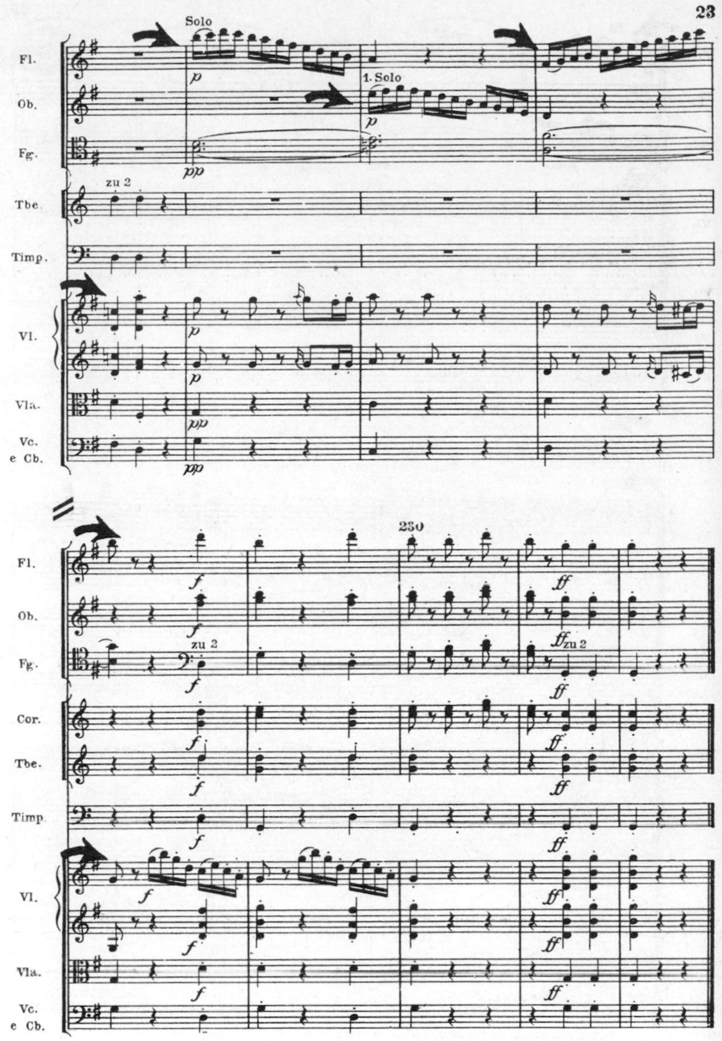

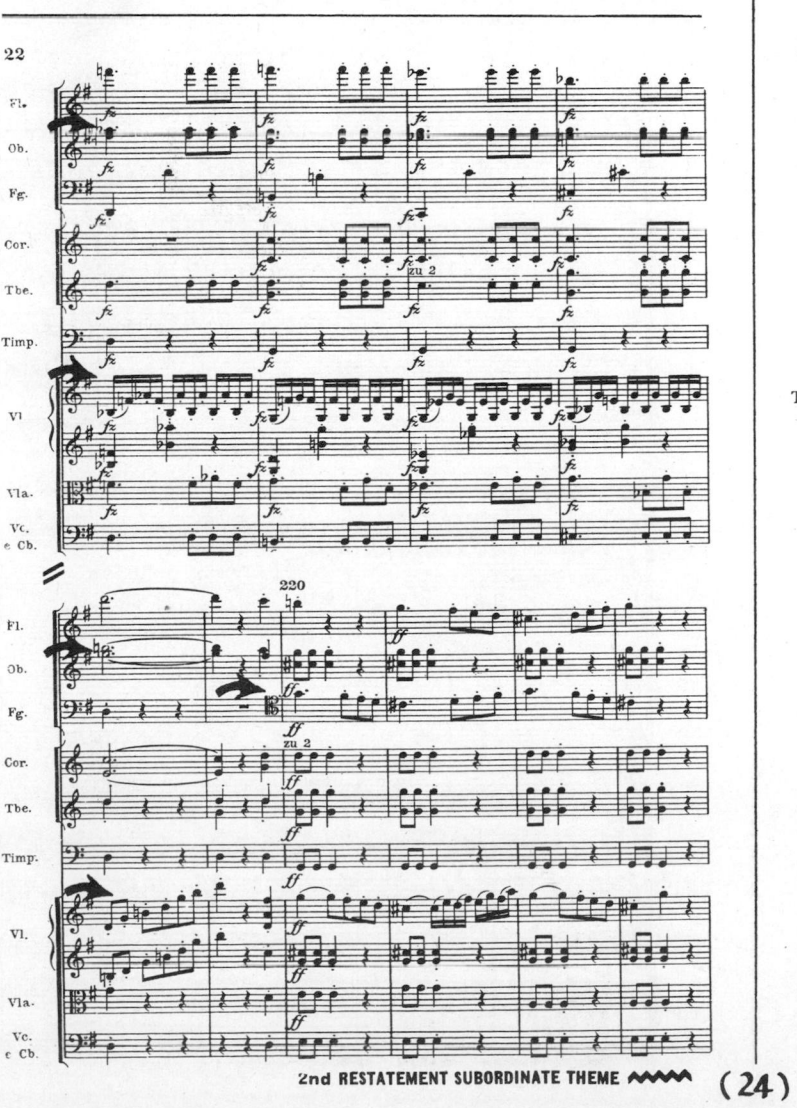

II

SONG FORM
Adagio

PRINCIPAL THEME—PART I

2nd RESTATEMENT SUBORDINATE THEME

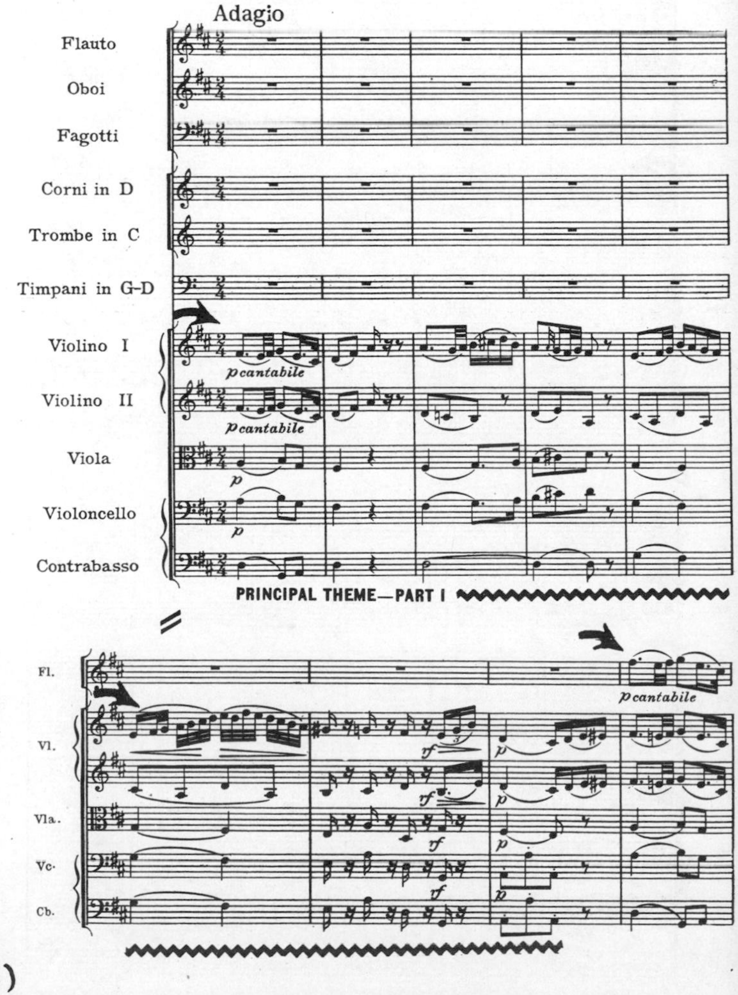

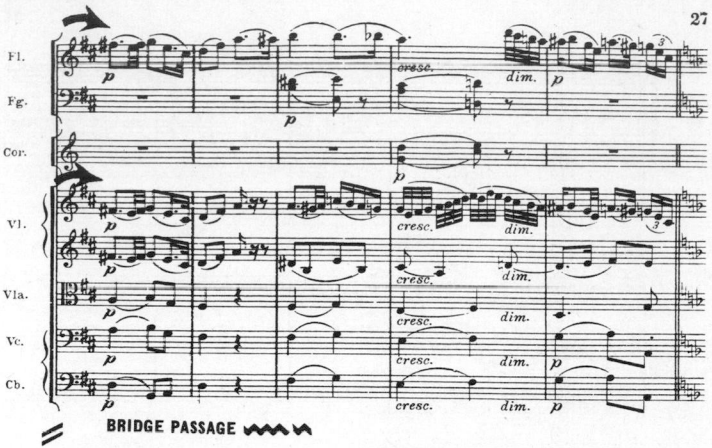

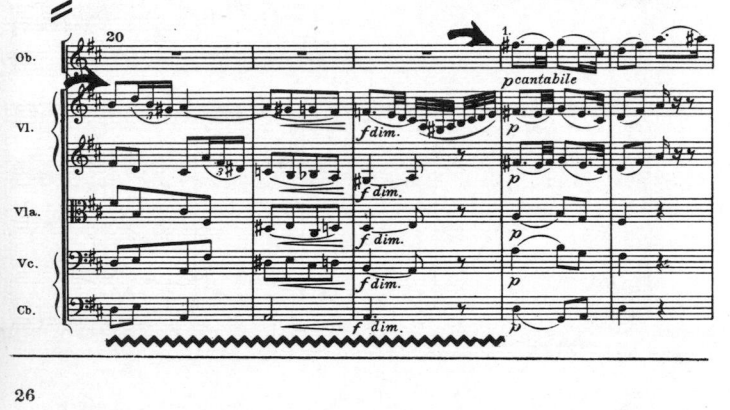

PRINCIPAL THEME—PART II ∿∿∿∿

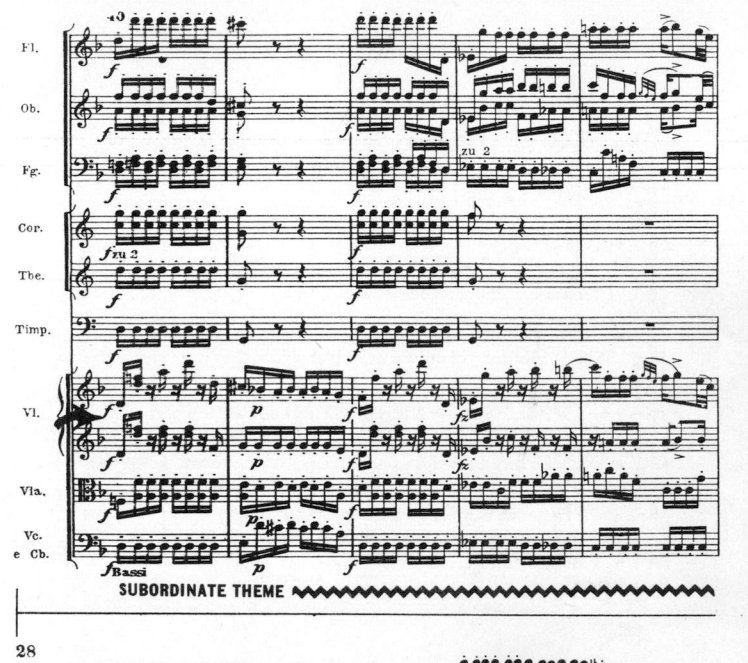

BRIDGE PASSAGE ∿∿∿∿

SUBORDINATE THEME ∿∿∿∿

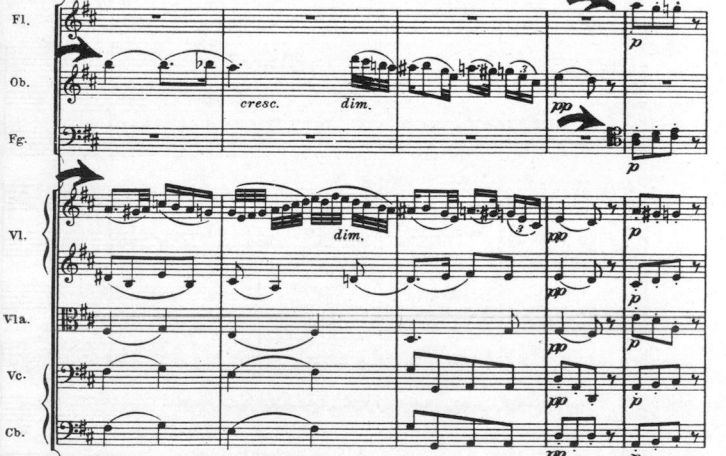

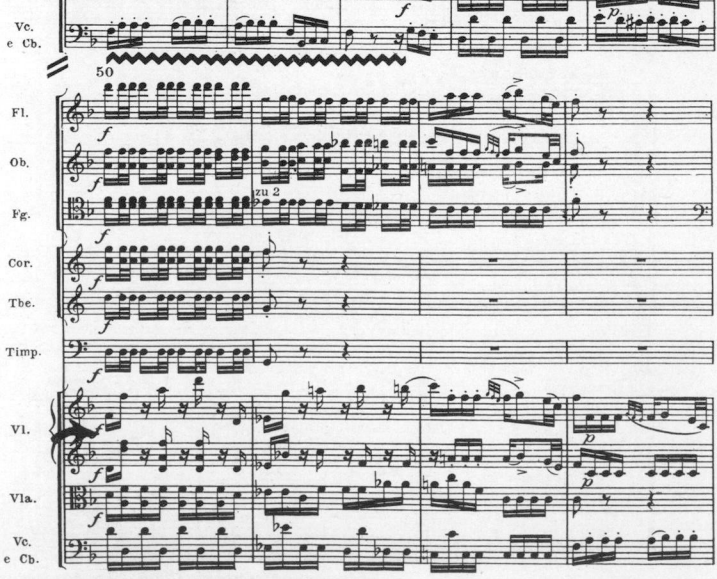

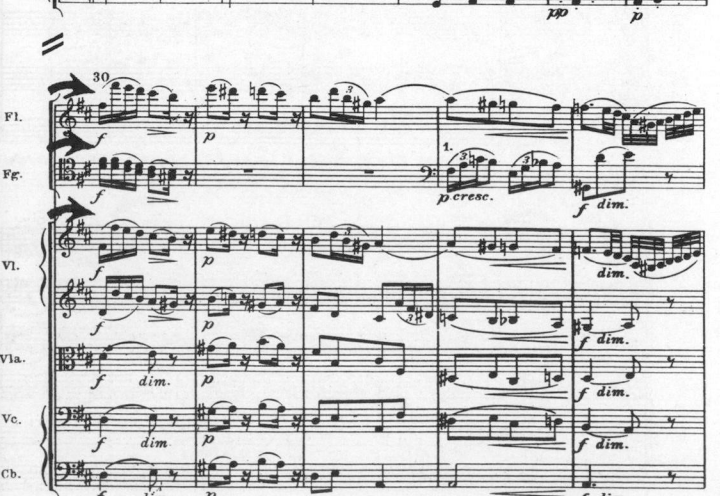

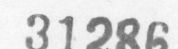

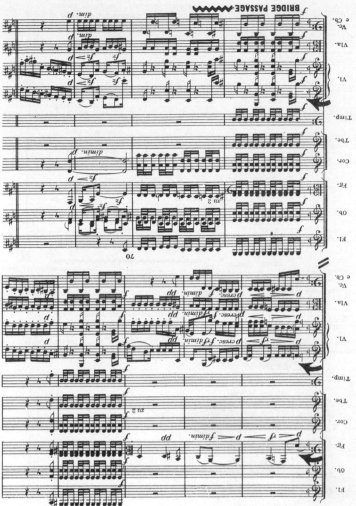
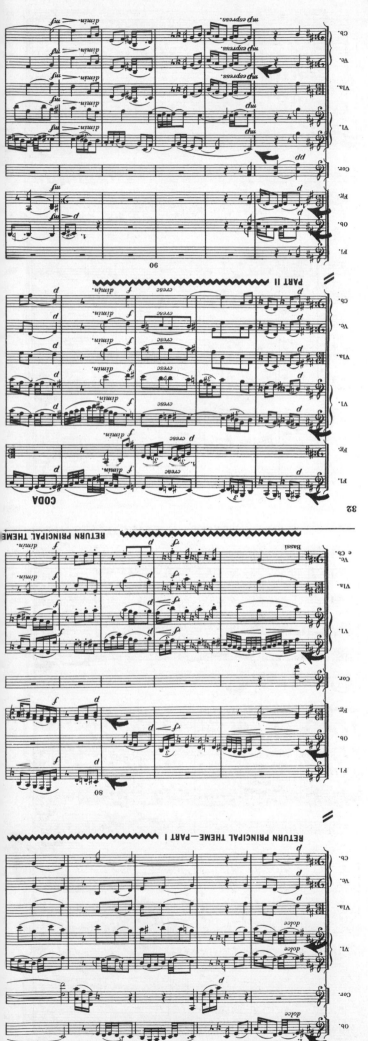
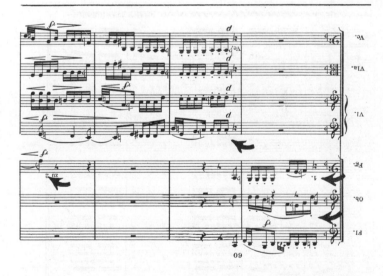
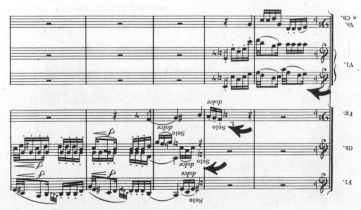

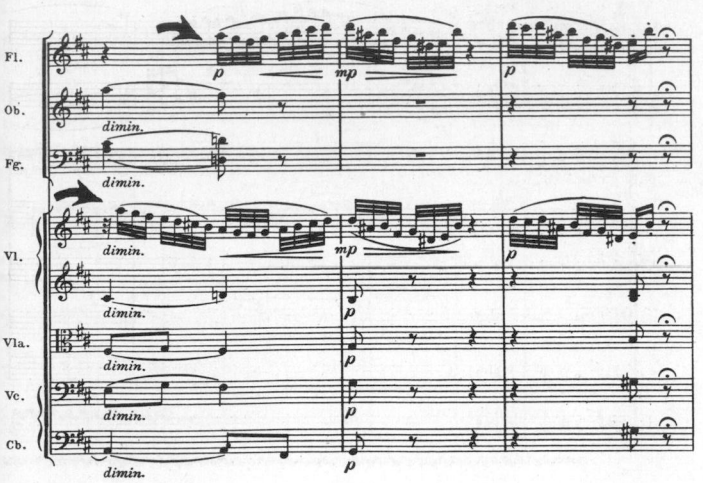

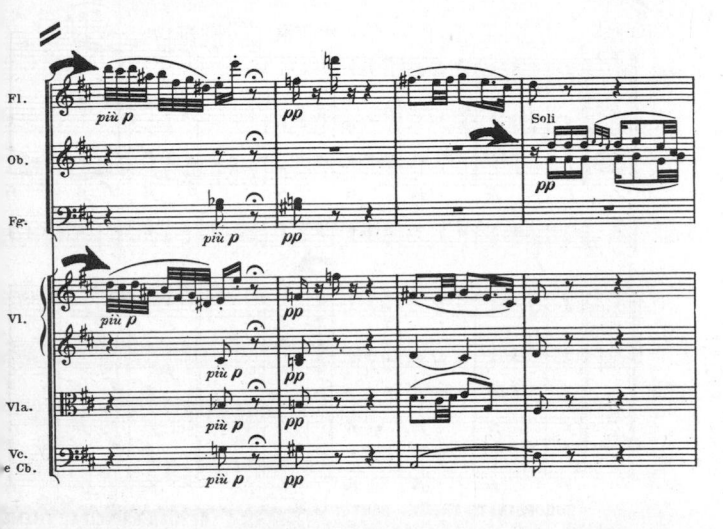

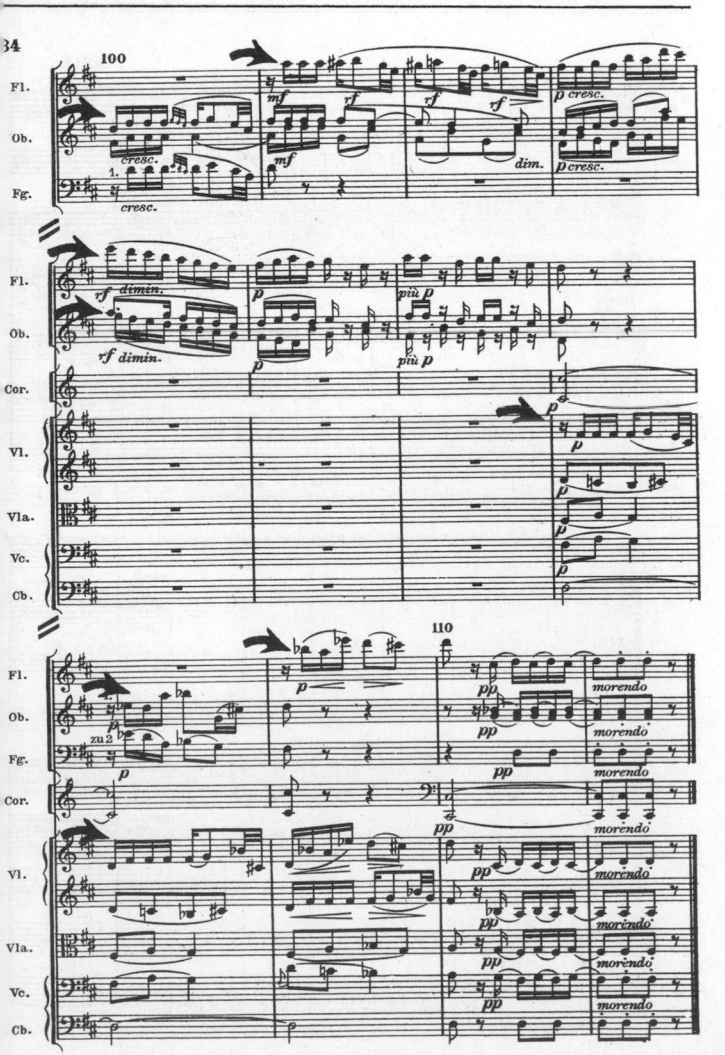

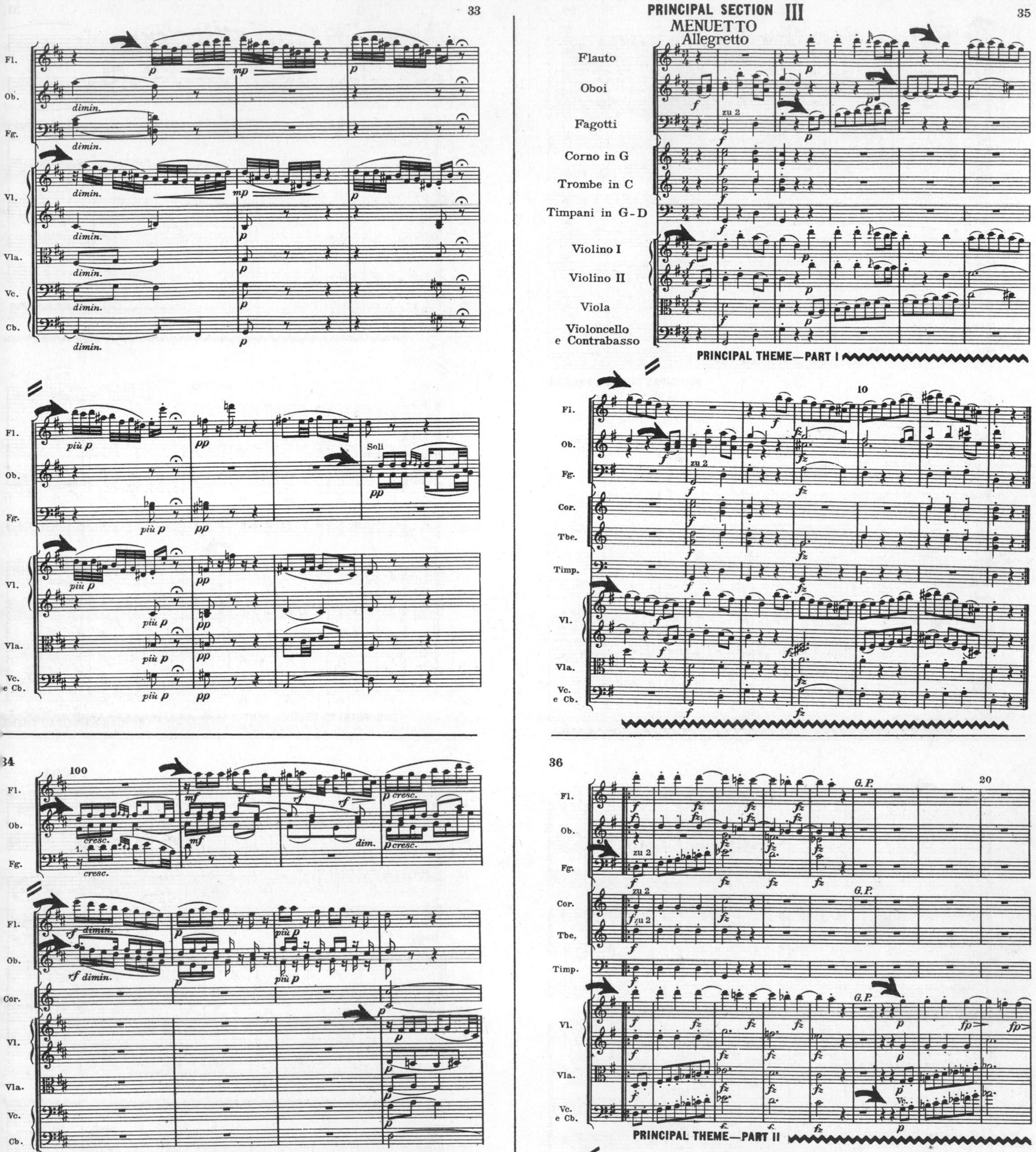
33
35
PRINCIPAL SECTION III
MENUETTO
Allegretto
Flauto
Oboi
Fagotti
Corno in G
Trombe in C
Timpani in G-D
Violino I
Violino II
Viola
Violoncello e Contrabasso
PRINCIPAL THEME—PART I
34
36
PRINCIPAL THEME—PART II
Soli
Solo
zu 2
dimin.
cresc.
morendo
più p
G.P.

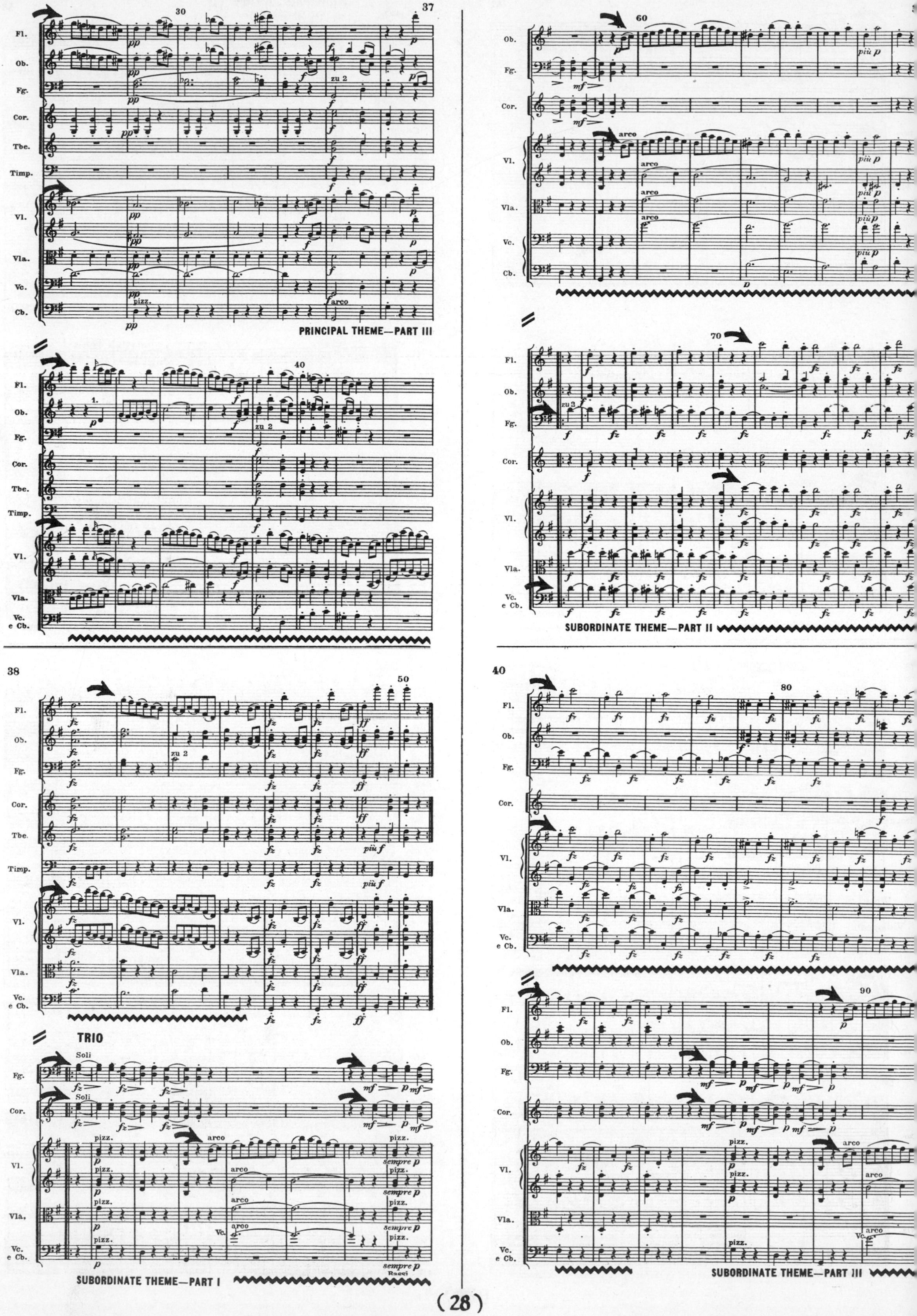
37
PRINCIPAL THEME—PART III
38
TRIO
SUBORDINATE THEME—PART I
SUBORDINATE THEME—PART II
40
SUBORDINATE THEME—PART III

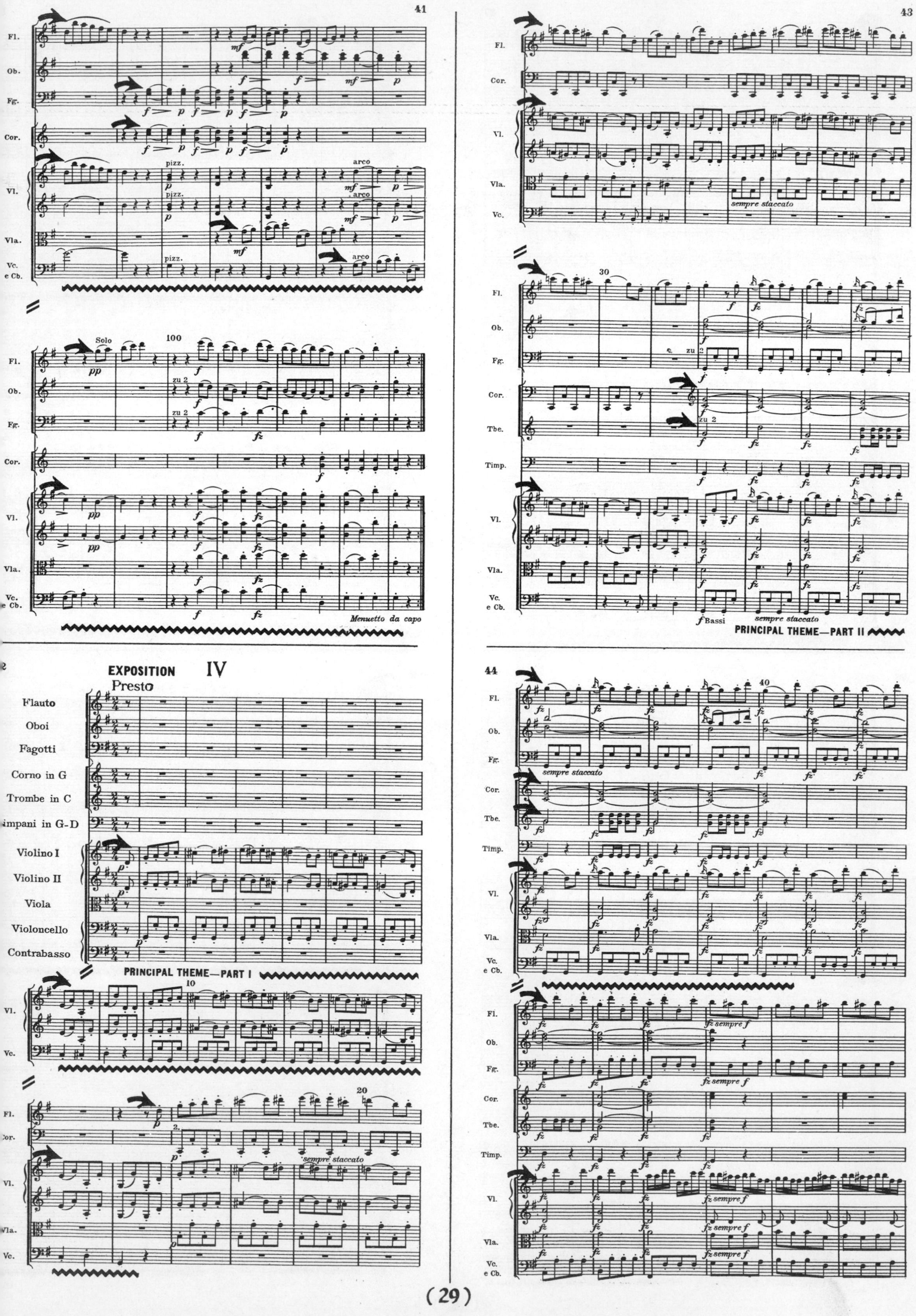

41
43
Menuetto da capo
EXPOSITION IV
Presto
Flauto
Oboi
Fagotti
Corno in G
Trombe in C
Timpani in G-D
Violino I
Violino II
Viola
Violoncello
Contrabasso
PRINCIPAL THEME—PART I
PRINCIPAL THEME—PART II
44
sempre staccato
fz sempre f

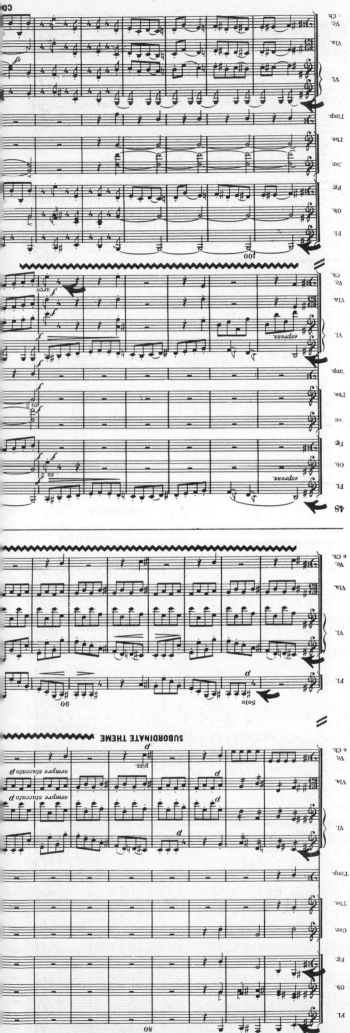

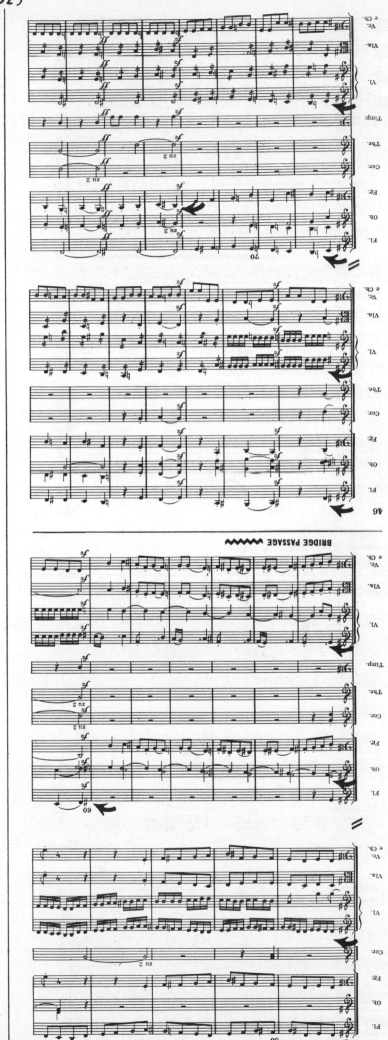

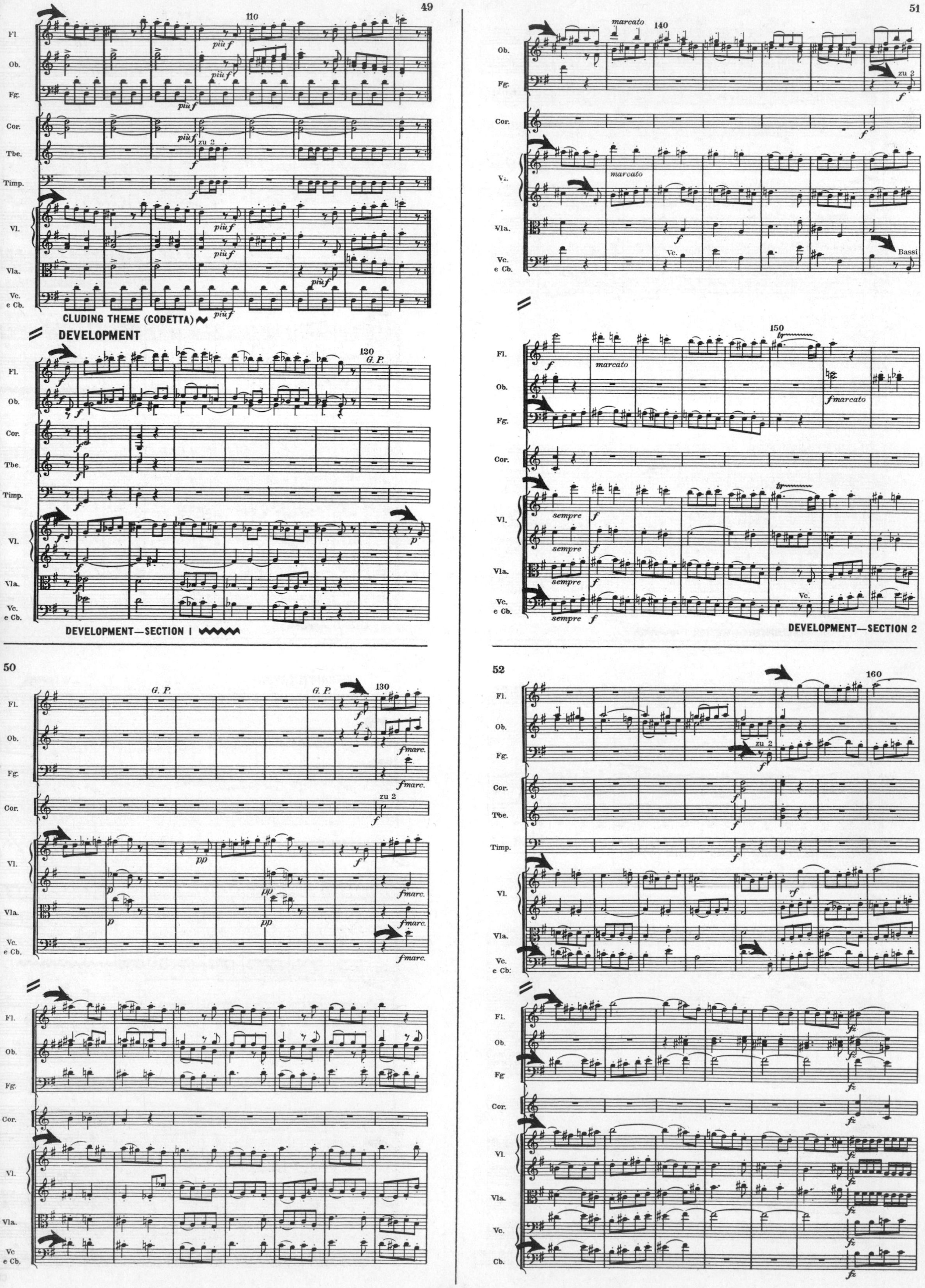

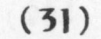

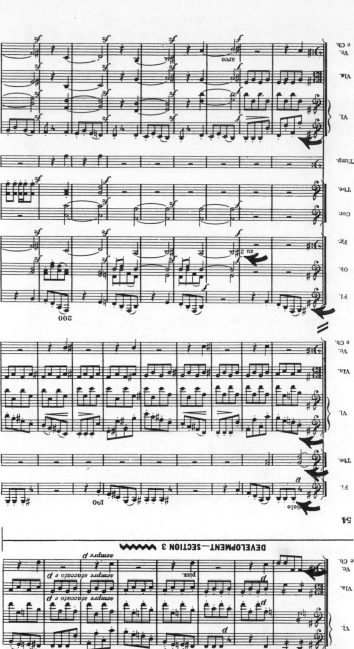
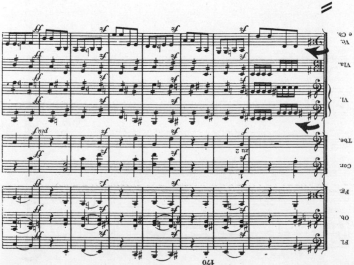
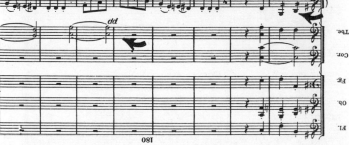
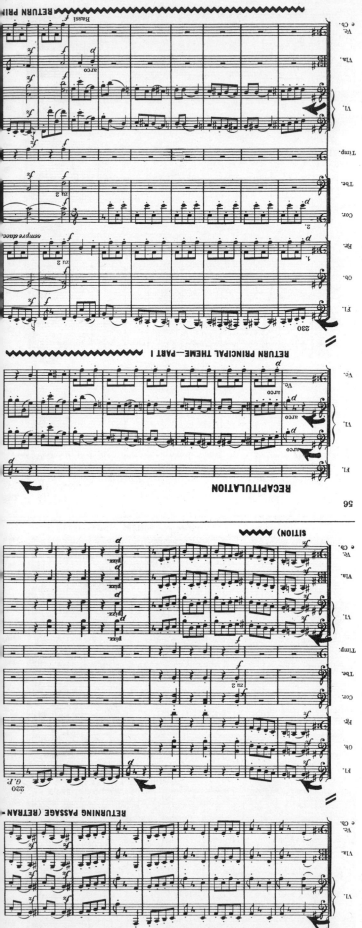
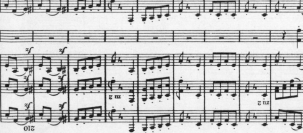

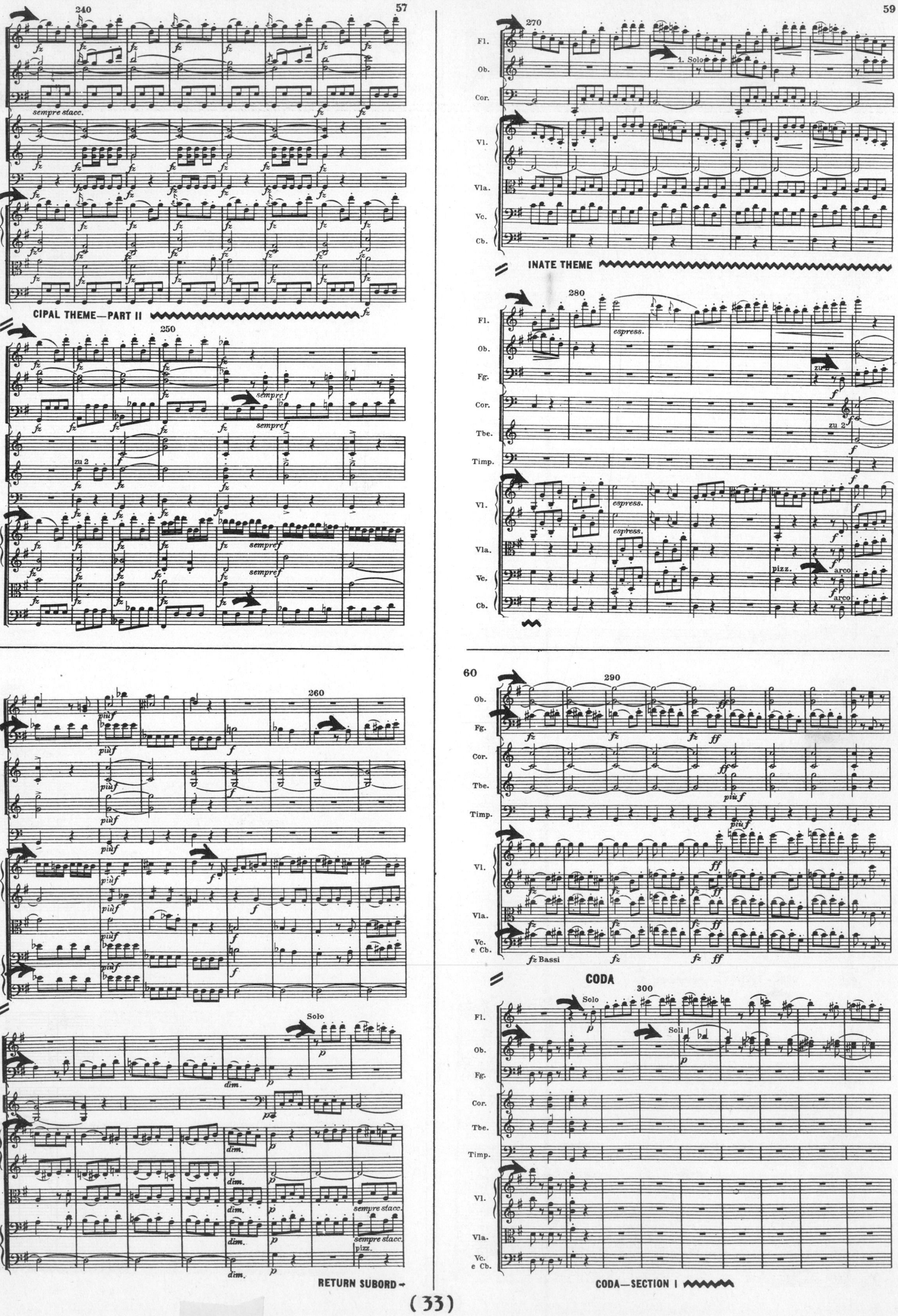
57
240
Fl.
Ob.
Fg.
sempre stacc.
Cor.
Tbe.
Timp.
Vl.
Vla.
Vc. e Cb.
CIPAL THEME—PART II
250
zu 2
sempre f
59
270
1. Solo
INATE THEME
280
espress.
zu 2
pizz.
arco
58
260
più f
Solo
dim.
sempre stacc.
pizz.
RETURN SUBORD→
60
290
ff
fz Bassi
CODA
300
Solo
Soli
CODA—SECTION I

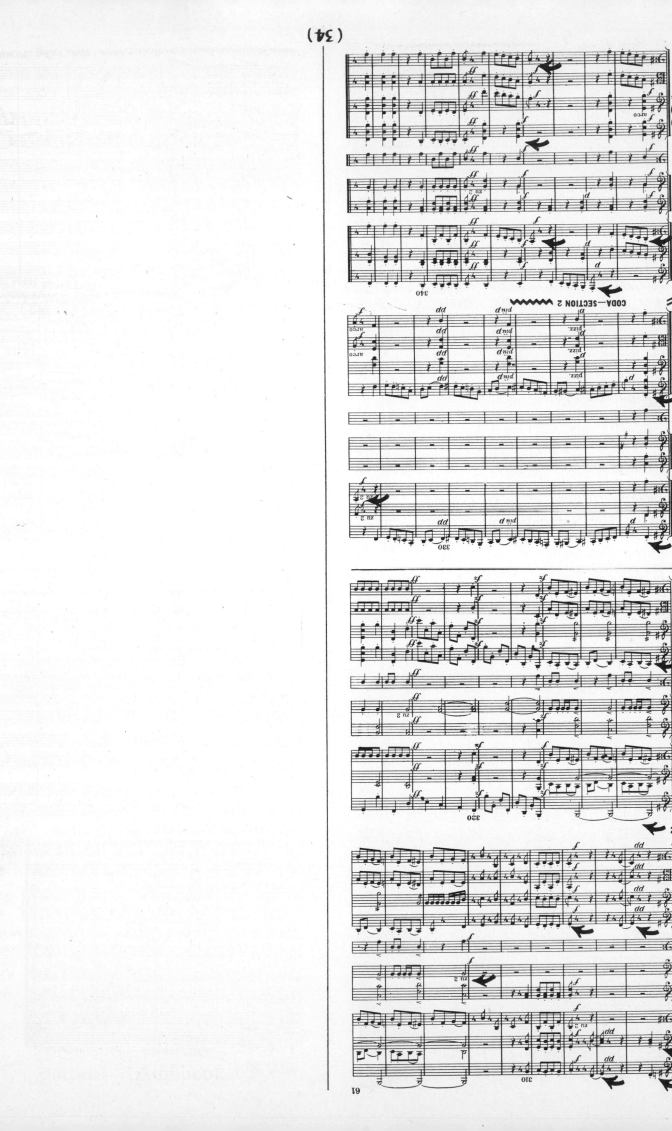

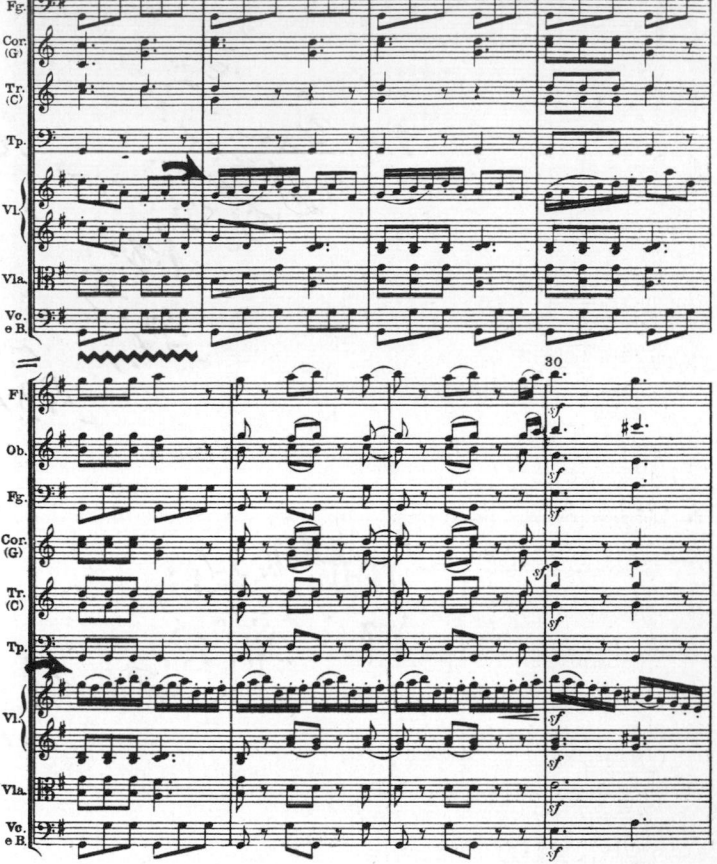

"Surprise" Symphony — Joseph Haydn (1732–1809)

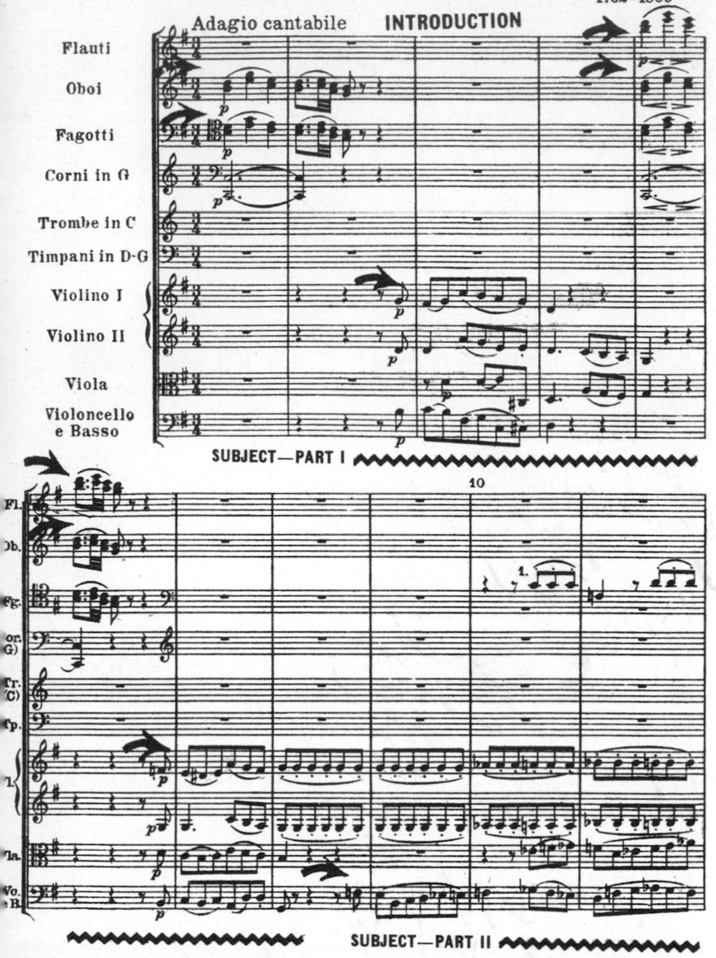

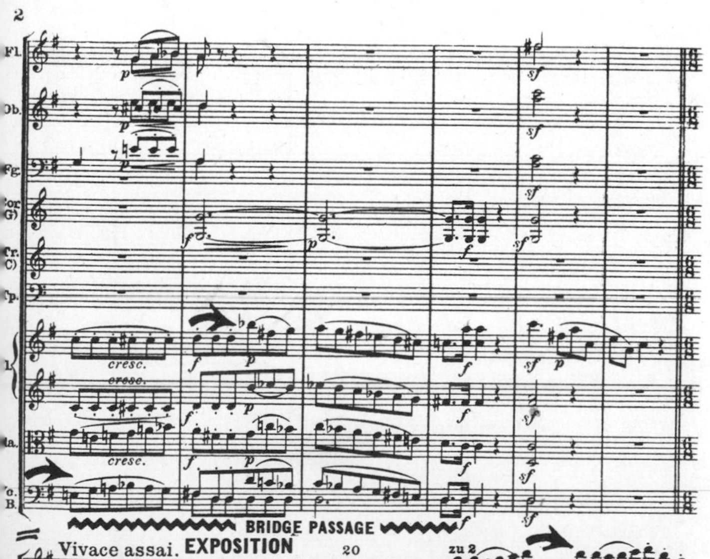

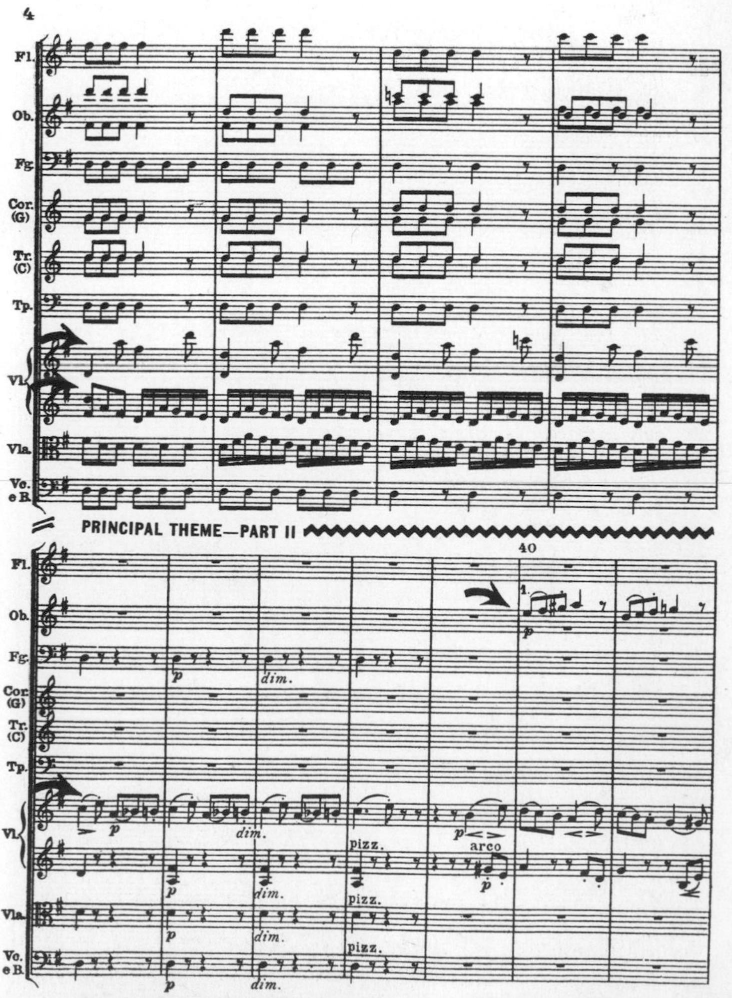

#9A in G major

(35)

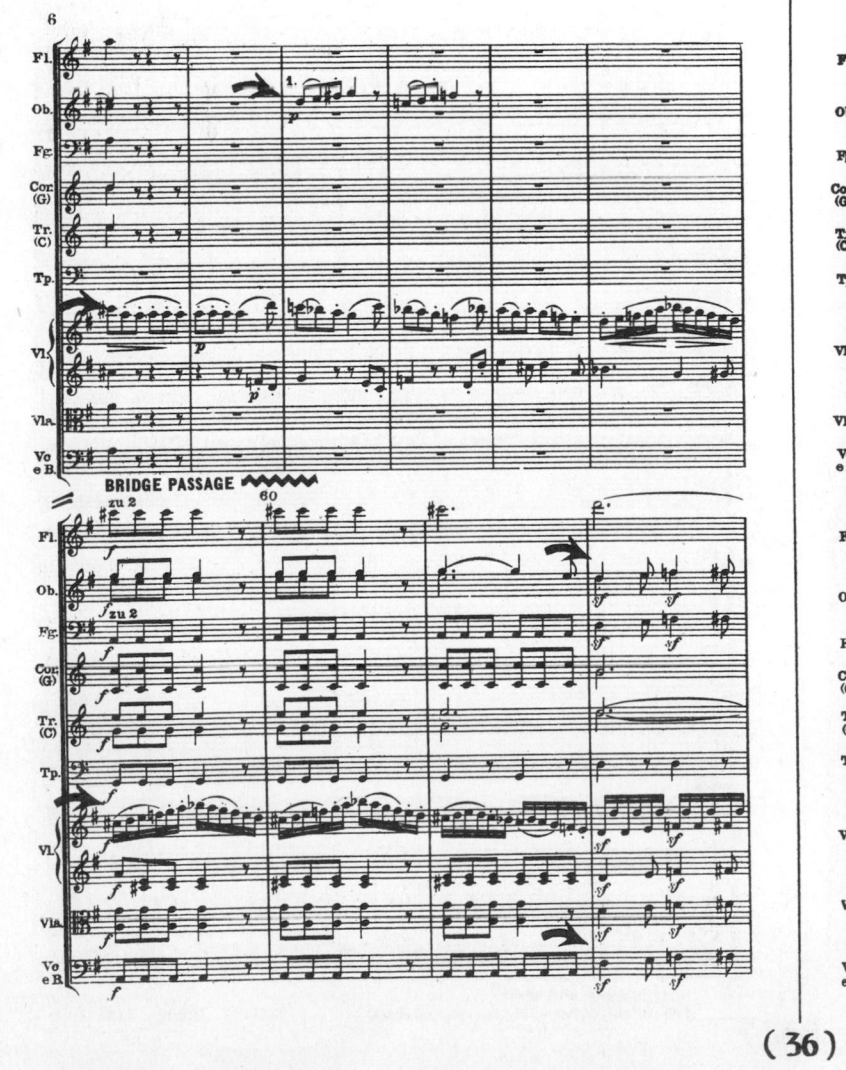

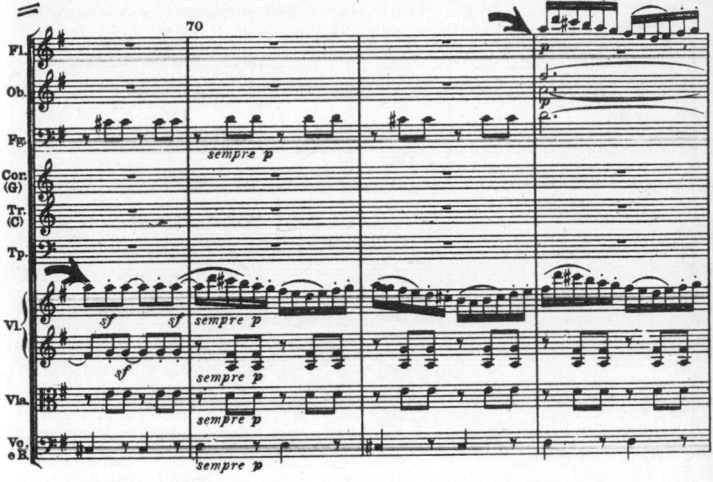

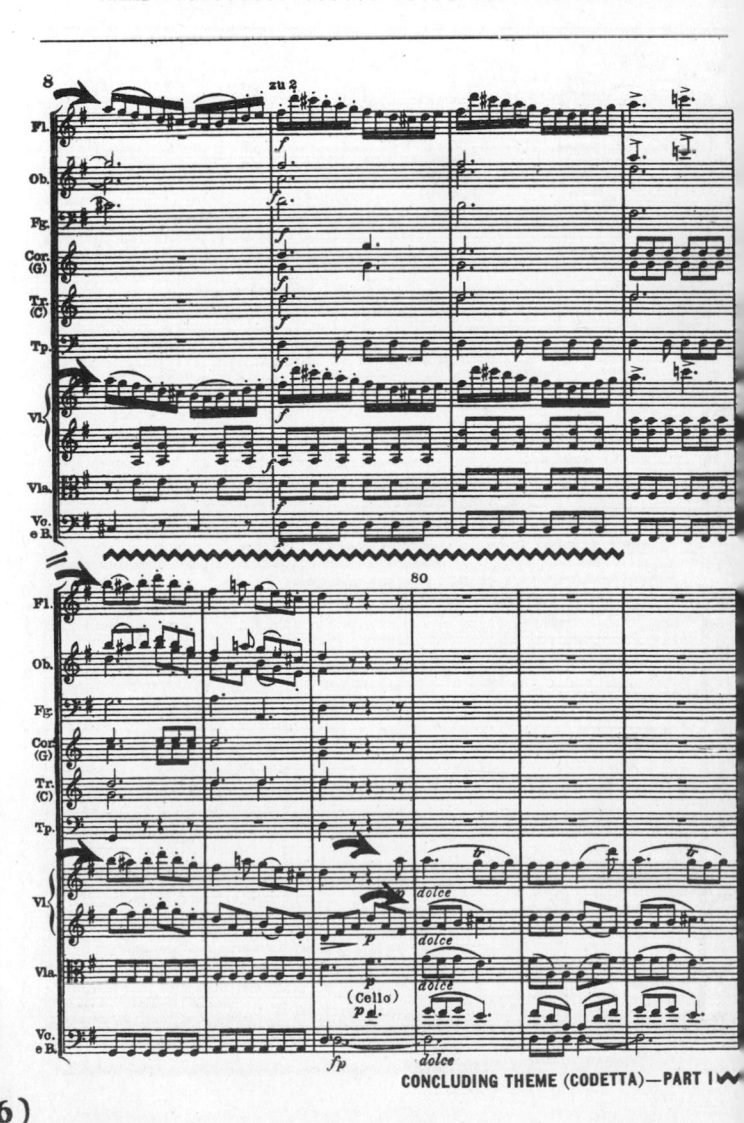

SUBORDINATE

THEME

BRIDGE PASSAGE

CONCLUDING THEME (CODETTA)—PART I

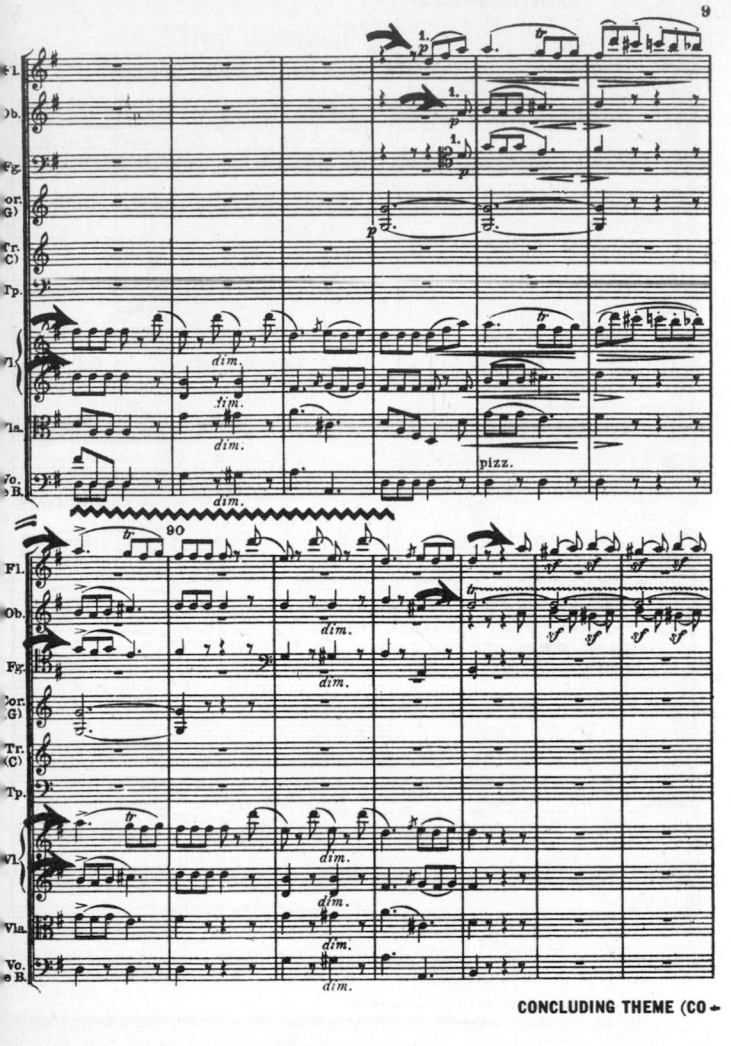

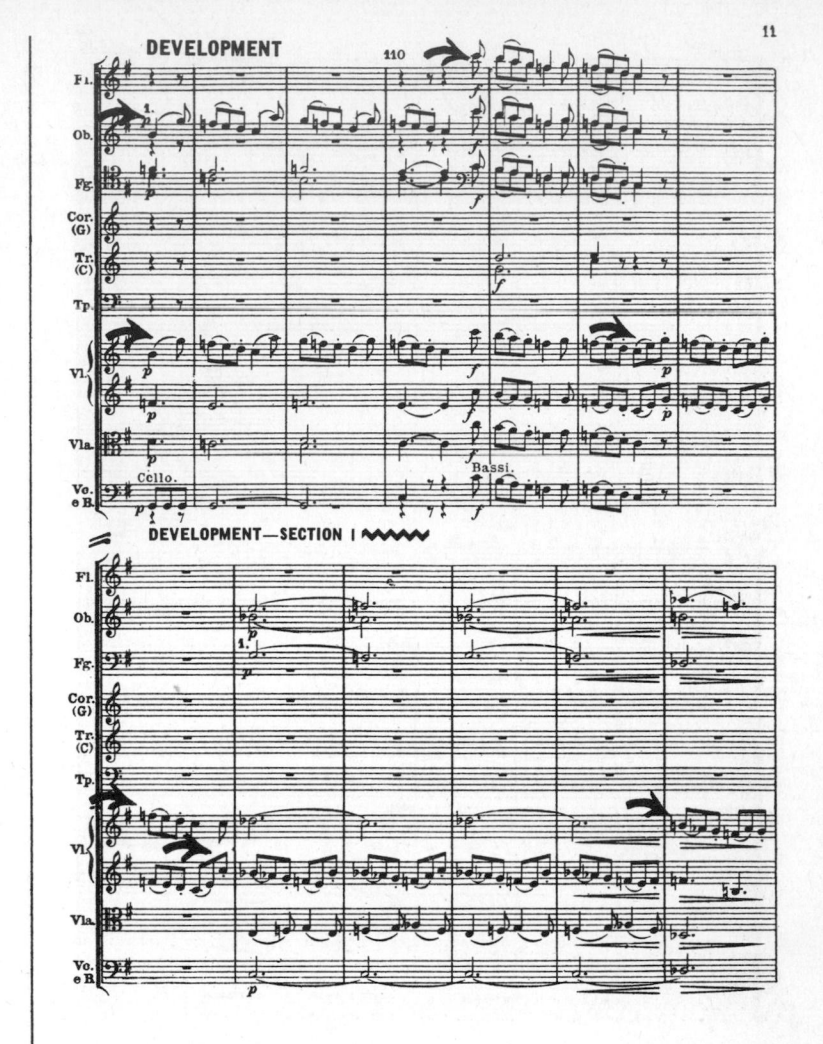

DEVELOPMENT—SECTION I ∿∿∿∿

CONCLUDING THEME (CO→

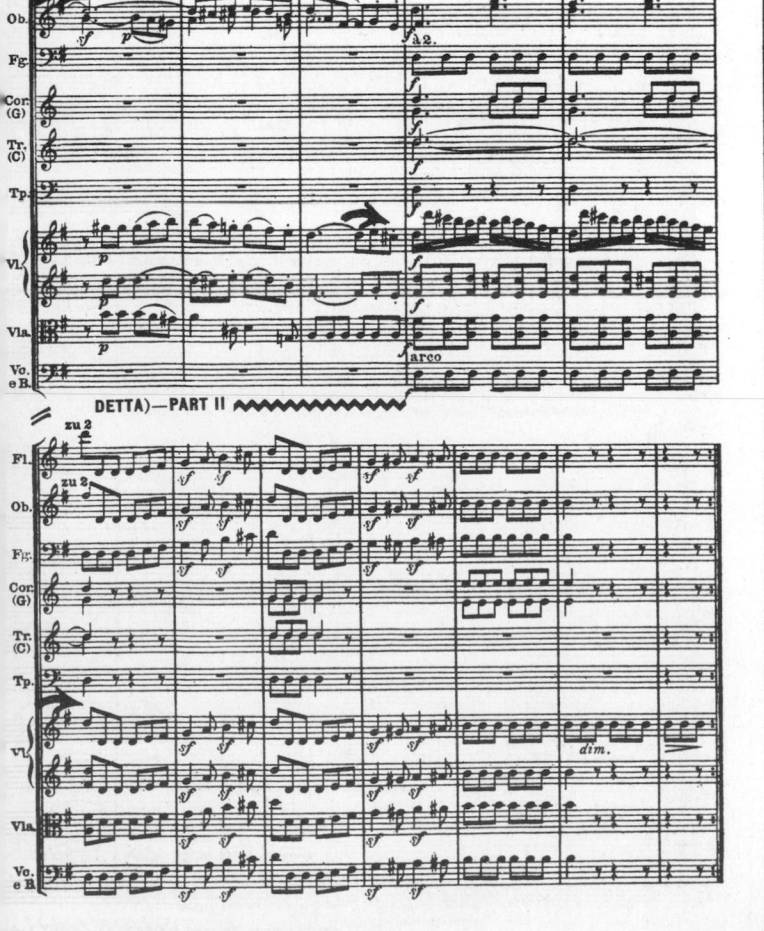

DETTA)—PART II ∿∿∿∿∿∿

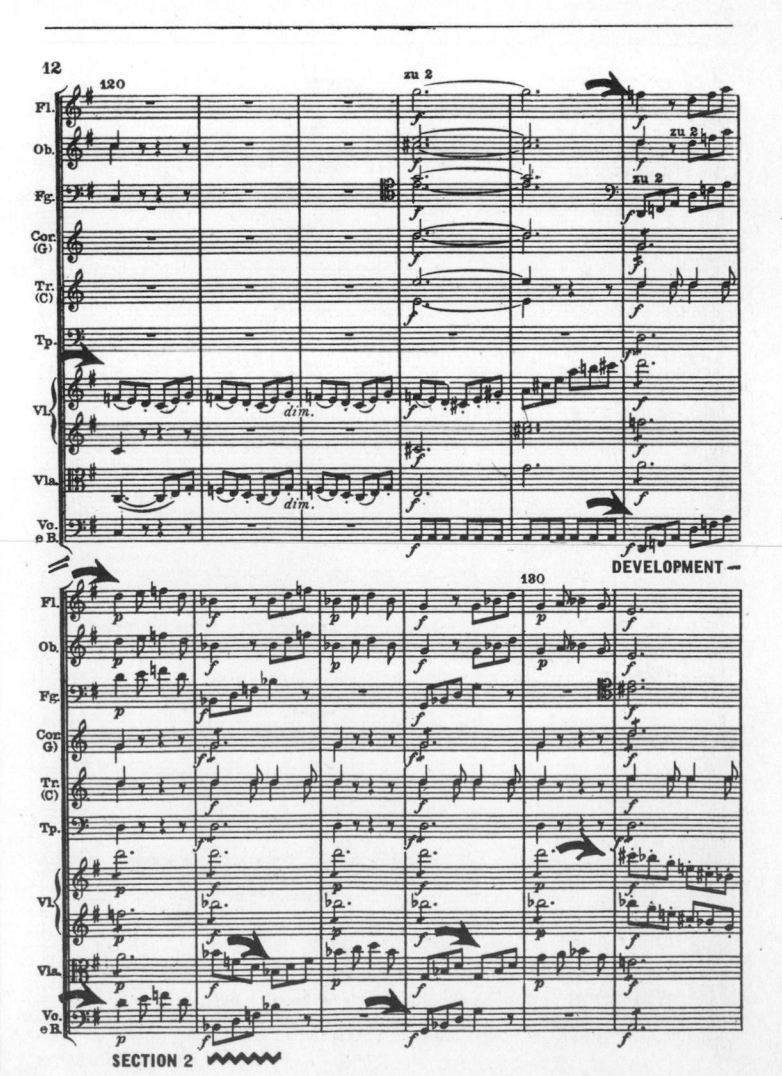

DEVELOPMENT—

SECTION 2 ∿∿∿∿

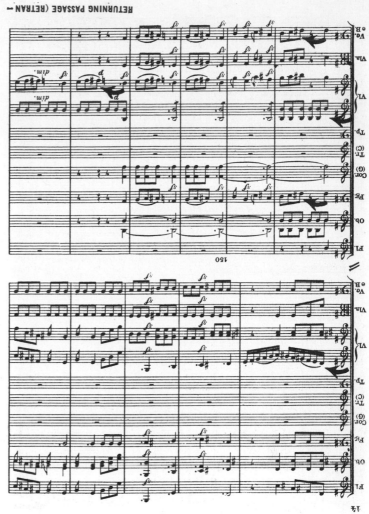
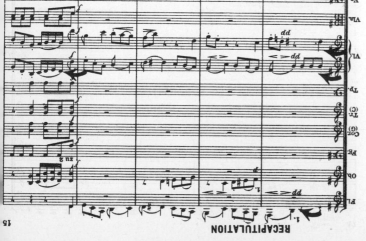
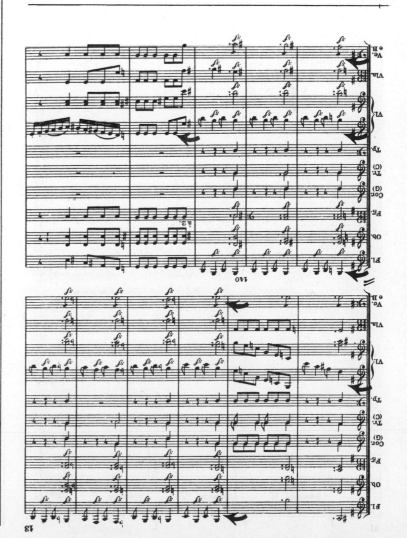
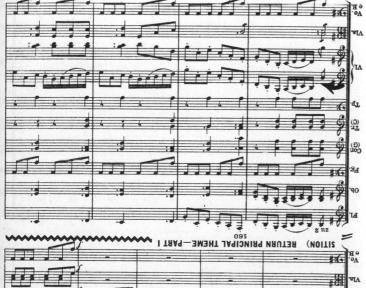

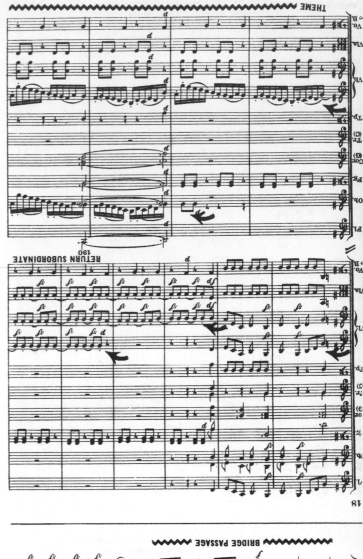

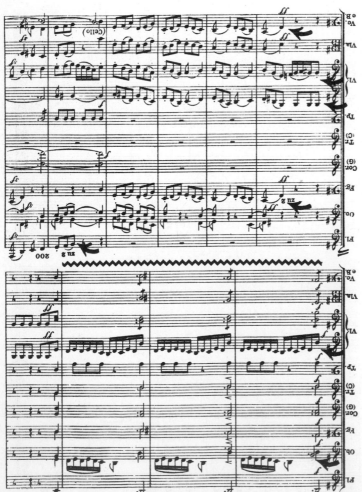

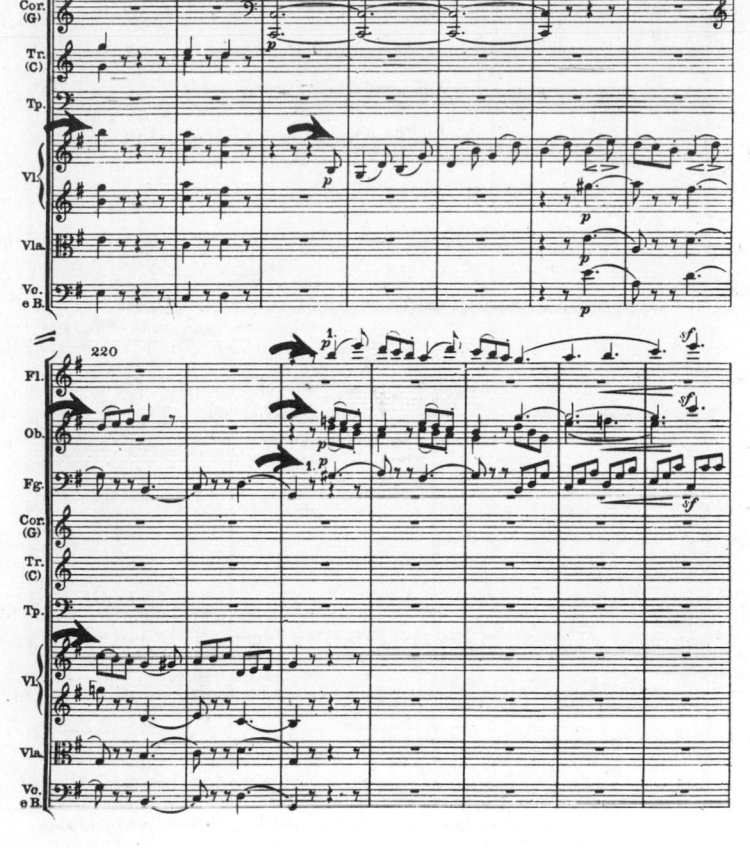

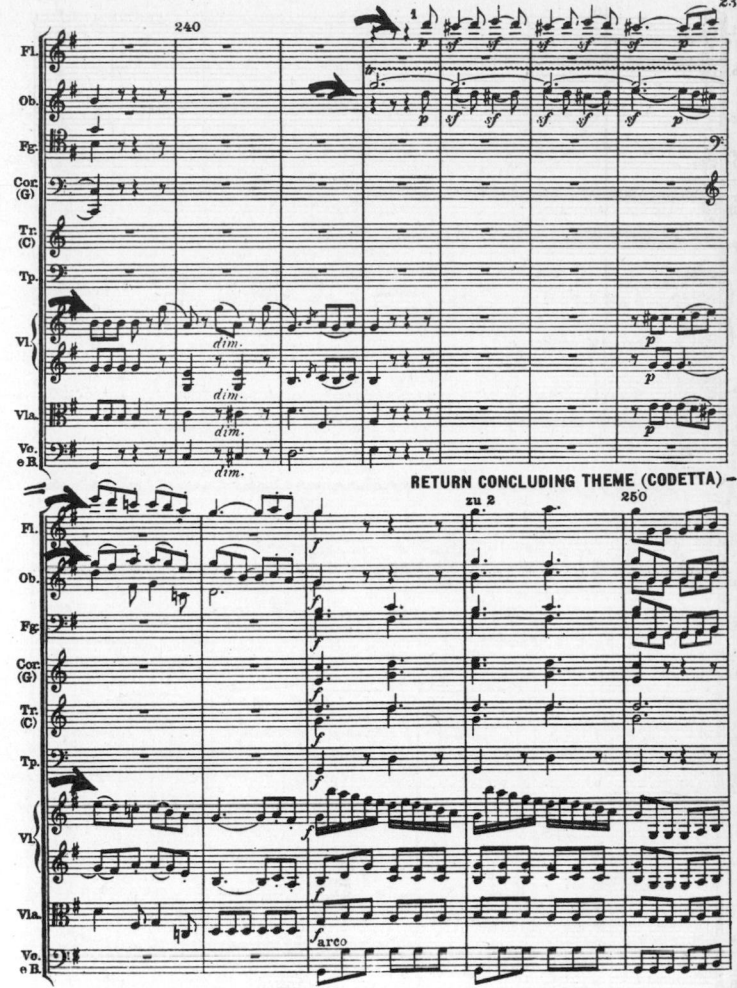

RETURN CONCLUDING THEME (CODETTA)—

PART II

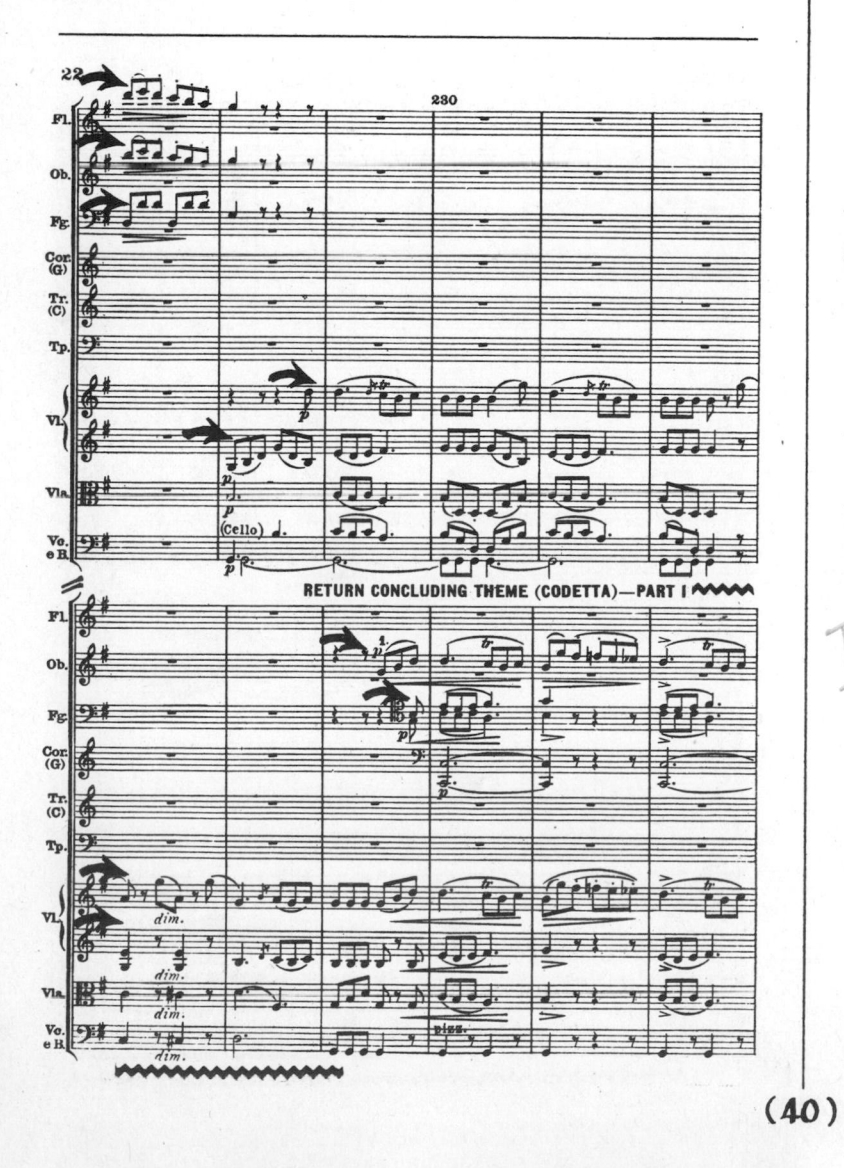

RETURN CONCLUDING THEME (CODETTA)—PART I

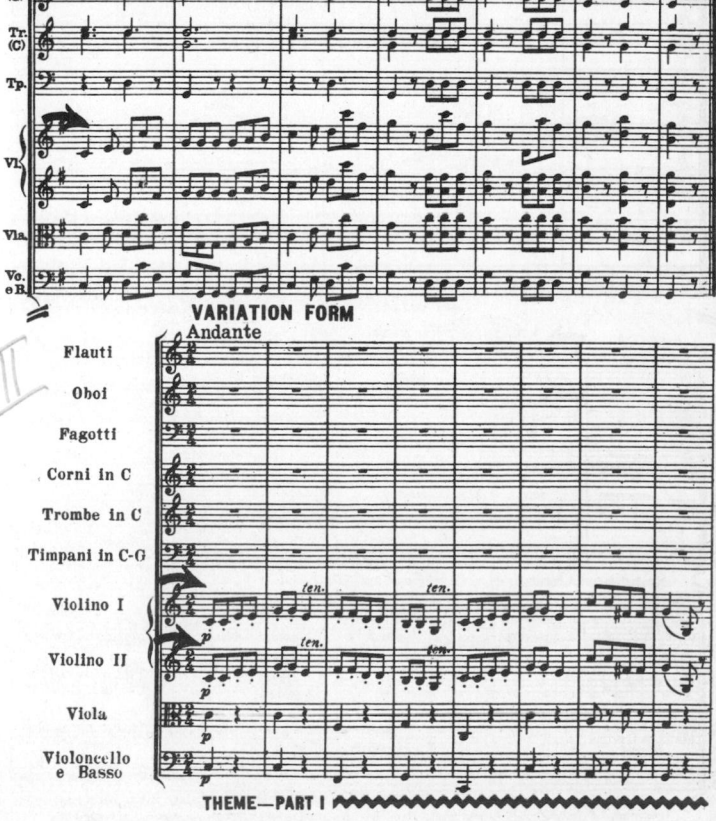

VARIATION FORM

Andante

Flauti	
Oboi	
Fagotti	
Corni in C	
Trombe in C	
Timpani in C-G	
Violino I	
Violino II	
Viola	
Violoncello e Basso	

THEME—PART I

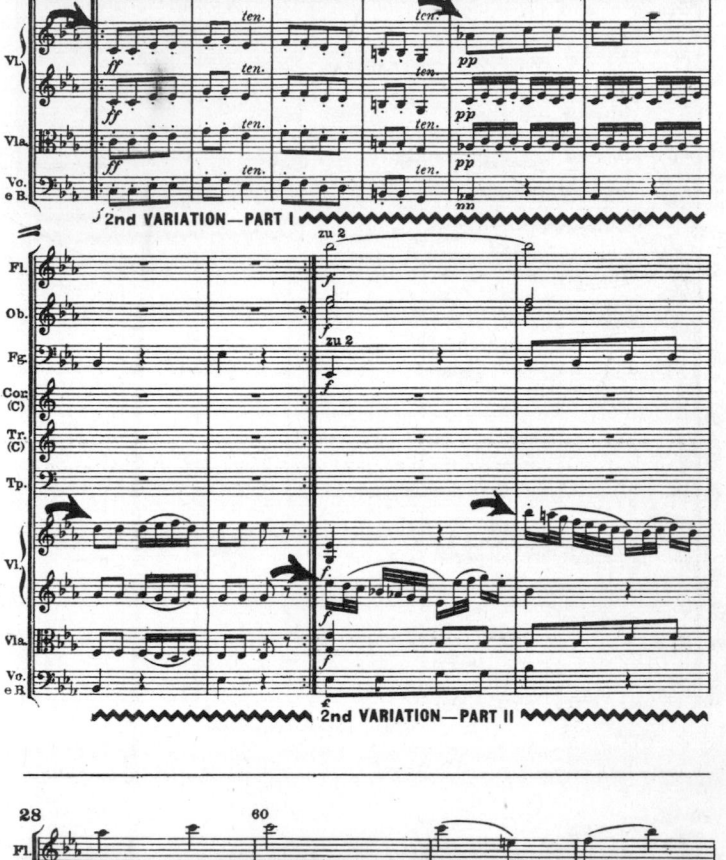

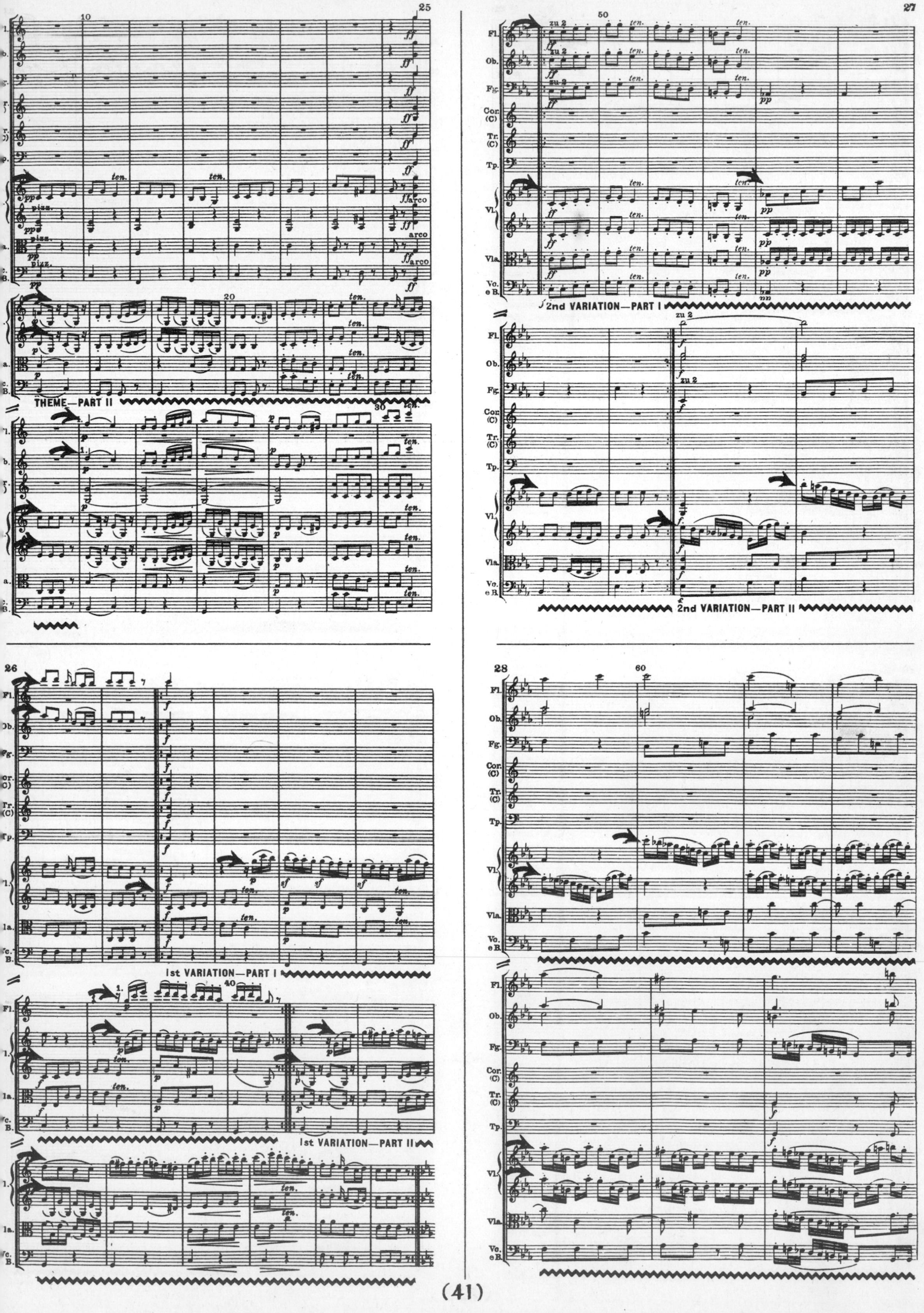
25
26
27
28
THEME—PART II
1st VARIATION—PART I
1st VARIATION—PART II
2nd VARIATION—PART I
2nd VARIATION—PART II
Fl.
Ob.
Fg.
Cor. (C)
Tr. (C)
Tp.
Vl.
Vla.
Vc. e B.
zu 2
ten.
pizz.
arco

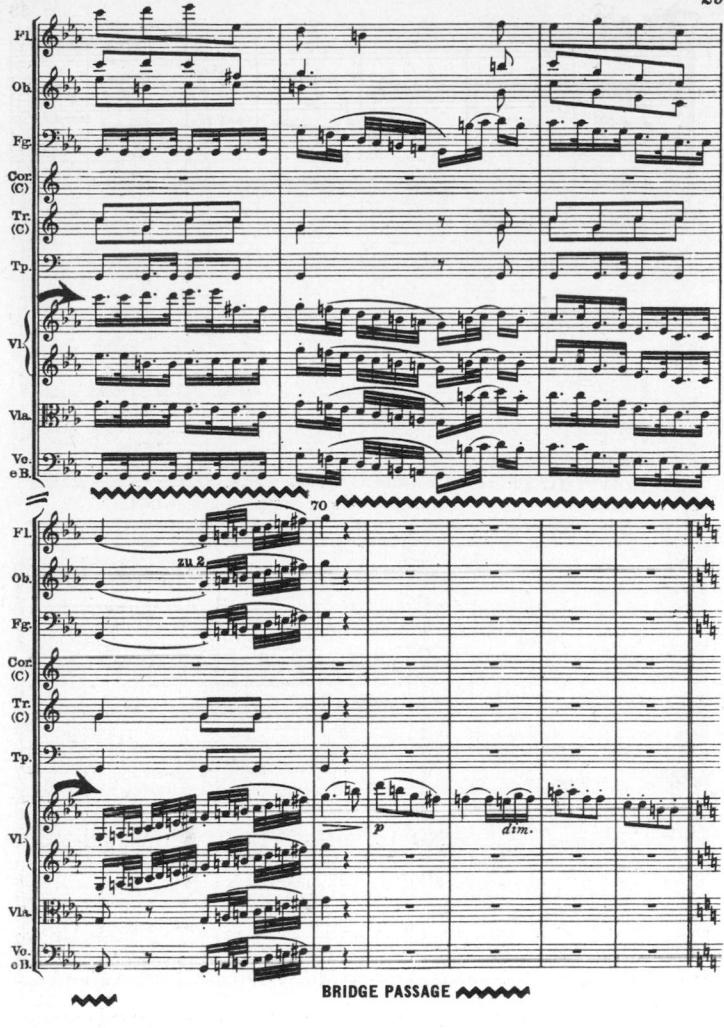

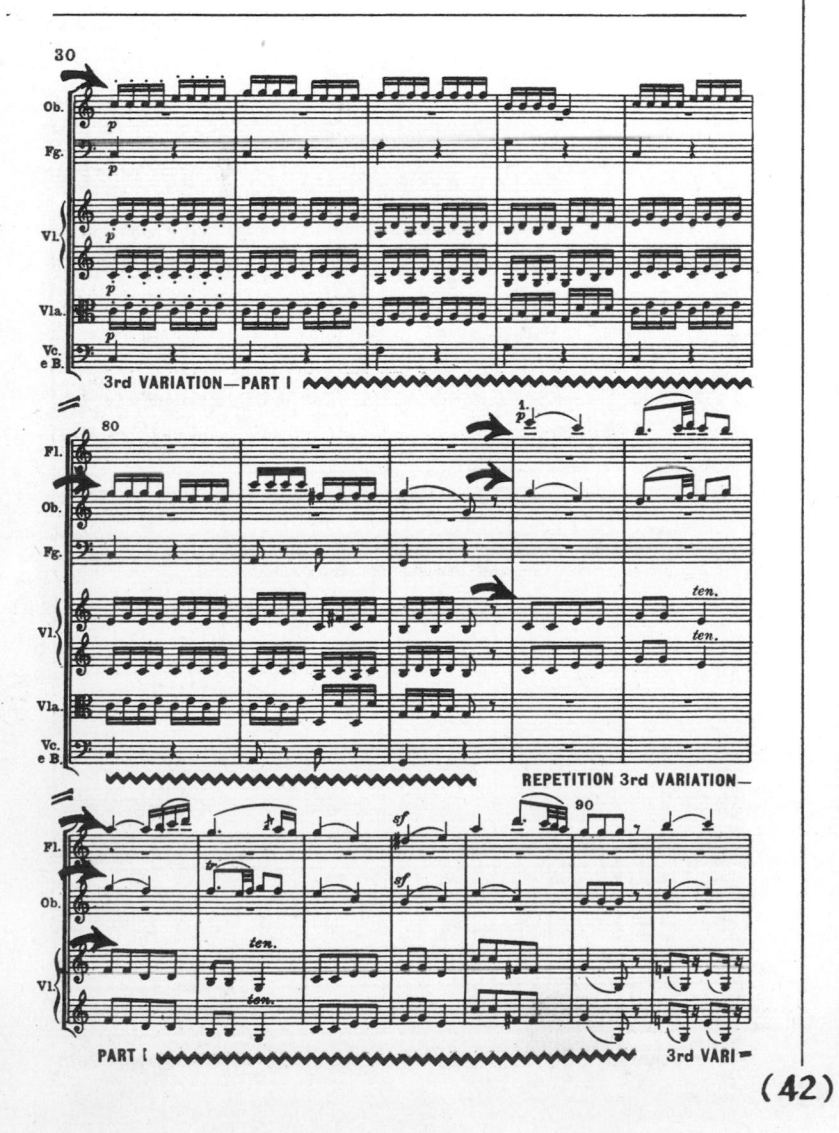

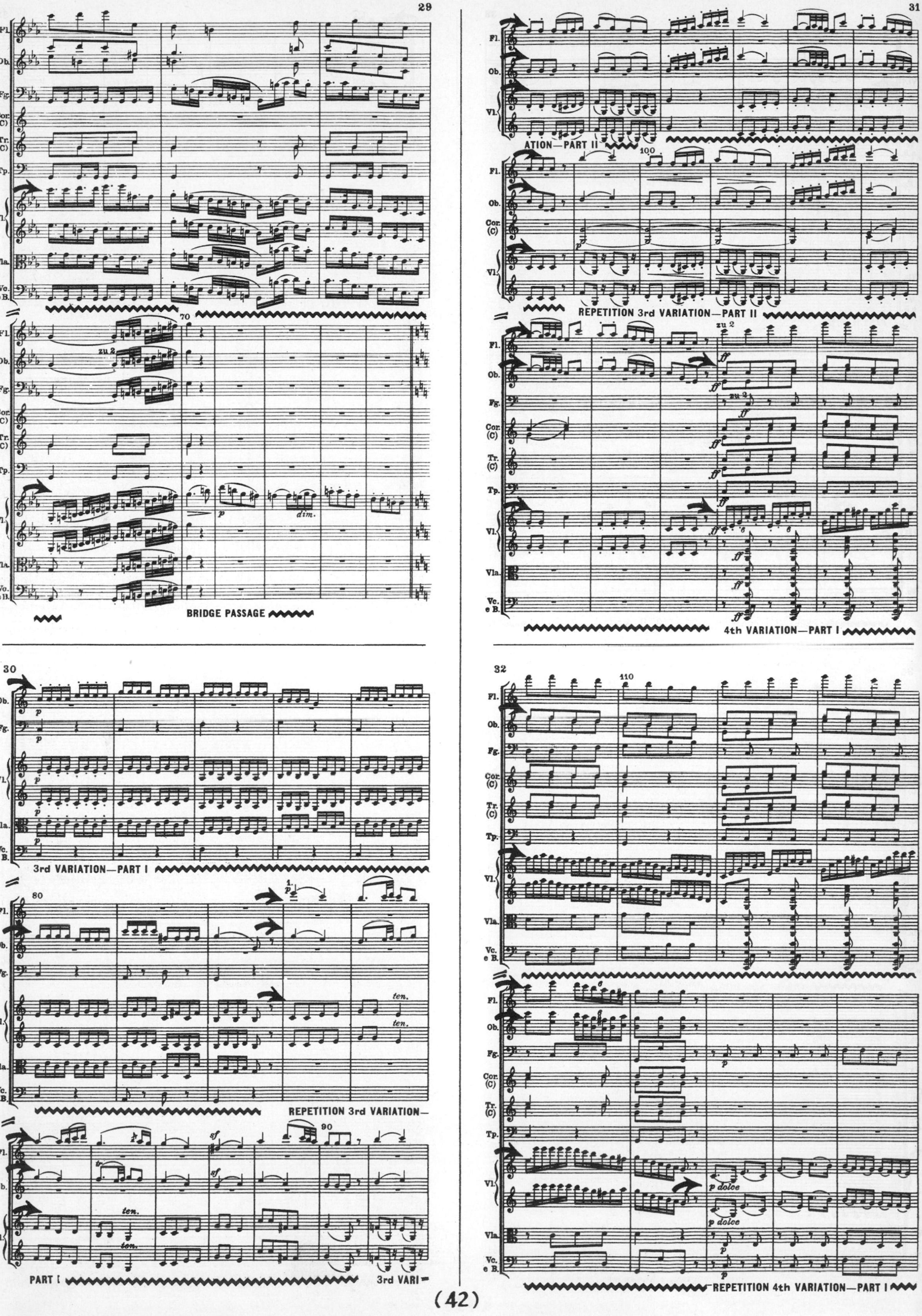

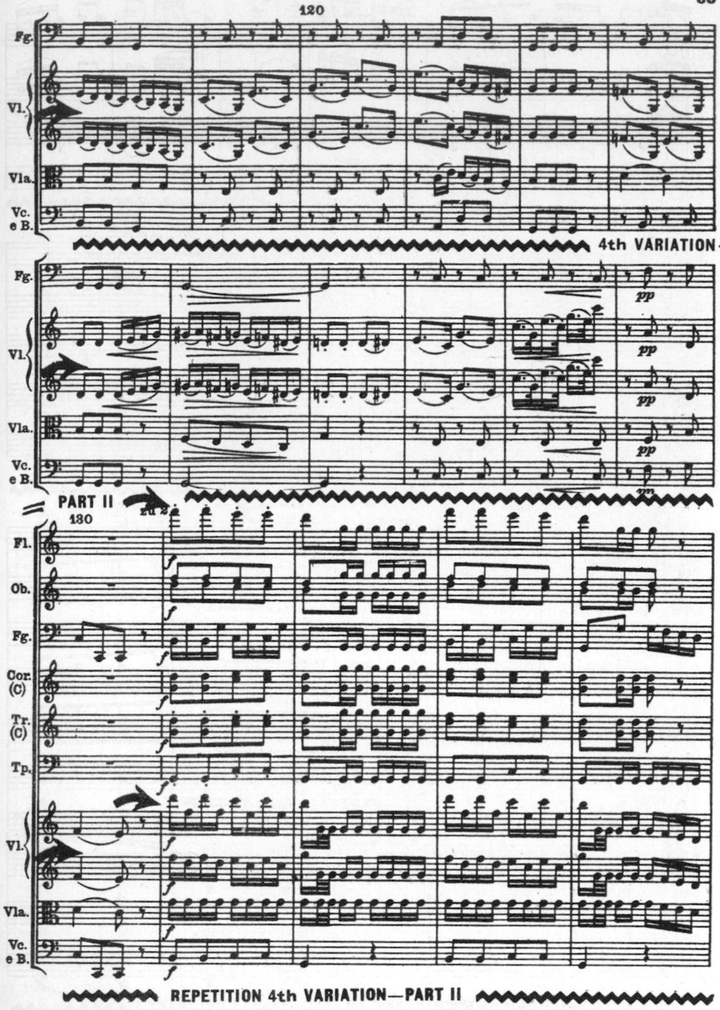
120
Fg.
Vl.
Vla.
Vc. e B.
4th VARIATION
pp
PART II
zu 2
130
Fl.
Ob.
Fg.
Cor. (C)
Tr. (C)
Tp.
f
REPETITION 4th VARIATION—PART II

Fl.
Ob.
Fg.
Cor. (C)
Tr. (C)
Tp.
Vl.
Vla.
Vc. e B.
1.
p
ten.
sempre dim.
CODA—SECTION 2
150
pp

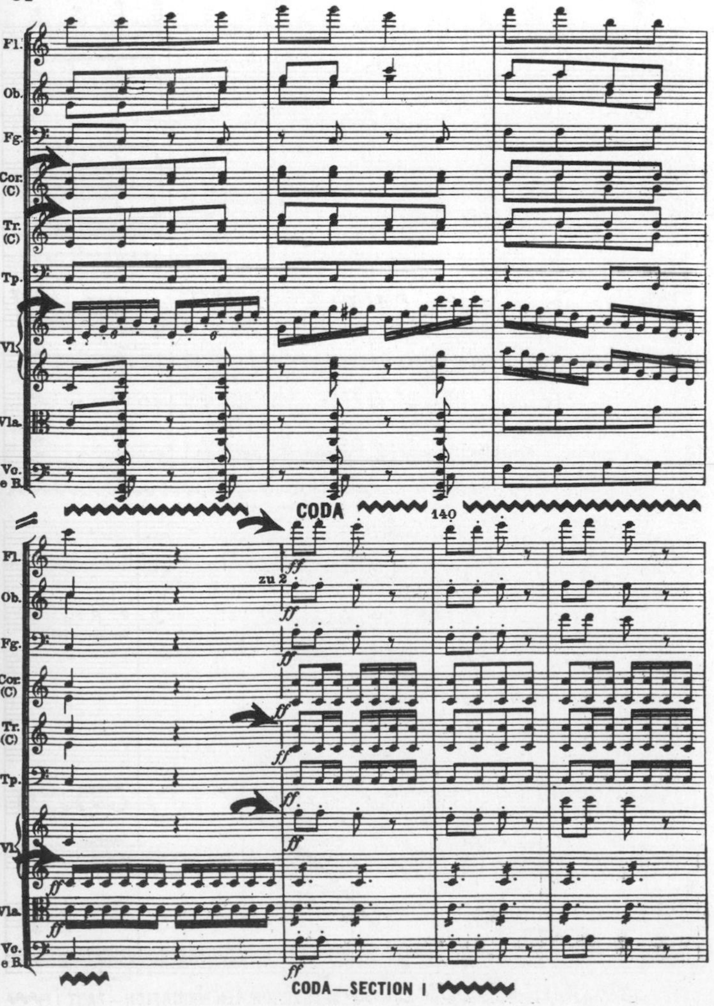
Fl.
Ob.
Fg.
Cor. (C)
Tr. (C)
Tp.
Vl.
Vla.
Vc. e B.
CODA
140
zu 2
ff
CODA—SECTION I

Menuetto SONG FORM

Allegro molto

zu 2
Flauti
Oboi
Fagotti
Corni in G
Trombe in C
Timpani in D-G
Violino I
Violino II
Viola
Violoncello e Basso
f
PRINCIPAL THEME—PART I, 1st PERIOD
1.
p
10
Fl.
Ob.
Fg.
Cor. (G)
Tr. (C)
Tp.
Vl.
Vla.
Vc. e B.
PRINCIPAL THEME—PART I, 2nd PERIOD

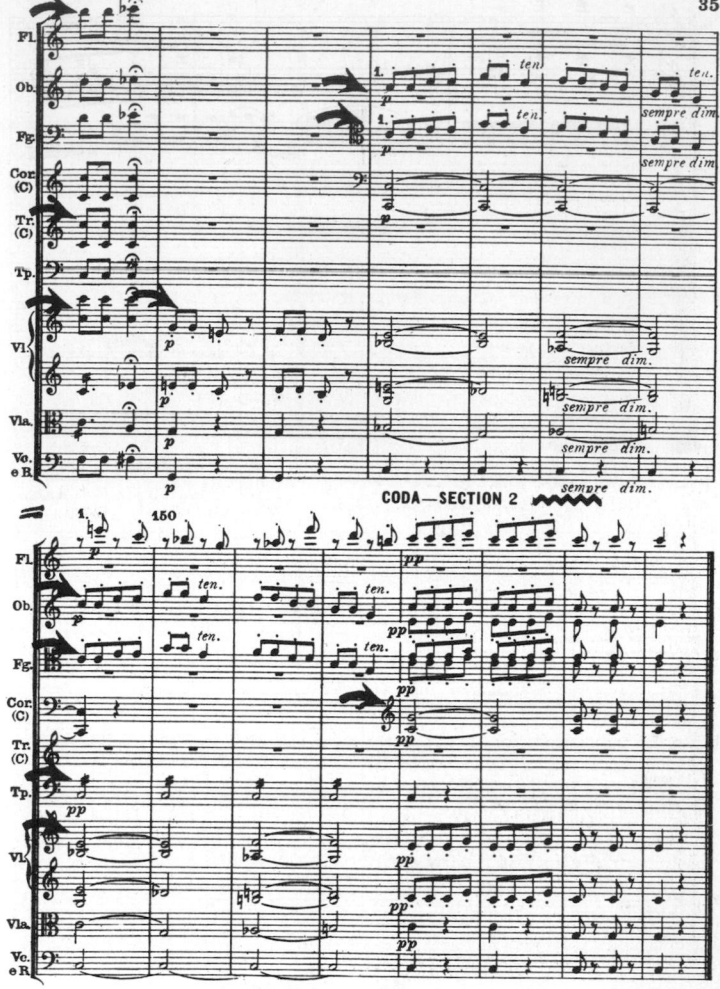

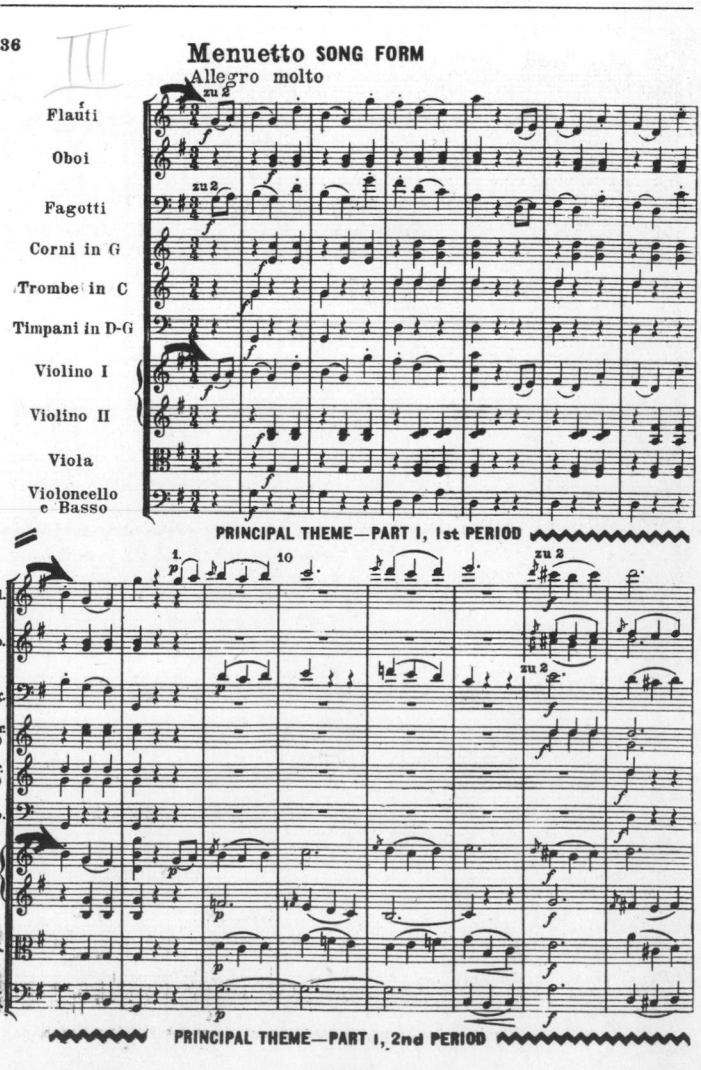

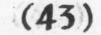

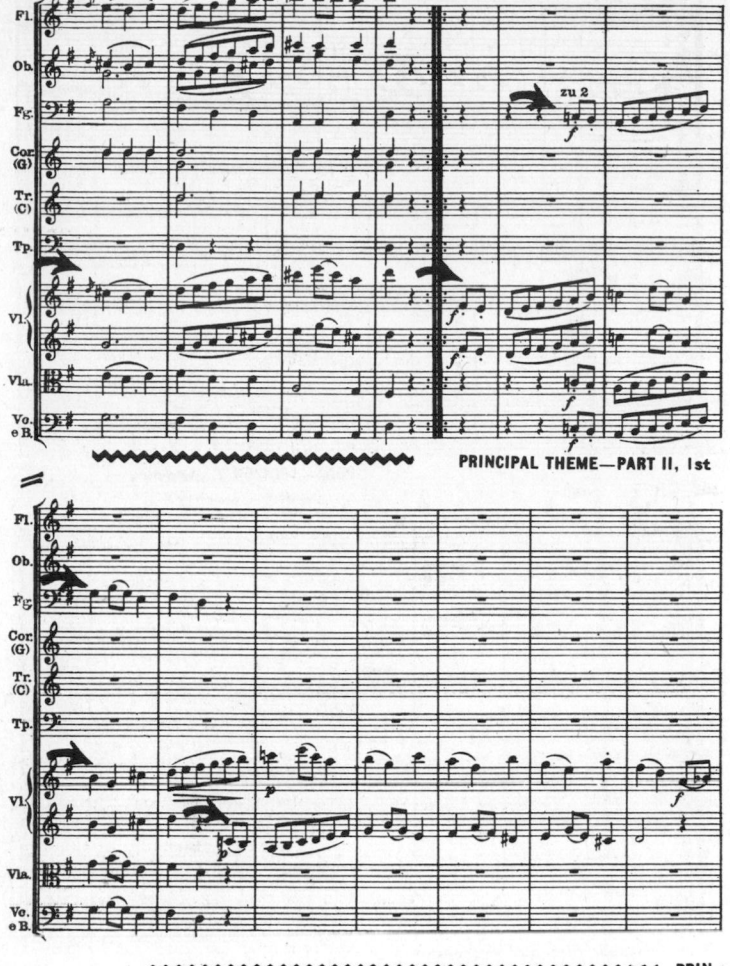

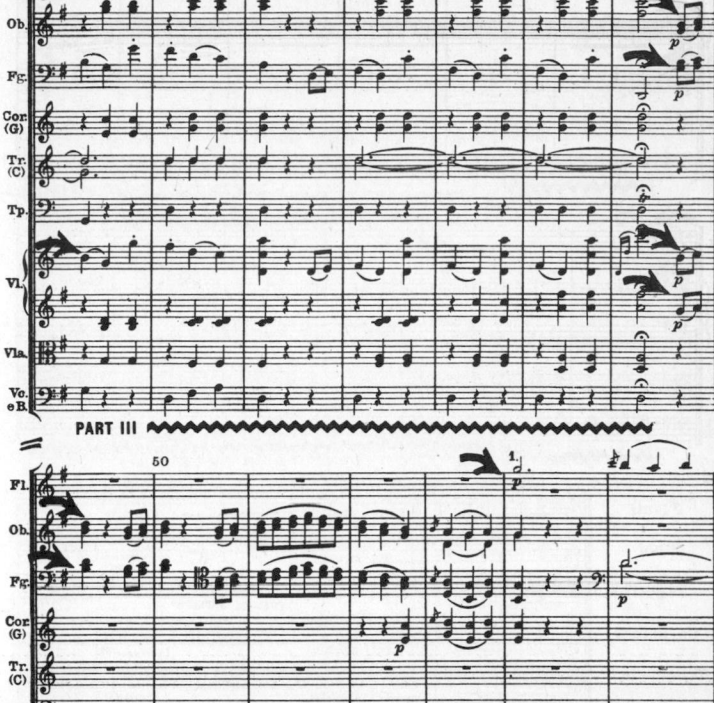

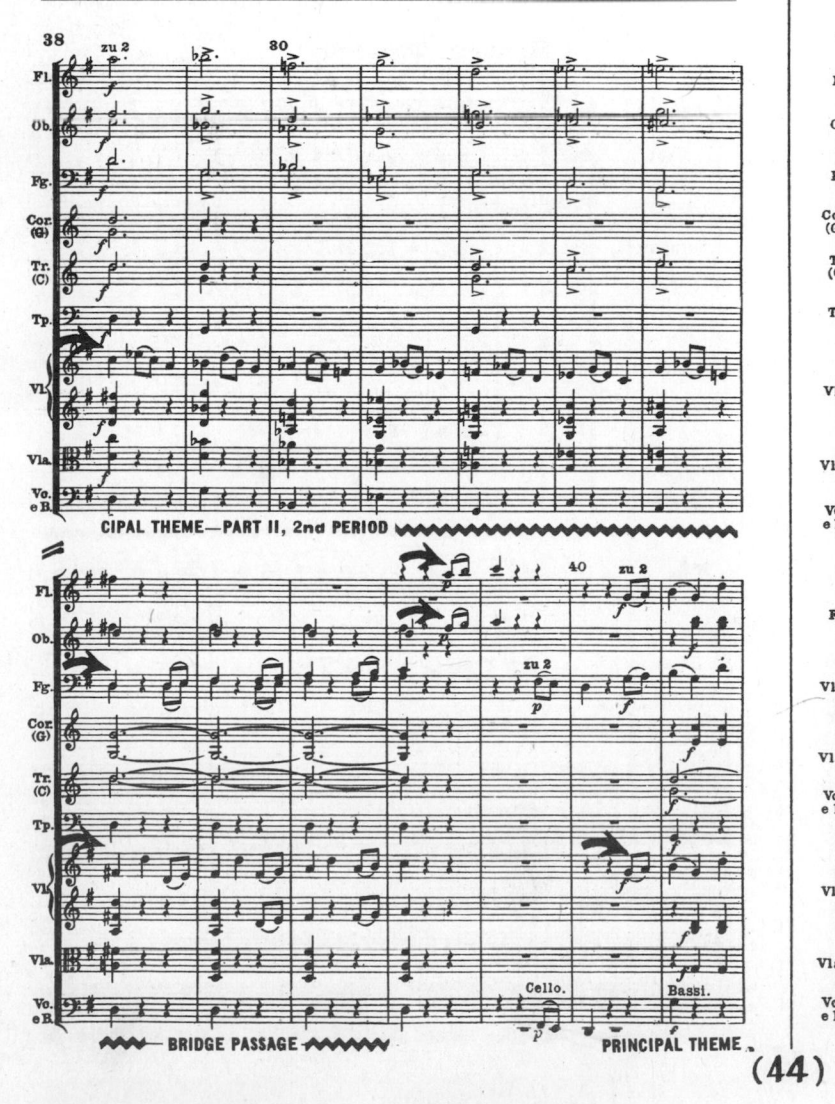

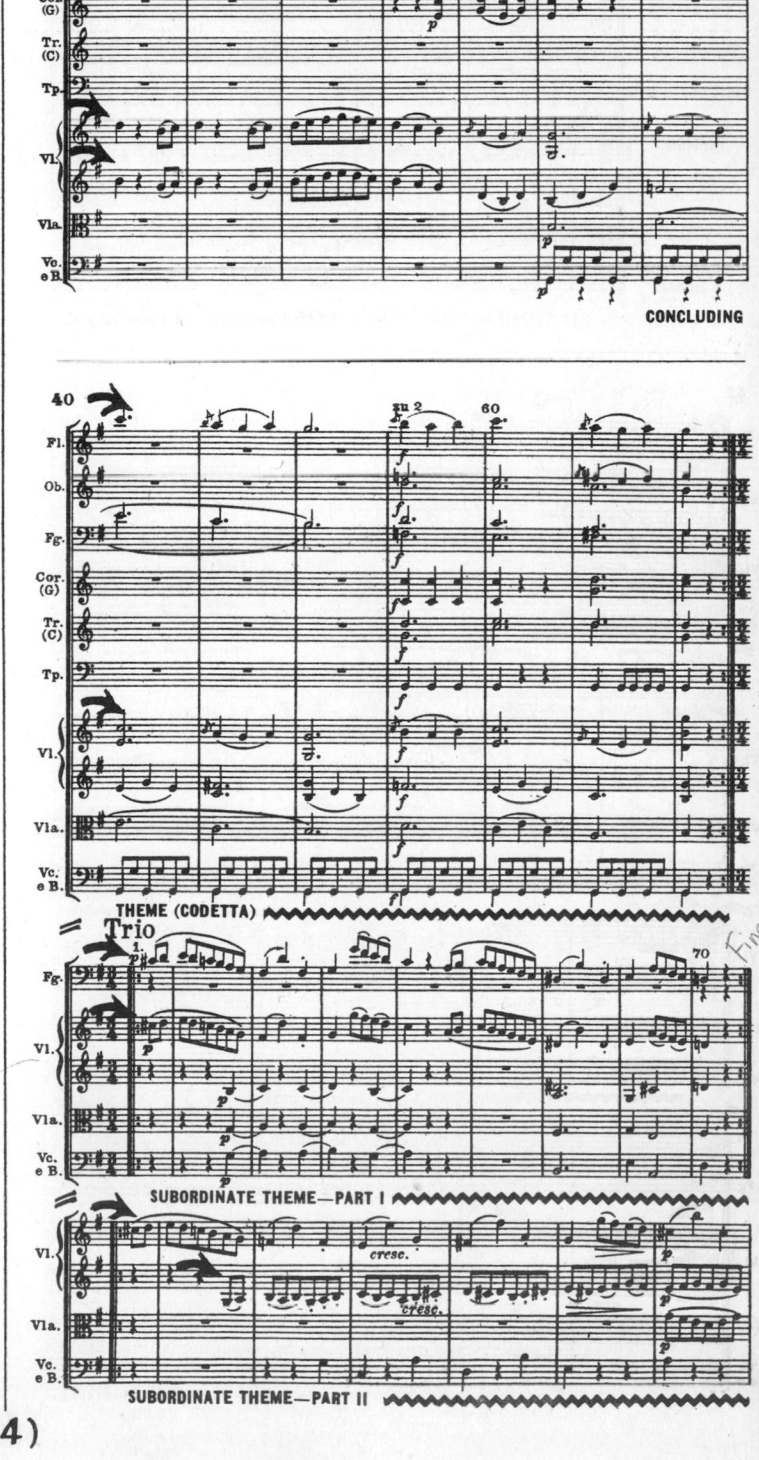

(44)

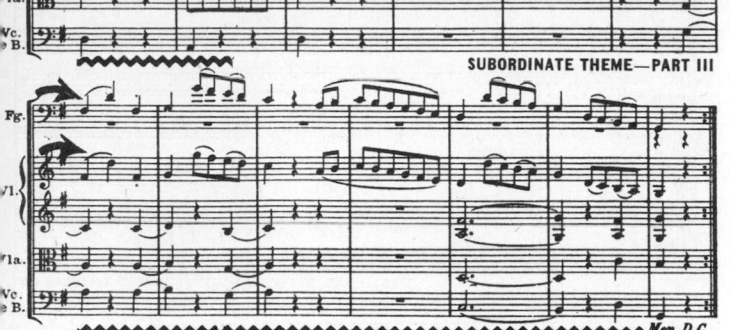

SUBORDINATE THEME—PART III

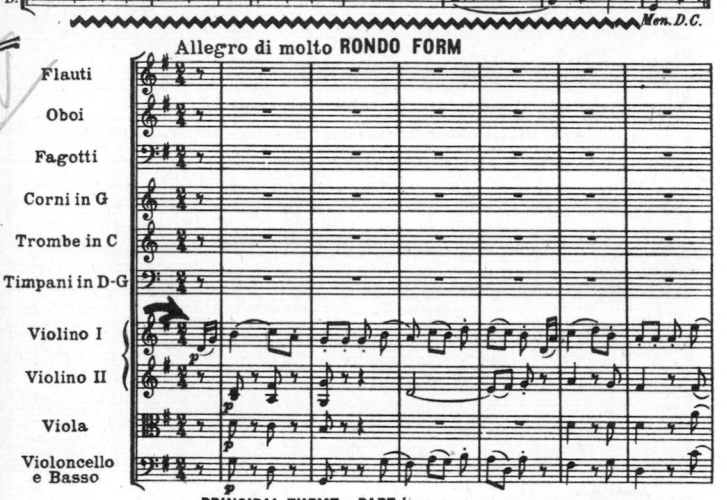

Men. D.C.

Allegro di molto RONDO FORM

Flauti
Oboi
Fagotti
Corni in G
Trombe in C
Timpani in D-G
Violino I
Violino II
Viola
Violoncello e Basso

PRINCIPAL THEME—PART I ～～～～

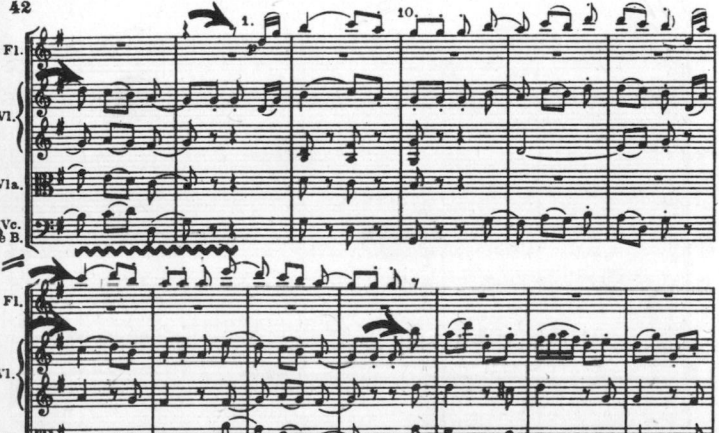

PRINCIPAL THEME—PART II ～～～

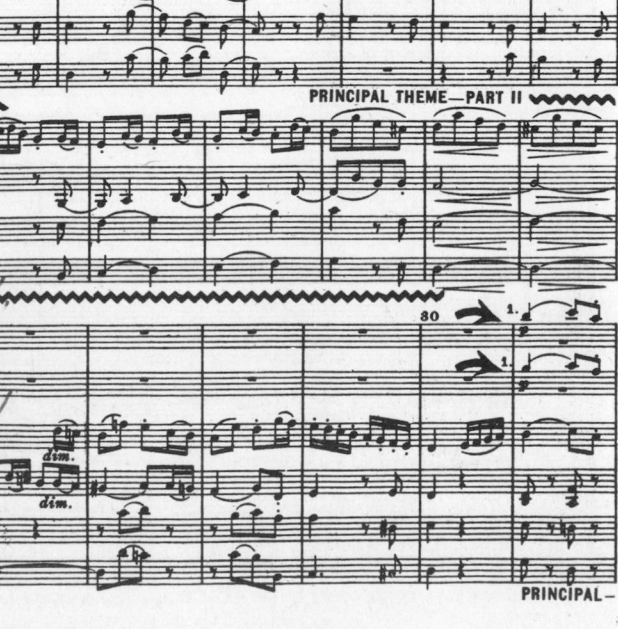

PRINCIPAL—

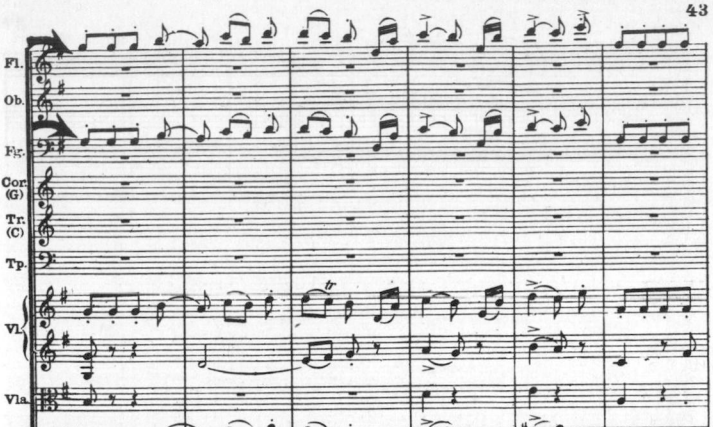

THEME—PART III ～～～～～～～～～～～

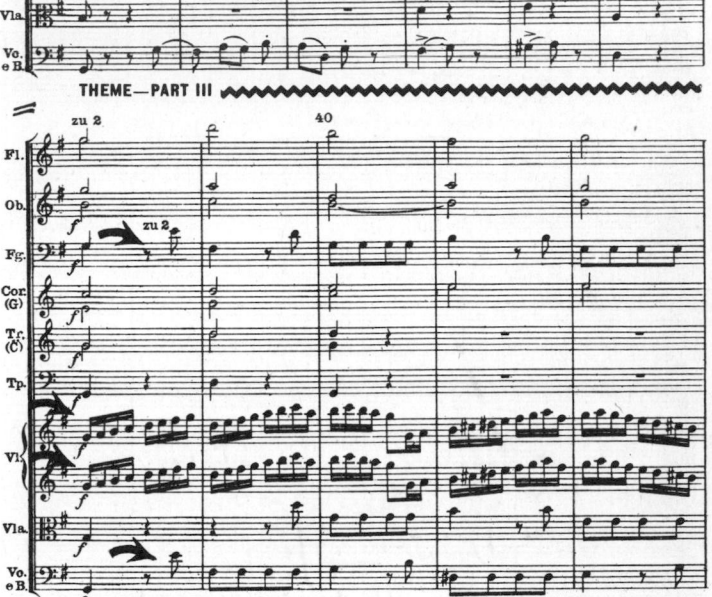

BRIDGE PASSAGE ～～～

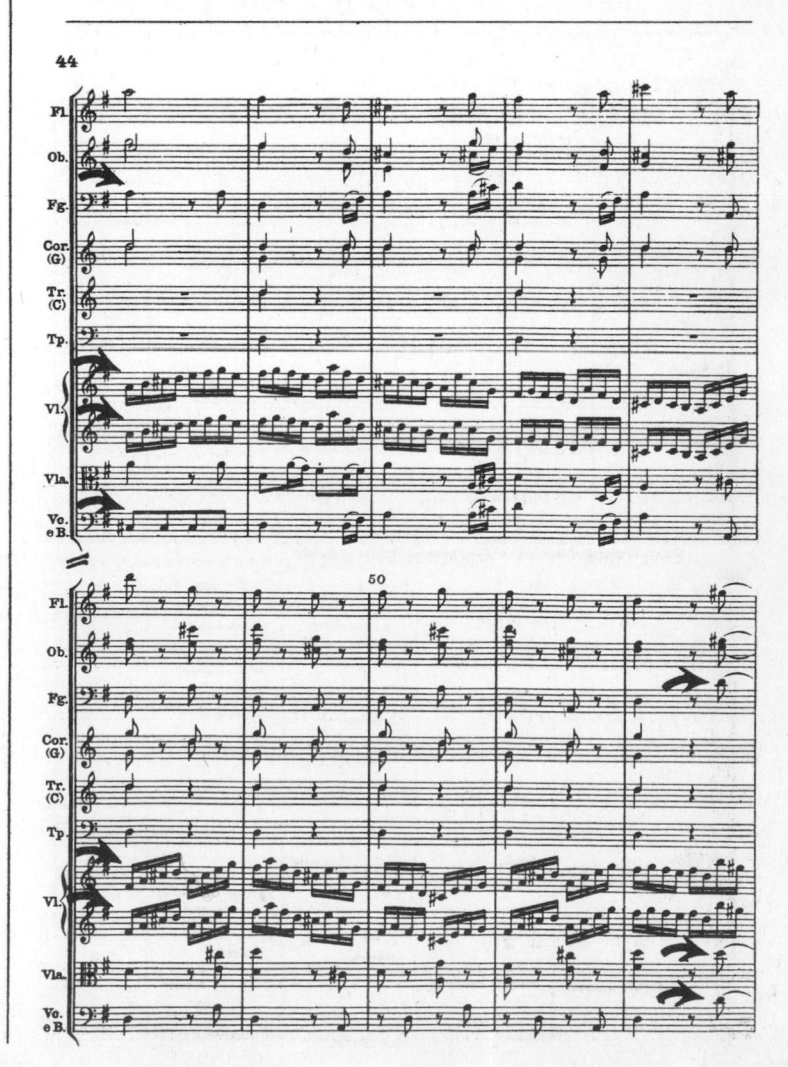

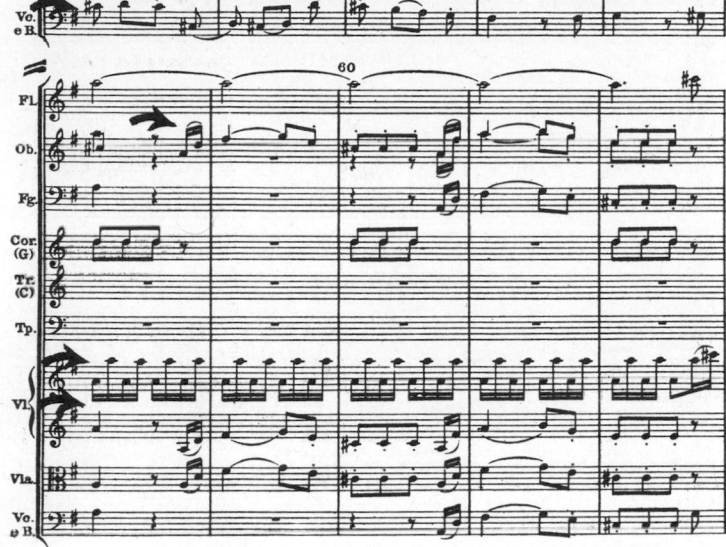

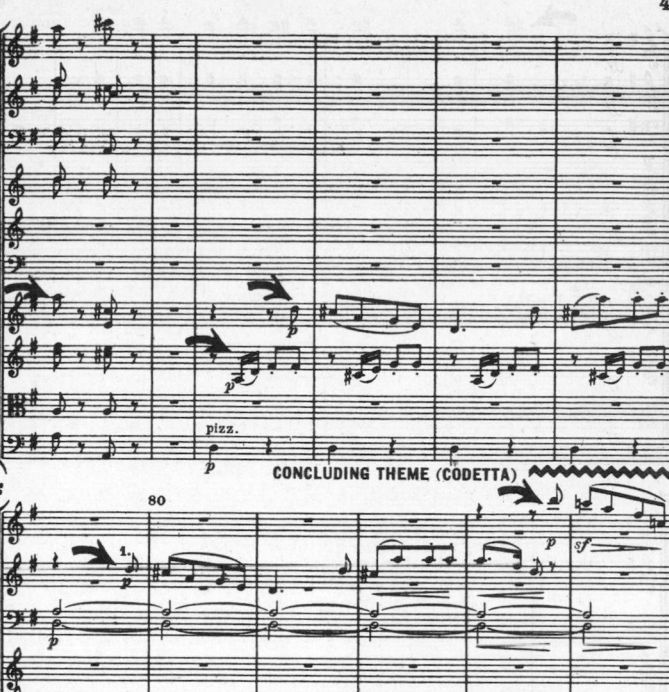

1st SUBORDINATE THEME

CONCLUDING THEME (CODETTA)

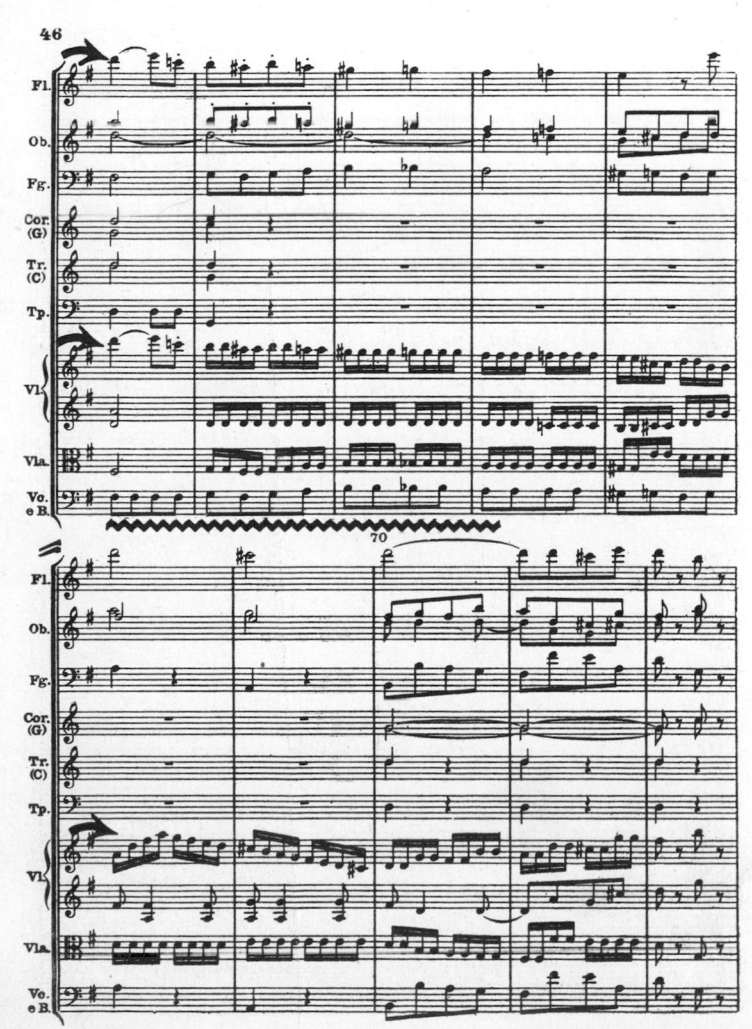

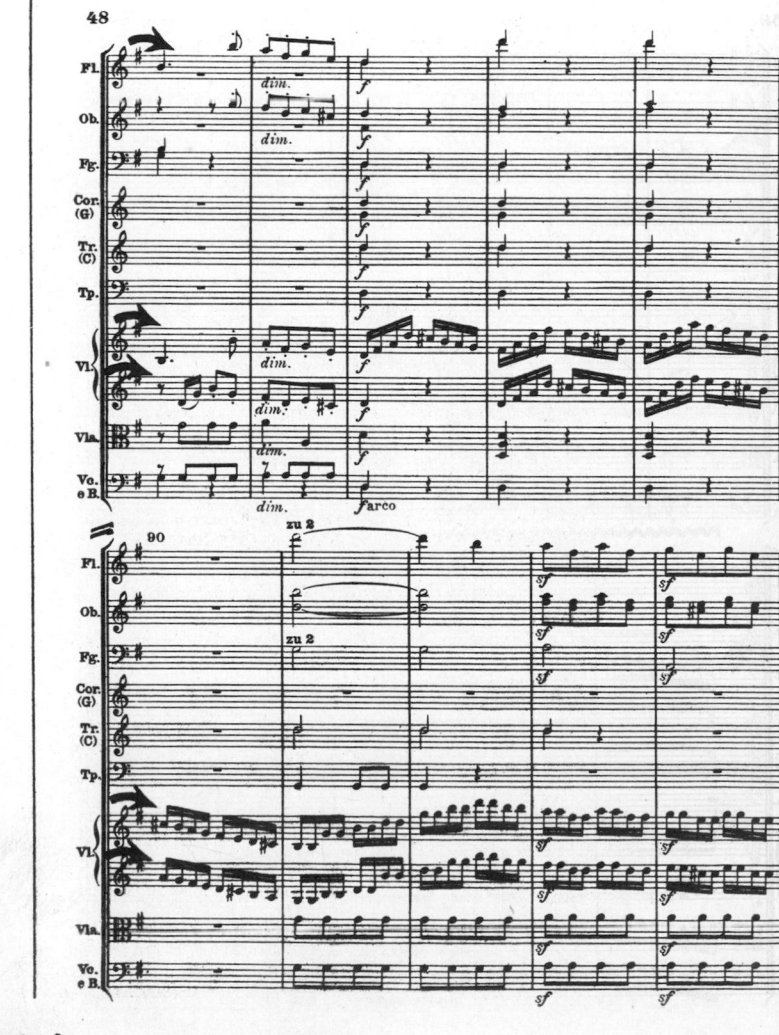

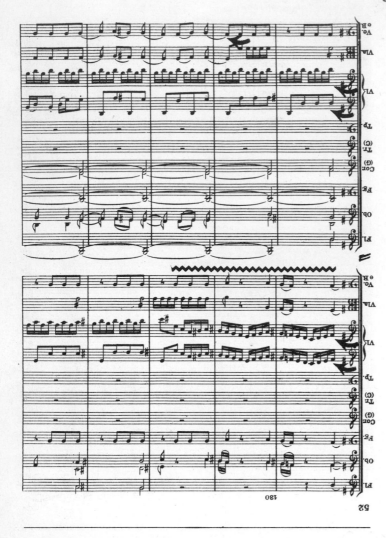
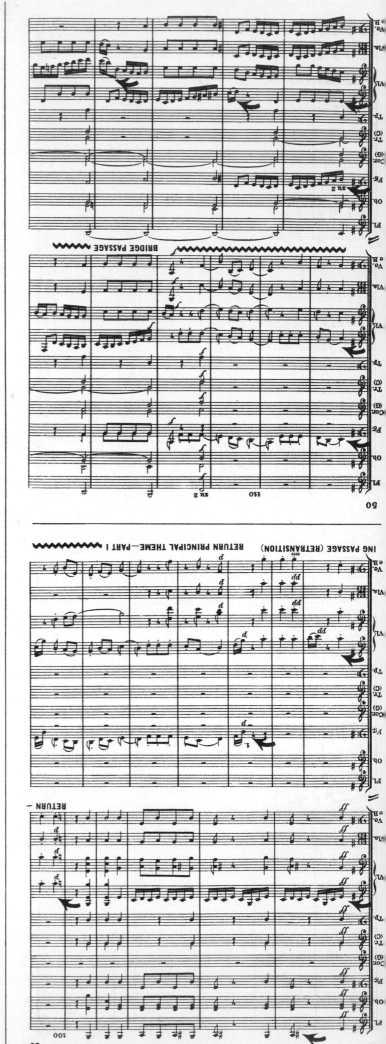
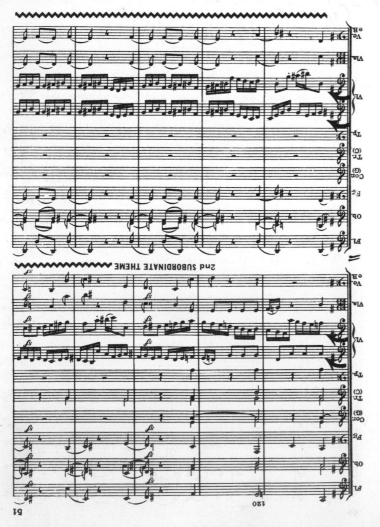

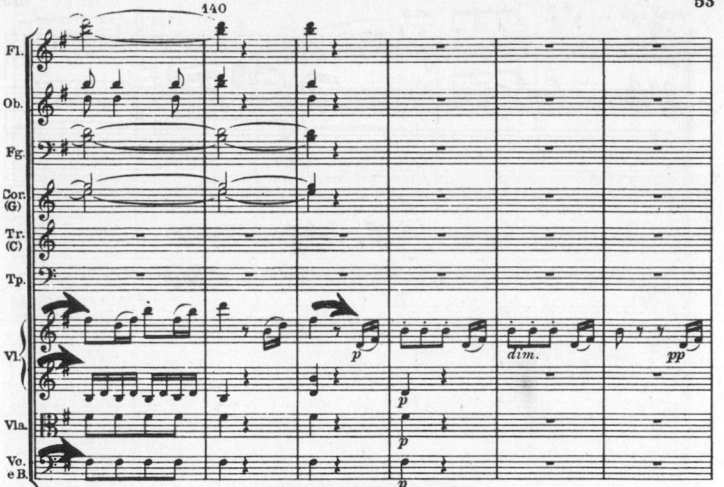

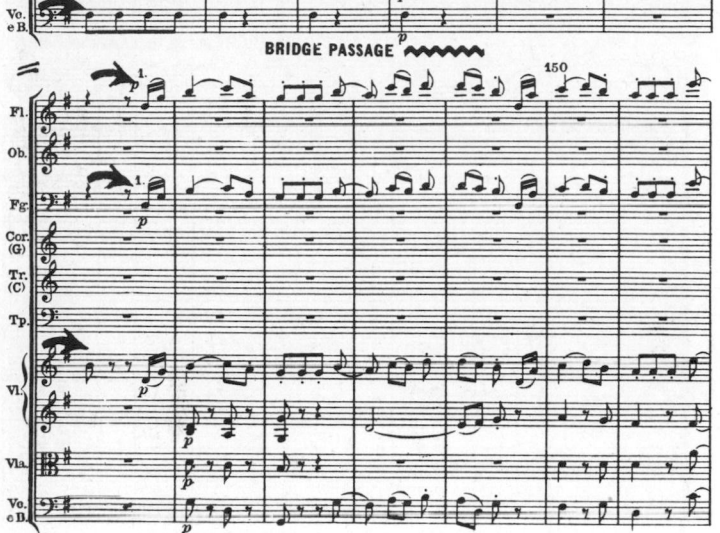

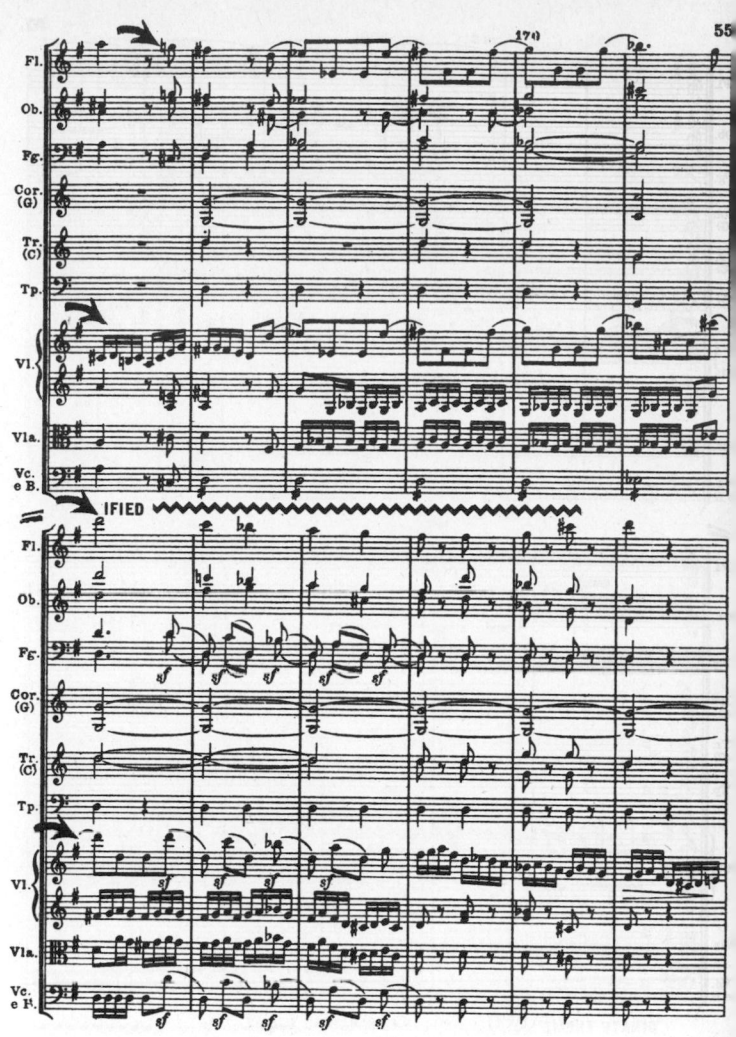

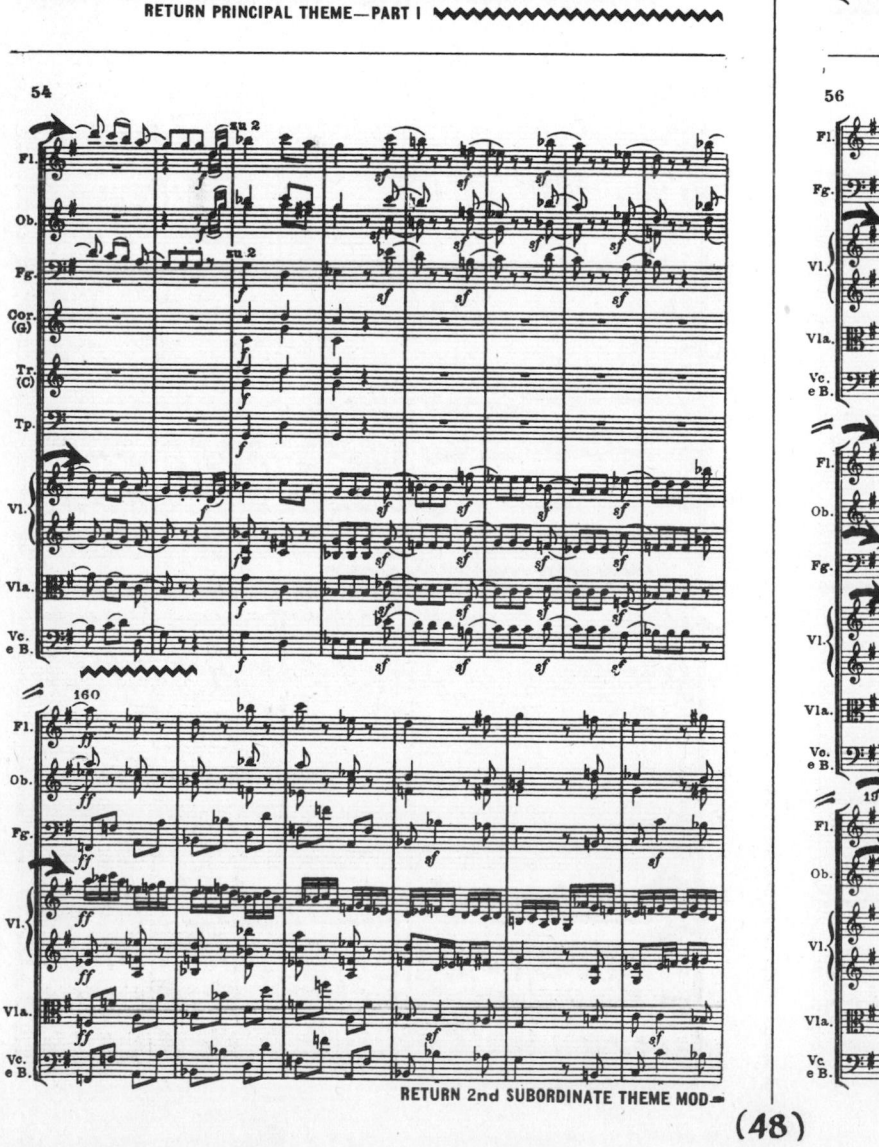

53

BRIDGE PASSAGE 〰〰〰〰

RETURN PRINCIPAL THEME—PART I 〰〰〰〰〰〰〰〰〰〰〰〰

54

RETURN 2nd SUBORDINATE THEME MOD—

55

—IFIED 〰〰〰〰〰〰〰〰〰〰〰〰〰〰〰〰〰

56

RETURN PRINCIPAL   THEME

PART I 〰〰〰〰〰〰〰〰〰〰〰〰〰〰〰〰〰〰〰〰RETURN

PRINCIPAL THEME—PART II 〰〰〰〰〰〰〰〰

(48)

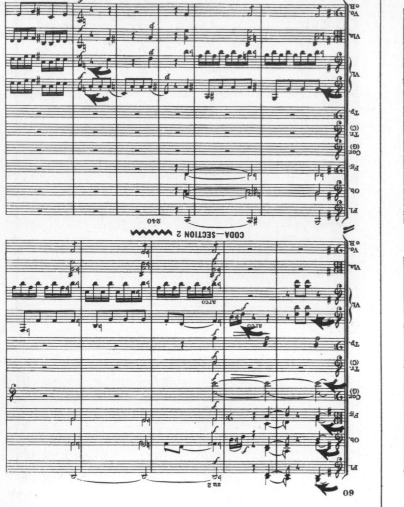
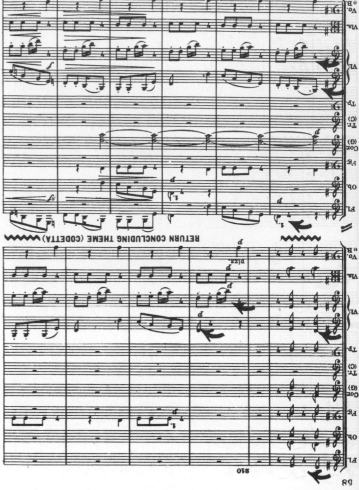
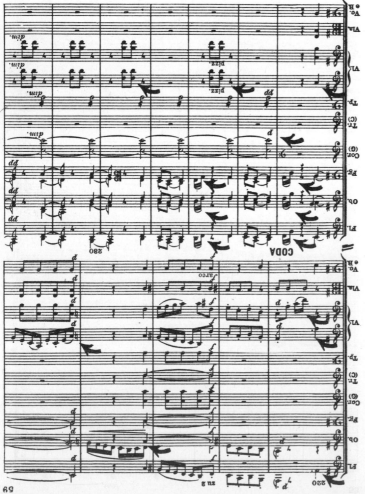
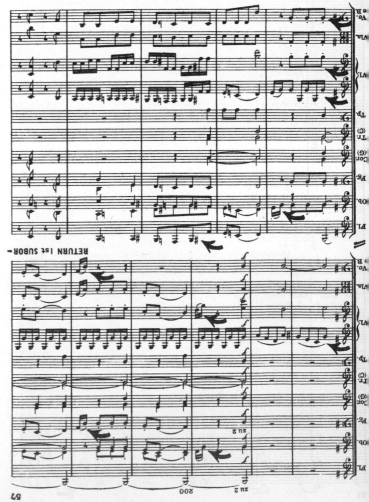

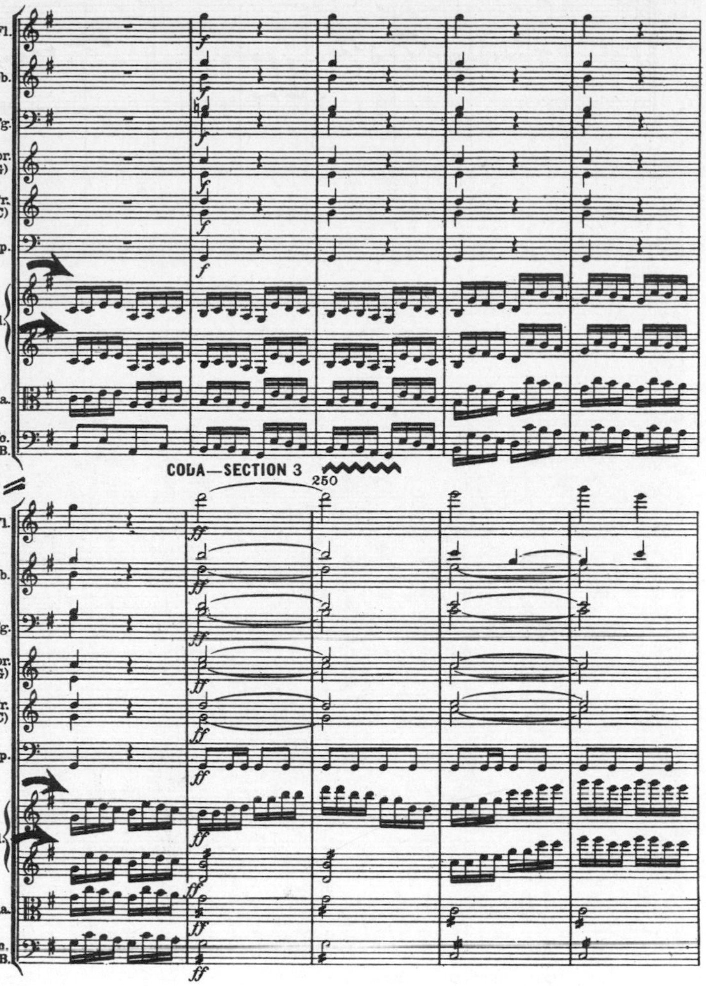
Fl.
Ob.
Fg.
Cor. (G)
Tr. (C)
Tp.
Vl.
Vla.
Vc. e B.
CODA—SECTION 3
250

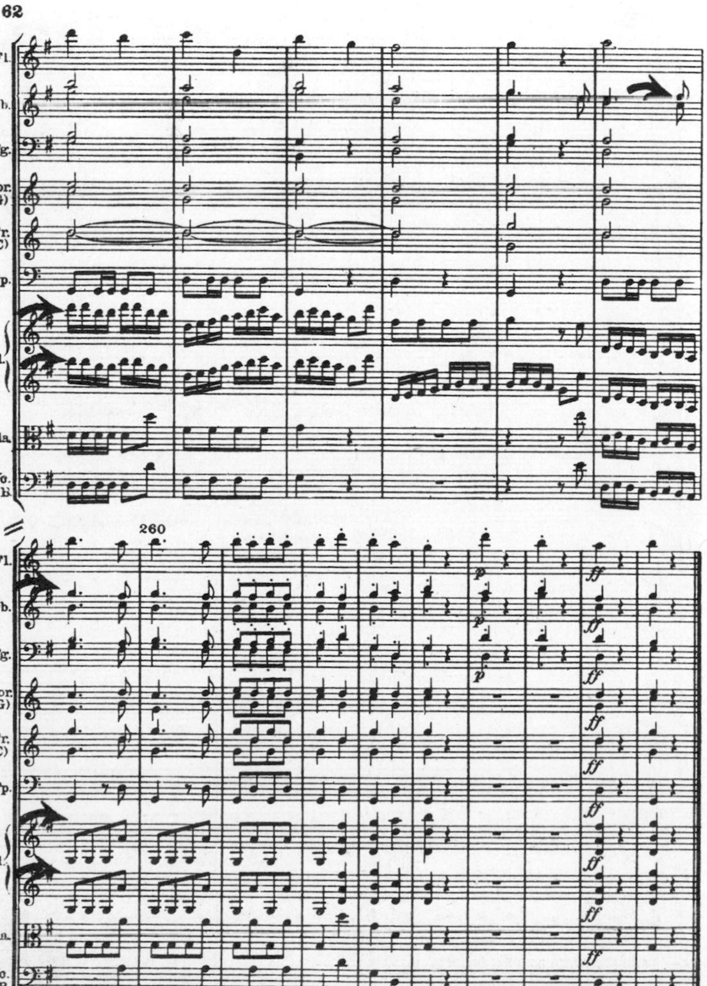
Fl.
Ob.
Fg.
Cor. (G)
Tr. (C)
Tp.
Vl.
Vla.
Vc. e B.
260

Symphony Nº 7
(Salomon)

Joseph Haydn
*1732-1809

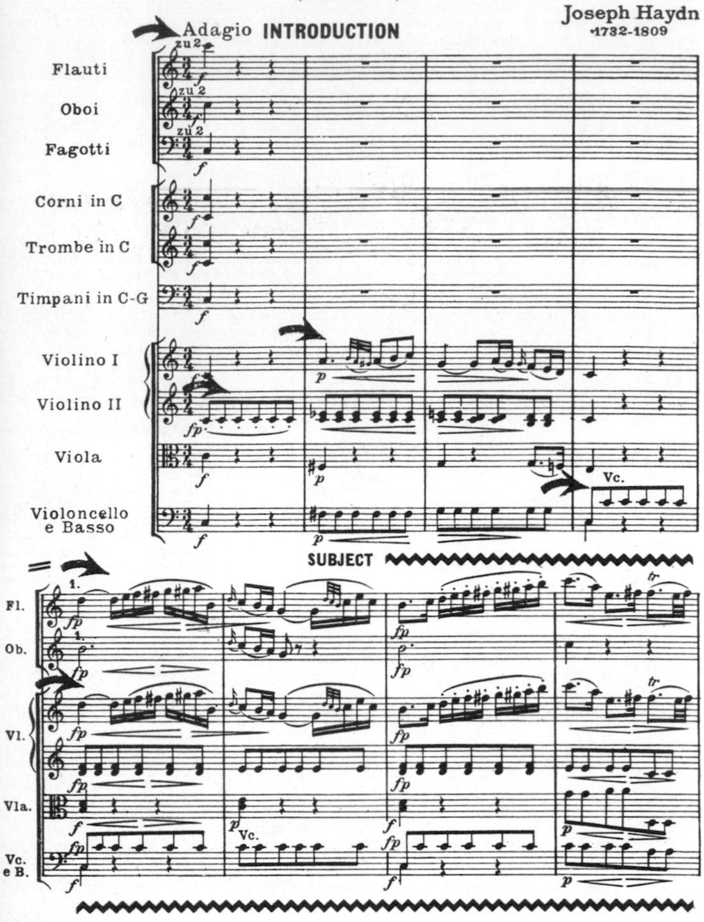

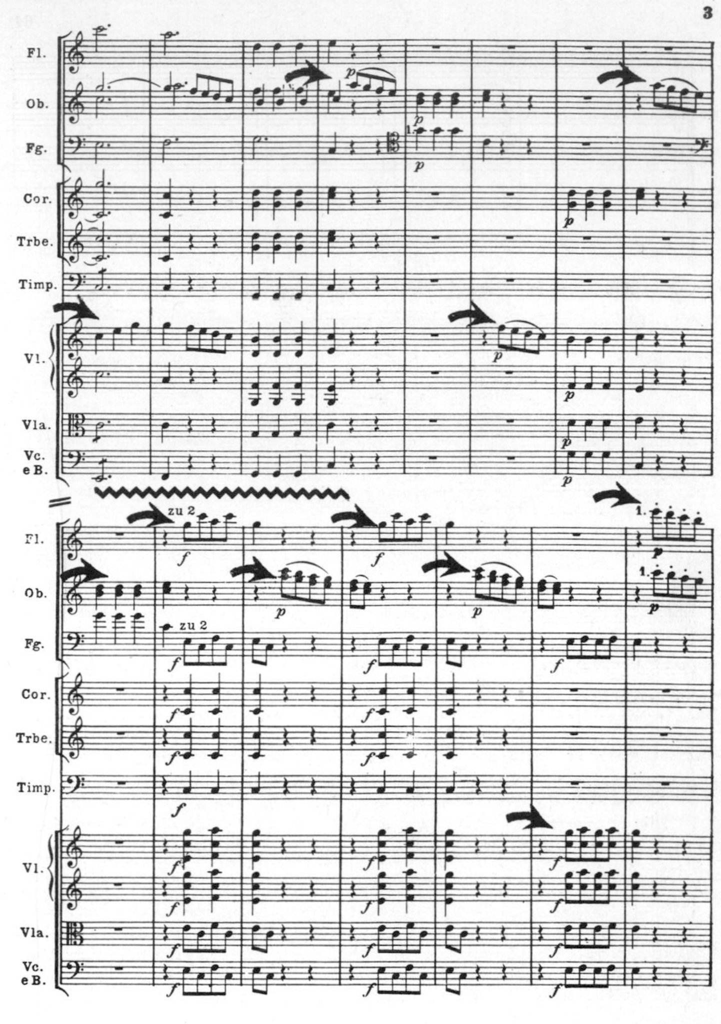

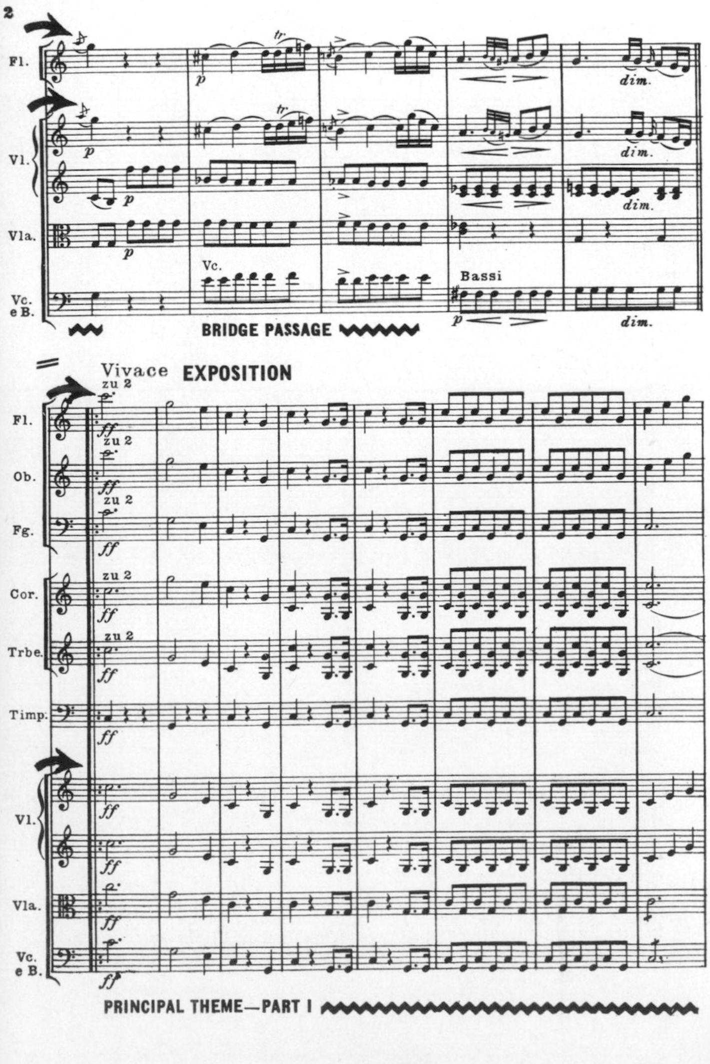

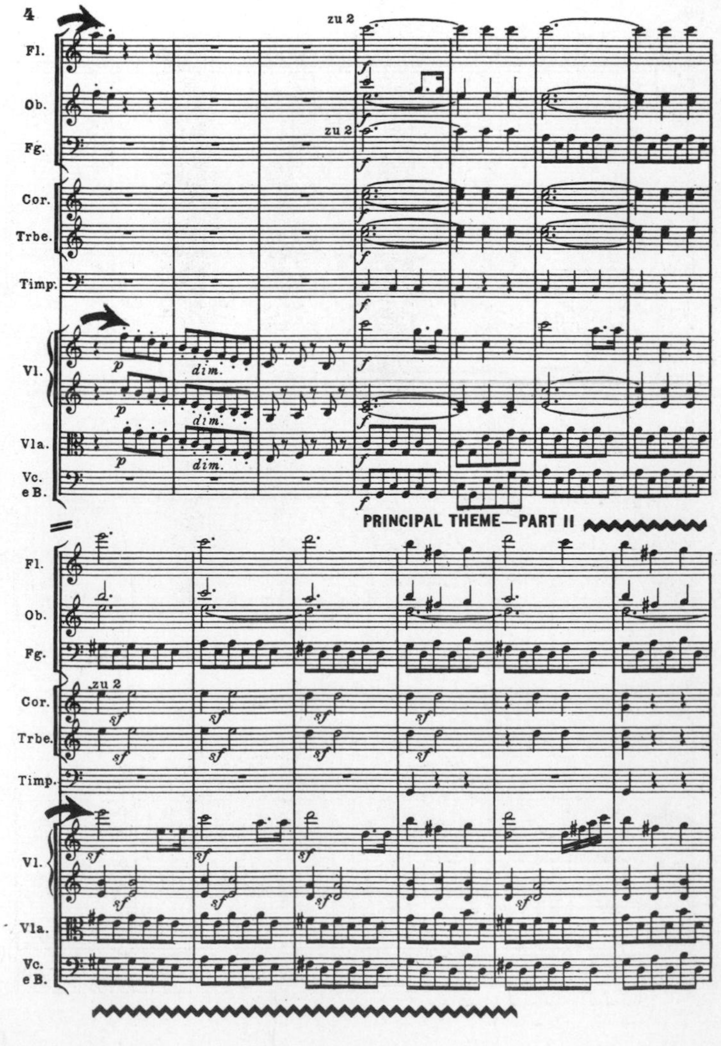

(51)

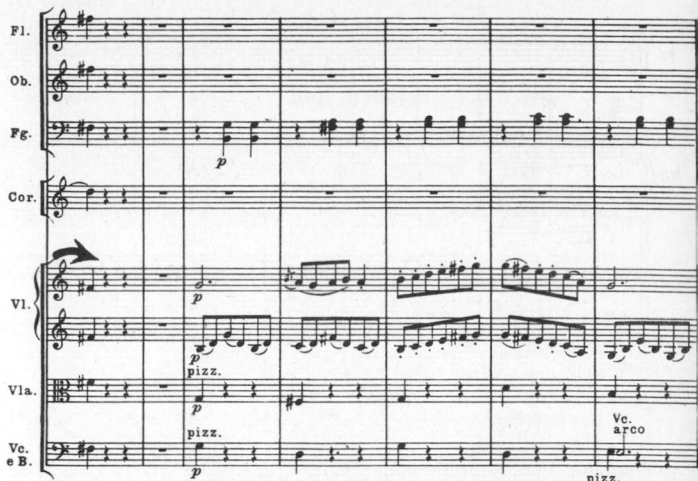

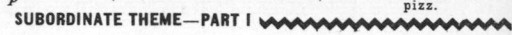

SUBORDINATE THEME—PART I ∿∿∿∿∿

BRIDGE PASSAGE ∿∿∿

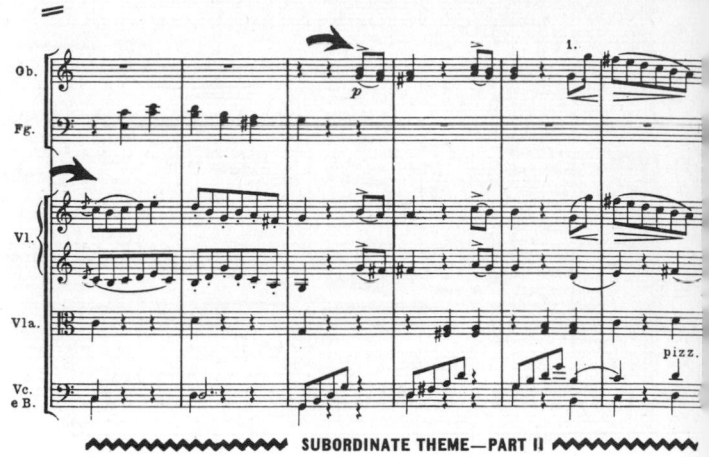

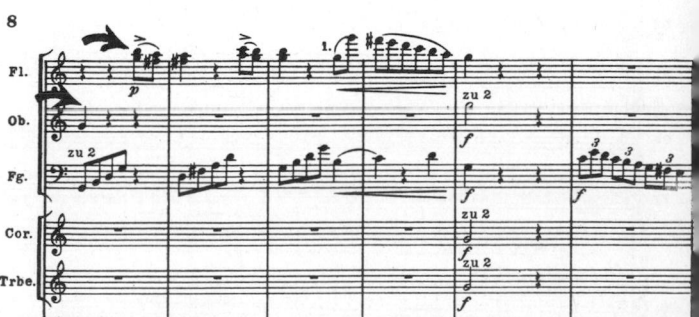

∿∿∿∿∿ **SUBORDINATE THEME—PART II** ∿∿∿∿∿

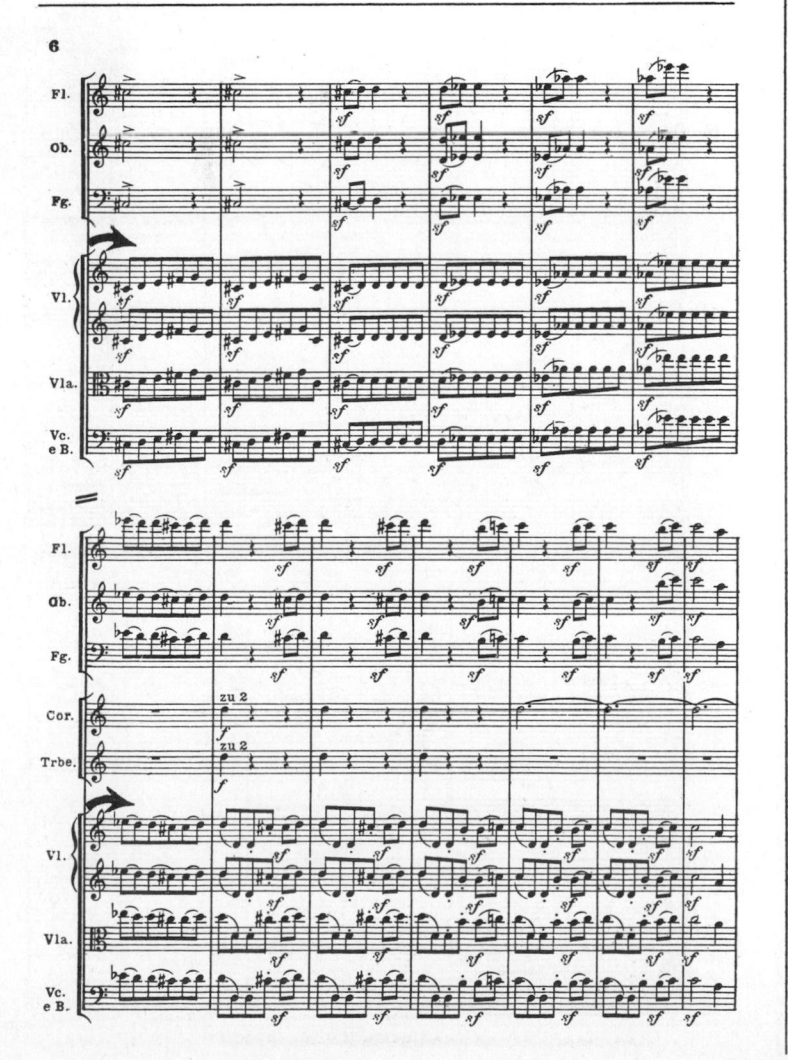

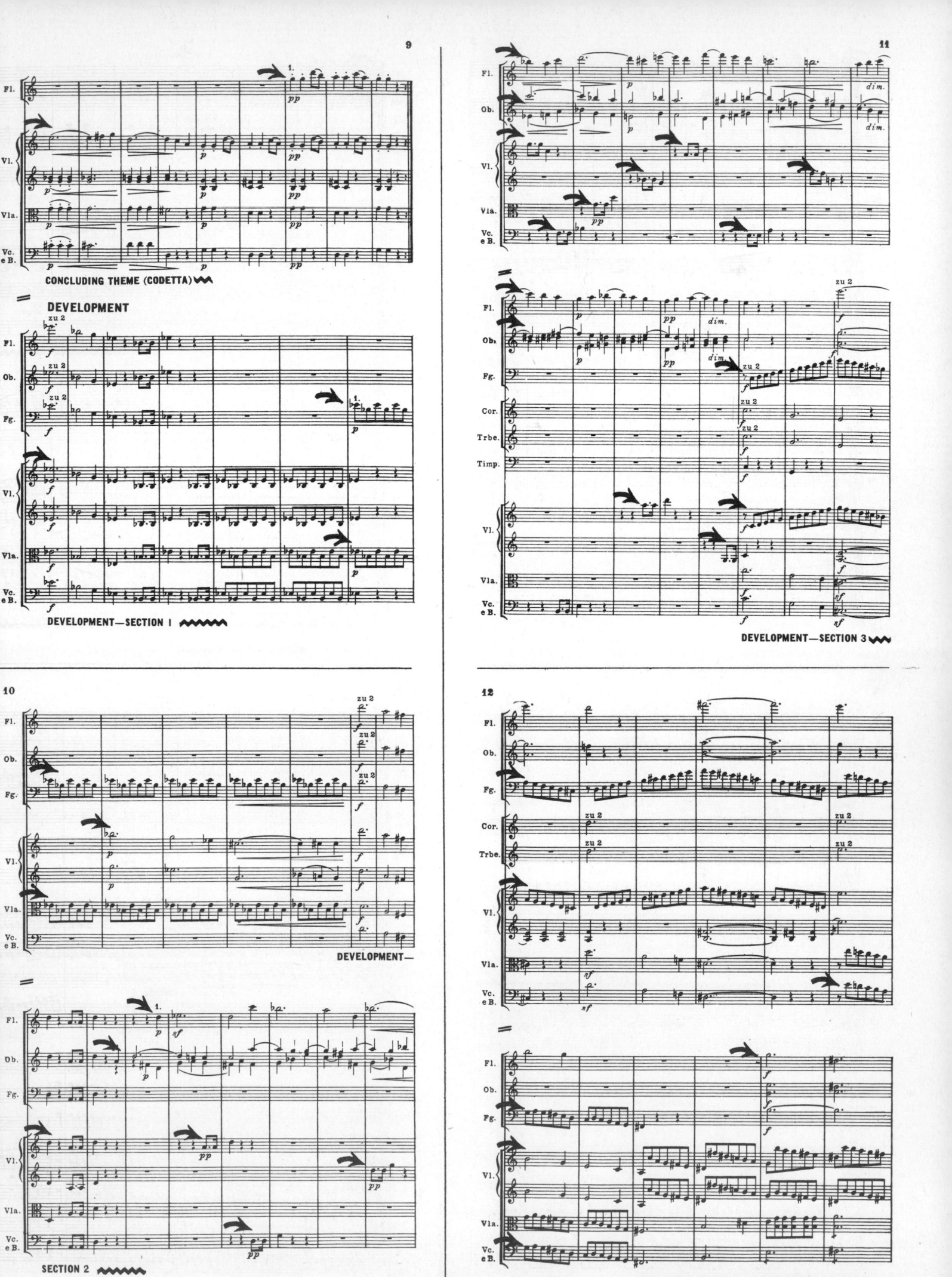

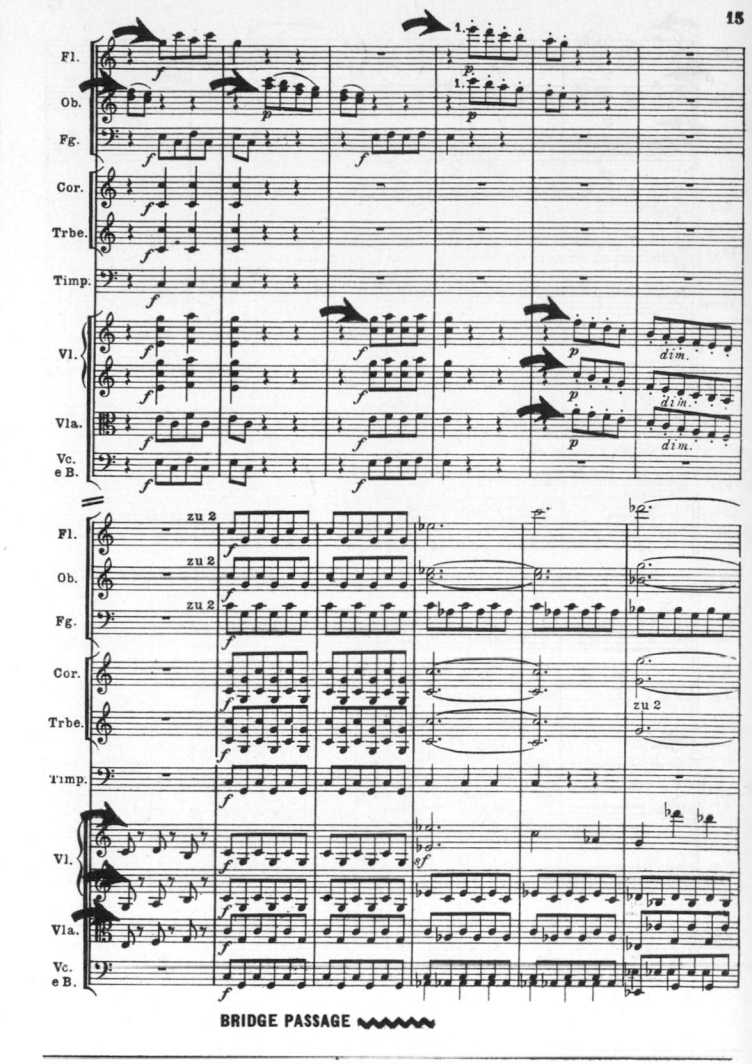

RECAPITULATION

RETURN PRINCIPAL THEME—PART I ∿∿

BRIDGE PASSAGE ∿∿∿

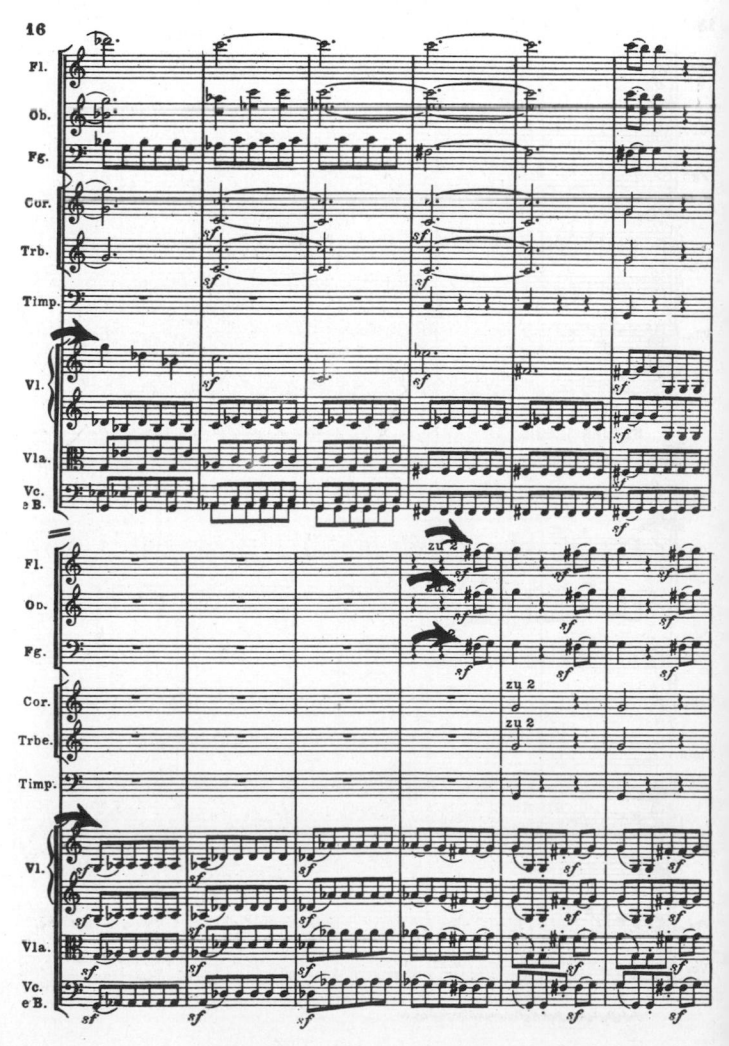

17

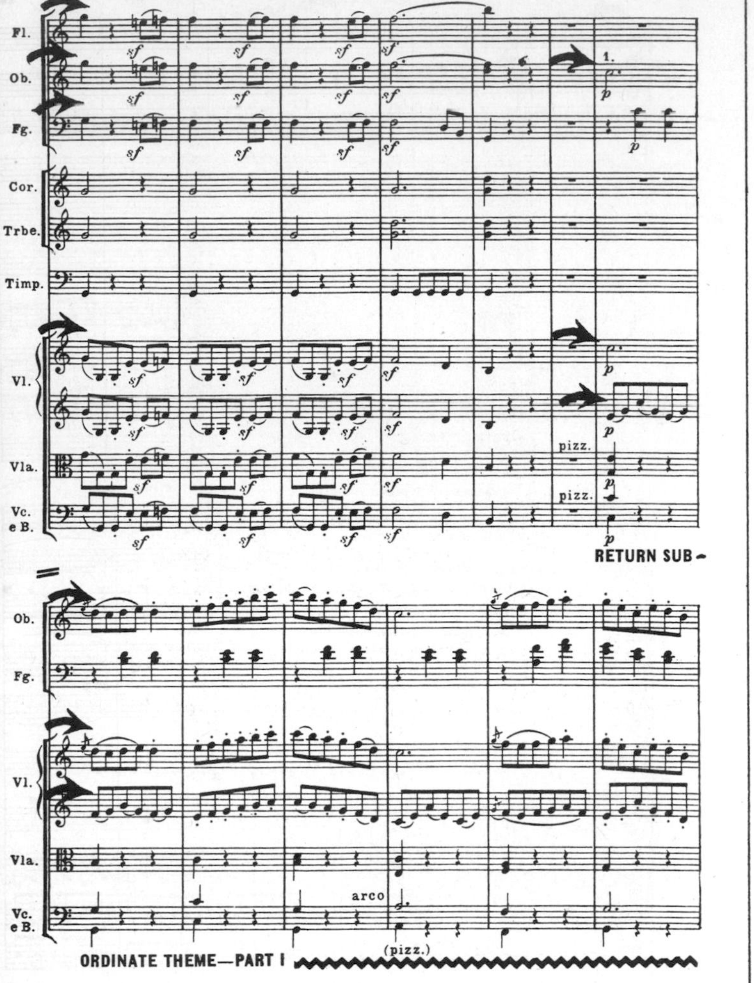
Fl.
Ob.
Fg.
Cor.
Trbe.
Timp.
Vl.
Vla.
Vc. e B.
sf
1.
p
pizz.
RETURN SUB-
ORDINATE THEME—PART I
arco
(pizz.)

18

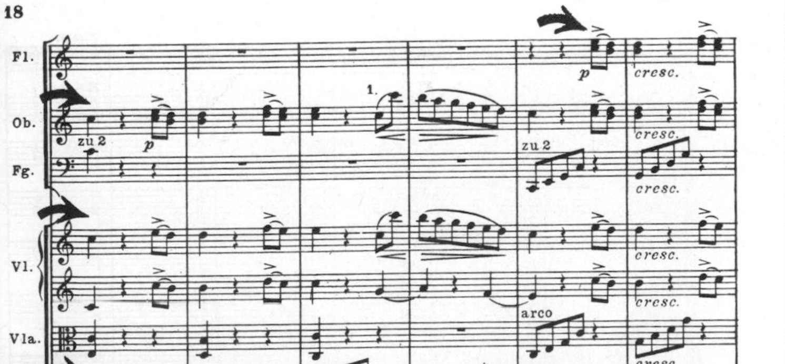
Fl.
Ob.
Fg.
Vl.
Vla.
Vc. e B.
zu 2
p
1.
cresc.
arco
pizz.
(Bassi)
RETURN SUBORDINATE THEME—PART II
Cor.
Trbe.
Timp.
f

19

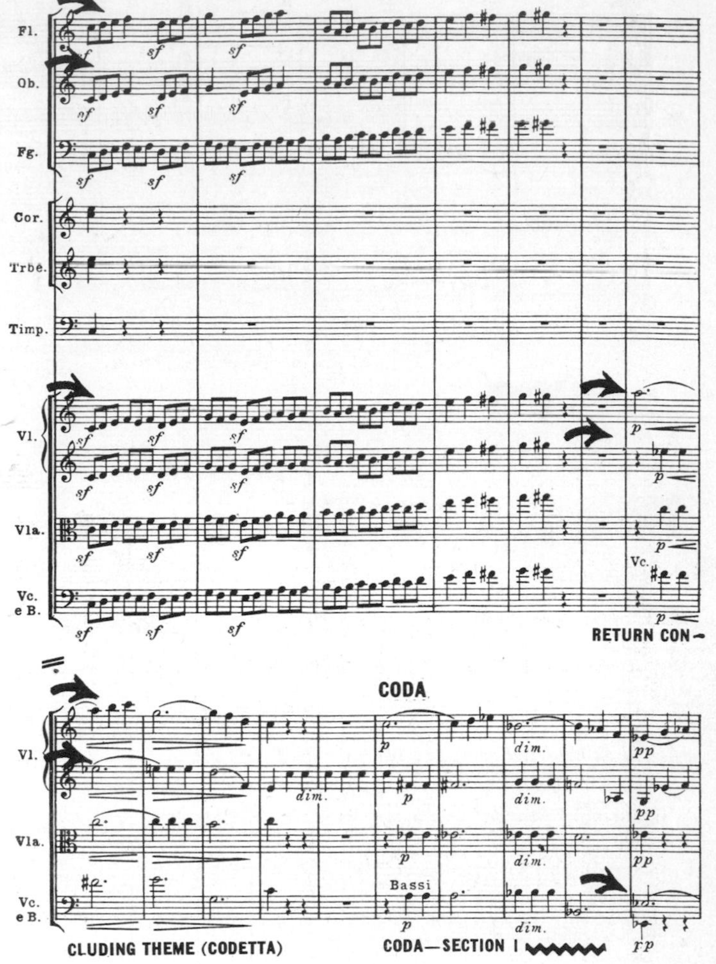
Fl.
Ob.
Fg.
Cor.
Trbe.
Timp.
Vl.
Vla.
Vc. e B.
sf
p
Vc.
RETURN CON-
CODA
dim.
pp
Bassi
CLUDING THEME (CODETTA)
CODA—SECTION I
fp

20

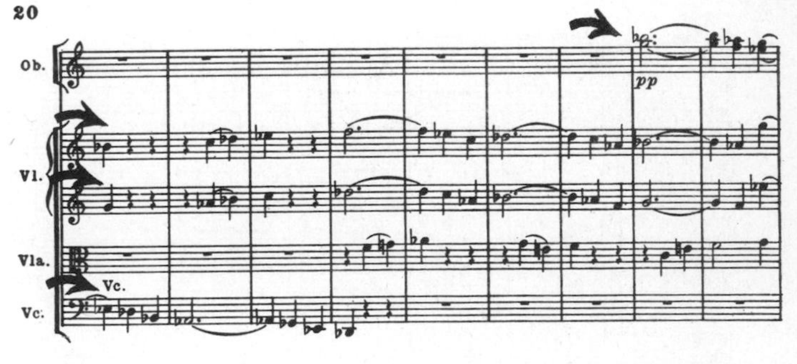
Ob.
Vl.
Vla.
Vc.
pp
Fl.
Fg.
Cor.
Trbe.
Timp.
B.
zu 2
p
cresc.
f
Bassi

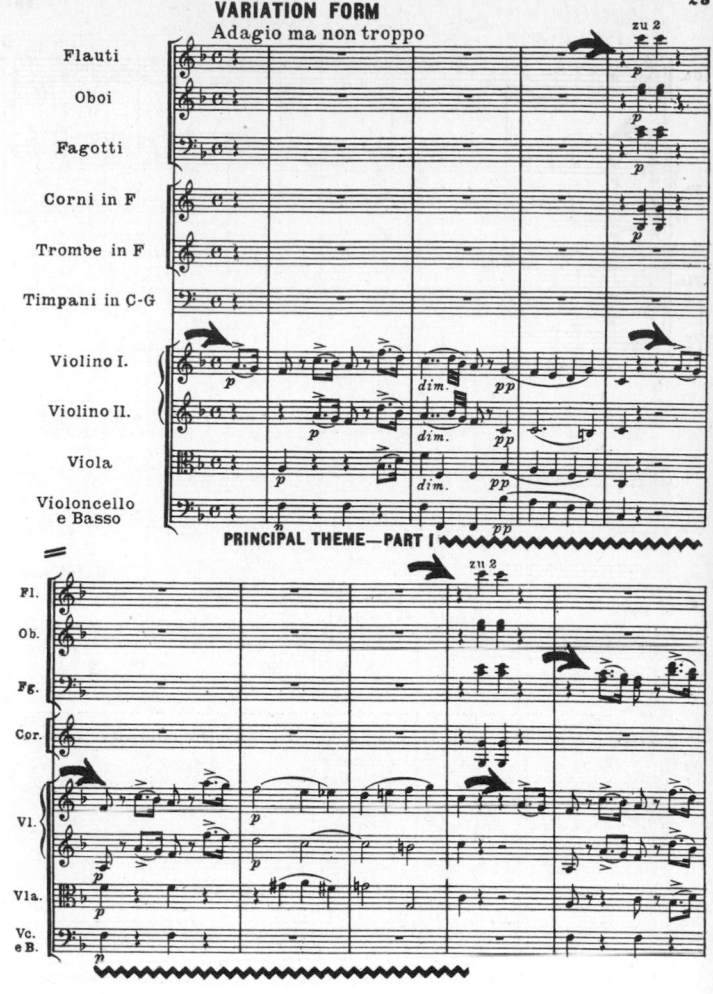

VARIATION FORM
Adagio ma non troppo

Flauti

Oboi

Fagotti

Corni in F

Trombe in F

Timpani in C-G

Violino I.

Violino II.

Viola

Violoncello
e Basso

PRINCIPAL THEME—PART I

CODA—SECTION 2

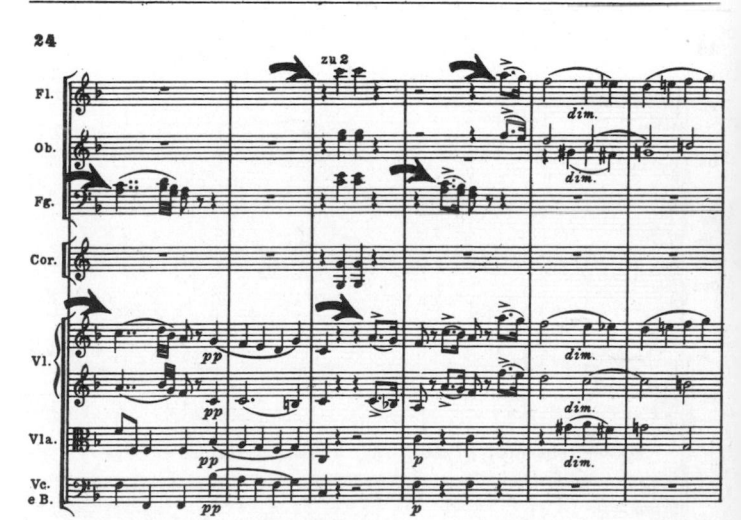

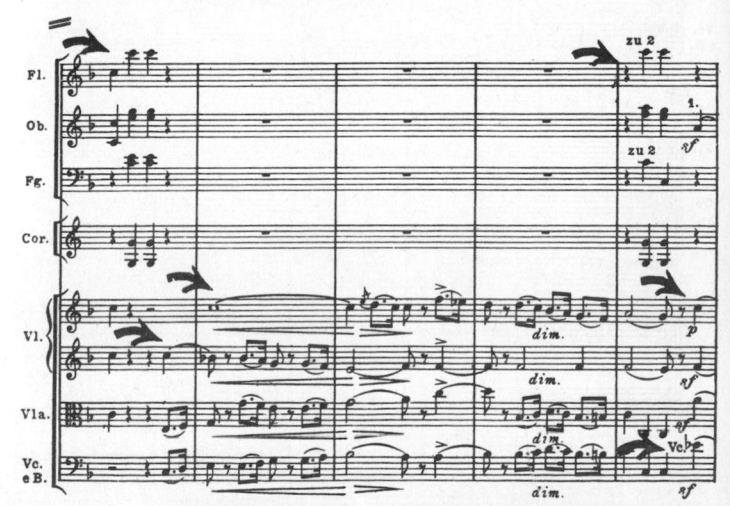

PRINCIPAL THEME—PART II

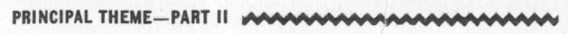

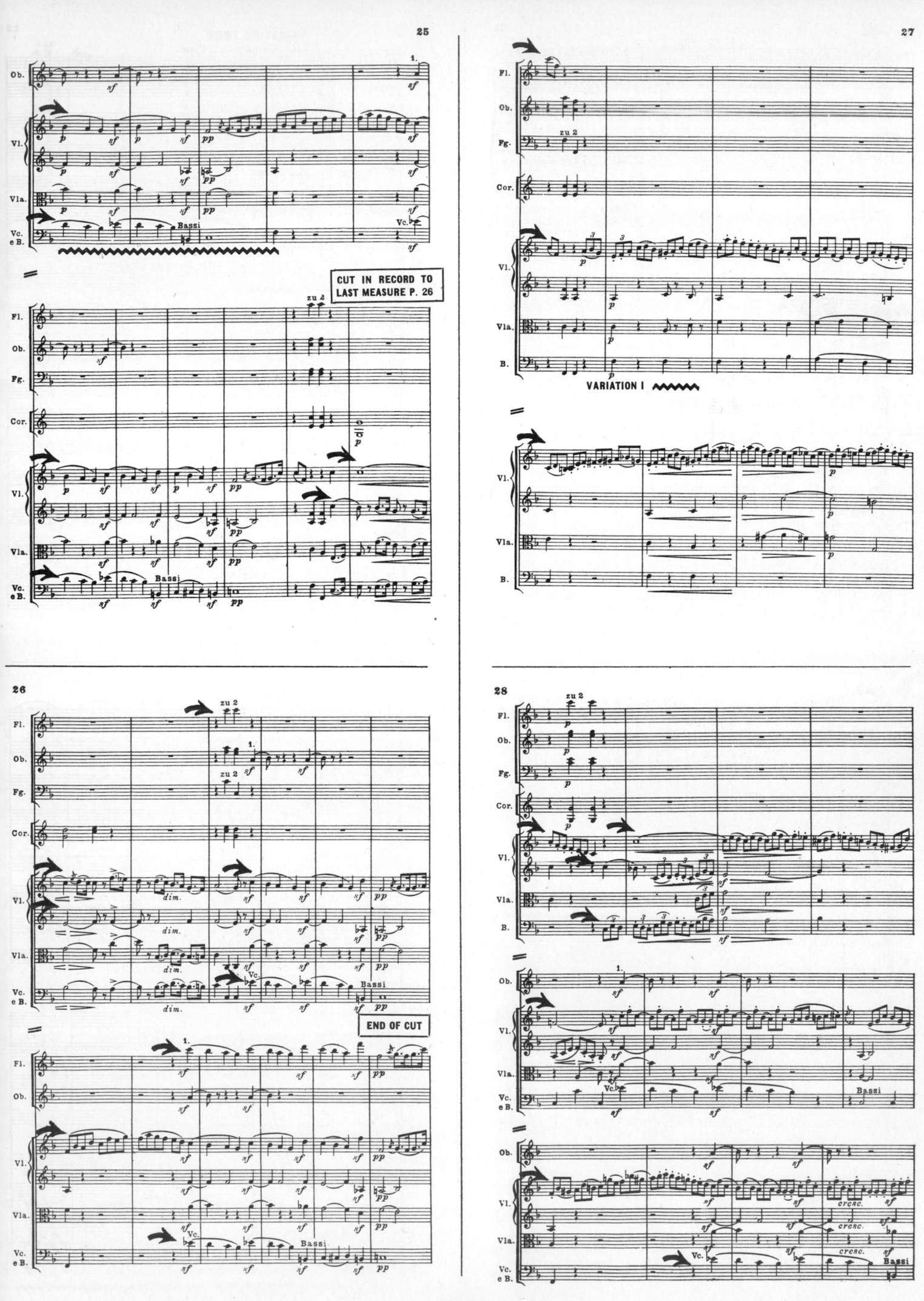

CUT IN RECORD TO
LAST MEASURE P. 26

VARIATION I

END OF CUT

29
30
31
32
Fl.
Ob.
Fg.
Cor.
Trbe.
Timp.
Vl.
Vla.
Vc. e B.
zu 2
dim.
VARIATION II
VARIATION III
un poco cresc.
pizz.
arco

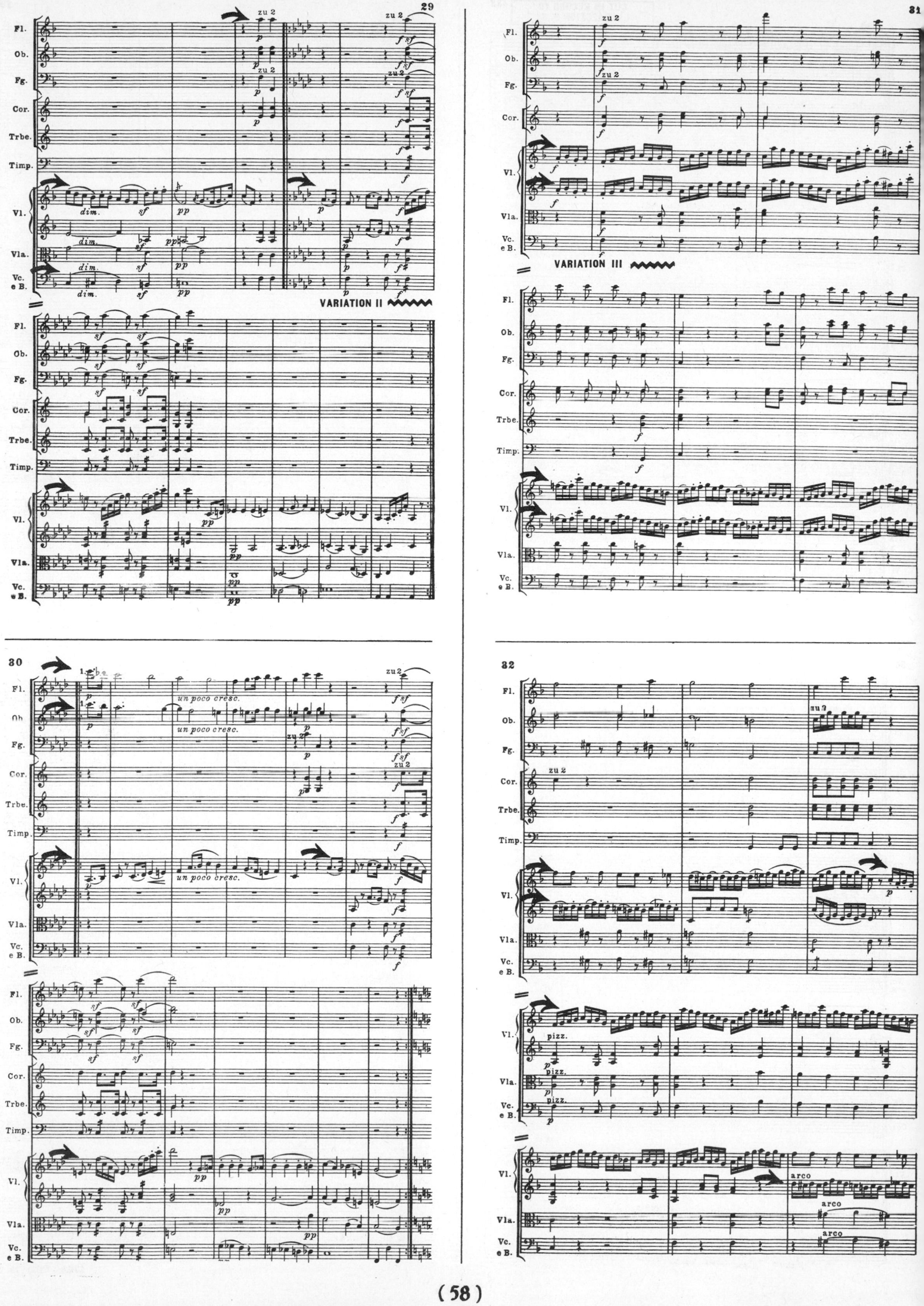

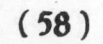

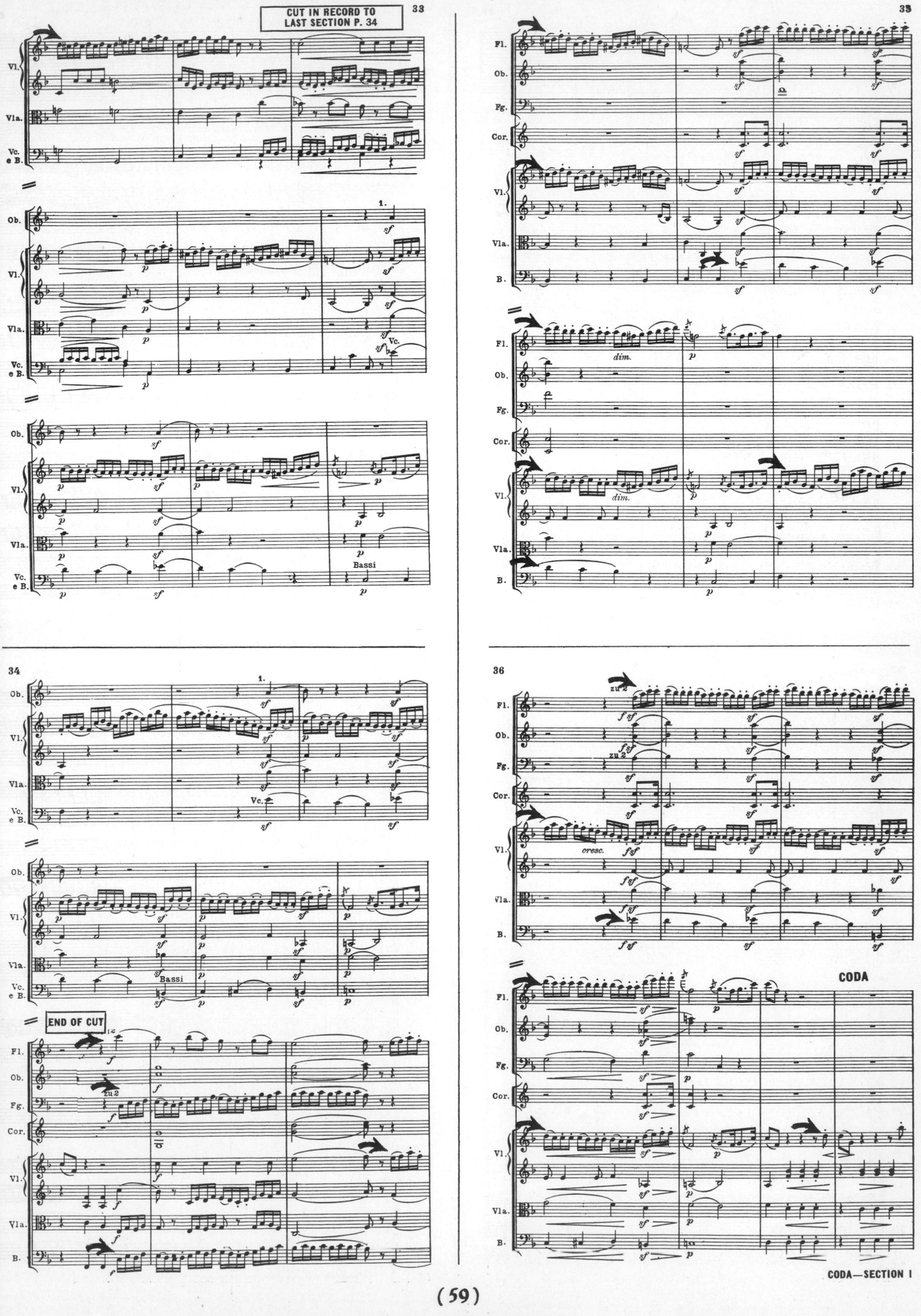
CUT IN RECORD TO LAST SECTION P. 34
33
33
34
END OF CUT
36
CODA
CODA—SECTION I
Fl.
Ob.
Fg.
Cor.
Vl.
Vla.
Vc. e B.
B.
Bassi
Vc.
zu 2
dim.
cresc.

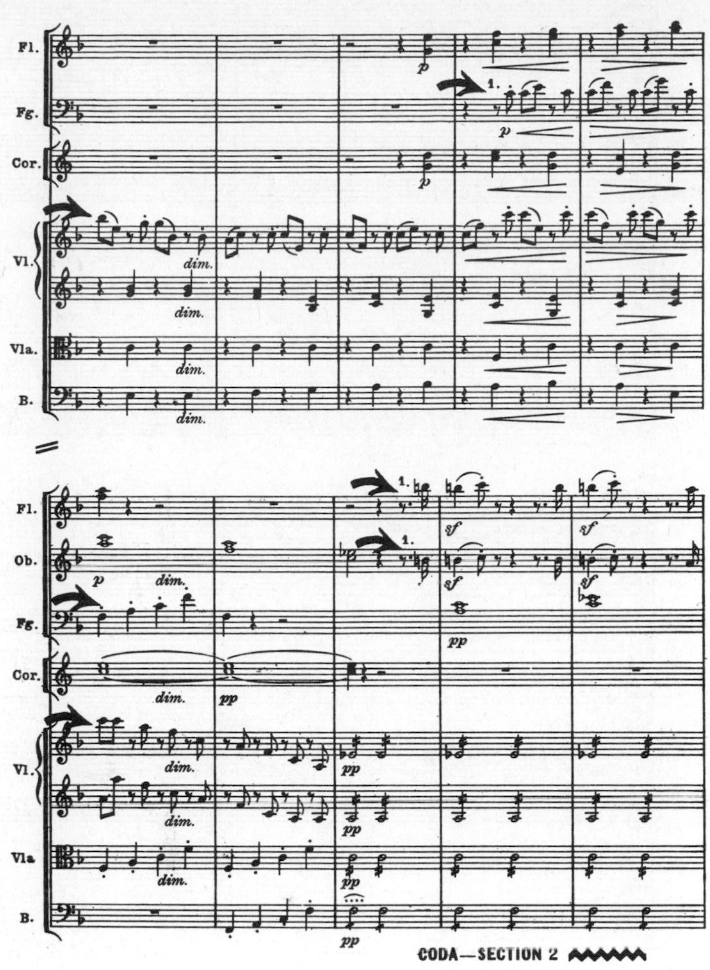

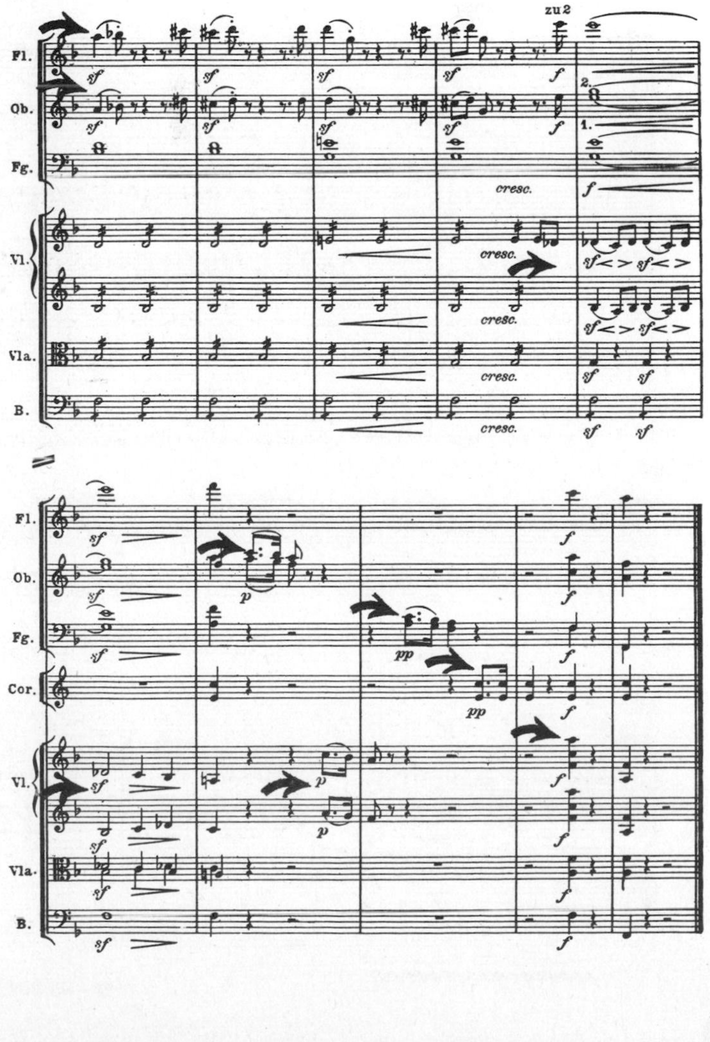

Fl.

Fg.

Cor.

Vl.

Vla.

B.

Fl.

Ob.

Fg.

Cor.

Vl.

Vla.

B.

CODA—SECTION 2 ∿∿∿∿

Flauti

Oboi

Fagotti

Corni in C

Trombe in C

Timpani in C-G

Violino I

Violino II

Viola

Violoncello e Basso

PRINCIPAL THEME—PART I ∿∿∿∿

Fl.

Ob.

Fg.

Cor.

Trbe.

Timp.

Vl.

Vla.

Vc. e B.

Fl.

Ob.

Fg.

Vl.

Vla.

B.

Fl.

Ob.

Fg.

Cor.

Vl.

Vla.

B.

Fl.

Ob.

Fg.

Cor.

Trbe.

Timp.

Vl.

Vla.

Vc. e B.

PRINCIPAL THEME—PART II ∿∿∿∿

Fl.

Ob.

Fg.

Cor.

Trbe.

Timp.

Vl.

Vla.

Vc. e B.

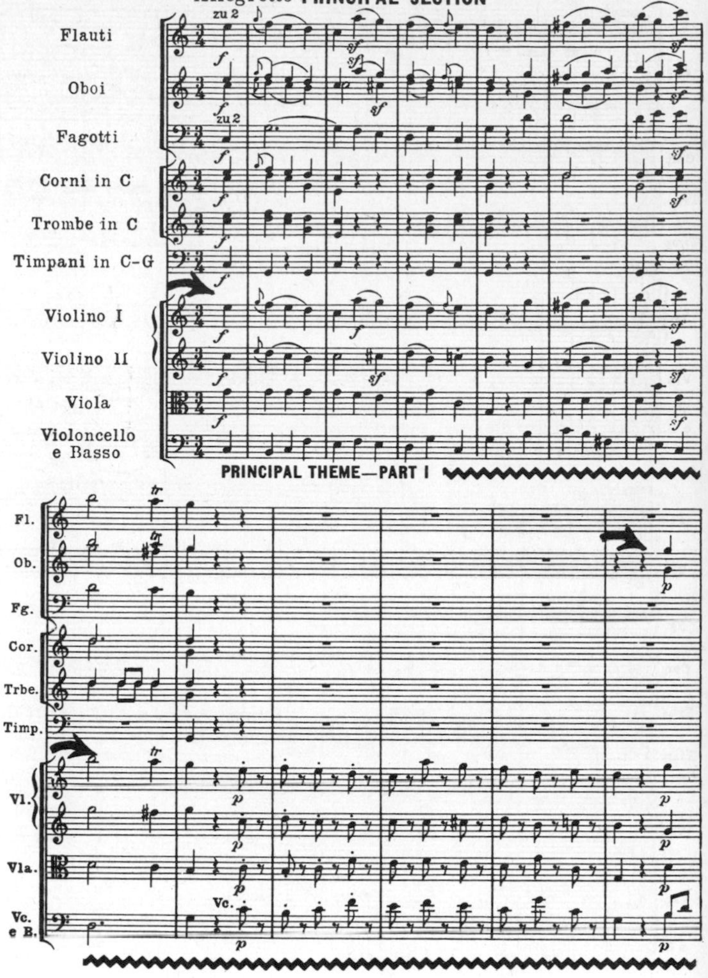

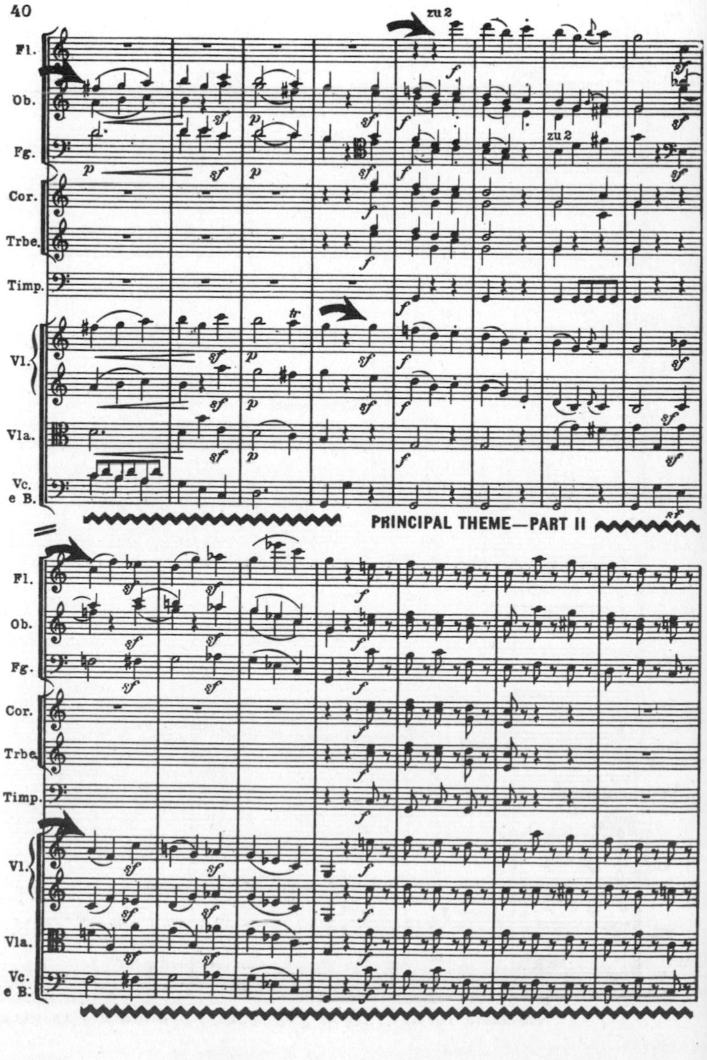

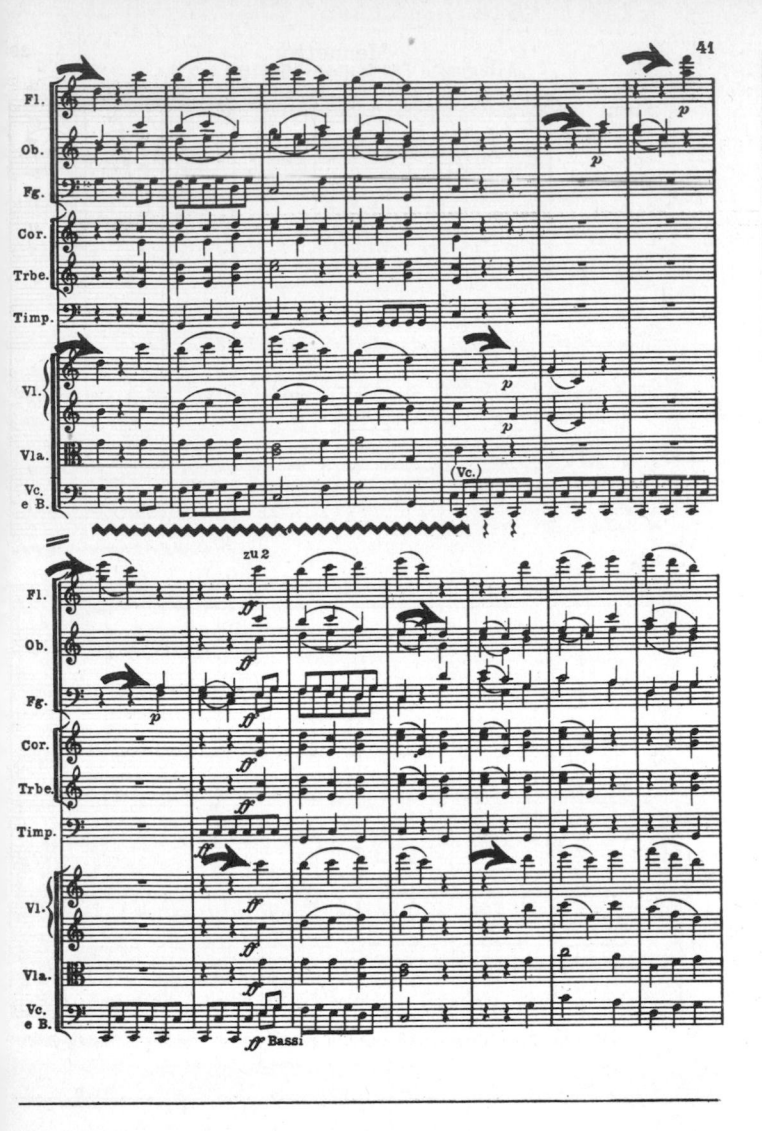

PRINCIPAL THEME—PART III

SUBORDINATE THEME—PART I

Trio

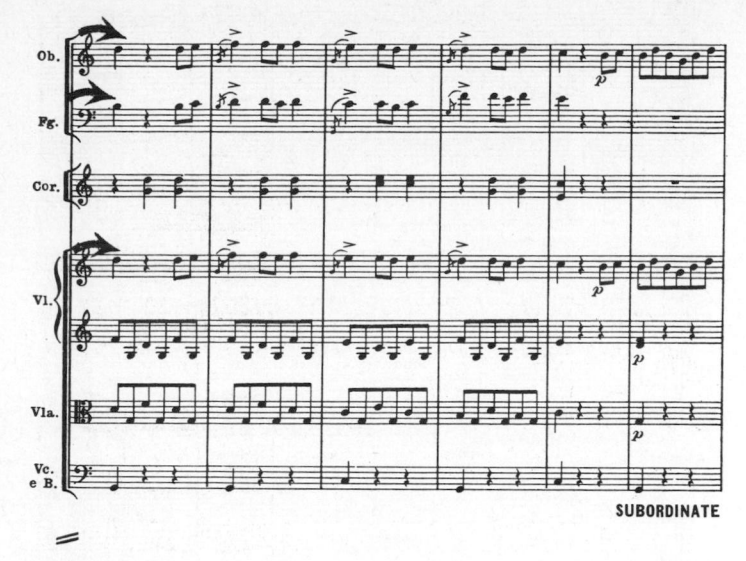

SUBORDINATE

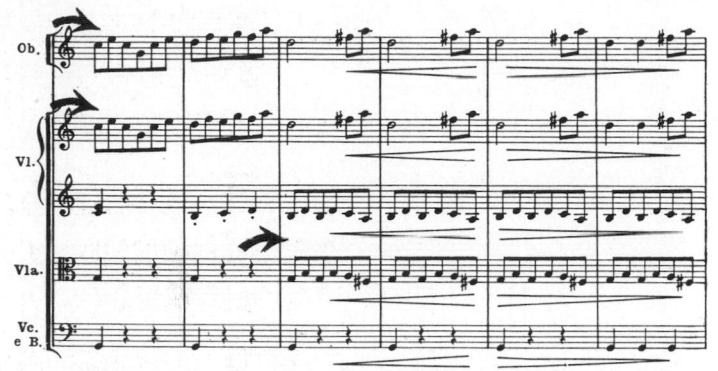

THEME—PART II

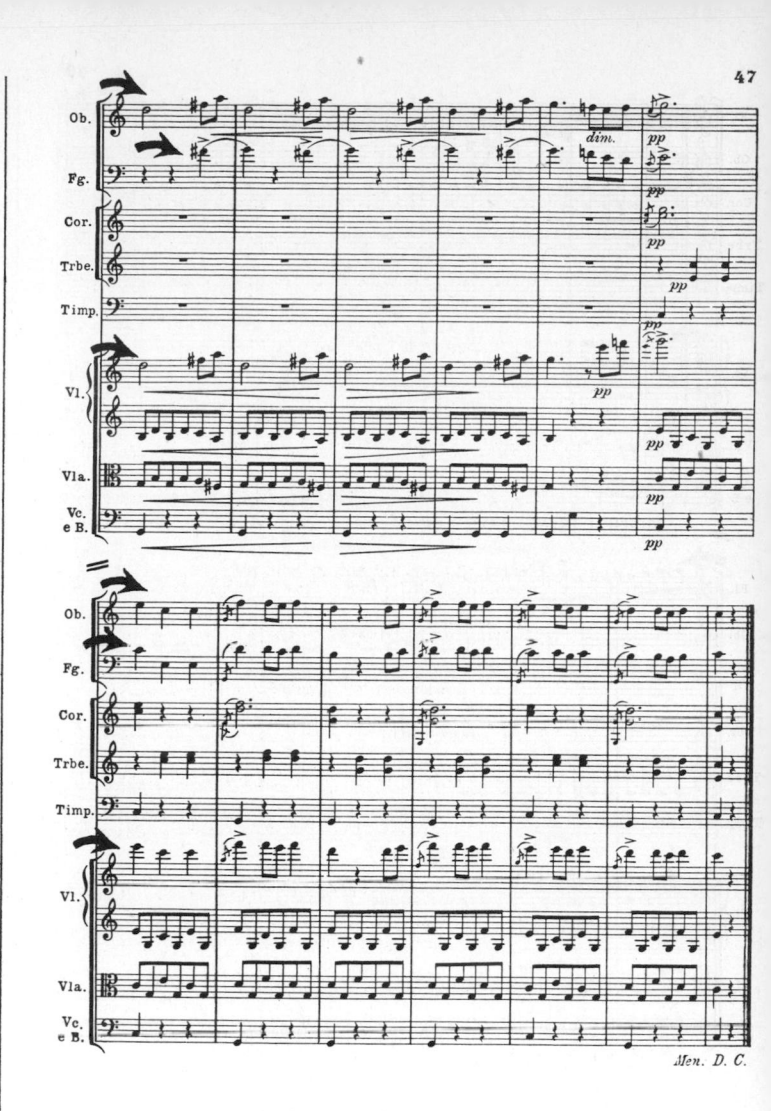

Men. D. C.

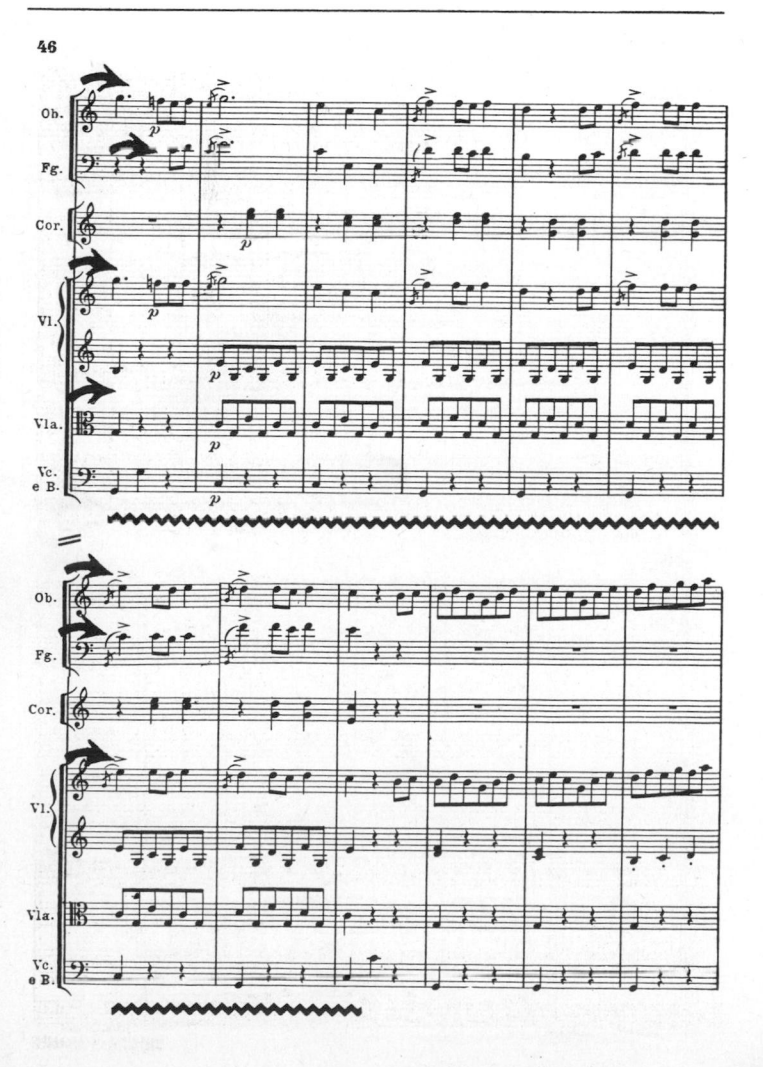

EXPOSITION   Finale
Presto assai

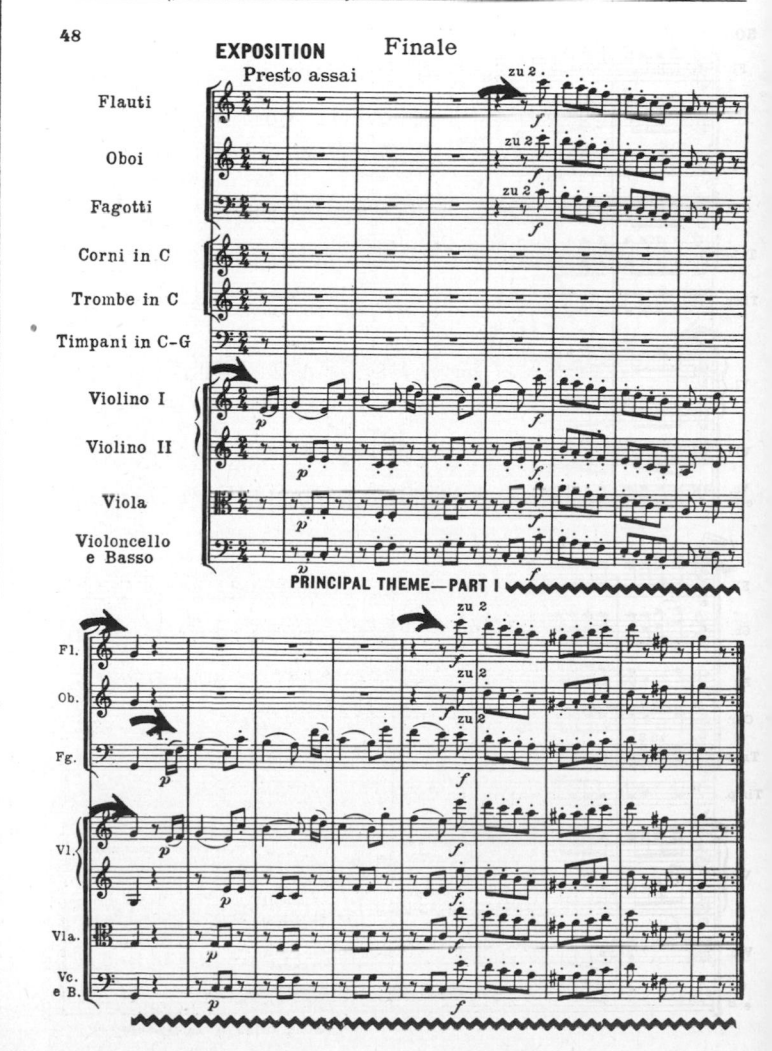

Flauti
Oboi
Fagotti
Corni in C
Trombe in C
Timpani in C-G
Violino I
Violino II
Viola
Violoncello e Basso

PRINCIPAL THEME—PART I

Fl.
Ob.
Fg.
Vl.
Vla.
Vc. e B.

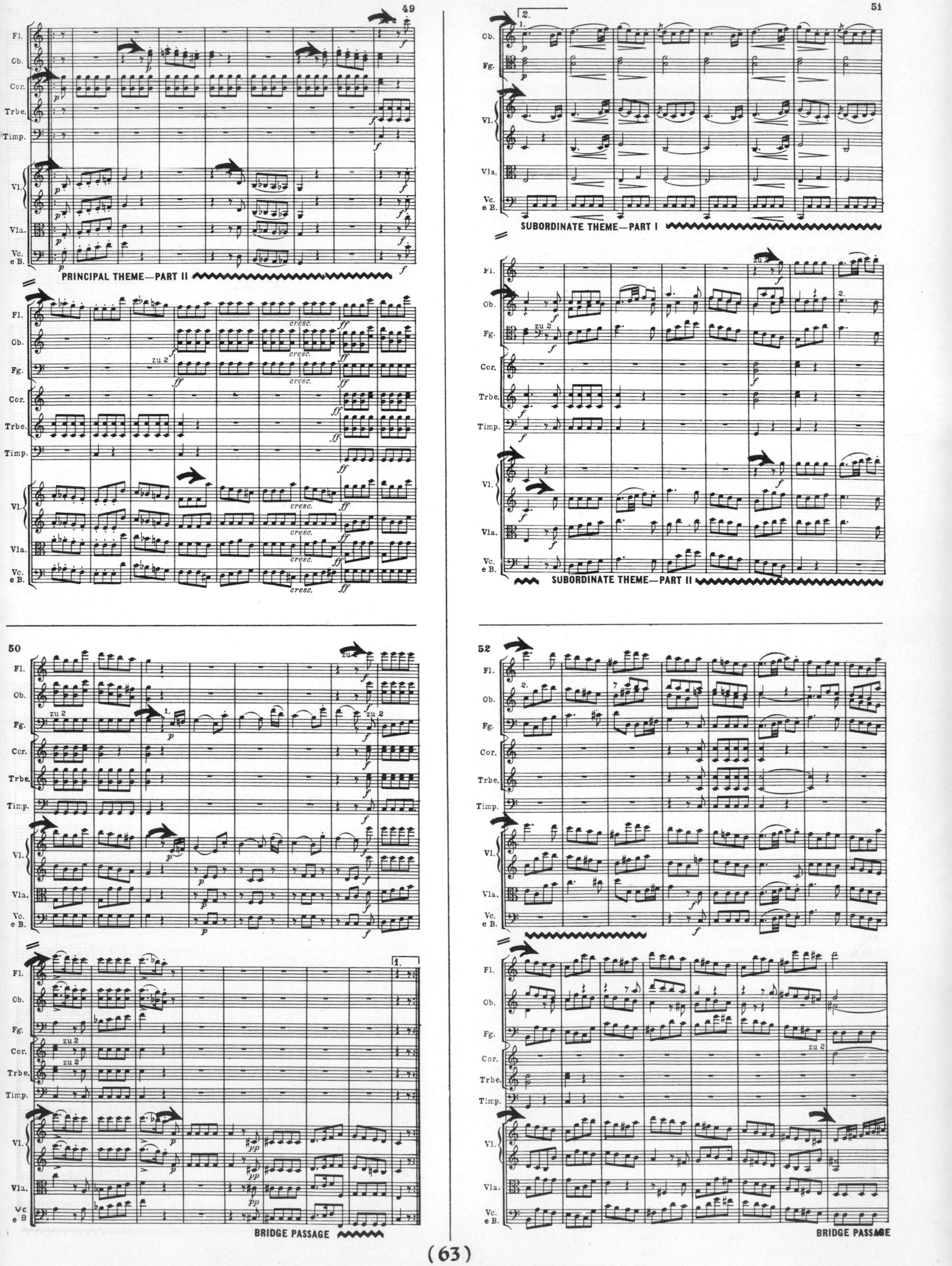
49
Fl.
Ob.
Cor.
Trbe.
Timp.
Vl.
Vla.
Vc. e B.
PRINCIPAL THEME—PART II
zu 2
cresc.
51
SUBORDINATE THEME—PART I
SUBORDINATE THEME—PART II
Fg.
50
52
BRIDGE PASSAGE

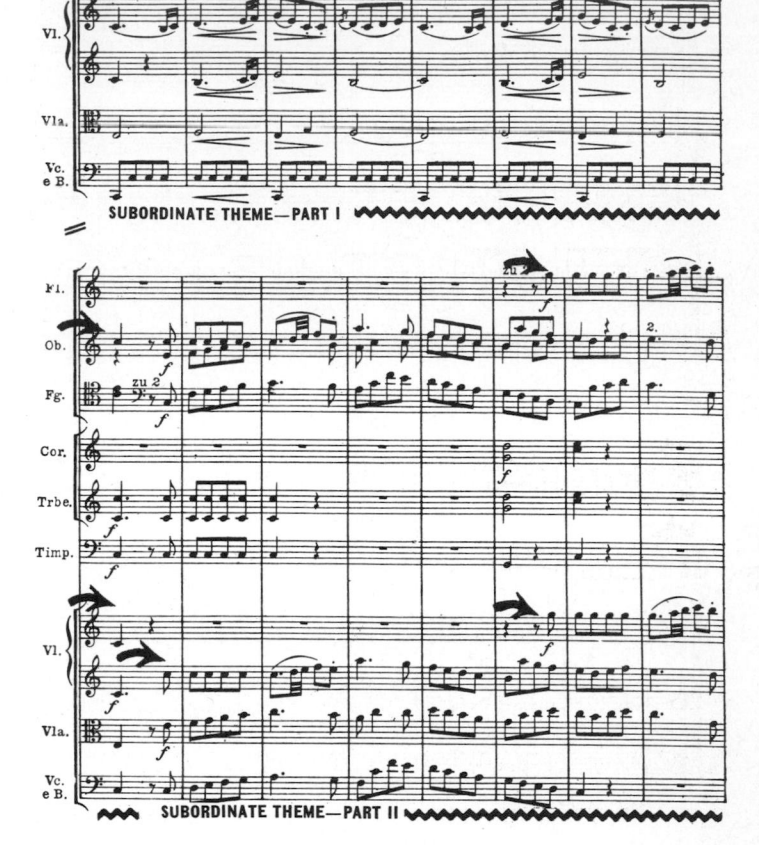

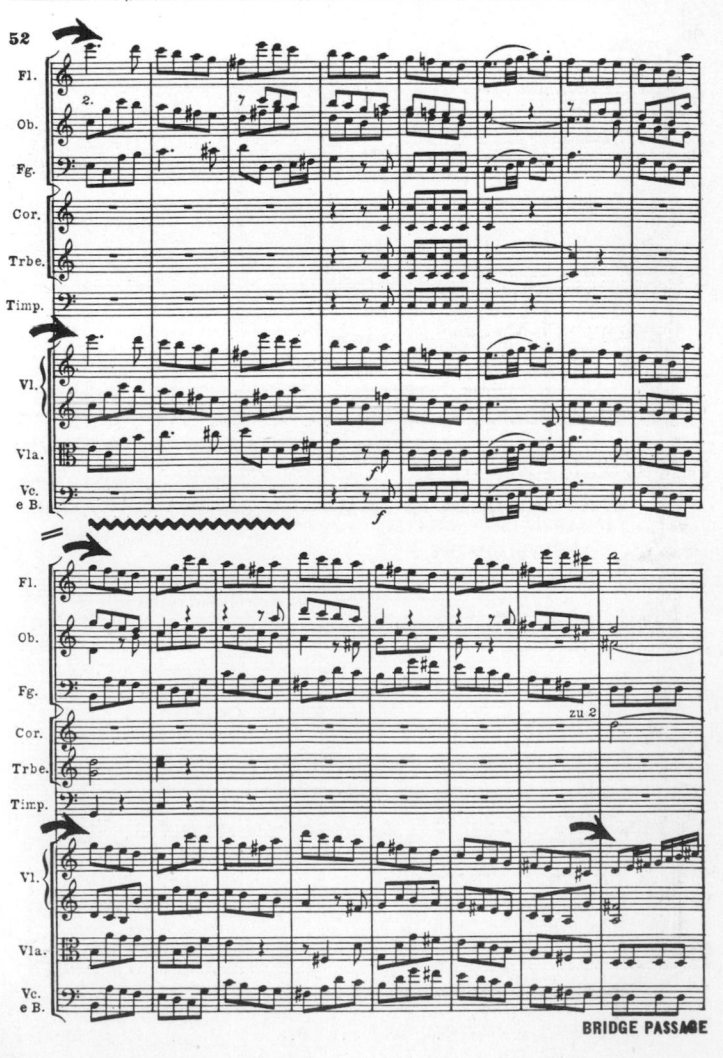

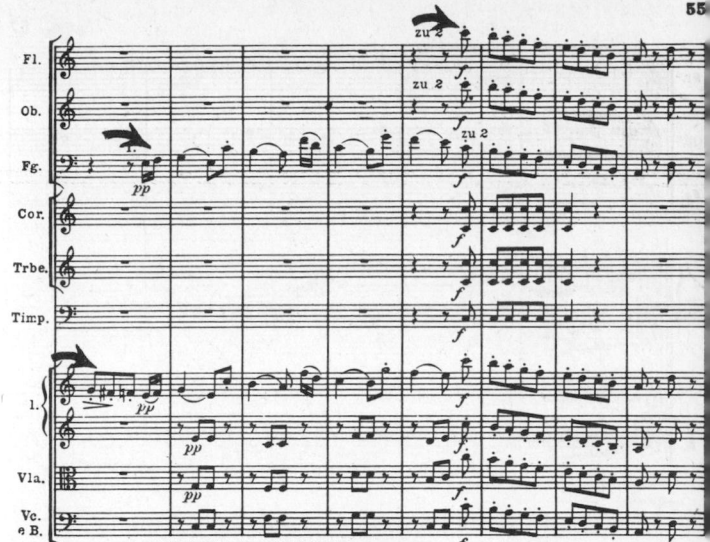

53

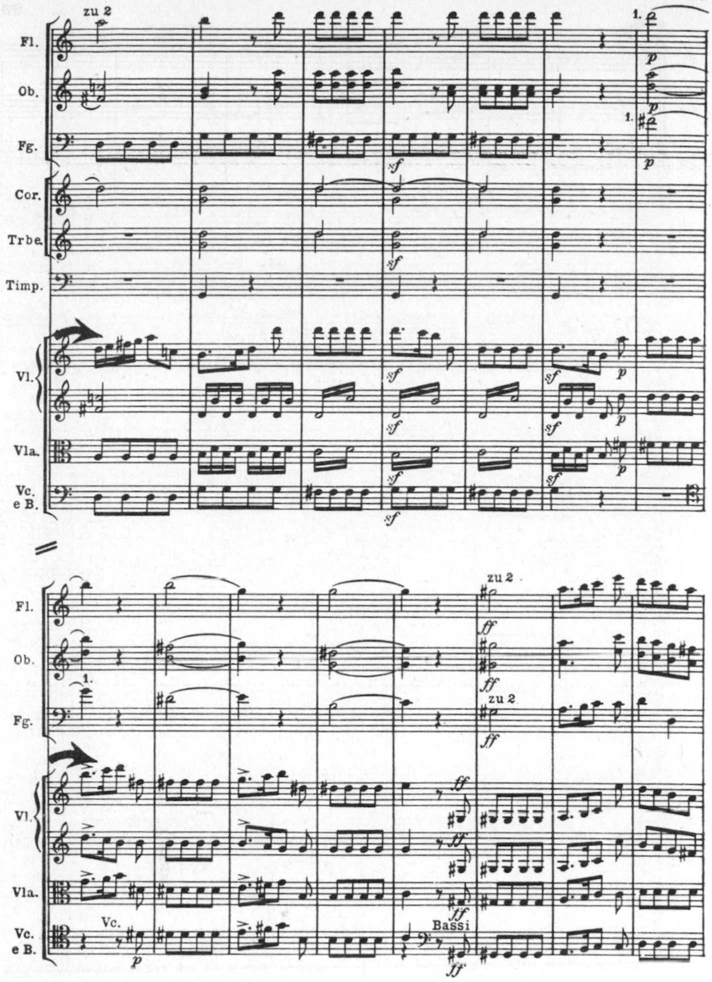
zu 2
Fl.
Ob.
Fg.
Cor.
Trbe.
Timp.
Vl.
Vla.
Vc. e B.
zu 2
Vc.
Bassi

55

zu 2
Fl.
Ob.
Fg.
Cor.
Trbe.
Timp.
1.
Vla.
Vc. e B.
DEVELOPMENT—SECTION 2
Vl.
Vc.
Bassi

54

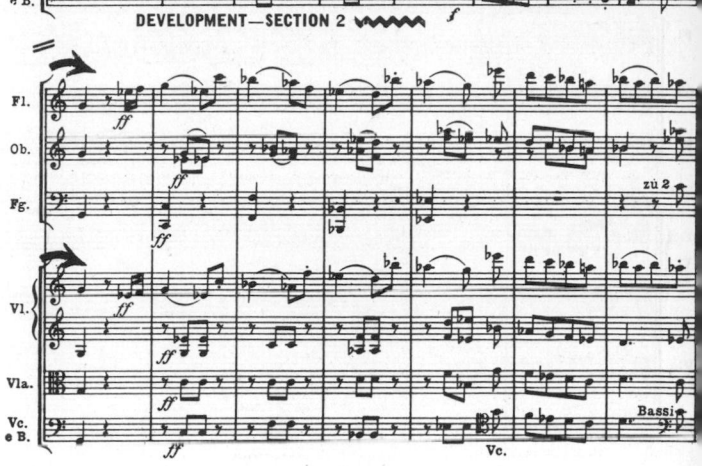

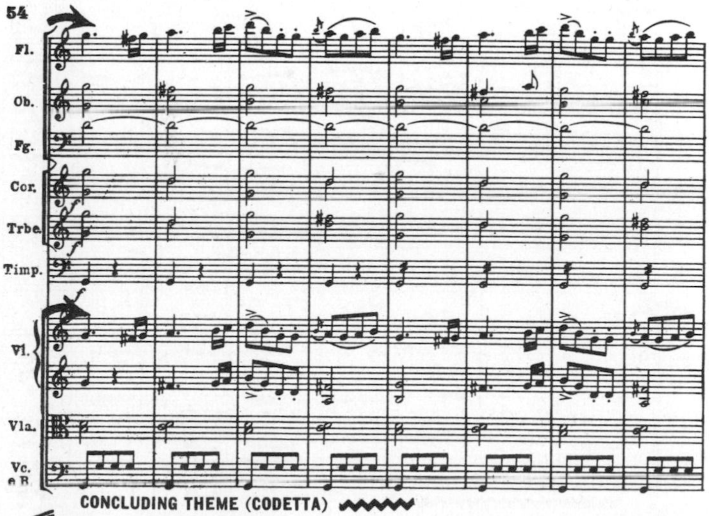
Fl.
Ob.
Fg.
Cor.
Trbe.
Timp.
Vl.
Vla.
Vc. e B.
CONCLUDING THEME (CODETTA)
DEVELOPMENT
dim.
DEVELOPMENT—SECTION I

56

Fl.
Ob.
Fg.
Vl.
Vla.
B.
DEVELOPMENT—SECTION 3

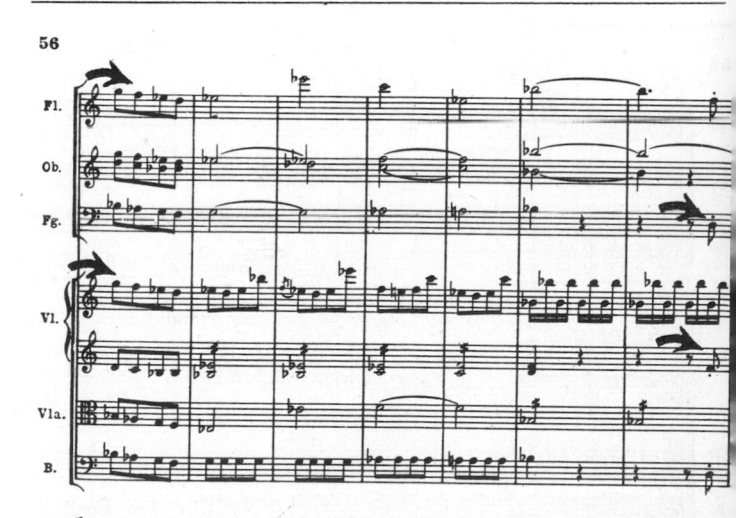

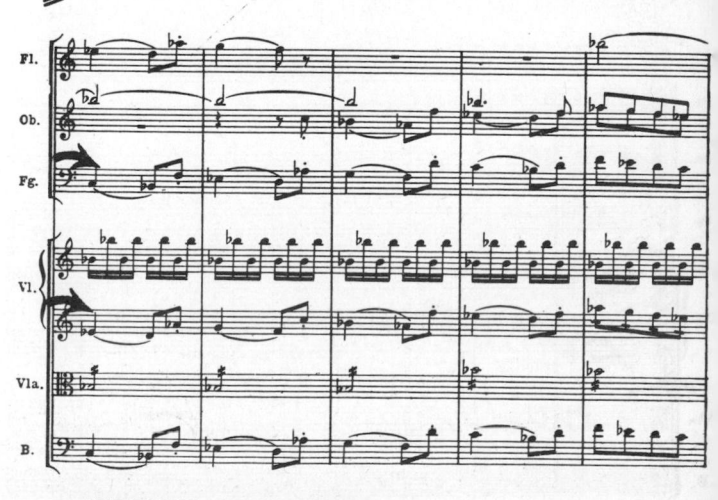

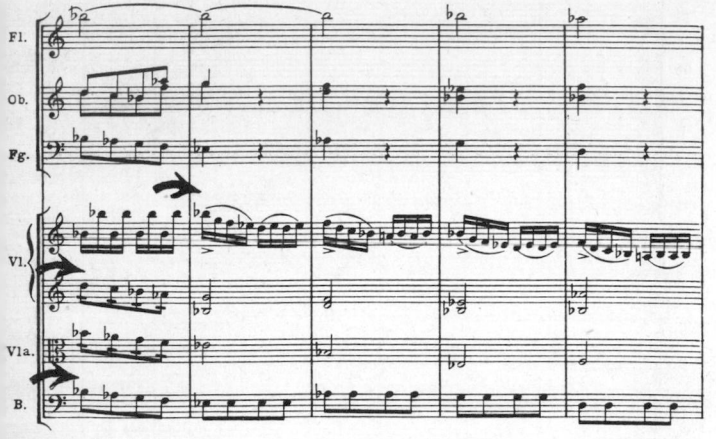

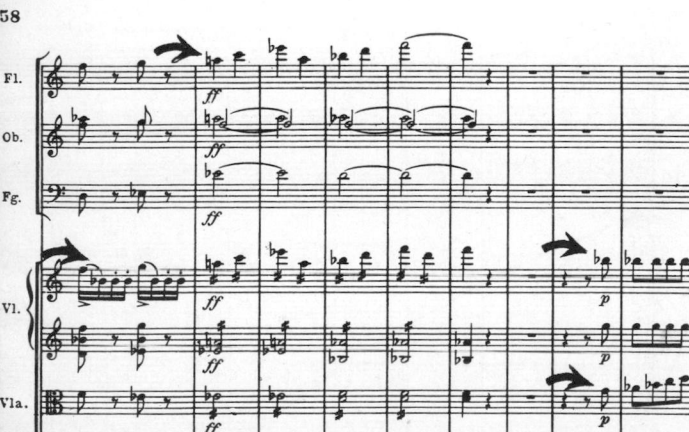

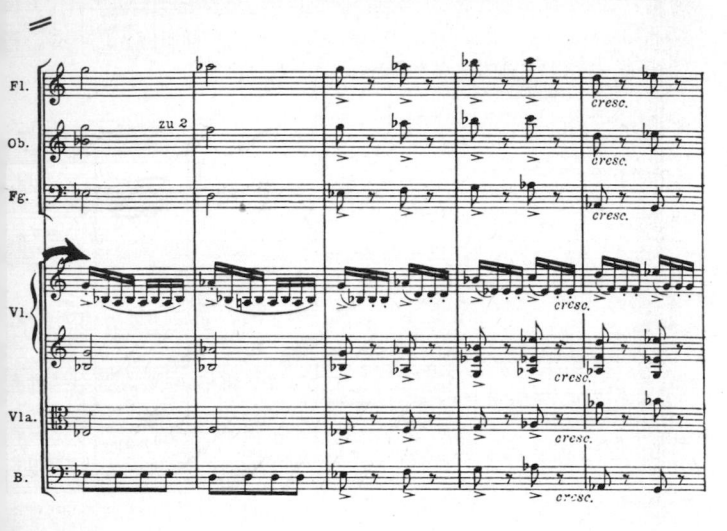

DEVELOPMENT—

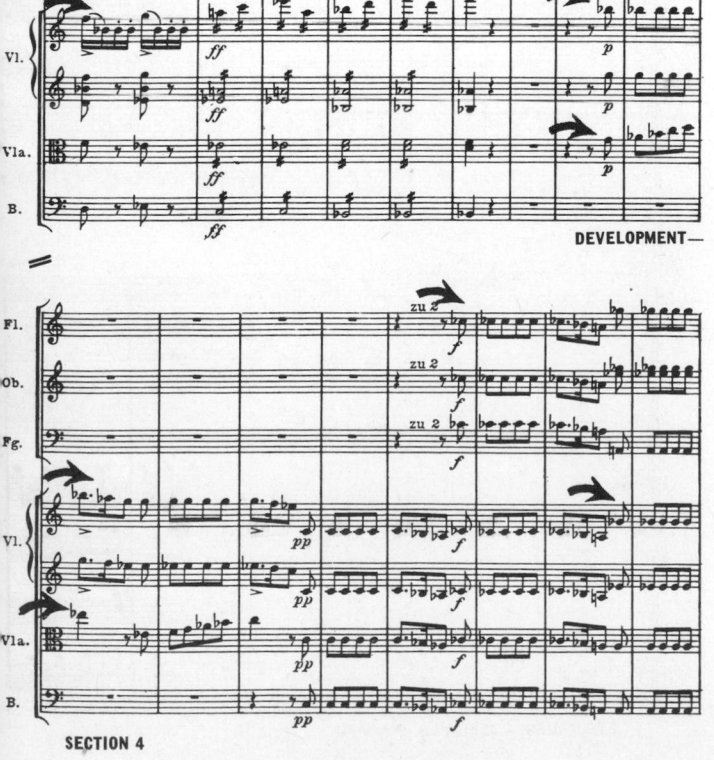

SECTION 4

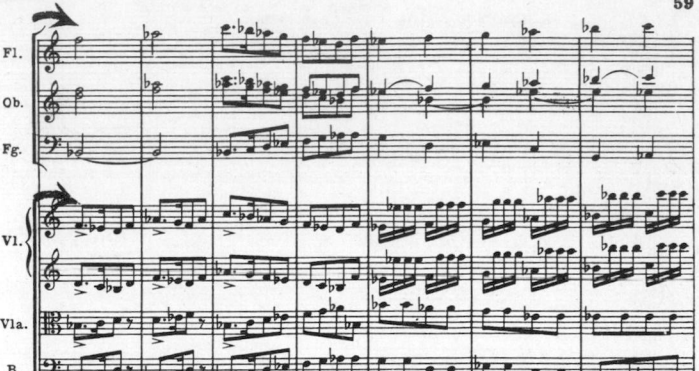

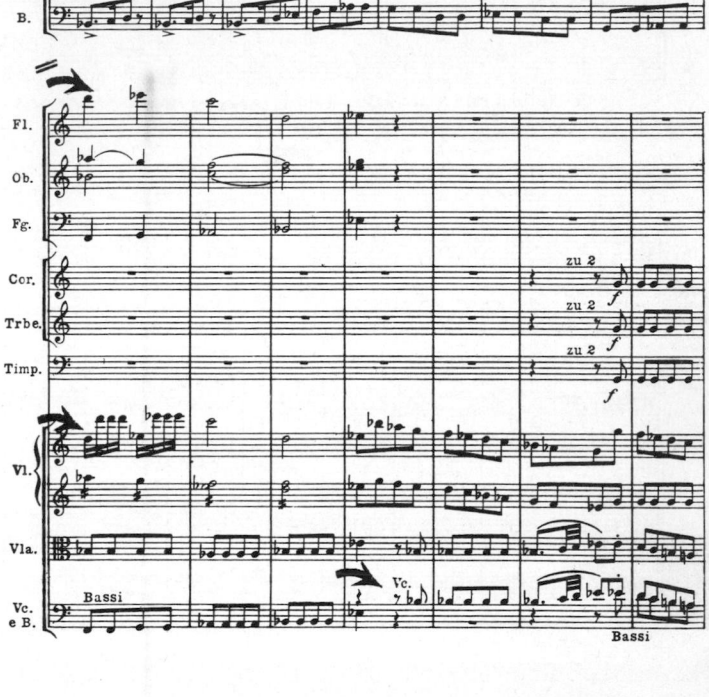

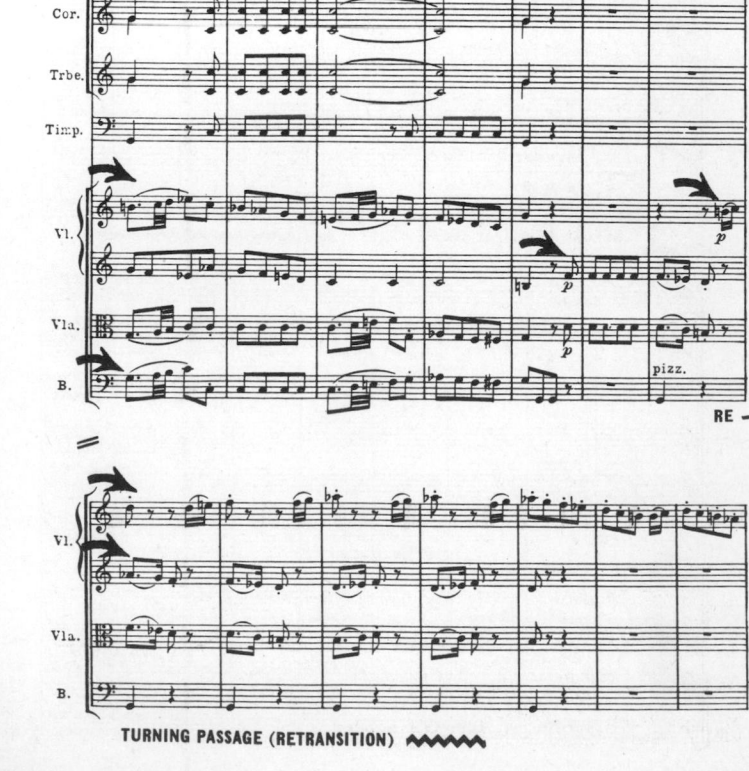

RE —

TURNING PASSAGE (RETRANSITION) ∿∿∿∿

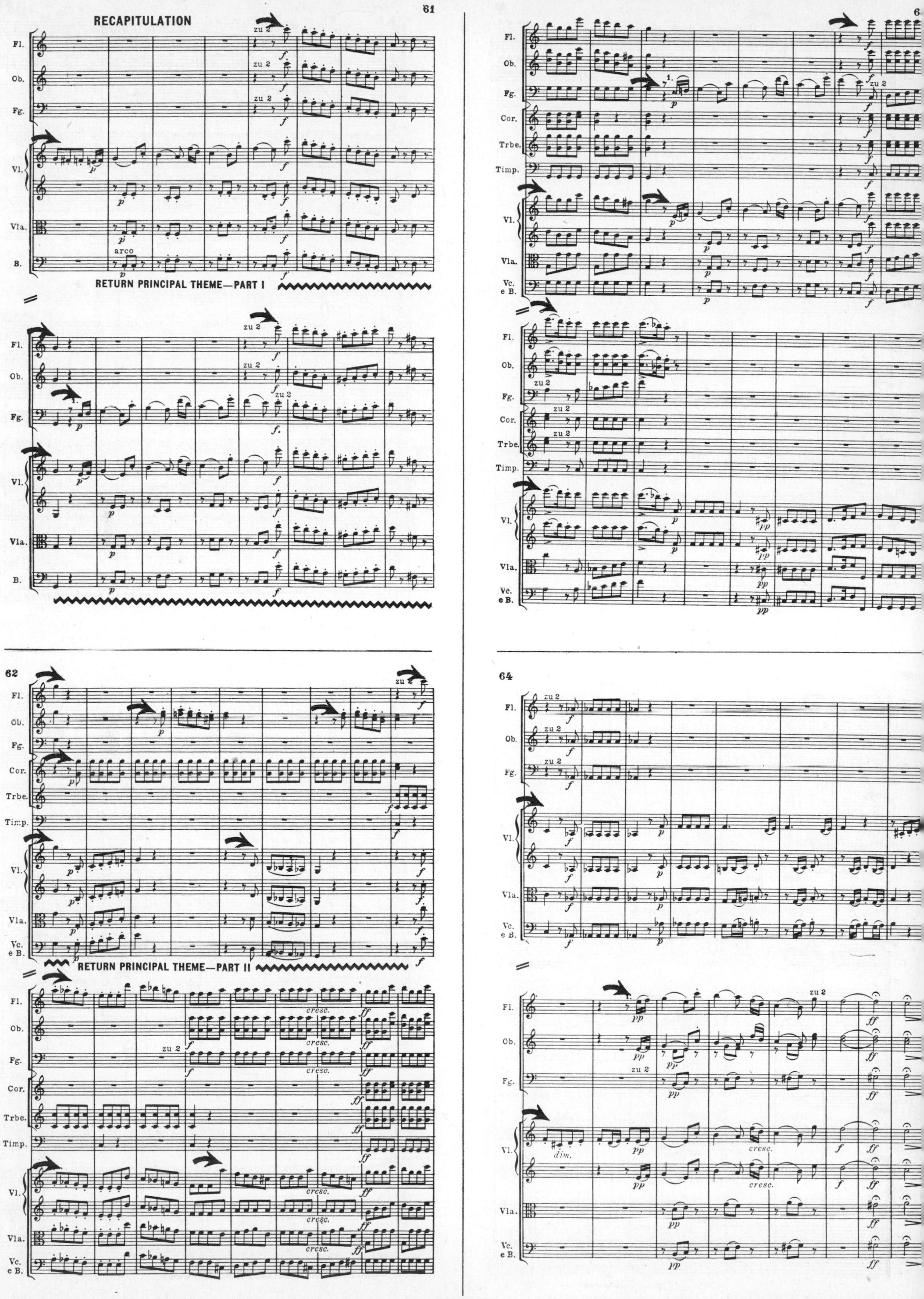

RECAPITULATION

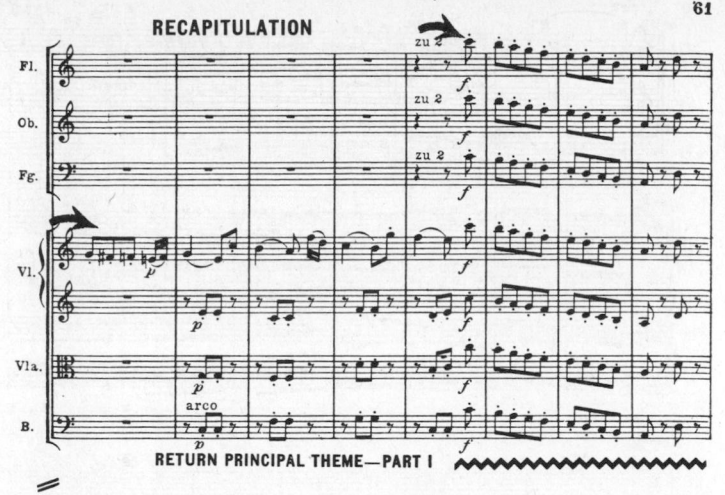

RETURN PRINCIPAL THEME—PART I

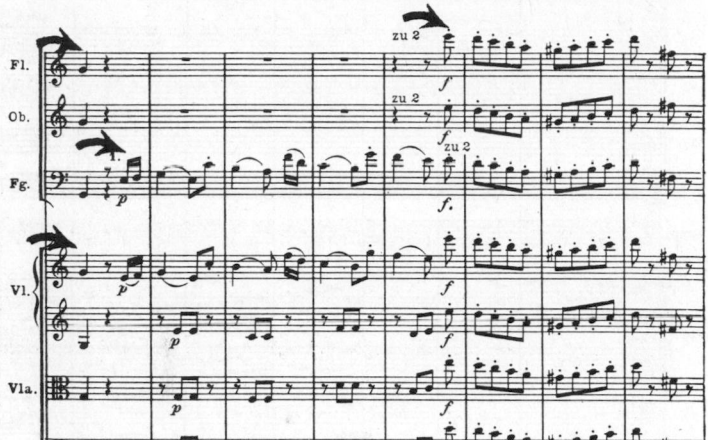

RETURN PRINCIPAL THEME—PART II

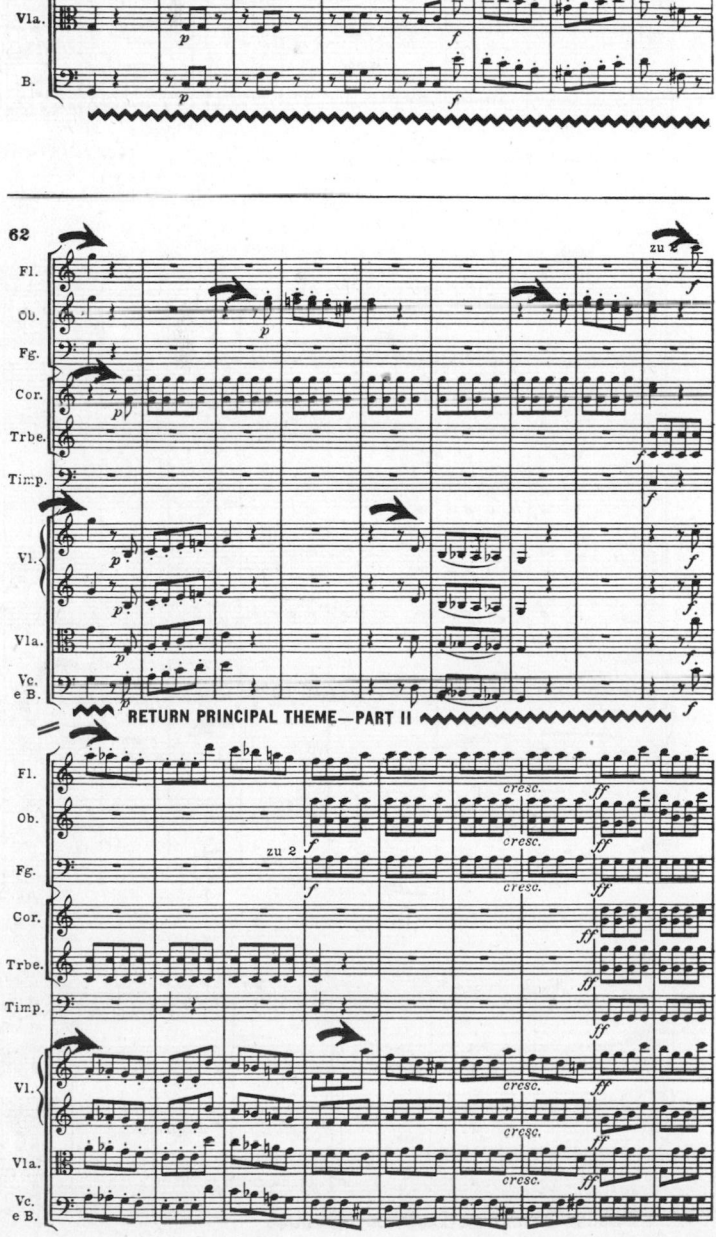

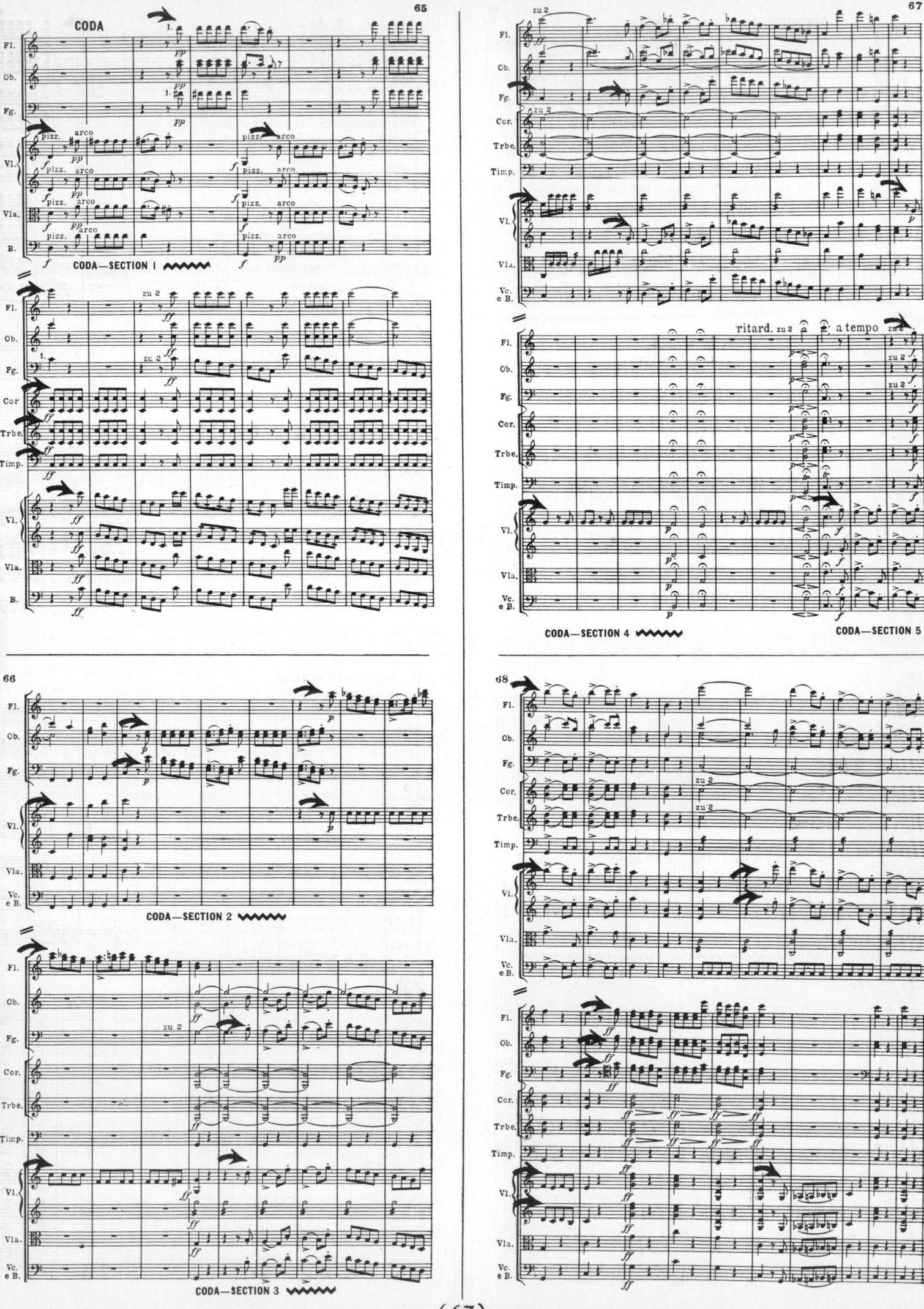

CODA

CODA—SECTION 1

CODA—SECTION 2

CODA—SECTION 3

CODA—SECTION 4

CODA—SECTION 5

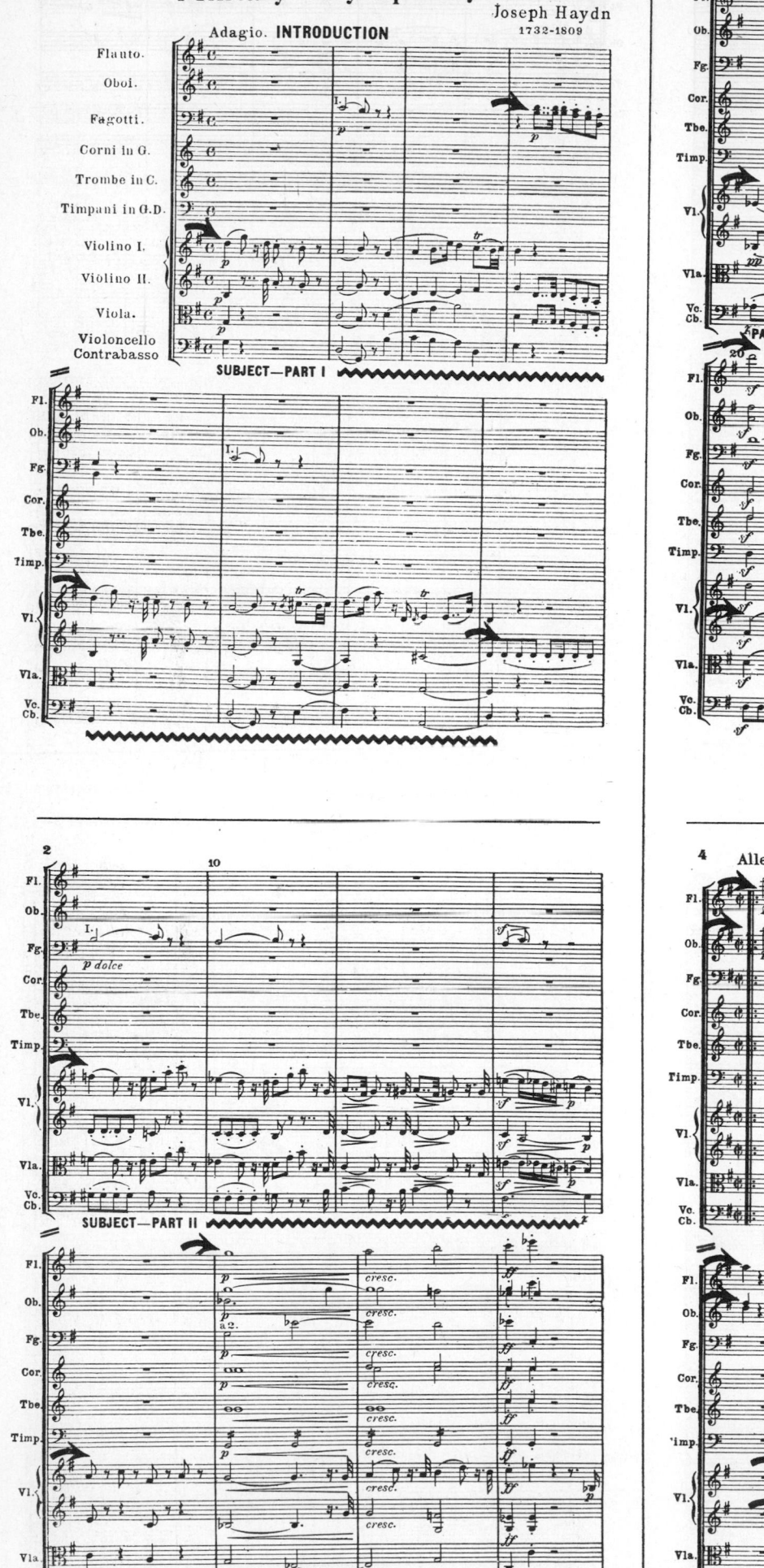

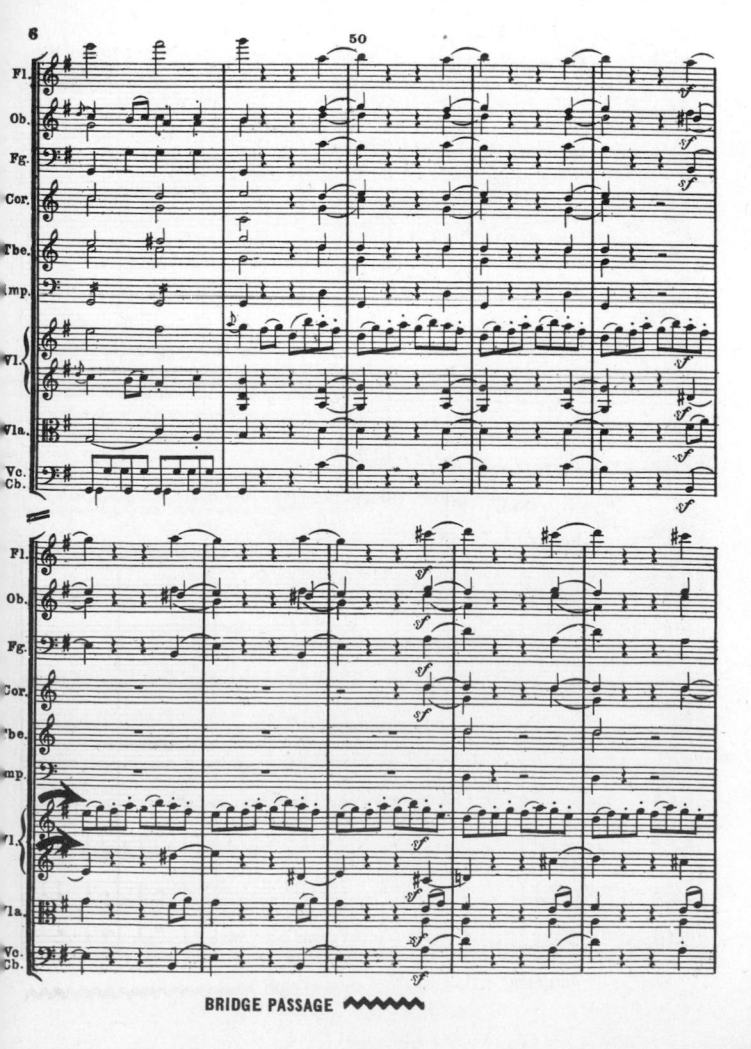

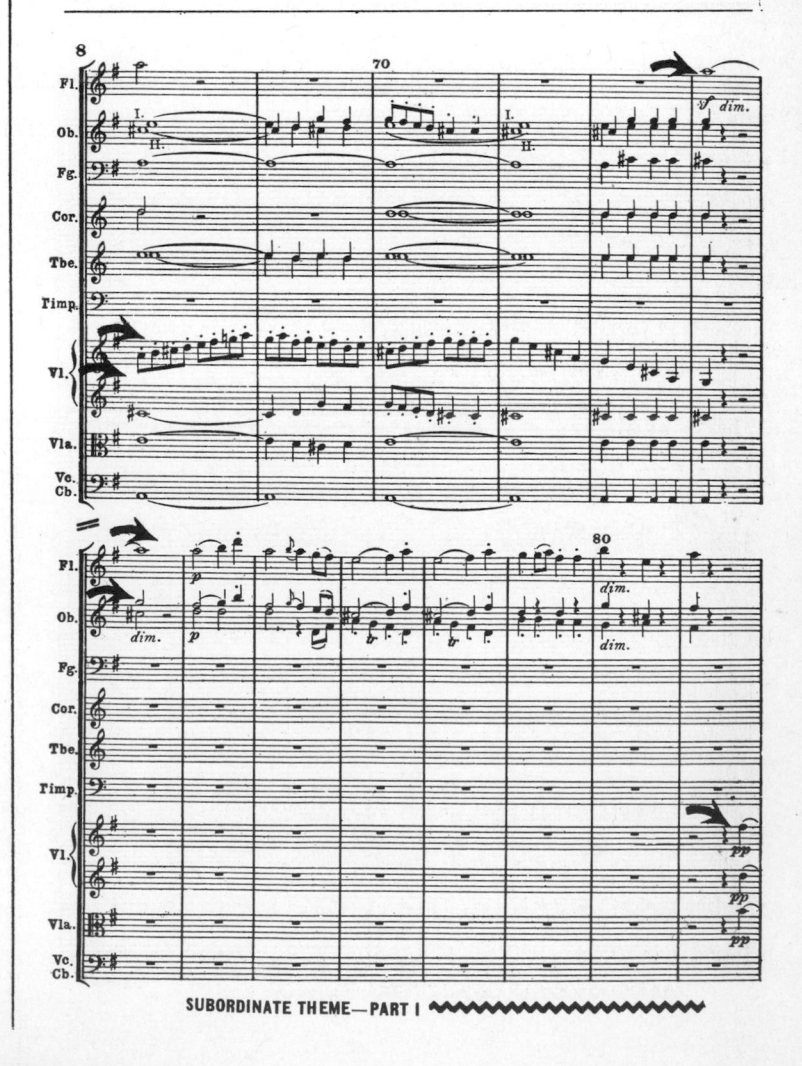

PRINCIPAL THEME—PART II

BRIDGE PASSAGE

SUBORDINATE THEME—PART I

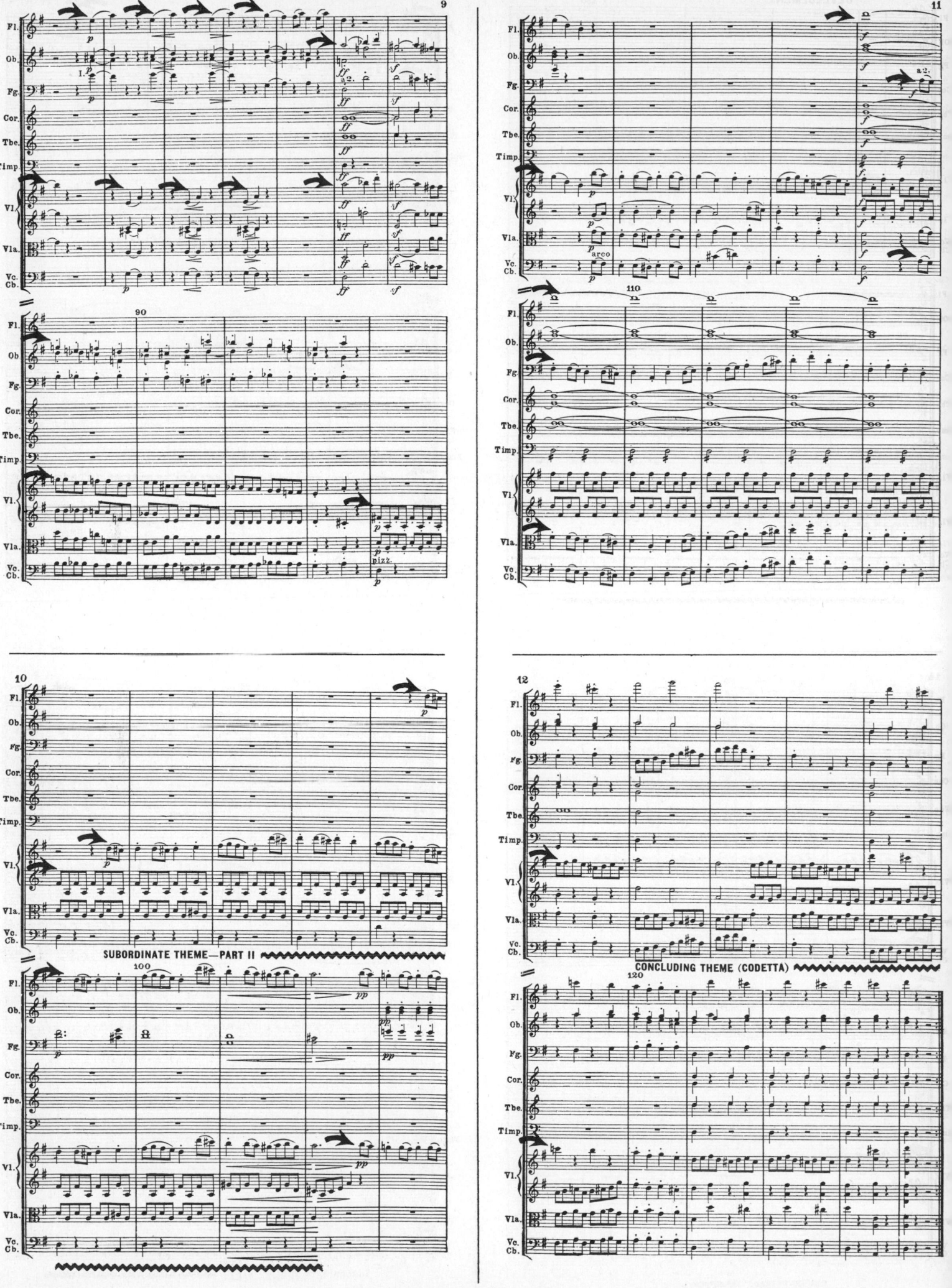

SUBORDINATE THEME—PART II

CONCLUDING THEME (CODETTA)

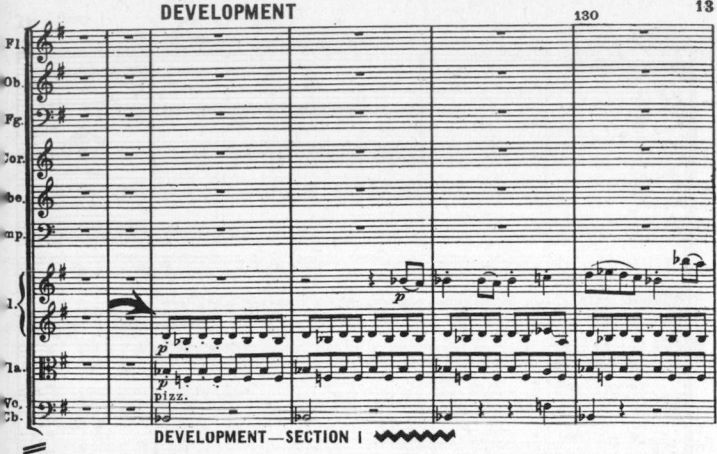

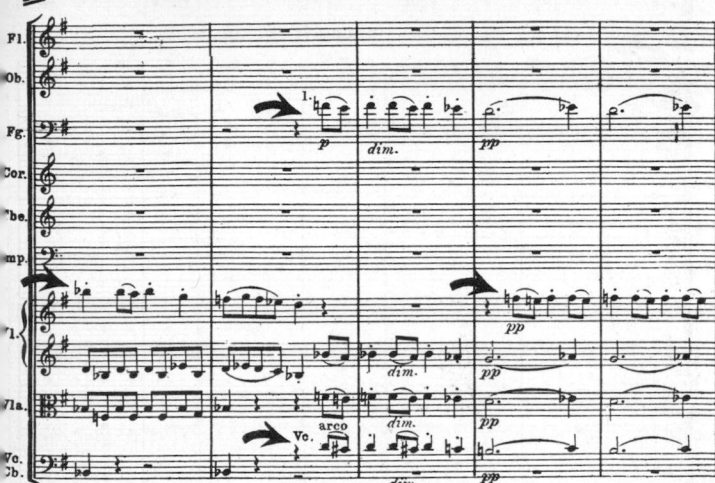

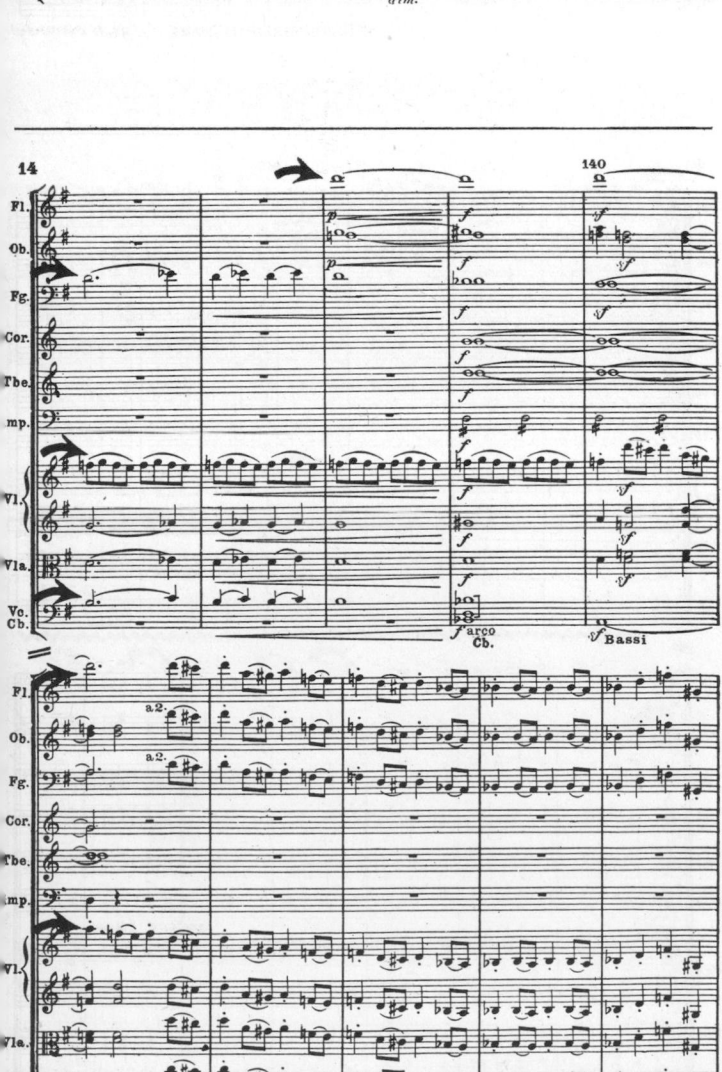

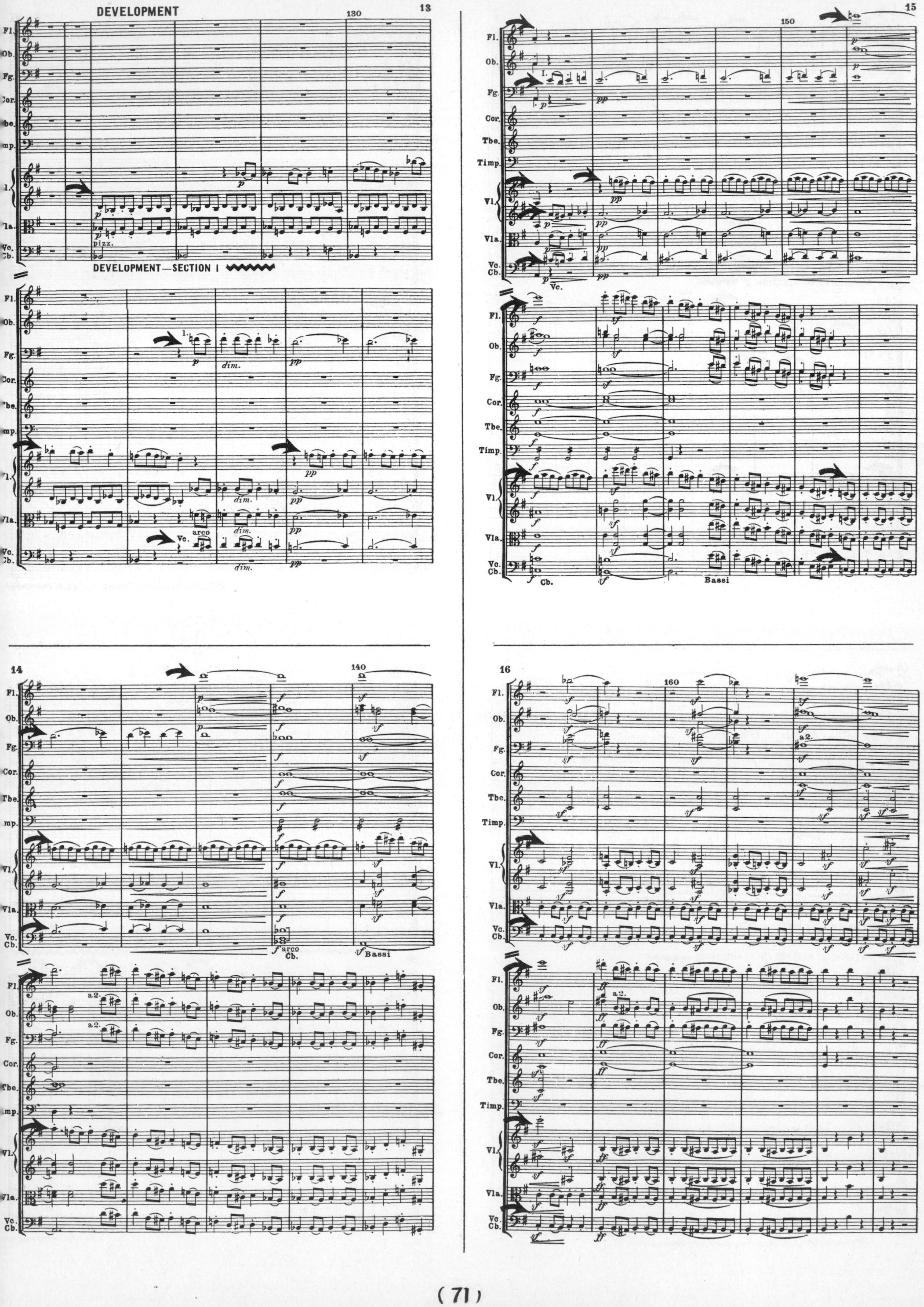

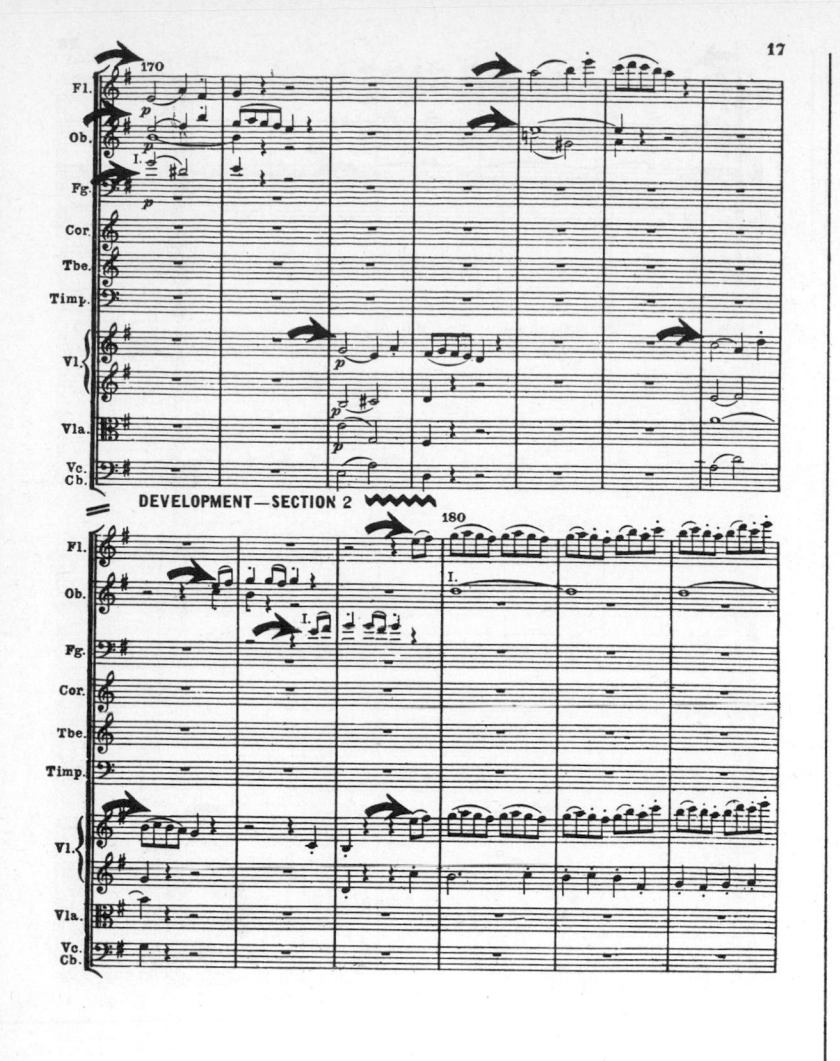

DEVELOPMENT—SECTION 2 〰〰〰

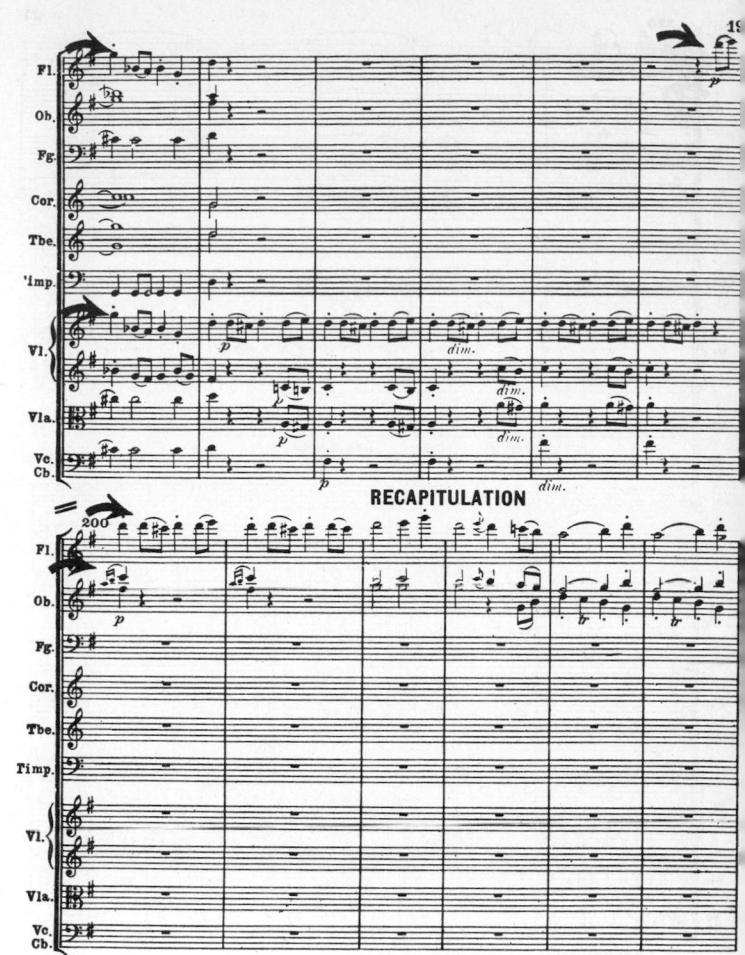

RECAPITULATION

RETURN PRINCIPAL THEME—PART I 〰〰〰

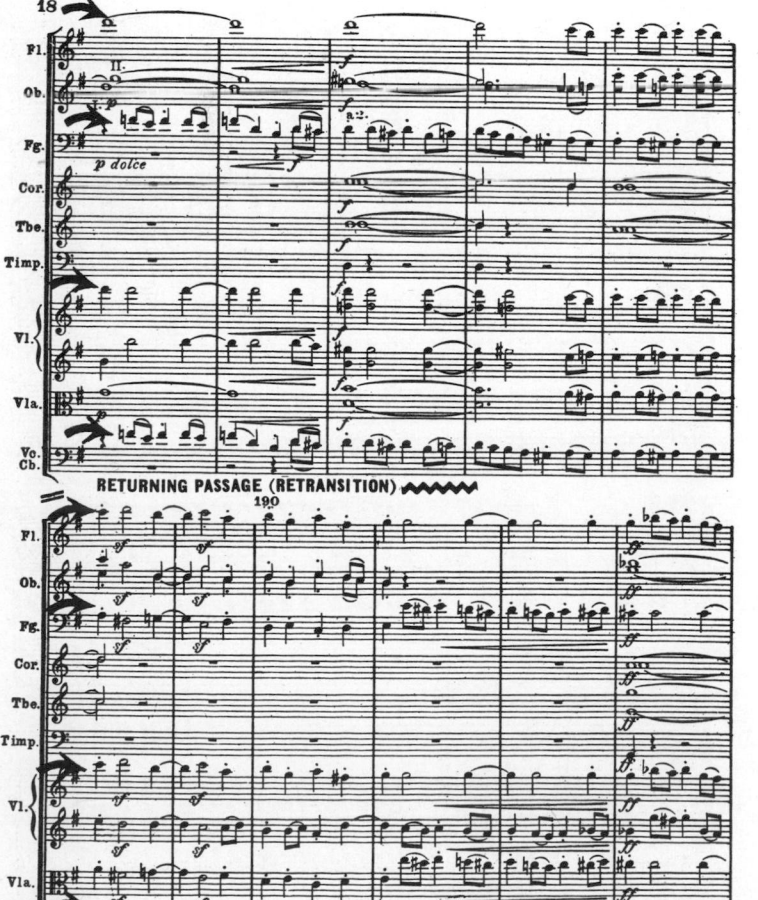

RETURNING PASSAGE (RETRANSITION) 〰〰〰〰

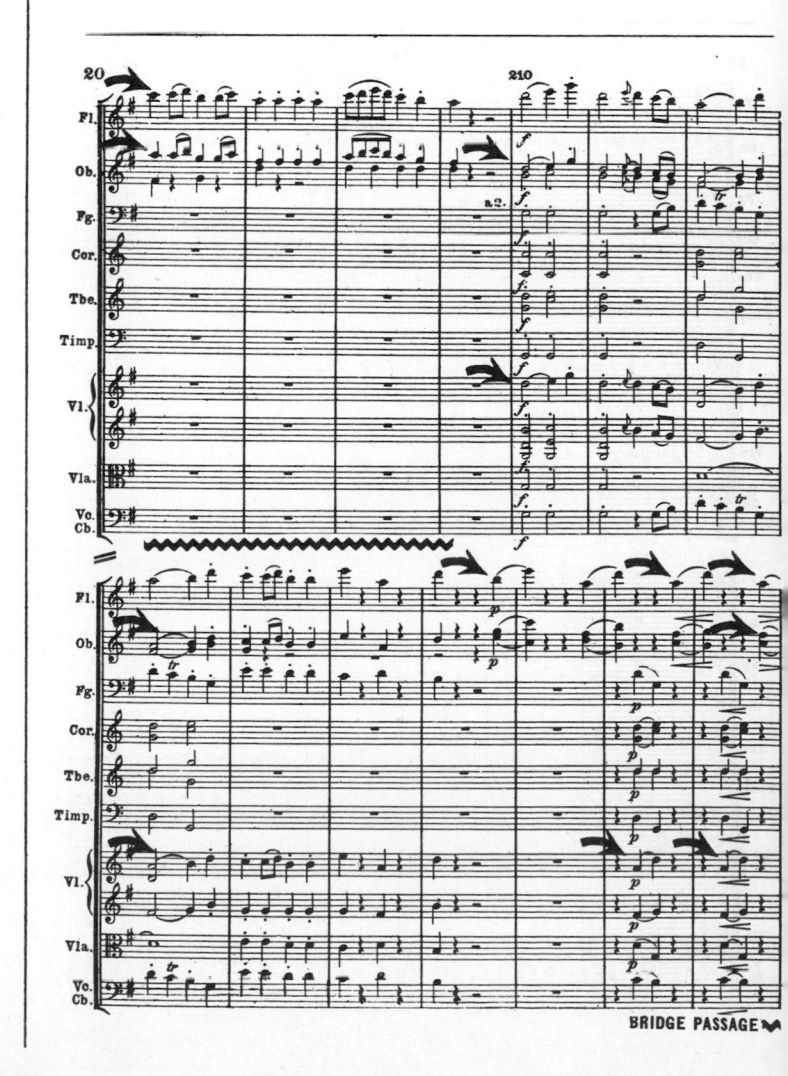

BRIDGE PASSAGE ◆

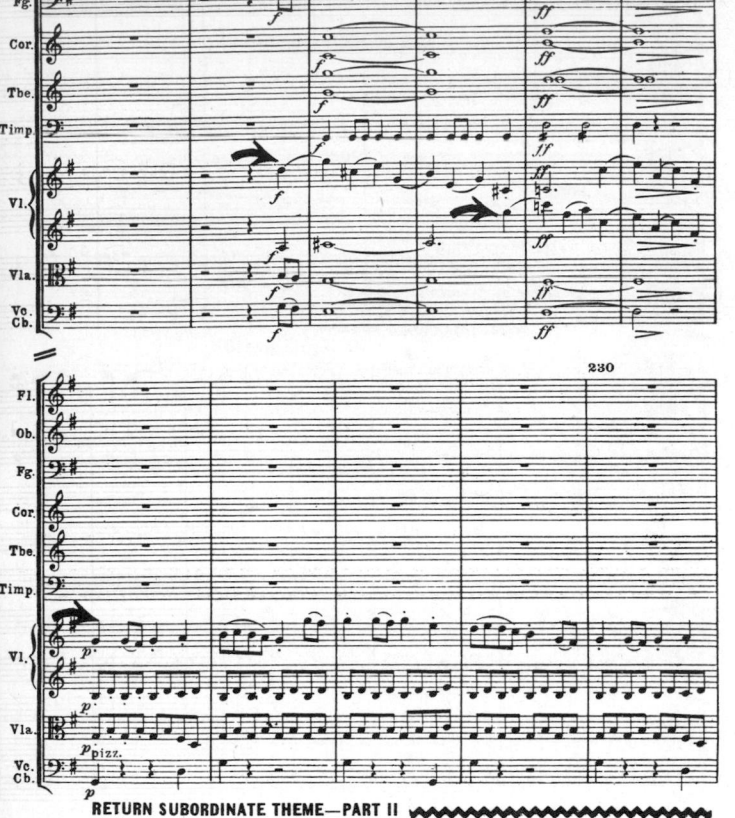

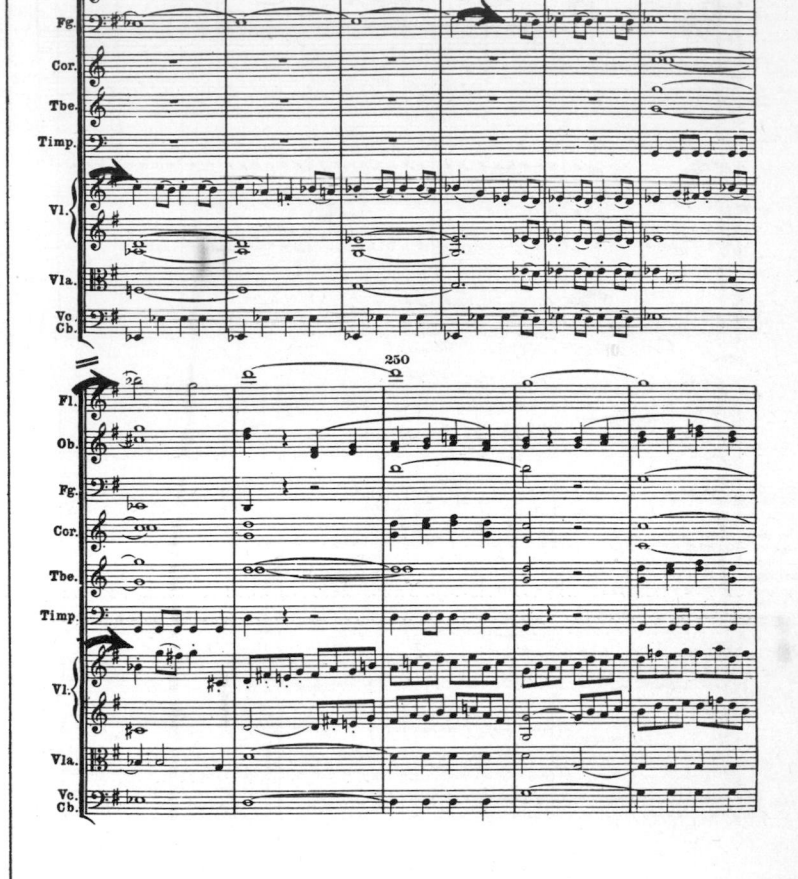

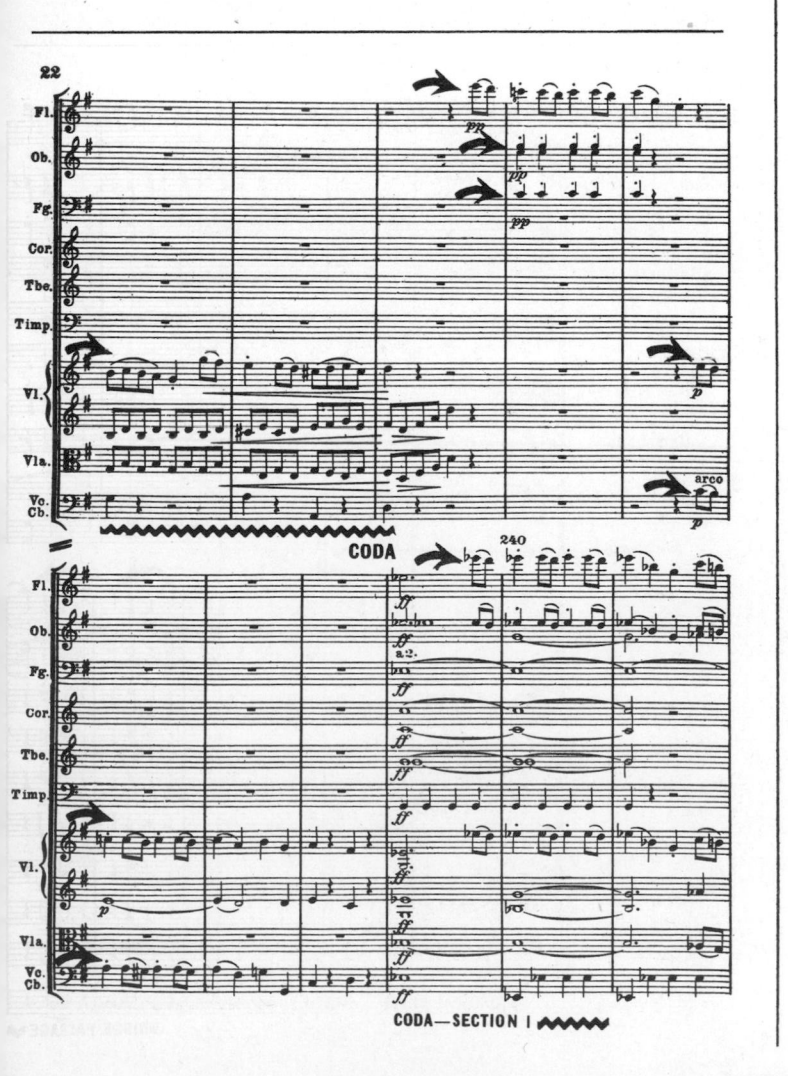

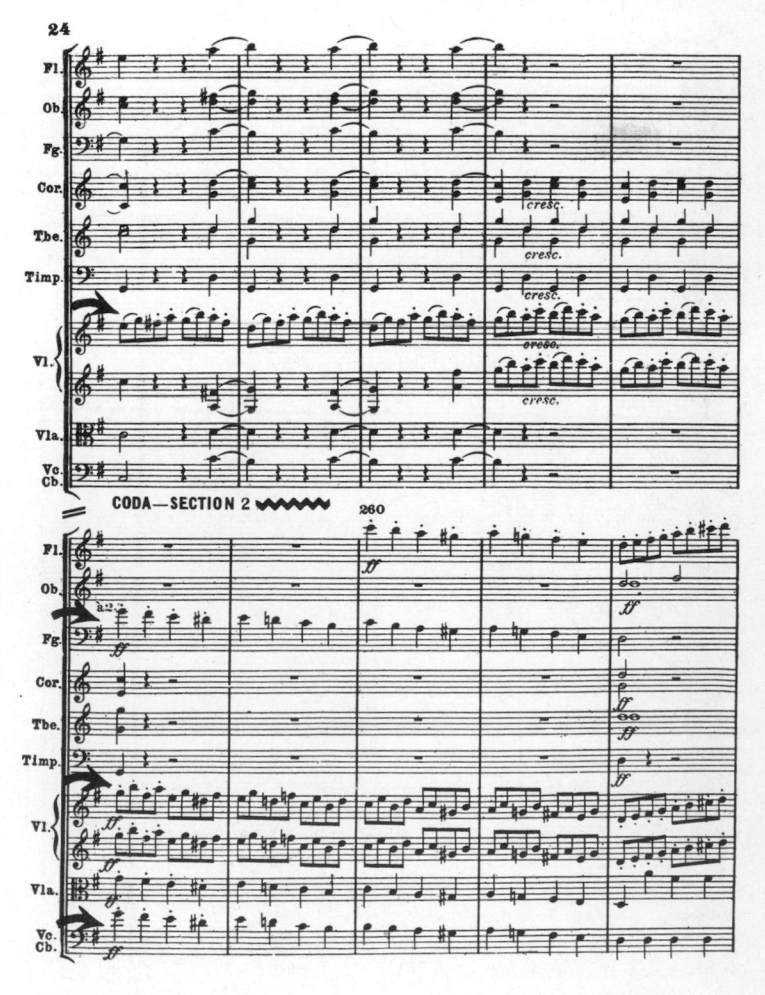

RETURN SUBORDINATE THEME—PART II

CODA

CODA—SECTION I

CODA—SECTION 2

(73)

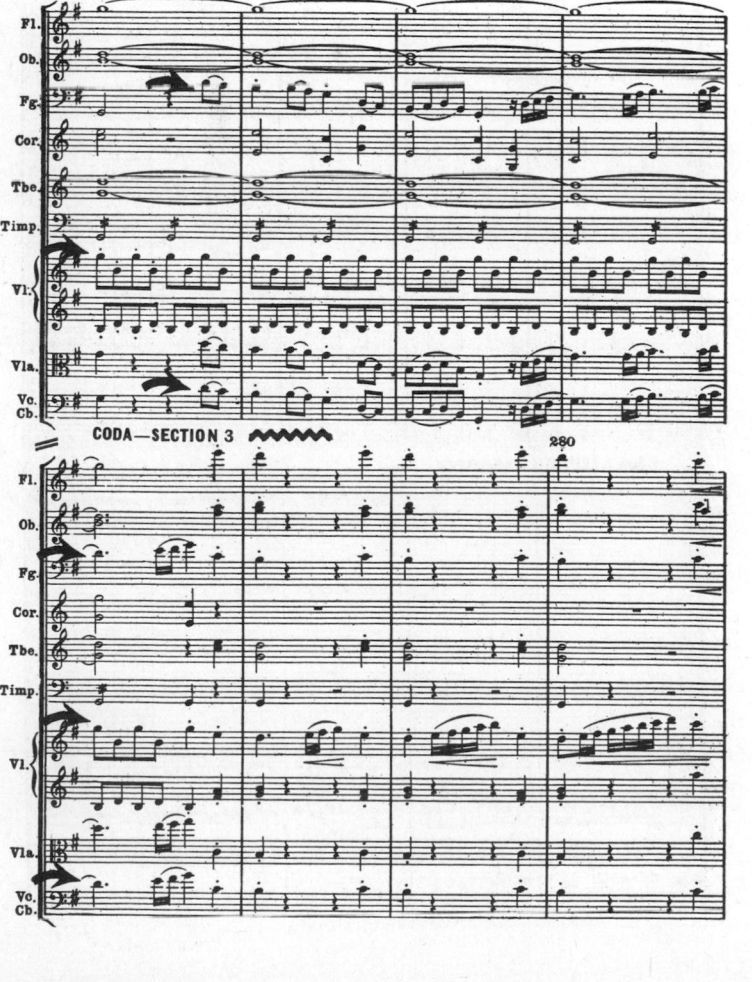

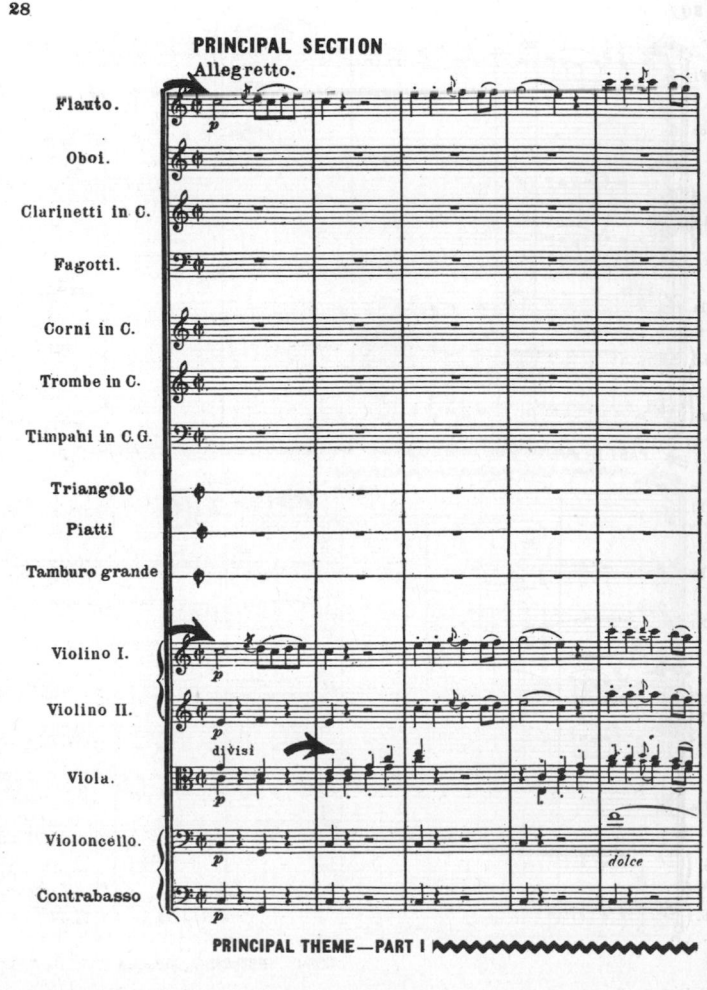

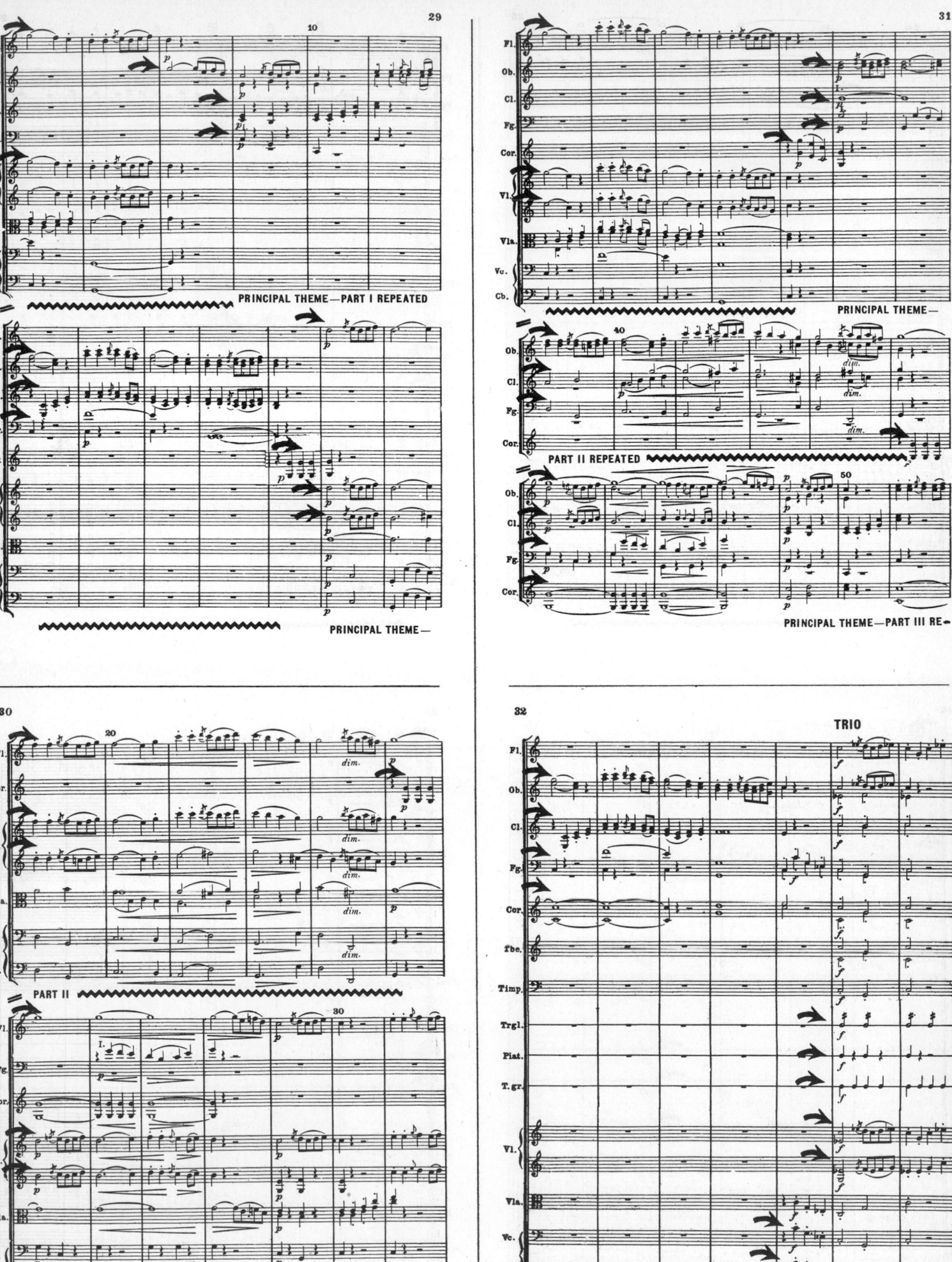

PRINCIPAL THEME—PART I REPEATED

PRINCIPAL THEME—

PRINCIPAL THEME—

PART II REPEATED

PRINCIPAL THEME—PART III RE—

TRIO

PART II

PRINCIPAL THEME—PART III

PEATED

SUBORDINATE THEME—

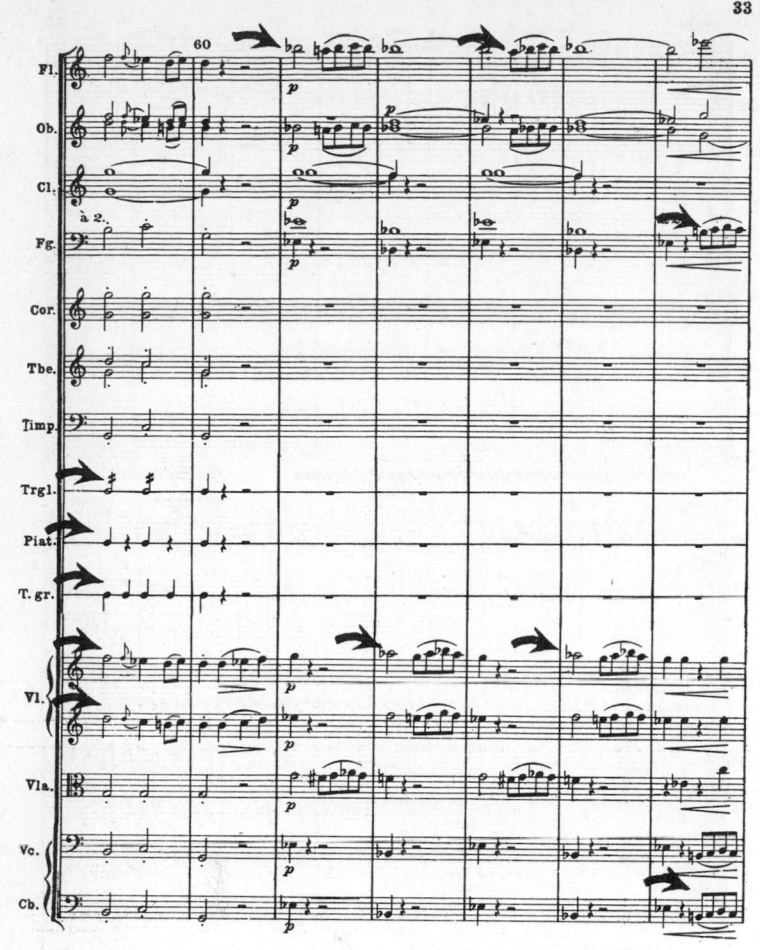

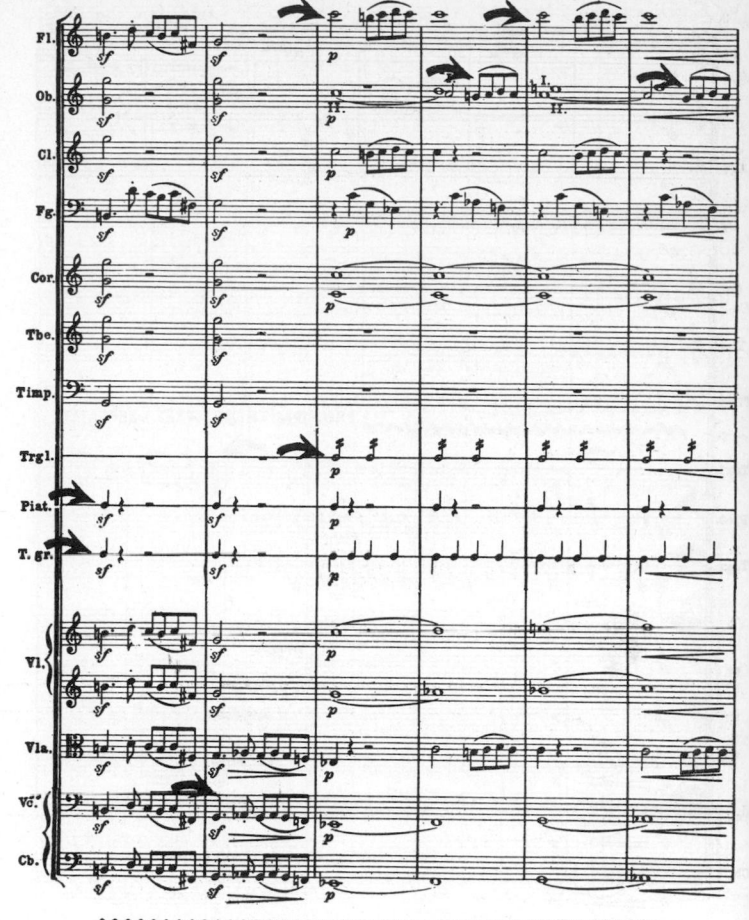

PART I ∿∿∿∿∿∿∿∿∿∿∿∿∿∿∿∿∿∿∿∿

∿∿∿∿∿∿∿∿∿∿∿∿∿∿∿∿∿∿∿∿∿∿∿

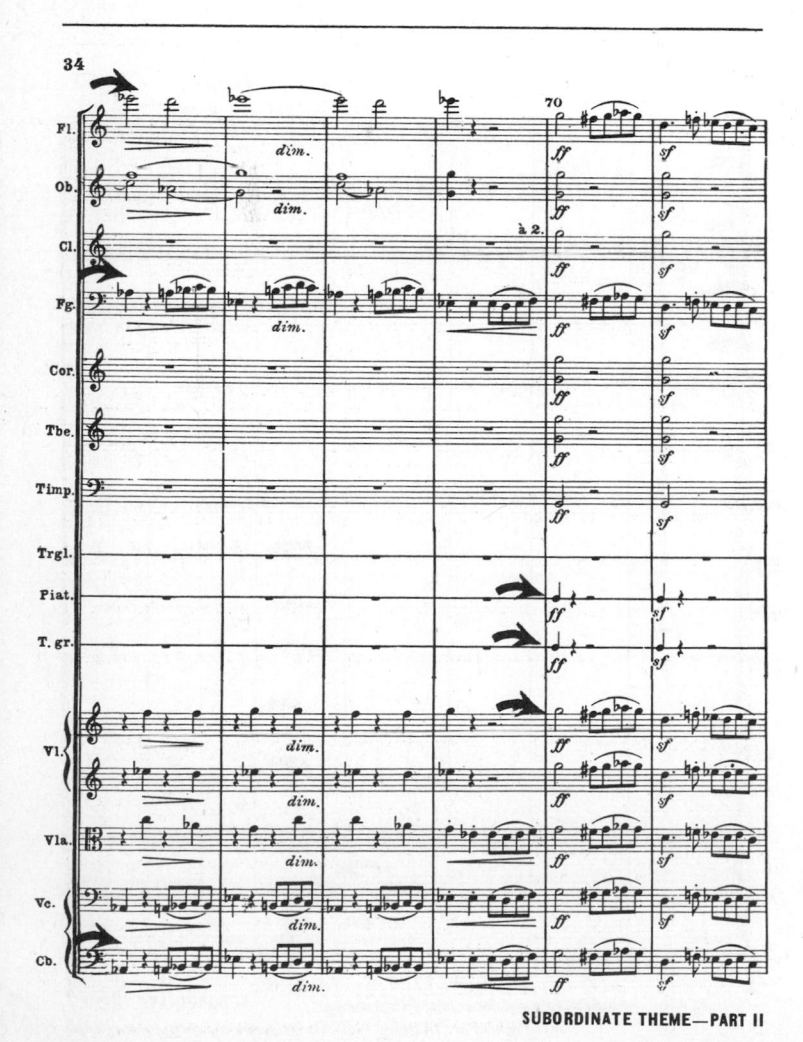

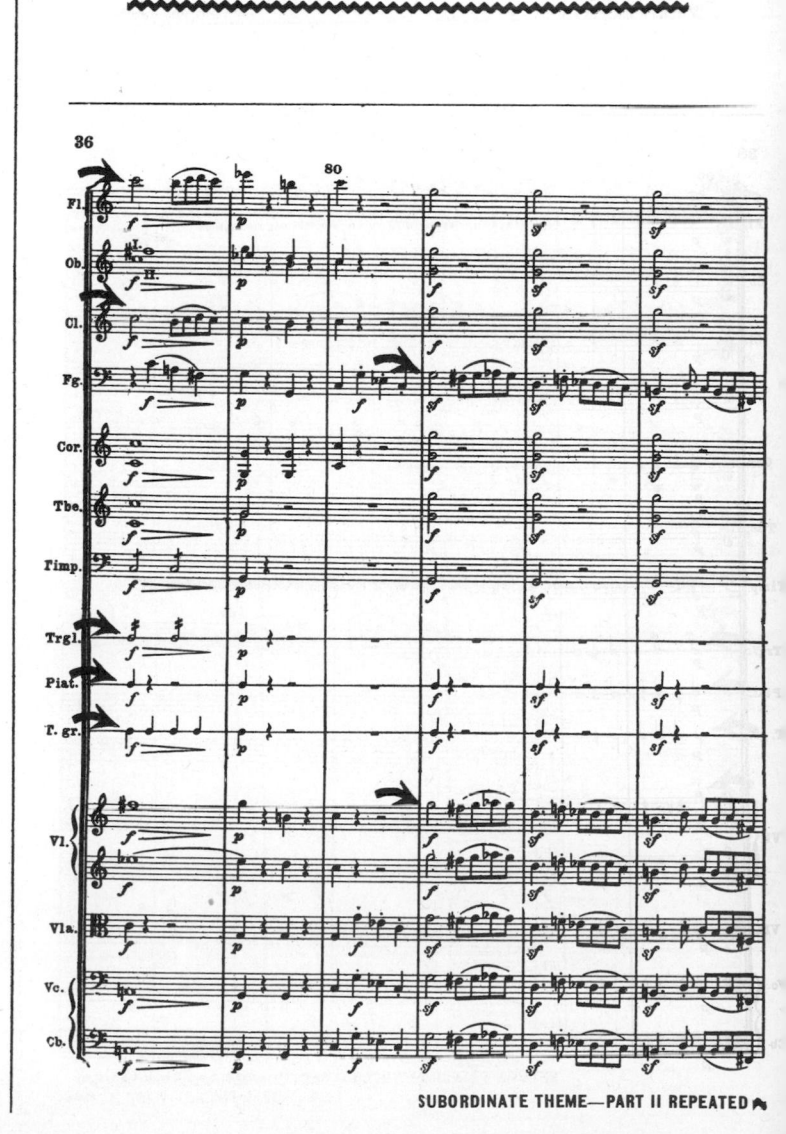

SUBORDINATE THEME—PART II

SUBORDINATE THEME—PART II REPEATED

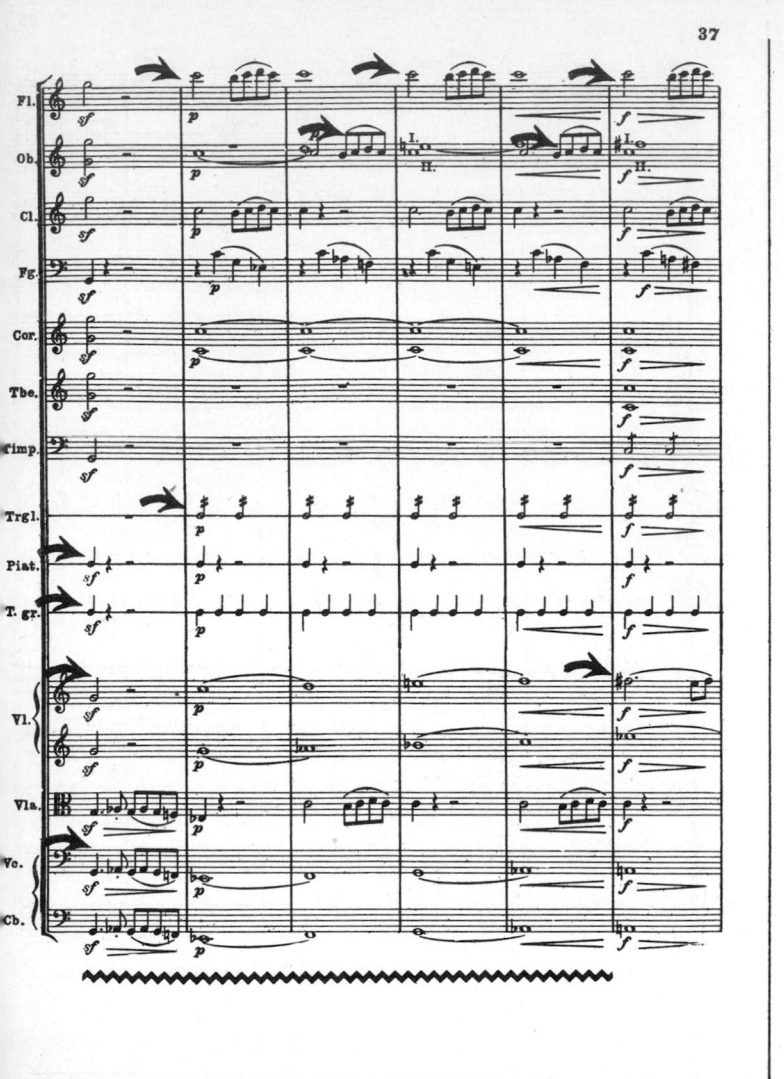

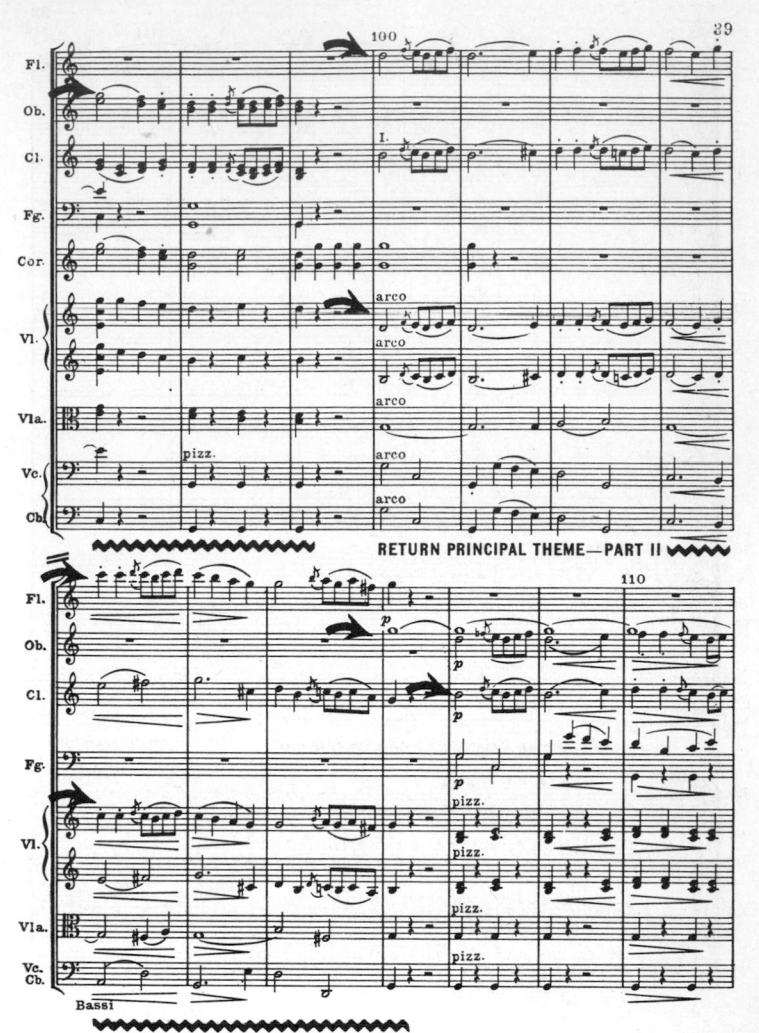

RETURN PRINCIPAL THEME—PART II

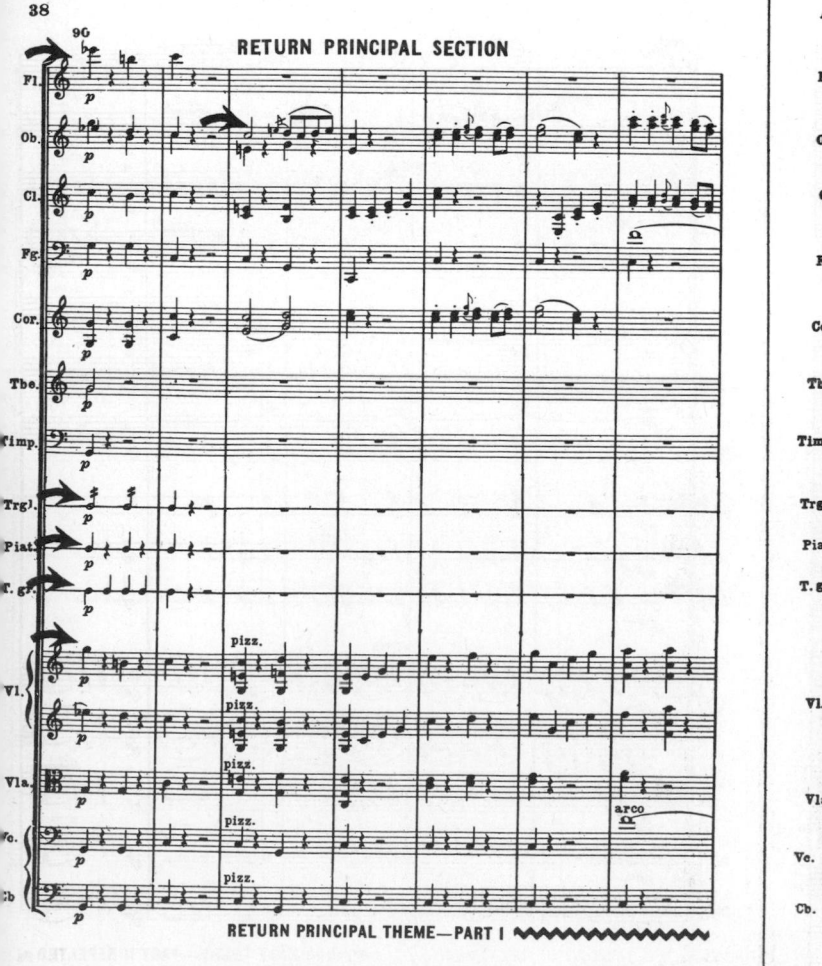

RETURN PRINCIPAL SECTION

RETURN PRINCIPAL THEME—PART I

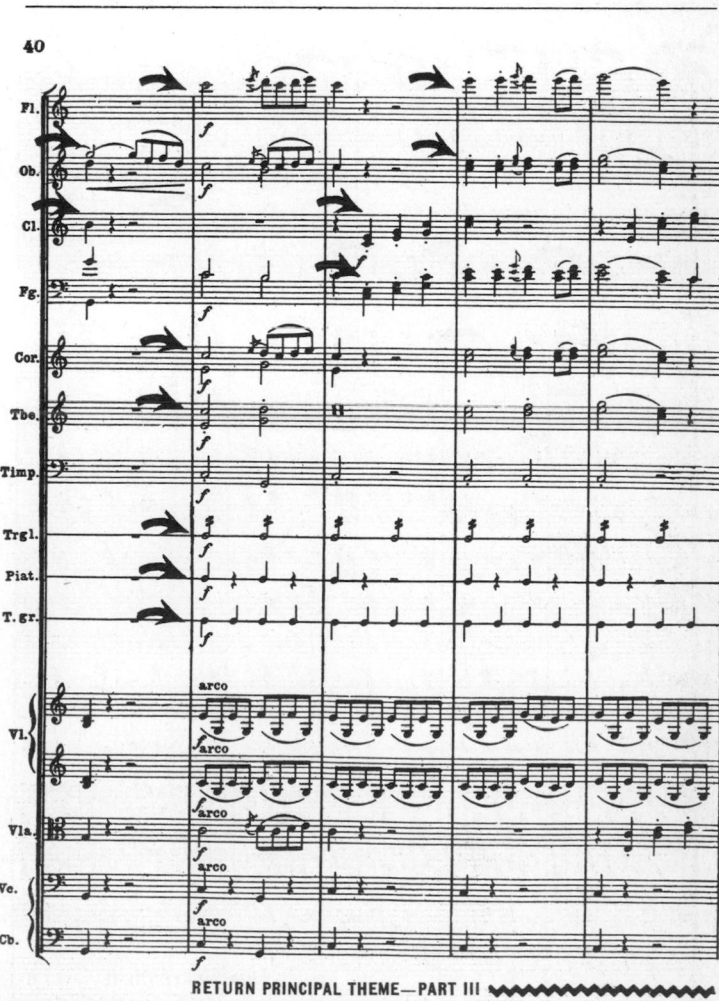

RETURN PRINCIPAL THEME—PART III

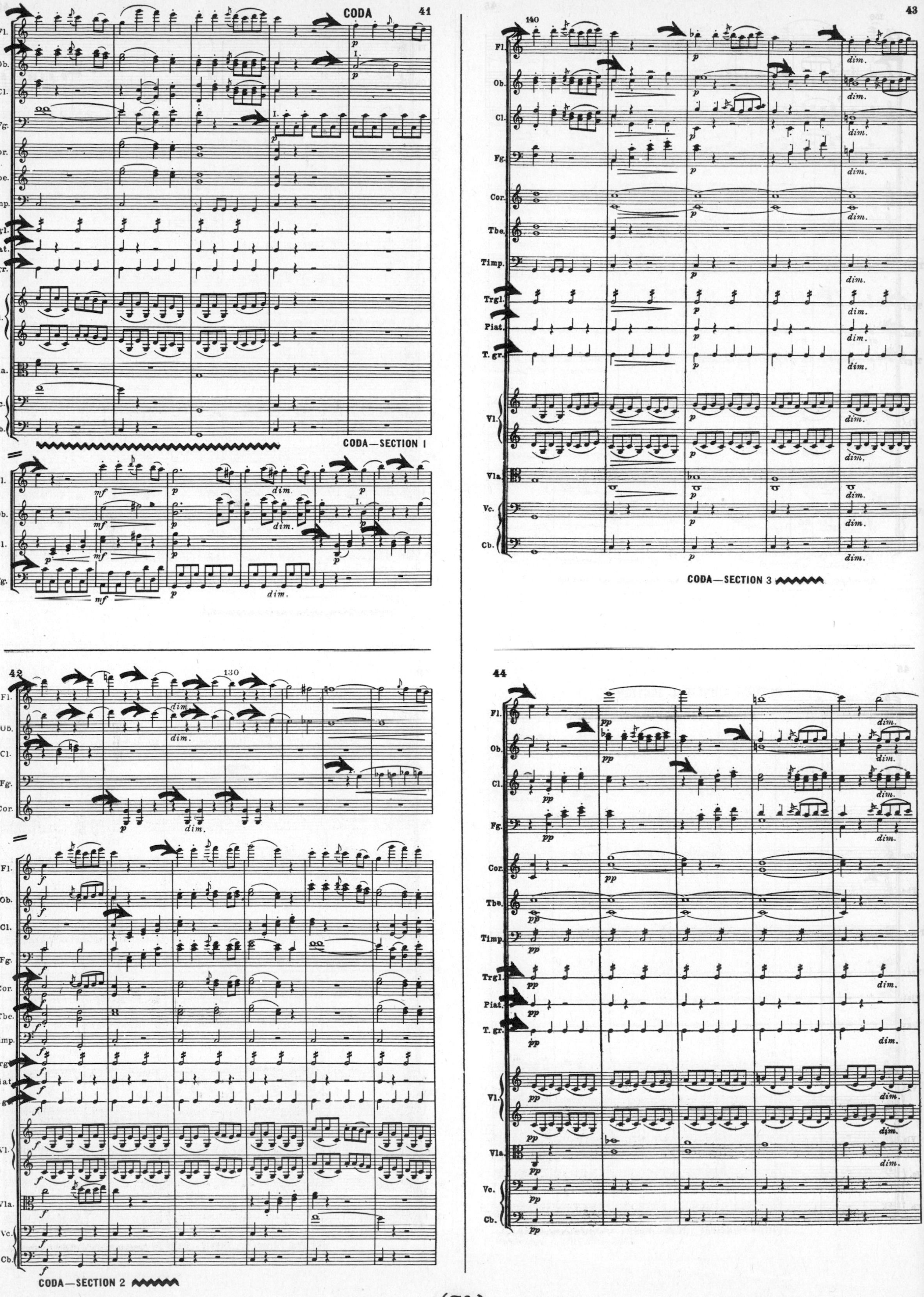
41
CODA
Fl.
Ob.
Cl.
Fg.
Cor.
Tbe.
Timp.
Trgl.
Piat.
T.gr.
Vl.
Vla.
Vc.
Cb.
CODA—SECTION 1
I.
p
mf
dim.
42
130
CODA—SECTION 2
f
43
140
CODA—SECTION 3
44
pp

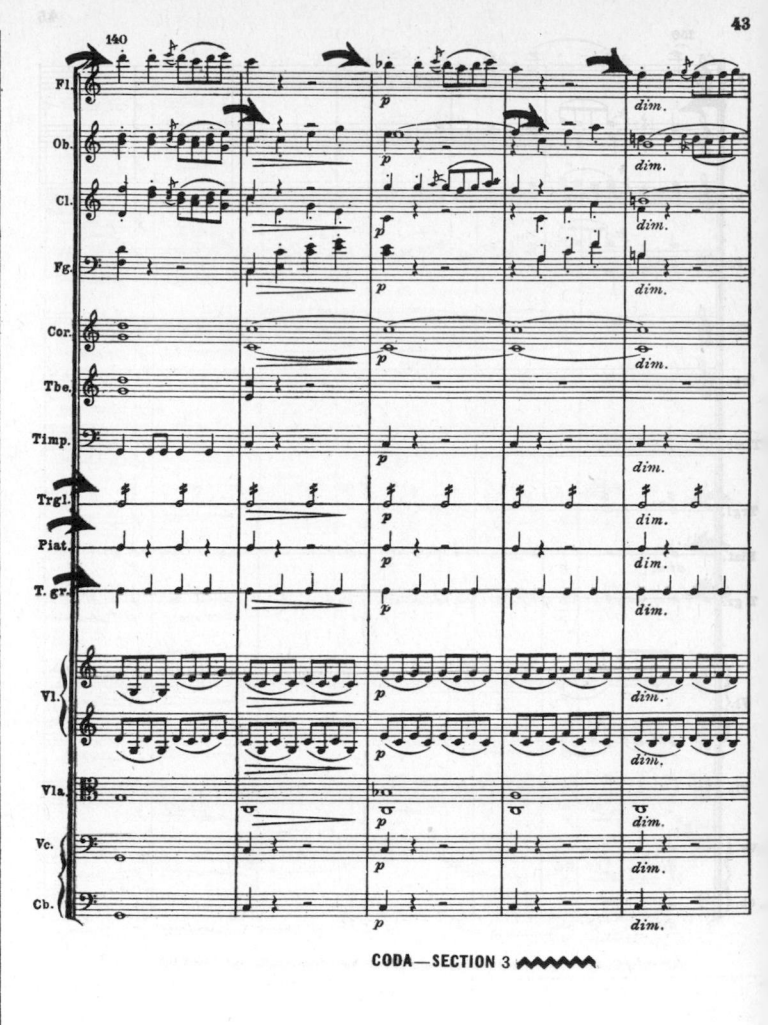

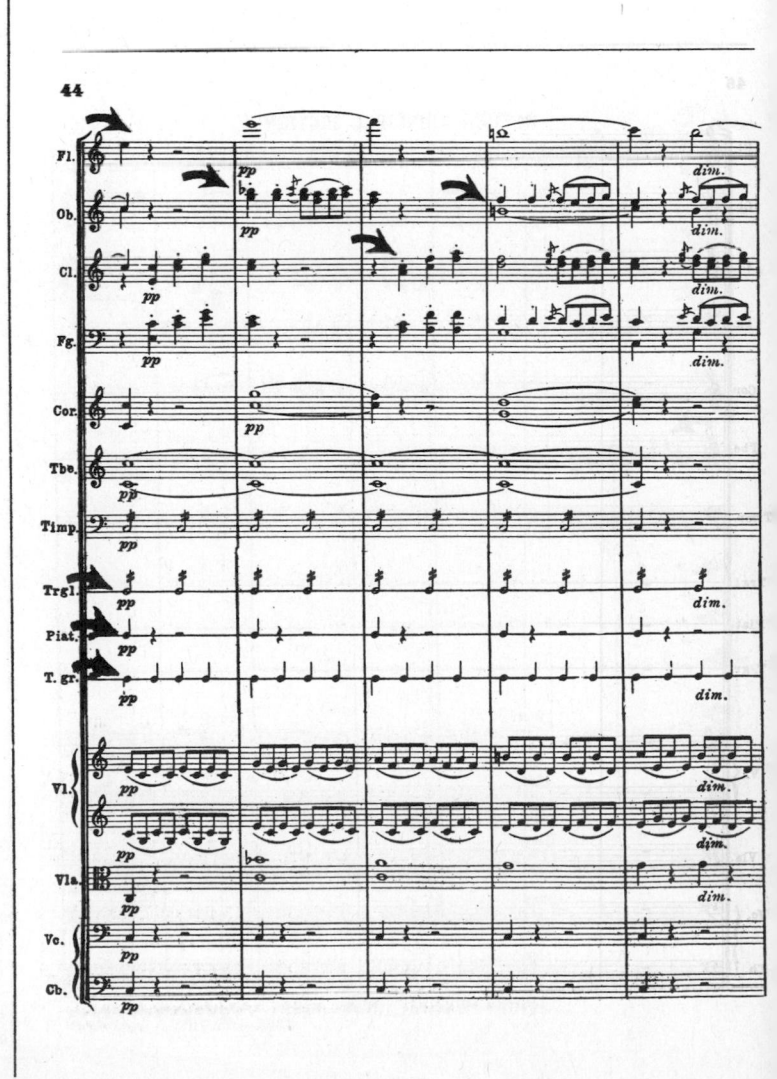

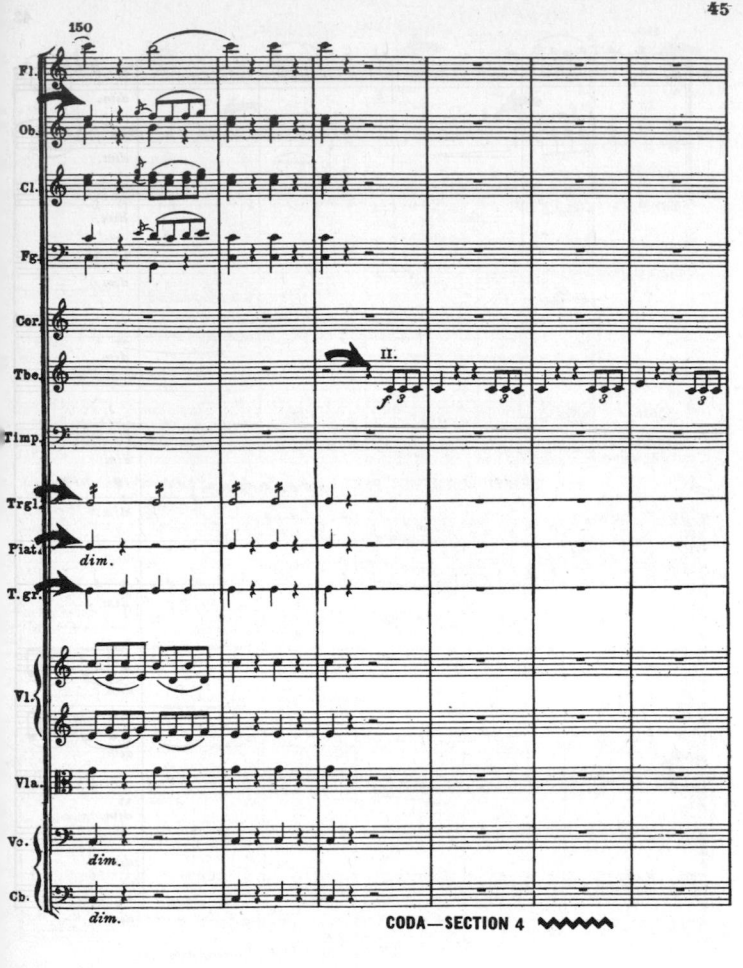

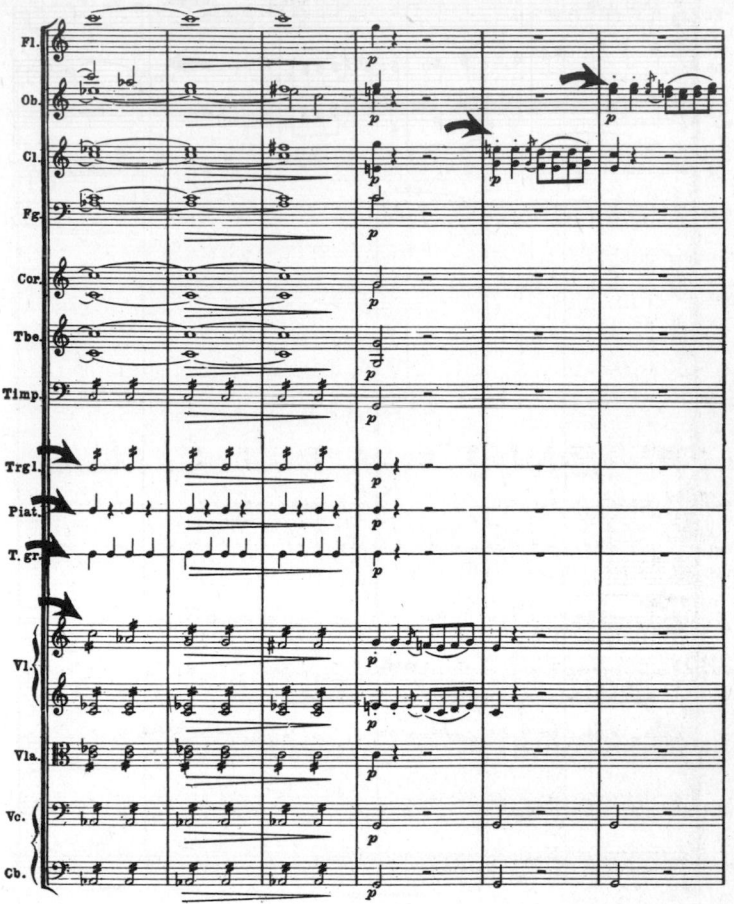

CODA—SECTION 4 〰〰〰

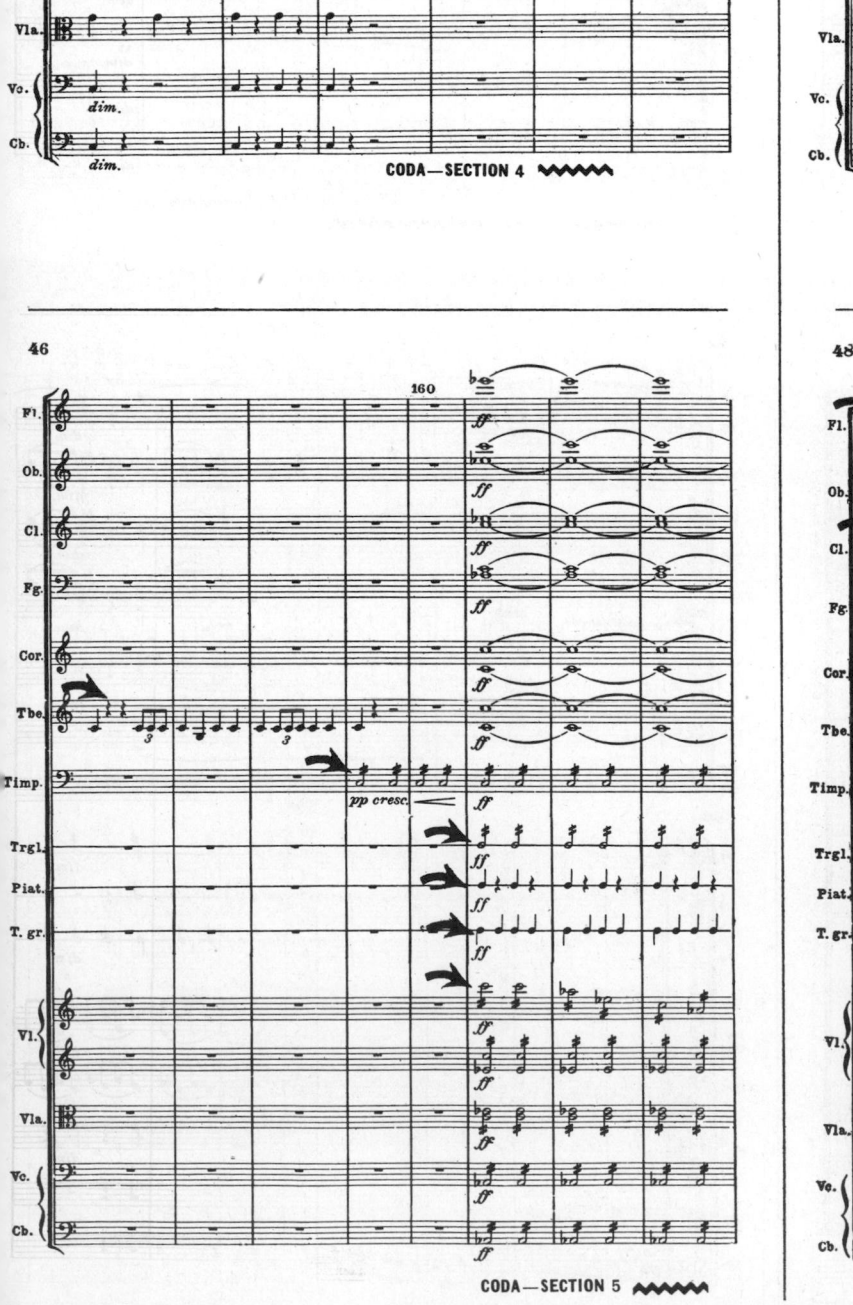

CODA—SECTION 5 〰〰〰

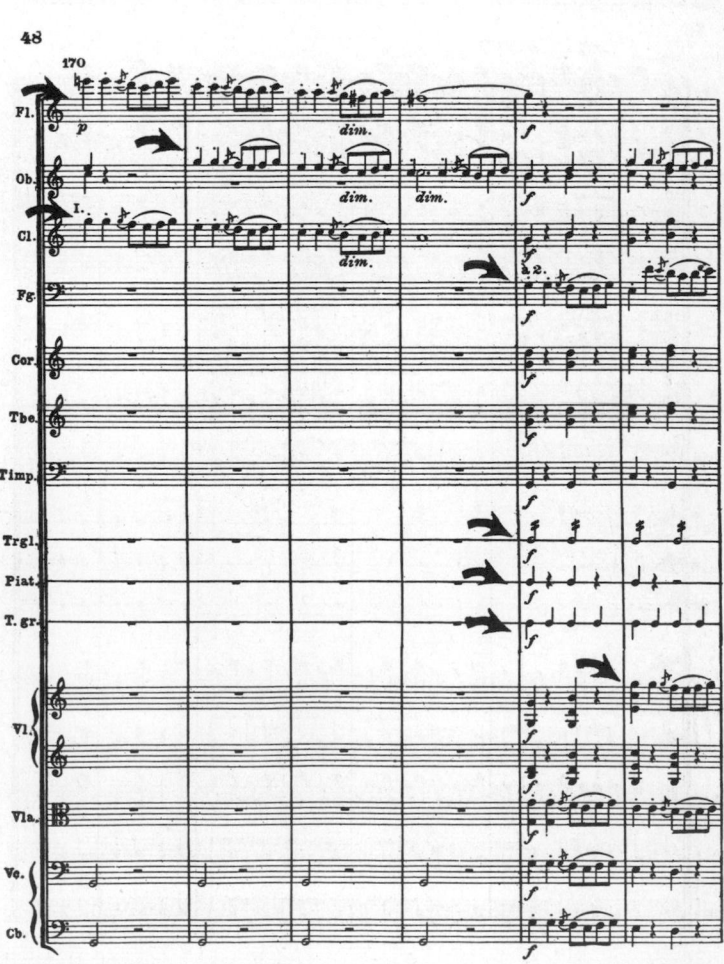

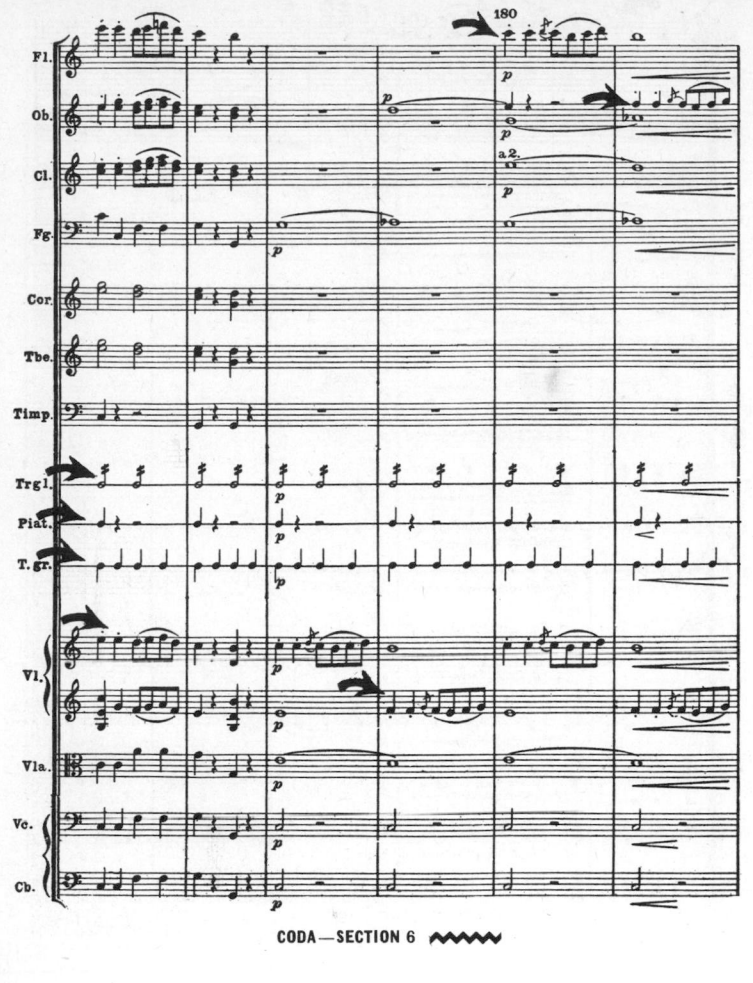

CODA—SECTION 6 〰〰

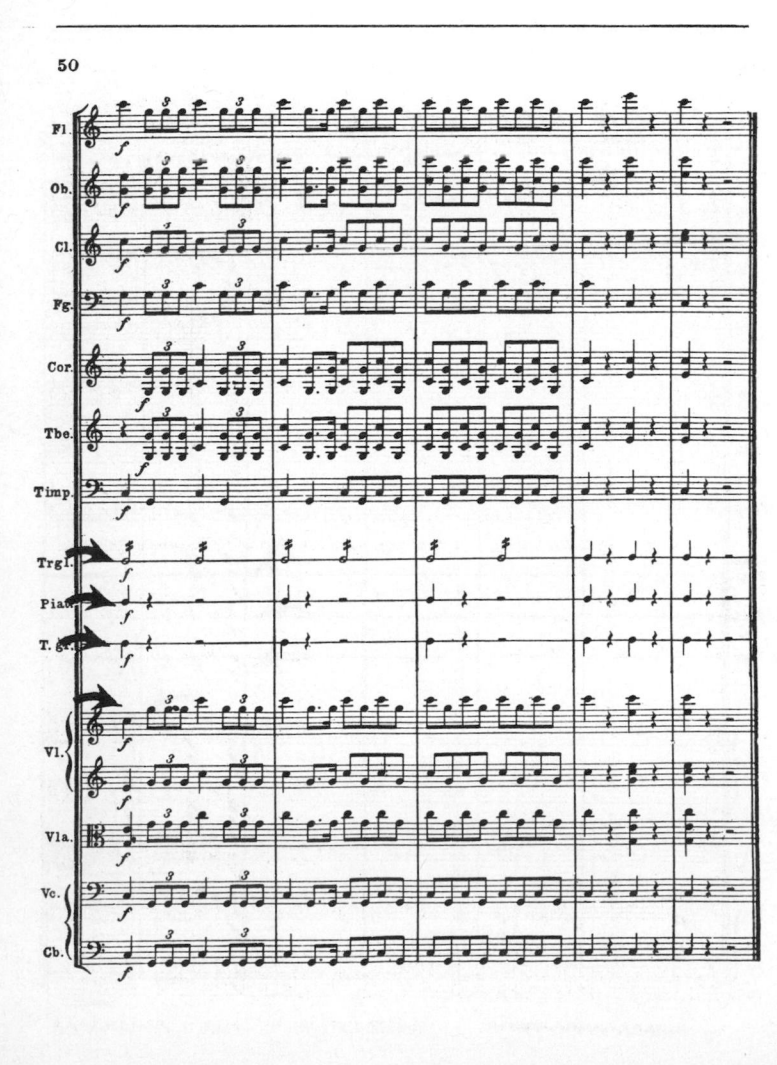

MENUETTO.
Moderato. PRINCIPAL SECTION

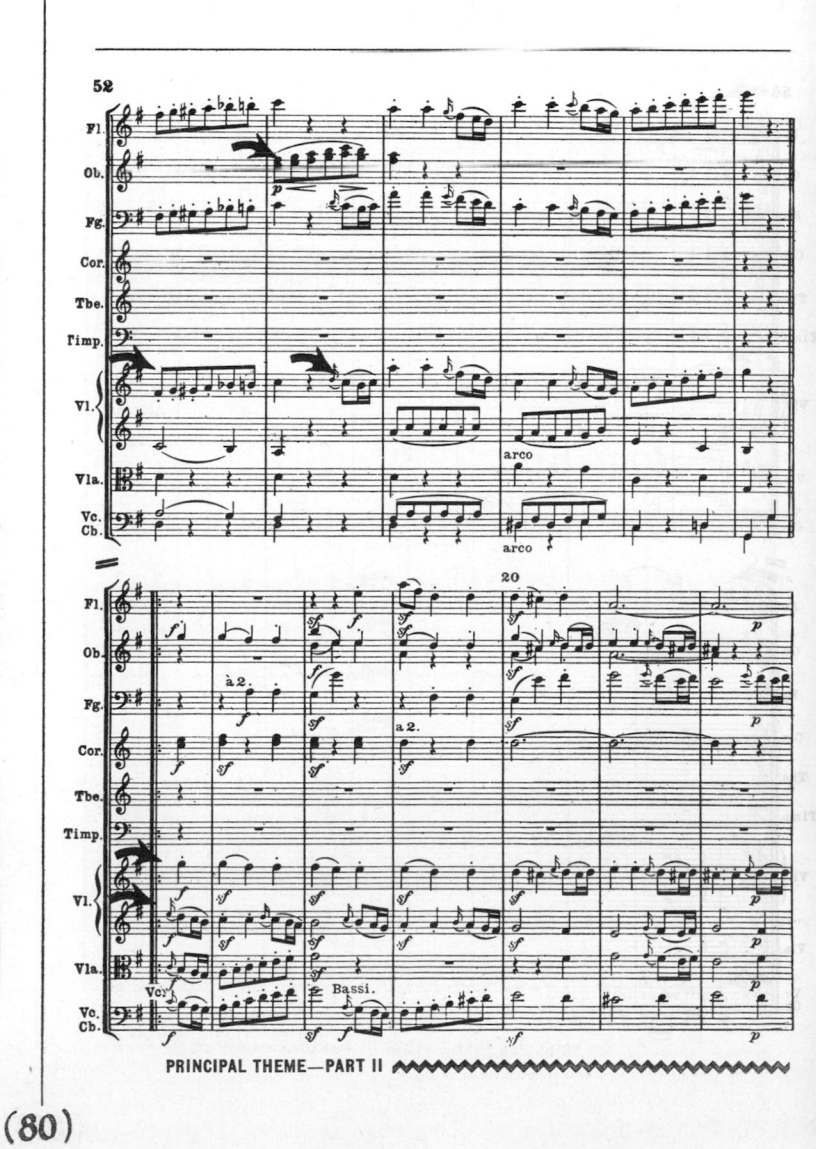

PRINCIPAL THEME—PART I 〰〰〰〰

PRINCIPAL THEME—PART II 〰〰〰〰

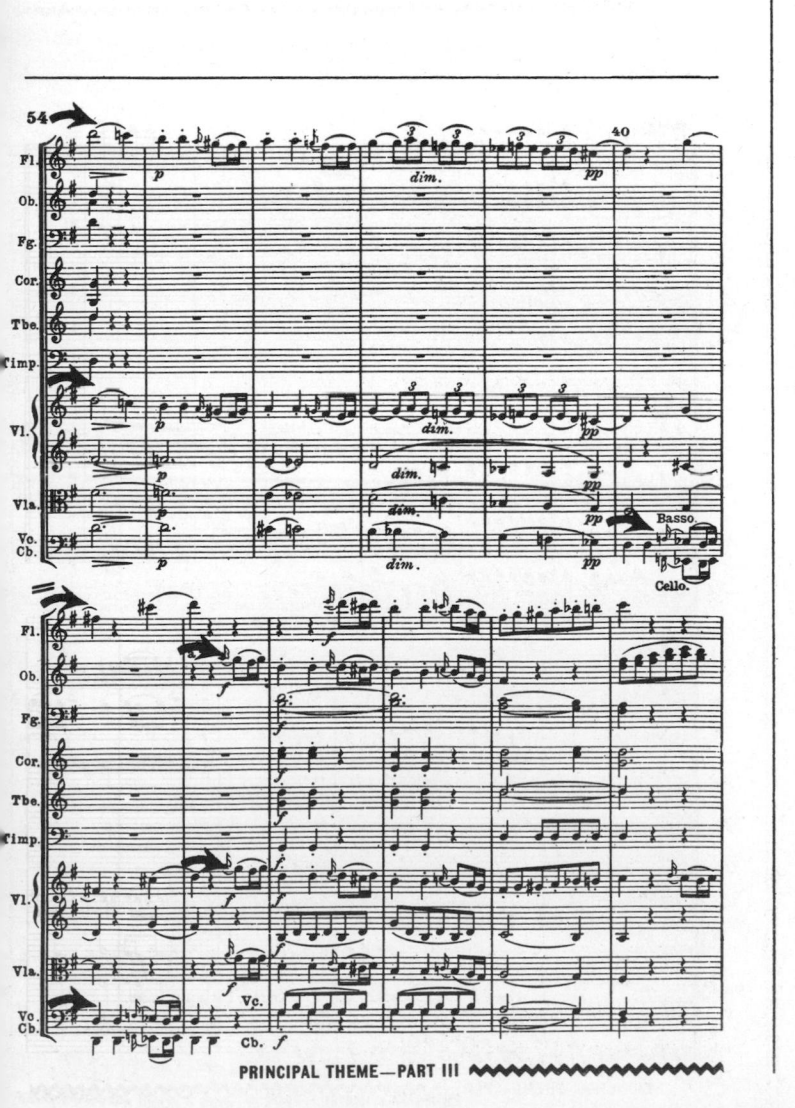

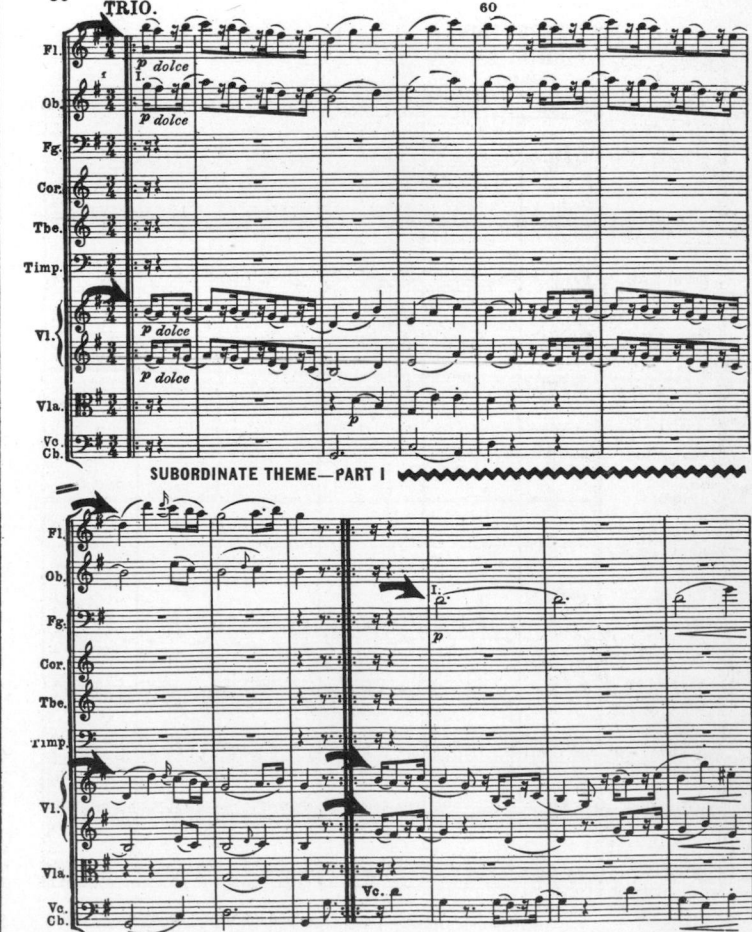

PRINCIPAL THEME—PART III 〰〰〰〰〰〰

SUBORDINATE THEME—PART II 〰〰〰〰

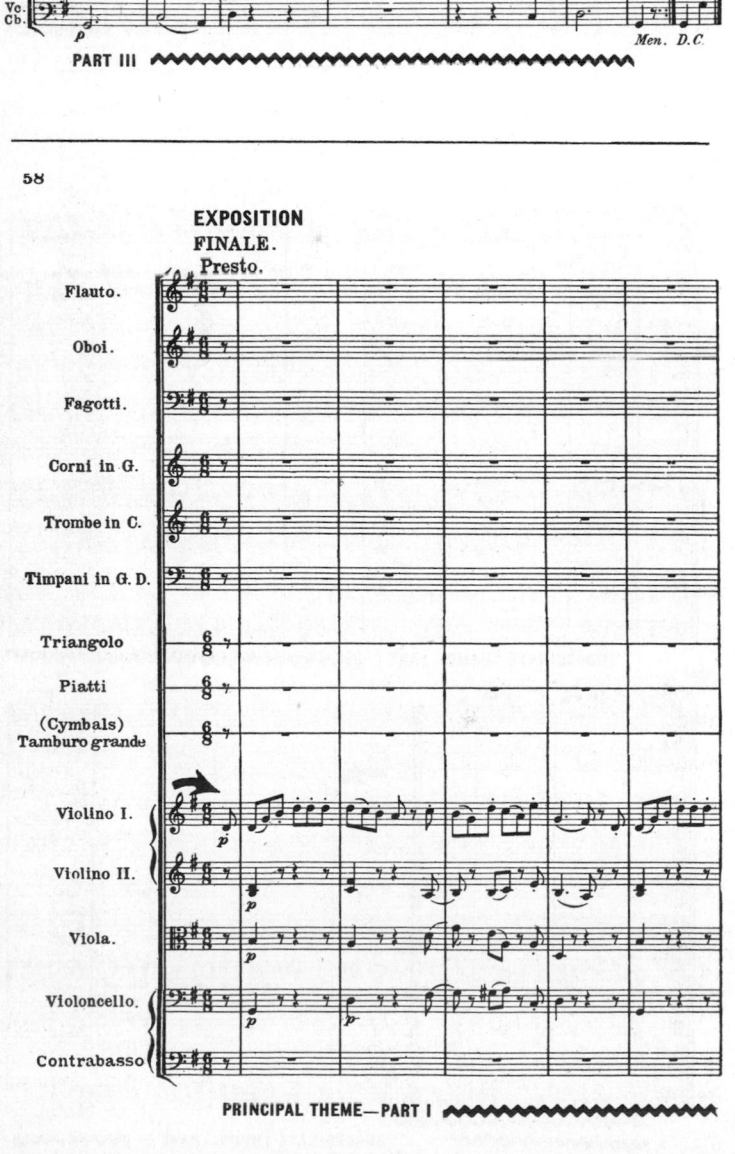

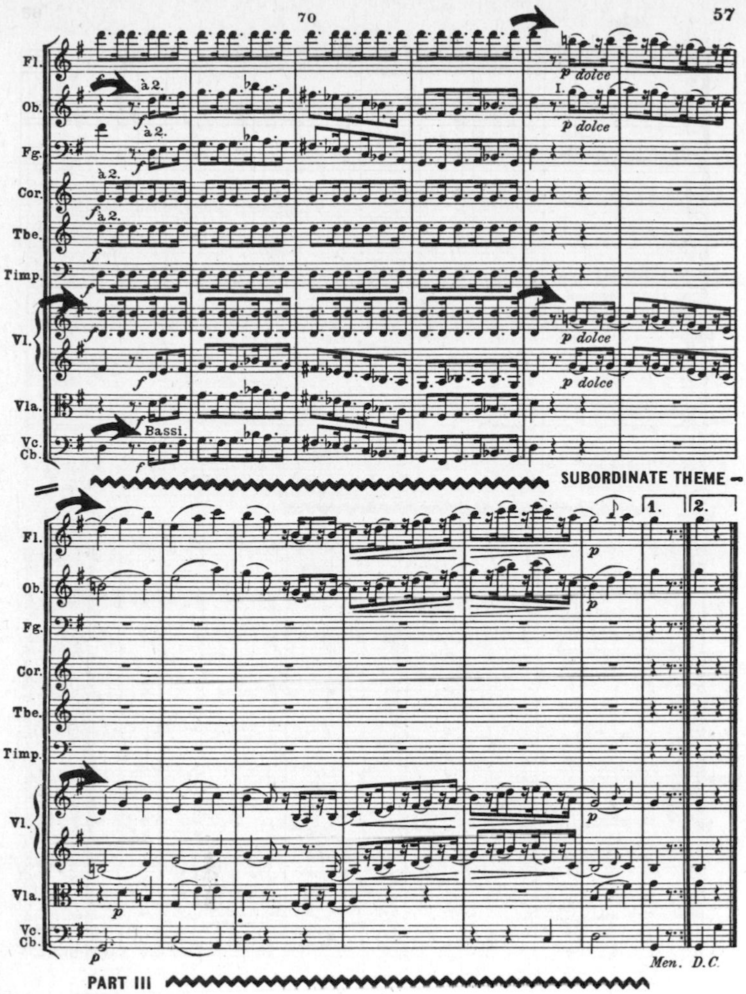
57
70
Fl.
Ob.
Fg.
Cor.
Tbe.
Timp.
Vl.
Vla.
Vc. Cb.
à 2.
p dolce
Bassi.
SUBORDINATE THEME
1.
2.
Men. D.C.
PART III

58
EXPOSITION
FINALE.
Presto.
Flauto.
Oboi.
Fagotti.
Corni in G.
Trombe in C.
Timpani in G. D.
Triangolo
Piatti
(Cymbals)
Tamburo grande
Violino I.
Violino II.
Viola.
Violoncello.
Contrabasso
PRINCIPAL THEME—PART I

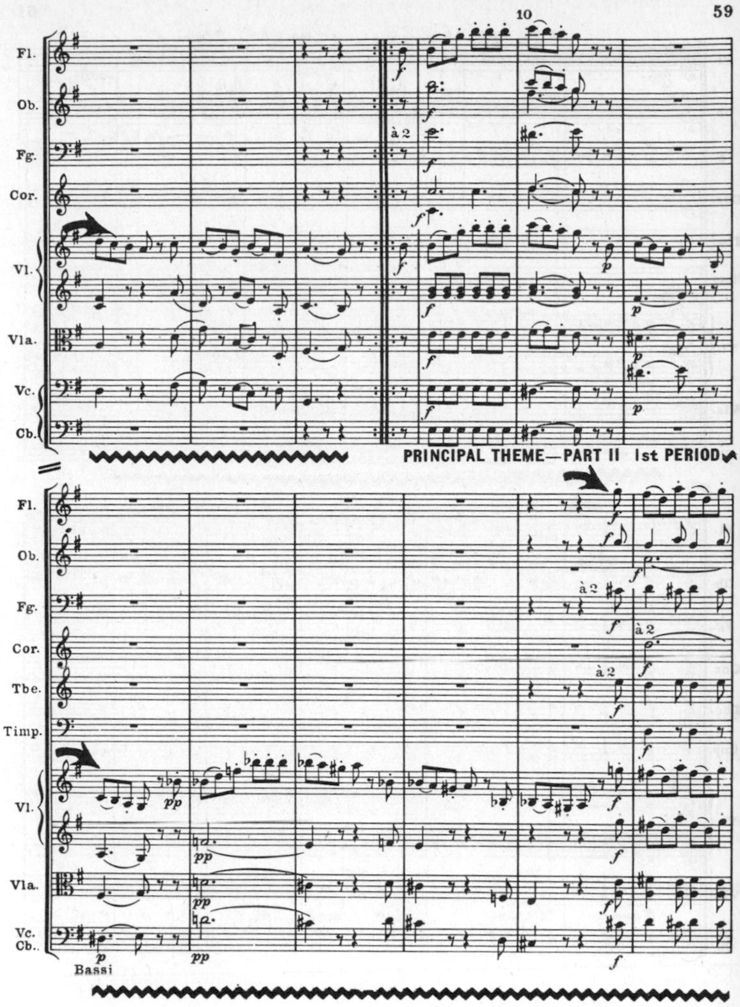
59
10
Fl.
Ob.
Fg.
Cor.
Tbe.
Timp.
Vl.
Vla.
Vc.
Cb.
à 2
PRINCIPAL THEME—PART II 1st PERIOD
pp
Bassi

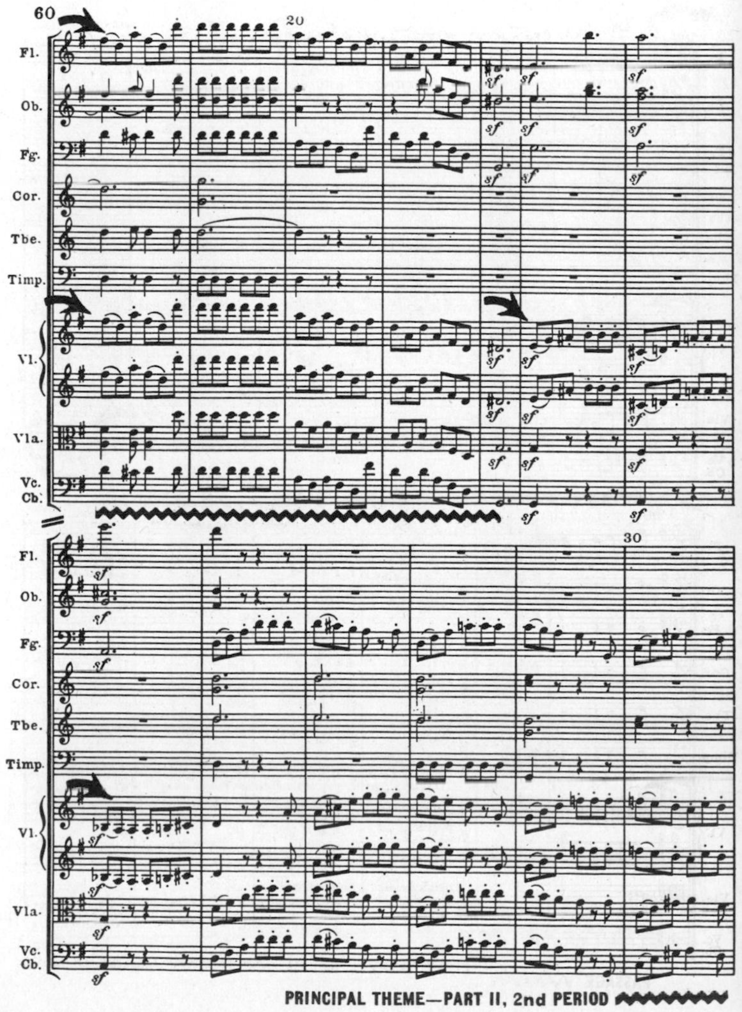
60
20
30
Fl.
Ob.
Fg.
Cor.
Tbe.
Timp.
Vl.
Vla.
Vc.
Cb.
sf
PRINCIPAL THEME—PART II, 2nd PERIOD

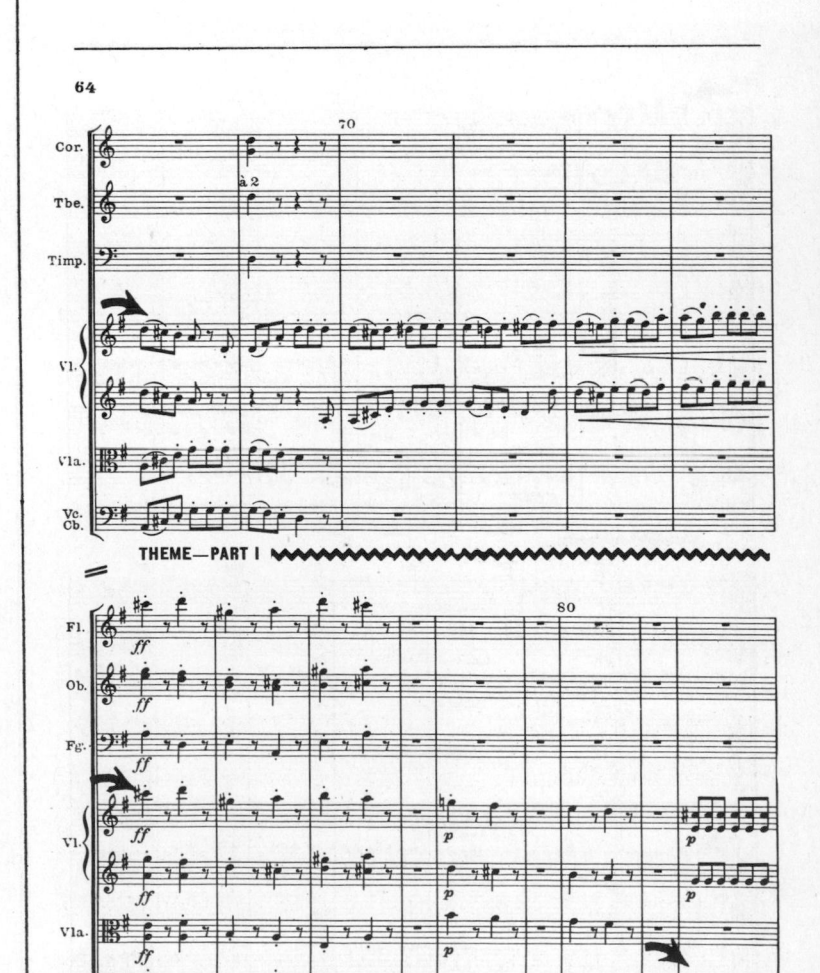

PRINCIPAL THEME—PART III

SUBORDINATE

BRIDGE

THEME—PART I

PASSAGE

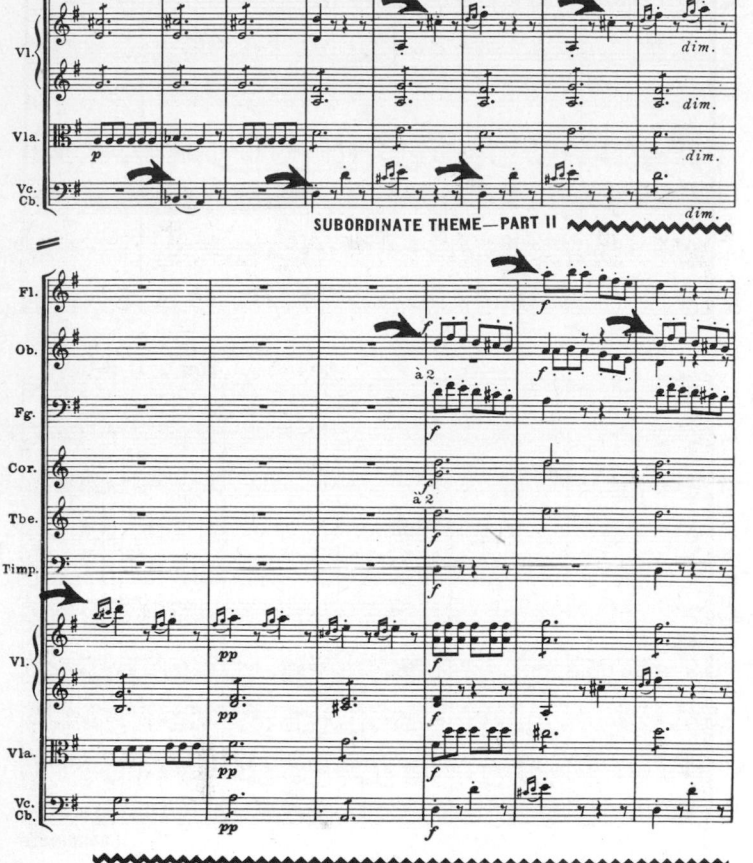

Fl.
Vl.
Vla.
Vc.
Cb.
dim.
SUBORDINATE THEME—PART II
Ob.
Fg.
Cor.
Tbe.
Timp.
à 2

Fl.
Ob.
Fg.
Cor.
Tbe.
Timp.
Vl.
Vla.
Vc.
Cb.
à 2
CONCLUD →

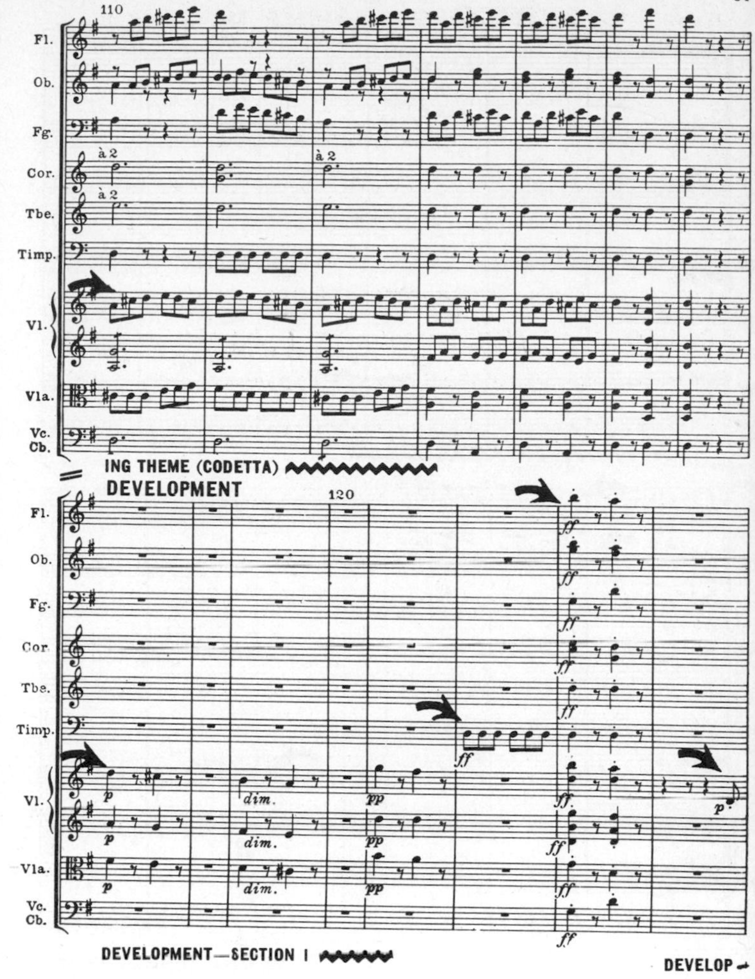
Fl.
Ob.
Fg.
Cor.
Tbe.
Timp.
Vl.
Vla.
Vc.
Cb.
à 2
ING THEME (CODETTA)
DEVELOPMENT
dim.
DEVELOPMENT—SECTION I
DEVELOP →

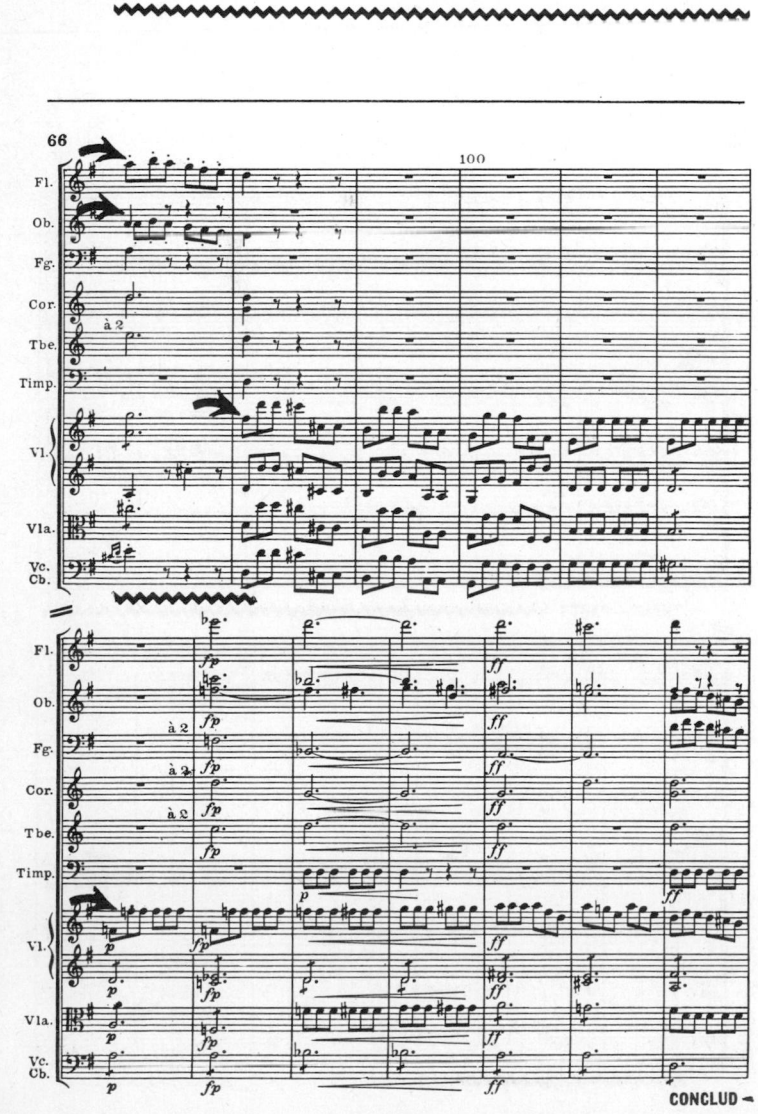

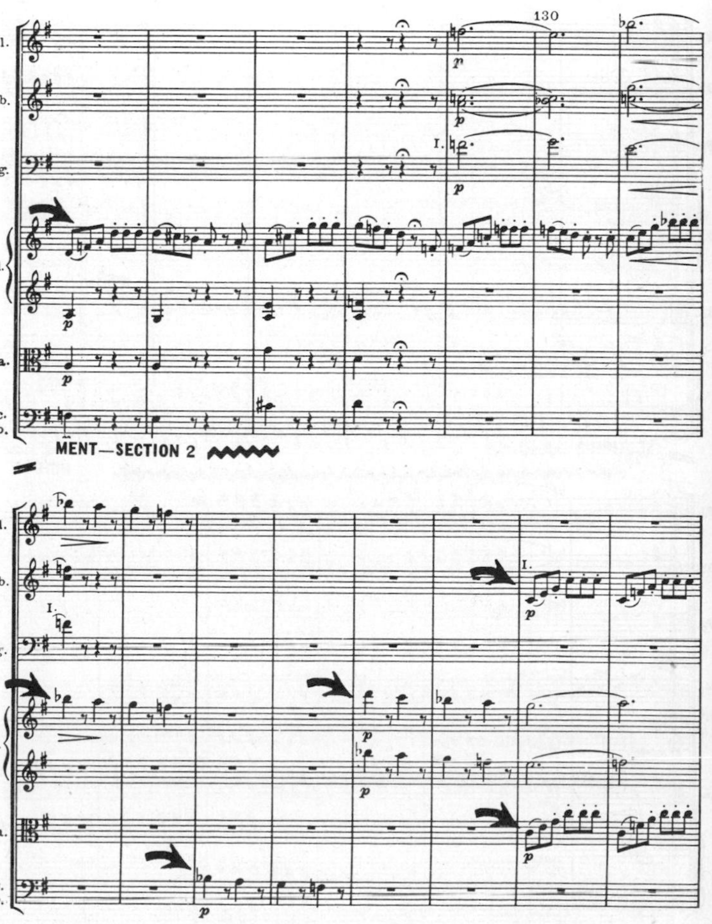
Fl.
Ob.
Fg.
Vl.
Vla.
Vc.
Cb.
I.
MENT—SECTION 2

69

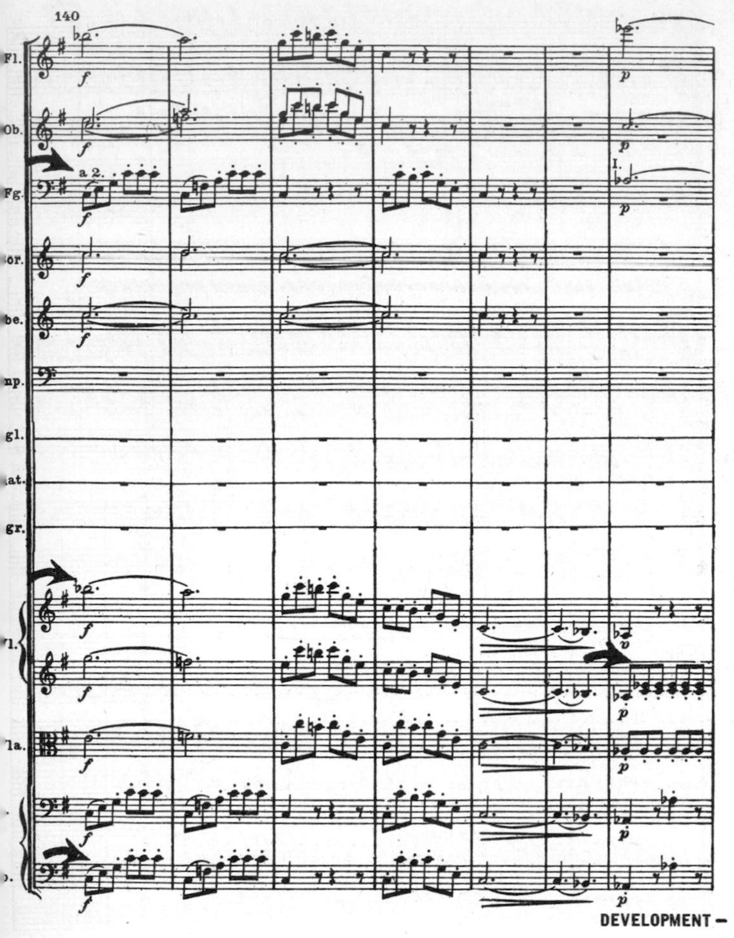
140
Fl.
Ob.
a 2.
Fg.
I.
Vl.
Vla.
DEVELOPMENT —

71

Fl.
Ob.
dim.
Fg.
Vl.
Vla.
Vc.
Cb.
DEVELOPMENT—SECTION 4
170
cresc.
p cresc.

70

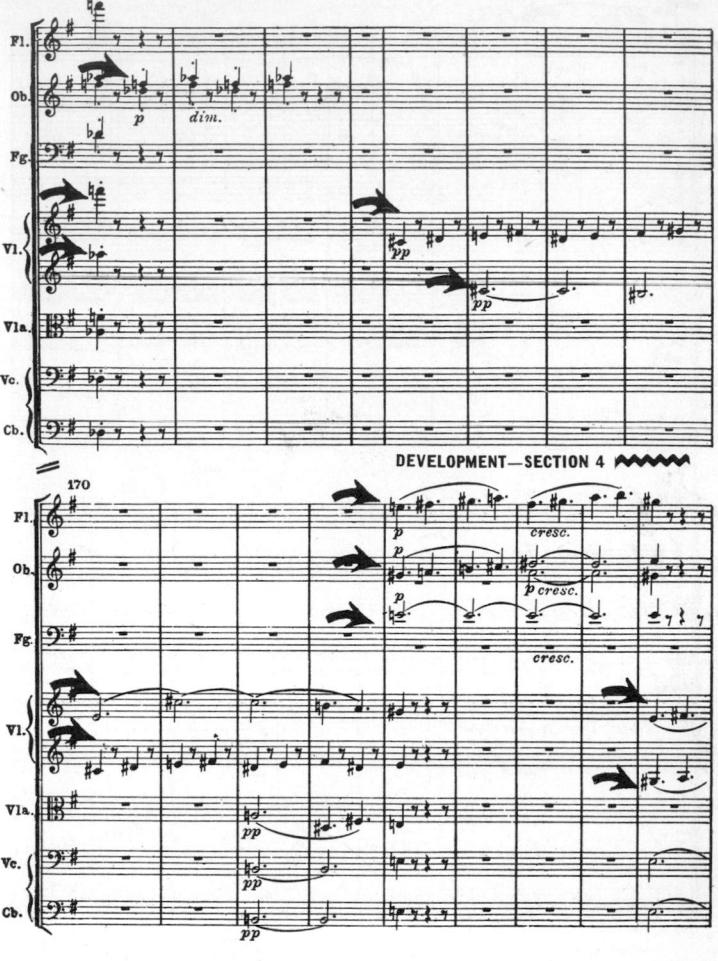

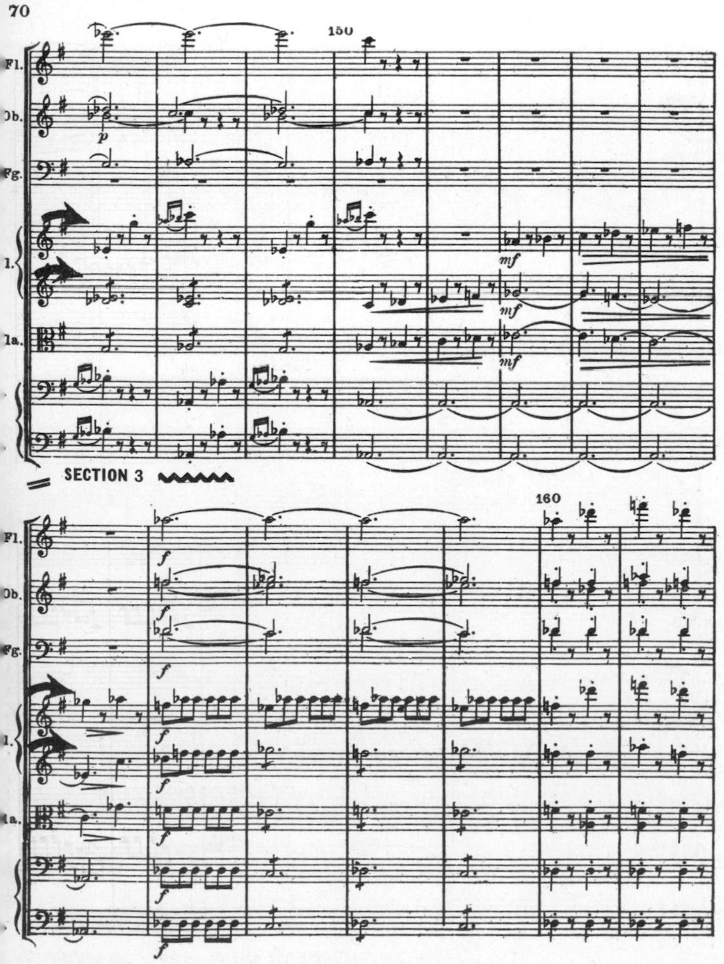
150
Fl.
Ob.
Fg.
SECTION 3
160

72

180
Fl.
Ob.
Fg.
Cor.
Tbe.
Vl.
Vla.
Vc.
Cb.
DEVELOPMENT—SECTION 5
a 2.

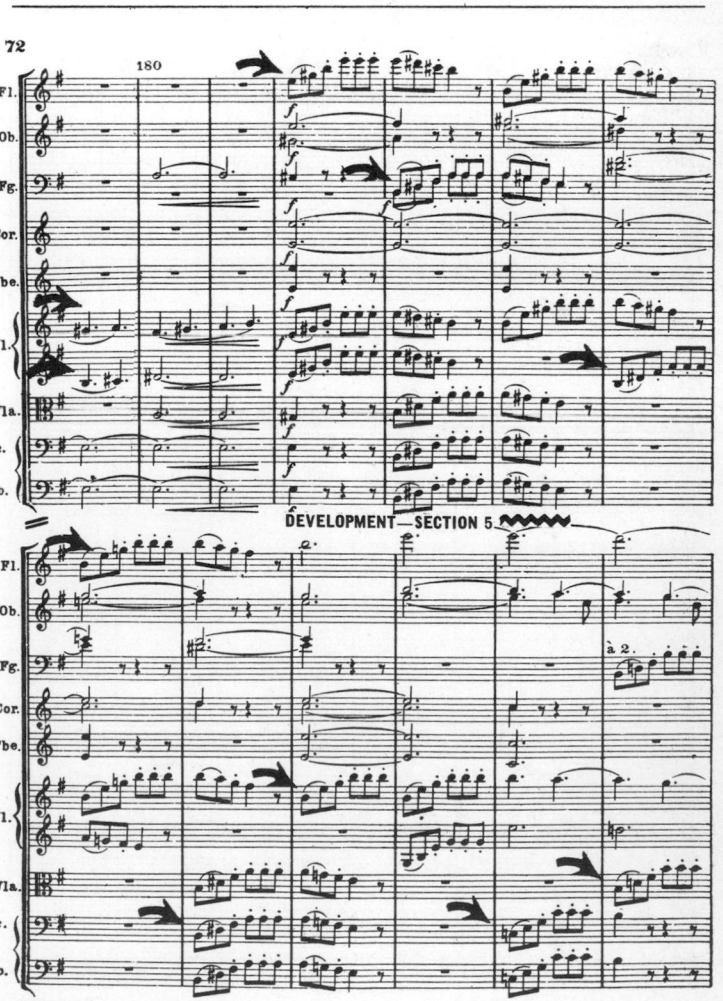

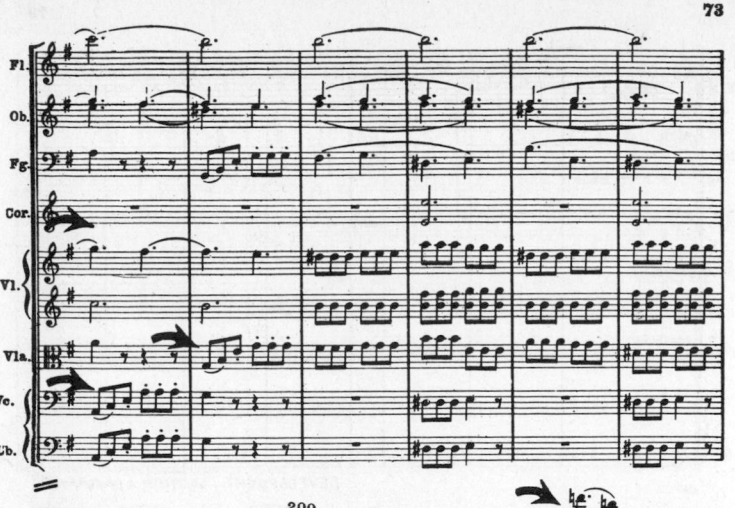
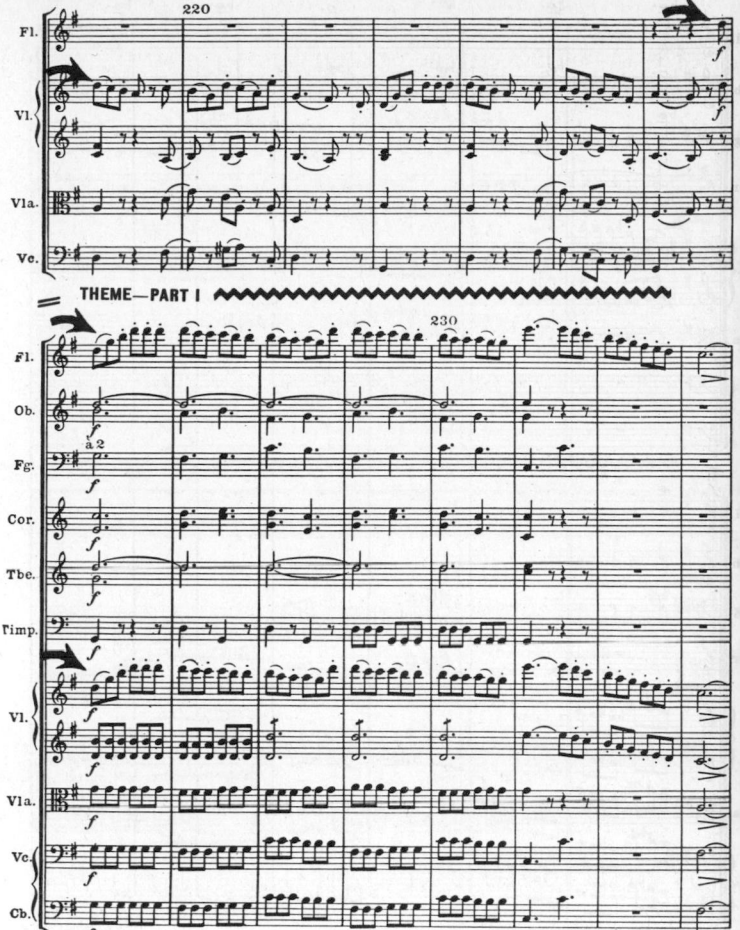
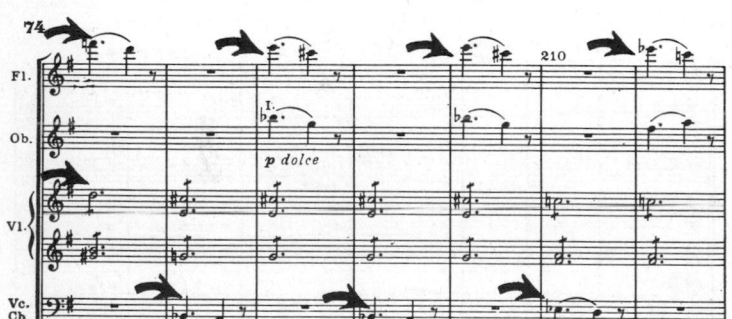
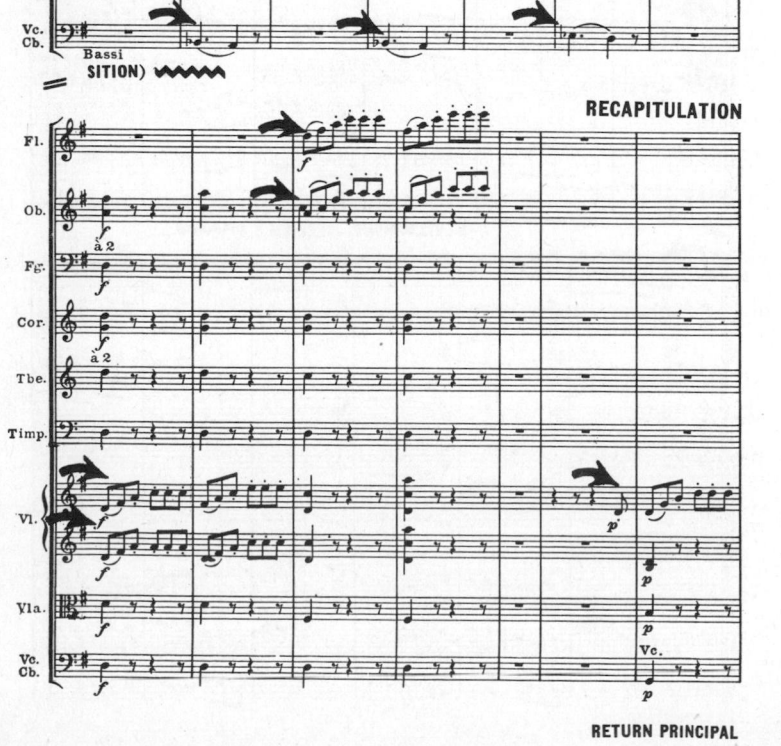
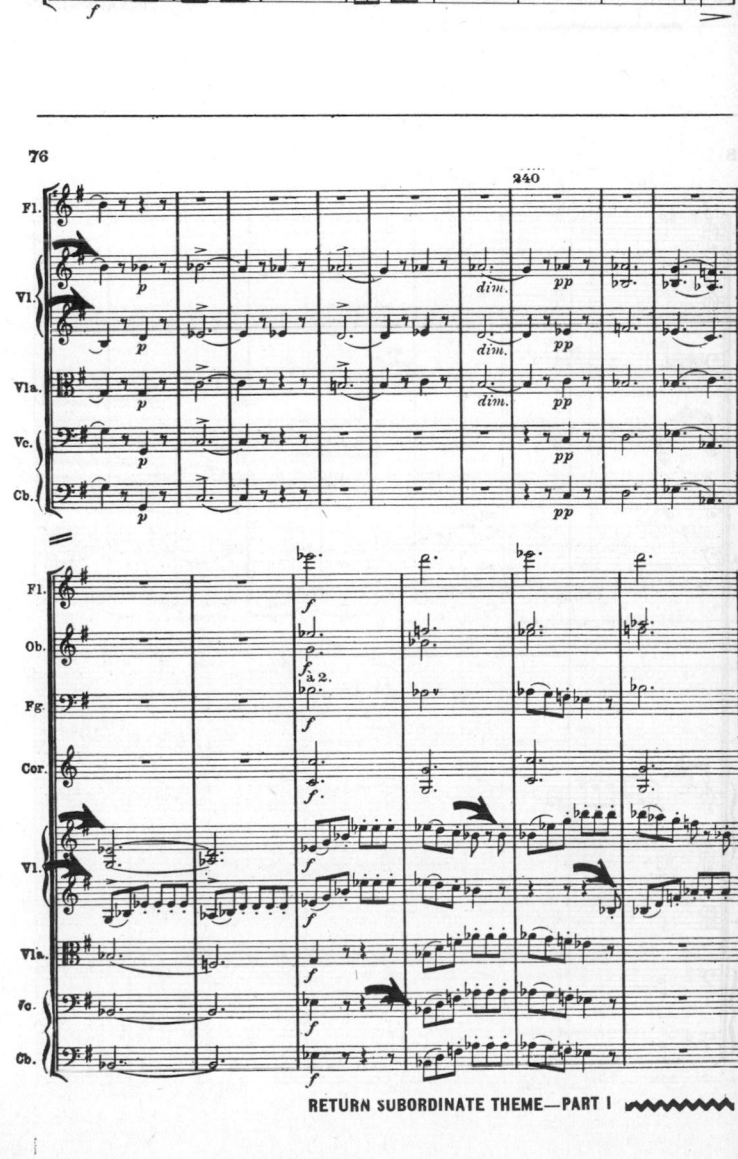

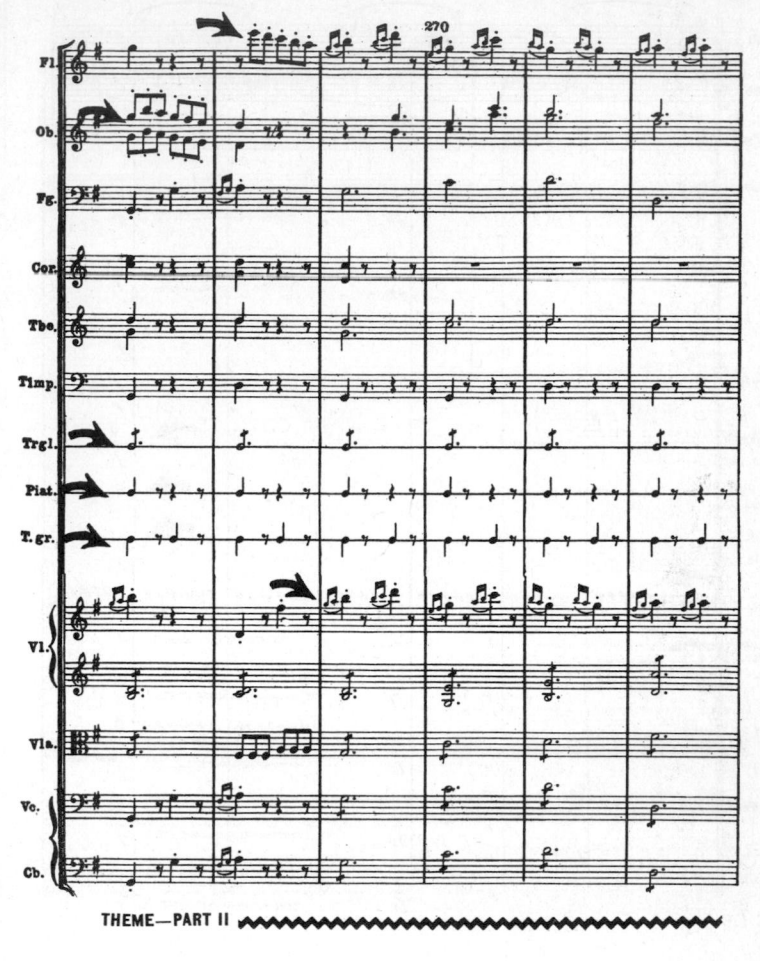

THEME—PART II

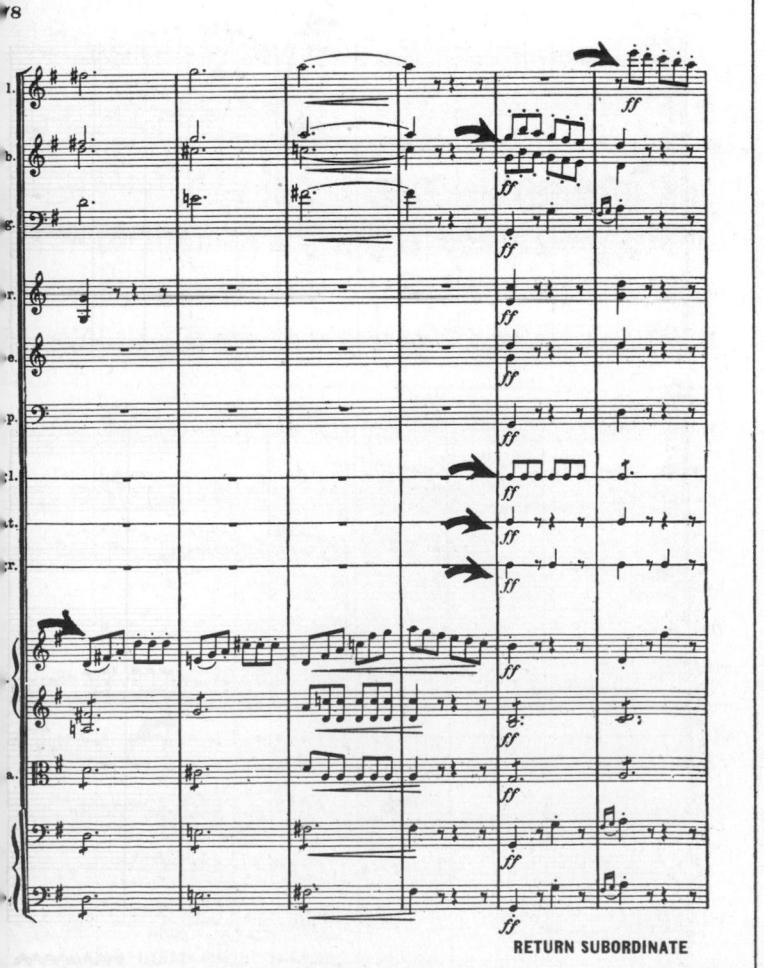

RETURN SUBORDINATE

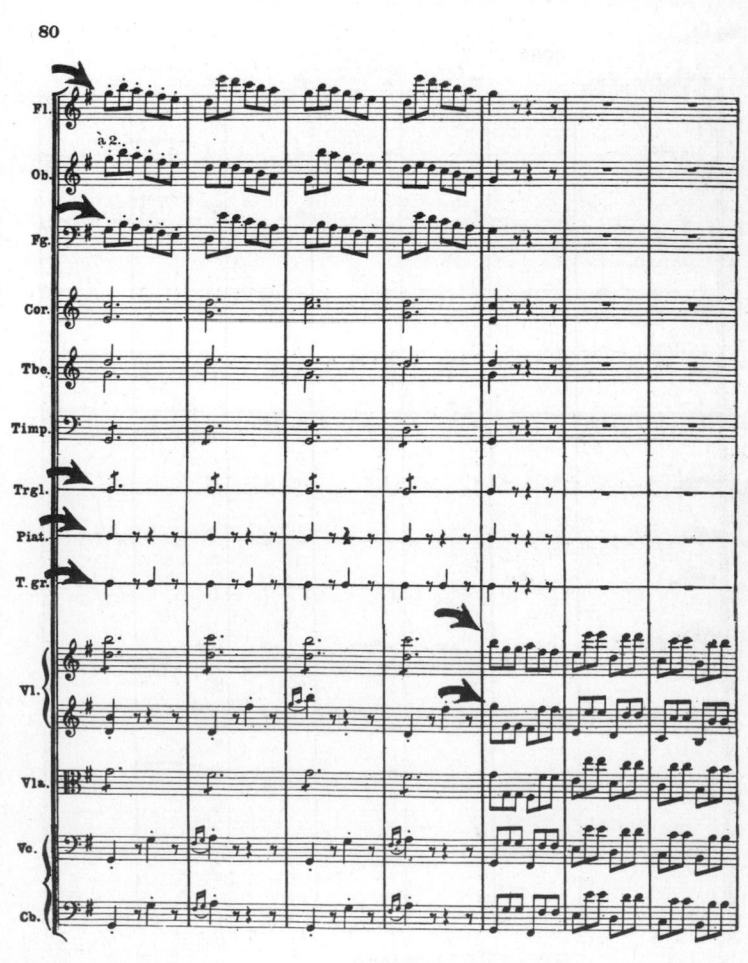

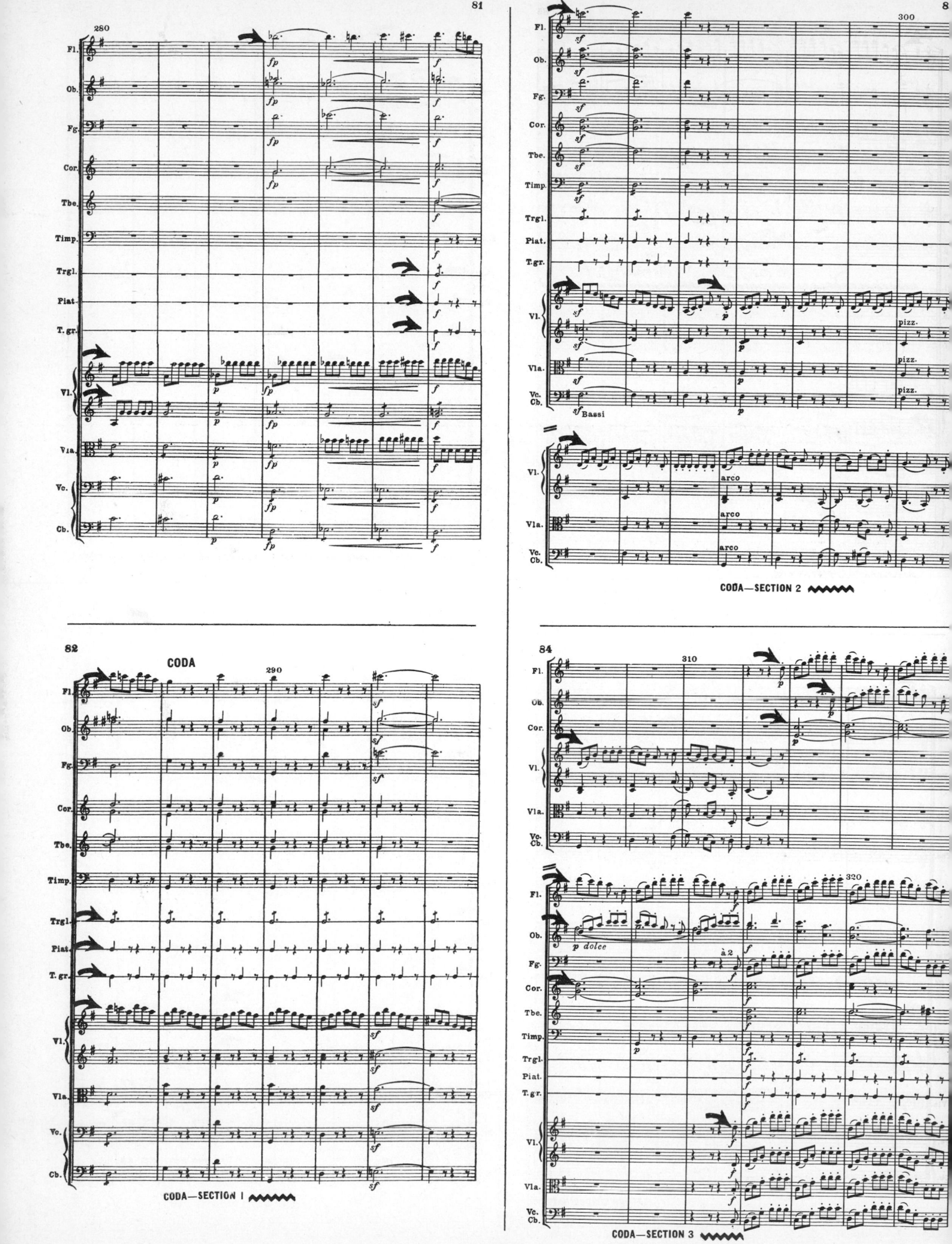

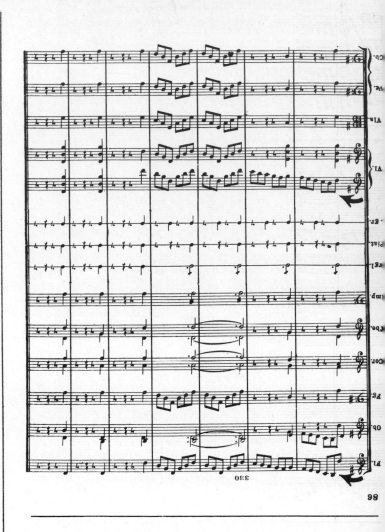

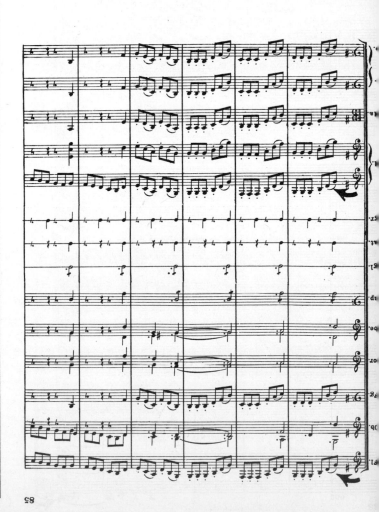

"Clock" Symphony

Joseph Haydn.
1732-1809.

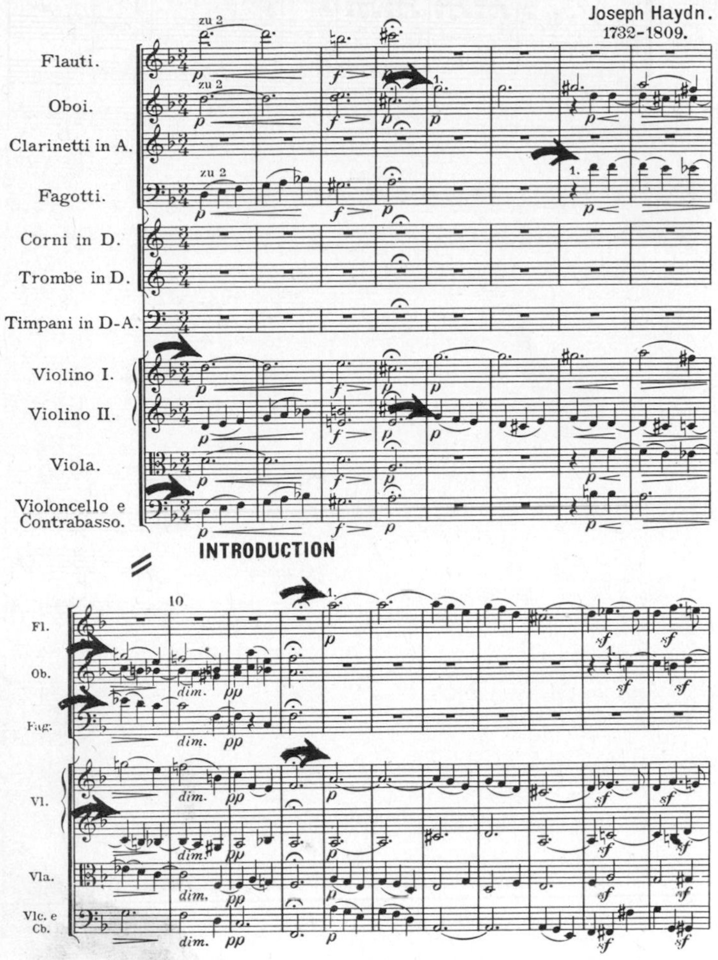

(90)

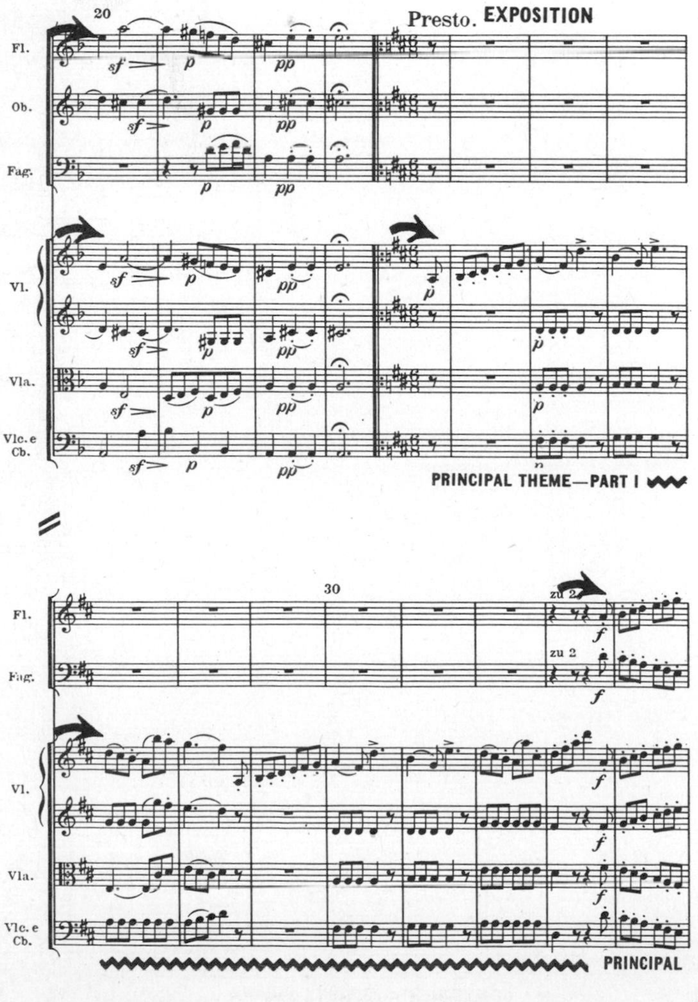

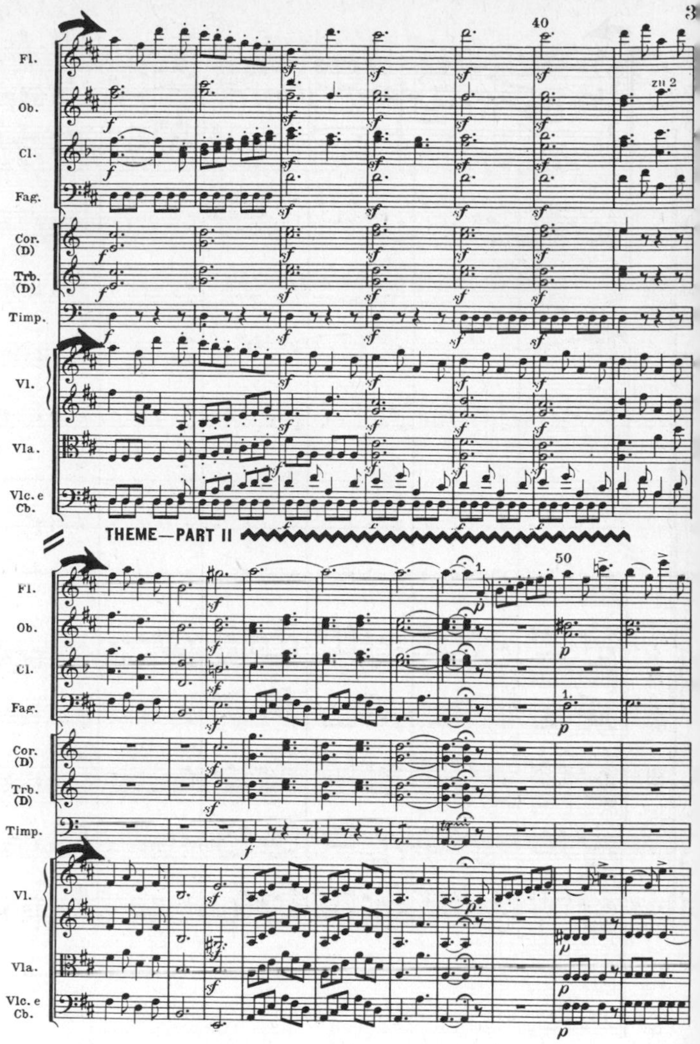

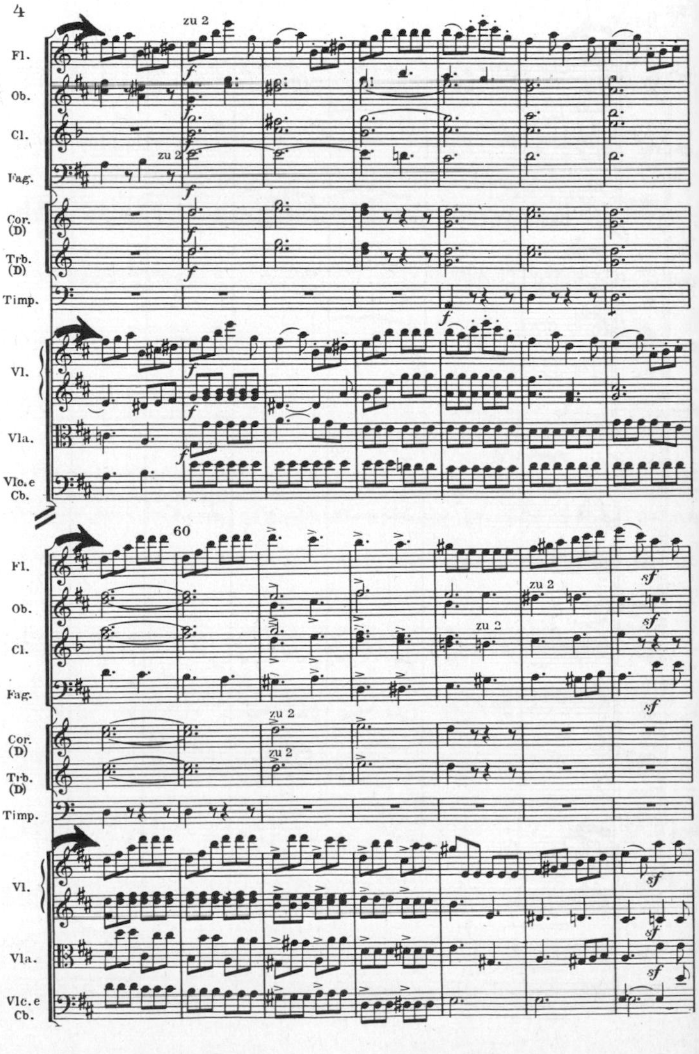

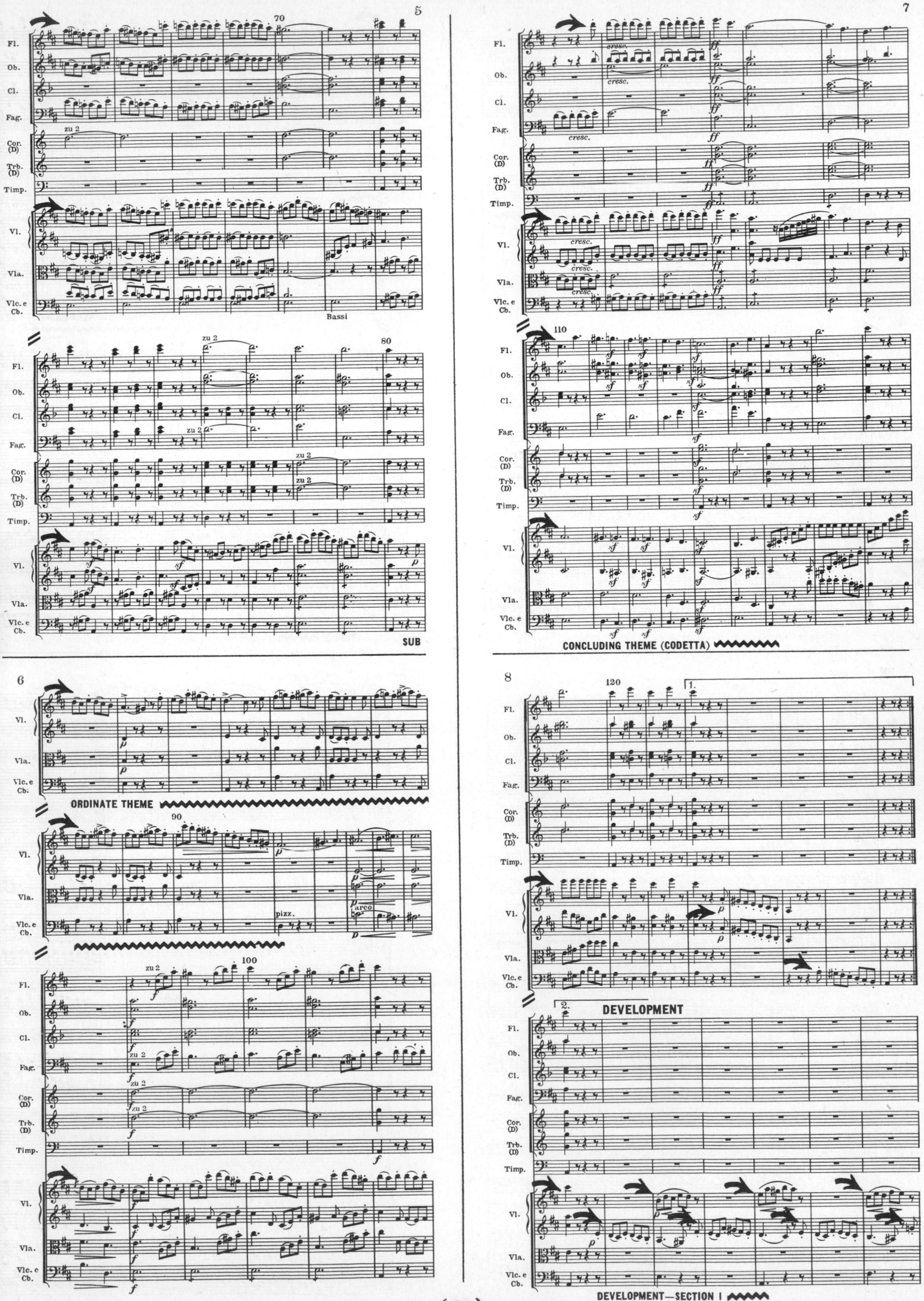

SUB

ORDINATE THEME

CONCLUDING THEME (CODETTA)

DEVELOPMENT

DEVELOPMENT—SECTION I

(91)

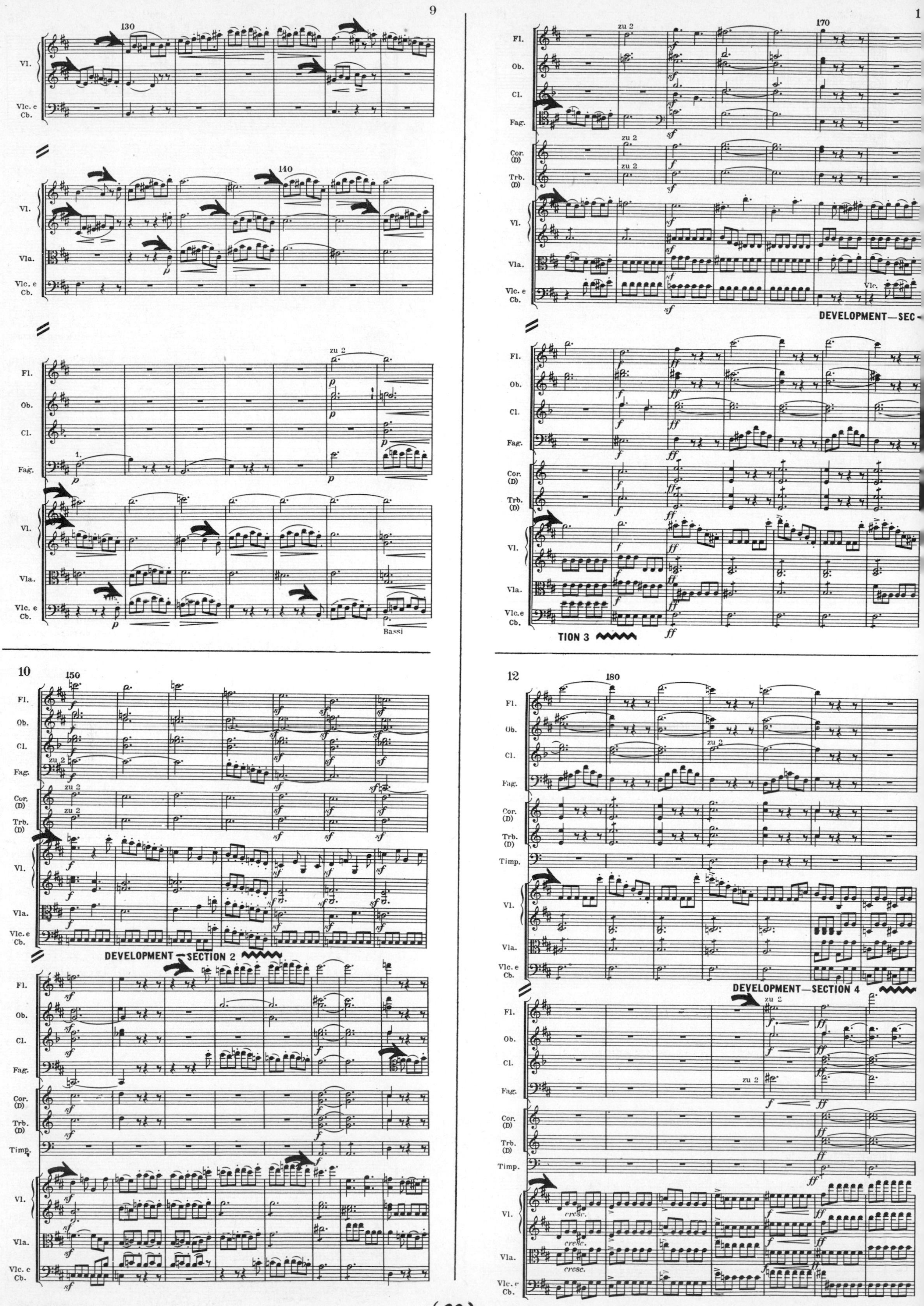
9
130
140
Fl.
Ob.
Cl.
Fag.
Cor. (D)
Trb. (D)
Timp.
Vl.
Vla.
Vlc. e Cb.
zu 2
1.
Bassi
10
150
DEVELOPMENT—SECTION 2
170
DEVELOPMENT—SEC-
TION 3
12
180
DEVELOPMENT—SECTION 4
cresc.

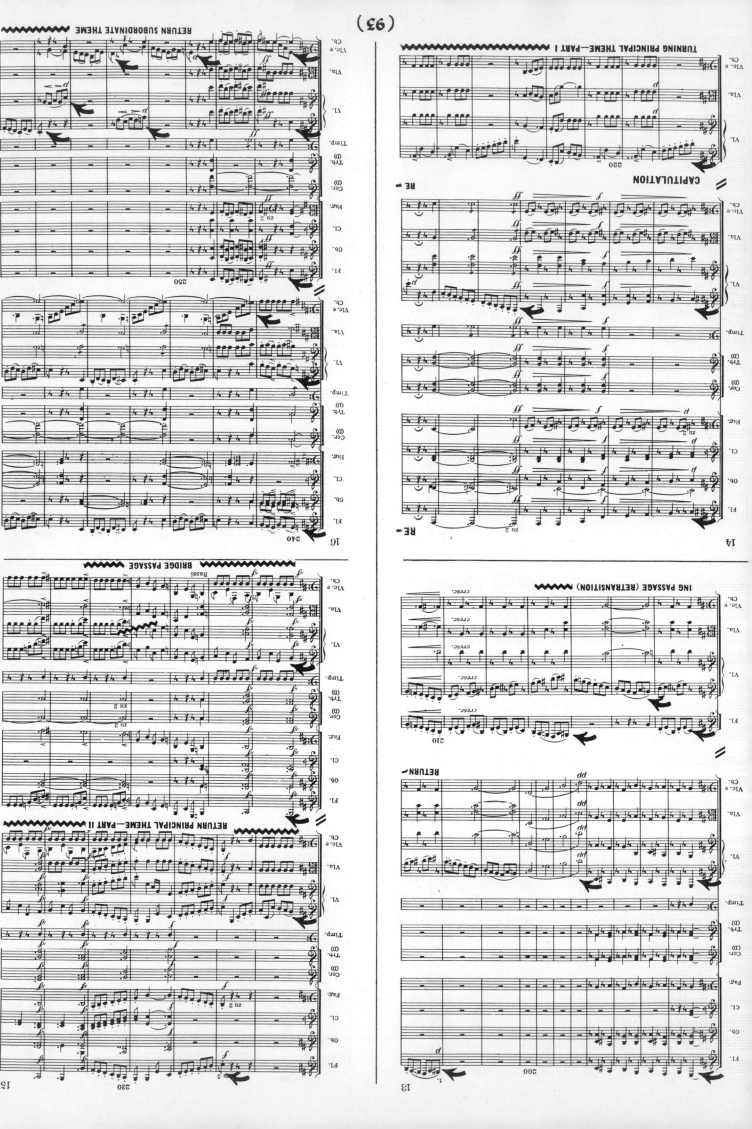

17
18
19
20
CODA
CODA—SECTION I
Fl.
Ob.
Cl.
Fag.
Cor. (D)
Trb. (D)
Timp.
Vl.
Vla.
Vlc. e Cb.
zu 2
cresc.
dim.
pizz.
arco
260
270
290
300
310
320

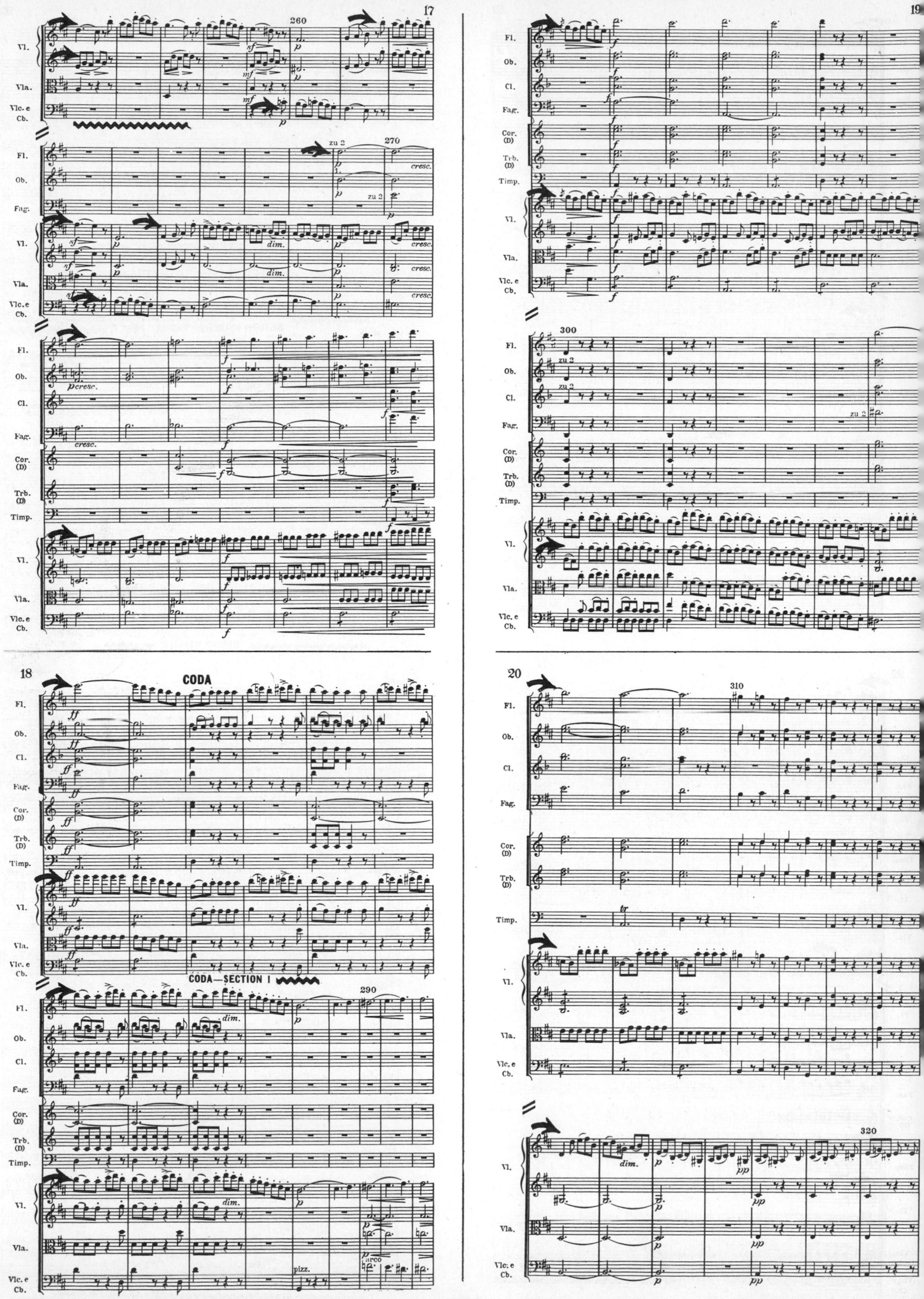

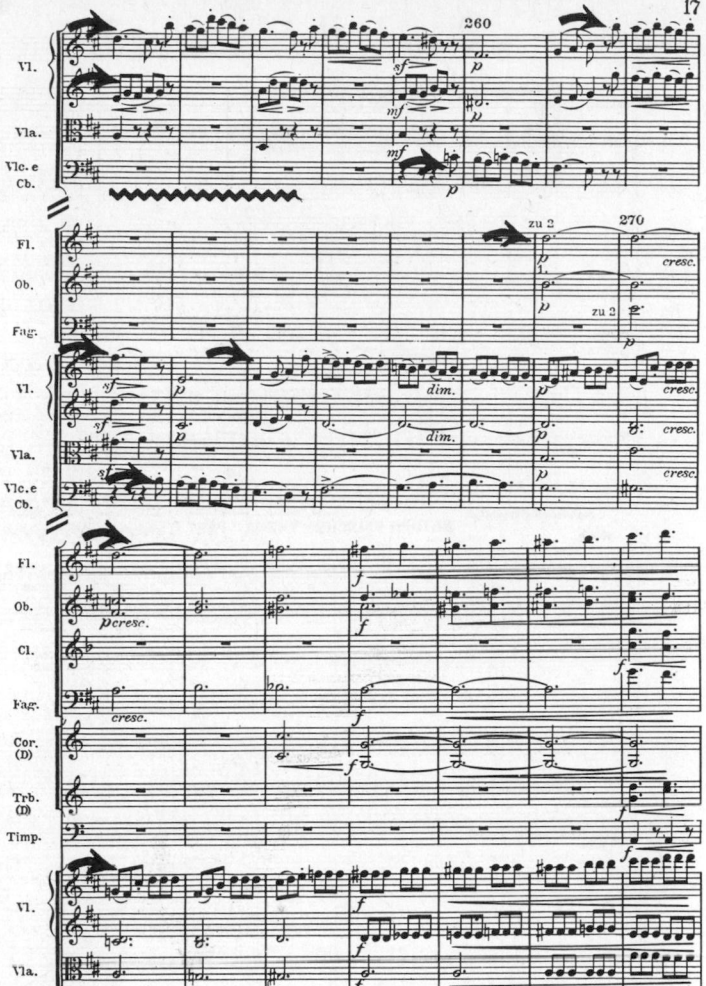

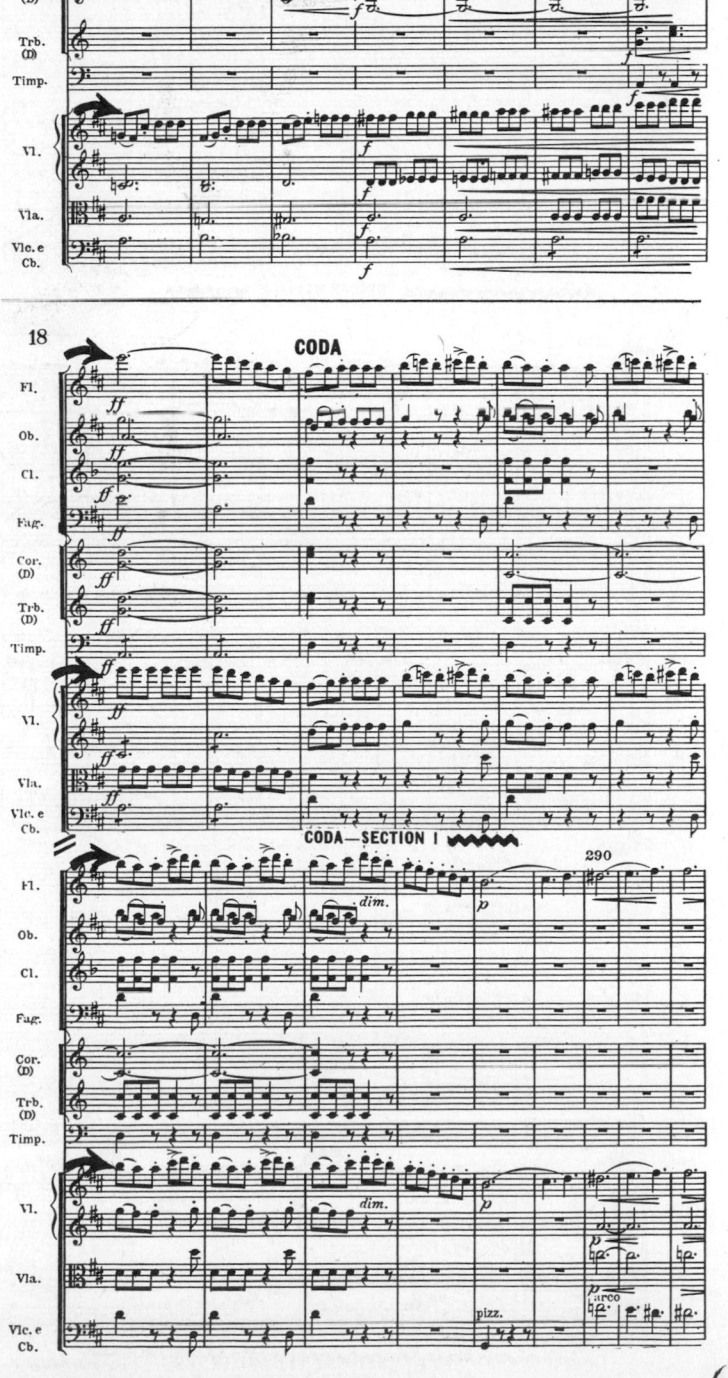

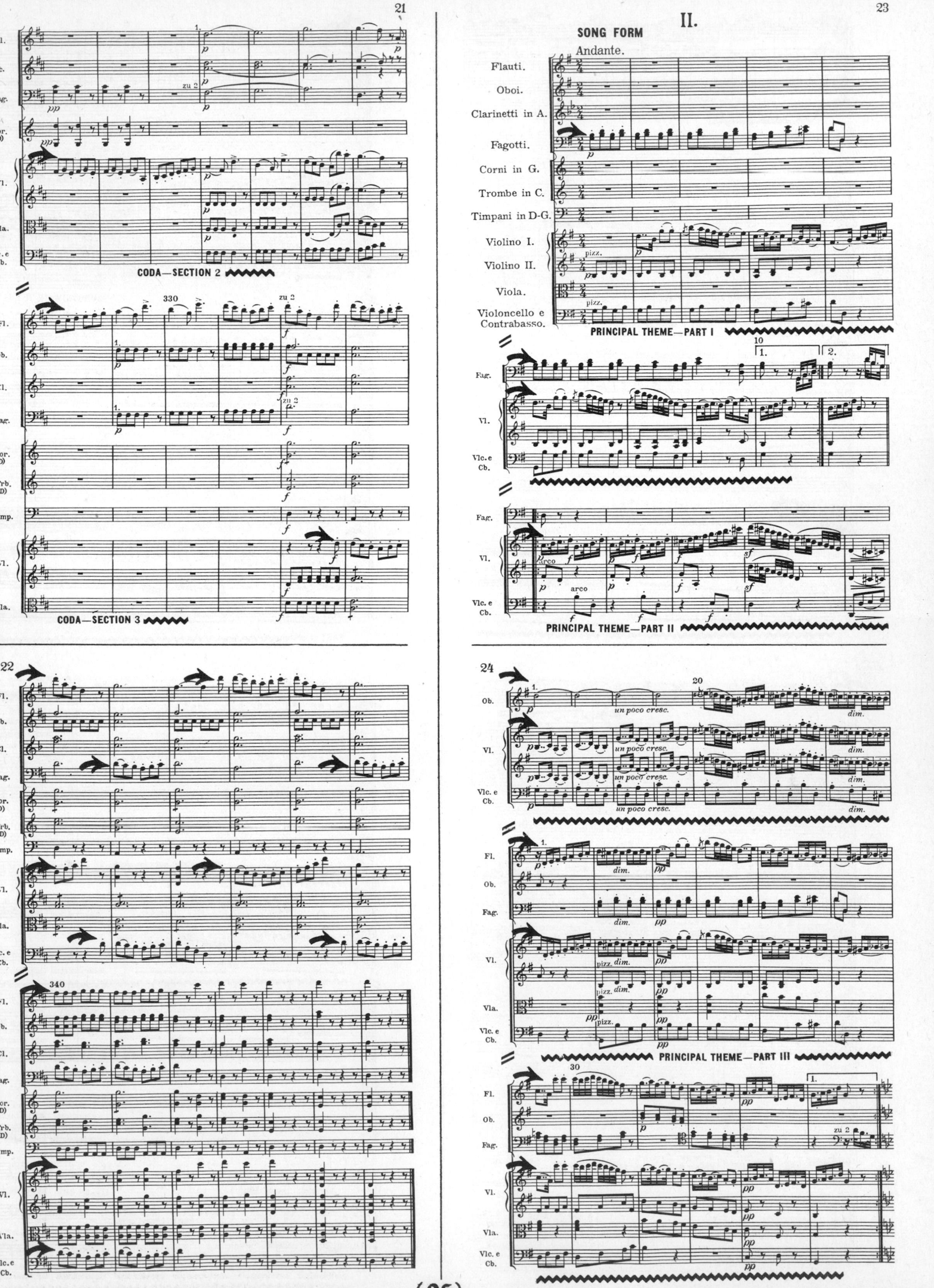
21
Fl.
Ob.
Fag.
Cor. (D)
Vl.
Vla.
Vlc. e Cb.
zu 2
CODA—SECTION 2
330
Cl.
Trb. (D)
Timp.
CODA—SECTION 3
22
340
23
II.
SONG FORM
Andante.
Flauti.
Oboi.
Clarinetti in A.
Fagotti.
Corni in G.
Trombe in C.
Timpani in D-G.
Violino I.
Violino II.
Viola.
Violoncello e Contrabasso.
pizz.
PRINCIPAL THEME—PART I
10
arco
PRINCIPAL THEME—PART II
24
20
un poco cresc.
dim.
PRINCIPAL THEME—PART III
30

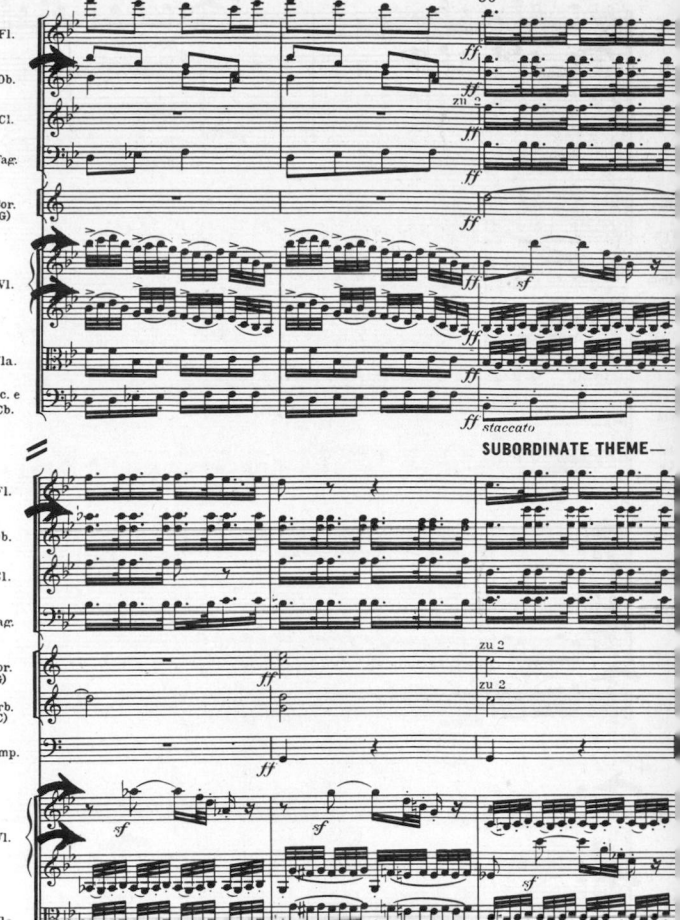

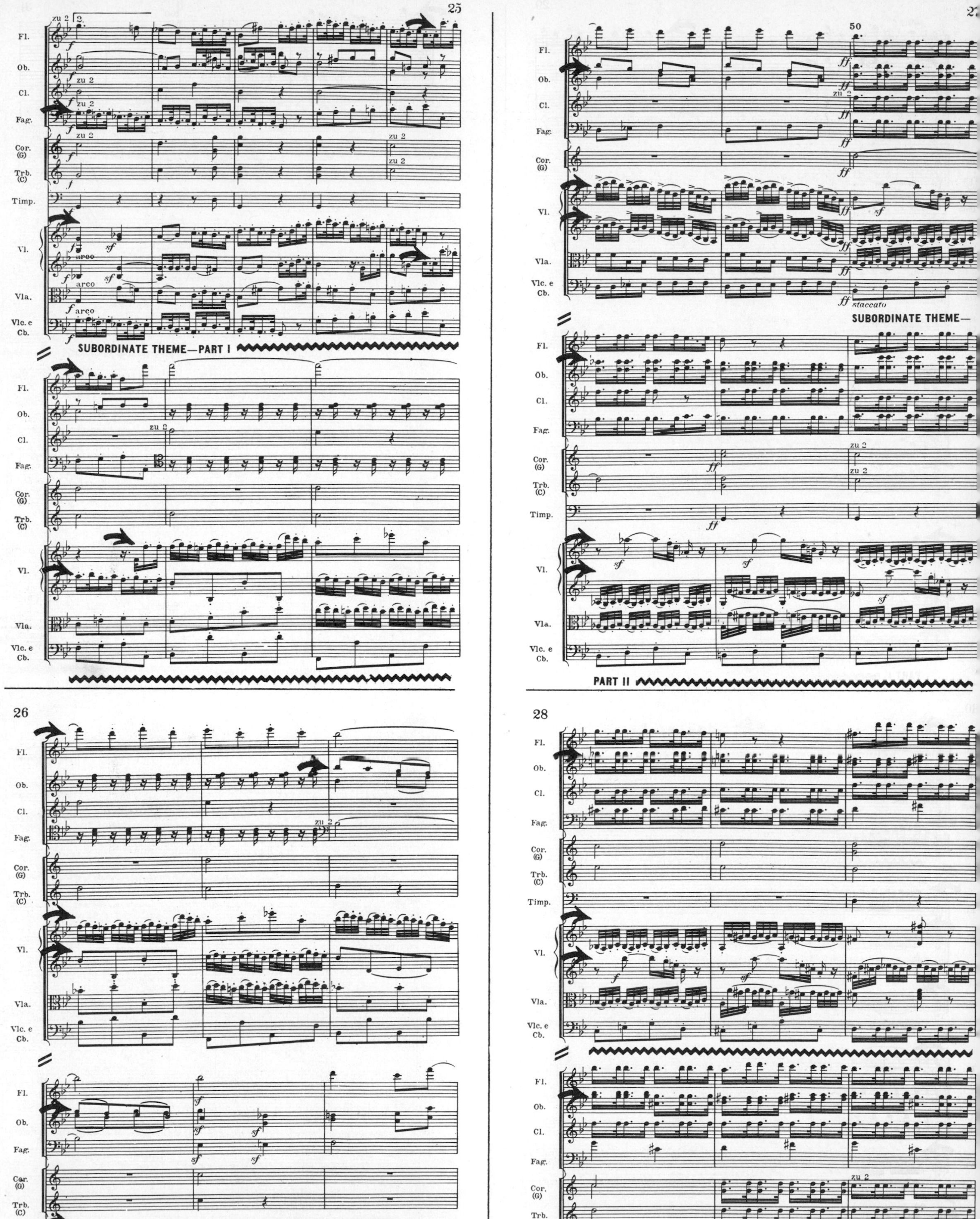
25
SUBORDINATE THEME—PART I
26
27
50
SUBORDINATE THEME—
PART II
28
Fl.
Ob.
Cl.
Fag.
Cor. (G)
Trb. (C)
Timp.
Vl.
Vla.
Vlc. e Cb.
zu 2
arco
staccato

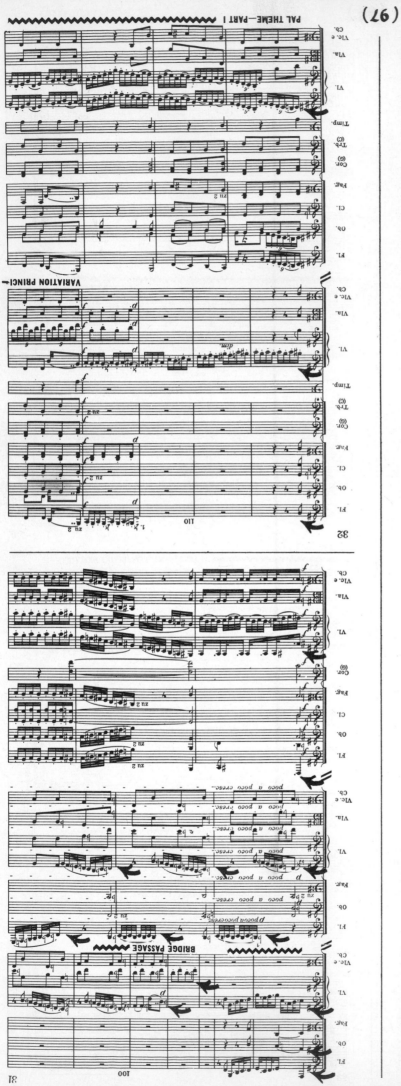
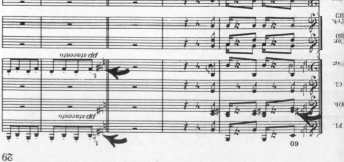

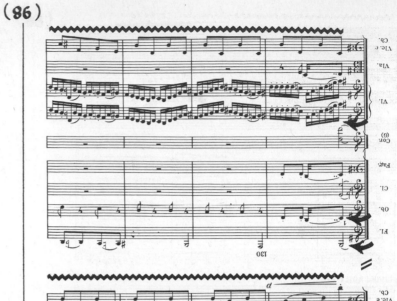
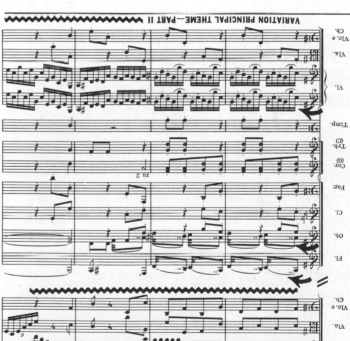

III.

PRINCIPAL SECTION

Menuetto. Allegretto.

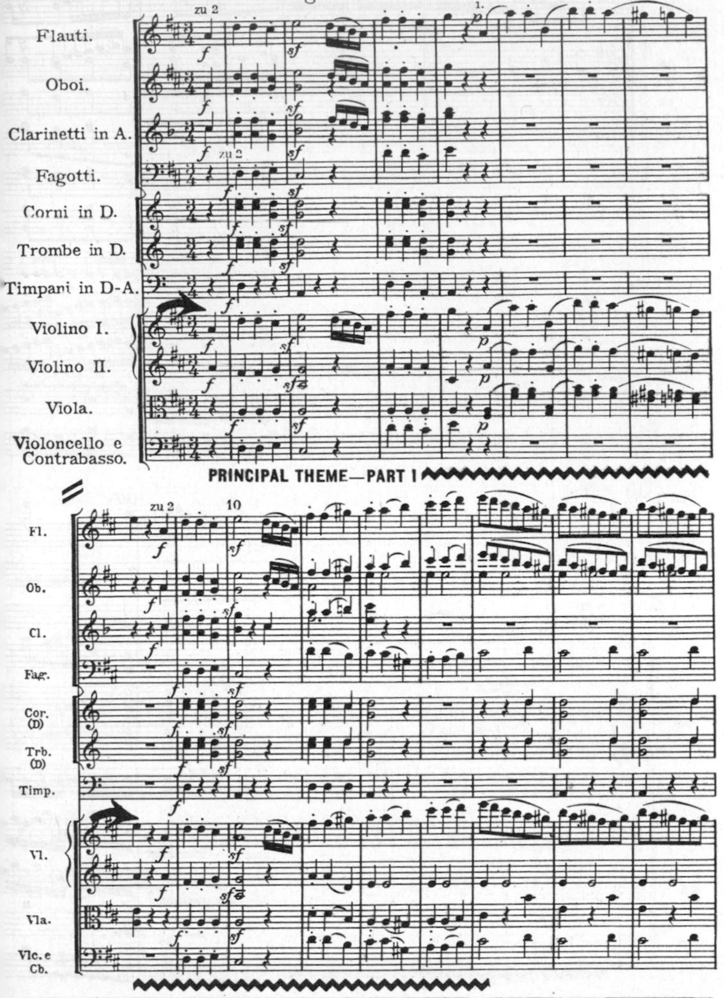
Flauti.
Oboi.
Clarinetti in A.
Fagotti.
Corni in D.
Trombe in D.
Timpani in D-A.
Violino I.
Violino II.
Viola.
Violoncello e Contrabasso.
zu 2
PRINCIPAL THEME—PART I
Fl.
Ob.
Cl.
Fag.
Cor. (D)
Trb. (D)
Timp.
Vl.
Vla.
Vlc. e Cb.

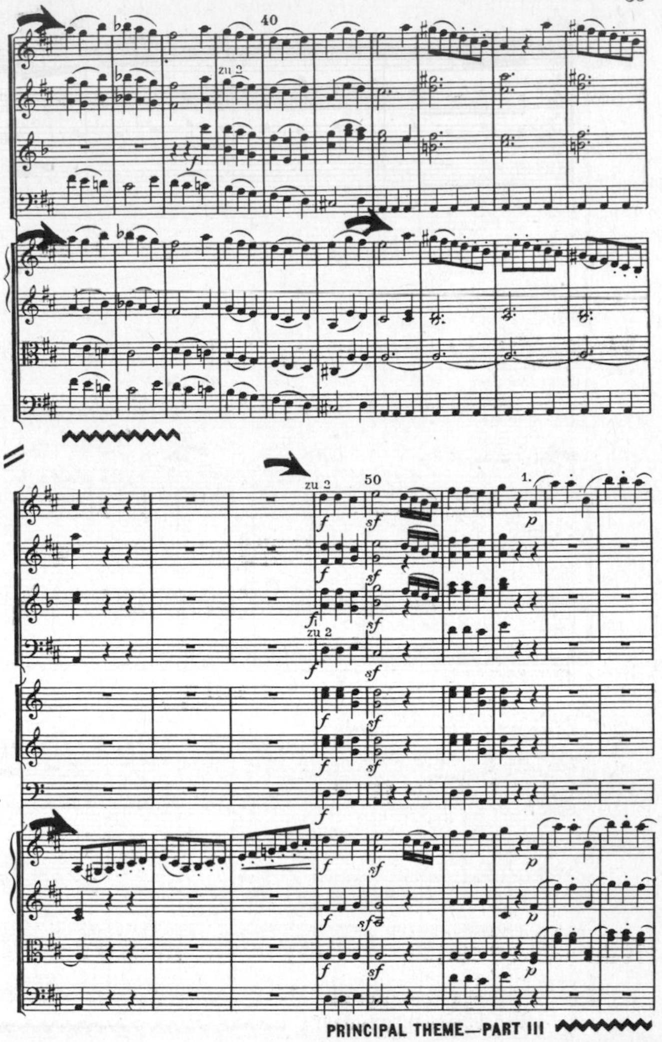
Fl.
Ob.
Cl.
Fag.
Vl.
Vla.
Vlc. e Cb.
zu 2
Cor. (D)
Trb. (D)
Timp.
PRINCIPAL THEME—PART III

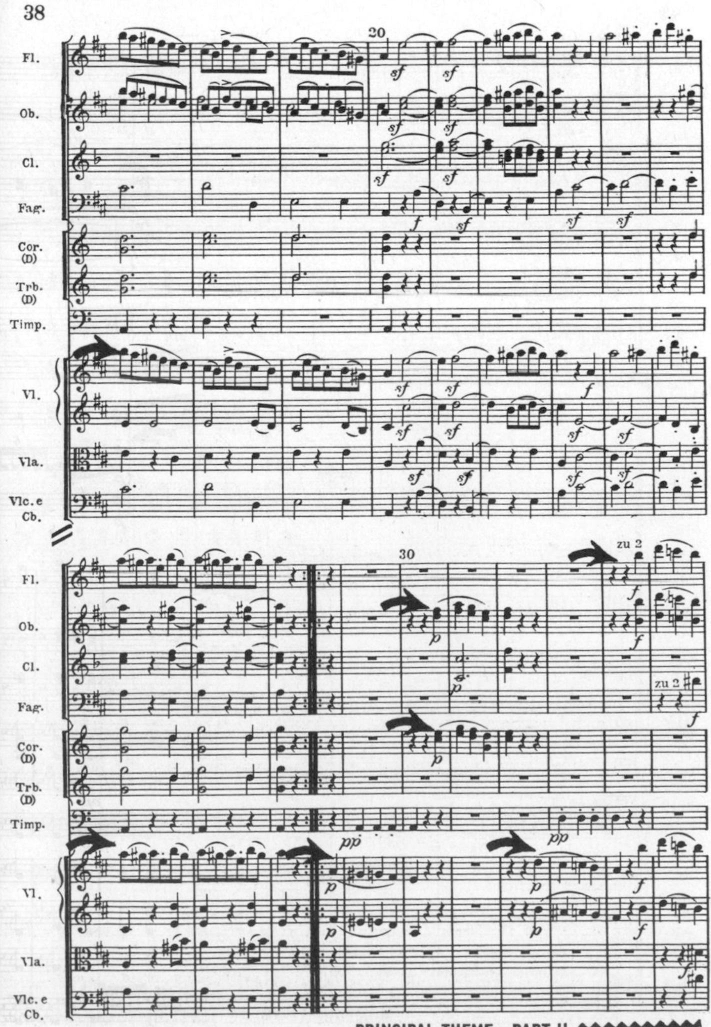
Fl.
Ob.
Cl.
Fag.
Cor. (D)
Trb. (D)
Timp.
Vl.
Vla.
Vlc. e Cb.
zu 2
PRINCIPAL THEME—PART II

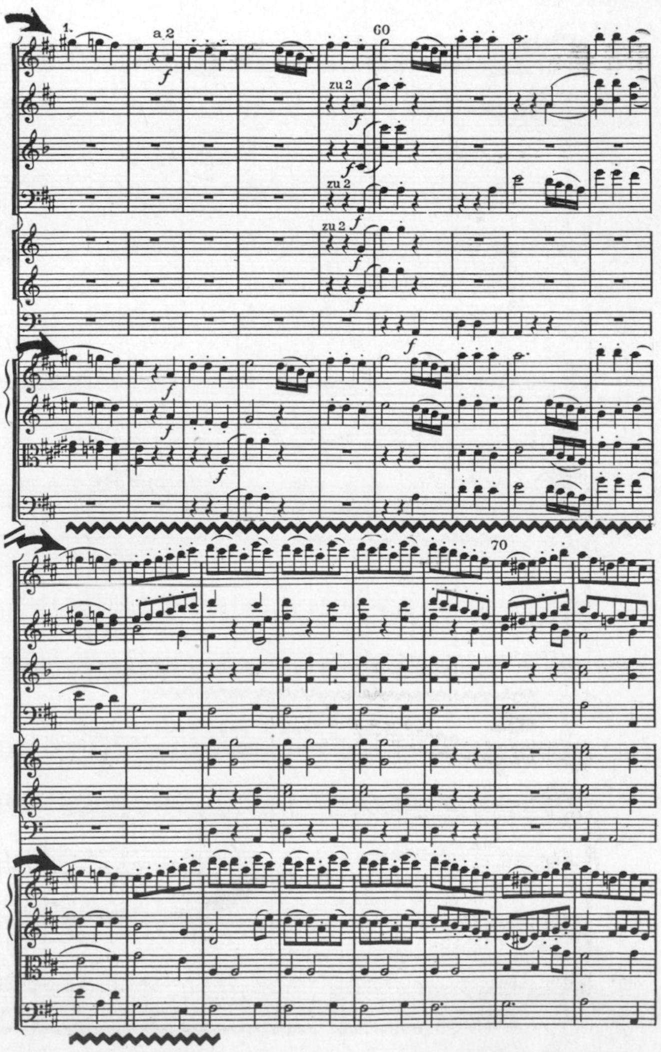
Fl.
Ob.
Cl.
Fag.
Cor. (D)
Trb. (D)
Timp.
Vl.
Vla.
Vlc. e Cb.
a 2
zu 2

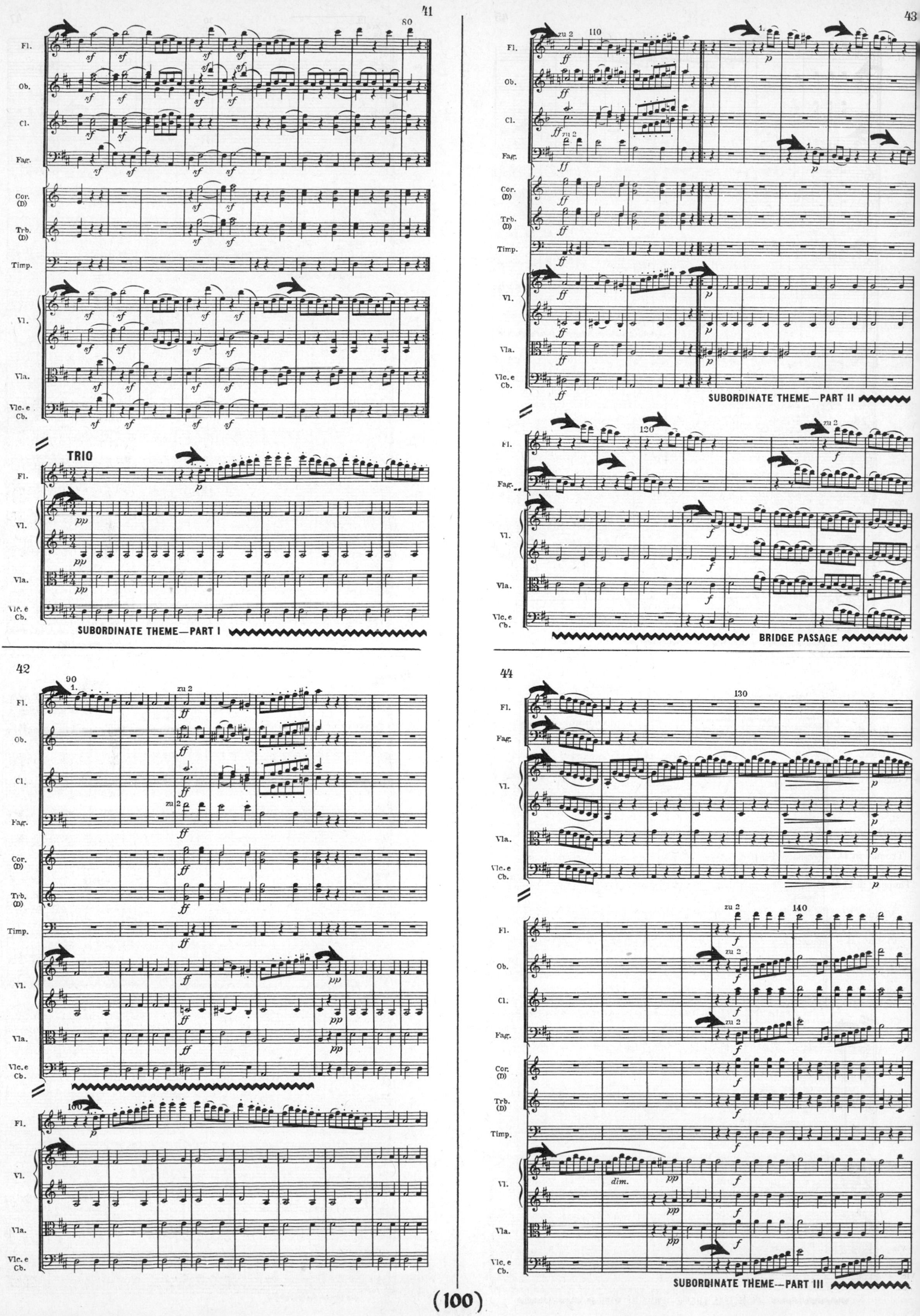
41
43
TRIO
SUBORDINATE THEME—PART I
SUBORDINATE THEME—PART II
BRIDGE PASSAGE
42
44
SUBORDINATE THEME—PART III
Fl.
Ob.
Cl.
Fag.
Cor. (D)
Trb. (D)
Timp.
Vl.
Vla.
Vlc. e Cb.

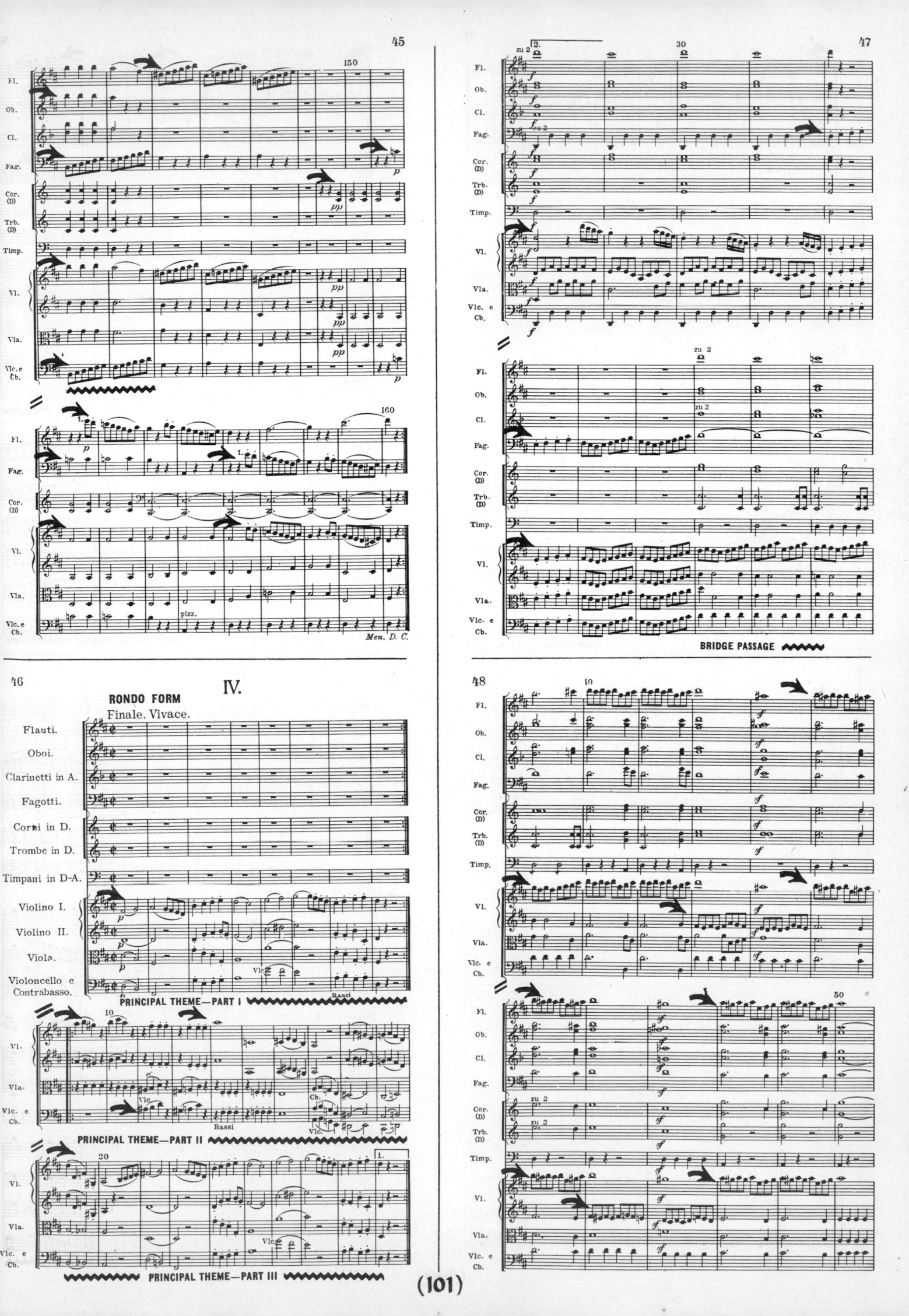

49

Fl.
Ob.
Cl.
Fag.
Cor. (D)
Trb. (D)
Timp.
Vl.
Vla.
Vlc. e Cb.
zu 2
60
1.
Vlc. arco
SUBORDINATE THEME

51

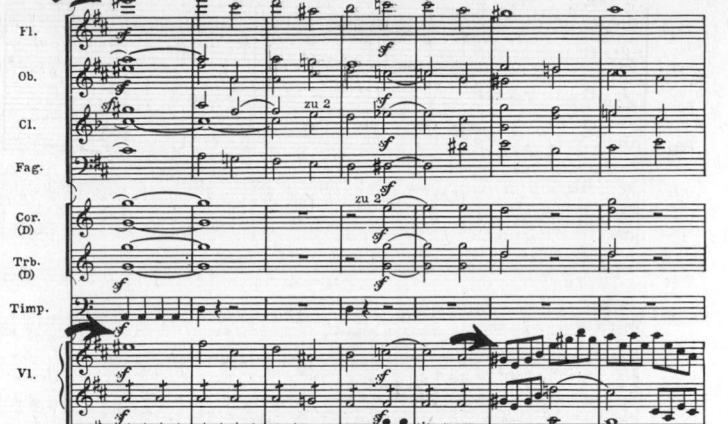

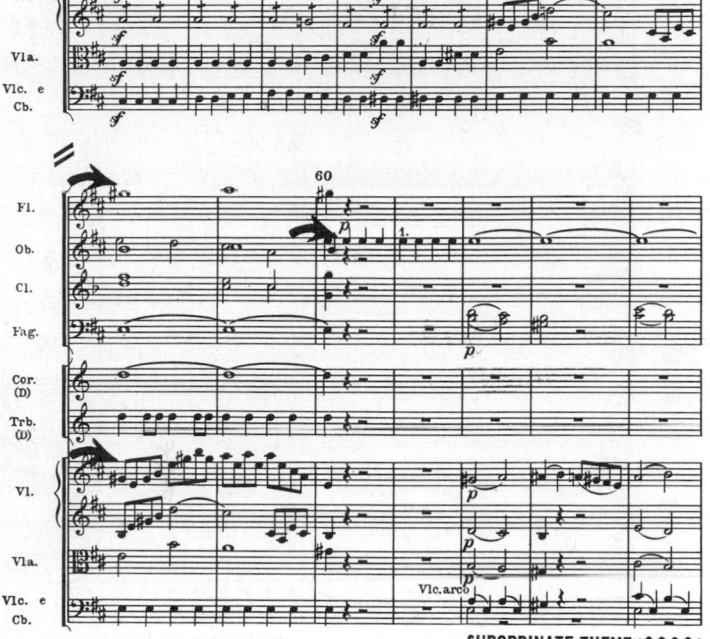

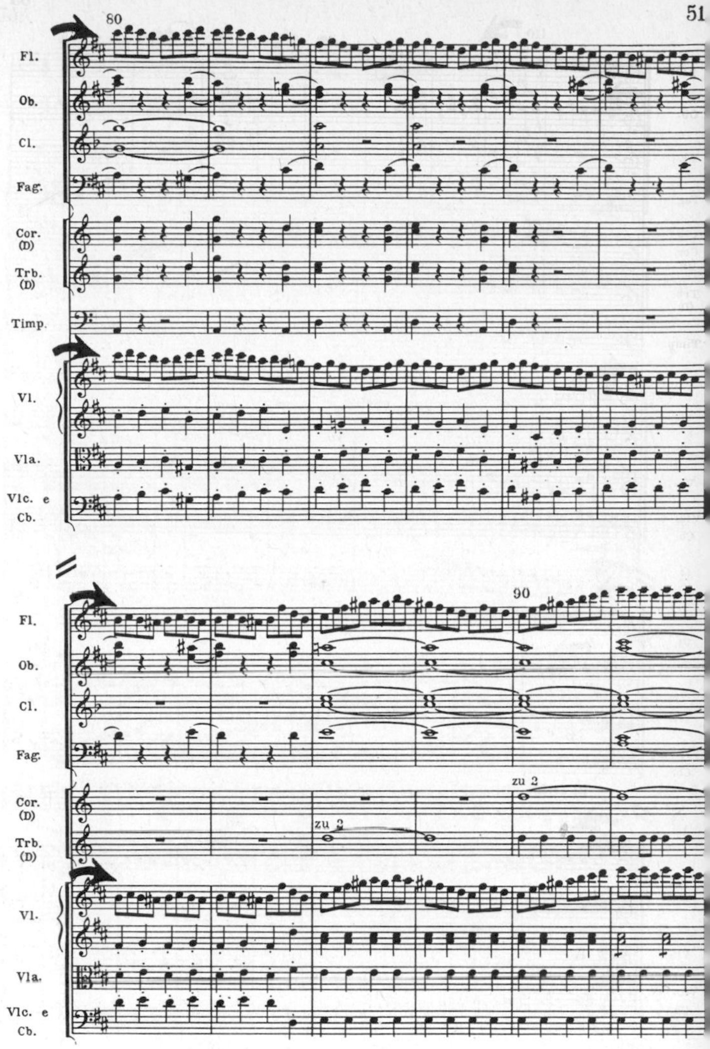

80
Fl.
Ob.
Cl.
Fag.
Cor. (D)
Trb. (D)
Timp.
Vl.
Vla.
Vlc. e Cb.
90
zu 2

50

Ob.
Fag.
Vl.
Vla.
Vlc. e Cb.
70
zu 2
Fl.
Cl.
Cor. (D)
Trb. (D)
Timp.
arco

52

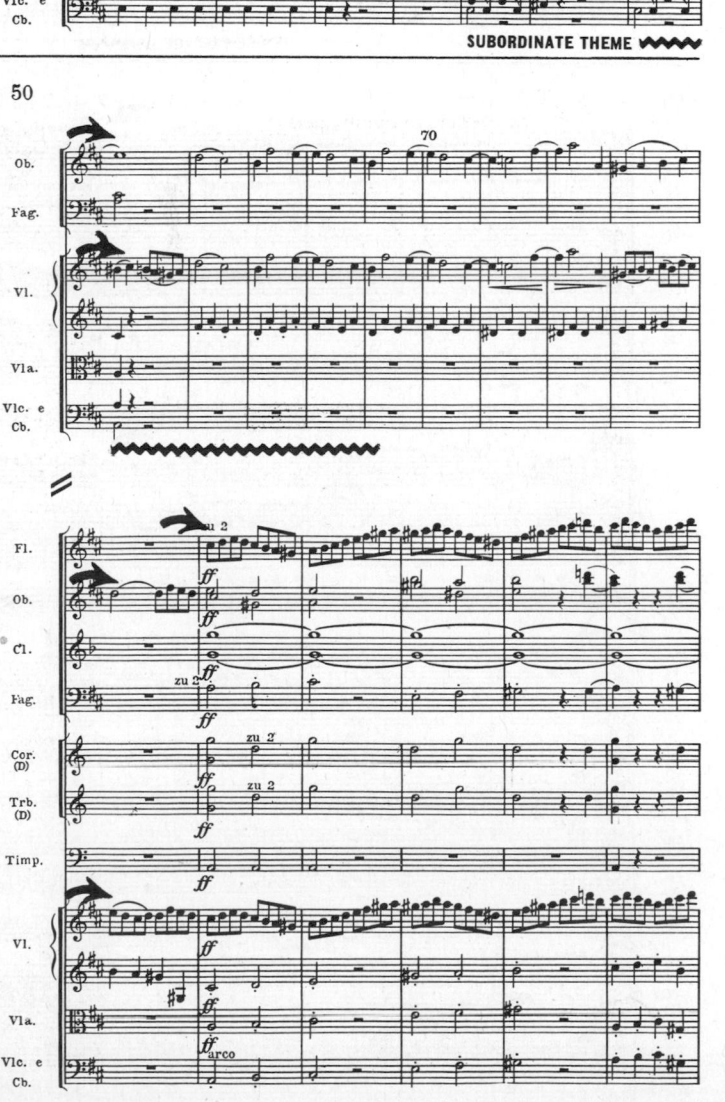

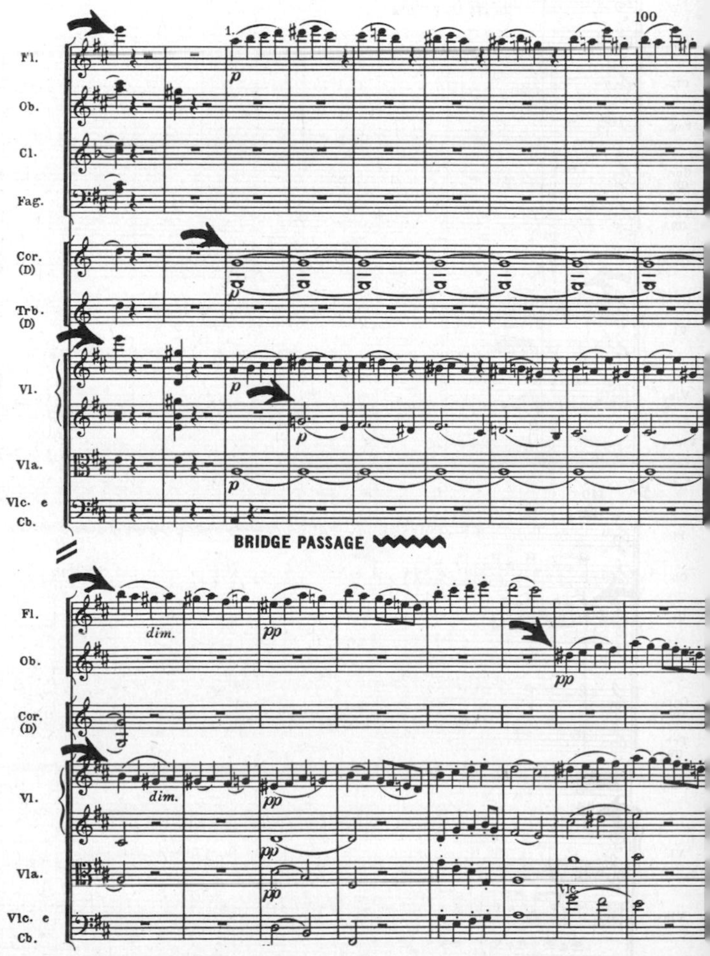

Fl.
Ob.
Cl.
Fag.
Cor. (D)
Trb. (D)
Vl.
Vla.
Vlc. e Cb.
1.
100
BRIDGE PASSAGE
dim.

53

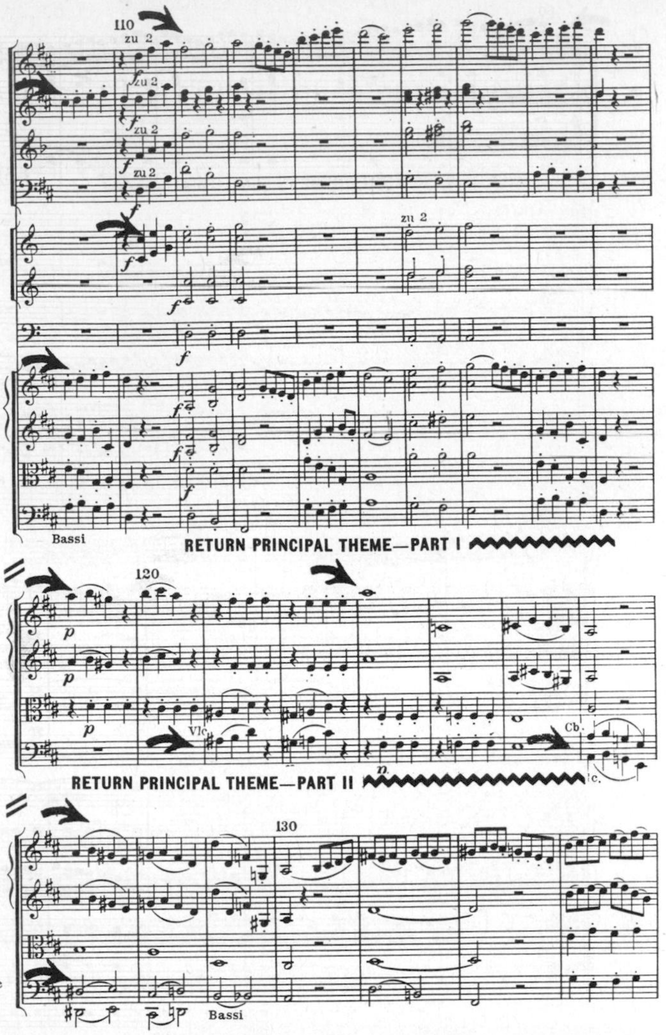
Fl.
Ob.
Cl.
Fag.
Cor. (D)
Trb. (D)
Timp.
Vl.
Vla.
Vlc. e Cb.
110
zu 2
Bassi
RETURN PRINCIPAL THEME—PART I
120
Vlc.
Cb.
RETURN PRINCIPAL THEME—PART II
130

54

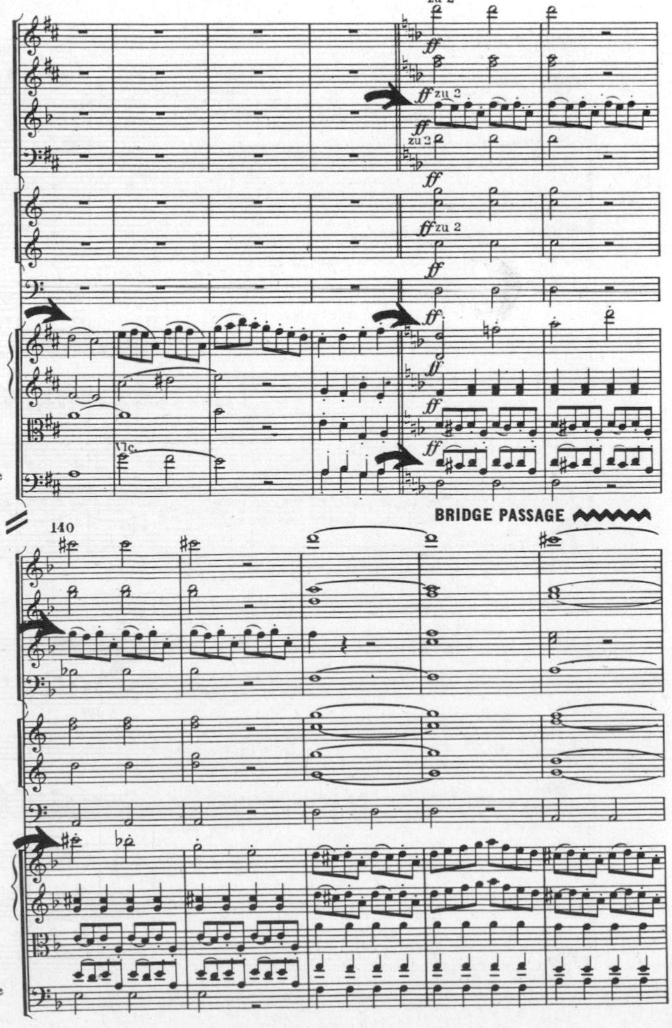
Fl.
Ob.
Cl.
Fag.
Cor. (D)
Trb. (D)
Timp.
Vl.
Vla.
Vlc. e Cb.
zu 2
Vlc.
BRIDGE PASSAGE
140

55

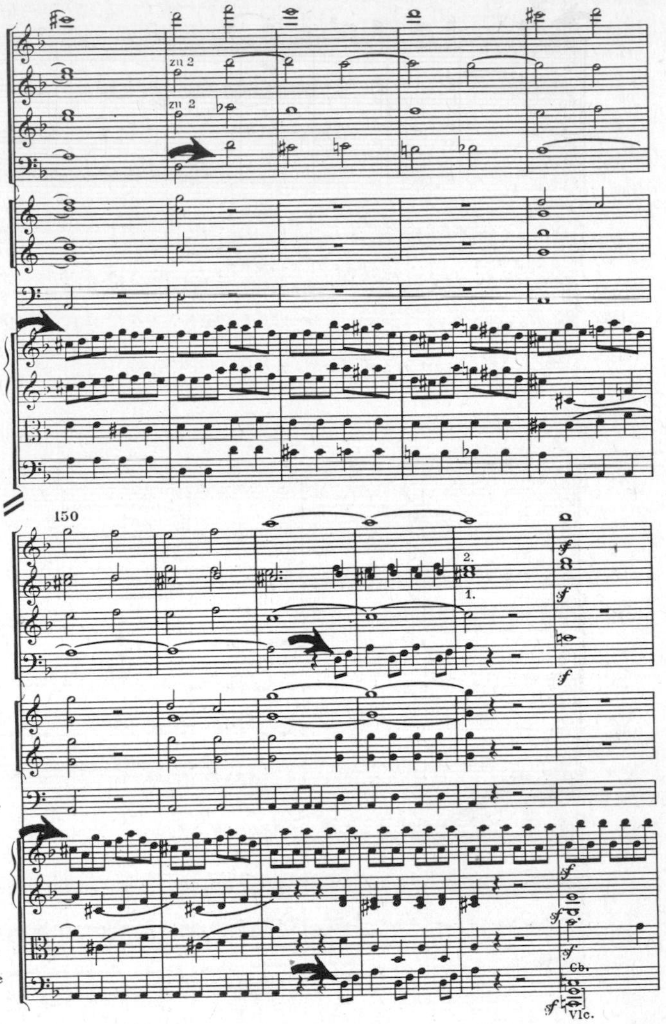
Fl.
Ob.
Cl.
Fag.
Cor. (D)
Trb. (D)
Timp.
Vl.
Vla.
Vlc. e Cb.
zu 2
150
Cb.
Vlc.

56

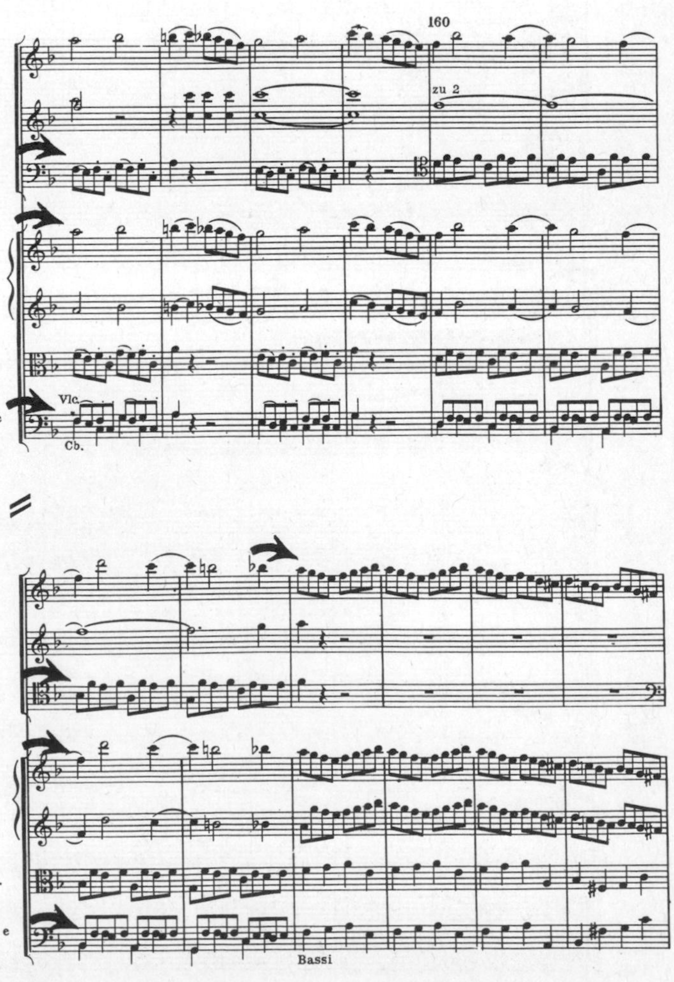
Fl.
Ob.
Fag.
Vl.
Vla.
Vlc. e Cb.
160
zu 2
Vlc.
Cb.
Bassi

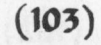

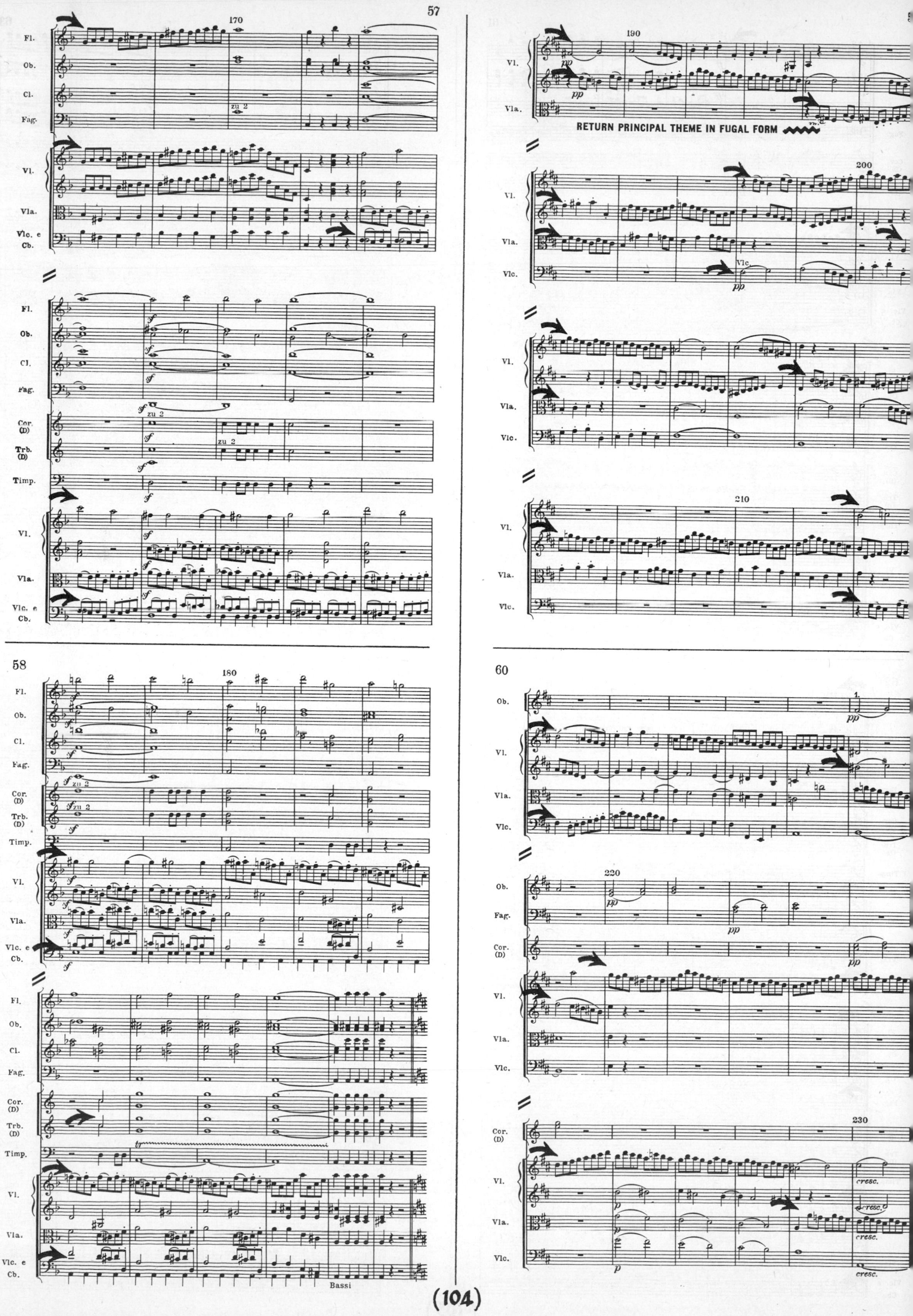

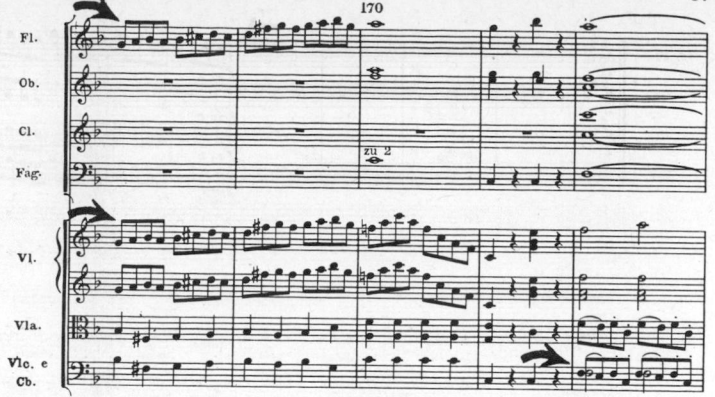

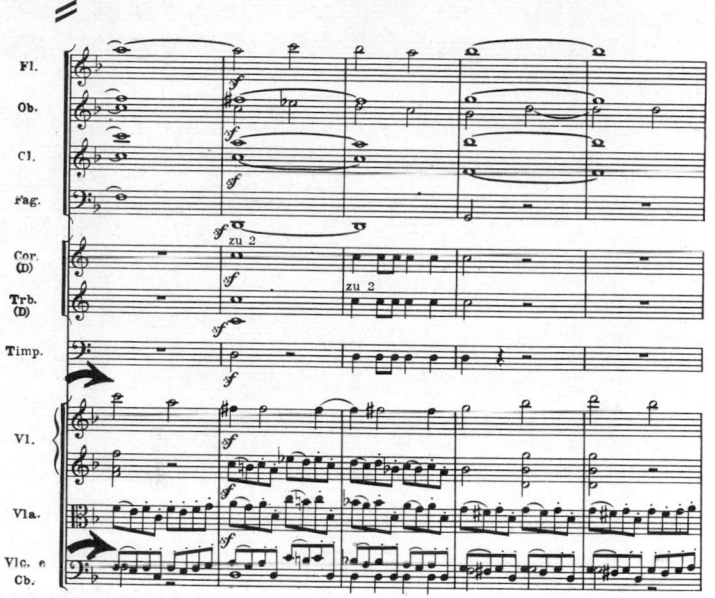

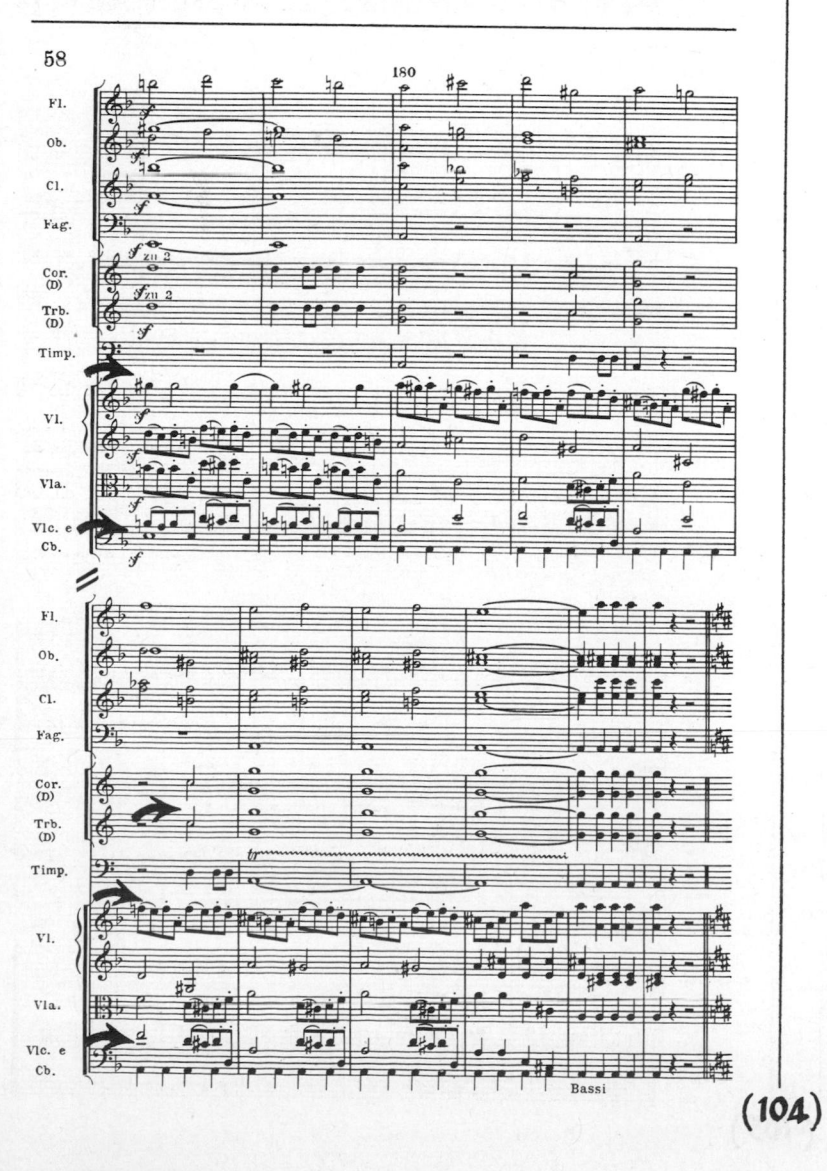

57

170

zu 2

58

180

zu 2

zu 2

Bassi

190

pp

pp

RETURN PRINCIPAL THEME IN FUGAL FORM ∿∿∿

200

Vlc

pp

210

60

1.
pp

220

pp

pp

230

cresc.

cresc.

cresc.

p

cresc.

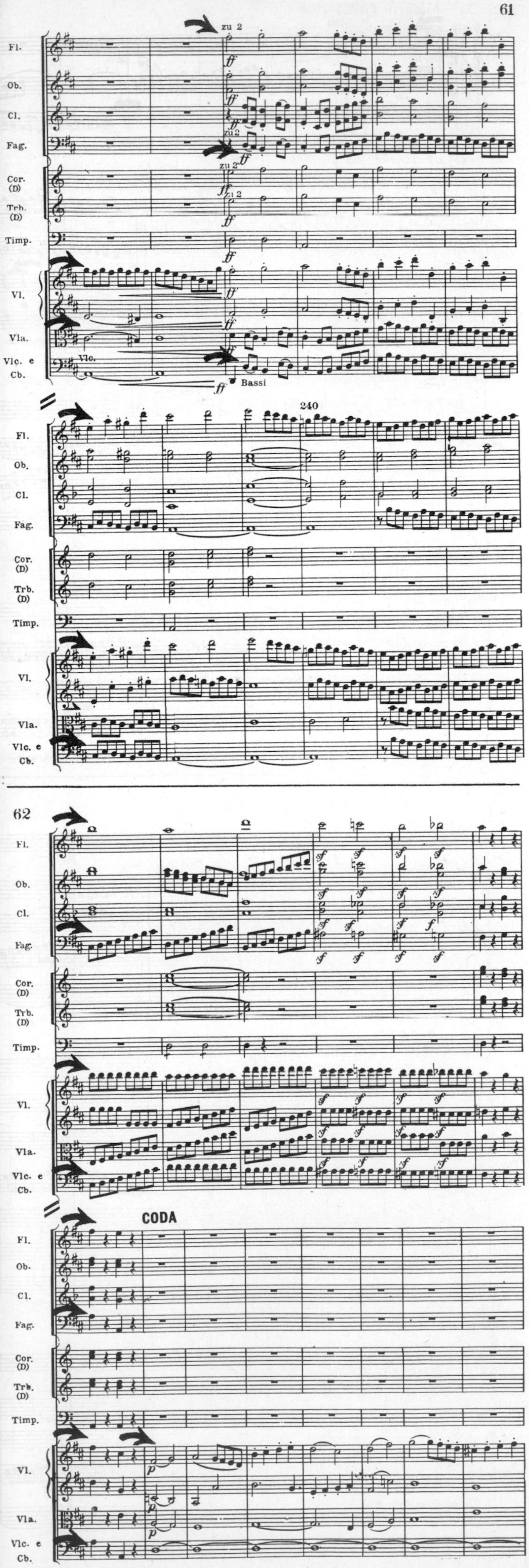
61
zu 2
Fl.
Ob.
Cl.
Fag.
Cor. (D)
Trb. (D)
Timp.
Vl.
Vla.
Vlc. e Cb.
Vlc.
Bassi
240
62
CODA

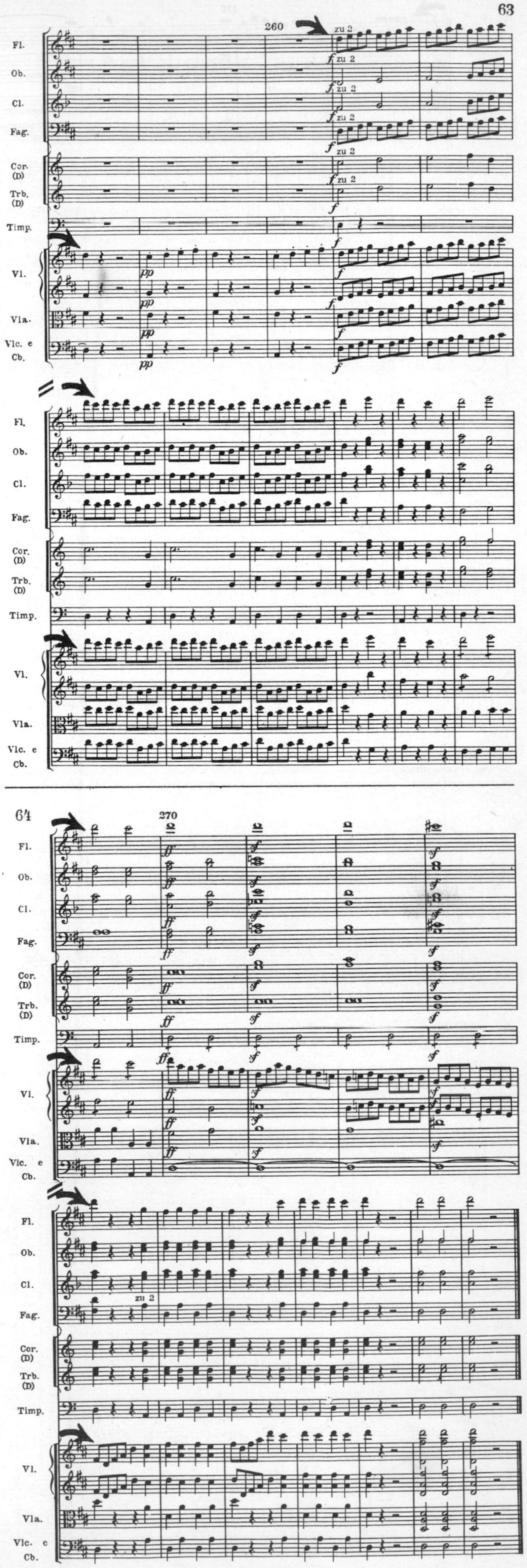
63
260
zu 2
Fl.
Ob.
Cl.
Fag.
Cor. (D)
Trb. (D)
Timp.
Vl.
Vla.
Vlc. e Cb.
64
270

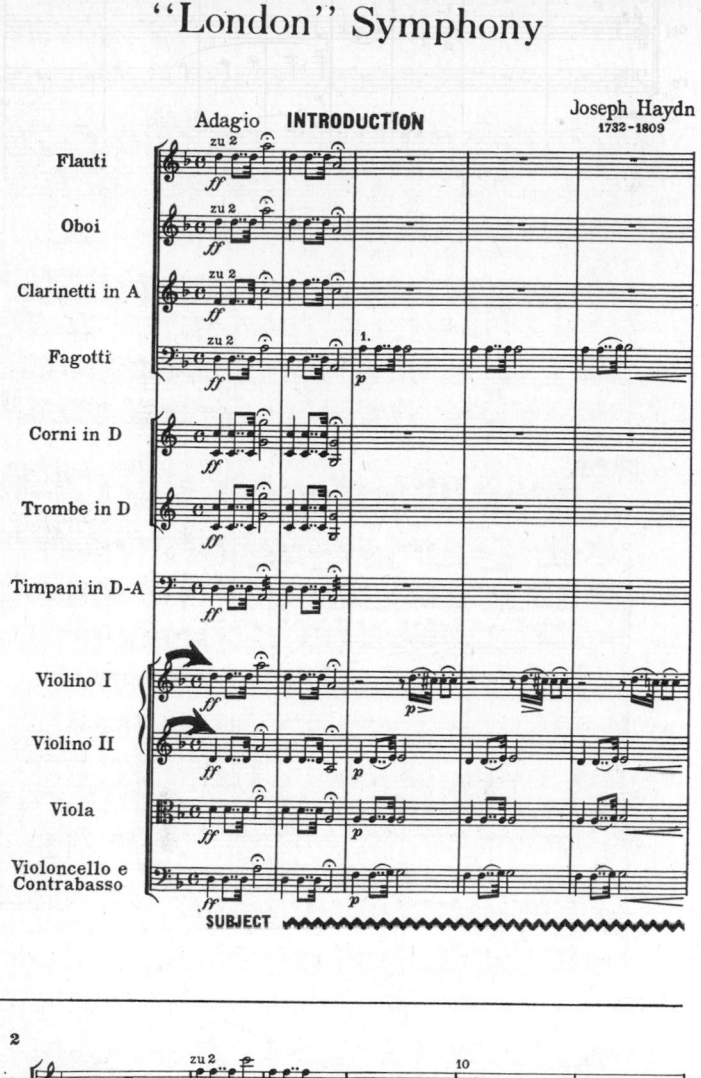

"London" Symphony

Adagio **INTRODUCTION**

Joseph Haydn
1732–1809

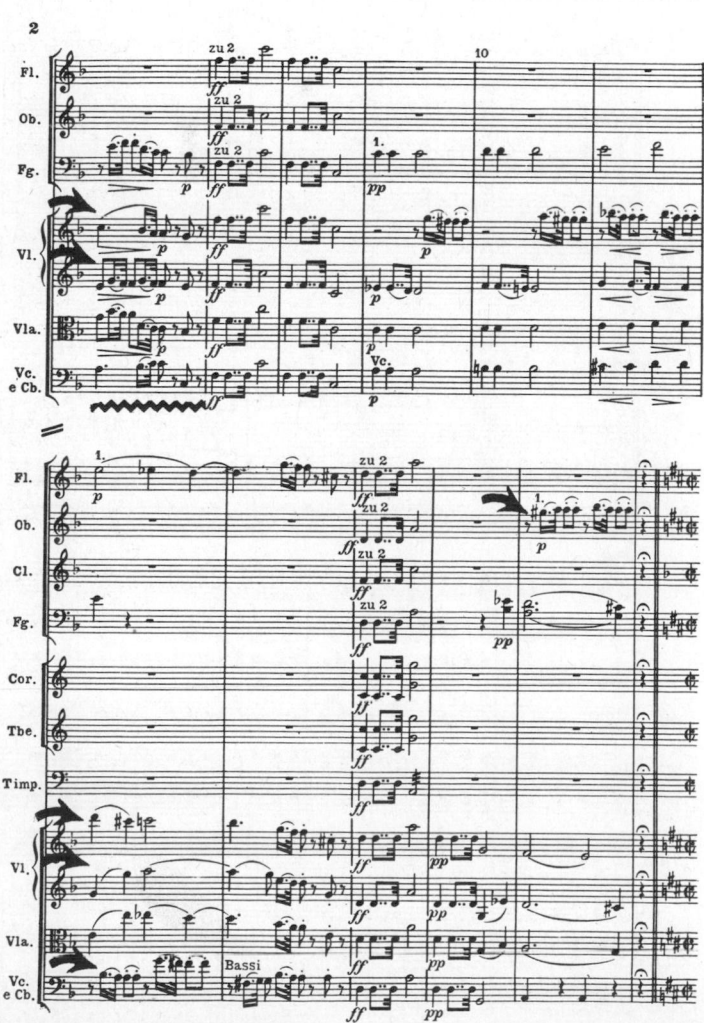

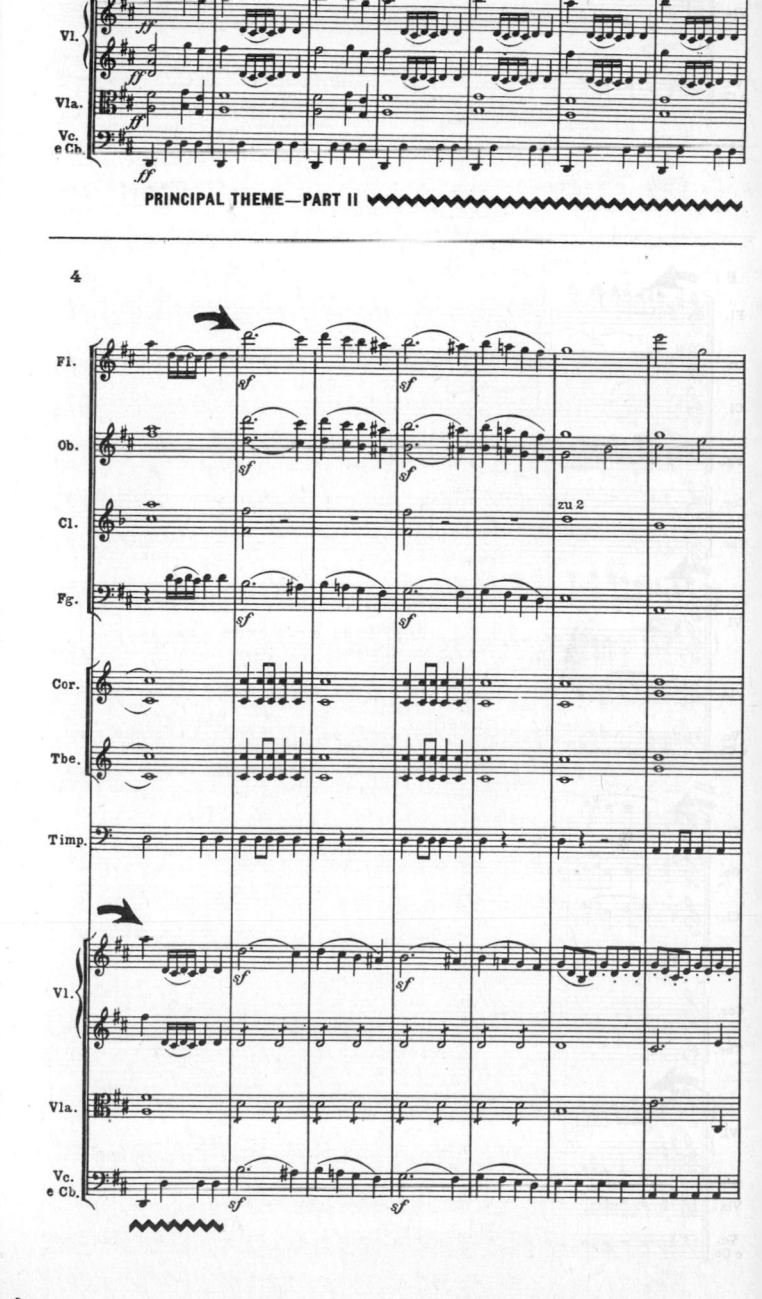

Allegro EXPOSITION

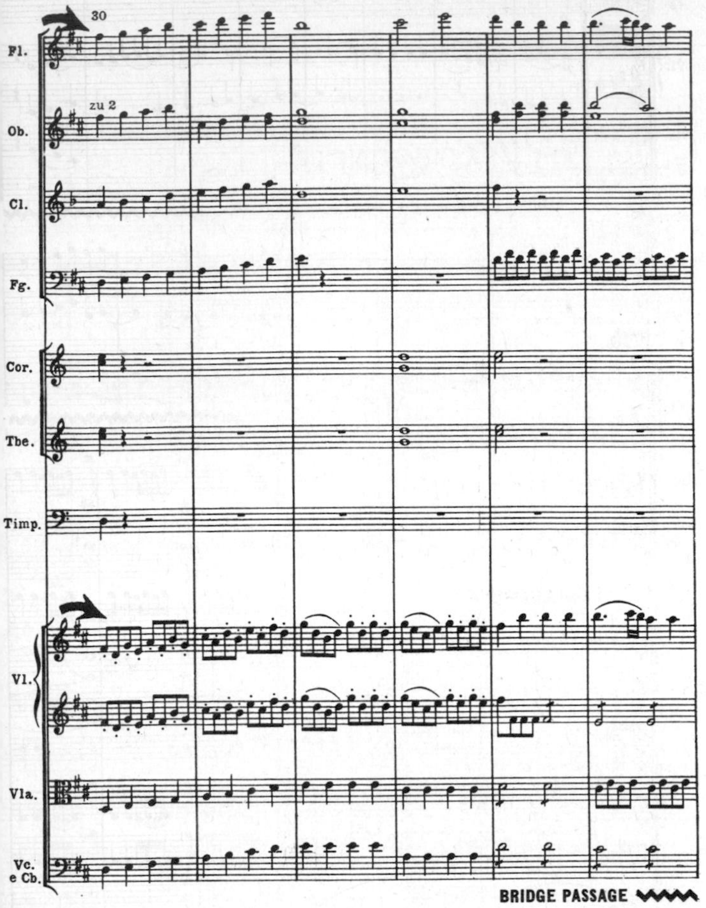

BRIDGE PASSAGE 〜〜〜〜

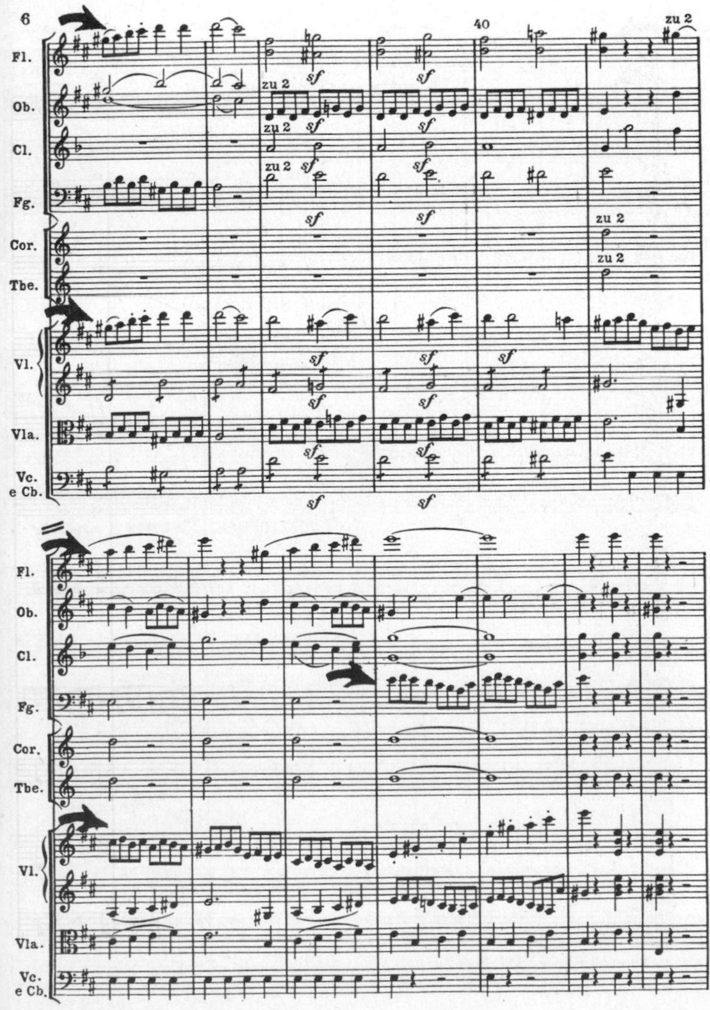

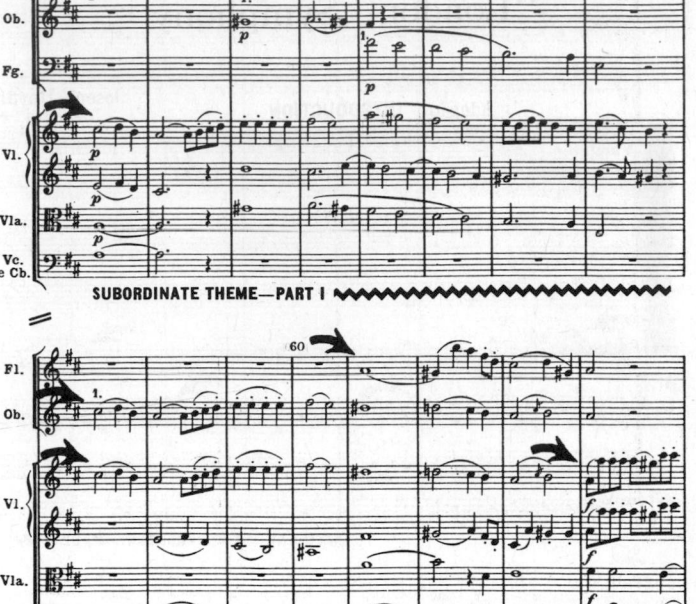

SUBORDINATE THEME—PART I 〜〜〜〜〜〜〜〜〜〜〜

SUBORDINATE THEME—PART II 〜〜〜〜〜〜〜〜 Bassi

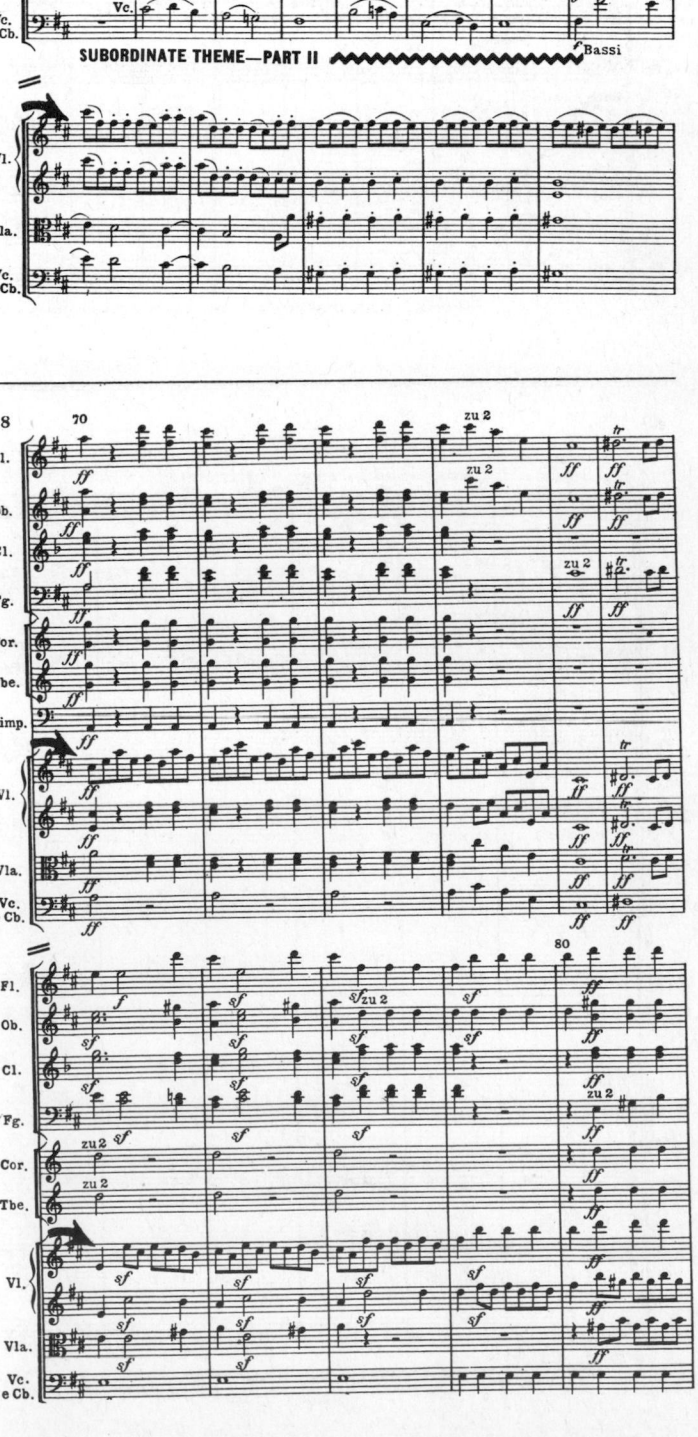

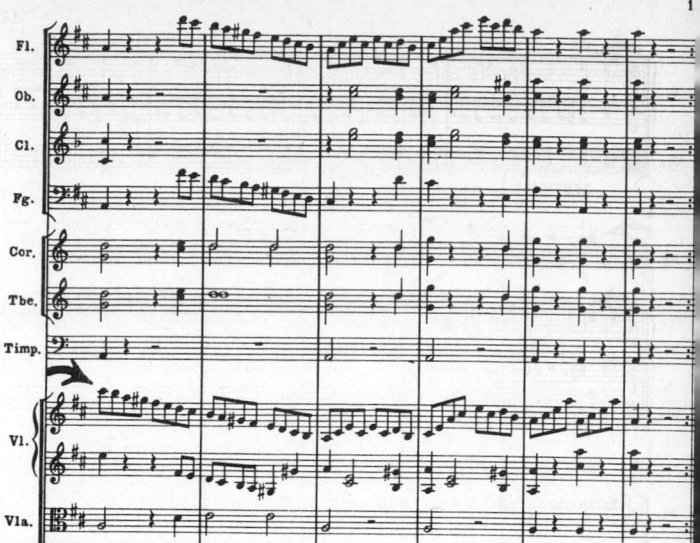

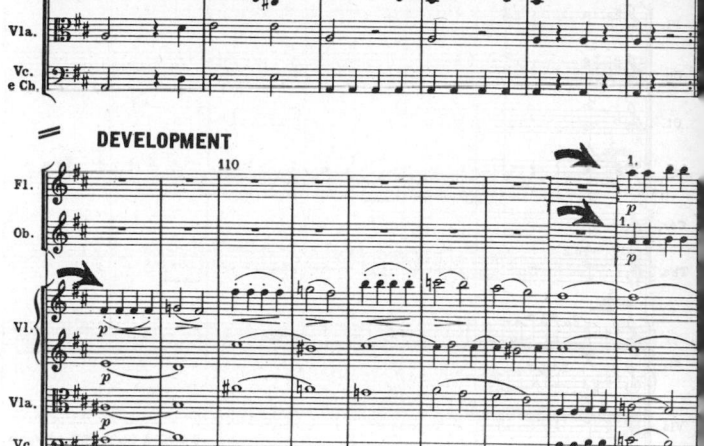

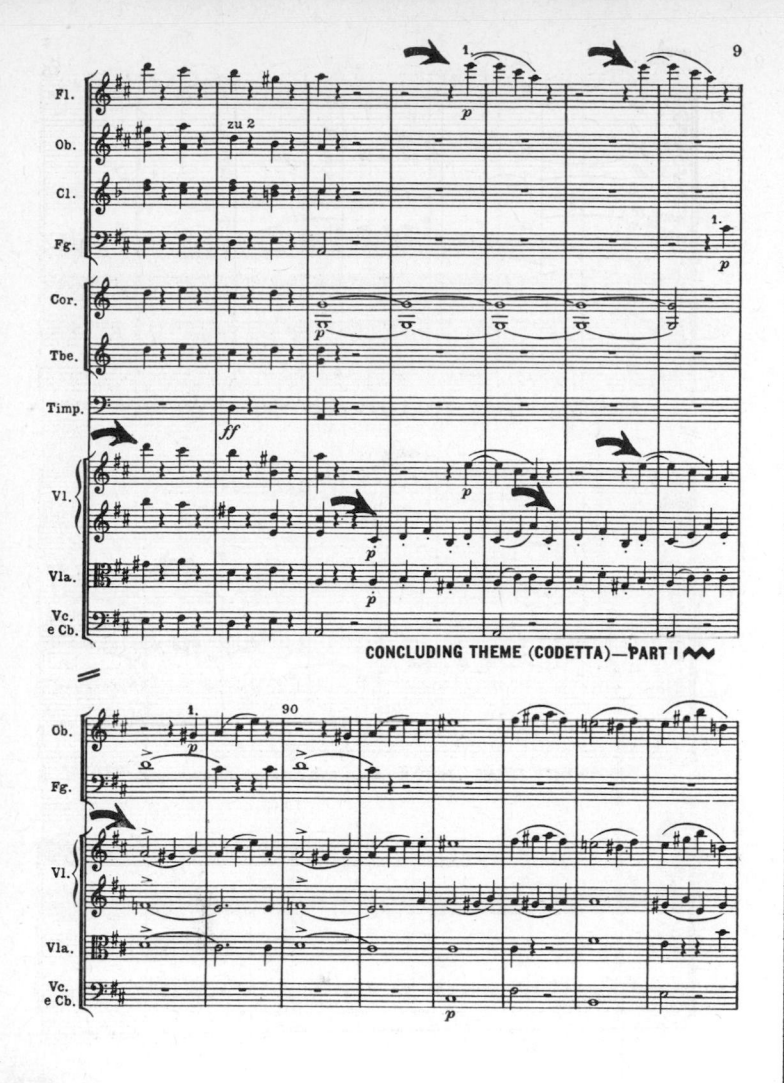

CONCLUDING THEME (CODETTA)—PART I ∿∿

DEVELOPMENT

DEVELOPMENT—SECTION I ∿∿∿∿∿

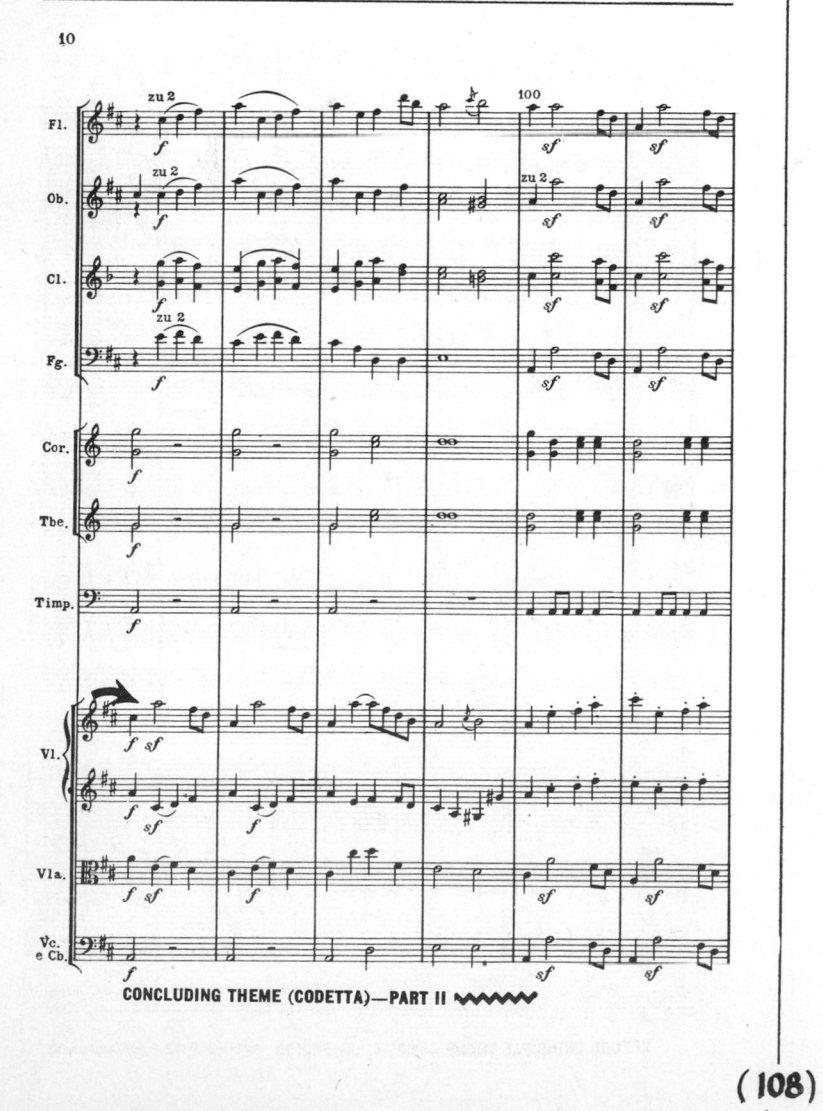

CONCLUDING THEME (CODETTA)—PART II ∿∿∿∿∿

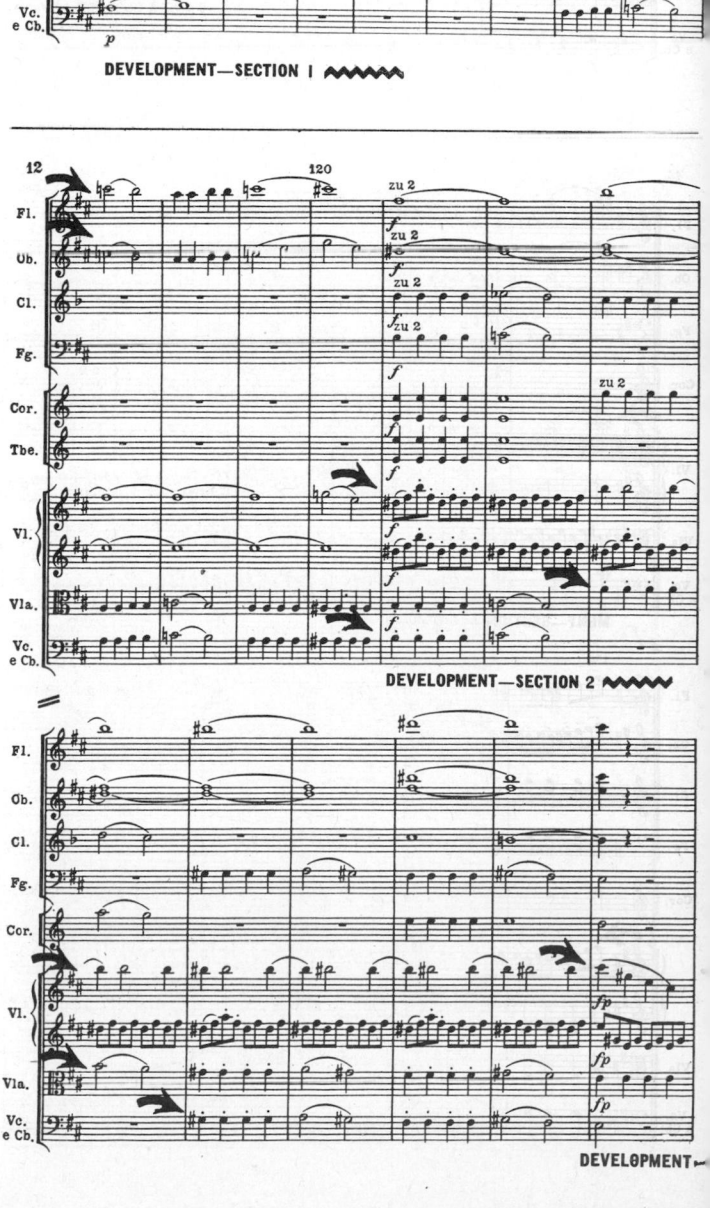

DEVELOPMENT—SECTION 2 ∿∿∿∿∿

DEVELOPMENT

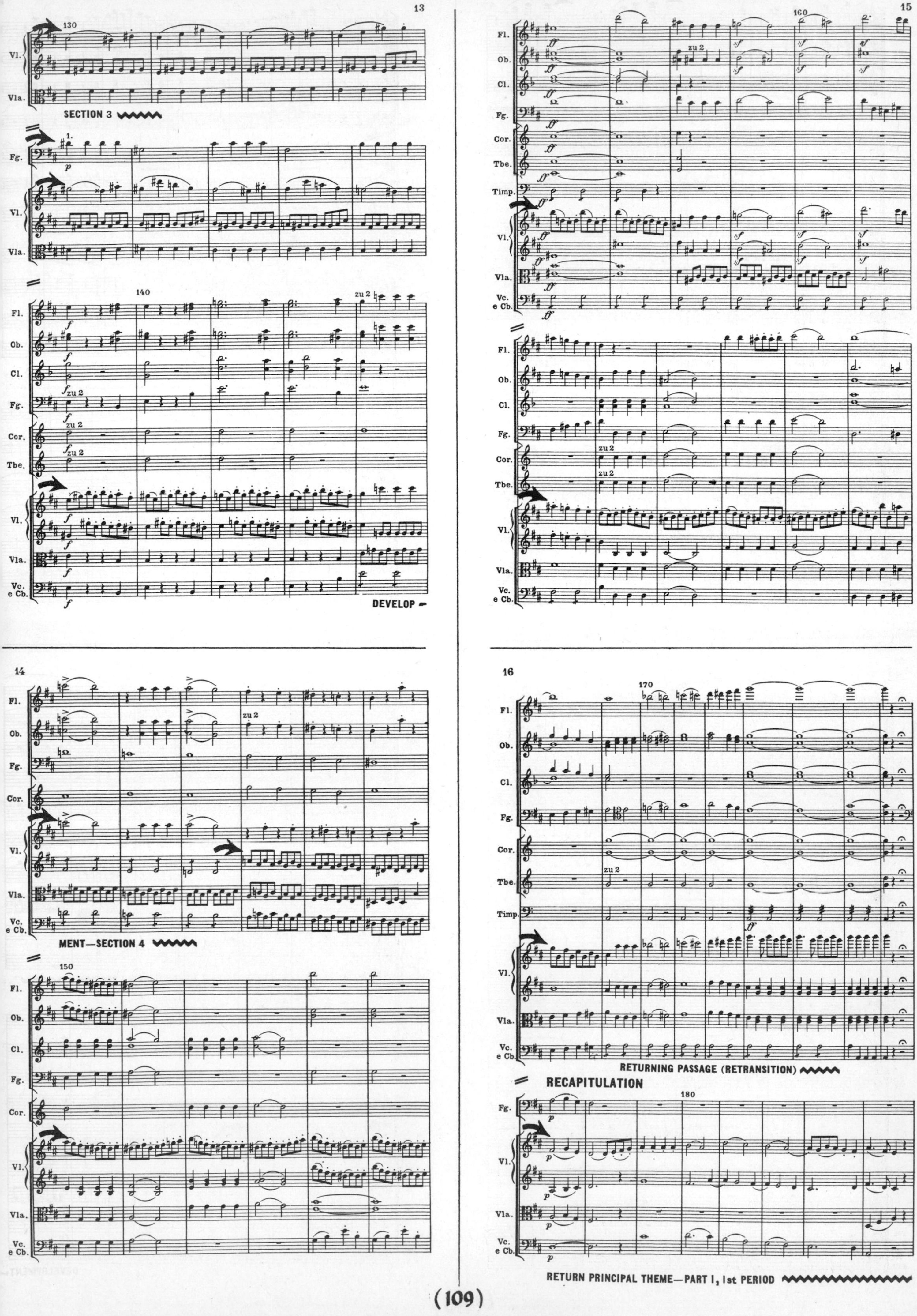
13
SECTION 3
DEVELOP –
14
MENT—SECTION 4
15
16
RETURNING PASSAGE (RETRANSITION)
RECAPITULATION
RETURN PRINCIPAL THEME—PART I, 1st PERIOD

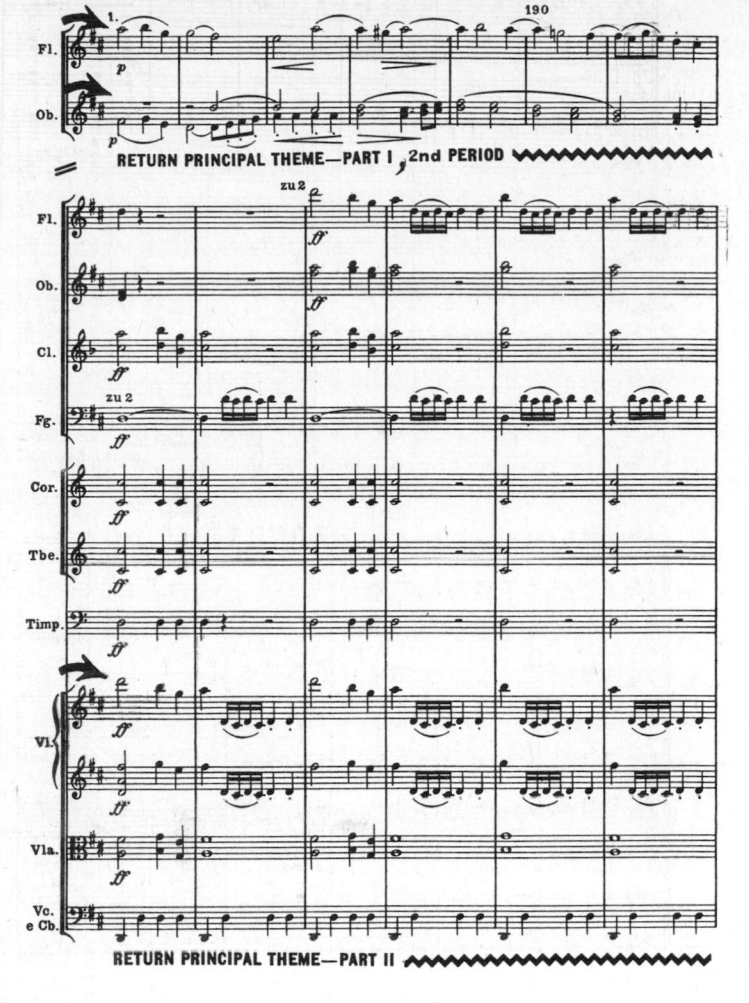

RETURN PRINCIPAL THEME—PART I, 2nd PERIOD

RETURN PRINCIPAL THEME—PART II

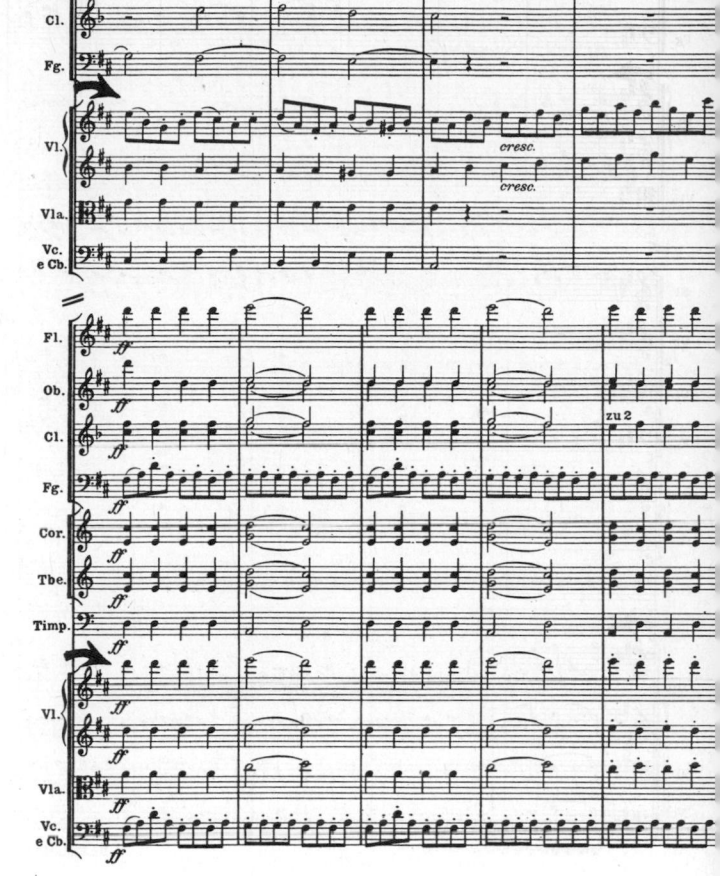

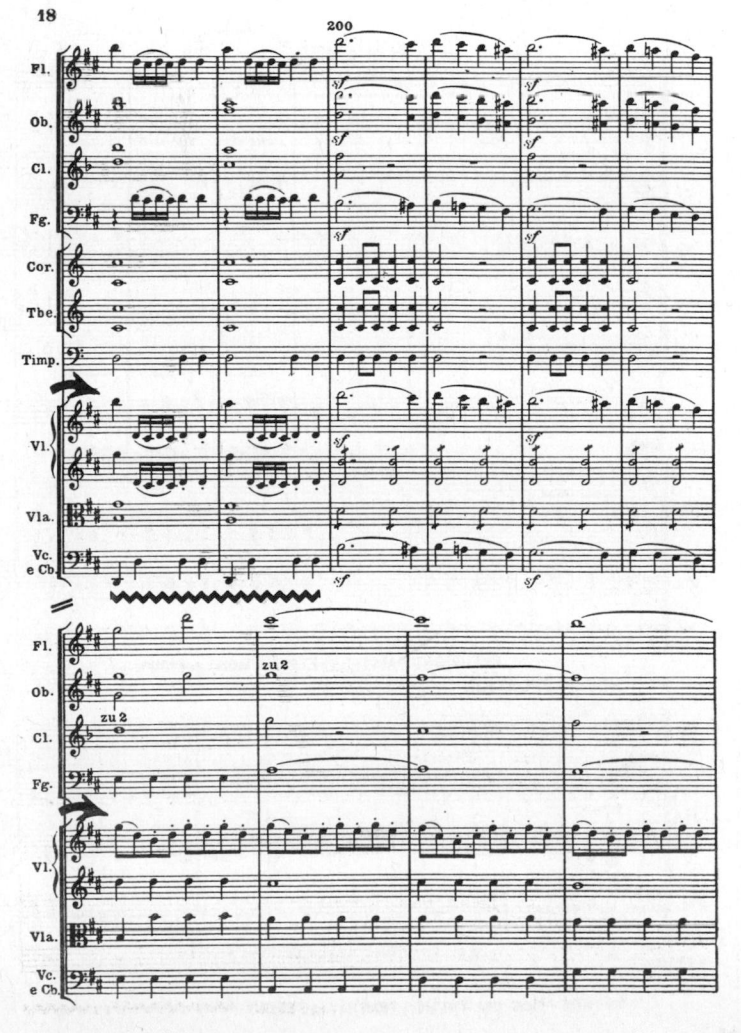

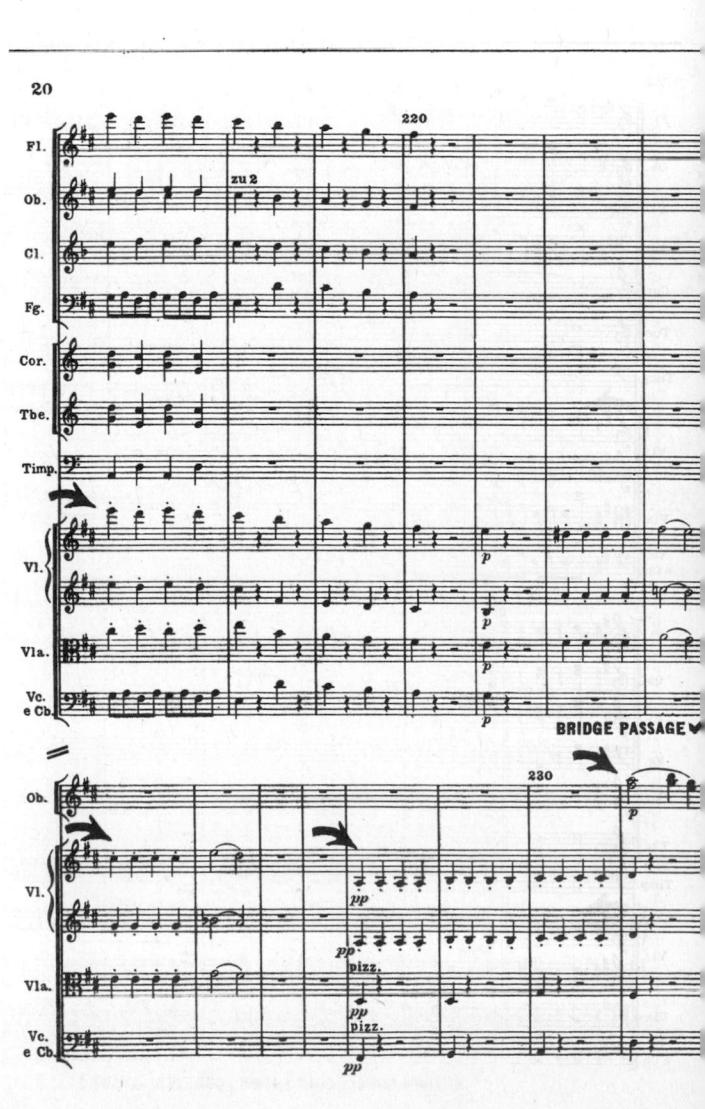

BRIDGE PASSAGE

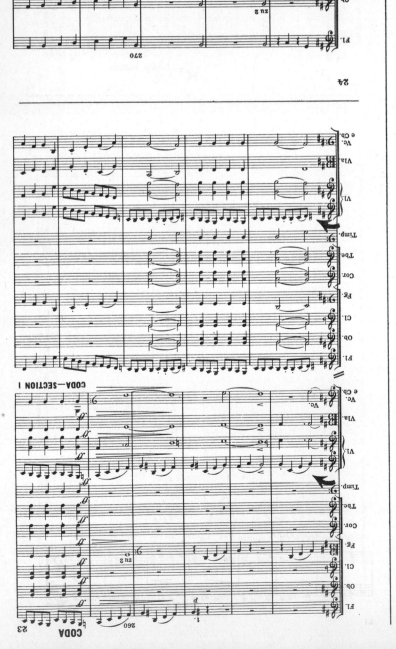

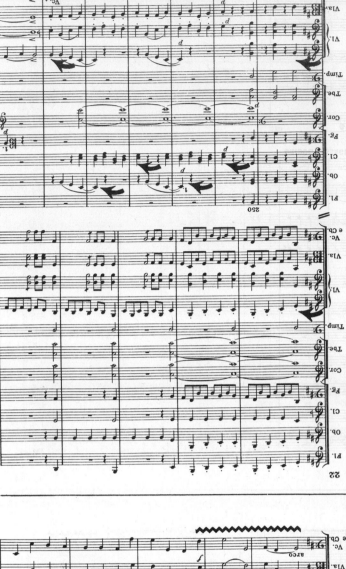

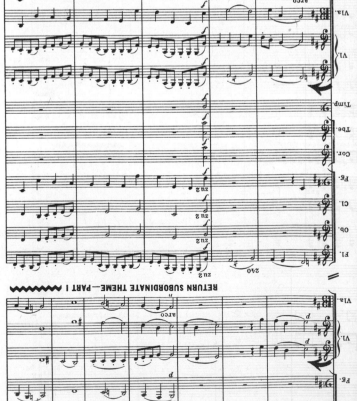

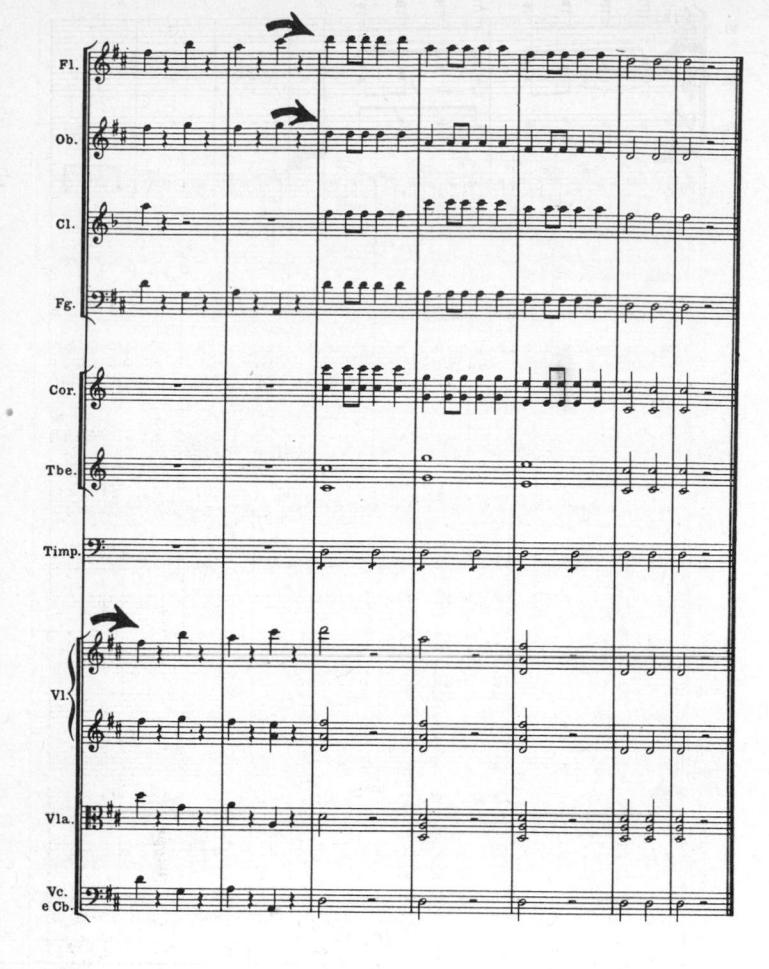

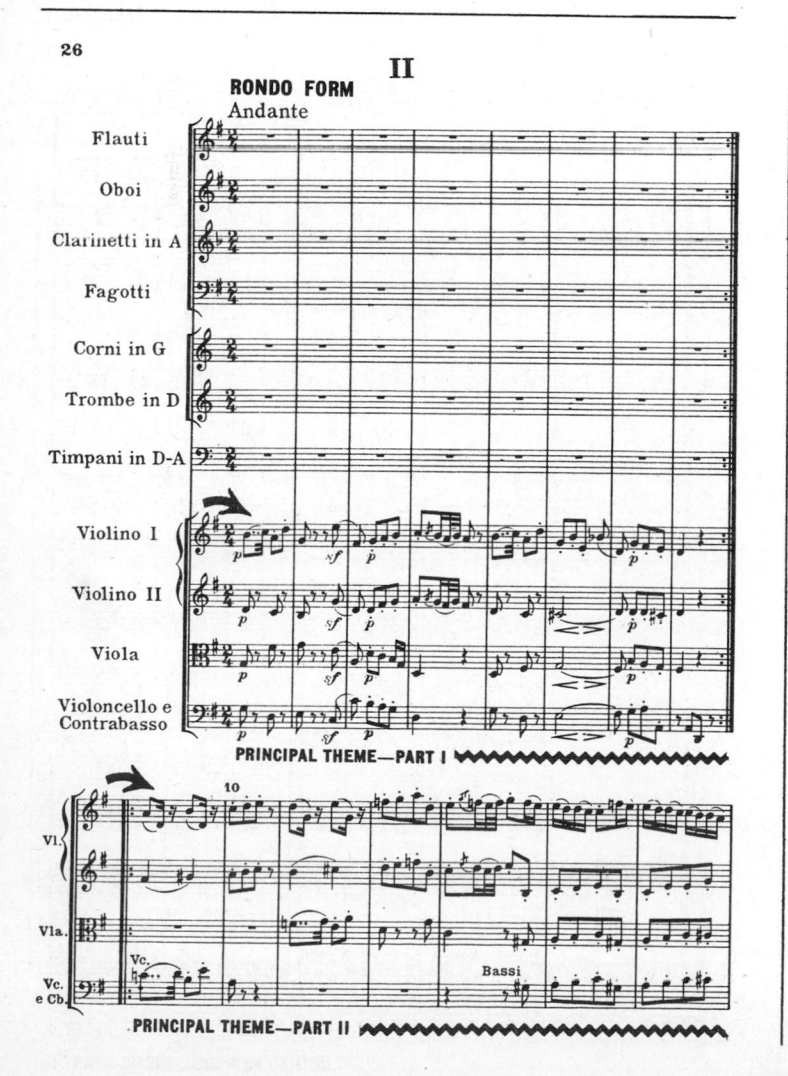

PRINCIPAL THEME—PART I ∿∿∿∿∿∿

PRINCIPAL THEME—PART II ∿∿∿∿∿∿

II

RONDO FORM
Andante

Flauti
Oboi
Clarinetti in A
Fagotti
Corni in G
Trombe in D
Timpani in D-A
Violino I
Violino II
Viola
Violoncello e Contrabasso

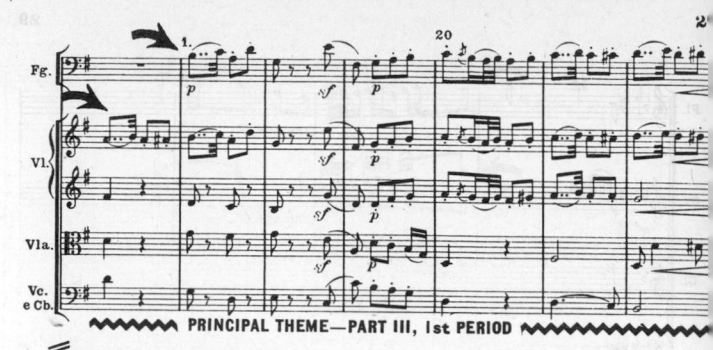

PRINCIPAL THEME—PART III, 1st PERIOD ∿∿∿∿∿∿

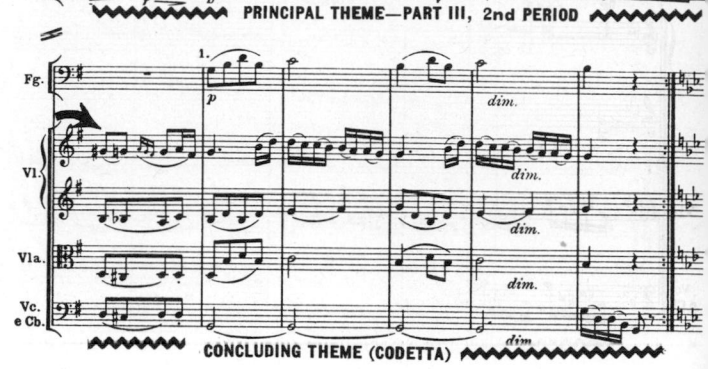

PRINCIPAL THEME—PART III, 2nd PERIOD ∿∿∿∿∿∿

CONCLUDING THEME (CODETTA) ∿∿∿∿∿∿

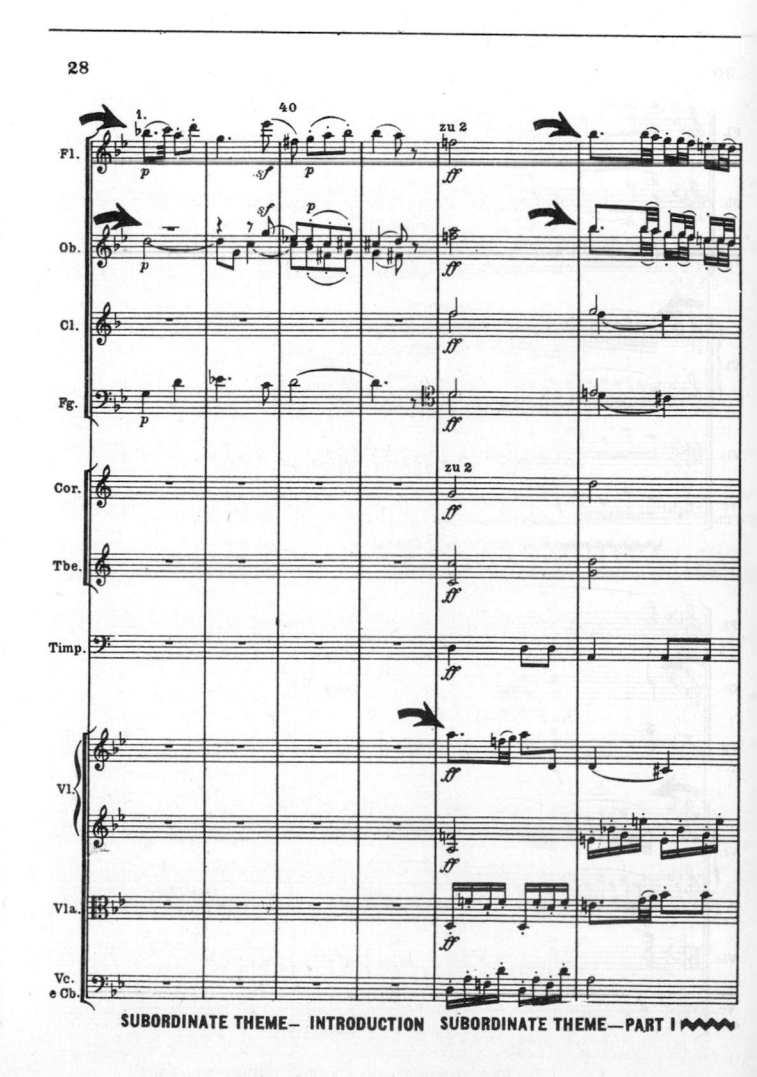

SUBORDINATE THEME— INTRODUCTION   SUBORDINATE THEME—PART I ∿∿∿

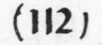

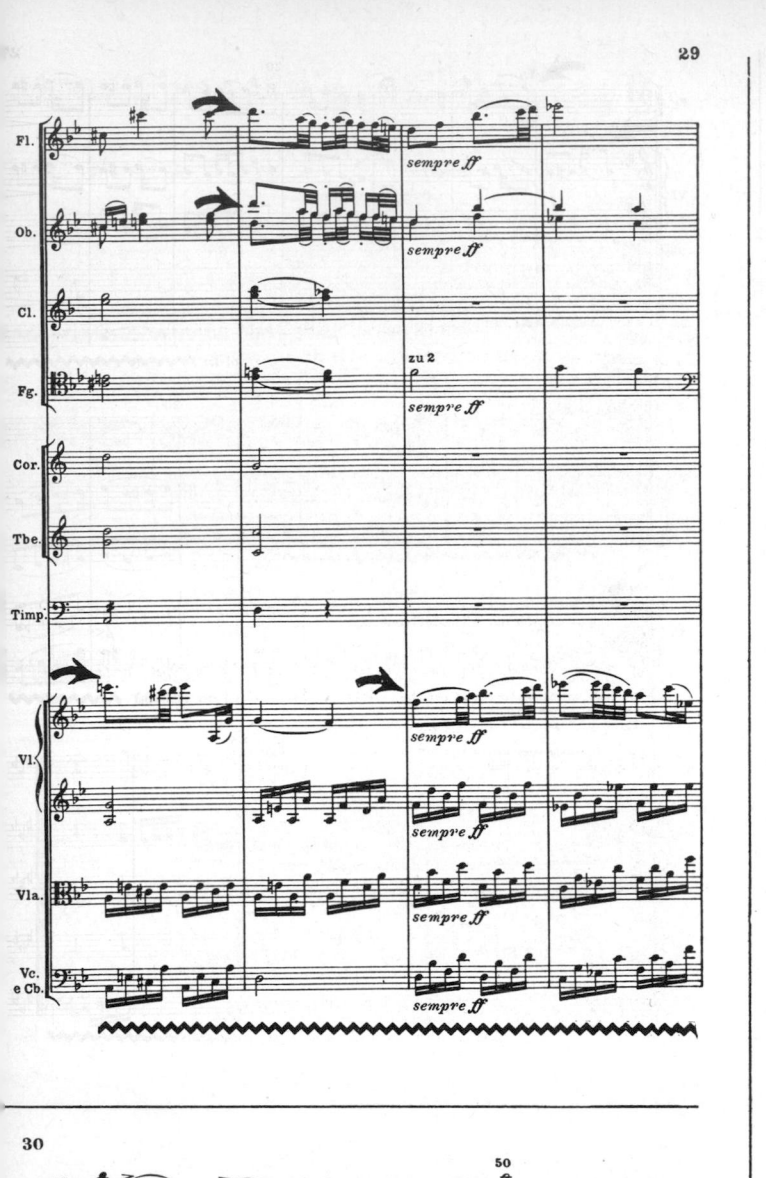

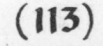

29

Fl.
Ob.
Cl.
Fg.
Cor.
Tbe.
Timp.
Vl.
Vla.
Vc. e Cb.
zu 2
sempre ff

30

50
Fl.
Ob.
Fg.
Vl.
Vla.
Vc. e Cb.
zu 2

31

Fl.
Ob.
Fg.
Vl.
Vla.
Vc. e Cb.
SUBORDINATE THEME—PART II (INTRO)
60
zu 2
Cor.
Tbe.
Timp.
Vc.
Cb.
SUBORDINATE THEME—PART II

32

70
Fl.
Ob.
Cl.
Fg.
Cor.
Tbe.
Timp.
Vl.
Vla.
Bassi
Vc. e Cb.
zu 2
RETURNING PASSAGE (RETRANSITION)
decresc.
pp
RETURN PRINCIPAL THEME—PART I

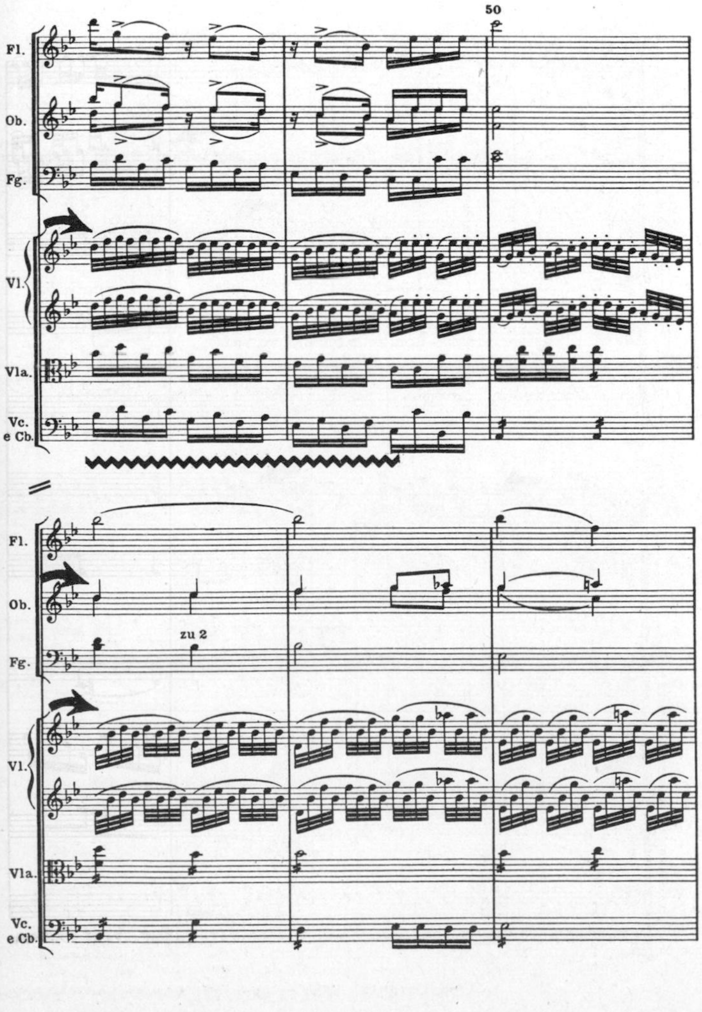

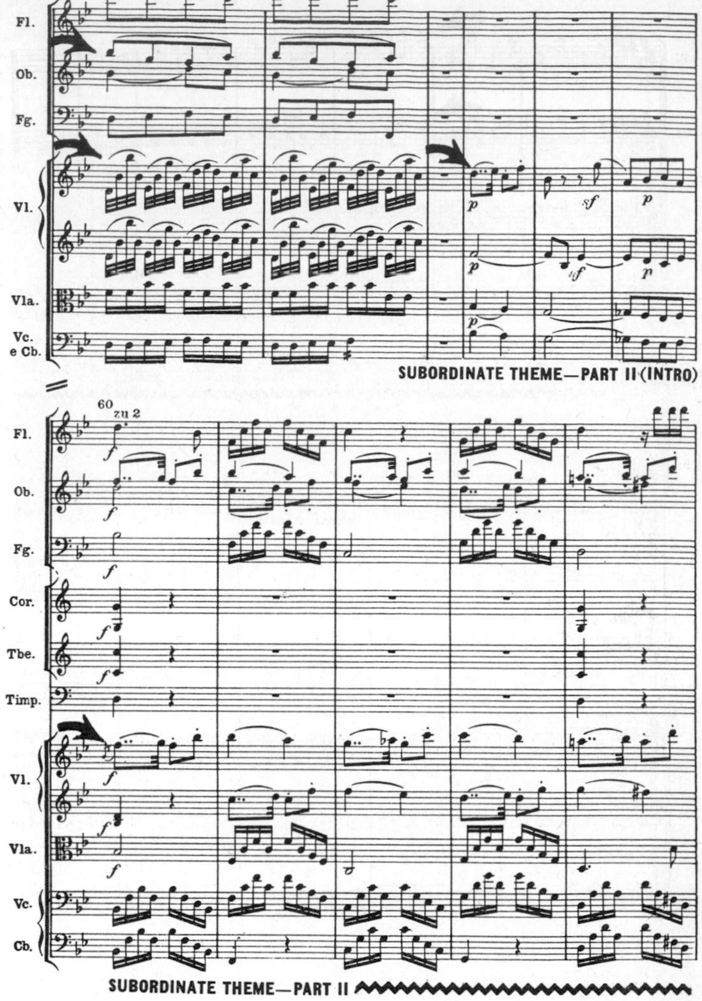

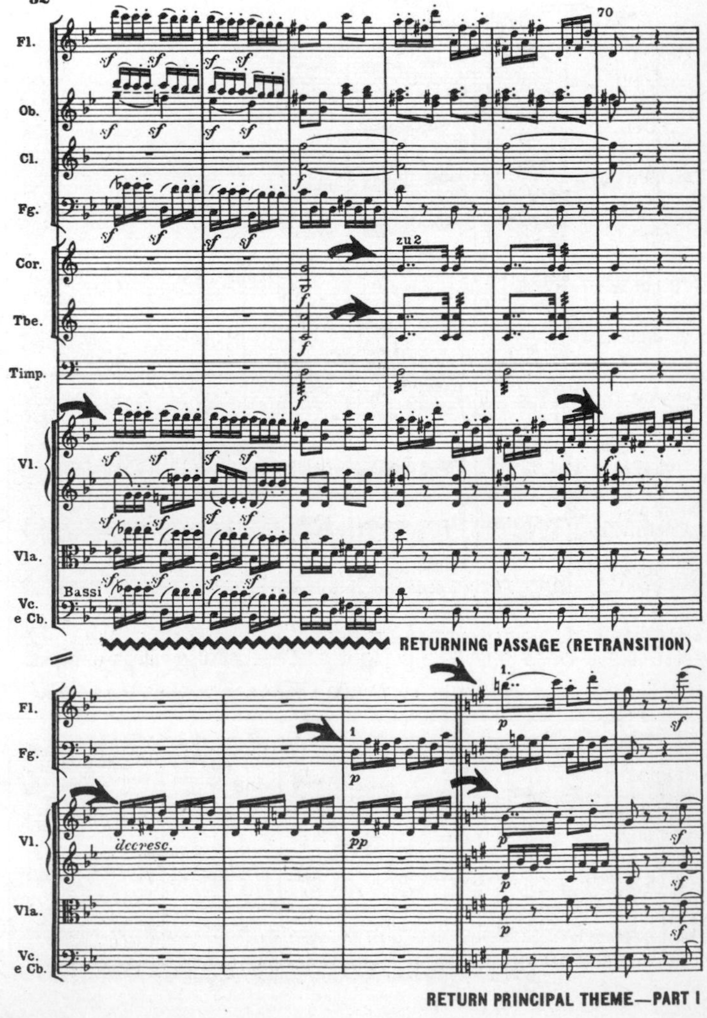

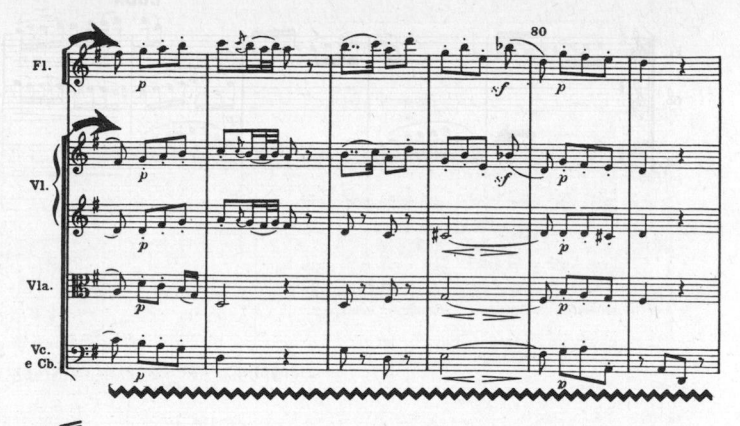

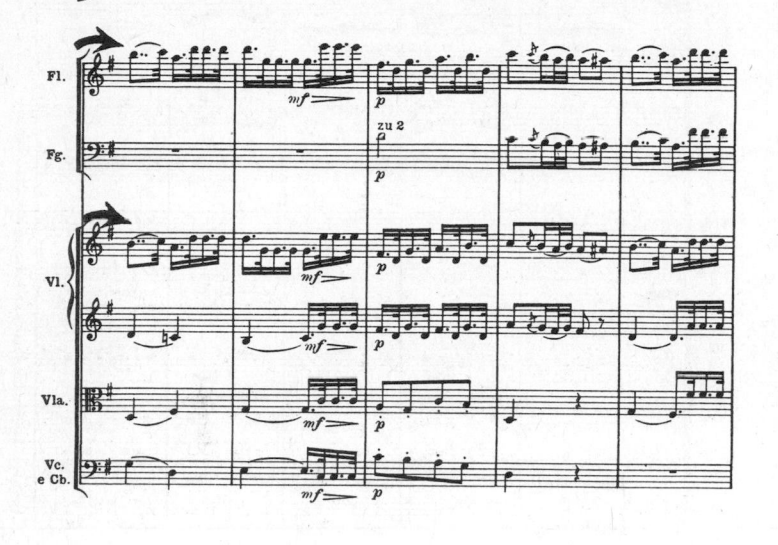

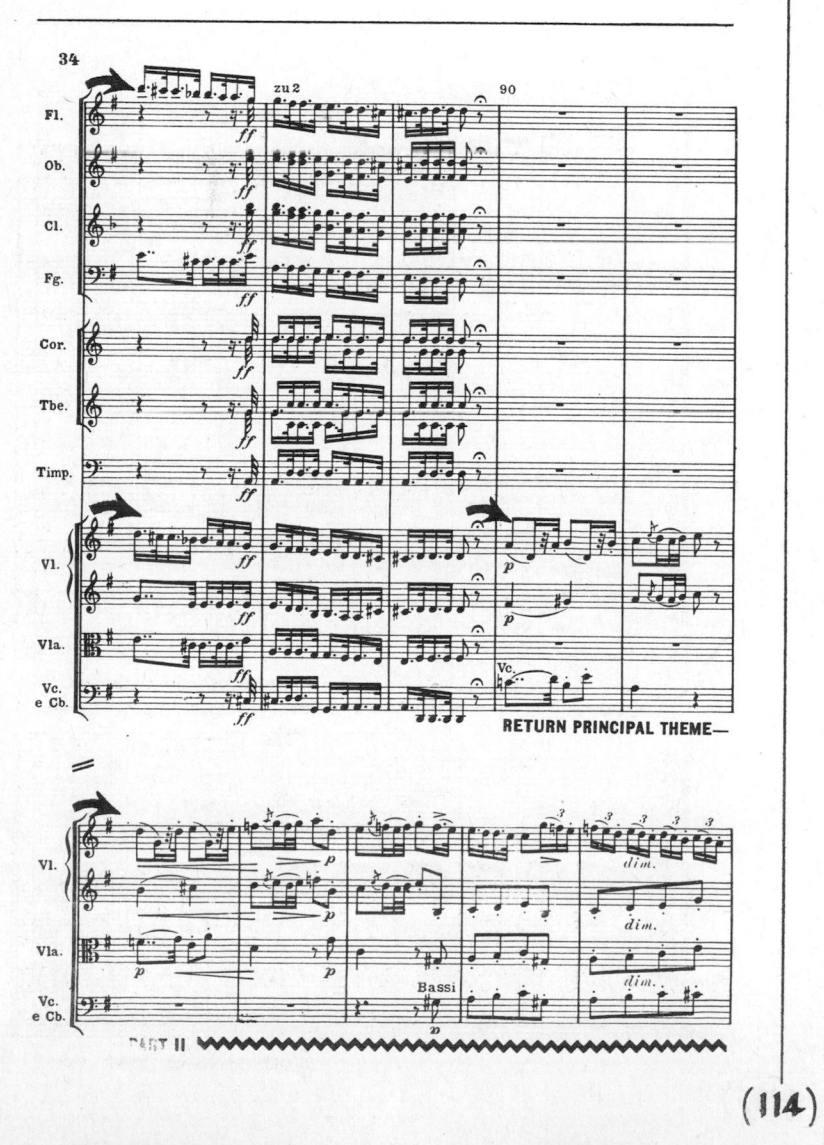

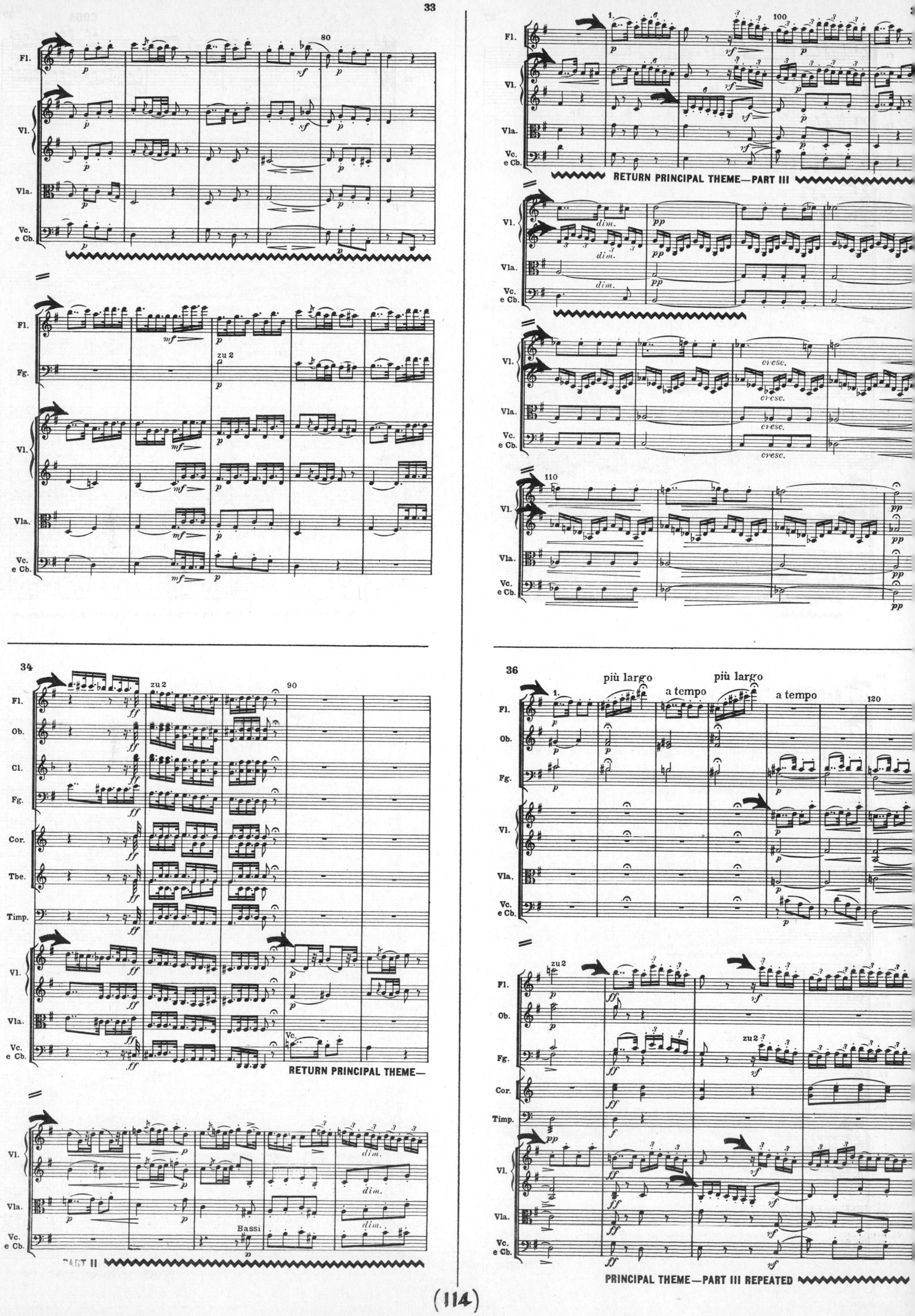
33
34
36
RETURN PRINCIPAL THEME—PART III
RETURN PRINCIPAL THEME—
PART II
PRINCIPAL THEME—PART III REPEATED
più largo
a tempo
più largo
a tempo
Fl.
Ob.
Cl.
Fg.
Cor.
Tbe.
Timp.
Vl.
Vla.
Vc. e Cb.
Bassi
zu 2
dim.
cresc.

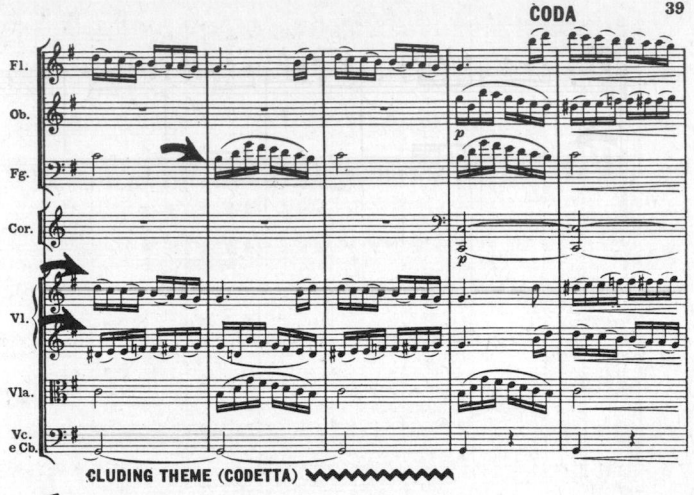

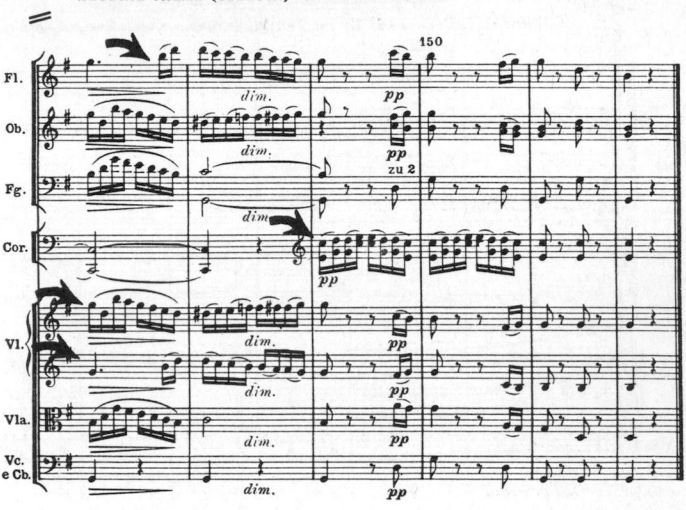

CLUDING THEME (CODETTA)

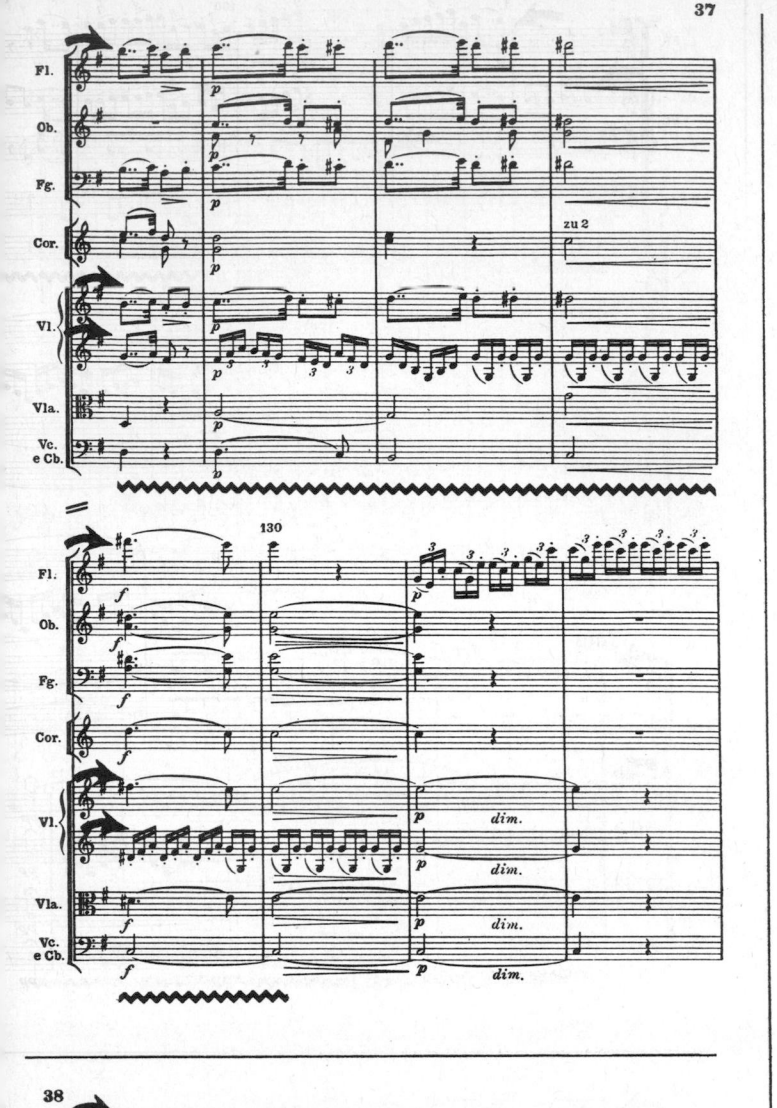

130

140

RETURN CON-

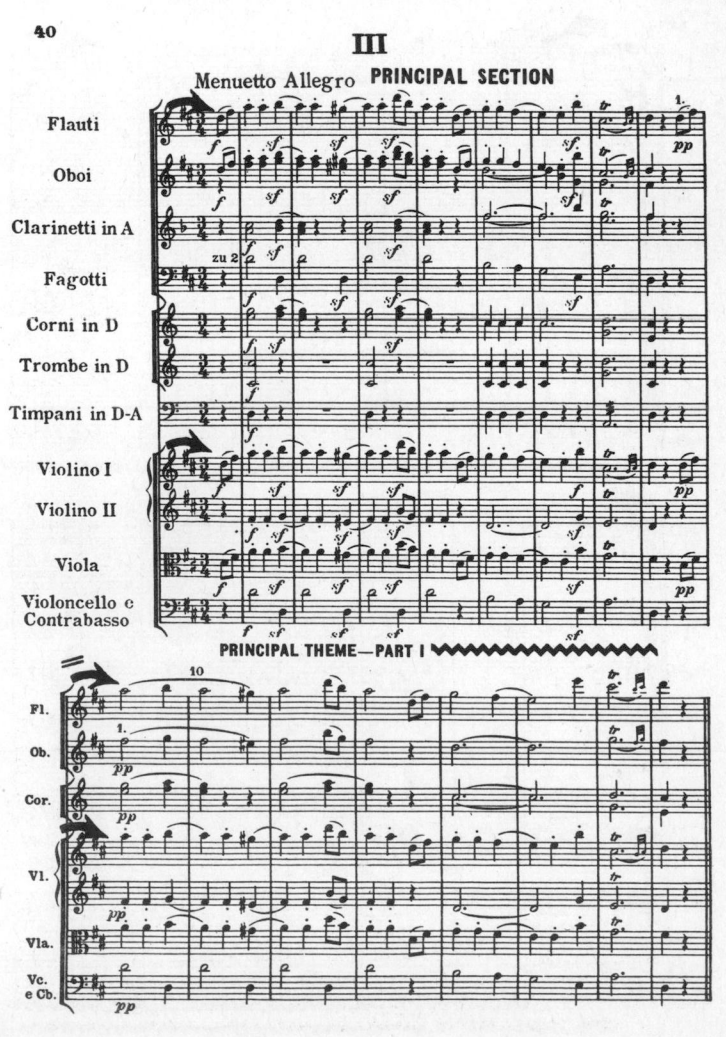

III

Menuetto Allegro **PRINCIPAL SECTION**

Flauti

Oboi

Clarinetti in A

Fagotti

Corni in D

Trombe in D

Timpani in D-A

Violino I

Violino II

Viola

Violoncello e
Contrabasso

PRINCIPAL THEME—PART I

10

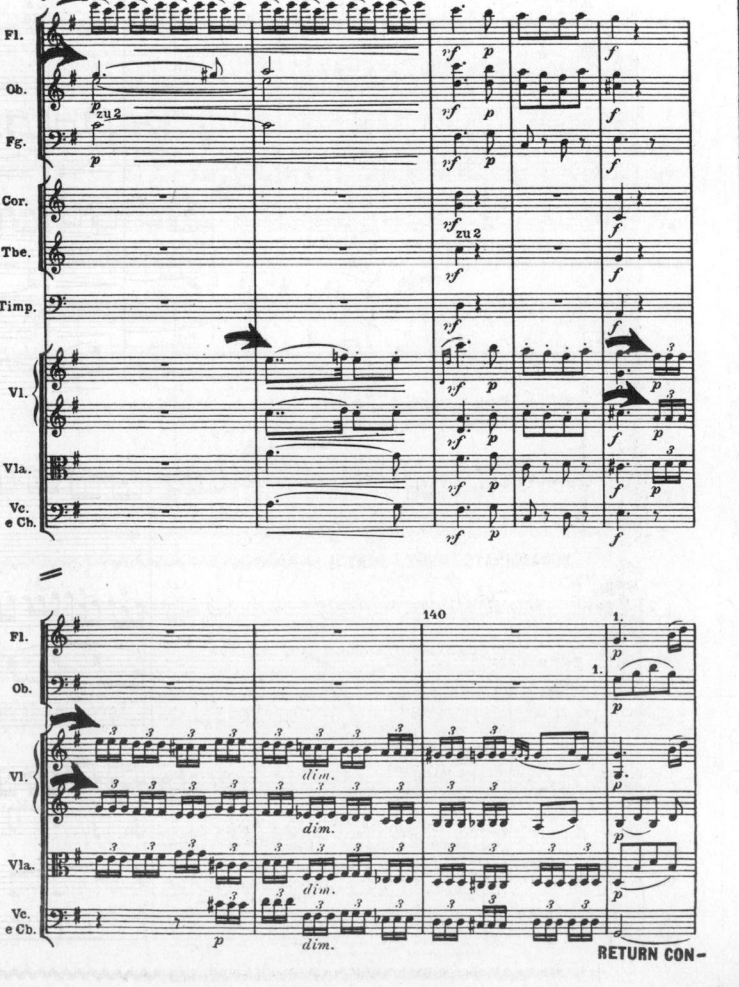

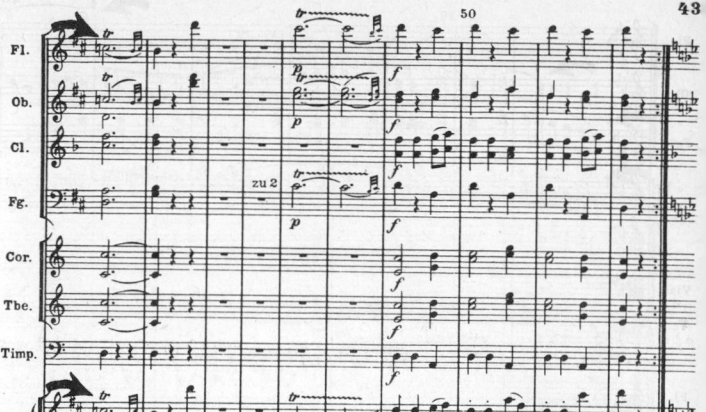

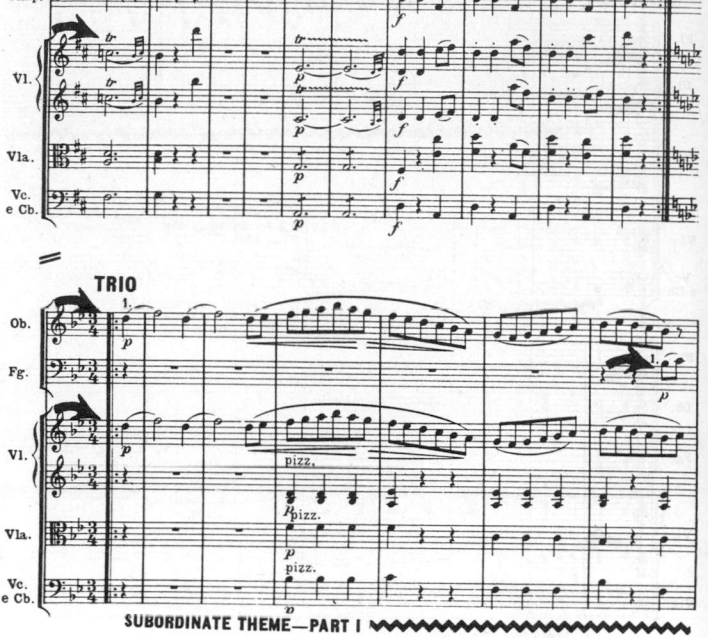

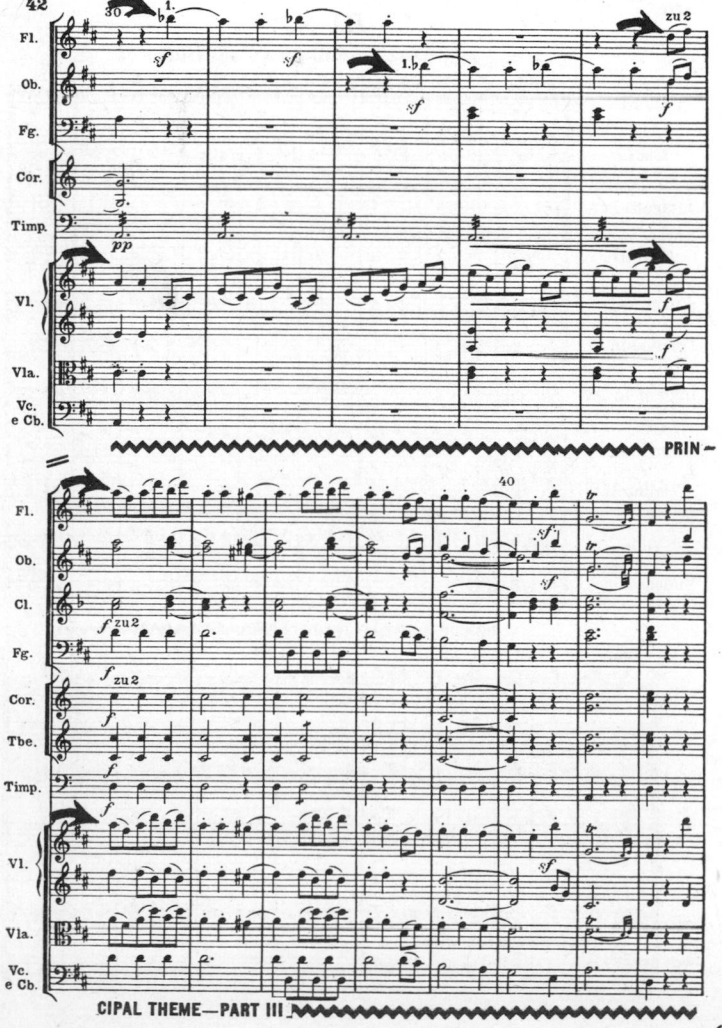

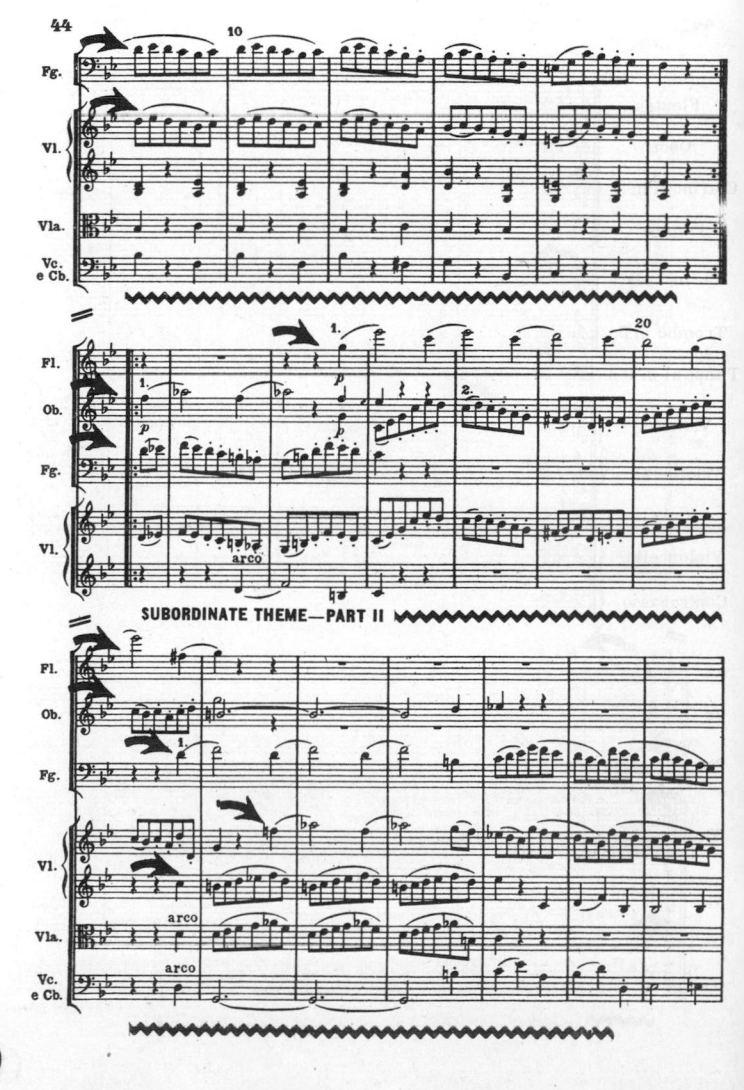

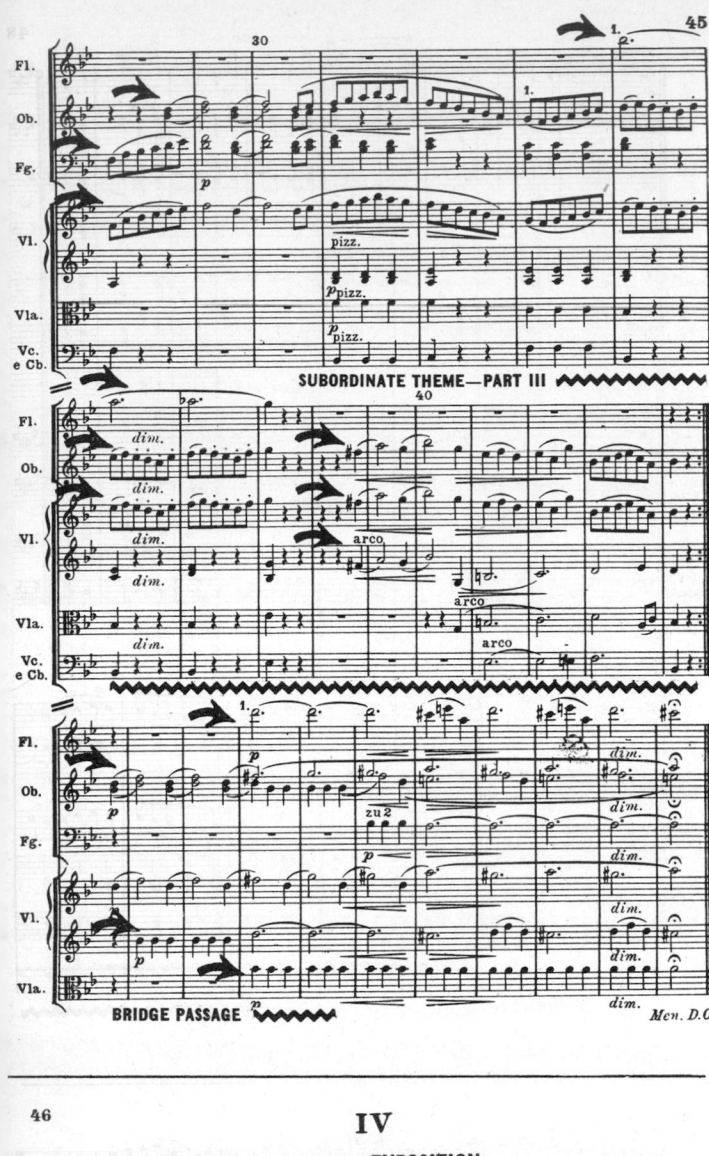

SUBORDINATE THEME—PART III ~~~~~~~

BRIDGE PASSAGE ~~~~~~

Men. D.C.

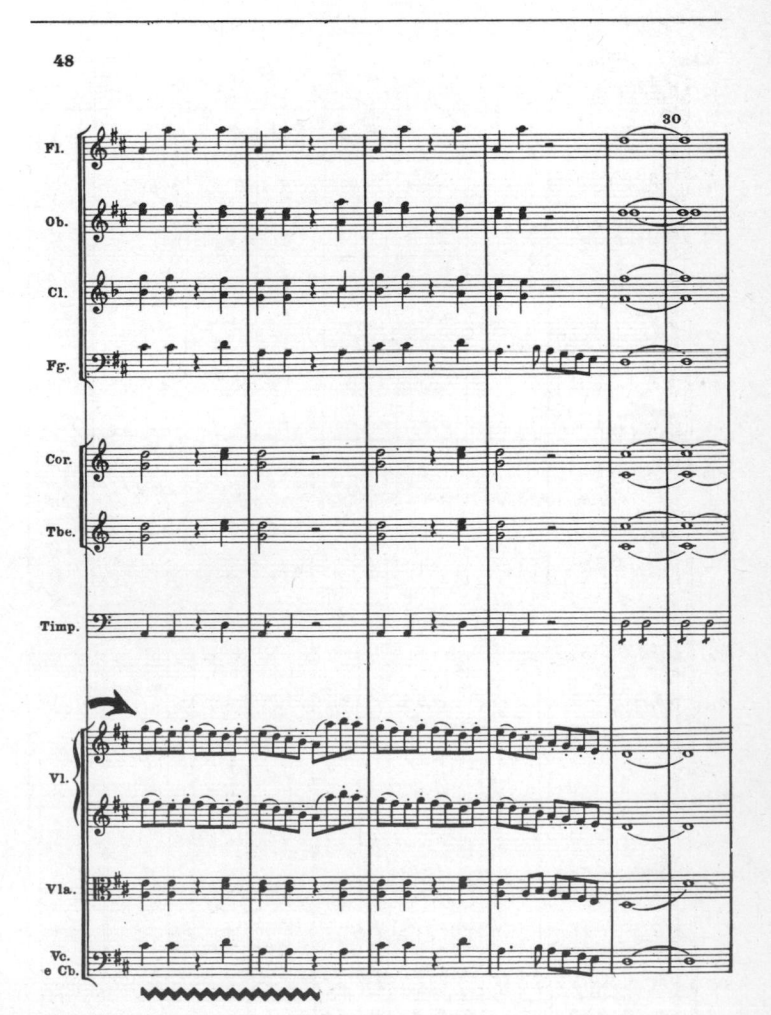

PRINCIPAL THEME—PART II ~~~~~~~~~~~~~~~~~

IV

Allegro spiritoso **EXPOSITION**

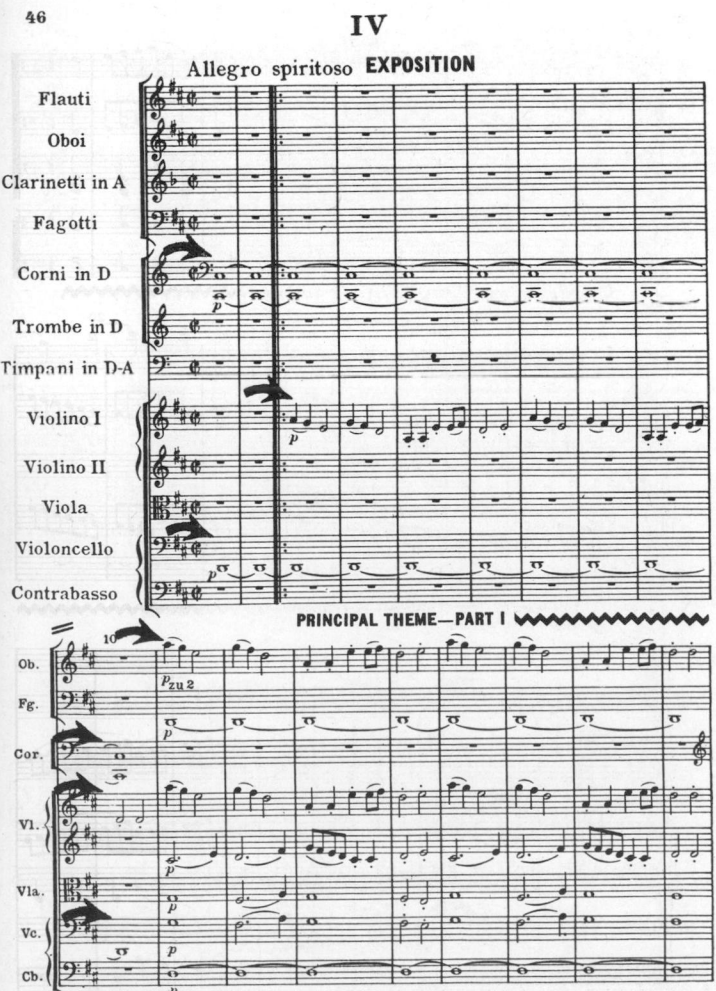

Flauti
Oboi
Clarinetti in A
Fagotti
Corni in D
Trombe in D
Timpani in D-A
Violino I
Violino II
Viola
Violoncello
Contrabasso

PRINCIPAL THEME—PART I ~~~~~~~

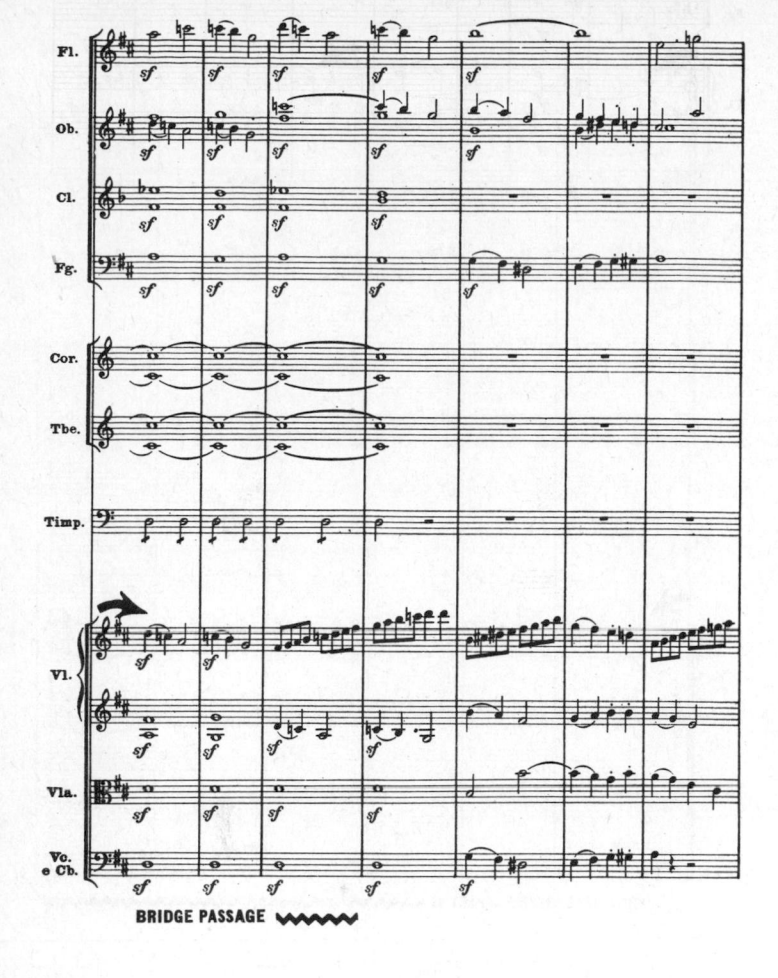

BRIDGE PASSAGE ～～～～

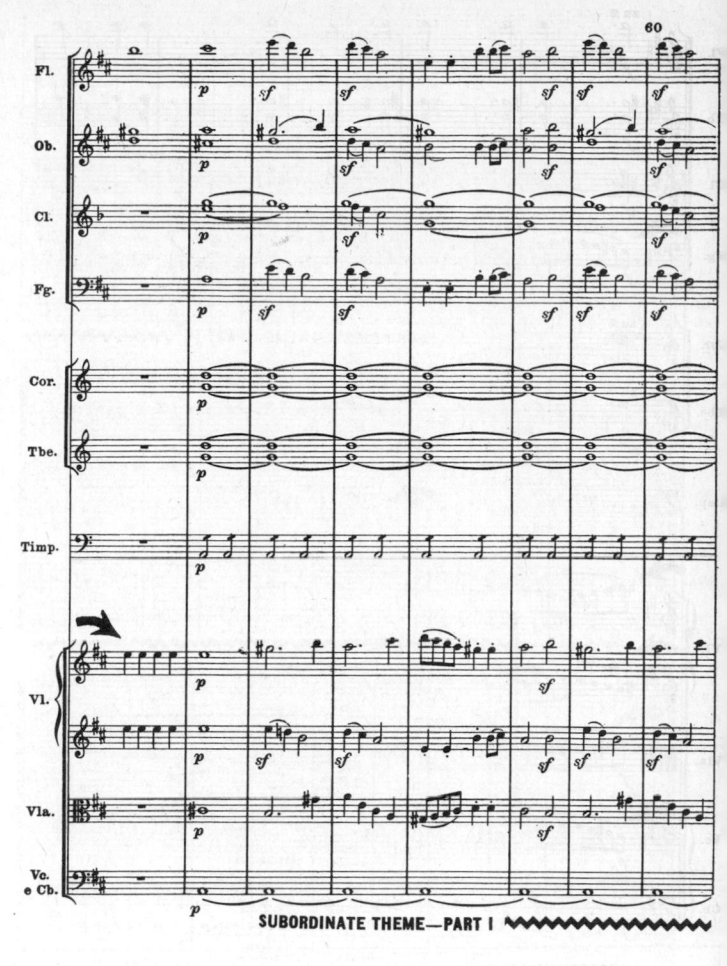

SUBORDINATE THEME—PART I ～～～～～

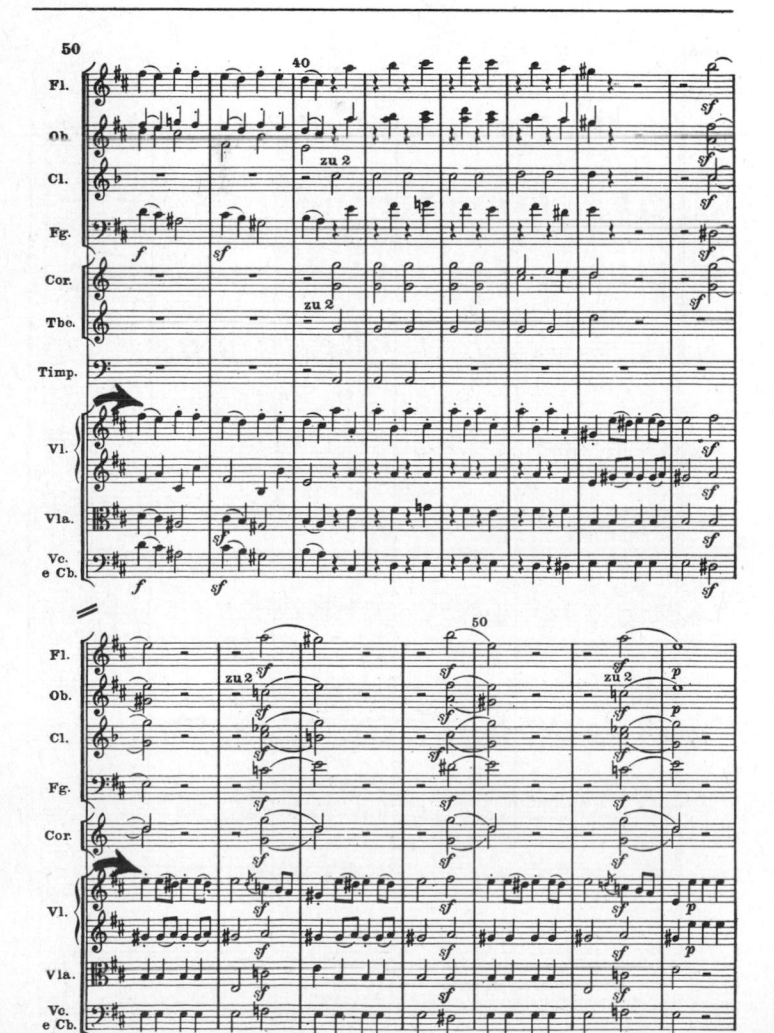

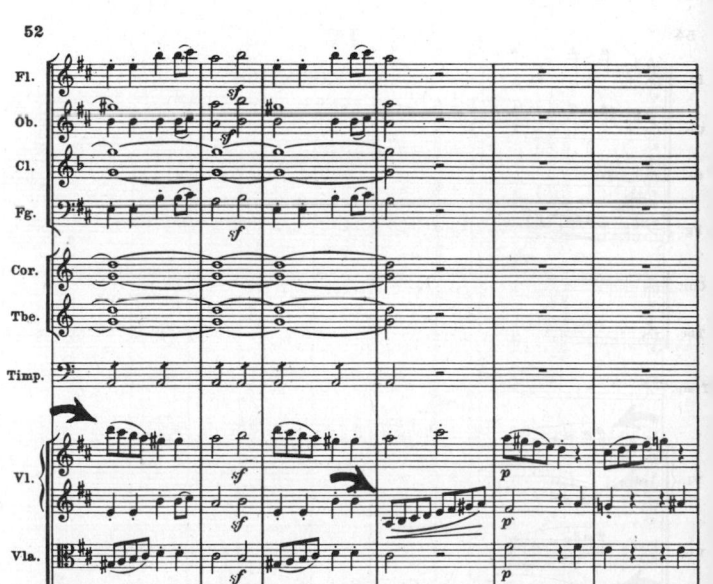

SUBORDINATE THEME—

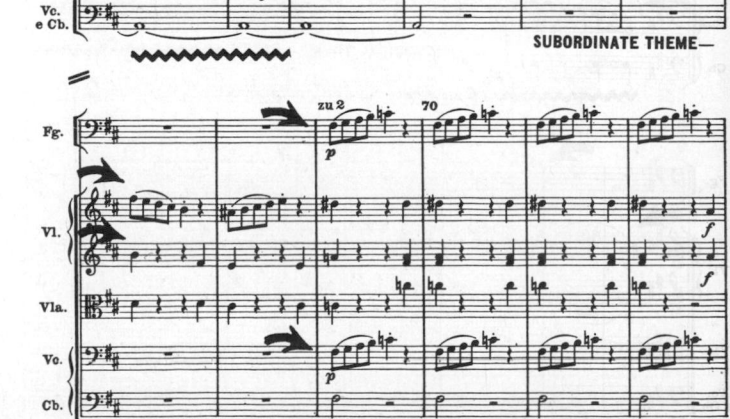

PART II, 1st PERIOD ～～～～～

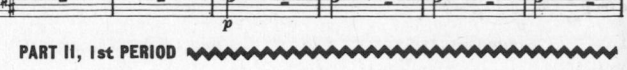

53

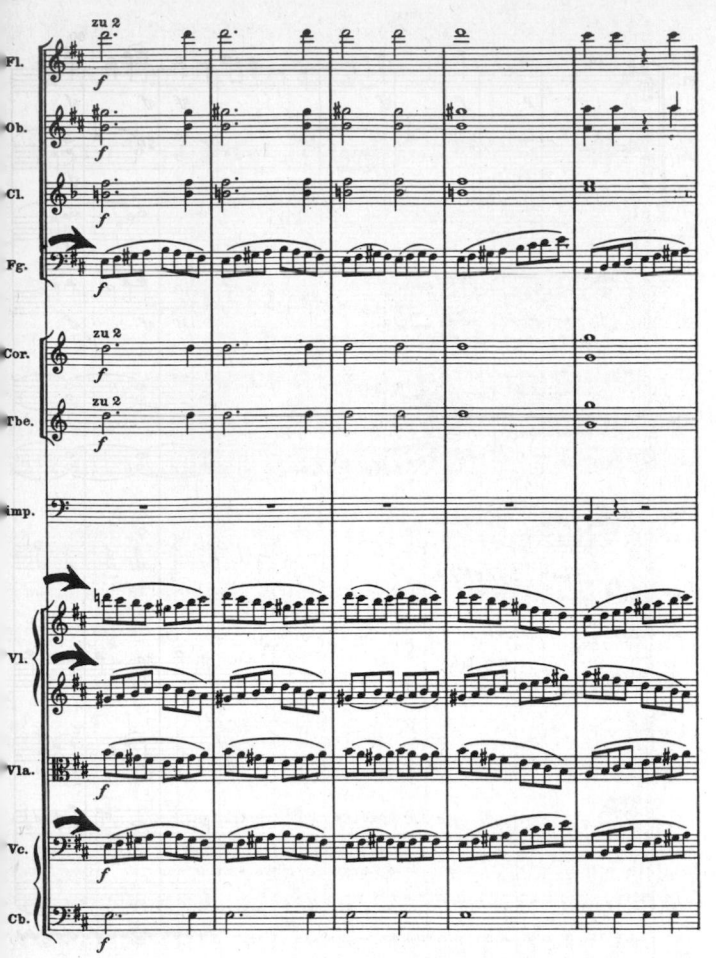

SUBORDINATE THEME—PART II, 2nd PERIOD ∿∿∿∿∿

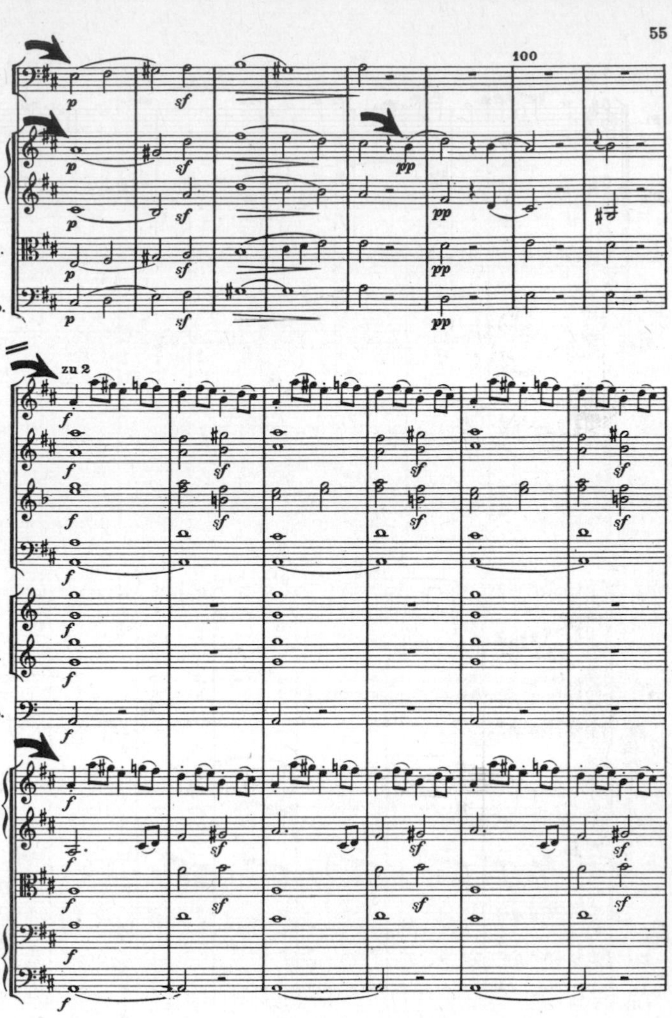

55

CONCLUDING THEME (CODETTA)—PART I ∿∿∿

54

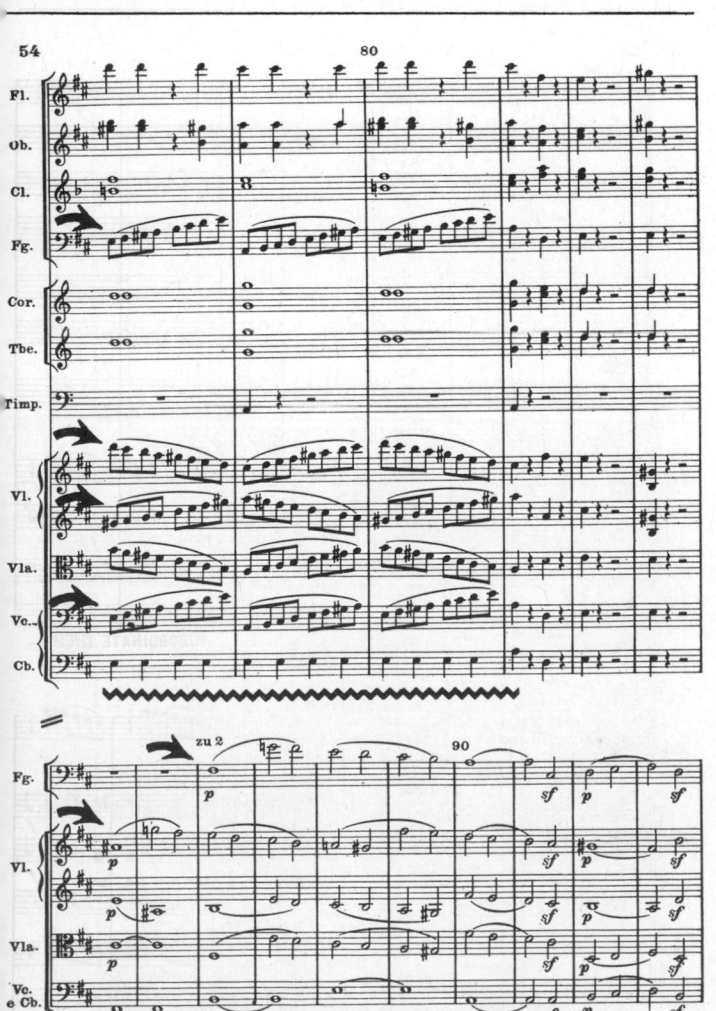

SUBORDINATE THEME—PART III ∿∿∿∿∿

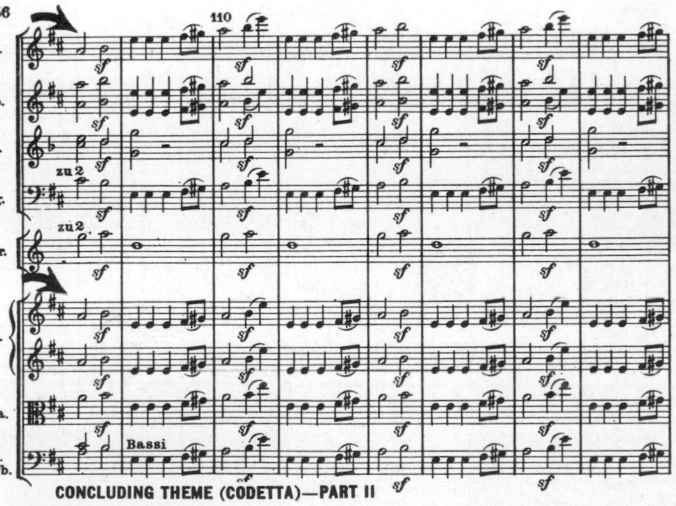

56

CONCLUDING THEME (CODETTA)—PART II

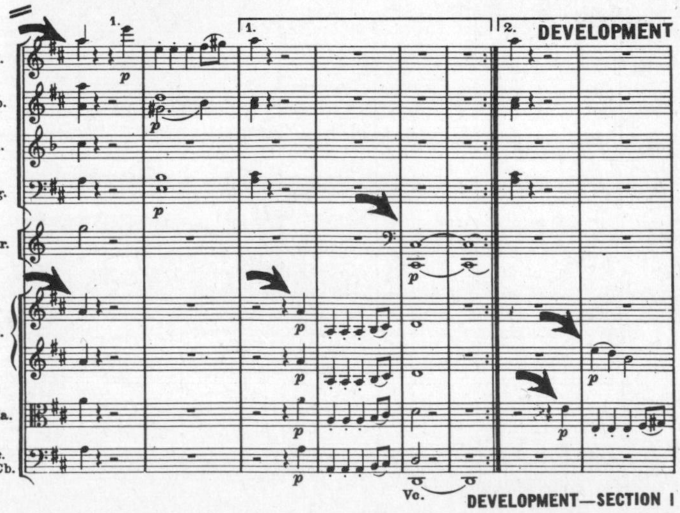

DEVELOPMENT

DEVELOPMENT—SECTION I

(119)

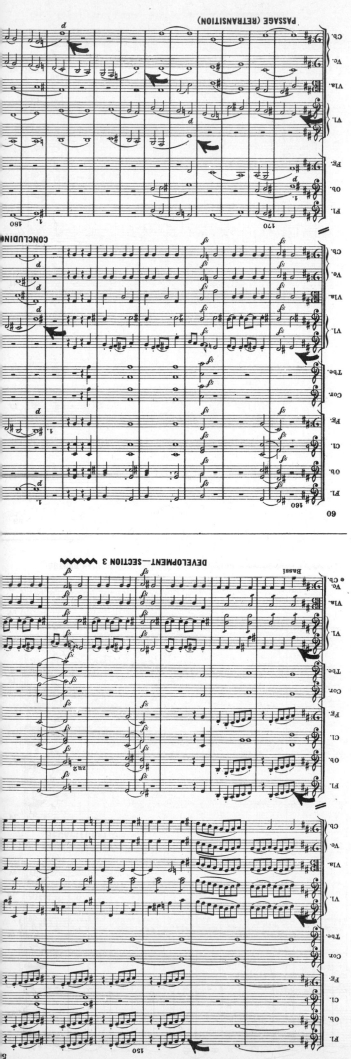

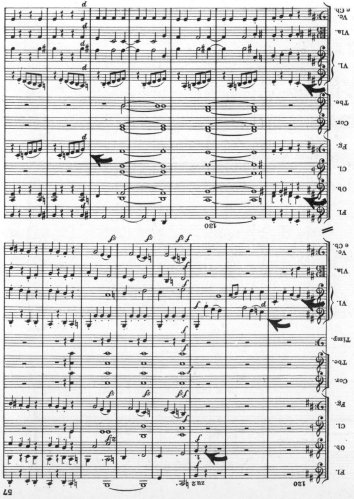

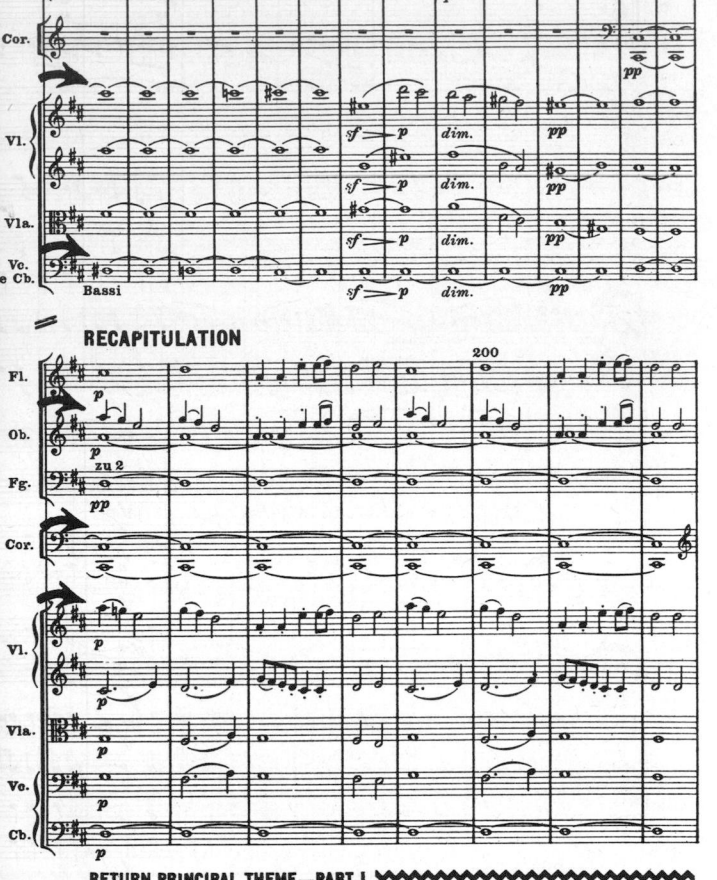

RECAPITULATION

RETURN PRINCIPAL THEME—PART I 〰〰〰〰〰〰〰〰

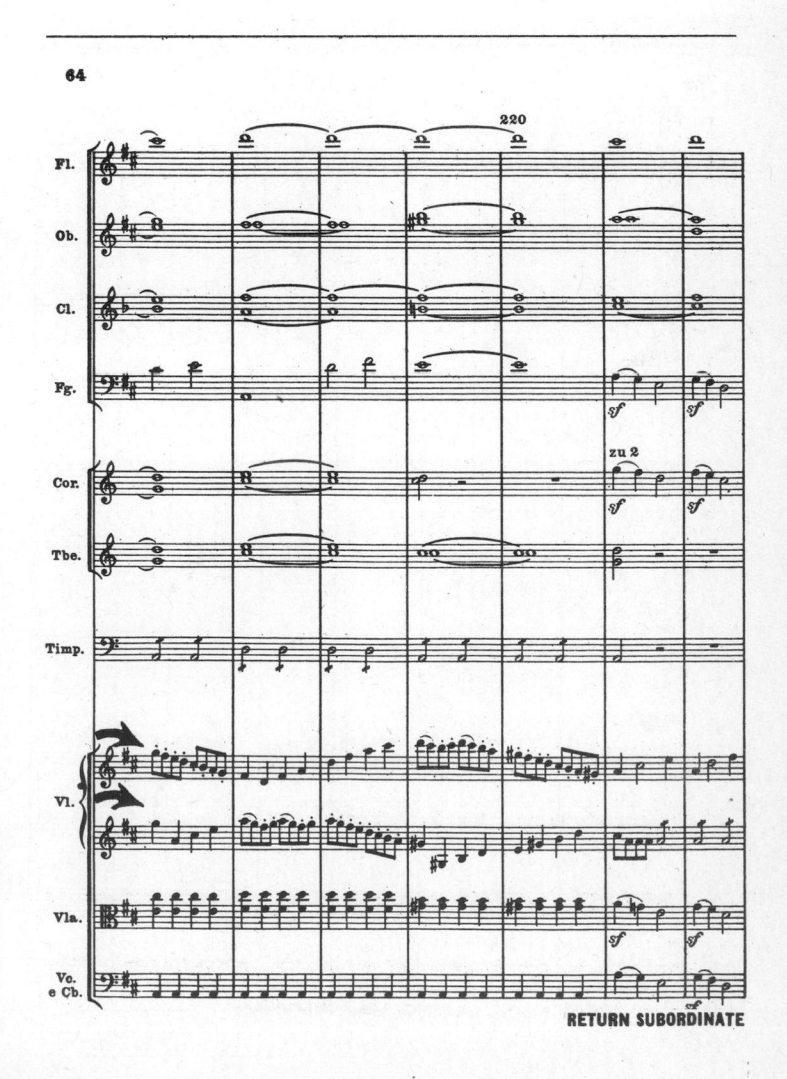

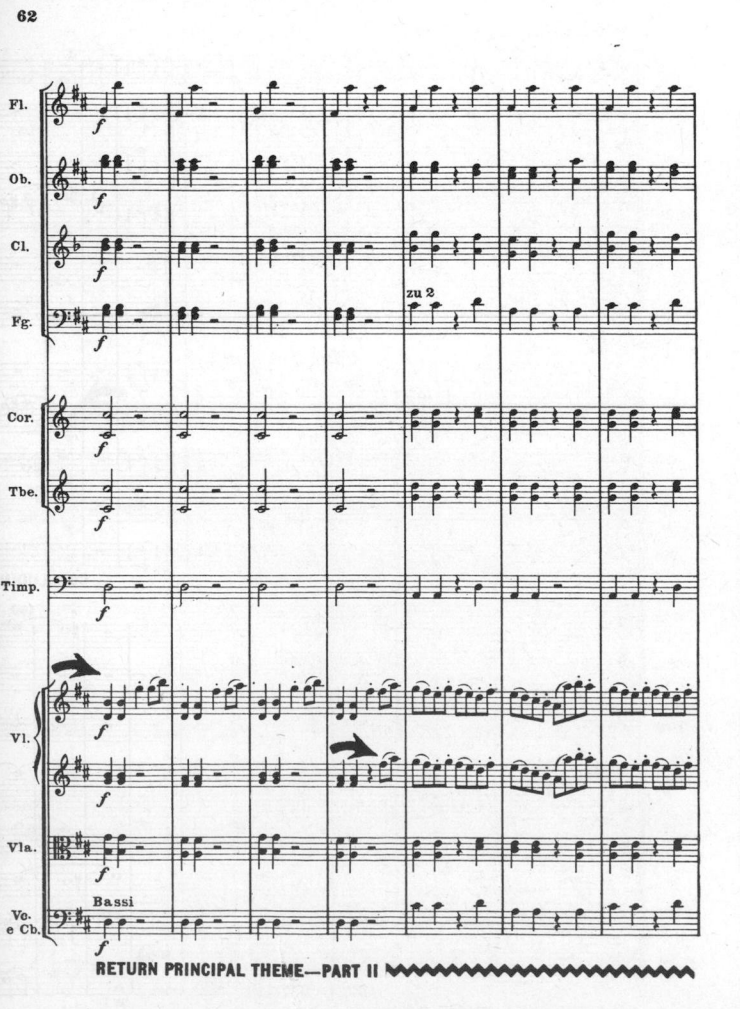

RETURN PRINCIPAL THEME—PART II 〰〰〰〰〰〰〰〰

RETURN SUBORDINATE

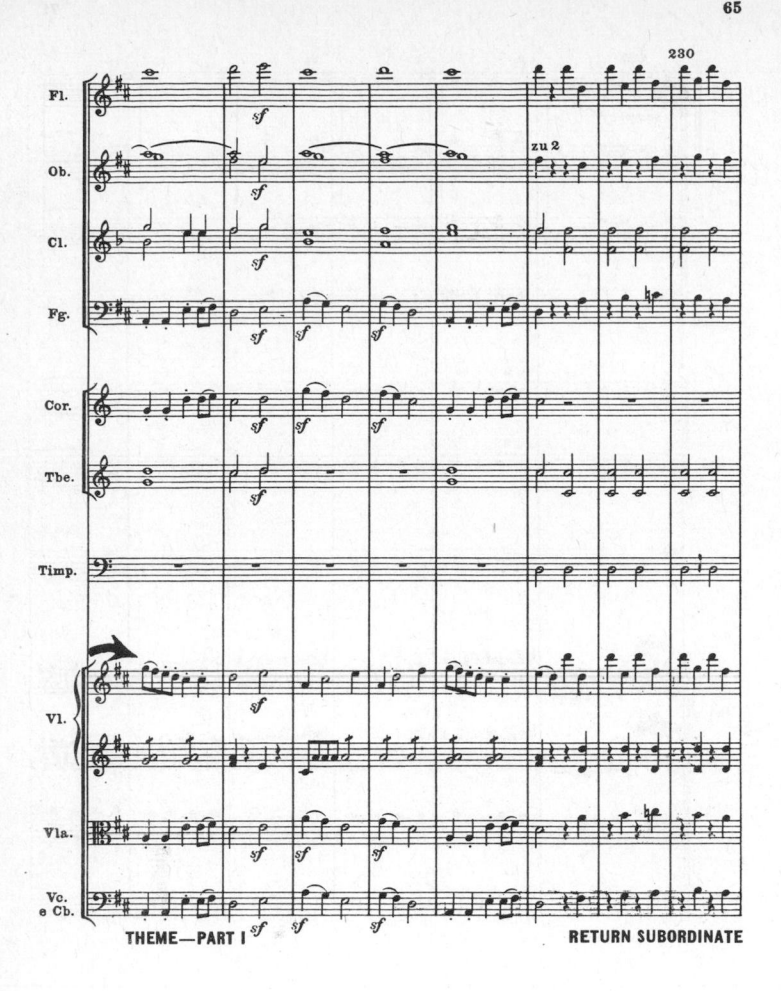

THEME—PART I   RETURN SUBORDINATE

65

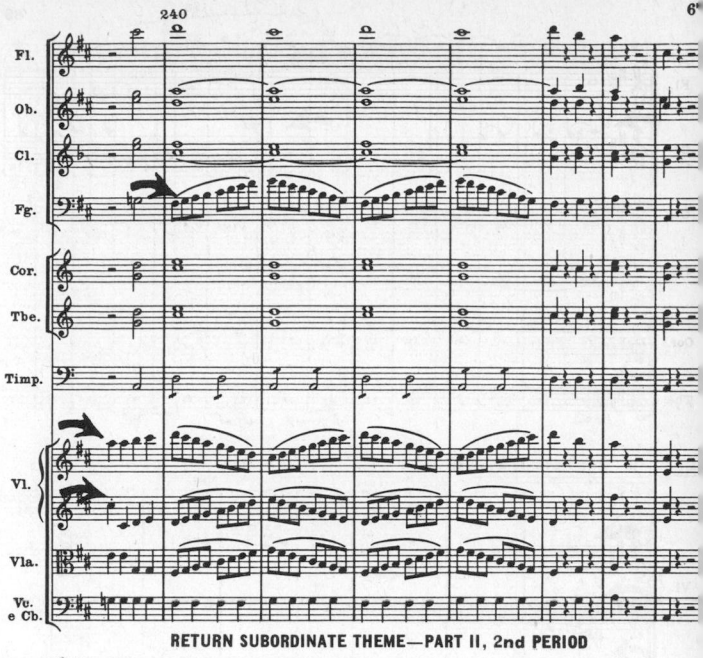

230

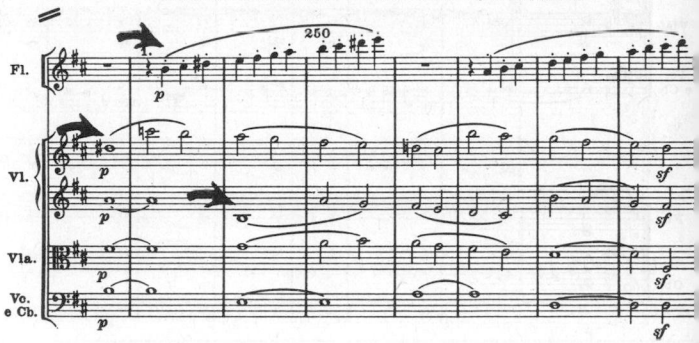

RETURN SUBORDINATE THEME—PART II, 2nd PERIOD

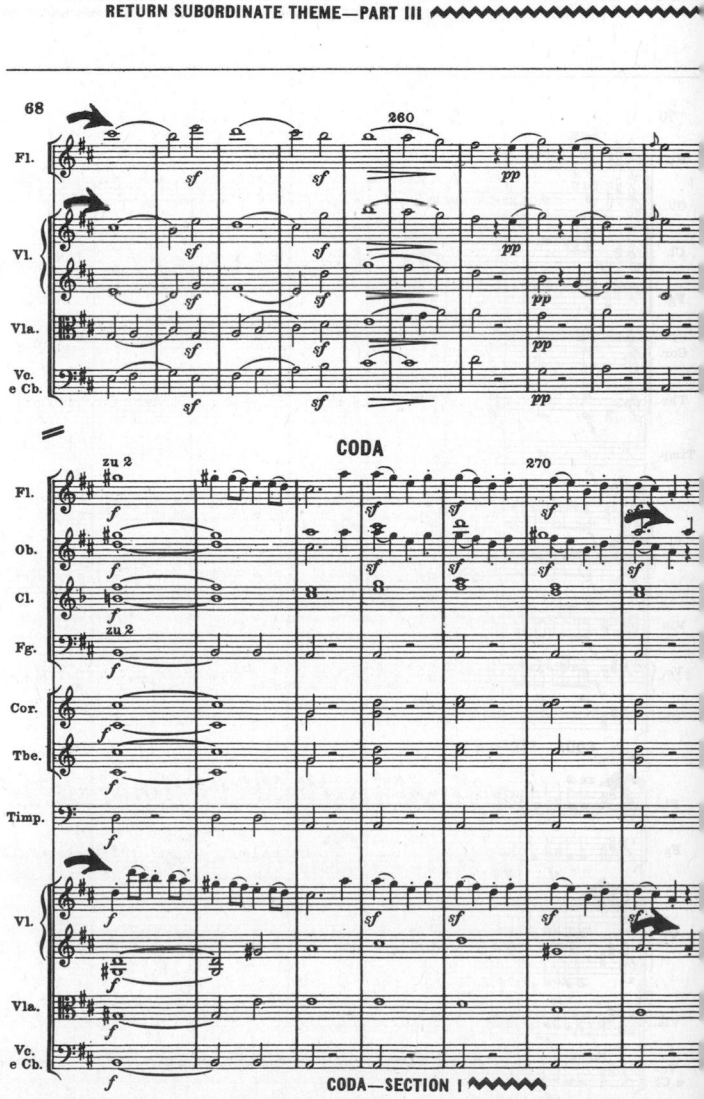

250

RETURN SUBORDINATE THEME—PART III ∿∿∿∿∿∿∿∿

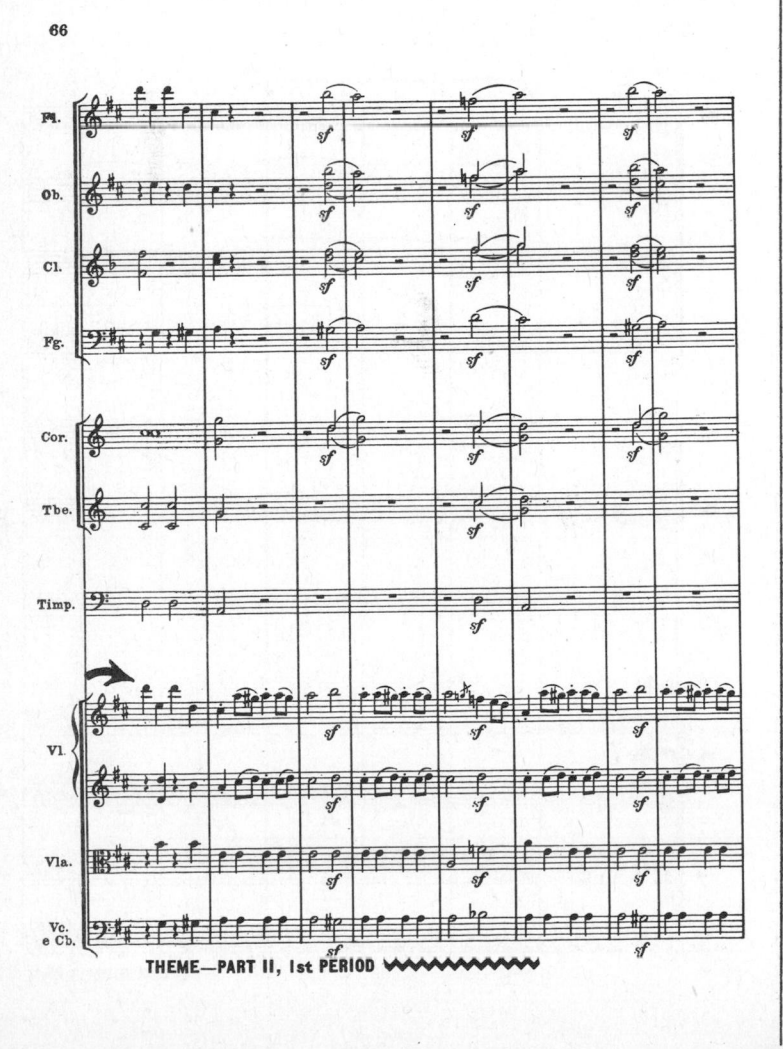

66

THEME—PART II, 1st PERIOD ∿∿∿∿∿∿∿∿

68

260

CODA

270

CODA—SECTION I ∿∿∿∿

69

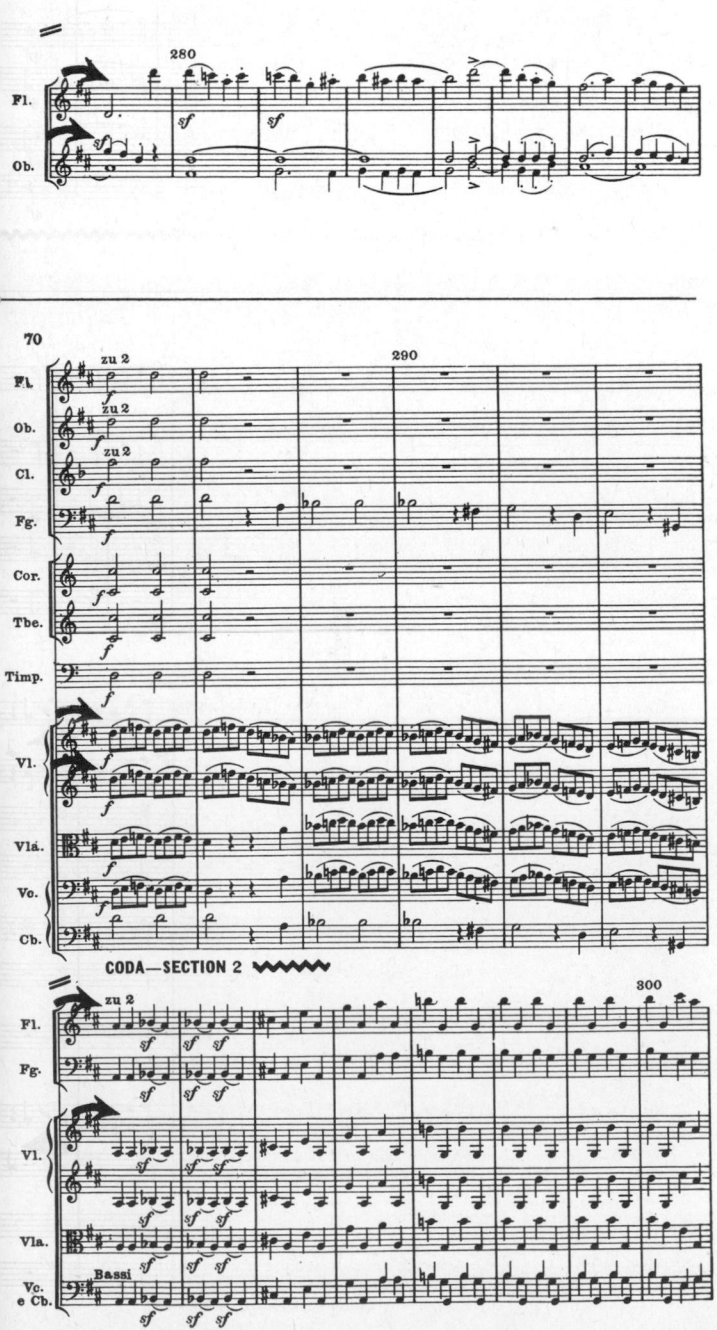

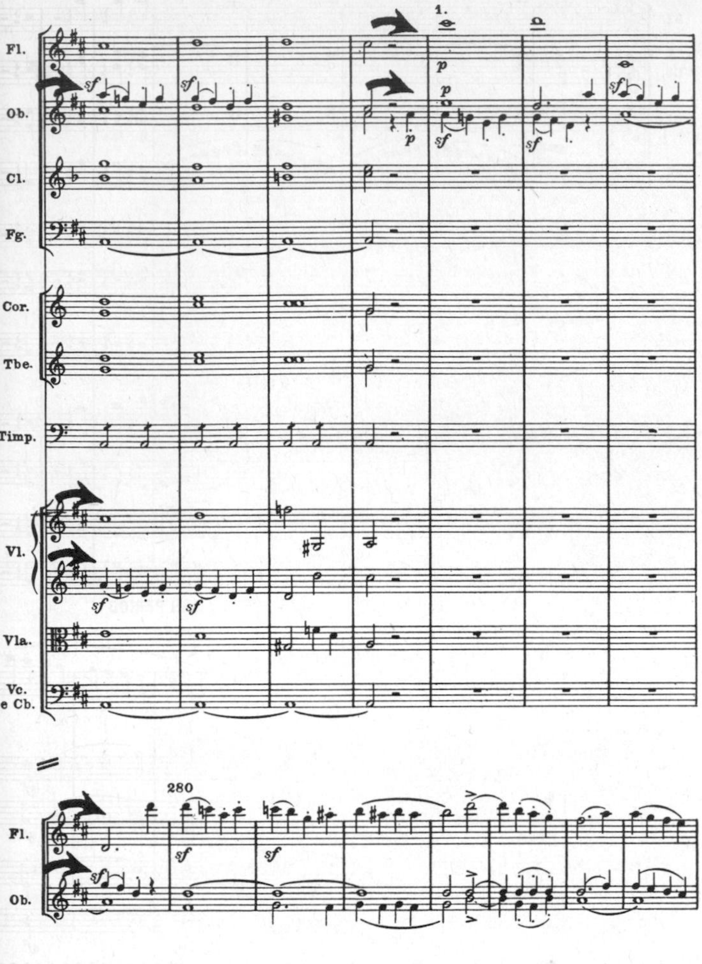
Fl.
Ob.
Cl.
Fg.
Cor.
Tbe.
Timp.
Vl.
Vla.
Vc. e Cb.
280

70

Fl.
Ob.
Cl.
Fg.
Cor.
Tbe.
Timp.
Vl.
Vla.
Vc.
Cb.
290
CODA—SECTION 2
zu 2
Bassi
300

71

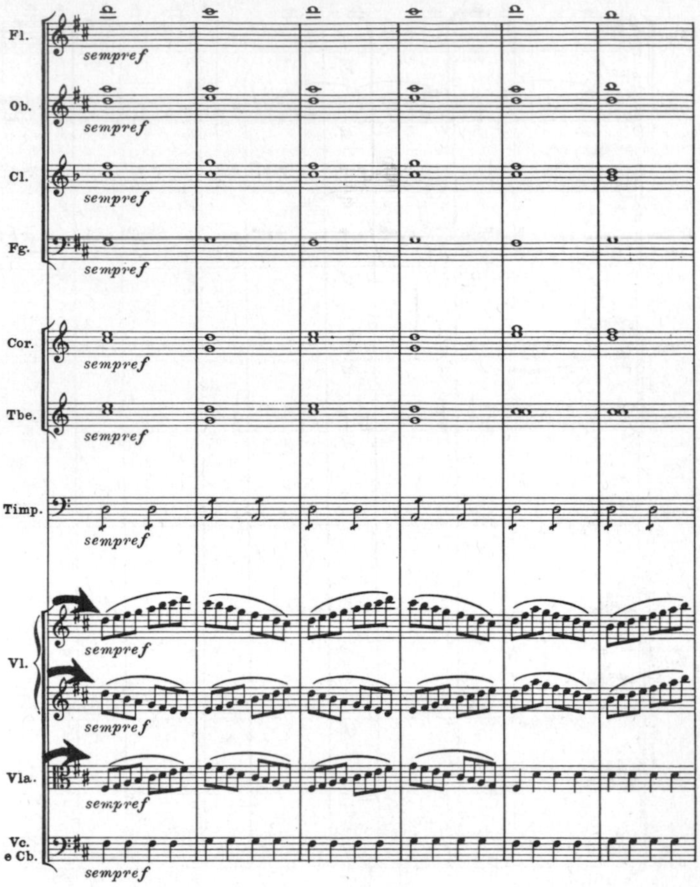
Fl.
Ob.
Cl.
Fg.
Cor.
Tbe.
Timp.
Vl.
Vla.
Vc. e Cb.
sempref

72

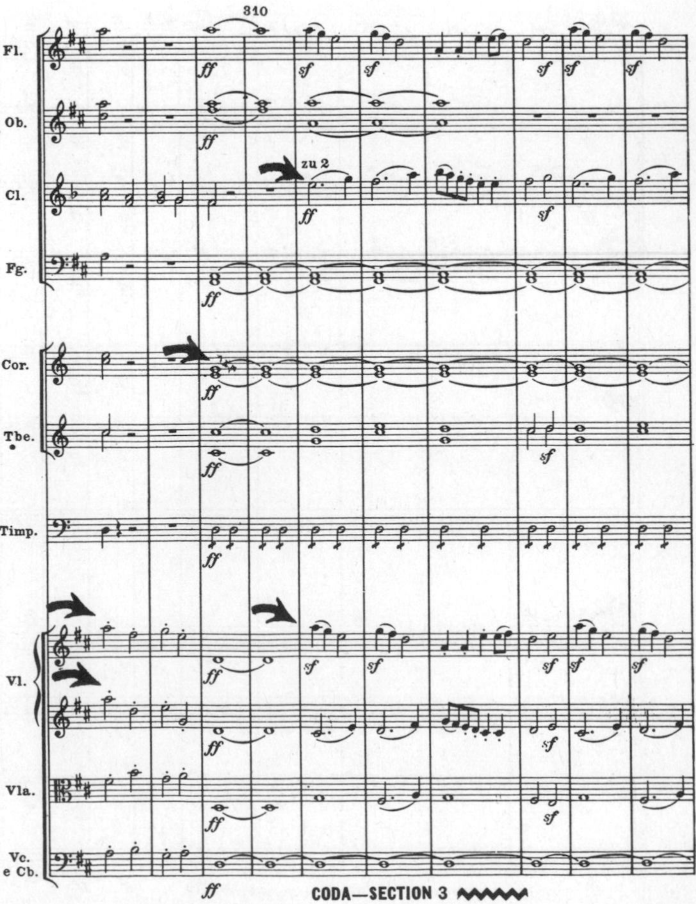
Fl.
Ob.
Cl.
Fg.
Cor.
Tbe.
Timp.
Vl.
Vla.
Vc. e Cb.
310
zu 2
CODA—SECTION 3

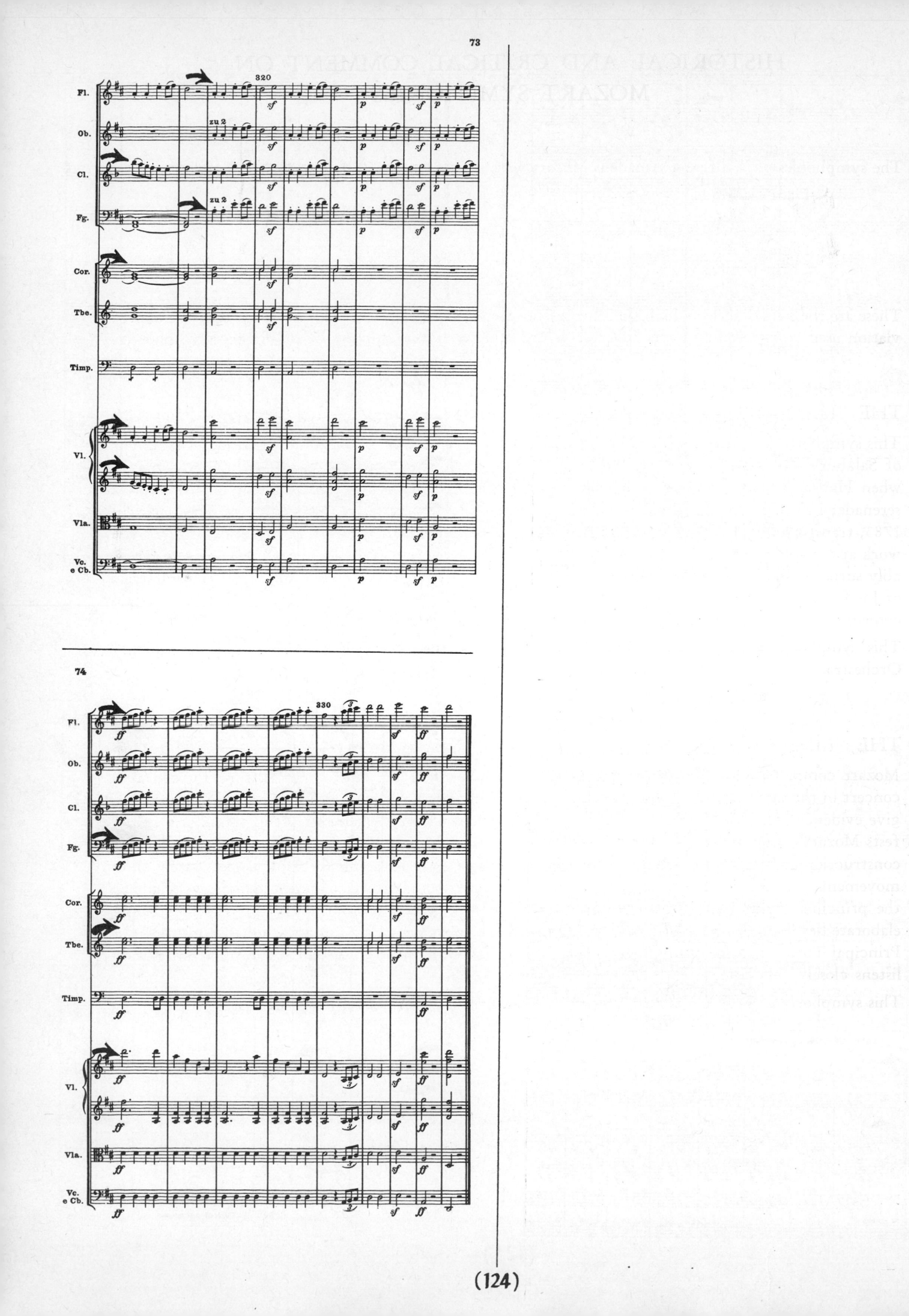

HISTORICAL AND CRITICAL COMMENT ON
MOZART SYMPHONIES

The symphonies of Wolfgang Amadeus Mozart were scored for the following instruments:

Flauti (Flutes)	*Fl.*	Timpani	*Timp.*
Oboi (Oboes)	*Ob.*	Violini (Violins)	*Vl.*
Clarinetti (Clarinets)	*Cl.*	Viola	*Vla.*
Fagotti (Bassoons)	*Fg.*	Violoncello	*Vc.*
Corni (Horns)	*Cor.*	Contrabasso (Basso)	*Cb. or B.*
Trombe (Trumpets)	*Tbe.*		

These are the names under which the instruments are listed on the first page of each score; the abbreviation used on succeeding pages follows. No trombones are used in any of the Mozart symphonies.

THE "HAFFNER" SYMPHONY   KÖCHEL CATALOGUE No. 385   Page 128

This symphony was written for some festive occasion in the house of Siegmund Haffner, the Mayor of Salzburg; six years previously, Mozart had composed the famous "Serenade" which was played when Haffner's daughter, Elizabeth, was married. The symphony was also originally intended as a serenade; in this form it had an introductory march and two minuets which Mozart eliminated in 1783, transforming the work into a four-movement symphony. It is said that, having composed the work at top speed, Mozart forgot all about it so that upon the return of the manuscript, he was agreeably surprised at its excellence. Critics are agreed that the symphony clearly manifests the influence of Josef Haydn; it would also appear that certain themes resemble airs to be found in Mozart's musical comedy "Die Entführung aus dem Serail" which was also composed in 1782.

This symphony is recorded by Arturo Toscanini and the New York Philharmonic Symphony Orchestra.

THE "LINZ" SYMPHONY   KÖCHEL CATALOGUE No. 425   Page 146

Mozart completed this symphony at Linz on November 3, 1783, and it was first performed at a concert in the same city the following day; hence its nickname. Just as Beethoven's first symphonies give evidence of his admiration for both Haydn and Mozart, in the same way this symphony manifests Mozart's deep veneration for Haydn, but his own individual style is clearly evident both in its construction and its instrumentation. Such innovations appear as the use of the trumpets in the slow movement, and the introduction of a subordinate theme in the same movement which overshadows the principal theme in importance. Another distinct departure from the Haydn tradition is the elaborate development period in both the first and last movements. It is interesting to note that the Principal Theme and the Subordinate Theme in the first movement are so much alike that unless one listens closely they appear to be exactly the same.

This symphony is recorded by Fritz Busch and the British Broadcasting Company Orchestra.

THE "PRAGUE" SYMPHONY Köchel Catalogue No. 504 Page 162

This work is also known as the *Symphony without a Minuet* because it consists of only three movements, like many of the earliest symphonies. In musical value it not only compares favorably with the three great symphonies composed in the last year of Mozart's life, but it actually surpasses them in respect to conciseness and plasticity in form. The work was written at Vienna in 1786, and had its first performance during January, 1787; at that time Mozart was enjoying the tremendous success of his opera "The Marriage of Figaro" at Prague. The symphony was played in a concert given at the opera-house; some concerted works followed, and then Mozart, seating himself at the clavier, in response to tumultuous applause, extemporized twelve marvellously brilliant and extremely difficult variations on the theme from the song *Non piu andrai* from "Figaro."

This symphony is recorded by Erich Kleiber and the Vienna Philharmonic Orchestra.

SYMPHONY IN E*b* MAJOR Köchel Catalogue No. 543 Page 180

Mozart composed his three greatest symphonies during the summer of 1788; they were completed in less than nine weeks. The first was the Symphony in E*b* Major, finished on June 26; the second was the Symphony in G Minor, completed in July; the third was the "Jupiter" Symphony completed on August 10. It is very interesting to note that while Mozart could dash off a piece of chamber music or a concerto for some intimate friend in a few hours, he looked upon his symphonic writing from a much more serious standpoint, and always spent no little time in revising or polishing the instrumentation. It may be true that he was the greatest melodist among the classic composers; it is equally true that his intuitive sense of proportion has rendered his symphonies architectural monuments from the standpoint of design.

This symphony is recorded by Bruno Walter and the British Broadcasting Symphony Orchestra.

SYMPHONY IN G MINOR Köchel Catalogue No. 550 Page 196

The earliest symphonies by Philipp Emanuel Bach, Gossec, Dittersdorf and Boccherini employed only the instruments of the string quartet, the double-bass, two oboes and two horns. Even Haydn's earlier symphonies had only this instrumentation; later the Austrian master added the flute, the bassoon, the trumpet and the kettle-drums—the clarinet was also used by him at times. Mozart employed this later instrumentation, but only utilized the clarinet in his more mature works after having heard the instrument and become greatly enamoured of its tone qualities. Neither Haydn nor Mozart used the trombone; it was first introduced by Beethoven and Schubert. The G Minor Symphony employed no clarinets in its original autograph score; a later revision by the composer added clarinet parts, and also made some changes in the oboe part. This is the version of which the score is used in this volume.

This symphony is recorded by Serge Koussevitzky and the London Philharmonic Orchestra.

A few words of information about Dr. Ludwig Köchel will have its interest at this point. Köchel was a learned musician whose name is now immortal through a chronological thematic catalogue which he compiled of all Mozart's works, assigning each work a number (in the instance of this symphony No. 551), and adding to it a list of compositions which have been lost or were doubtful in origin. He also aided in the preparation of the complete edition of Mozart's works published by Breitkopf and Härtel, and was an intimate friend of Otto Jahn, author of an important biography of Mozart.

This symphony was the last of three written by Mozart in 1788; the composer is not responsible for the subtitle "Jupiter" which is probably an appellation bestowed by some ardent admirer of the work. The *Andante* is regarded as not only one of the most impressive slow movements conceived by Mozart but also as a striking example of classic beauty in symphonic composition.

The *Finale* of this symphony is one of the most remarkable examples of contrapuntal writing in all symphonic literature, whether it be classic or modern. Five themes, selected from the material used in this movement, are combined together in the *Coda,* revealing an extraordinary fugal exposition in quintuple counterpoint. It constitutes a unique example of the magnificent effects which can be secured by combining the severest of musical forms with inspired thematic material.

This symphony is recorded by Sir Thomas Beecham and the London Philharmonic Orchestra.

"Haffner" Symphony

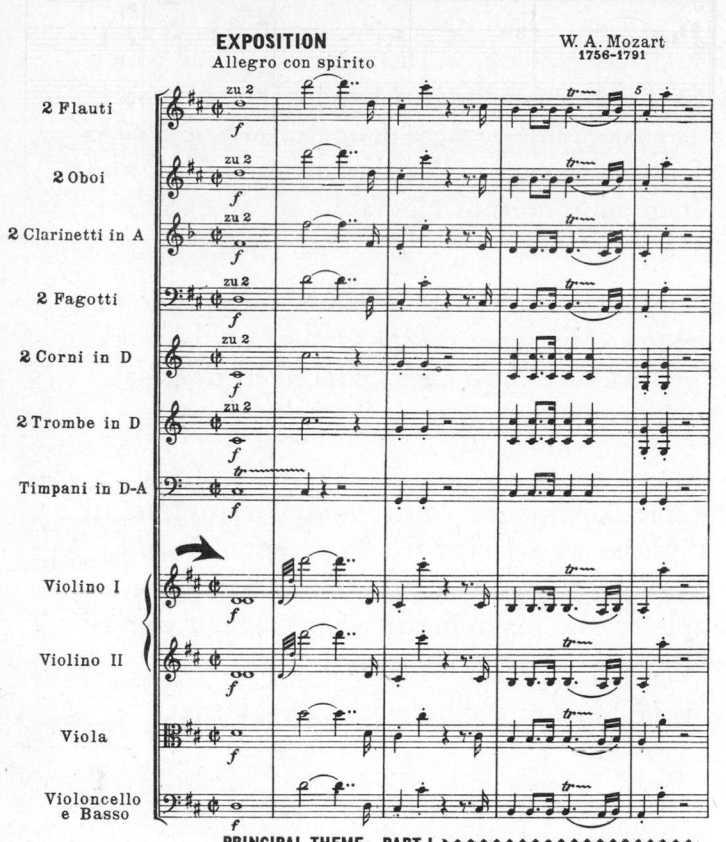

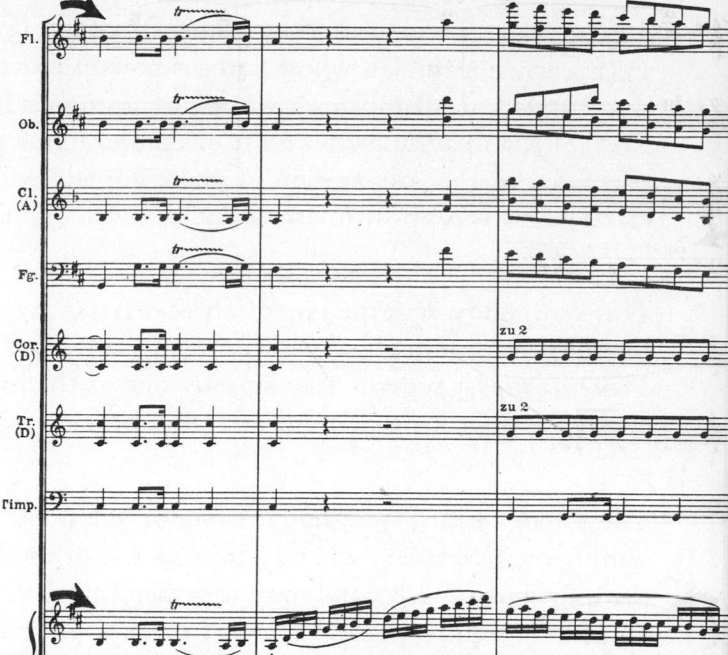

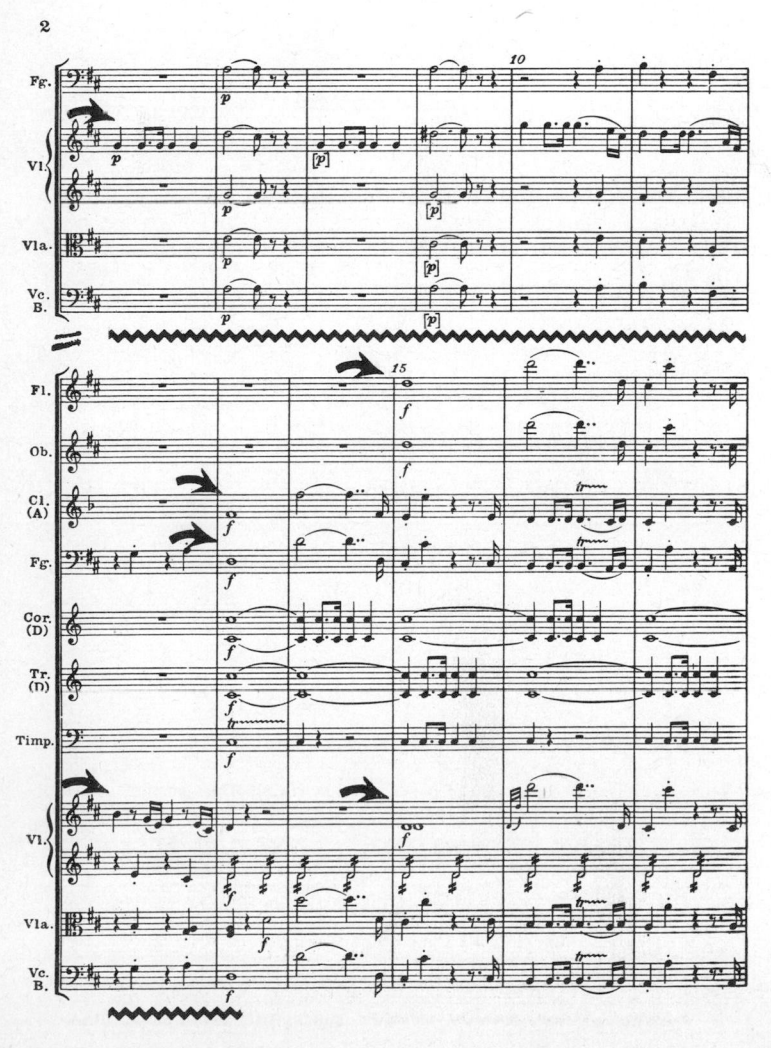

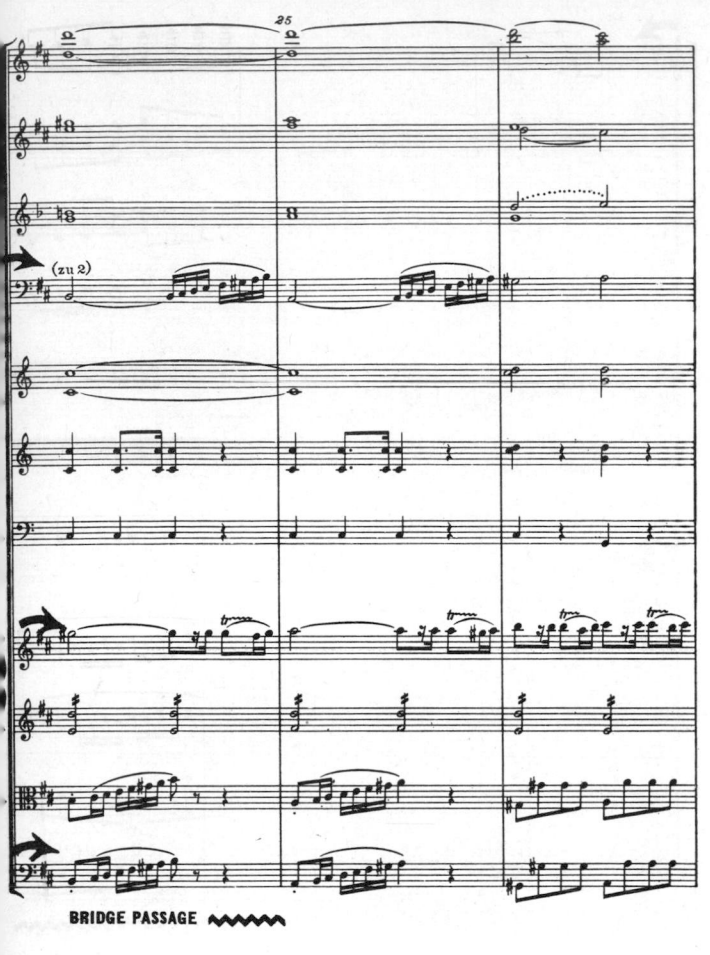

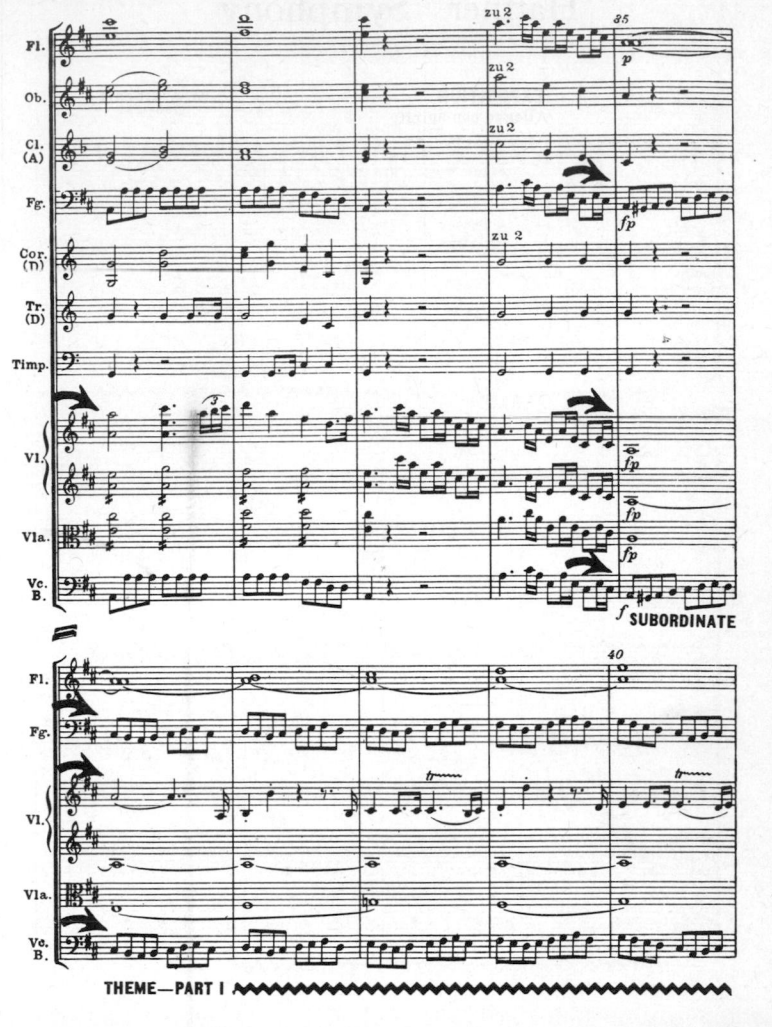

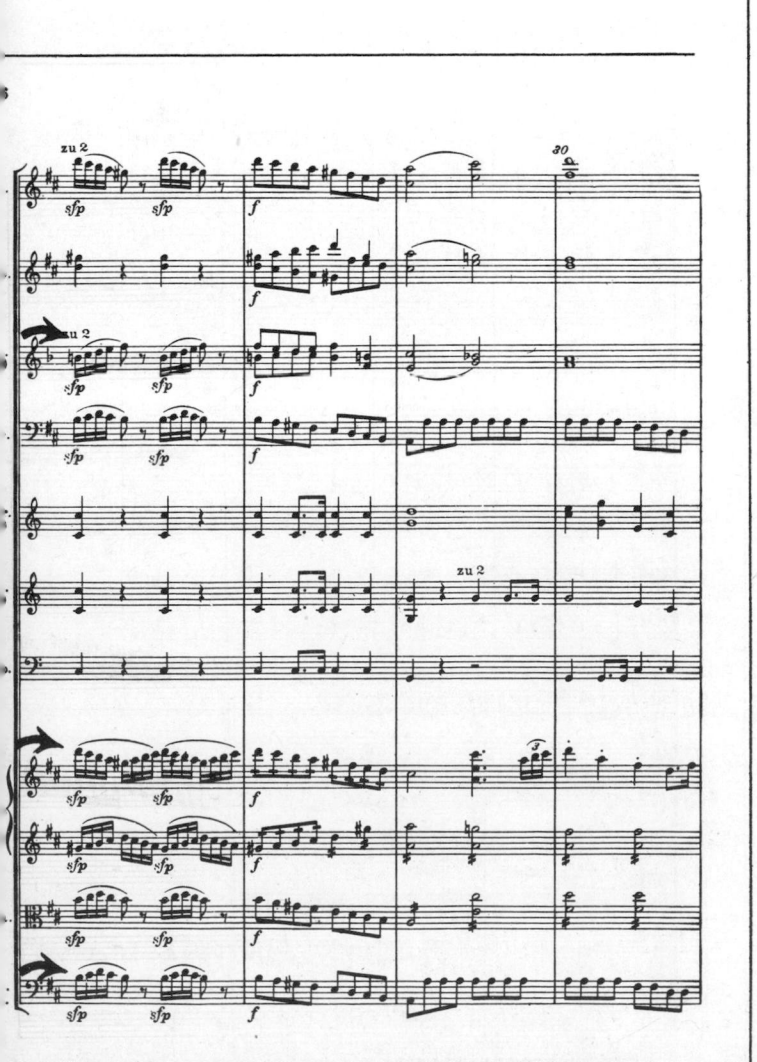

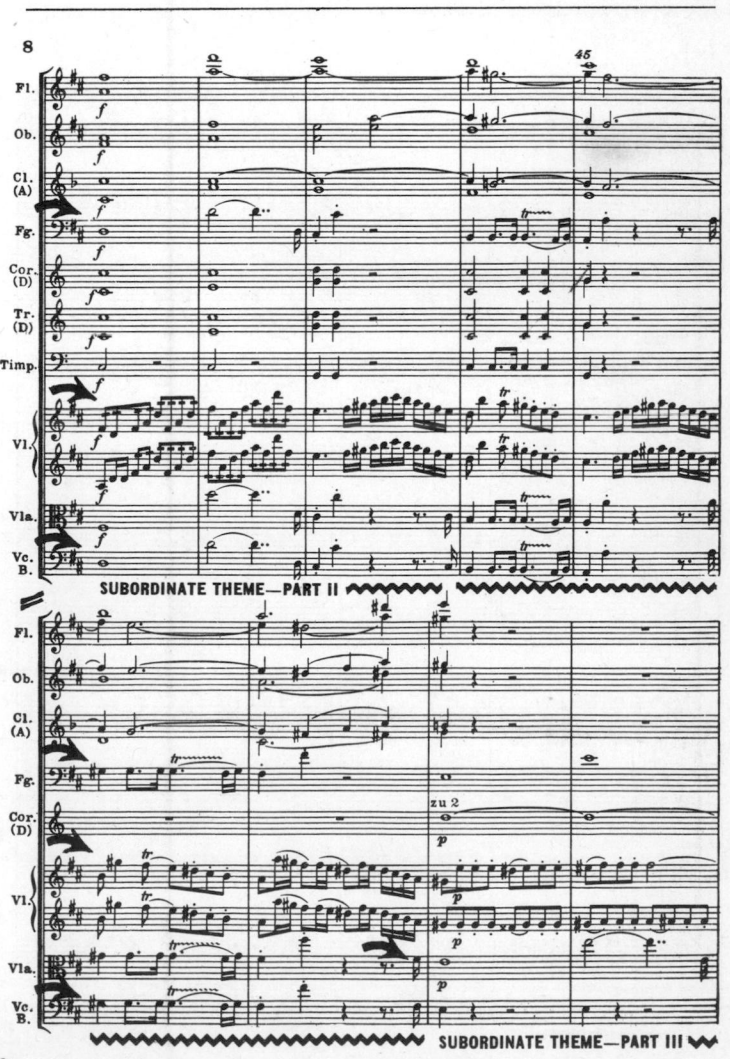

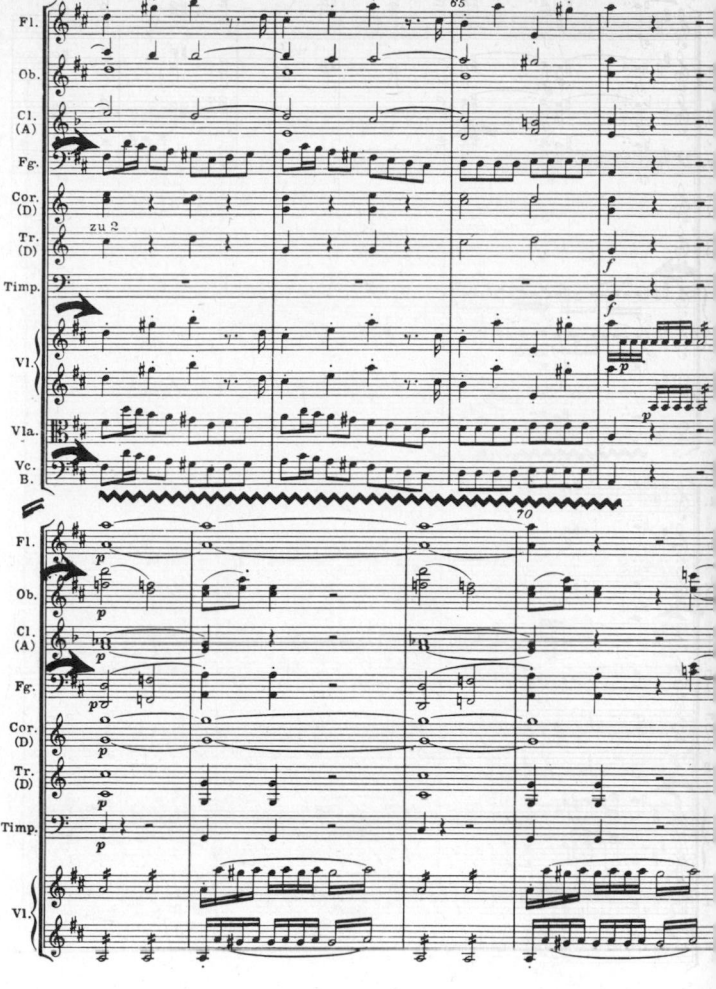

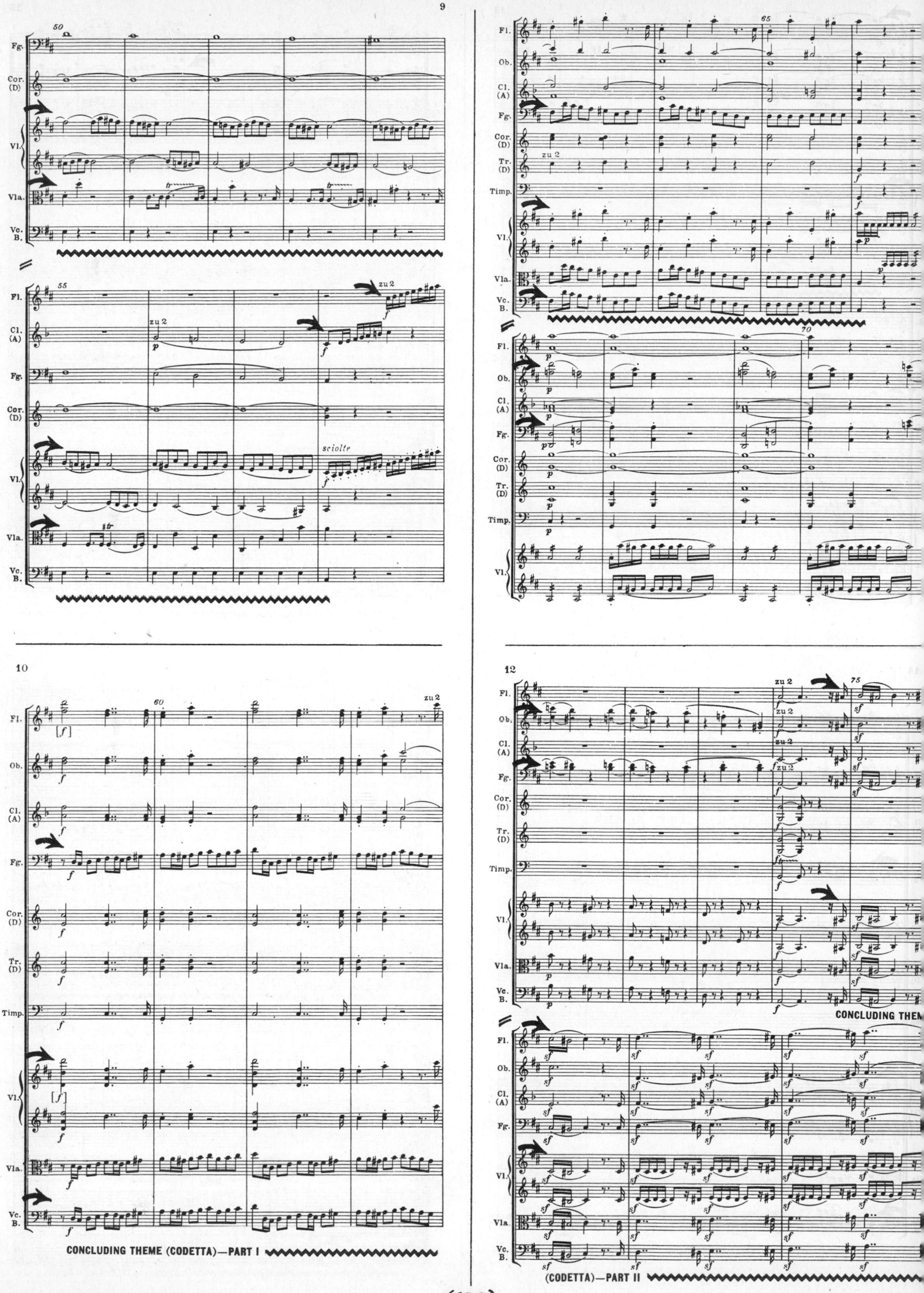
9
10
12
Fl.
Ob.
Cl. (A)
Fg.
Cor. (D)
Tr. (D)
Timp.
Vl.
Vla.
Vc. B.
zu 2
sciolte
CONCLUDING THEME (CODETTA)—PART I
CONCLUDING THEME
(CODETTA)—PART II

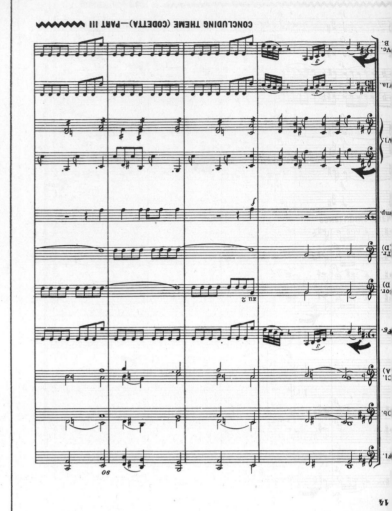

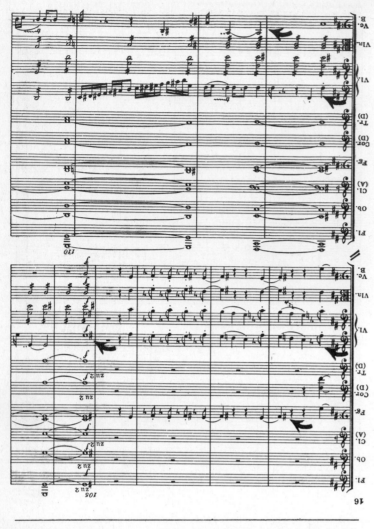

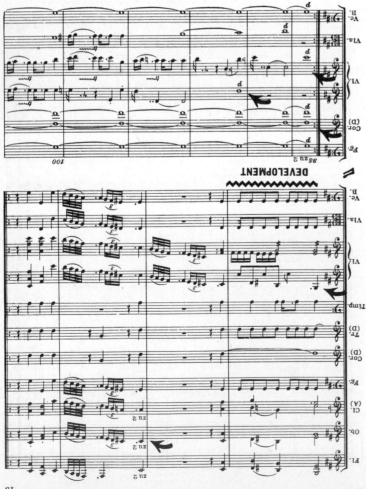

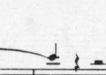

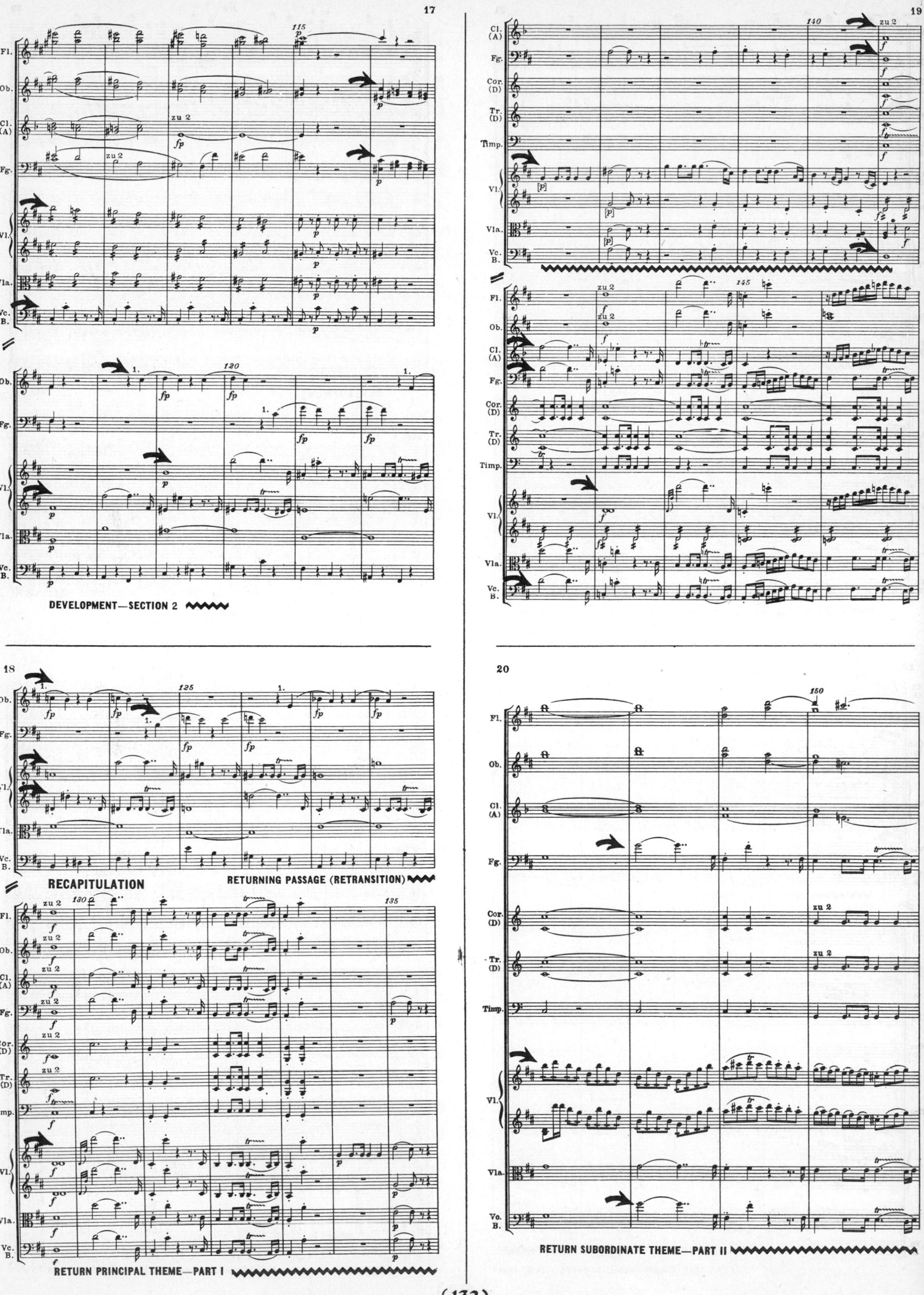
17
19
DEVELOPMENT—SECTION 2
18
RECAPITULATION
RETURNING PASSAGE (RETRANSITION)
RETURN PRINCIPAL THEME—PART I
20
RETURN SUBORDINATE THEME—PART II
Fl.
Ob.
Cl. (A)
Fg.
Cor. (D)
Tr. (D)
Timp.
Vl.
Vla.
Vc. B.
zu 2

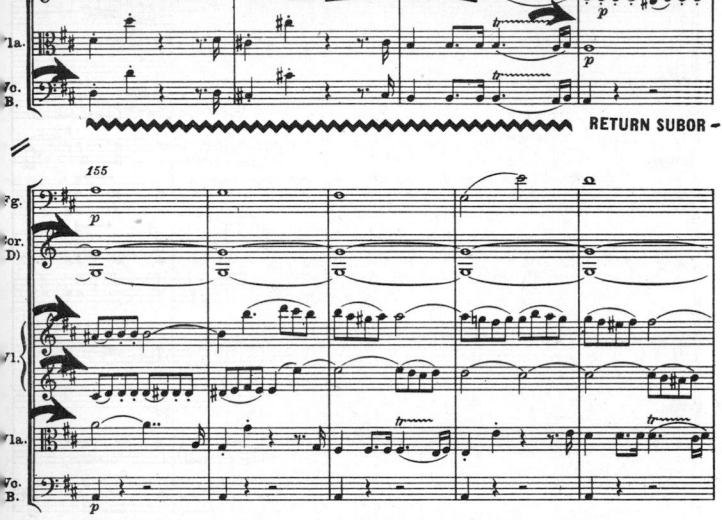

RETURN SUBOR-

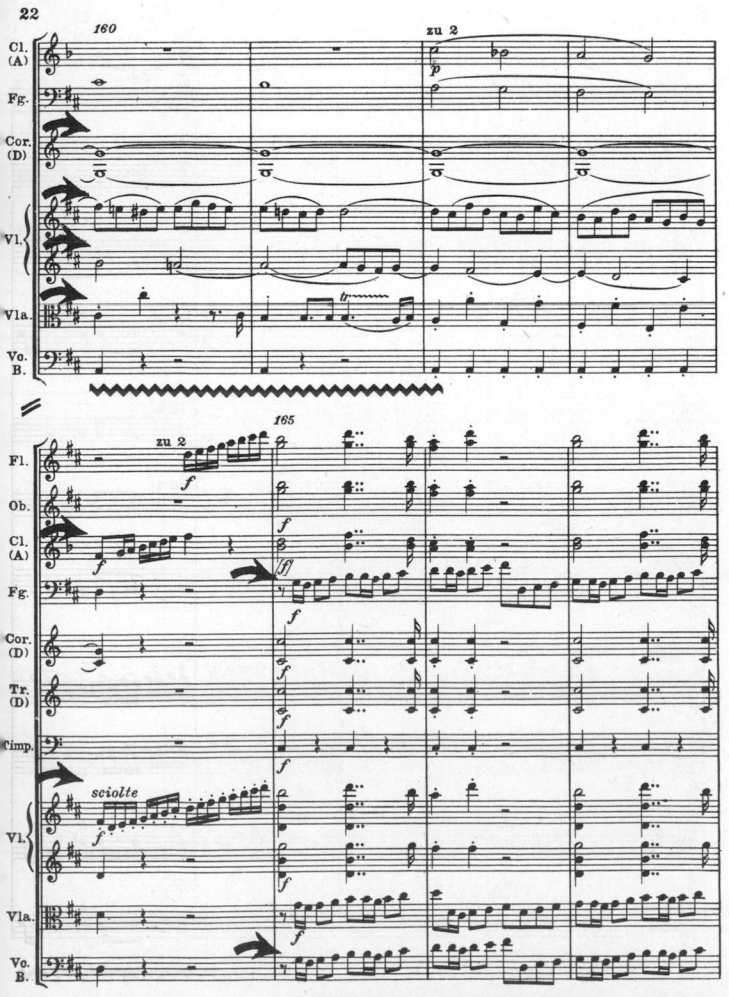

DINATE THEME—PART III

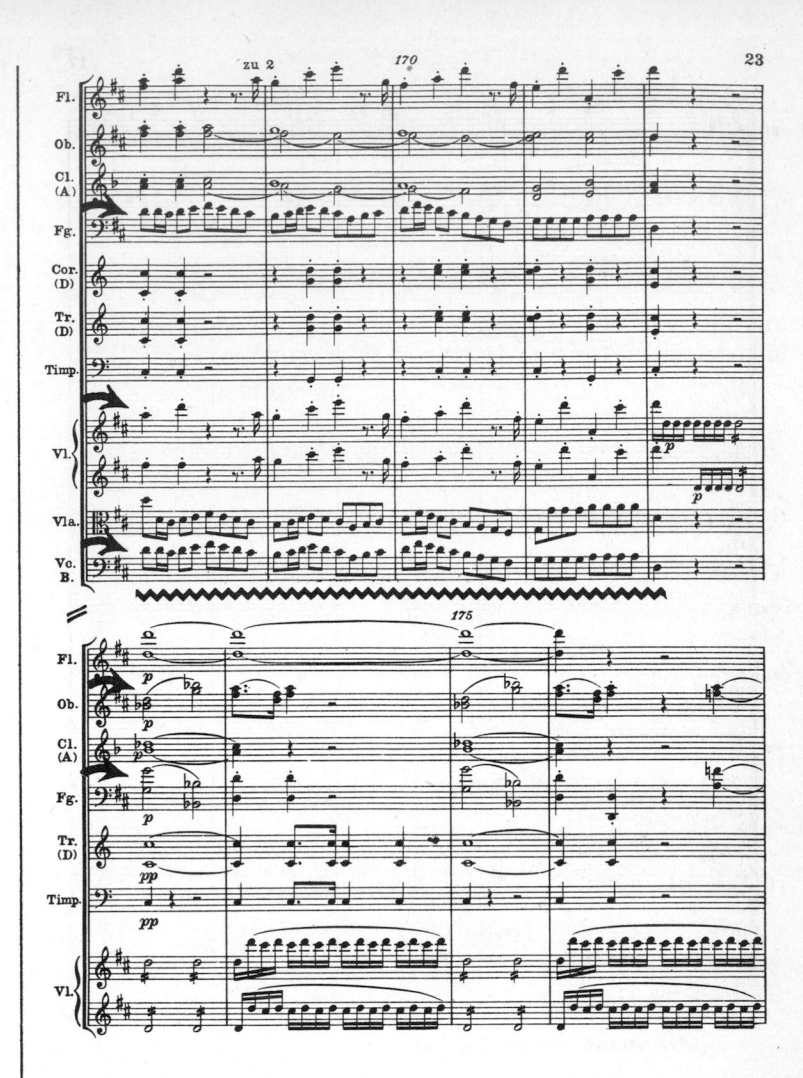

RETURN CONCLUDING THEME (CODETTA)—PART I

RETURN CONCLUDING THEME

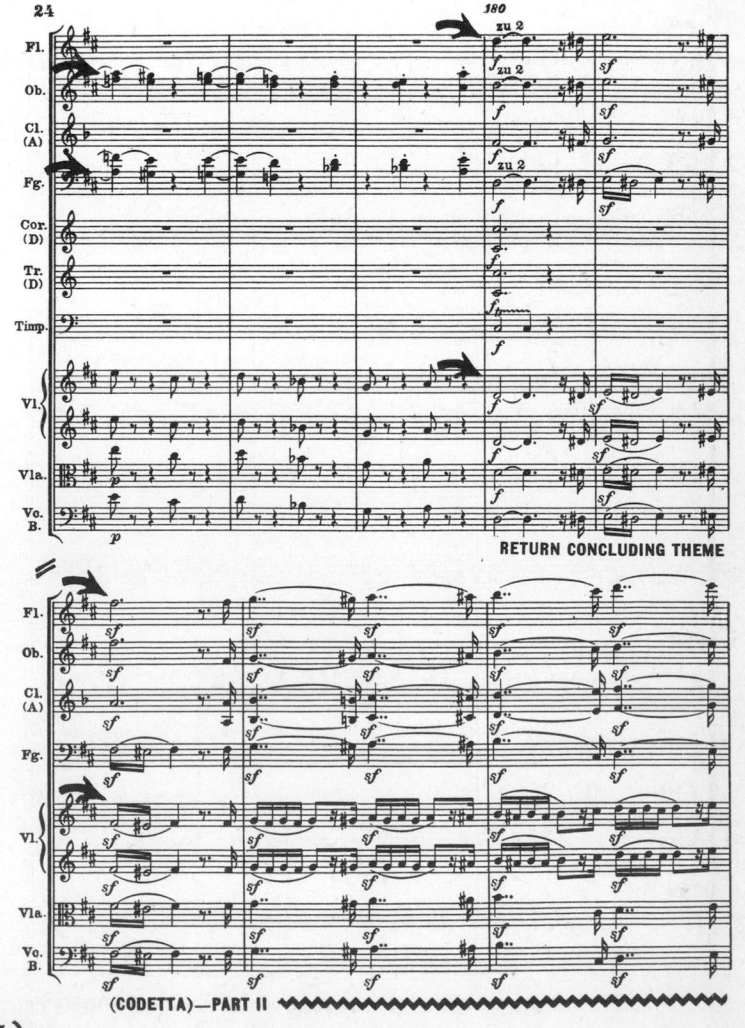

(CODETTA)—PART II

25

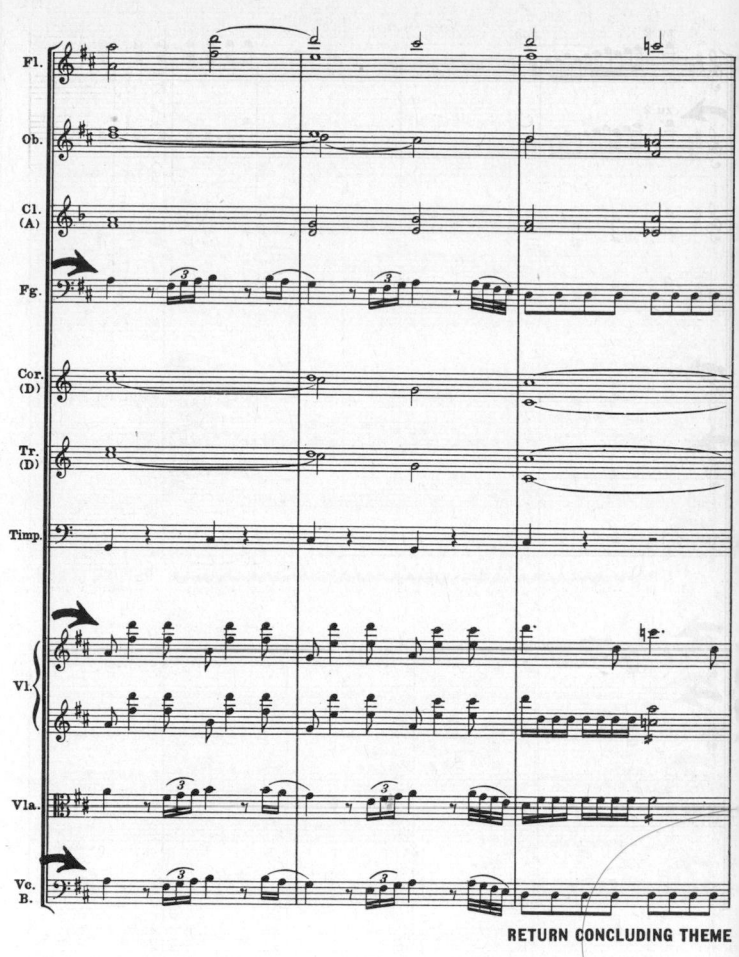

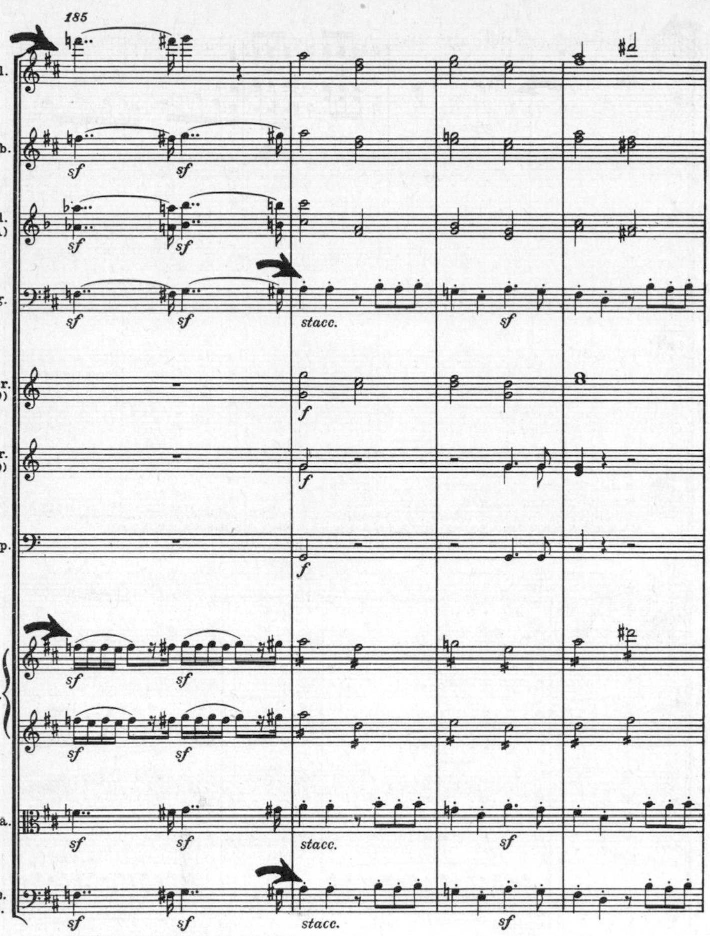

26

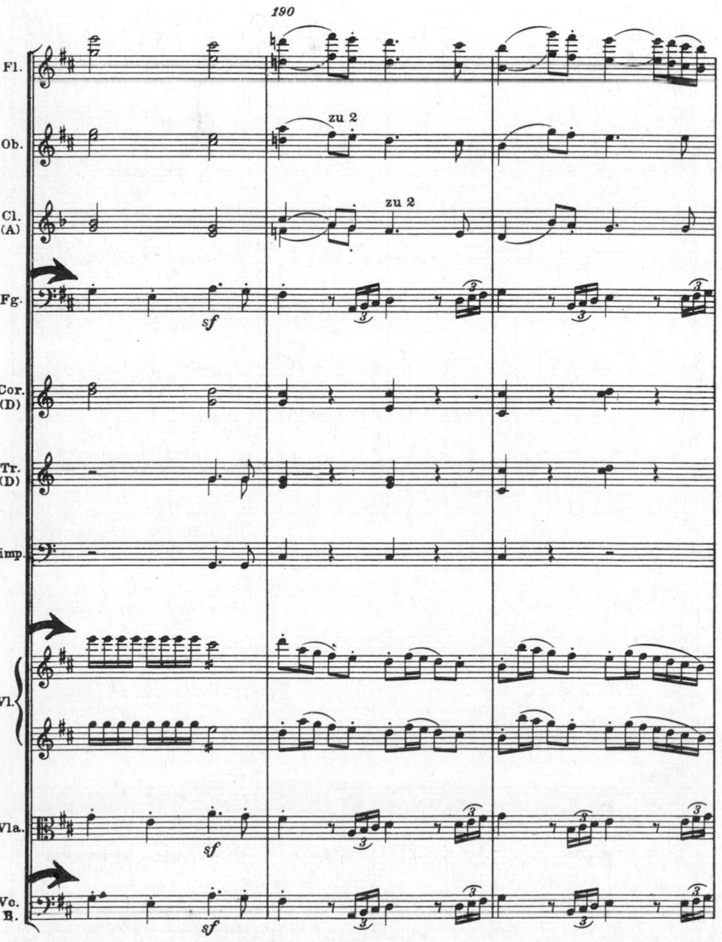

27

RETURN CONCLUDING THEME

28

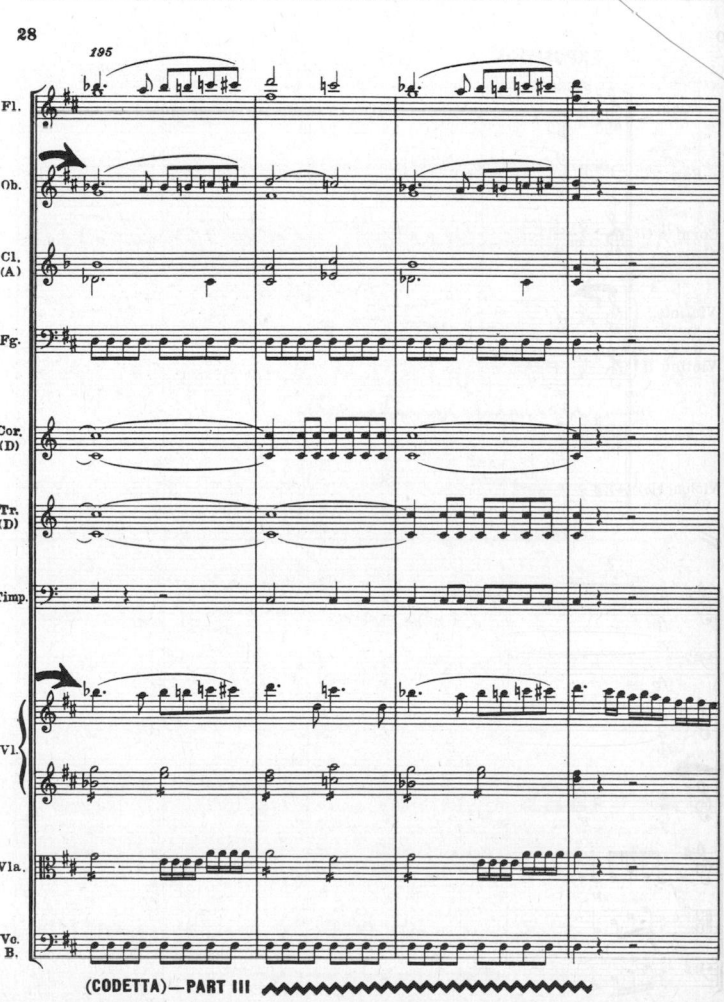

(CODETTA)—PART III

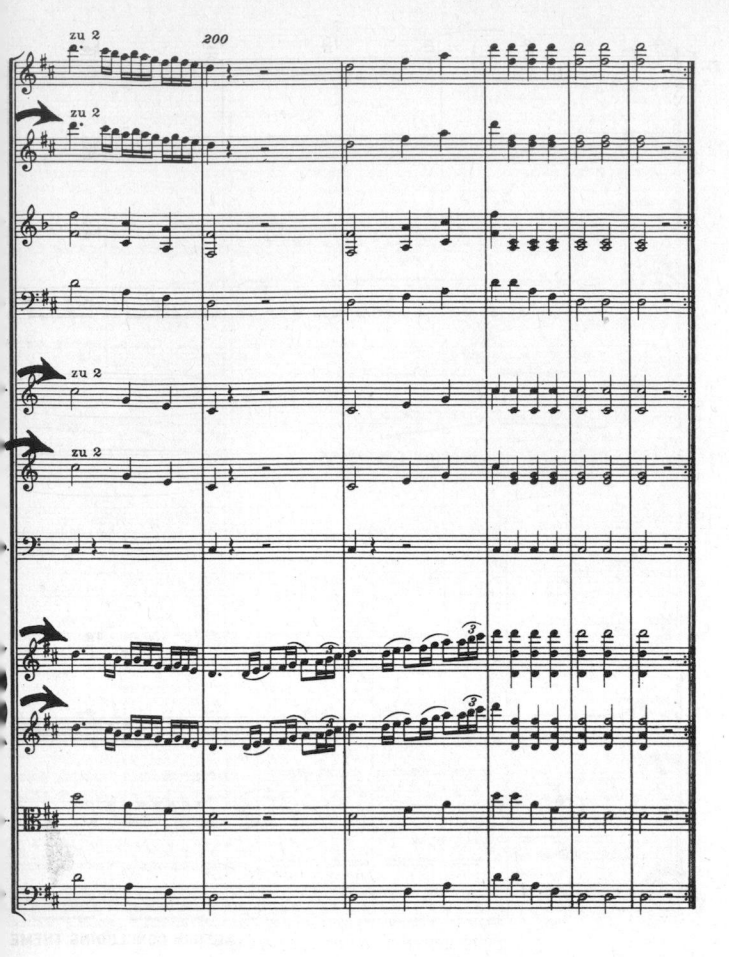

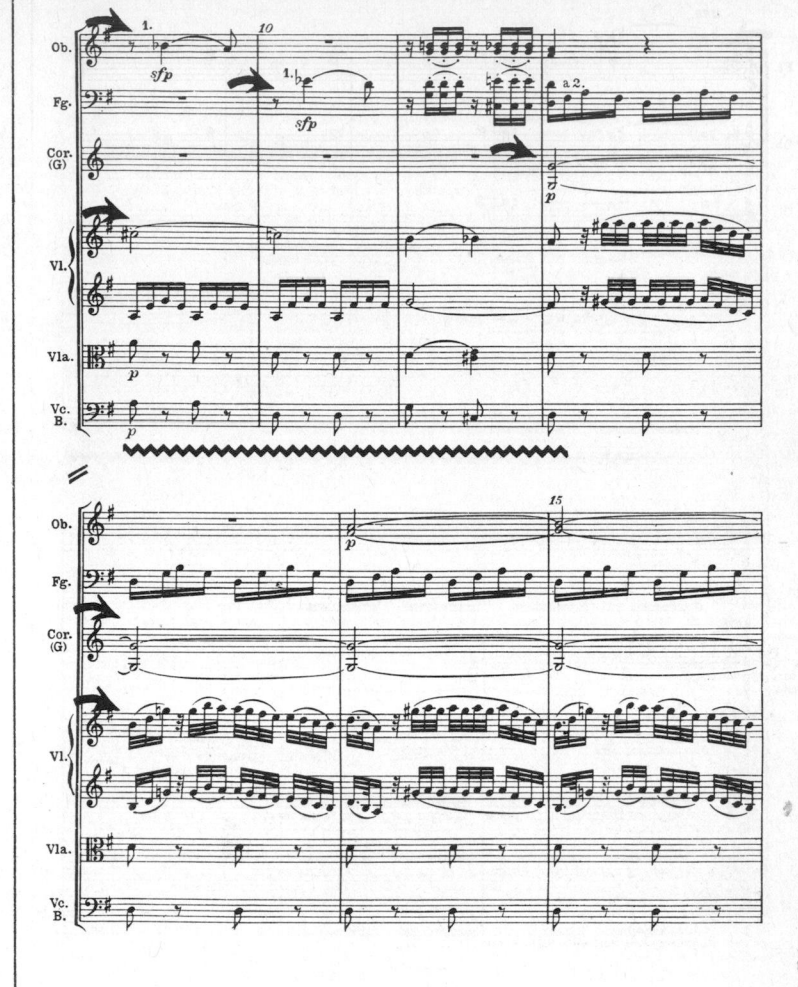

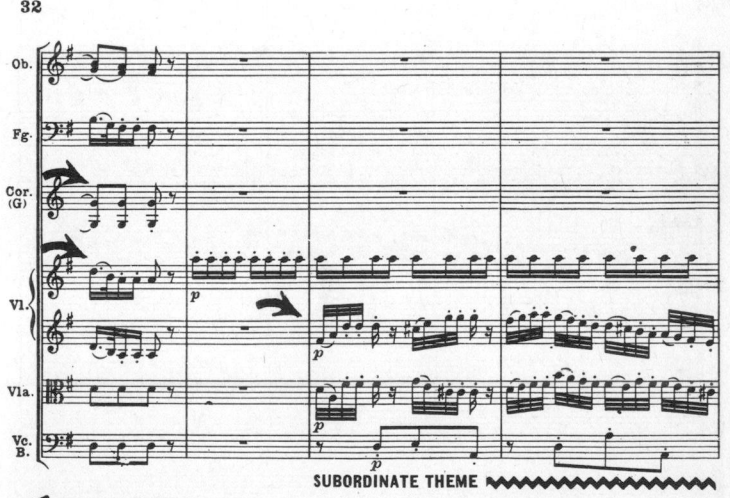

EXPOSITION II

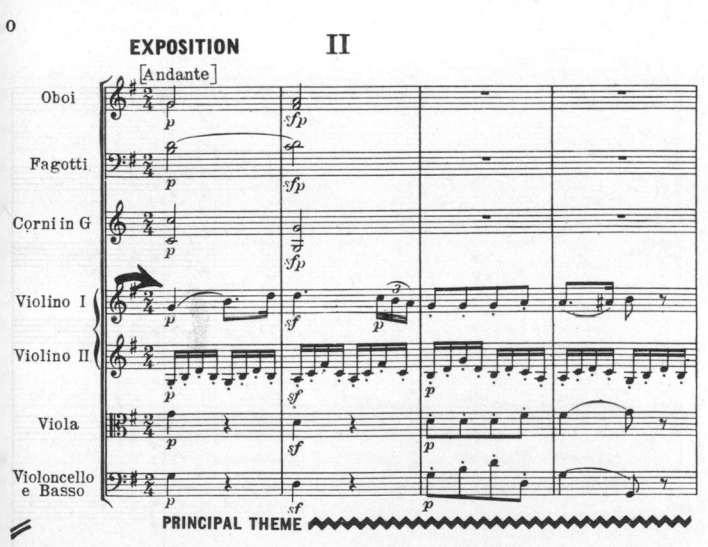

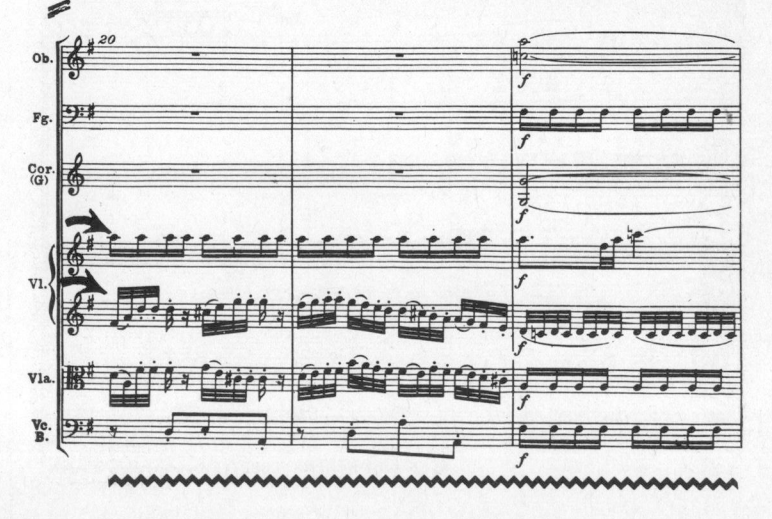

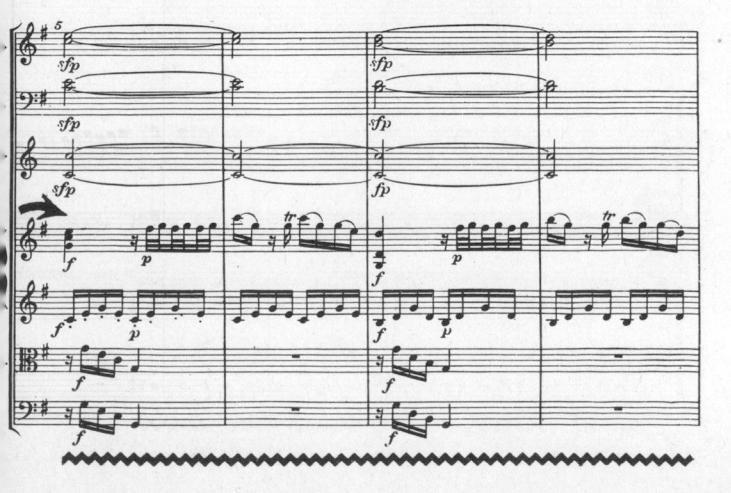

DEVELOPMENT

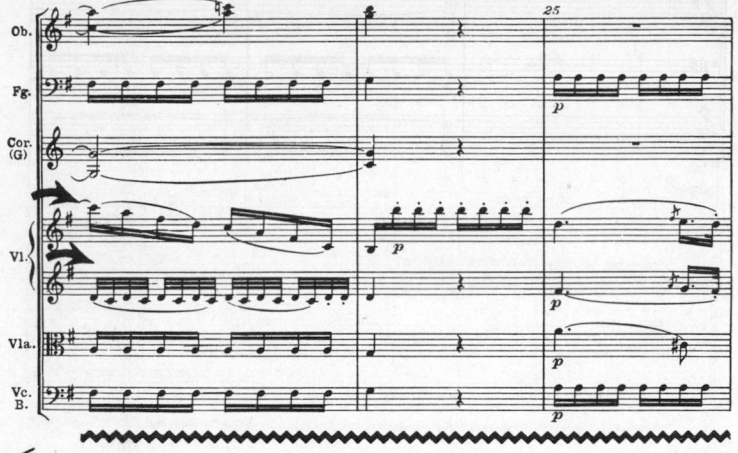

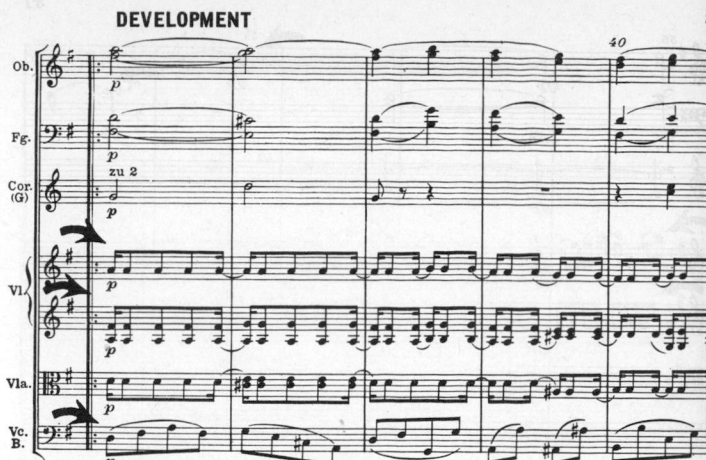

DEVELOPMENT—SECTION 1 ~~~~

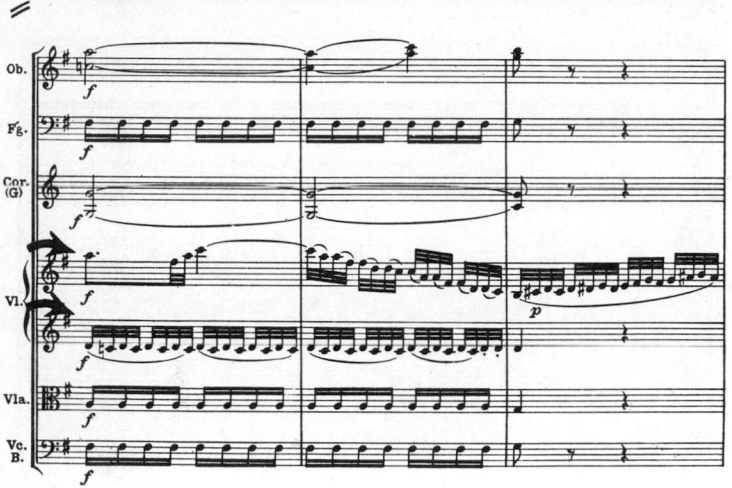

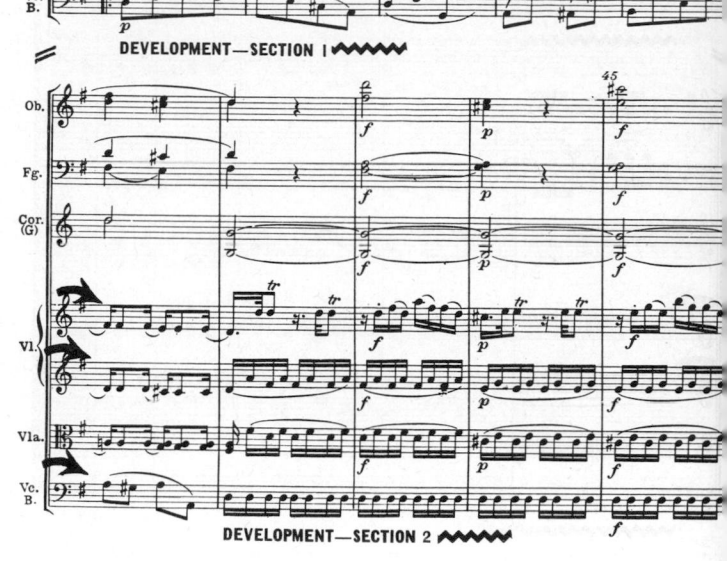

DEVELOPMENT—SECTION 2 ~~~~

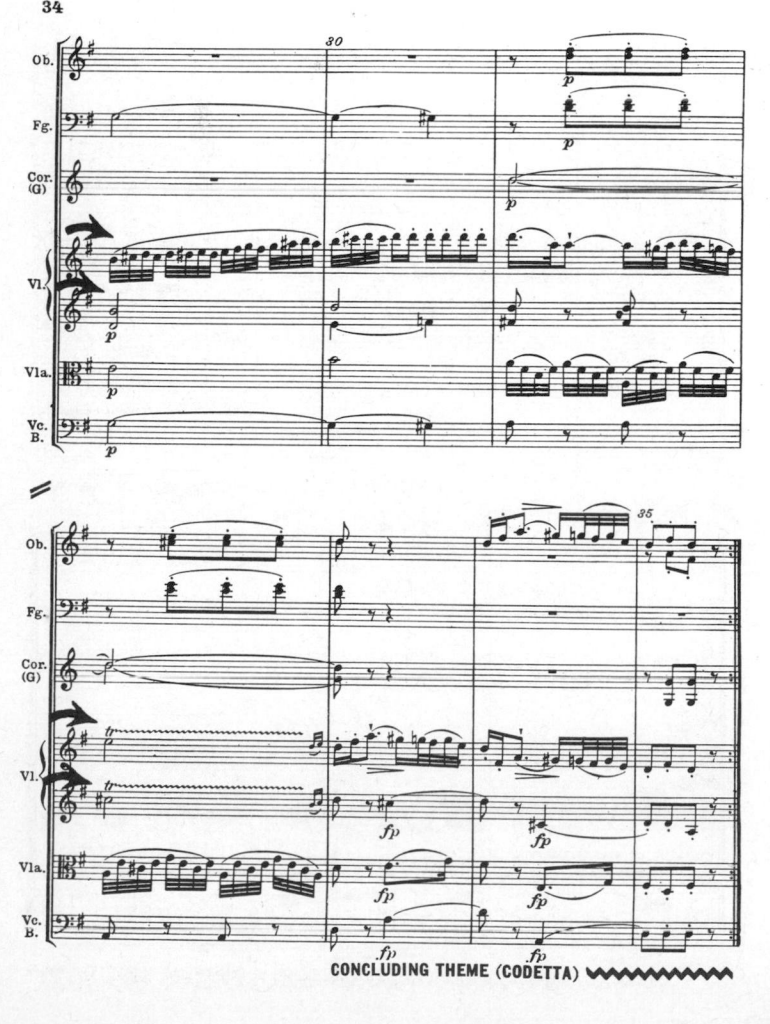

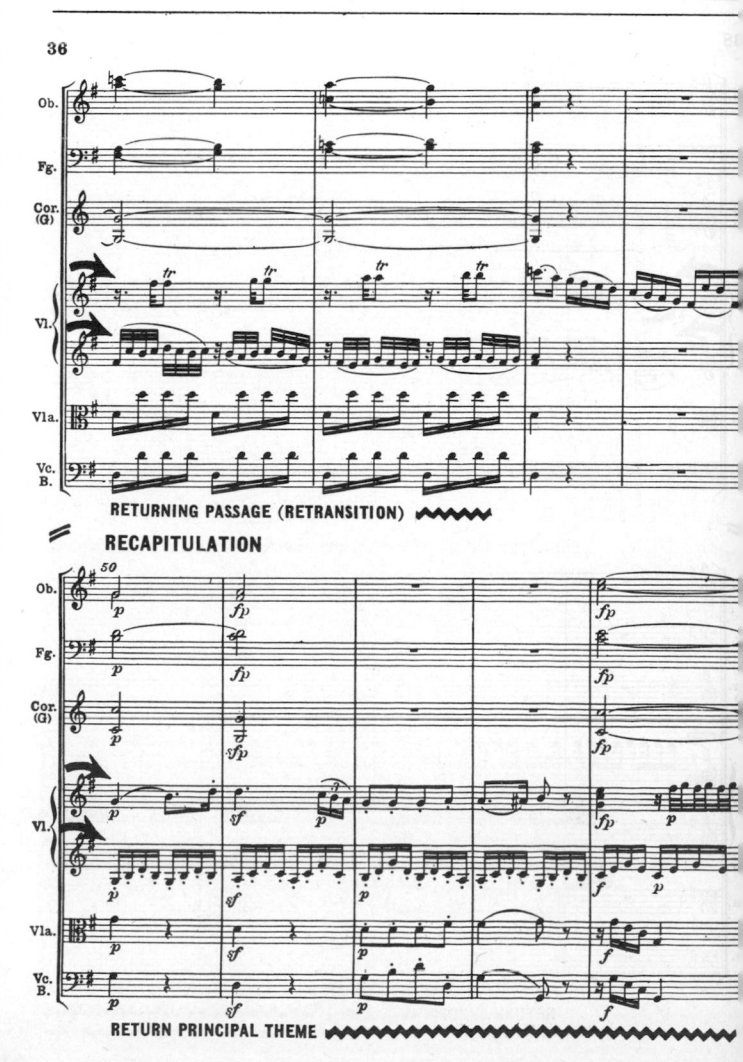

CONCLUDING THEME (CODETTA) ~~~~

RETURNING PASSAGE (RETRANSITION) ~~~~

RECAPITULATION

RETURN PRINCIPAL THEME ~~~~

DEVELOPMENT

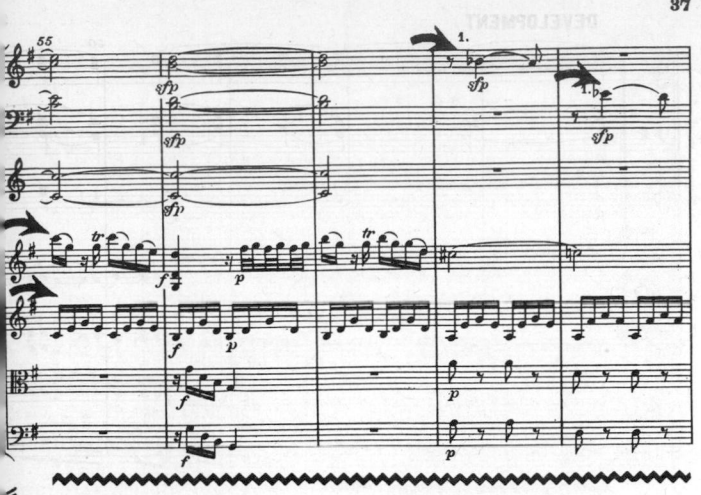

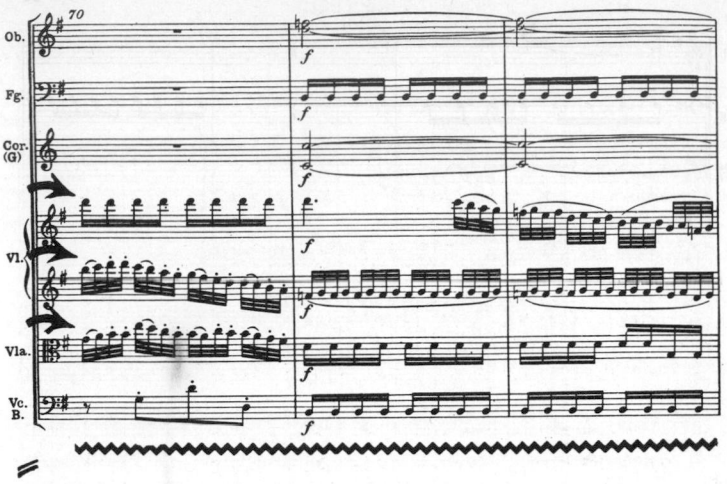

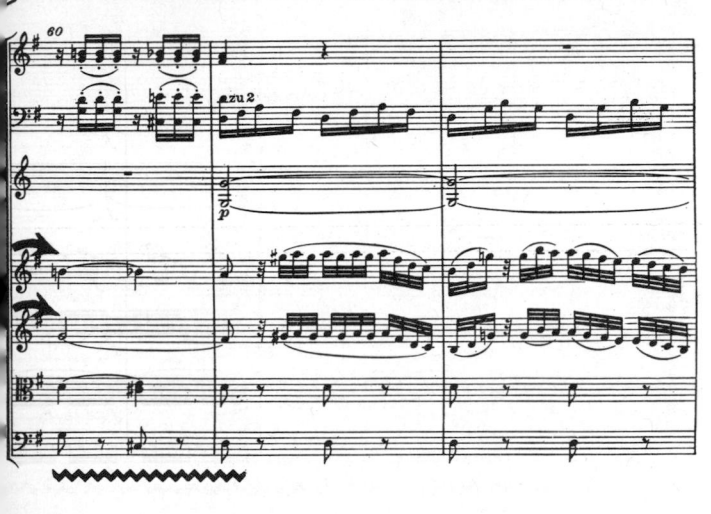

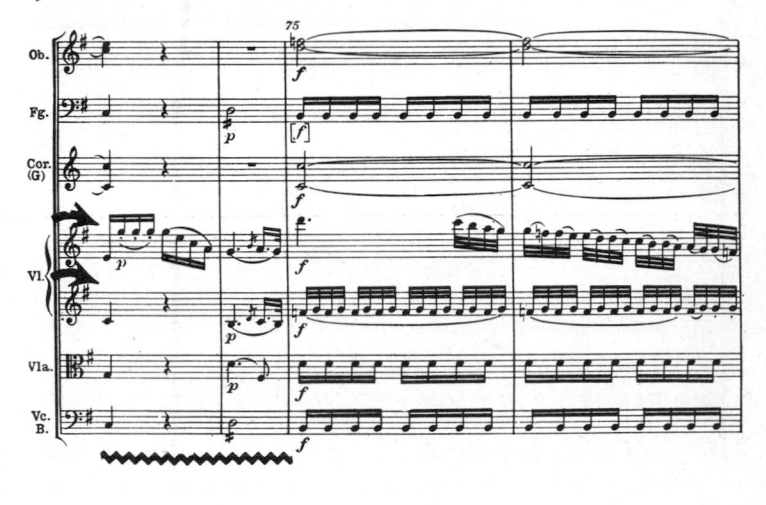

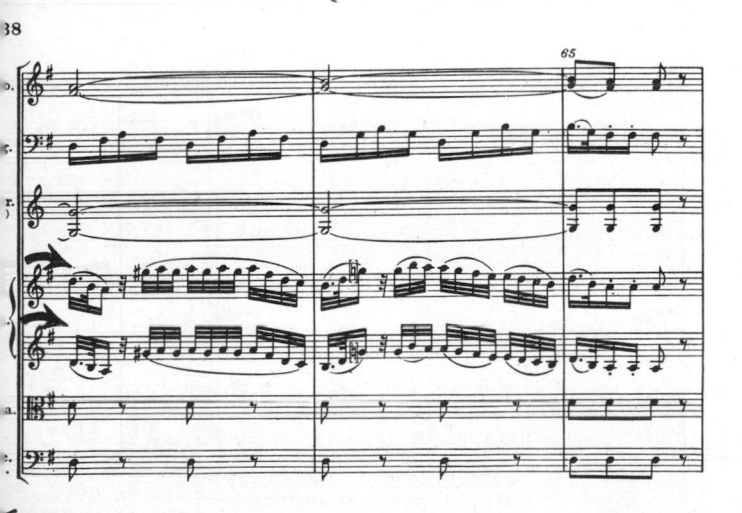

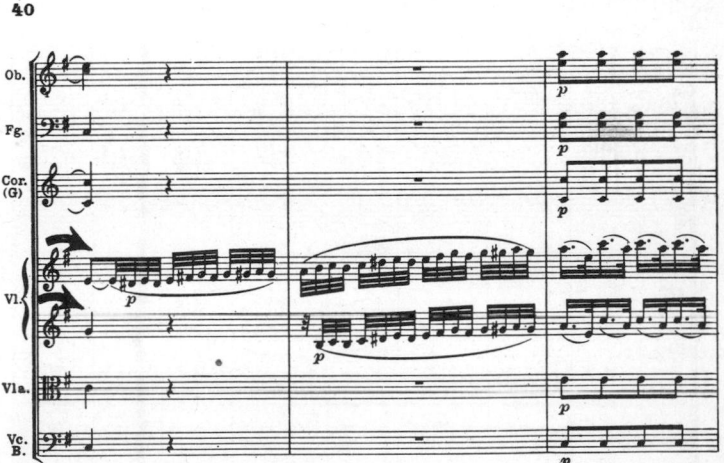

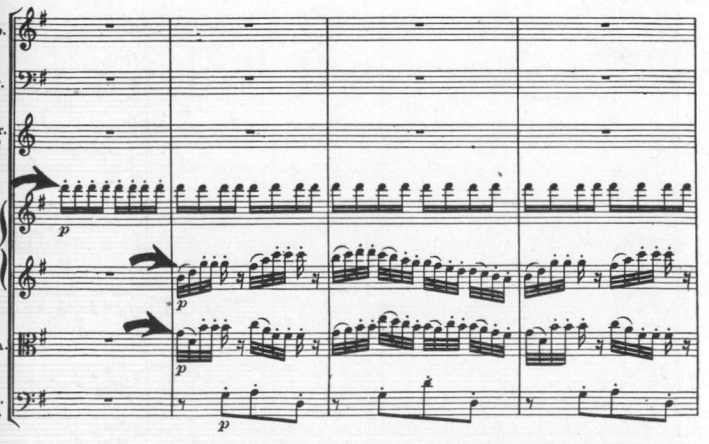

RETURN SUBORDINATE THEME 〜〜〜〜〜〜

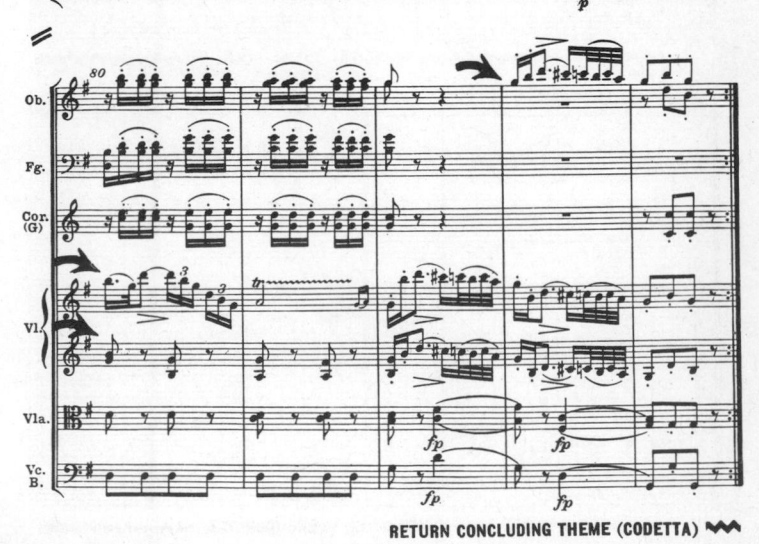

RETURN CONCLUDING THEME (CODETTA) 〜〜〜

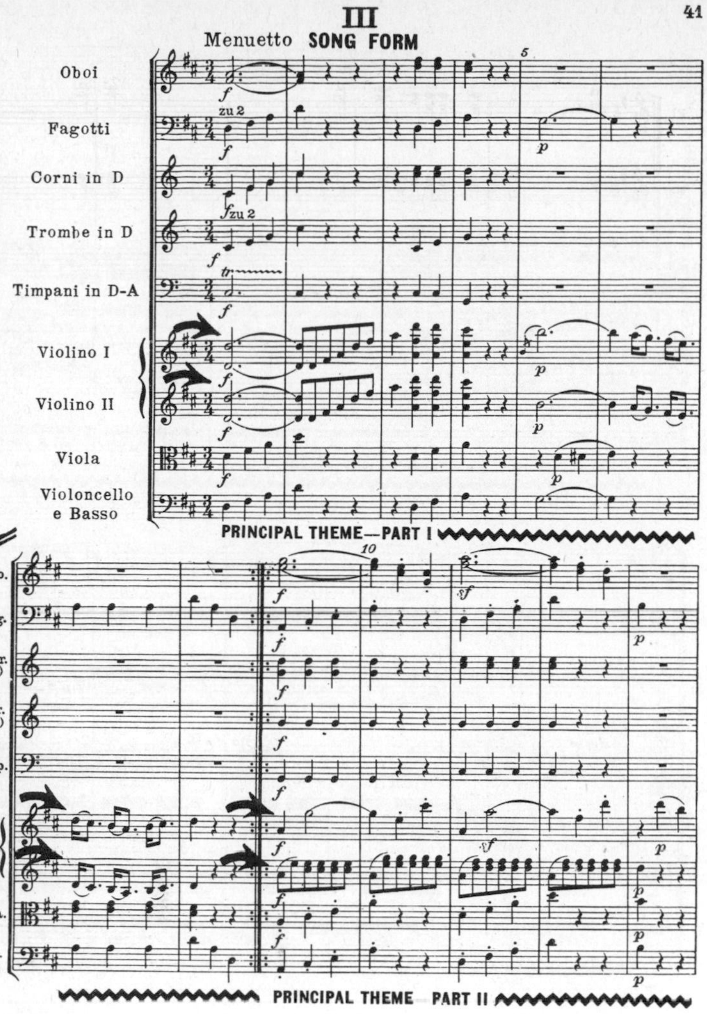
III
Menuetto SONG FORM
Oboi
Fagotti
Corni in D
Trombe in D
Timpani in D-A
Violino I
Violino II
Viola
Violoncello e Basso
PRINCIPAL THEME—PART I
PRINCIPAL THEME—PART II

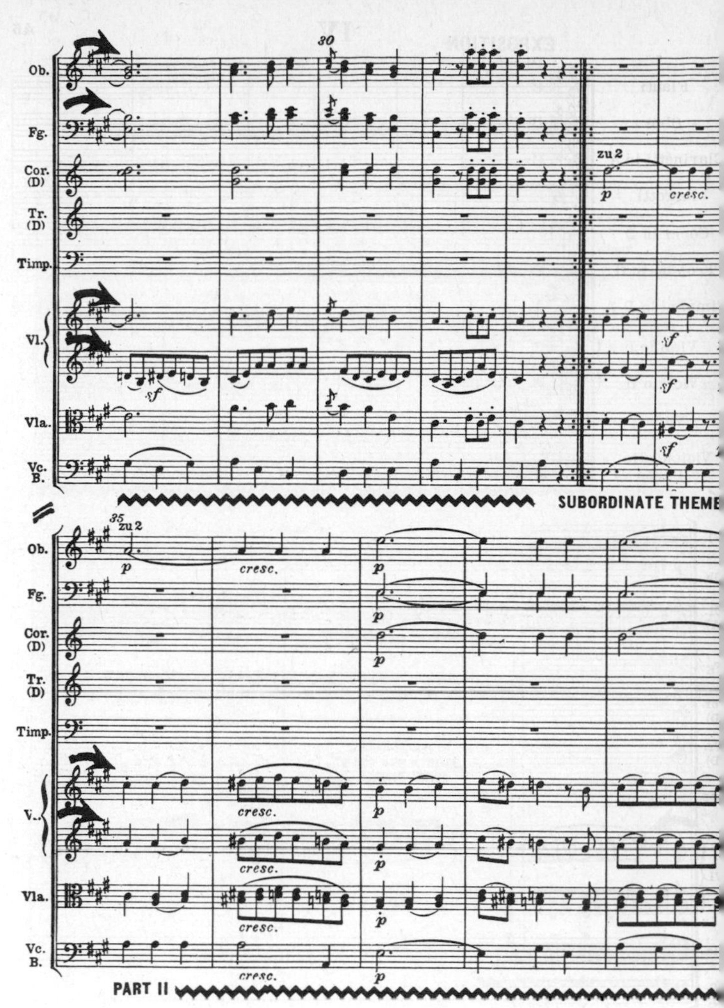
SUBORDINATE THEME
PART II

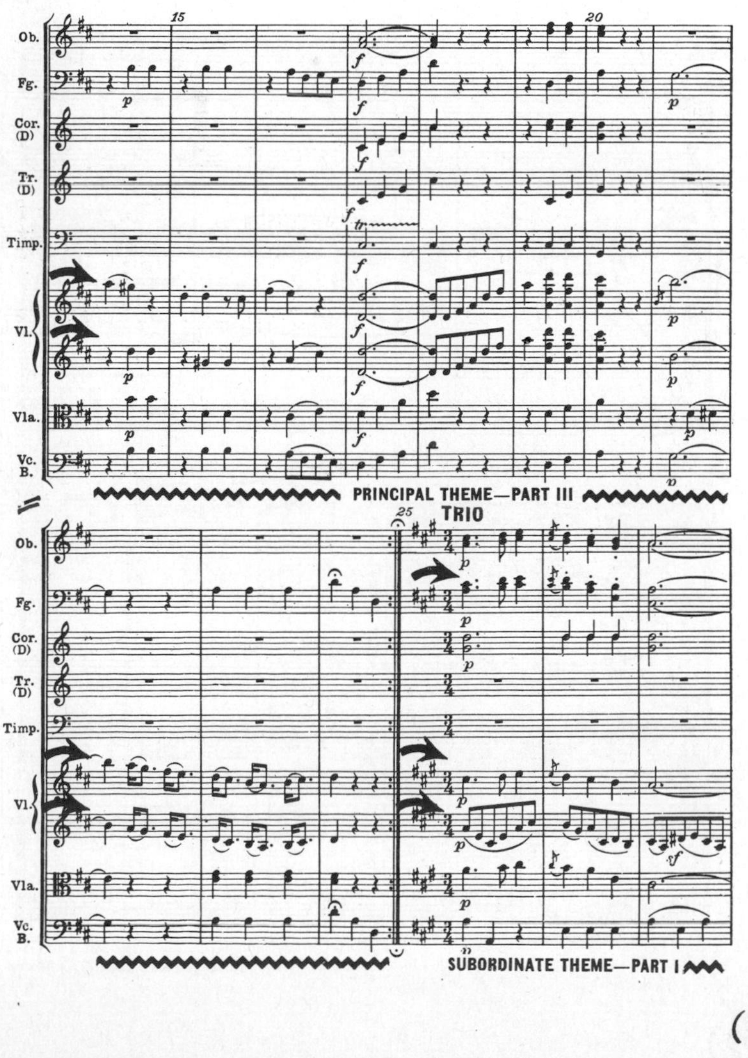
PRINCIPAL THEME—PART III
TRIO
SUBORDINATE THEME—PART I

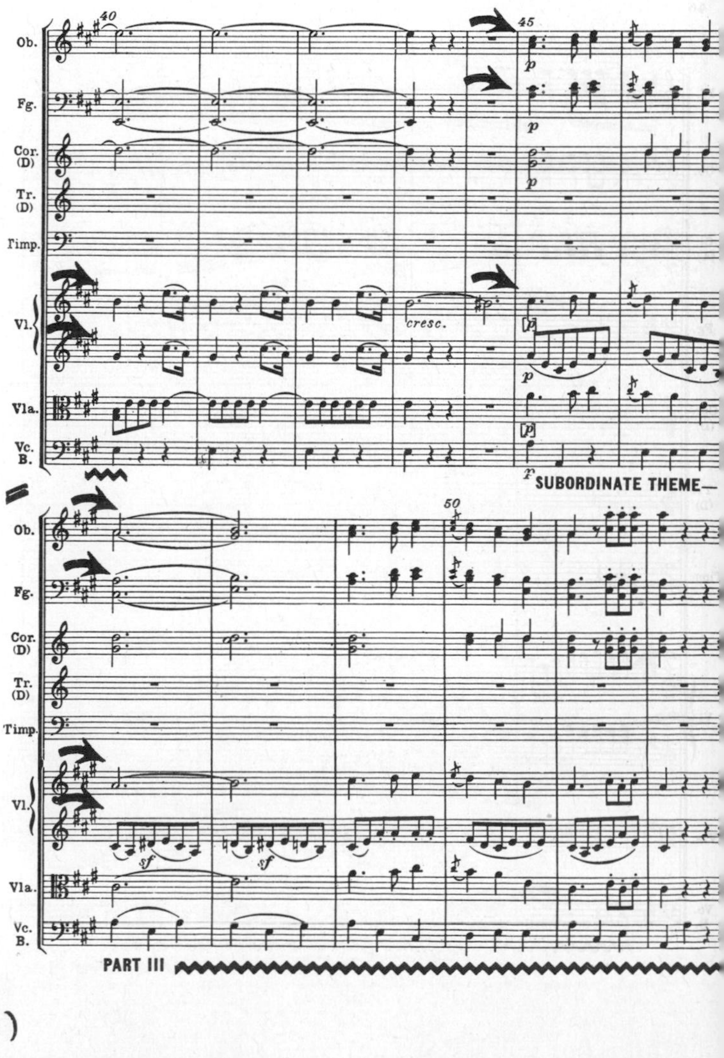
SUBORDINATE THEME—
PART III

Menuetto: SONG FORM

EXPOSITION
Presto

Flauti
Oboi
Clarinetti in A
Fagotti
Corni in D
Trombe in D
Timpani in D-A
Violino I
Violino II
Viola
Violoncello e Basso

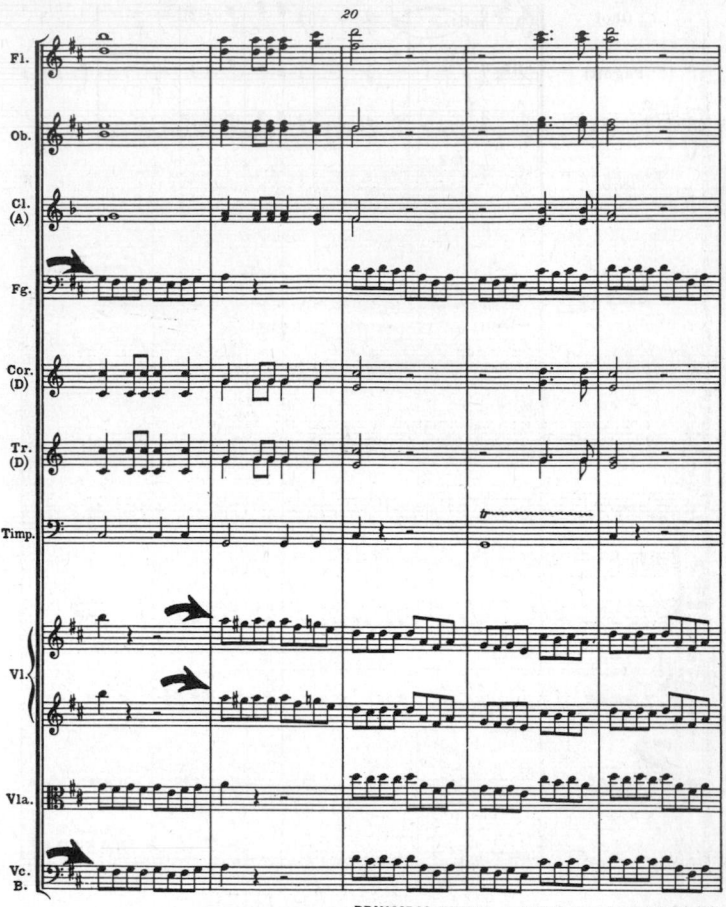

PRINCIPAL THEME—PART I, 1st PERIOD

PRINCIPAL THEME—PART I, 2nd PERIOD

PRINCIPAL THEME—PART II

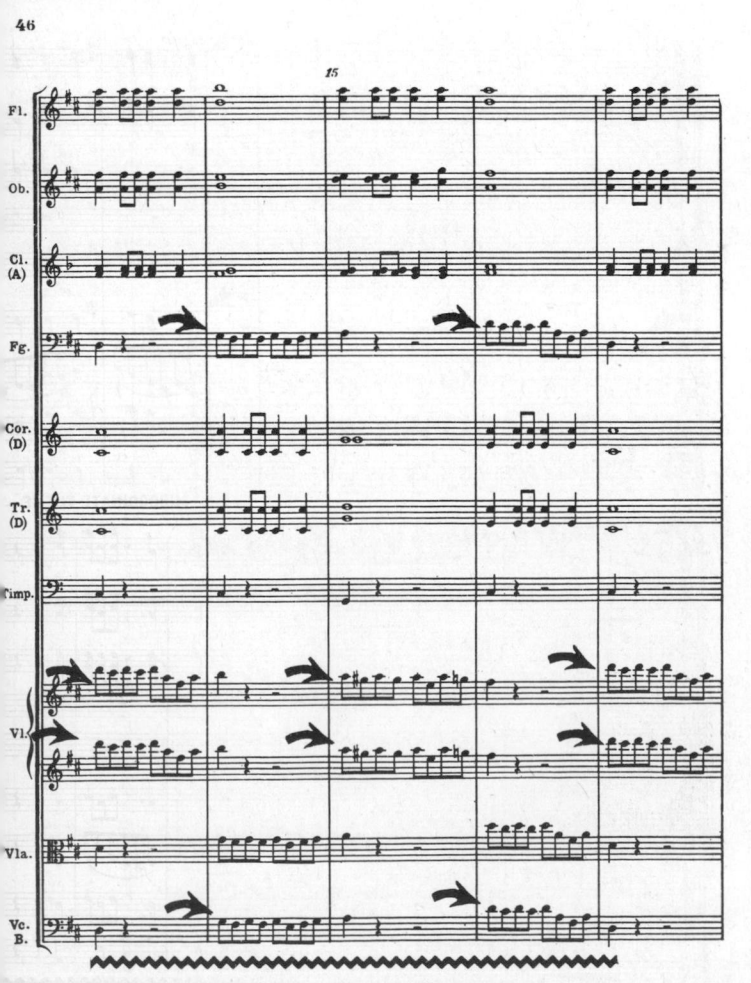

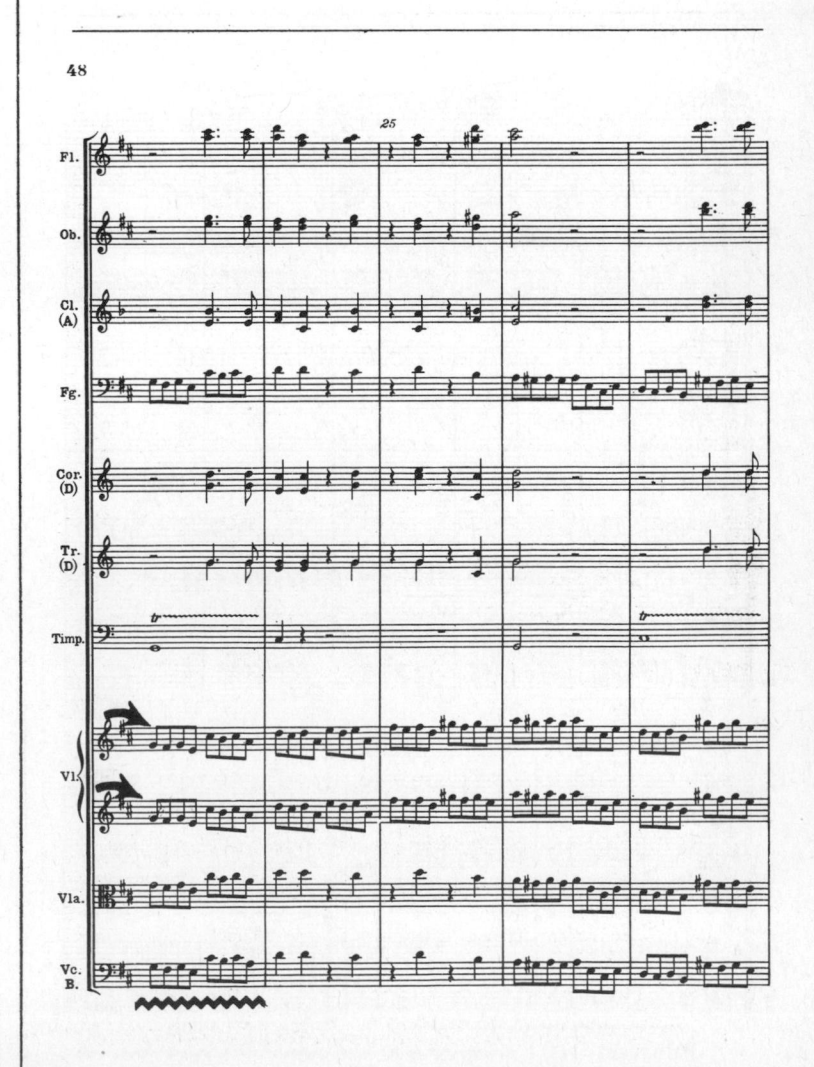

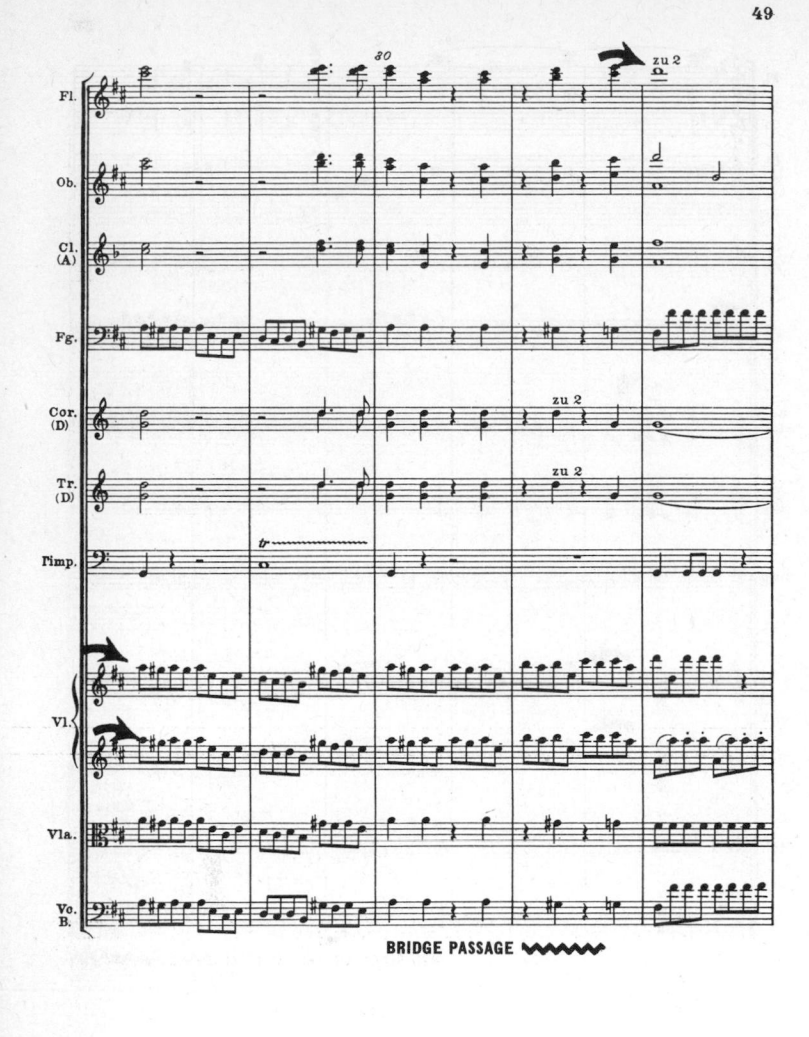

BRIDGE PASSAGE 〰〰〰

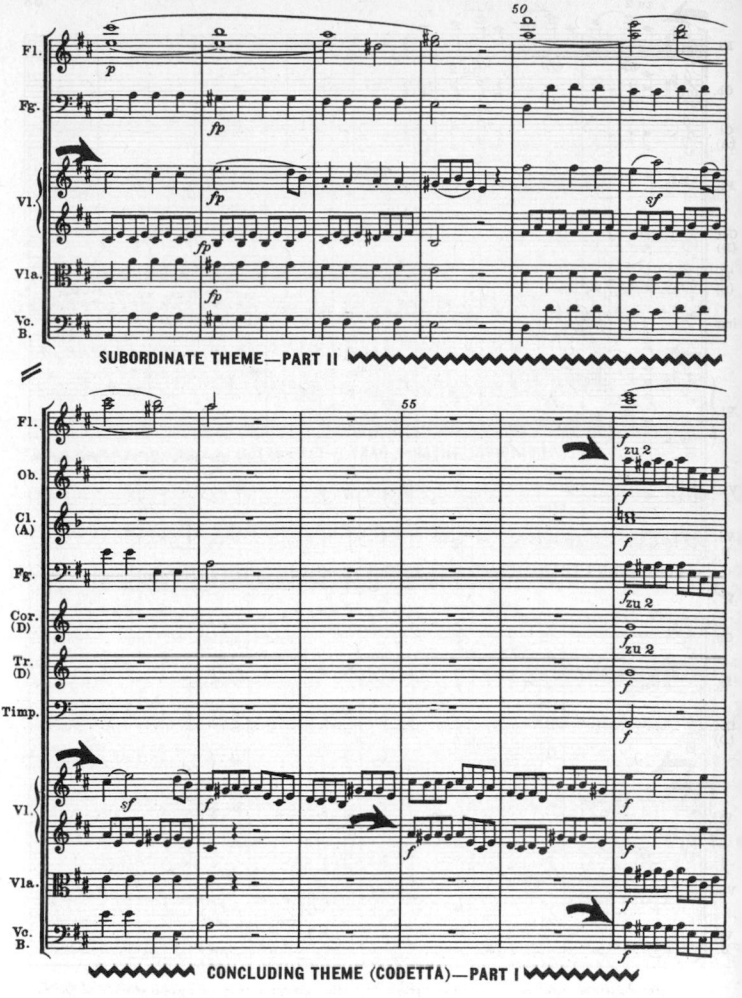

SUBORDINATE THEME—PART II 〰〰〰〰〰〰〰〰〰〰〰〰〰〰〰〰

〰〰〰〰〰 CONCLUDING THEME (CODETTA)—PART I 〰〰〰〰

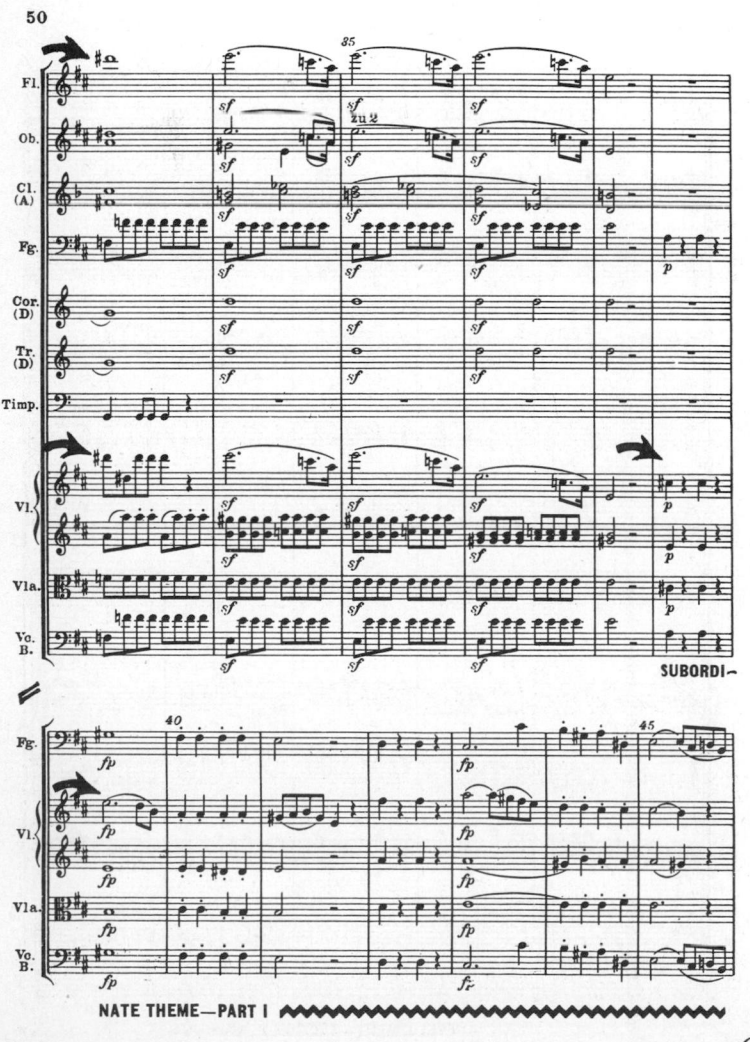

SUBORDI‐

NATE THEME—PART I 〰〰〰〰〰〰〰〰〰〰〰〰〰〰〰〰〰〰〰

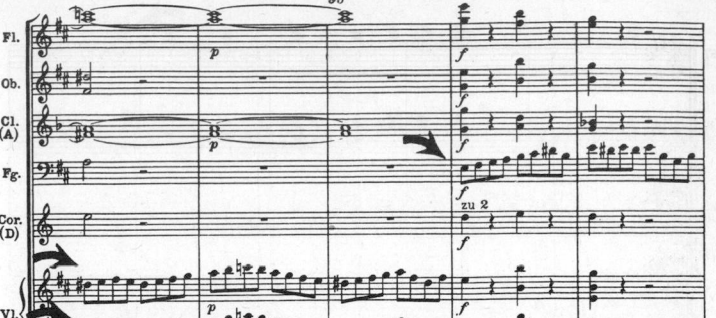

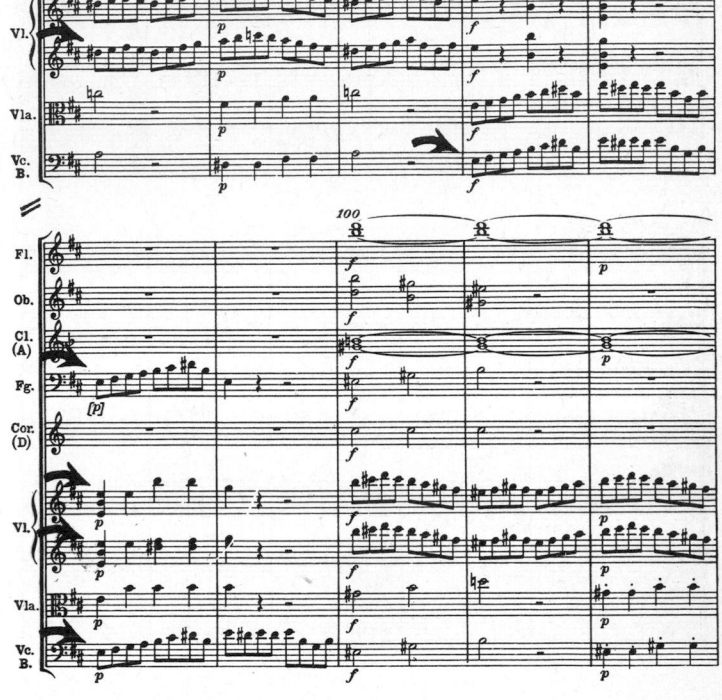

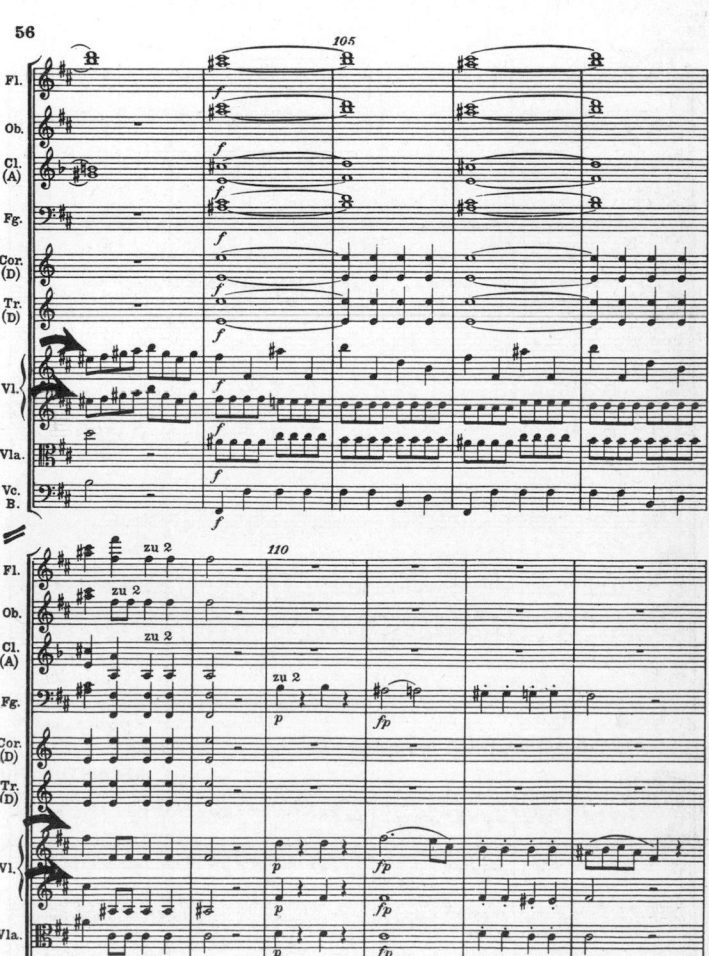

53

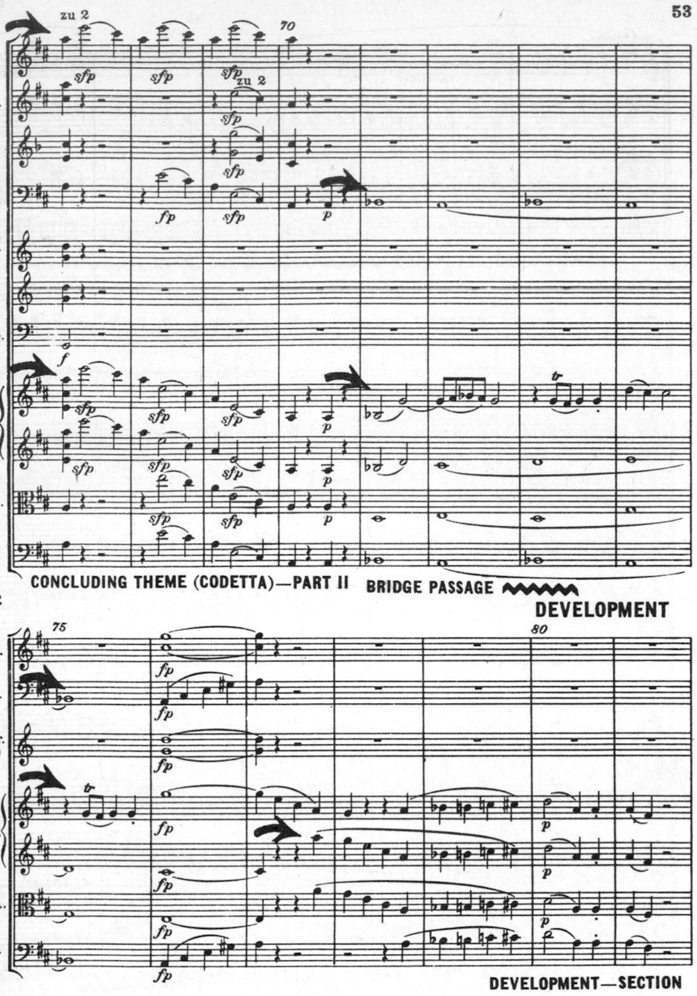

zu 2
Fl.
Ob.
Cl. (A)
Fg.
Cor. (D)
Tr. (D)
Timp.
Vl.
Vla.
Vc. B.
CONCLUDING THEME (CODETTA)—PART II
BRIDGE PASSAGE
DEVELOPMENT
DEVELOPMENT—SECTION

54

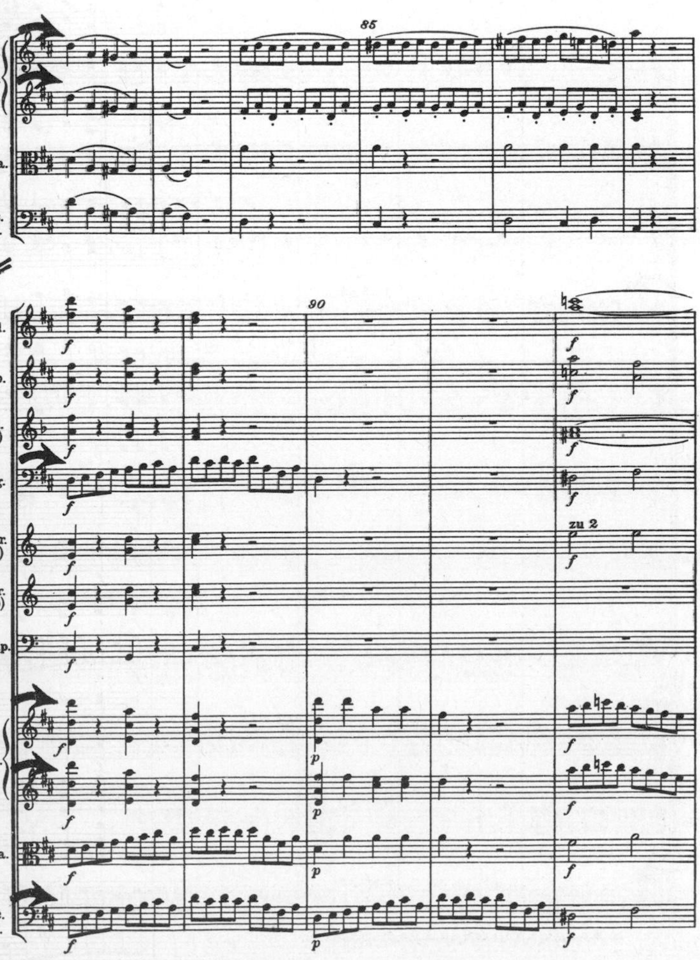

Vl.
Vla.
Vc. B.
Fl.
Ob.
Cl. (A)
Fg.
Cor. (D)
Tr. (D)
Timp.
zu 2

55

Fl.
Ob.
Cl. (A)
Fg.
zu 2
Cor. (D)
Vl.
Vla.
Vc. B.

56

Fl.
Ob.
Cl. (A)
Fg.
Cor. (D)
Tr. (D)
Vl.
Vla.
Vc. B.
zu 2
DEVELOPMENT—SECTION 2

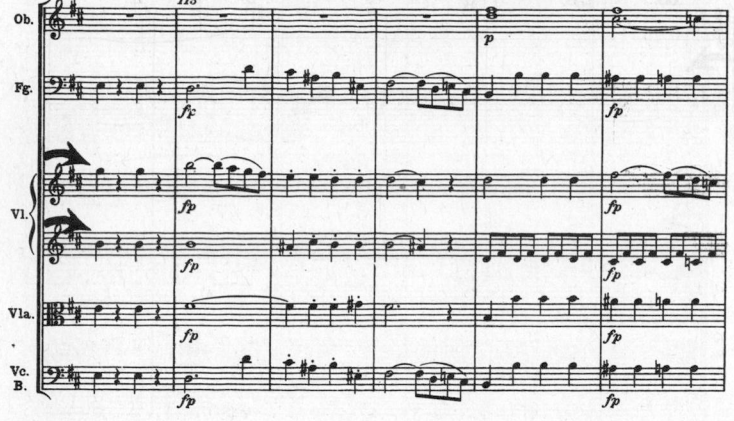

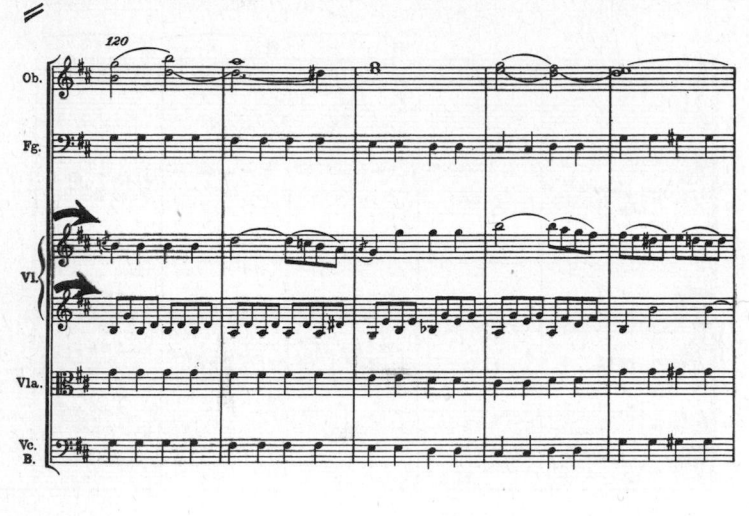

60

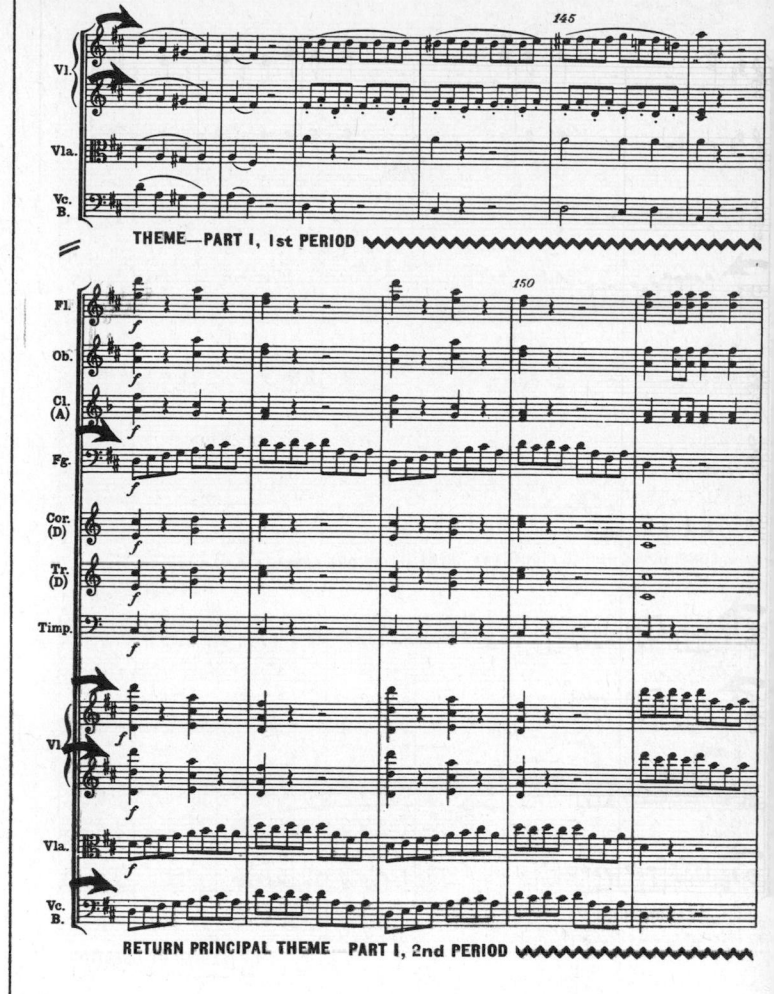

RETURNING

PASSAGE (RETRANSITION) 〜〜〜

RECAPITULATION

RETURN PRINCIPAL

THEME—PART I, 1st PERIOD 〜〜〜〜〜〜〜

RETURN PRINCIPAL THEME   PART I, 2nd PERIOD 〜〜〜

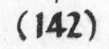

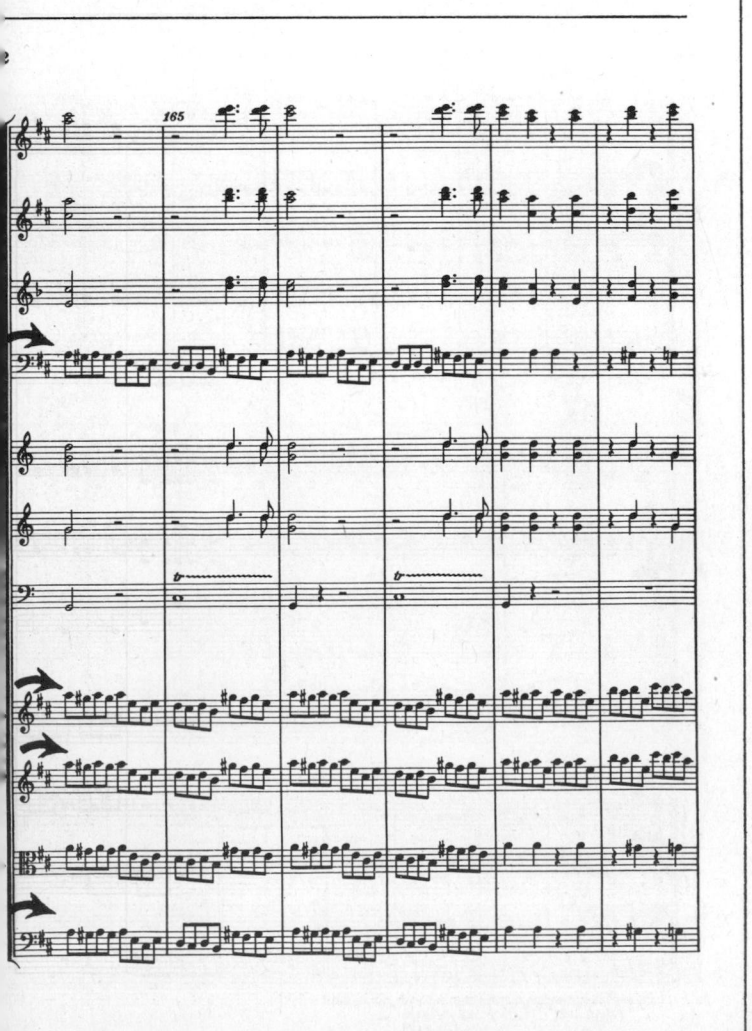

RETURN PRINCIPAL THEME—PART II ᴧᴧᴧᴧᴧᴧᴧ

Fl.

Ob.

Cl.
(A)

Fg.

Cor.
(D)

Tr.
(D)

Timp.

Vl.

Vla.

Vc.
B.

Fl.

Ob.

Cl.
(A)

Fg.

Cor.
(D)

Tr.
(D)

Timp.

Vl.

Vla.

Vc.
B.

Fg.

Vl.

Vla.

Vc.
B.

RETURN SUBORDINATE THEME—PART I ᴧᴧᴧᴧᴧᴧᴧᴧᴧᴧᴧᴧ

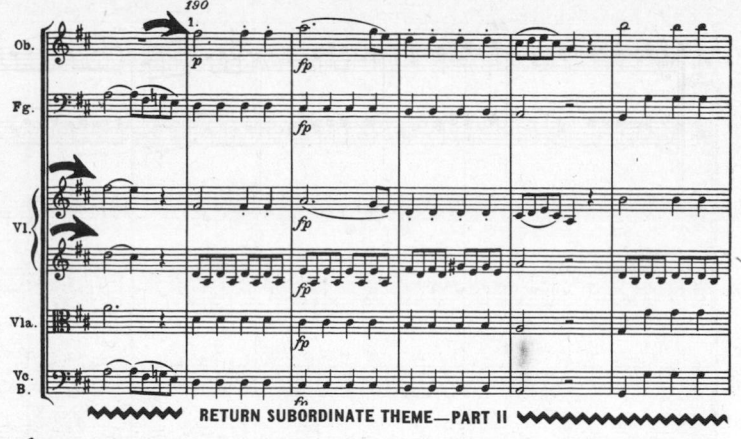

RETURN SUBORDINATE THEME—PART II

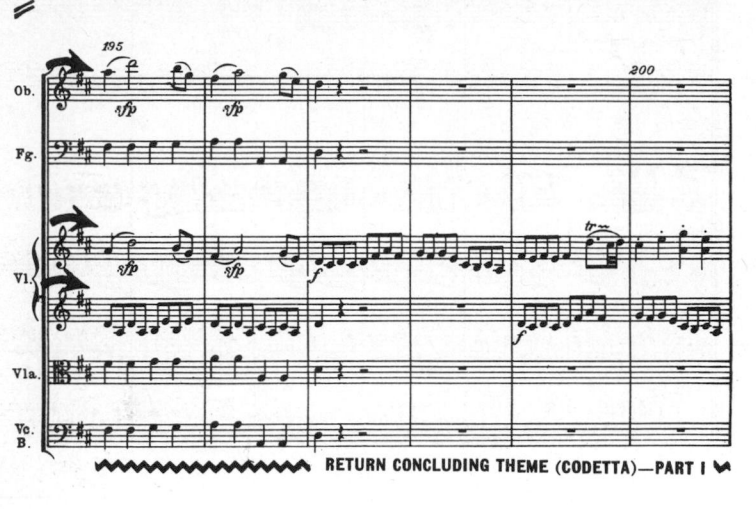

RETURN CONCLUDING THEME (CODETTA)—PART I

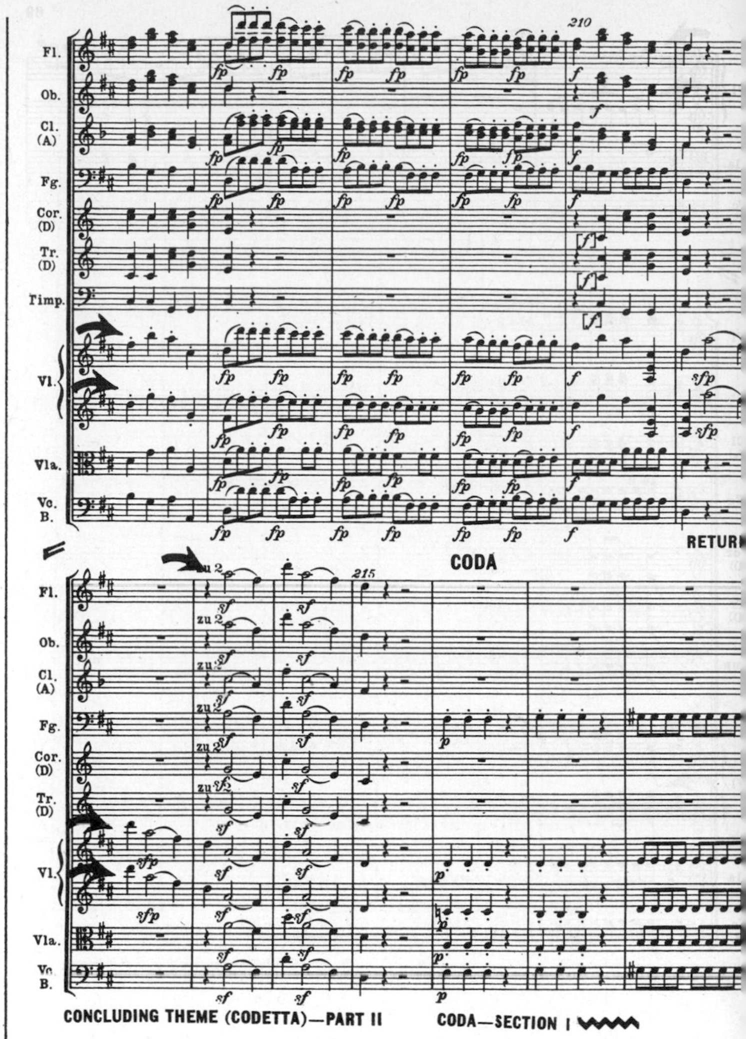

CODA

CONCLUDING THEME (CODETTA)—PART II   CODA—SECTION I

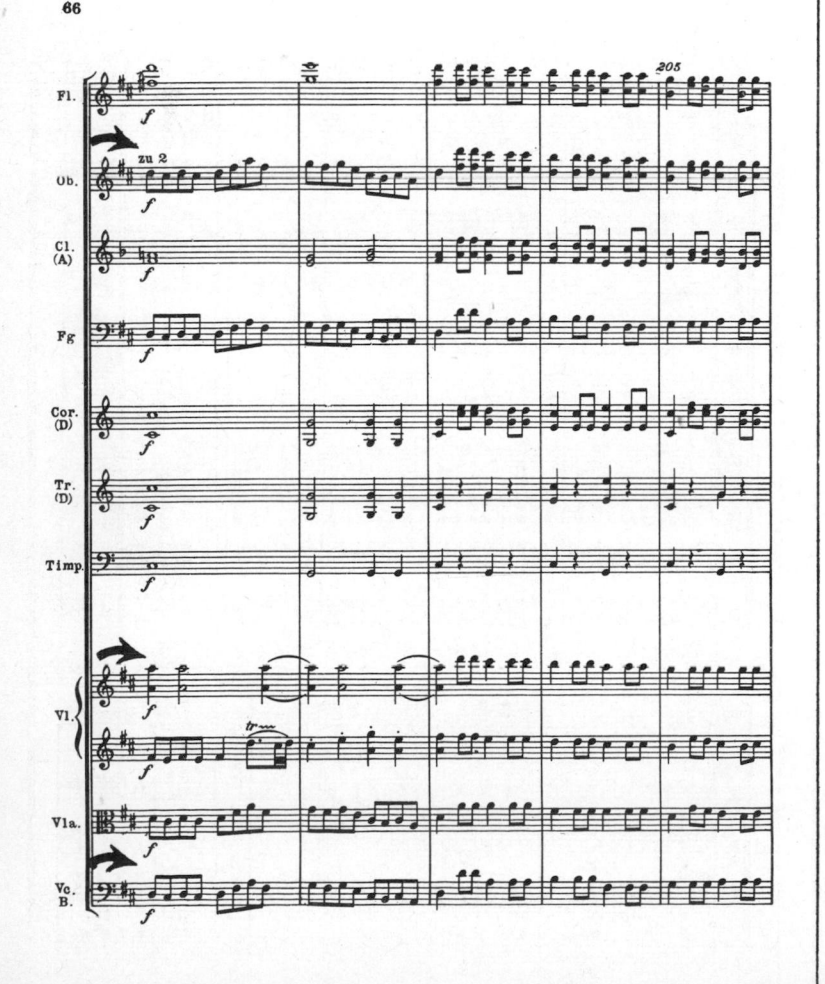

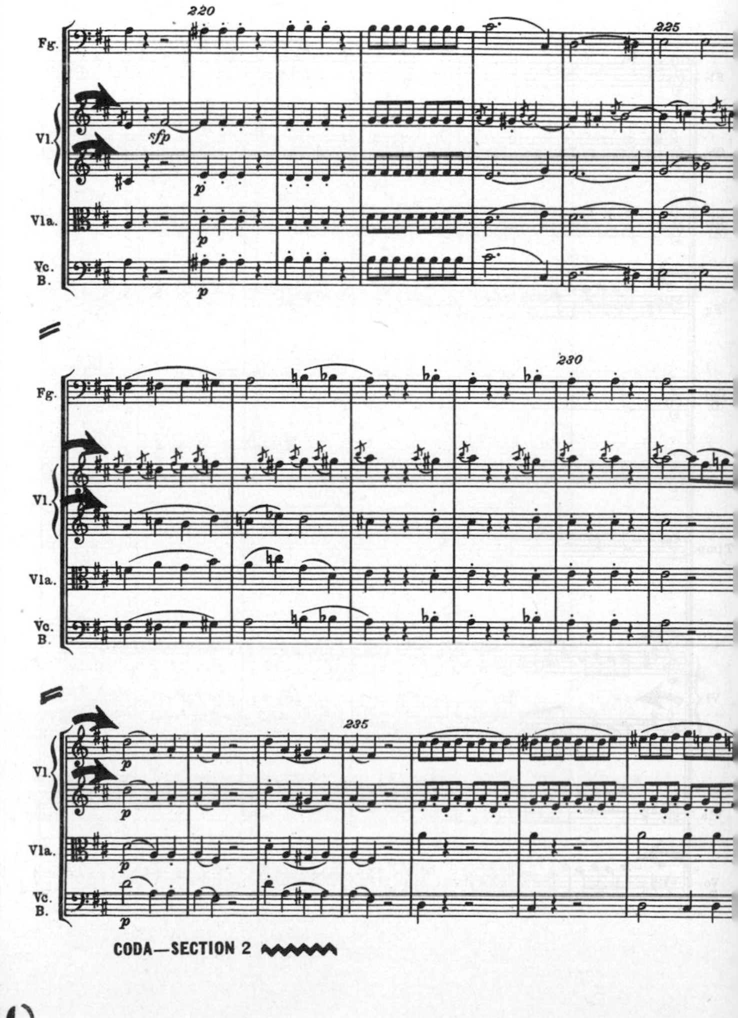

CODA—SECTION 2

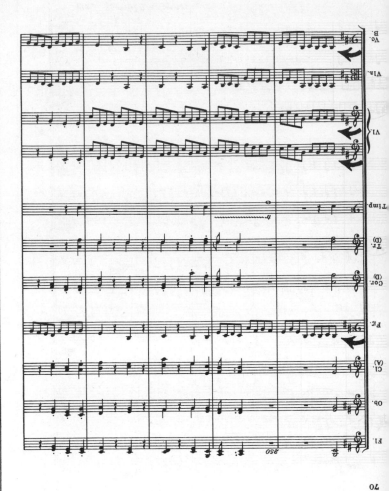

"Linz" Symphony

W. A. Mozart.
1756–1791.

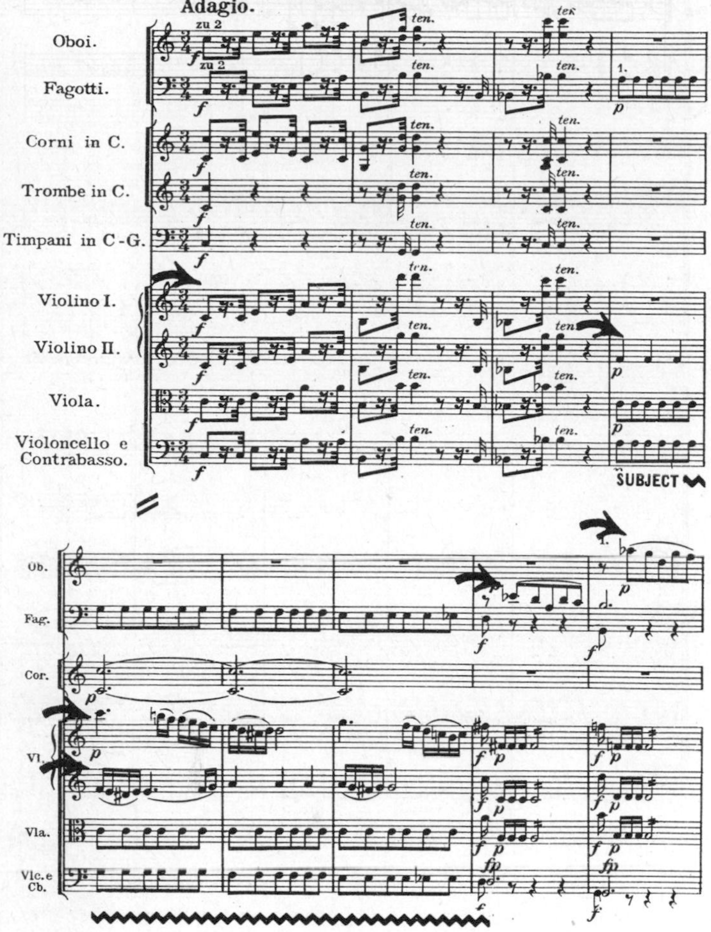

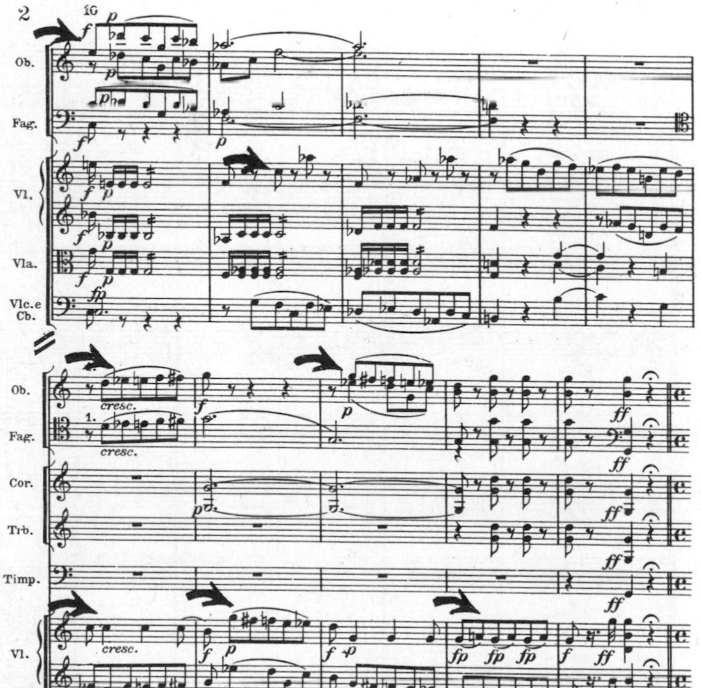

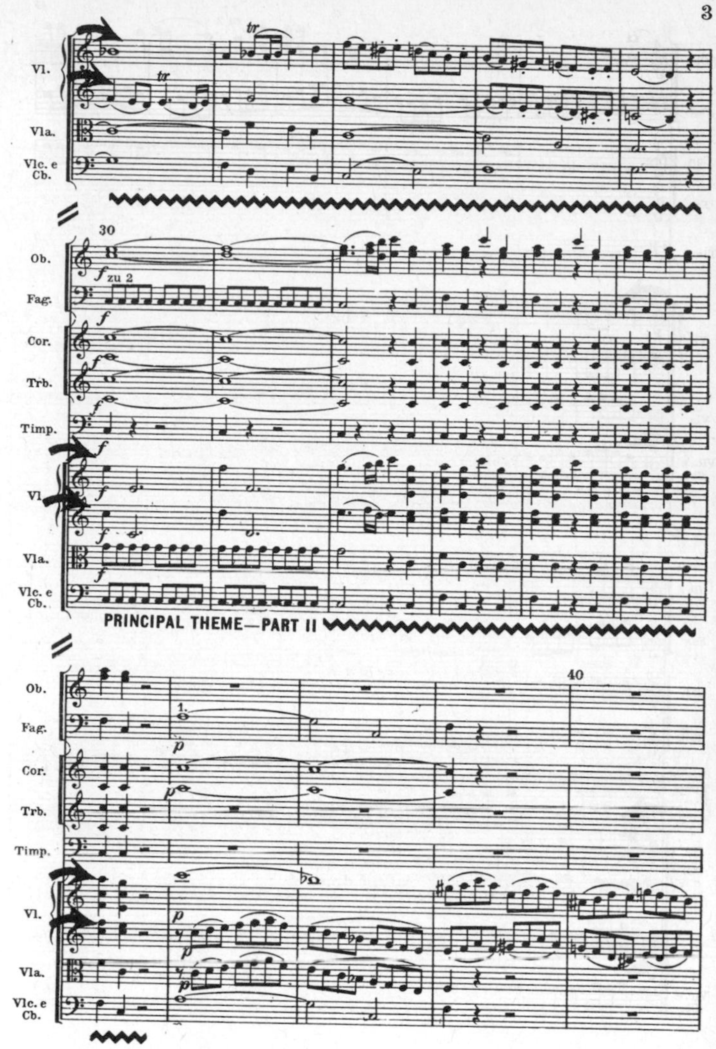

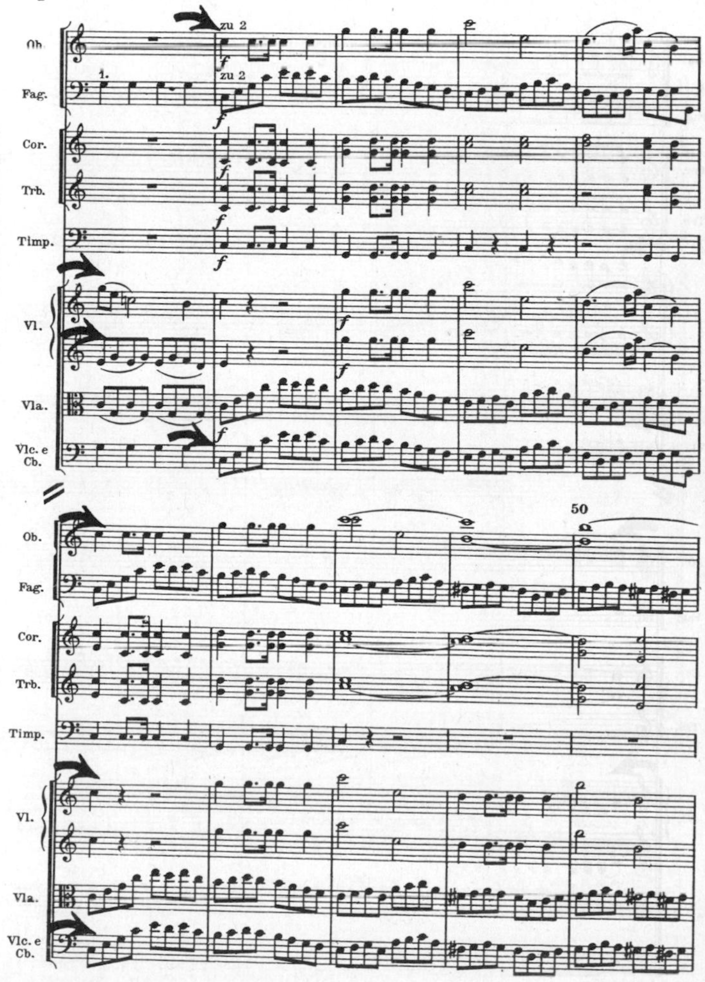

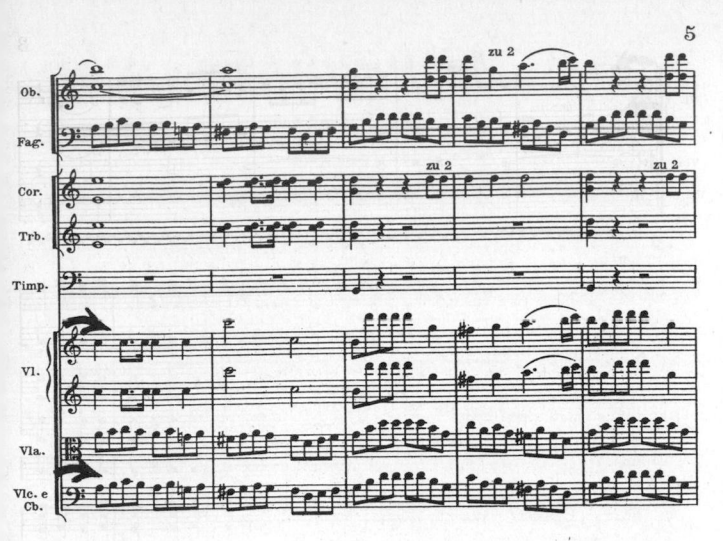

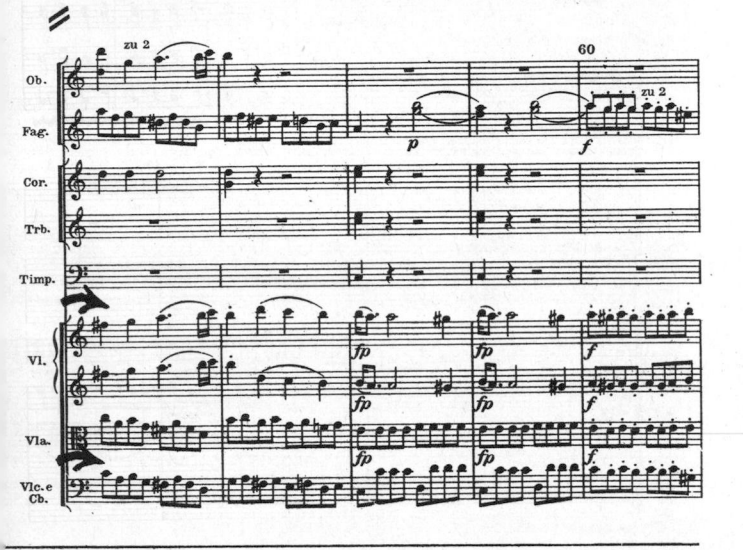

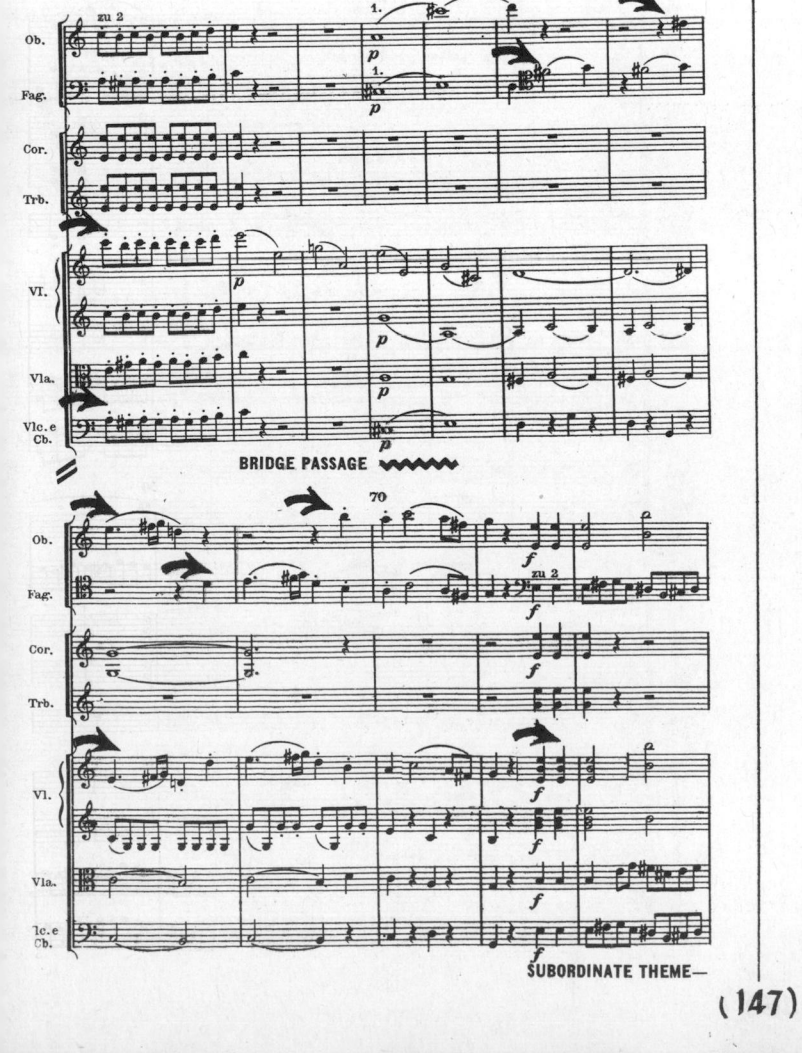

PART I

SUBORDINATE THEME—PART II

BRIDGE PASSAGE

SUBORDINATE THEME—

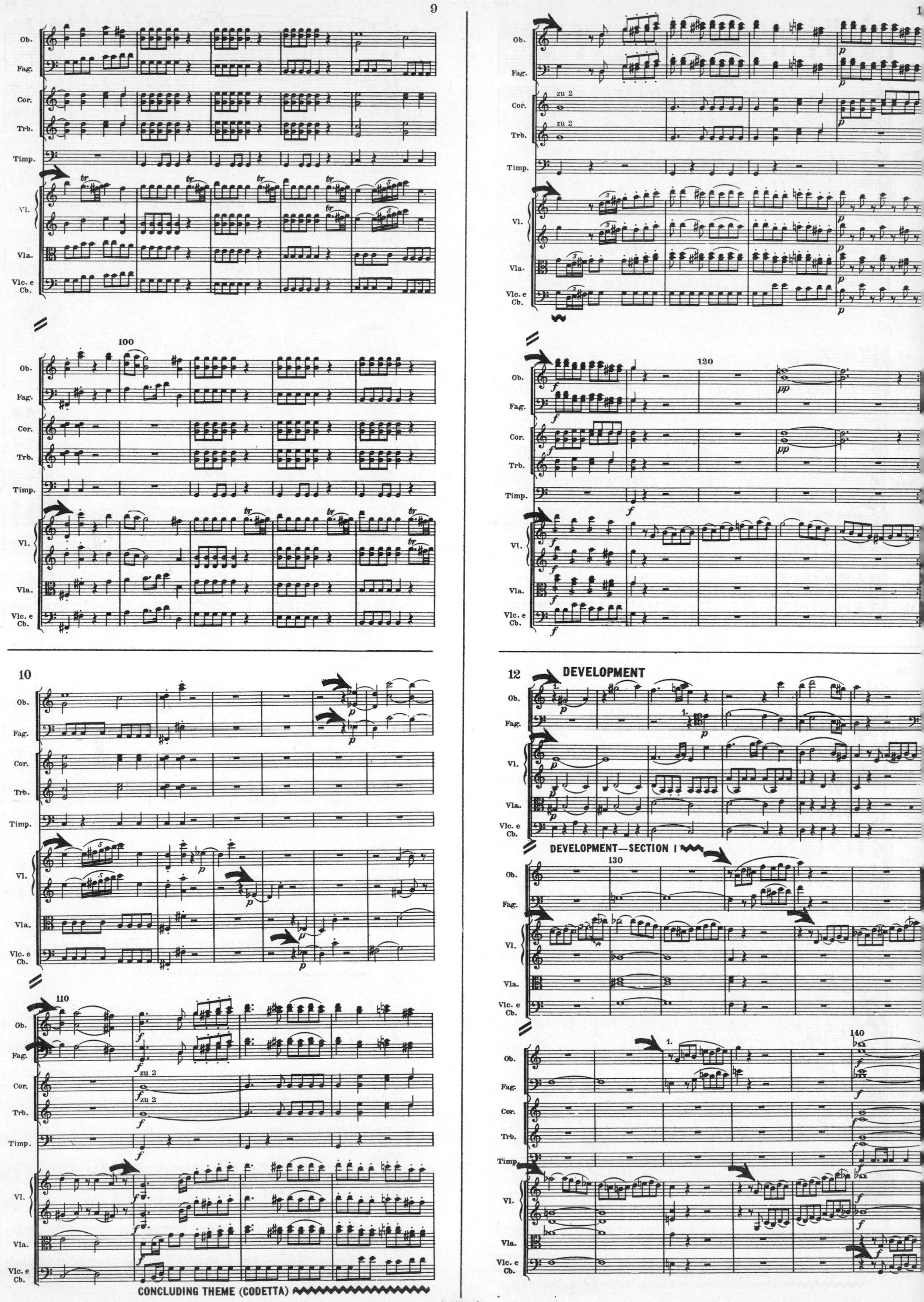
9
Ob.
Fag.
Cor.
Trb.
Timp.
Vl.
Vla.
Vlc. e Cb.
zu 2
100
120
10
12
DEVELOPMENT
DEVELOPMENT—SECTION I
130
110
140
CONCLUDING THEME (CODETTA)

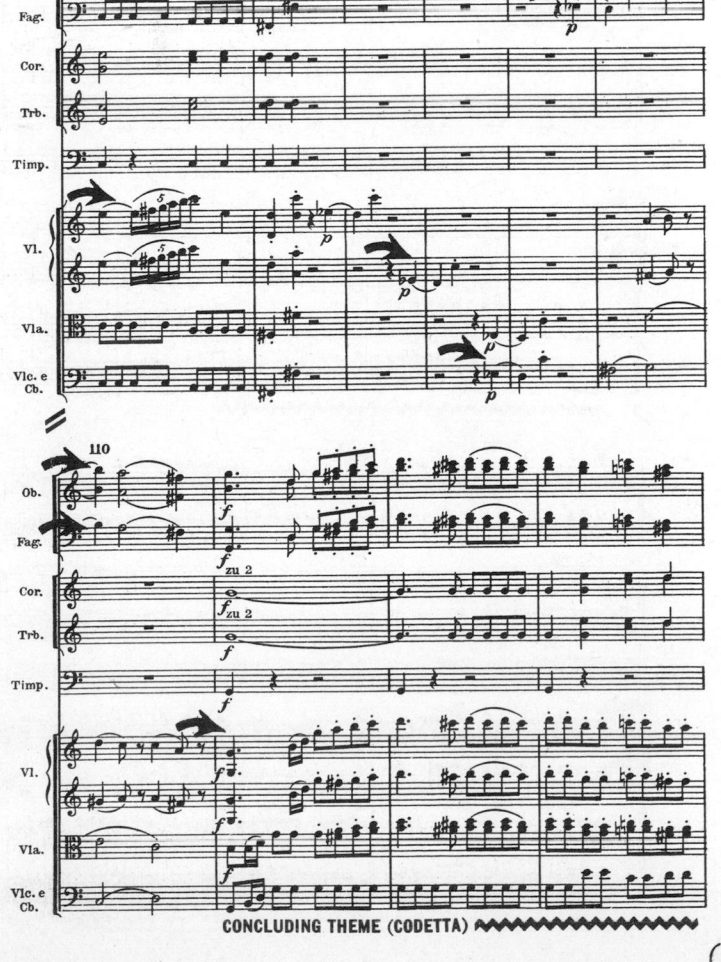

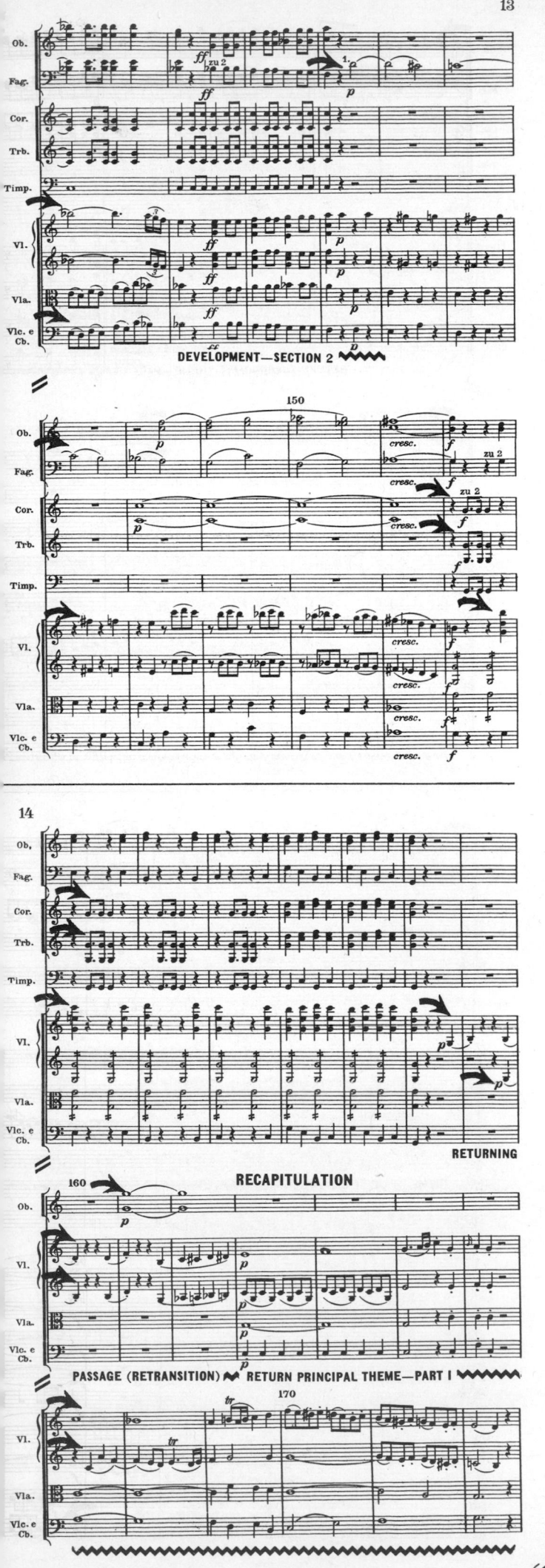

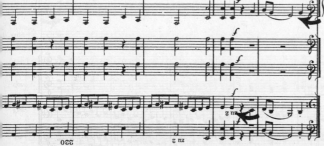

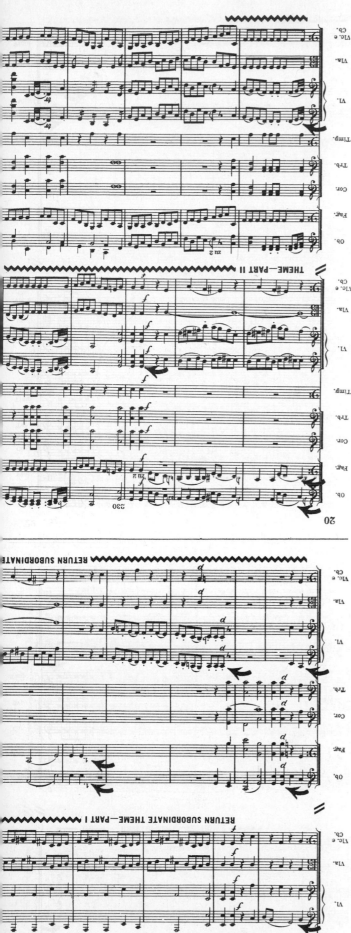

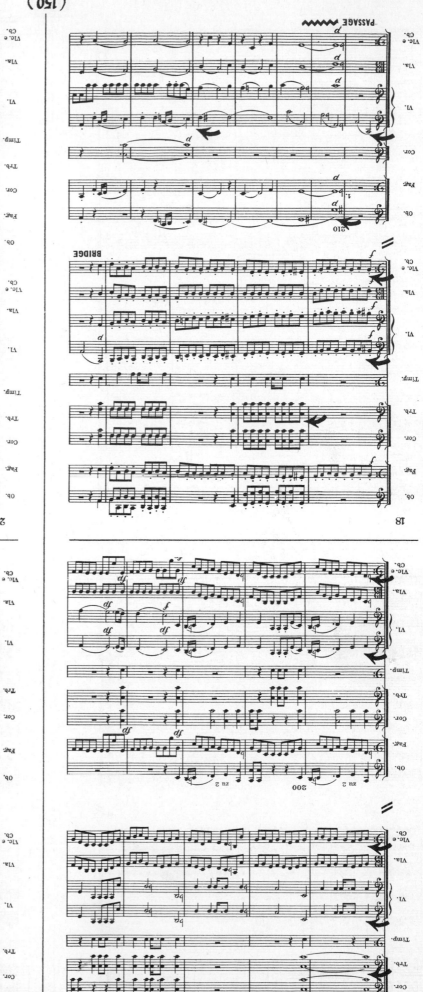

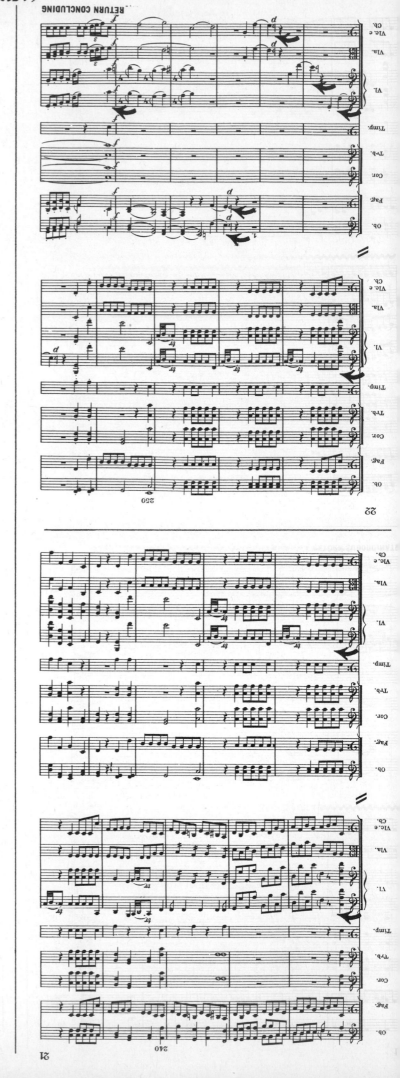
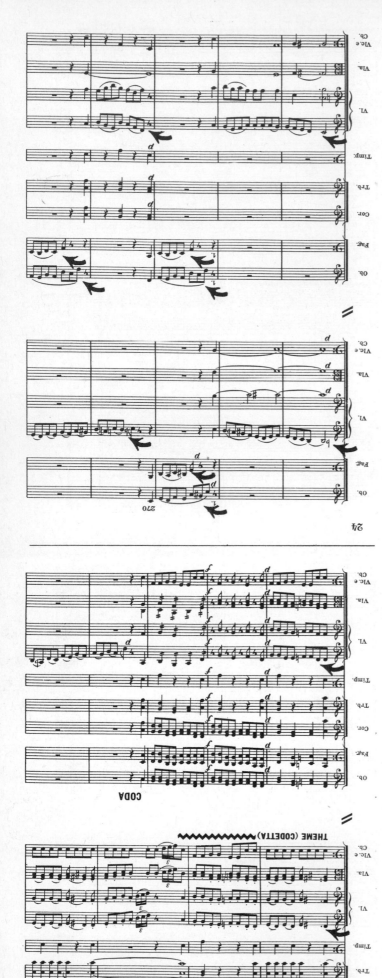

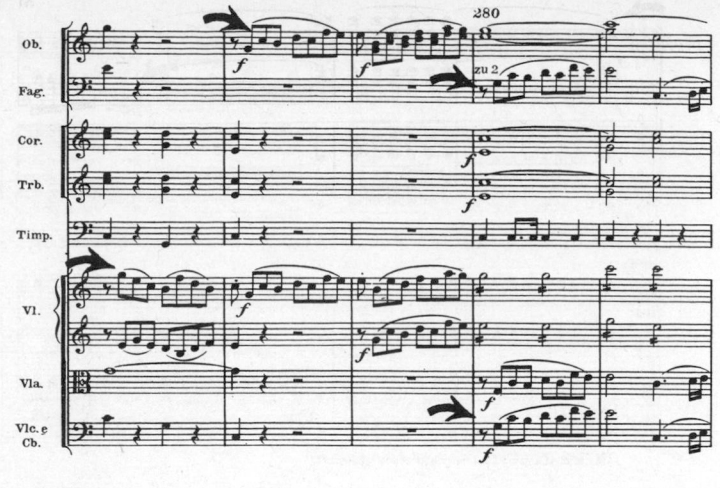

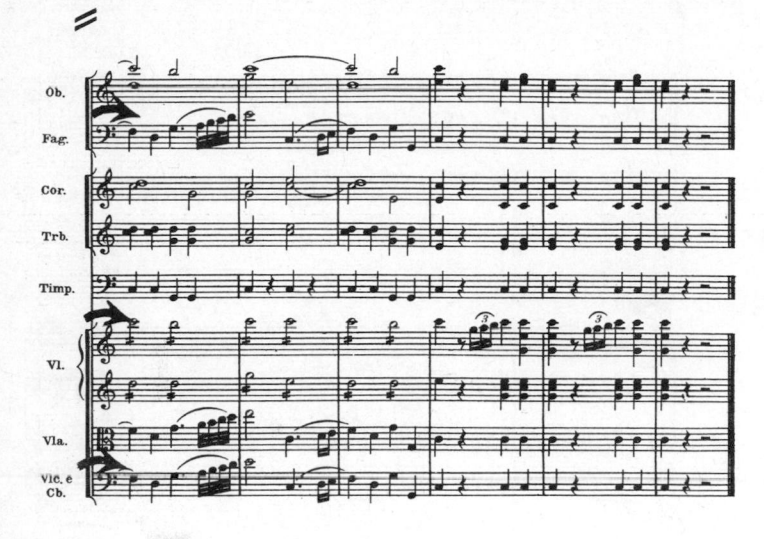

II.
Poco Adagio. EXPOSITION

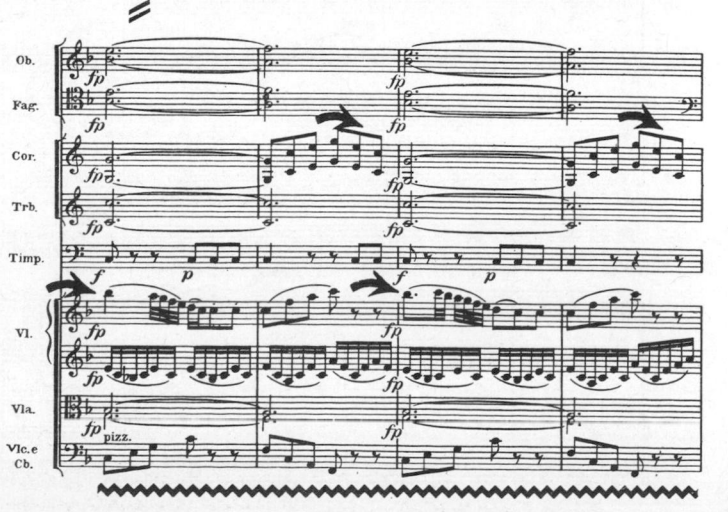

PRINCIPAL THEME—PART I

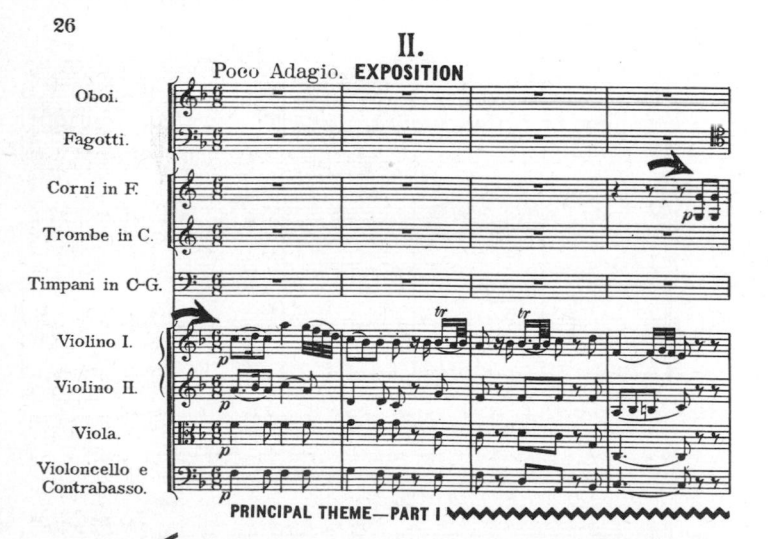

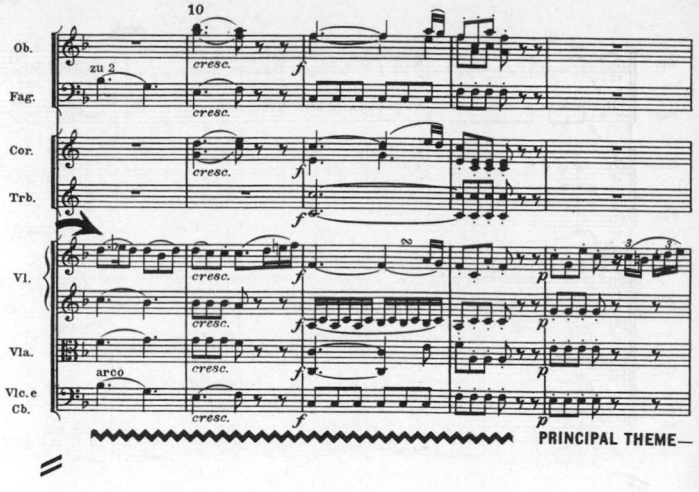

PRINCIPAL THEME—

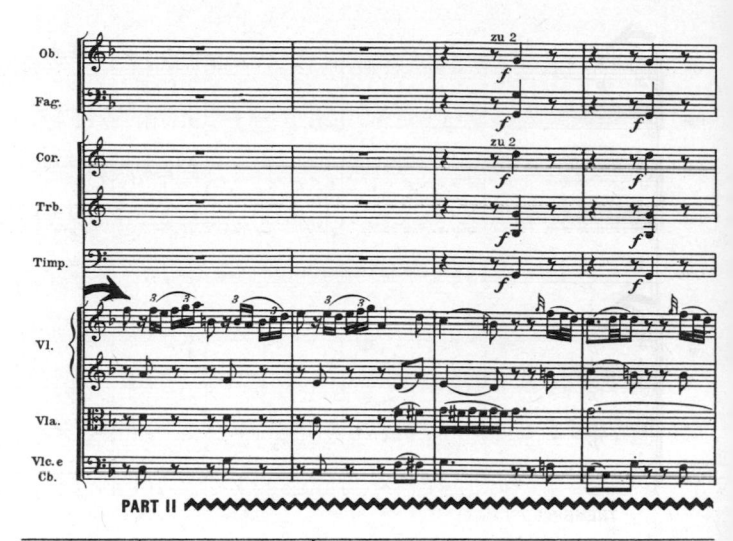

PART II

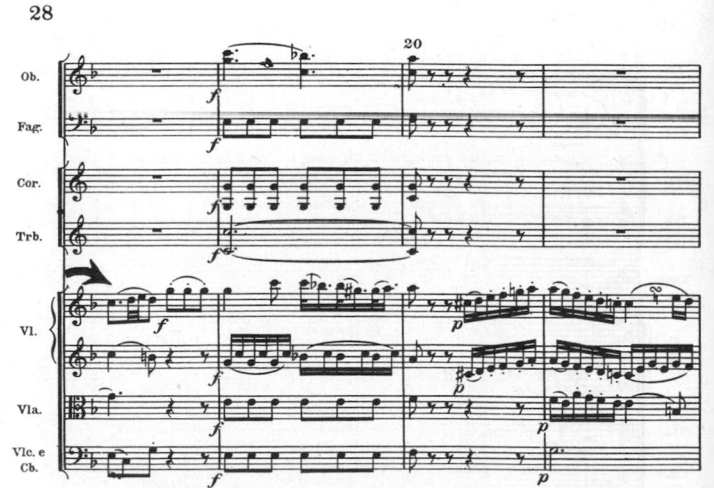

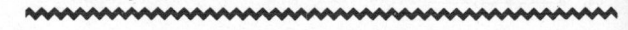

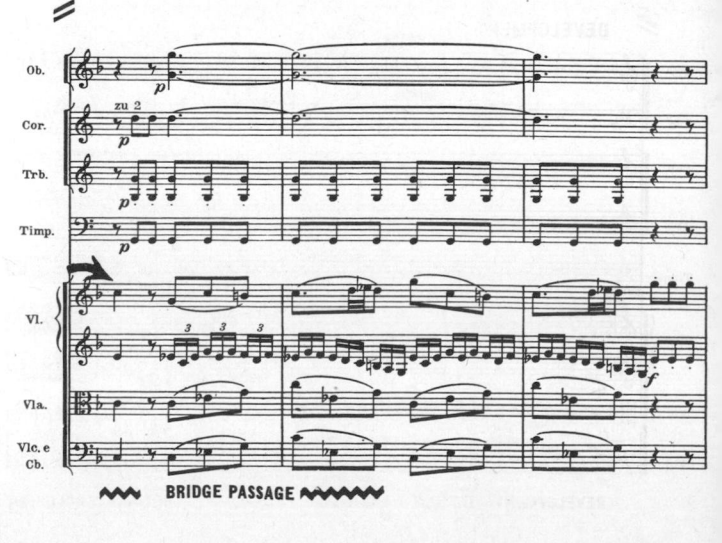

BRIDGE PASSAGE

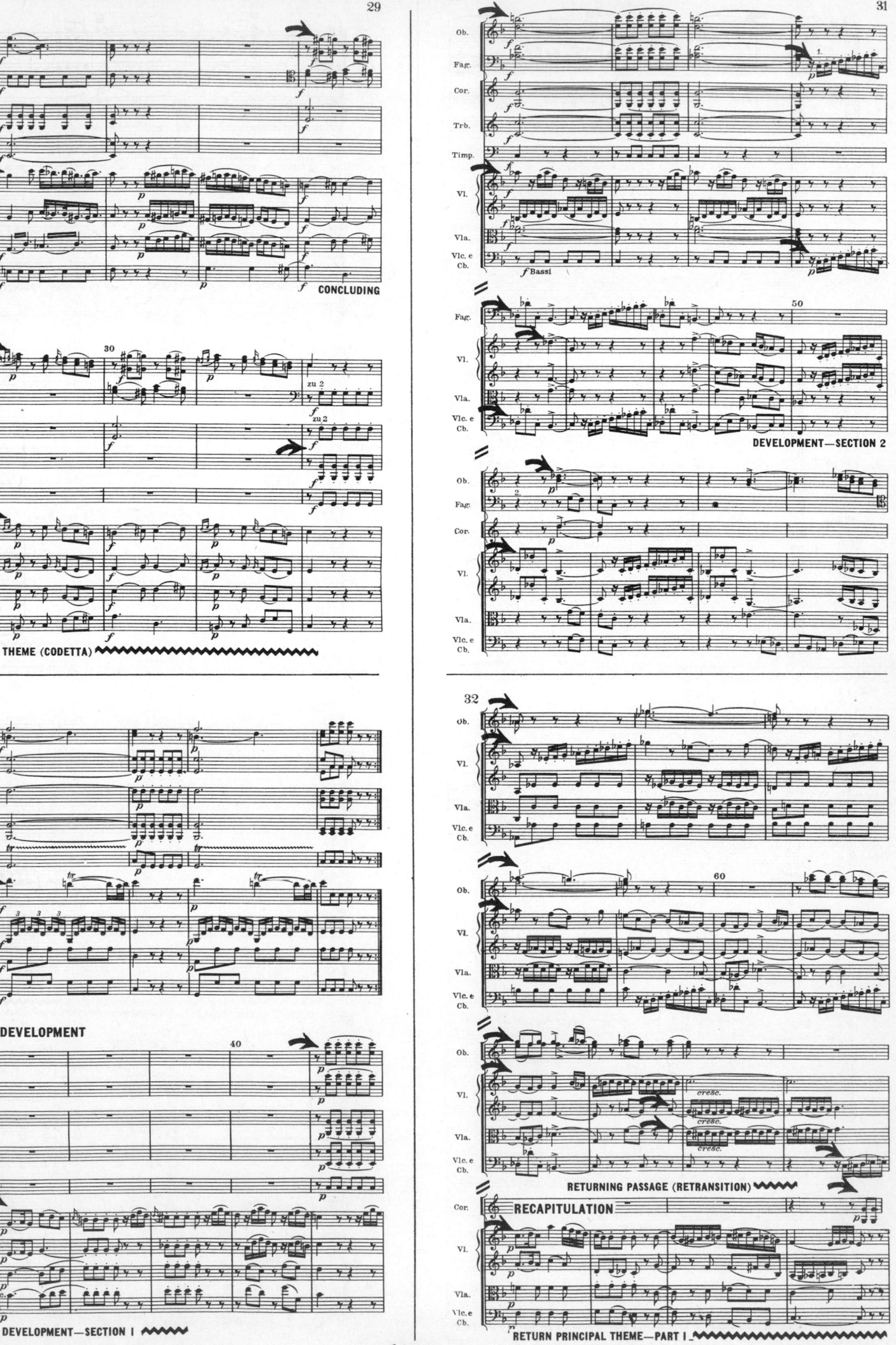

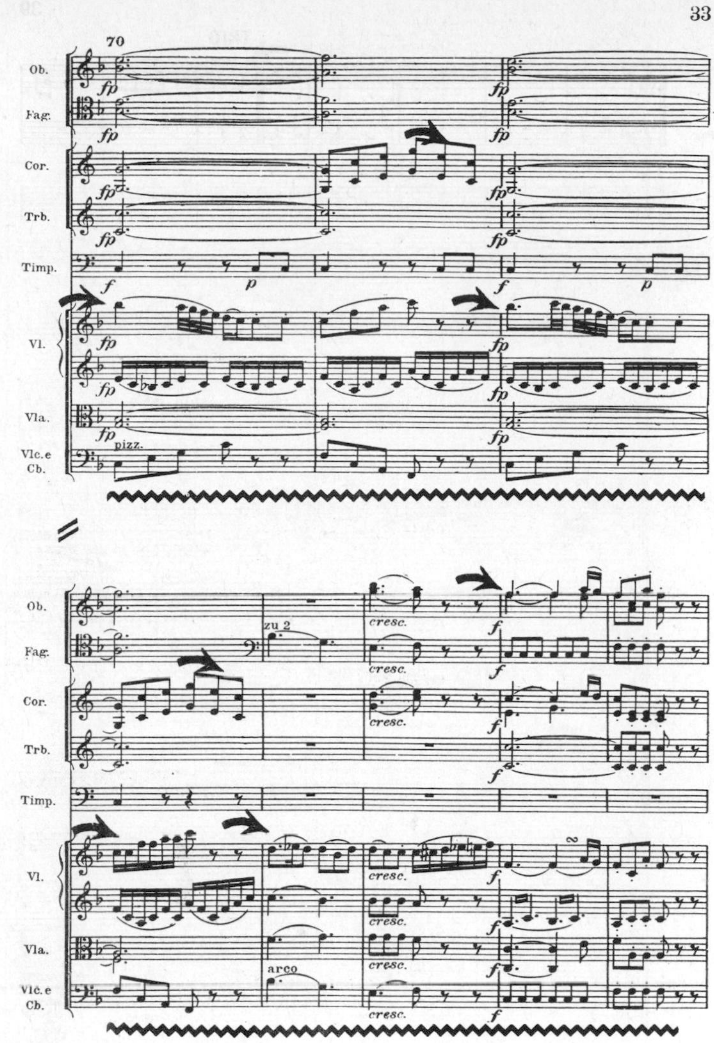

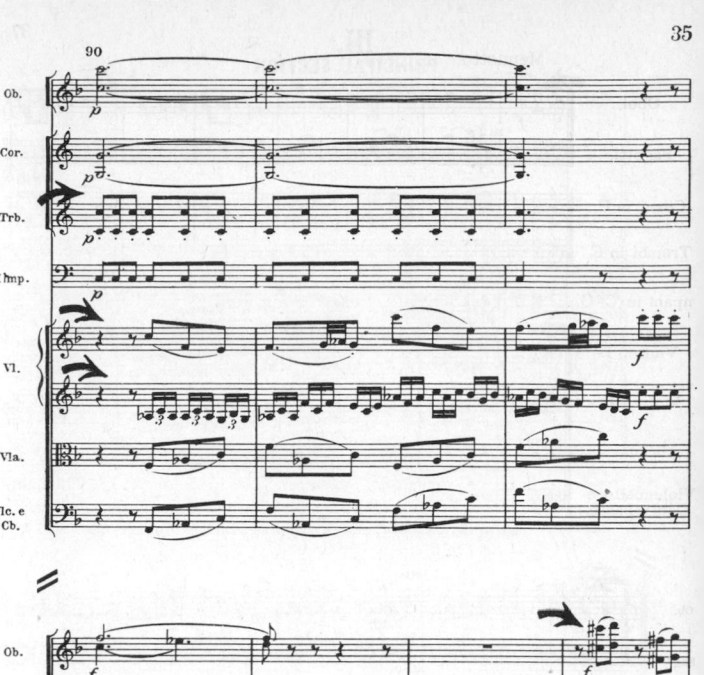

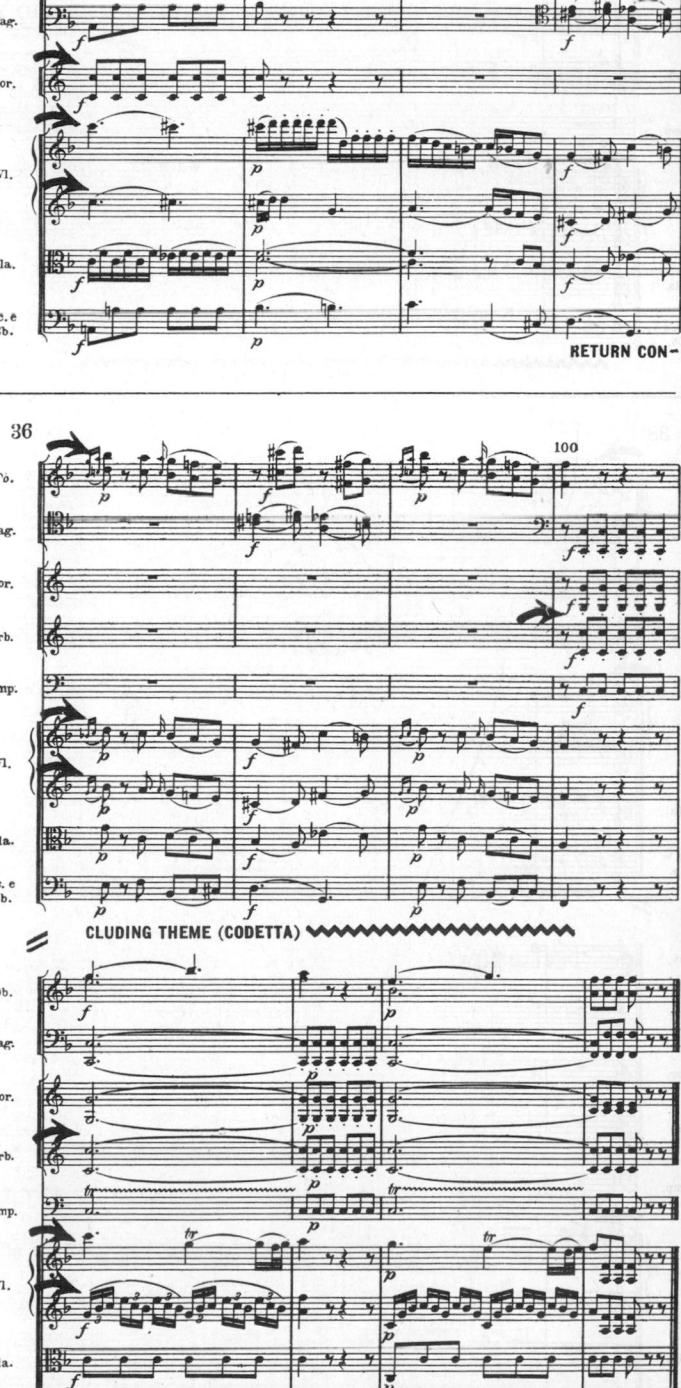

RETURN CON-

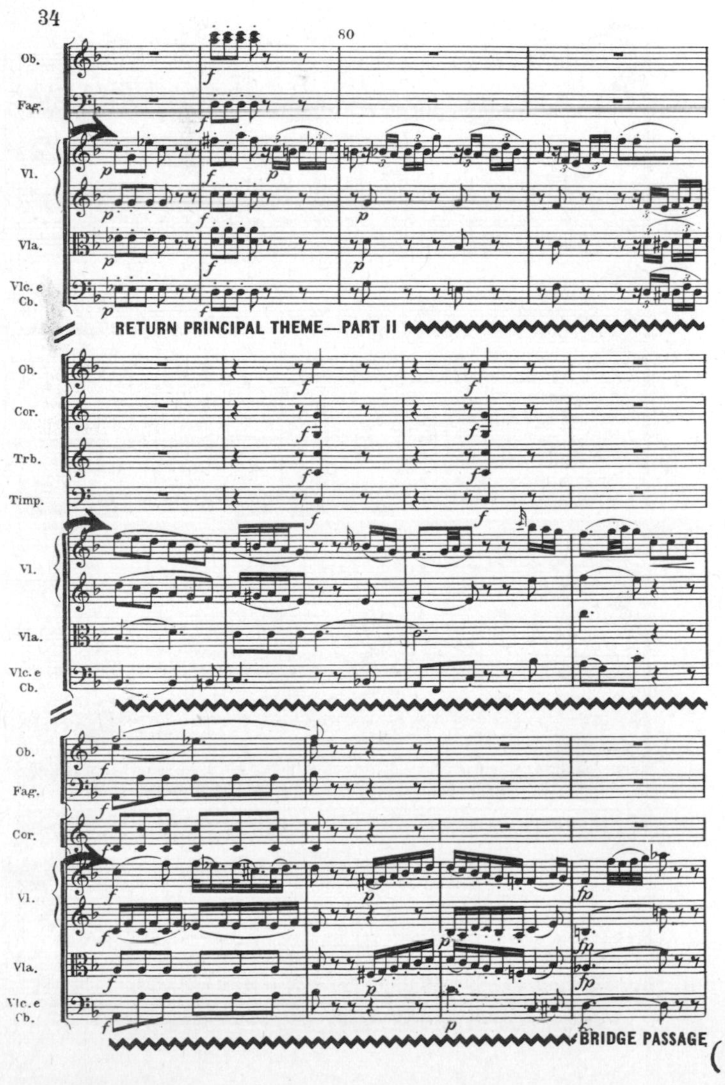

RETURN PRINCIPAL THEME—PART II

BRIDGE PASSAGE

CLUDING THEME (CODETTA)

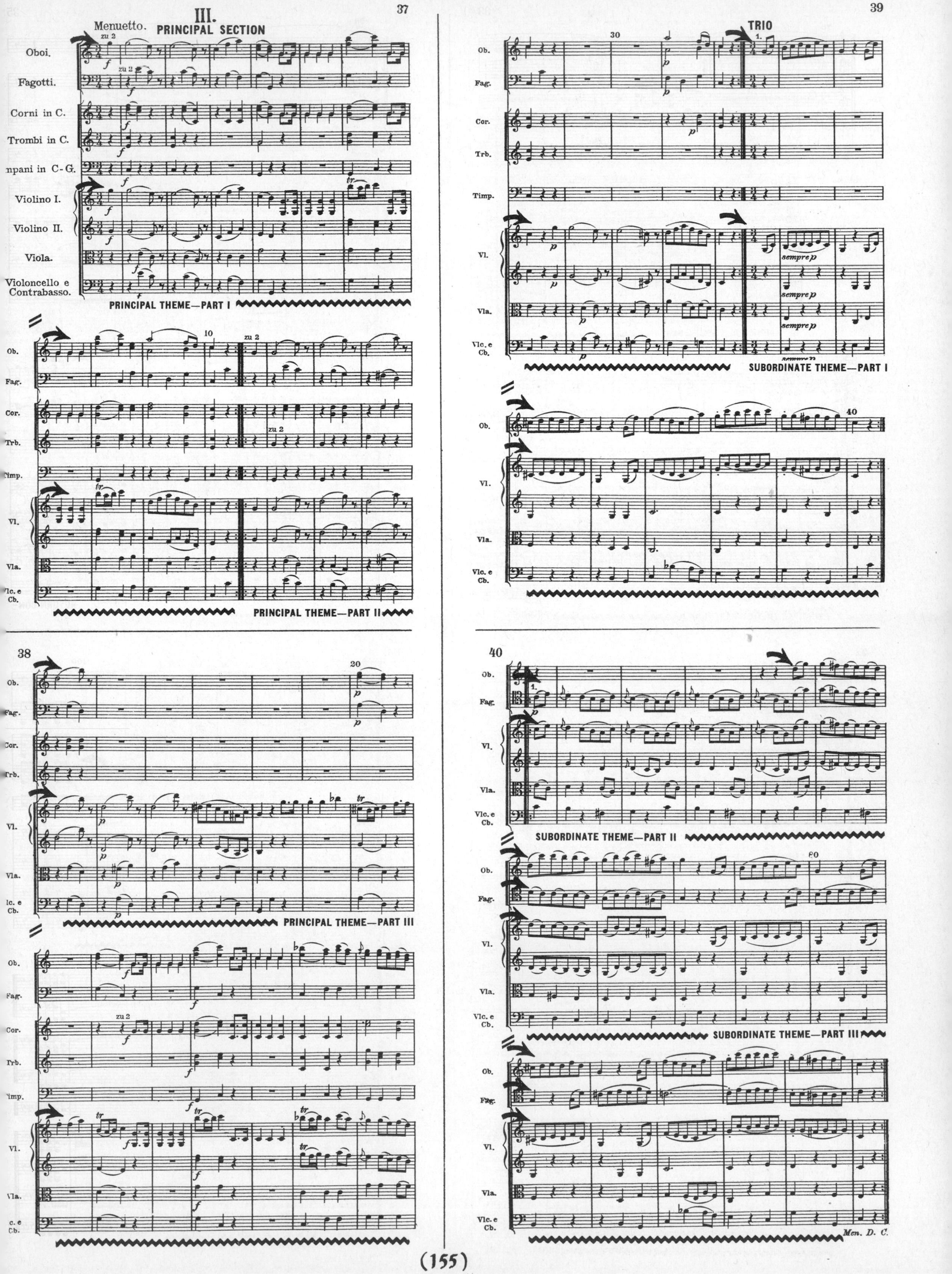

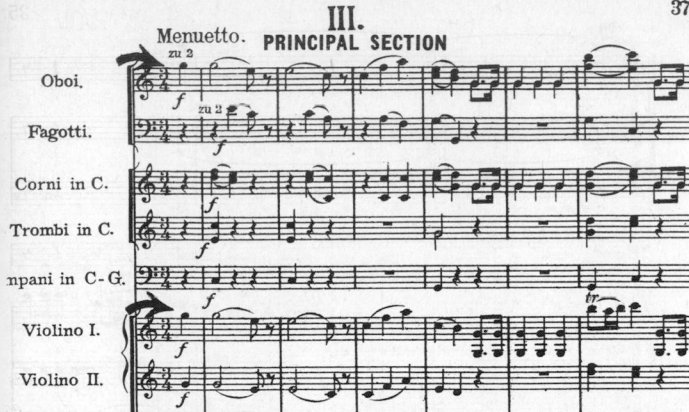

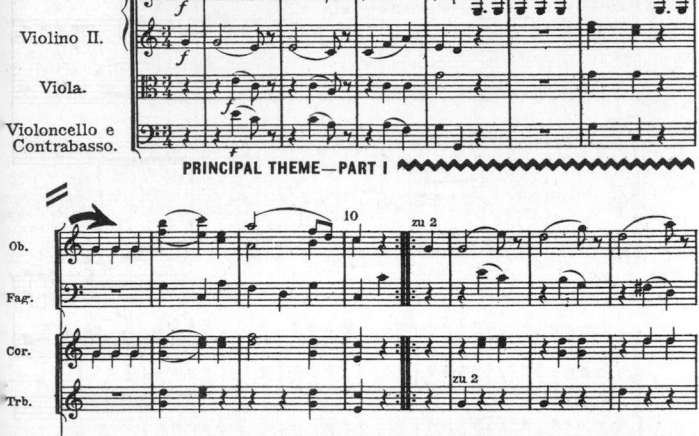

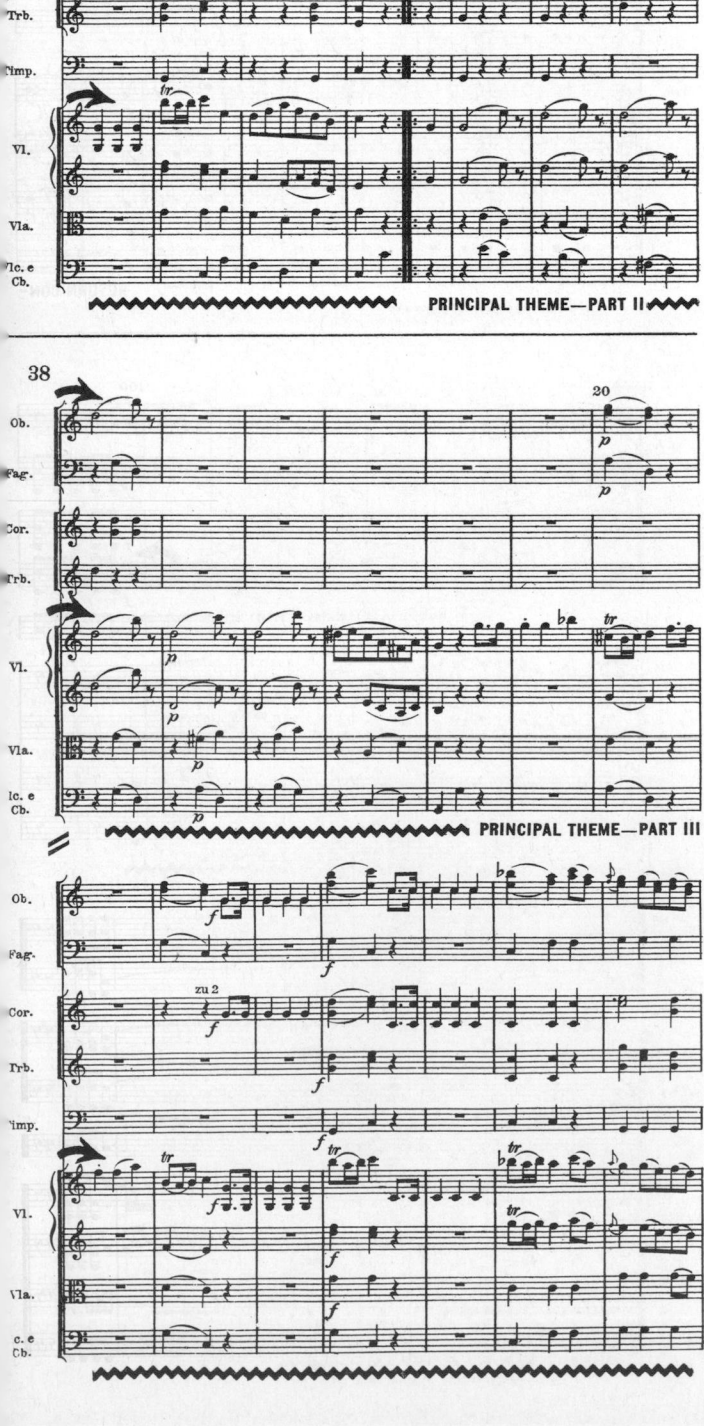

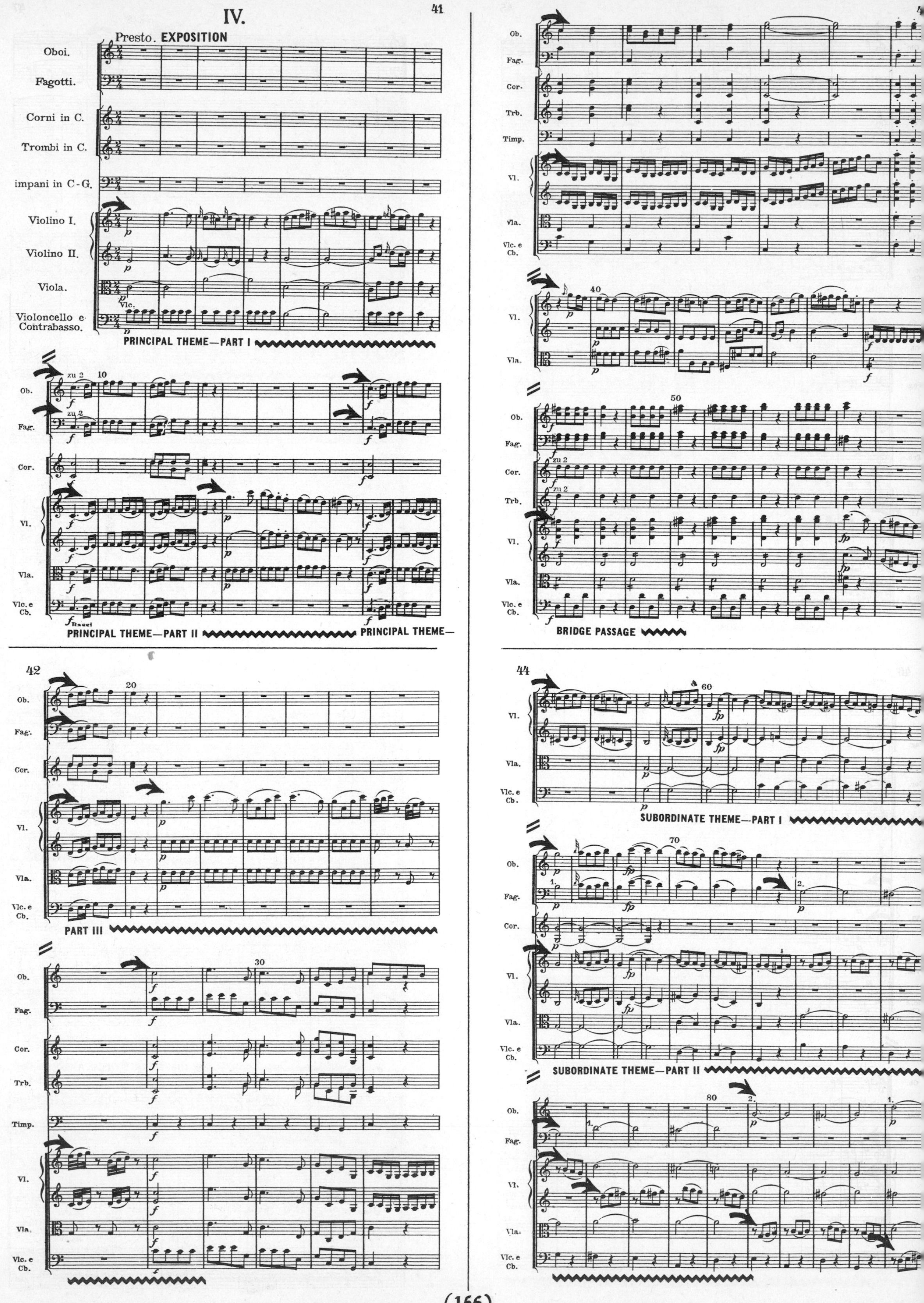
41
IV.
Presto. EXPOSITION
Oboi.
Fagotti.
Corni in C.
Trombi in C.
impani in C-G.
Violino I.
Violino II.
Viola.
Violoncello e Contrabasso.
Vlc.
PRINCIPAL THEME—PART I
zu 2
10
Ob.
Fag.
Cor.
Vl.
Vla.
Vlc. e Cb.
Bassi
PRINCIPAL THEME—PART II
PRINCIPAL THEME—
42
20
PART III
30
Timp.
Trb.
40
50
BRIDGE PASSAGE
44
60
SUBORDINATE THEME—PART I
70
SUBORDINATE THEME—PART II
80

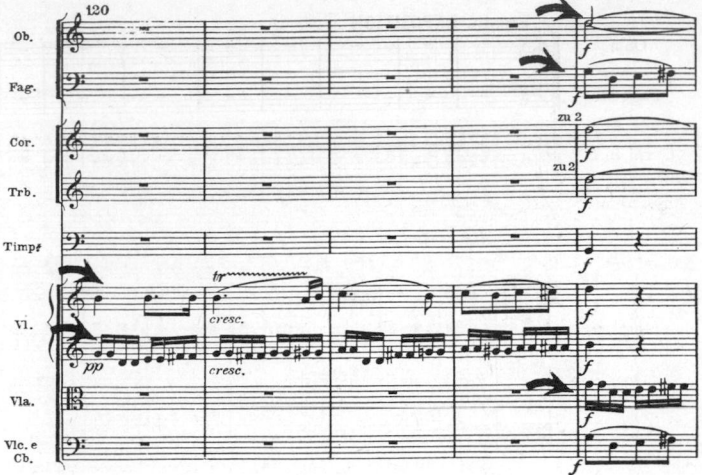

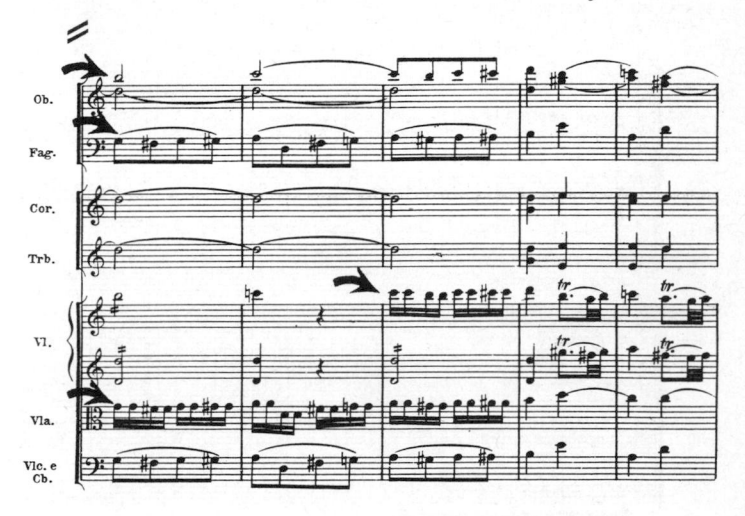

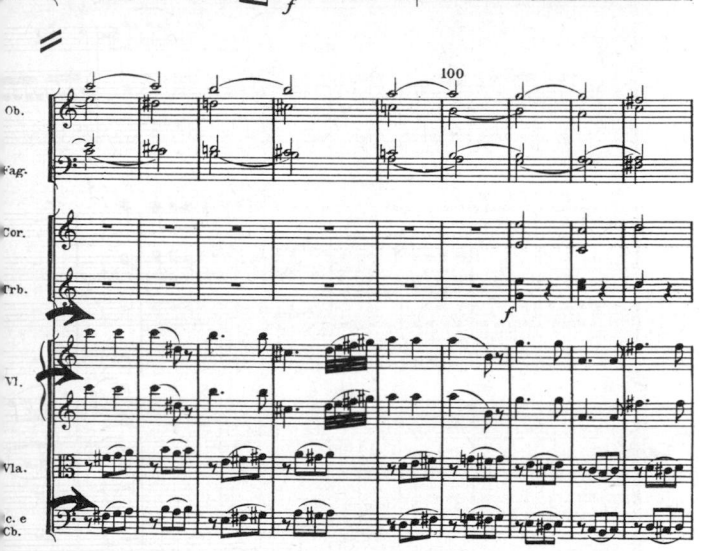

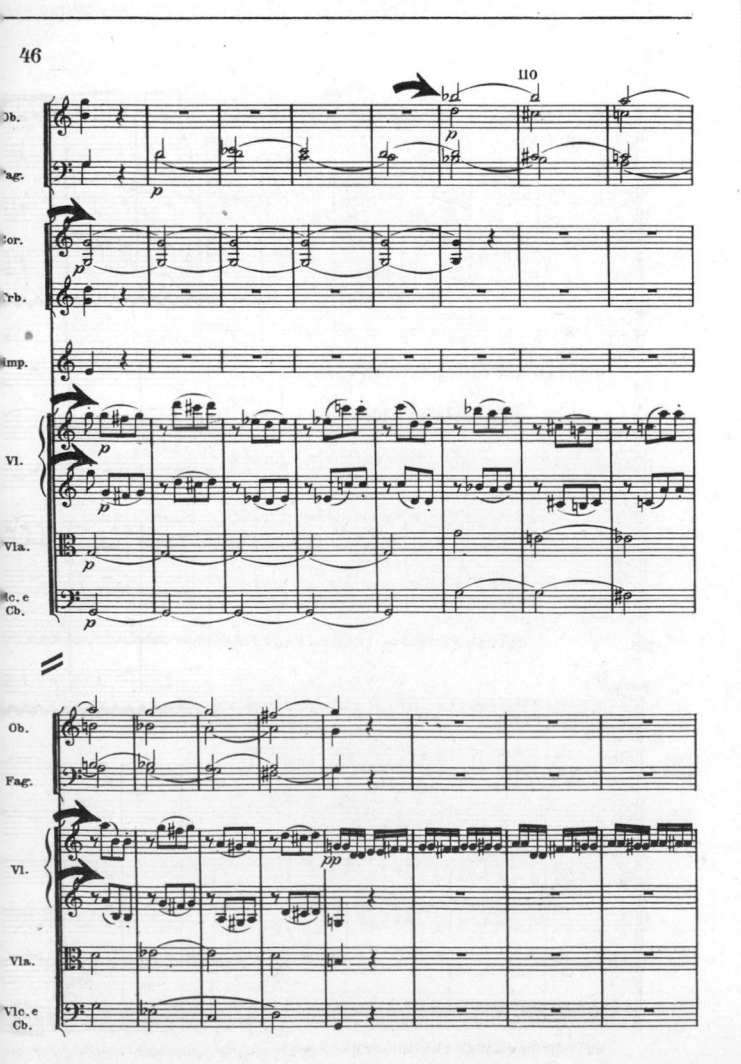

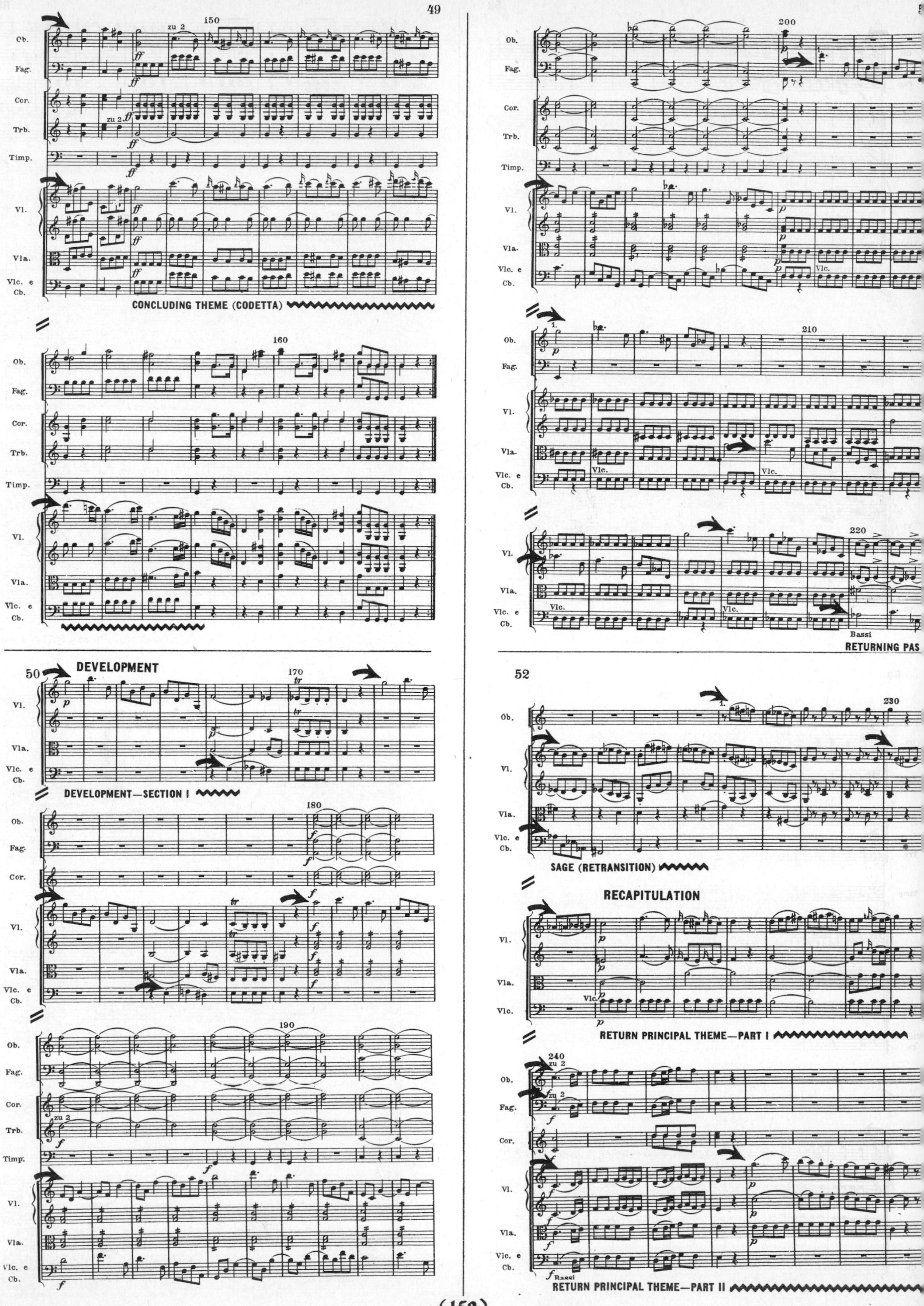
49
CONCLUDING THEME (CODETTA)
50
DEVELOPMENT
DEVELOPMENT—SECTION I
RETURNING PAS
52
SAGE (RETRANSITION)
RECAPITULATION
RETURN PRINCIPAL THEME—PART I
RETURN PRINCIPAL THEME—PART II

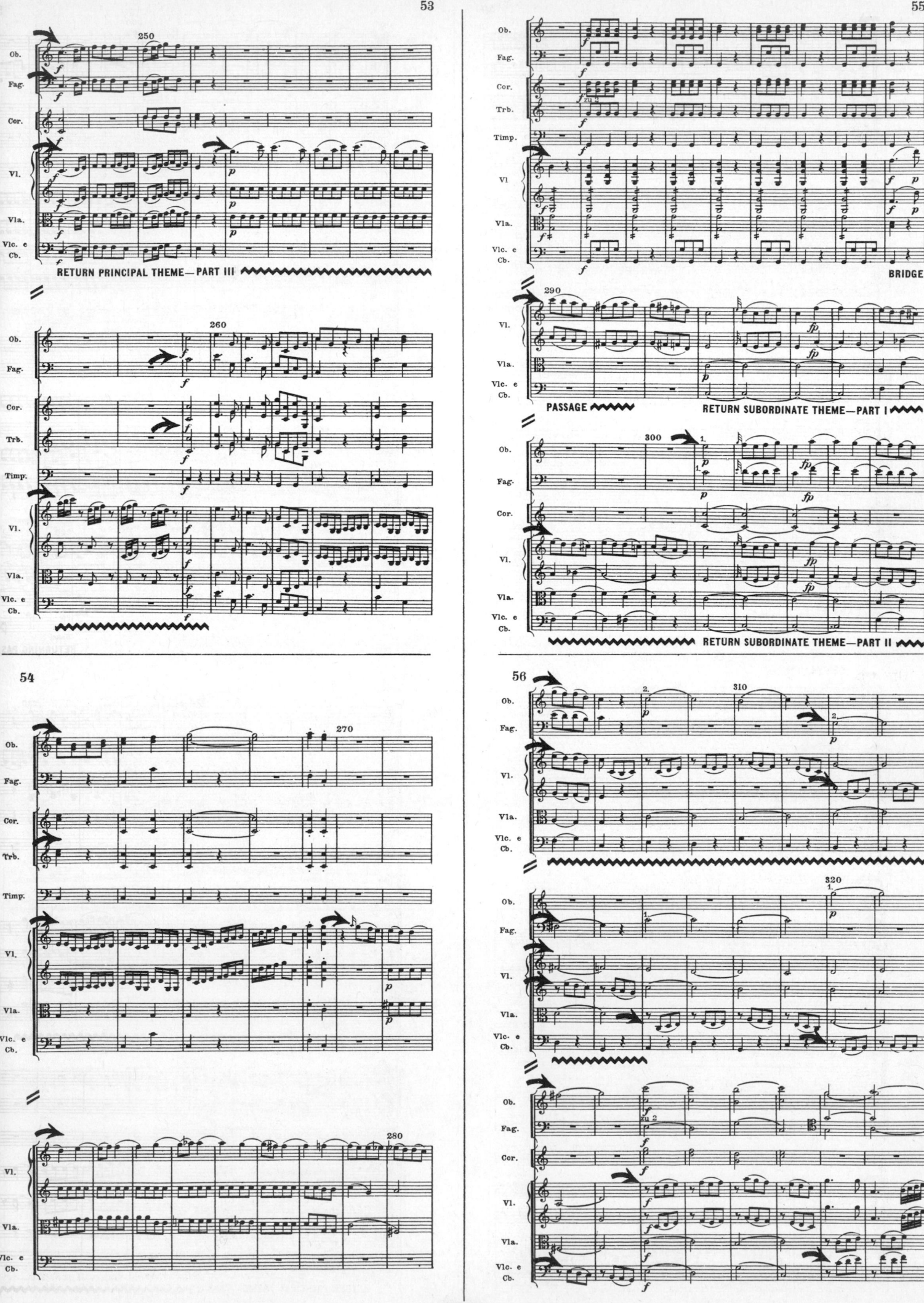

RETURN PRINCIPAL THEME—PART III

BRIDGE

PASSAGE

RETURN SUBORDINATE THEME—PART I

RETURN SUBORDINATE THEME—PART II

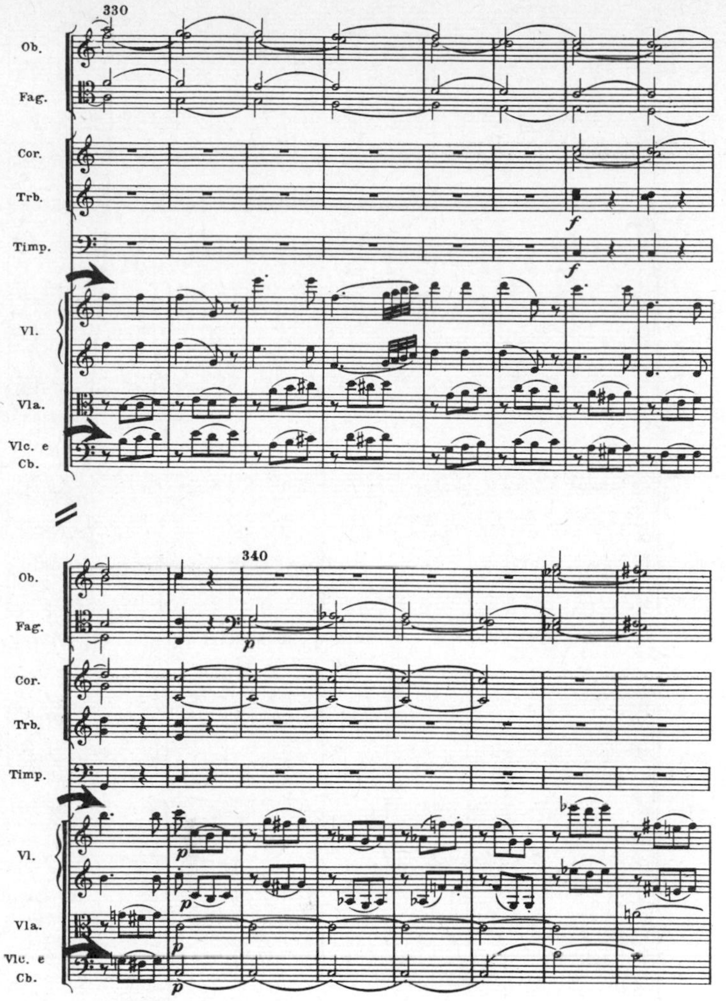

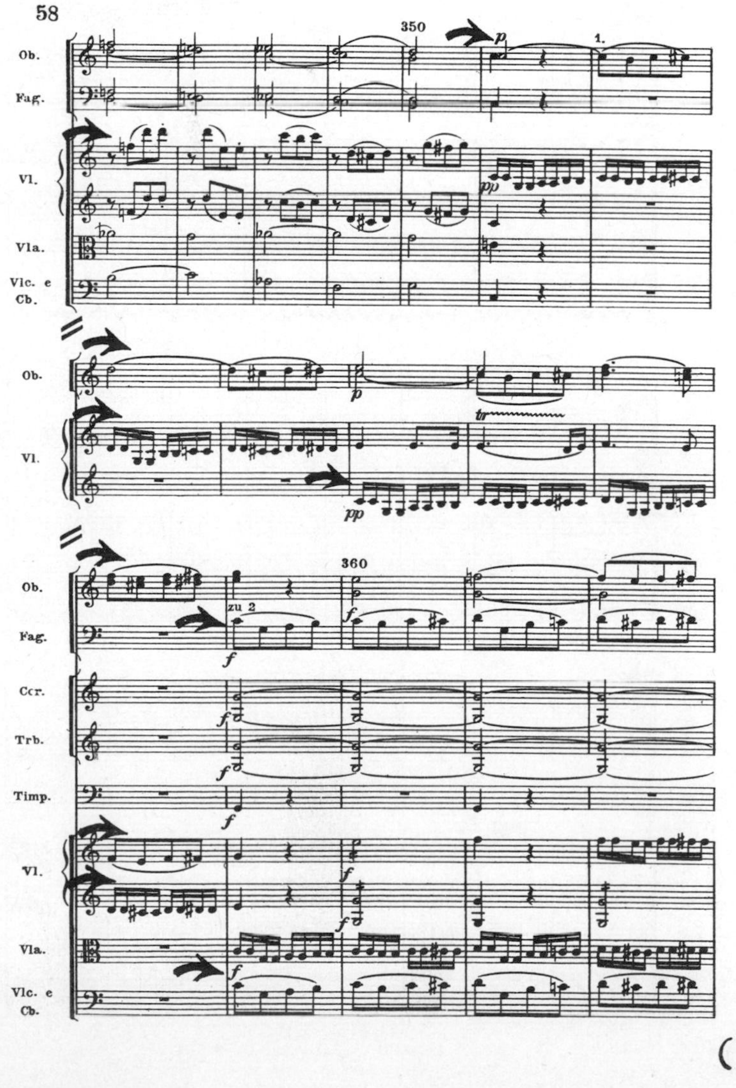

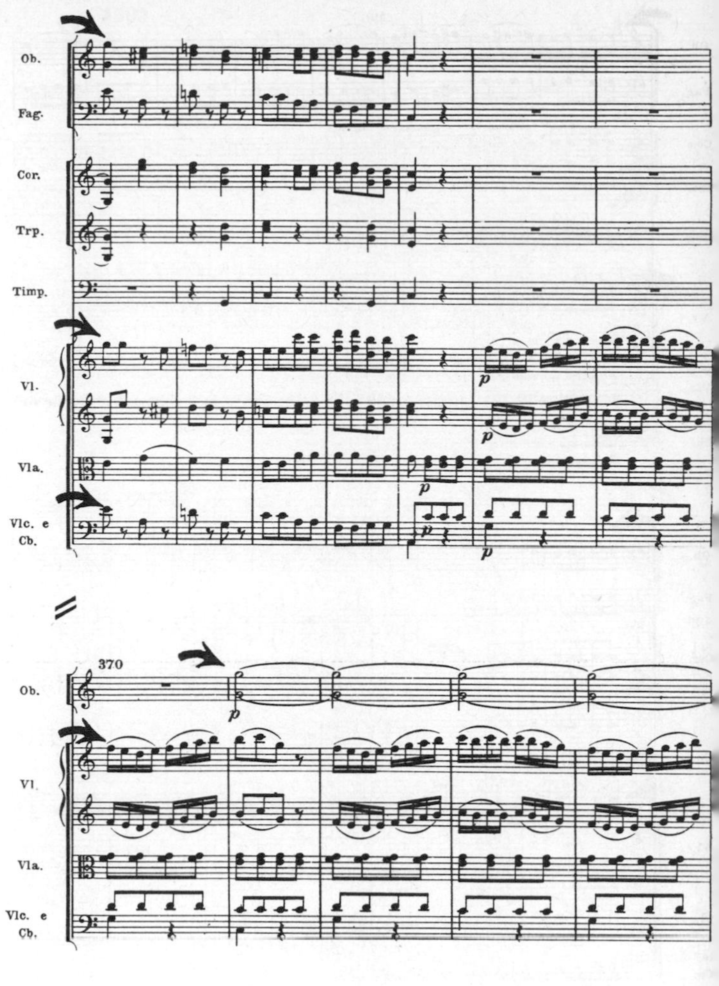

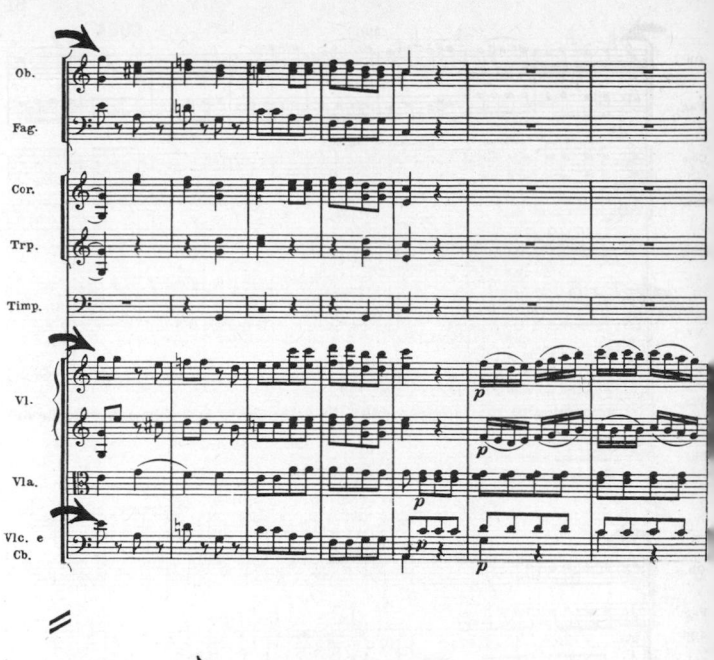

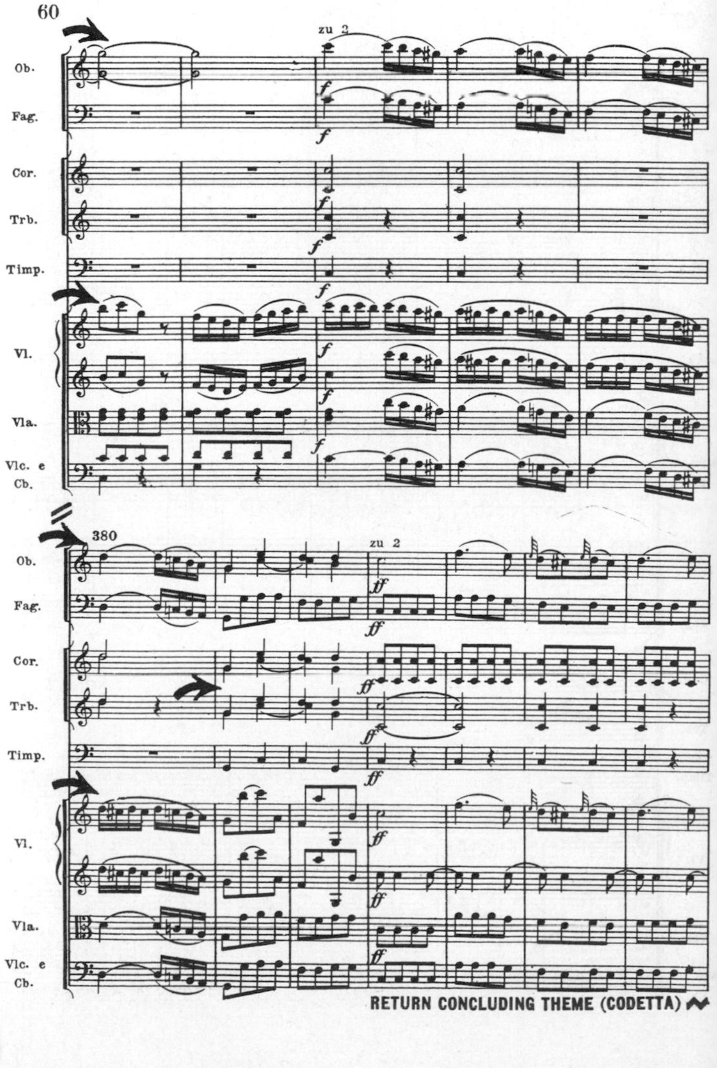

(160)

RETURN CONCLUDING THEME (CODETTA)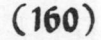

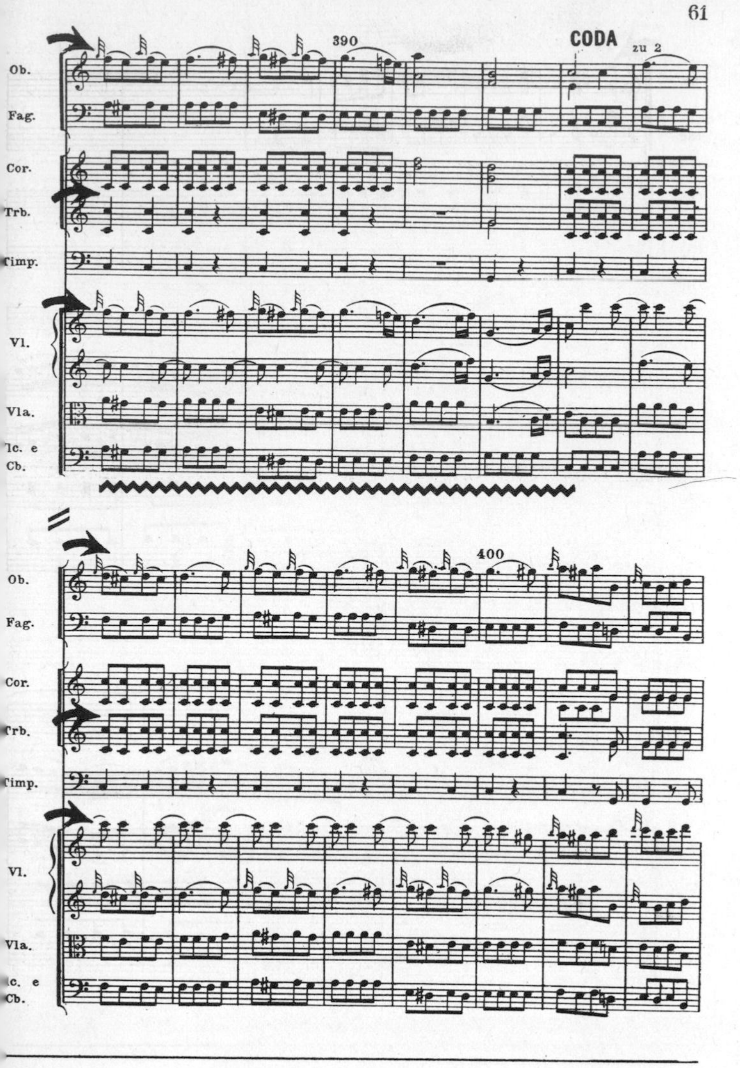
390
CODA
zu 2
Ob.
Fag.
Cor.
Trb.
Timp.
Vl.
Vla.
Vlc. e Cb.
400

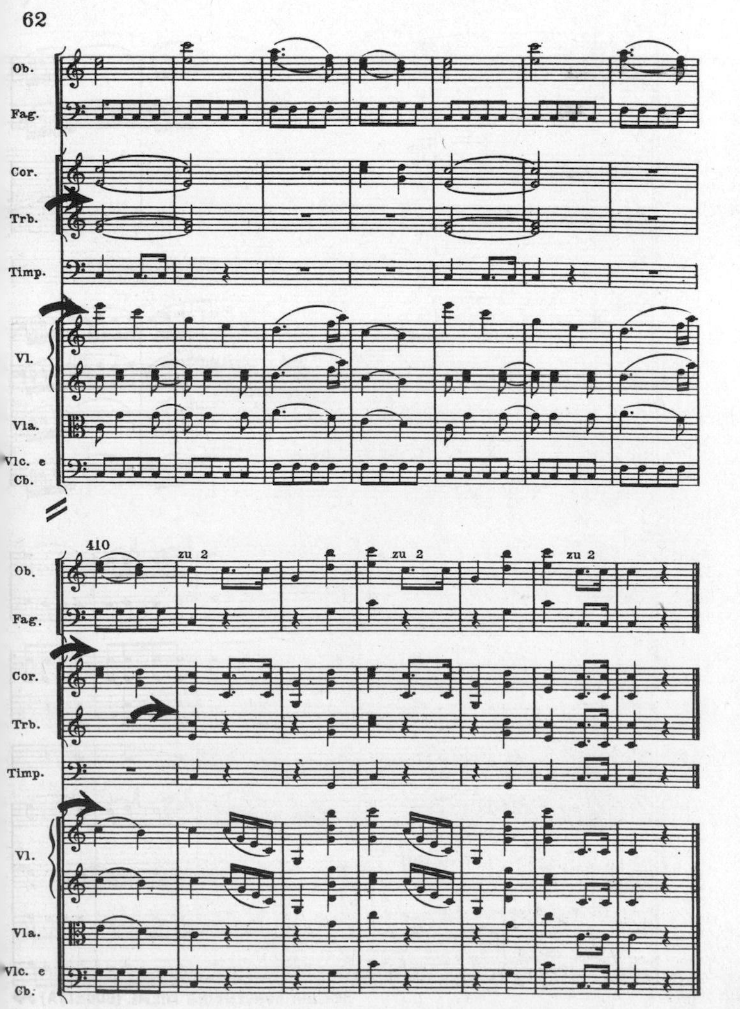
Ob.
Fag.
Cor.
Trb.
Timp.
Vl.
Vla.
Vlc. e Cb.
410
zu 2
zu 2
zu 2

"Prague" Symphony

W. A. Mozart
(1756-1791)

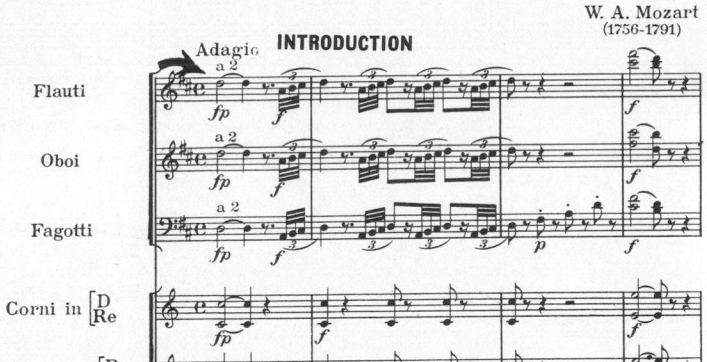

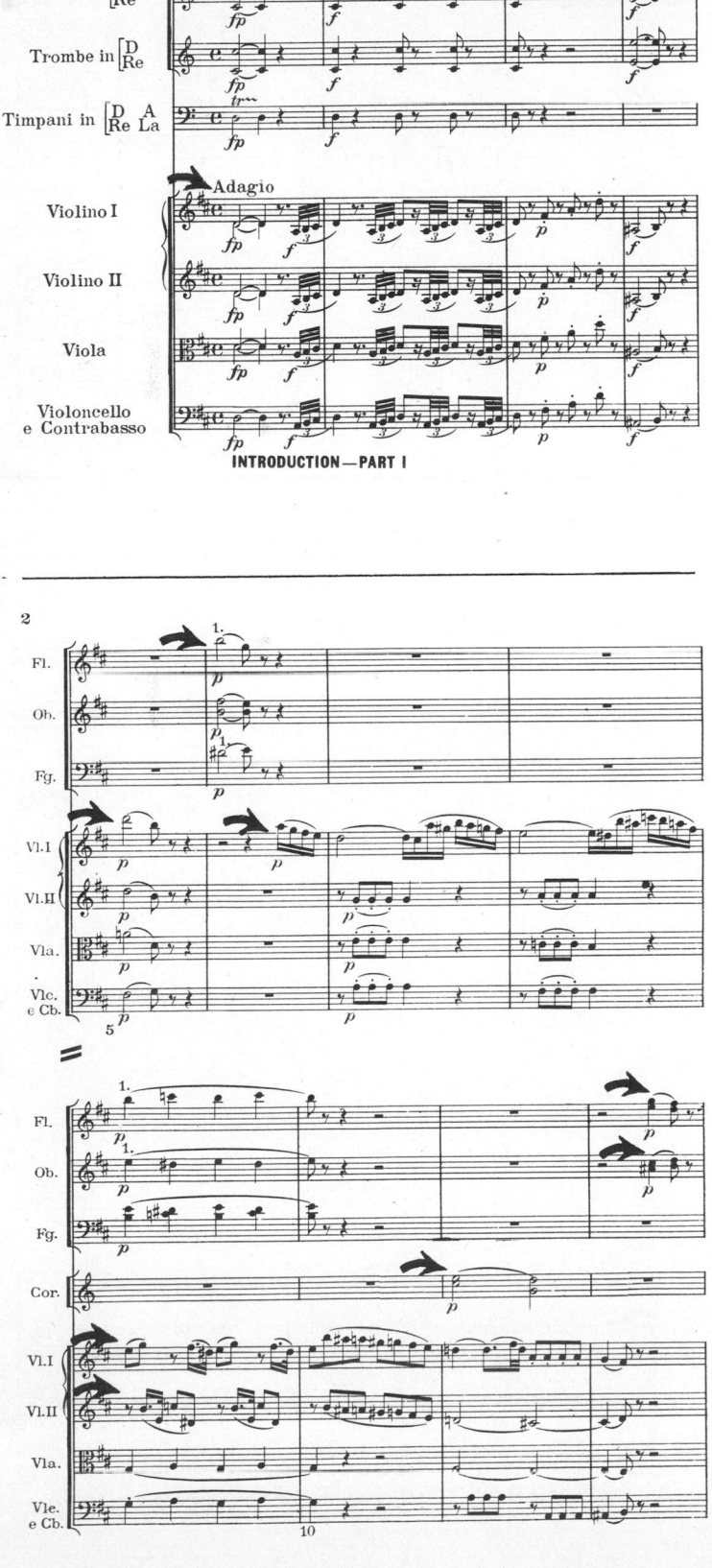

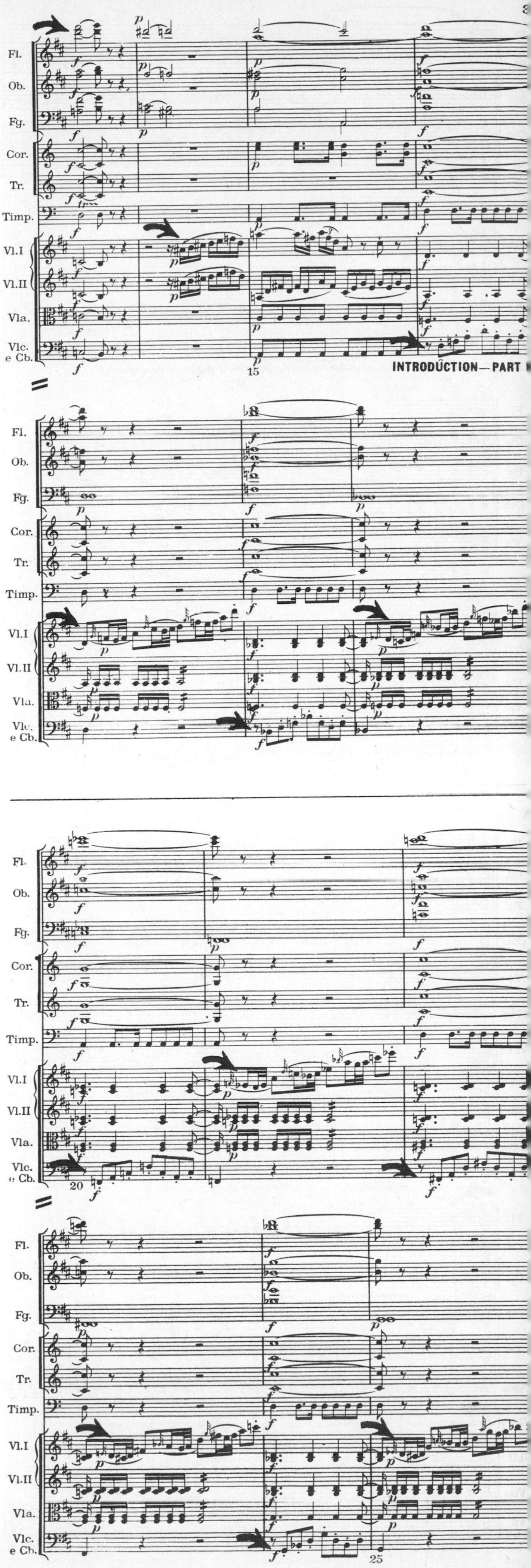

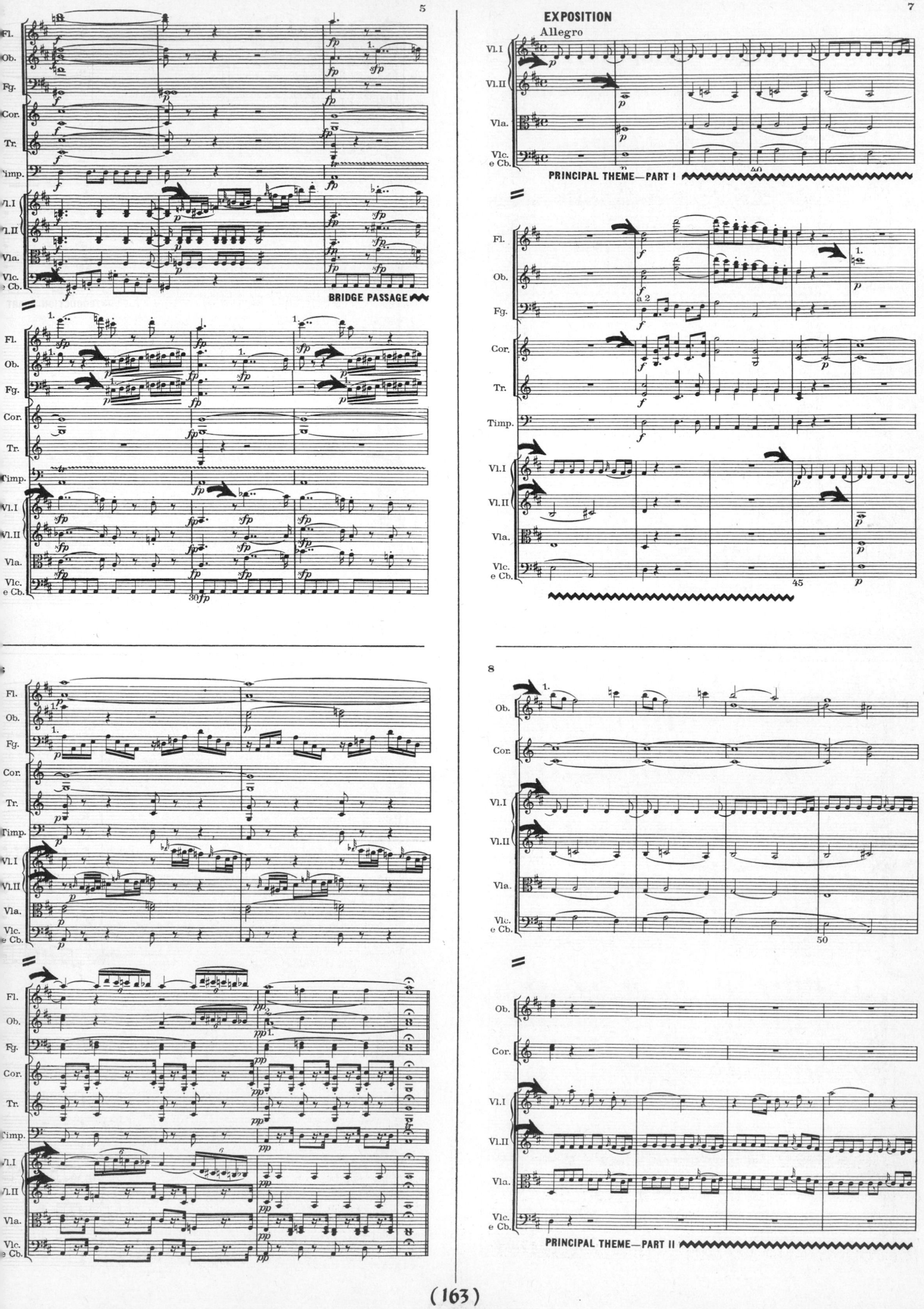

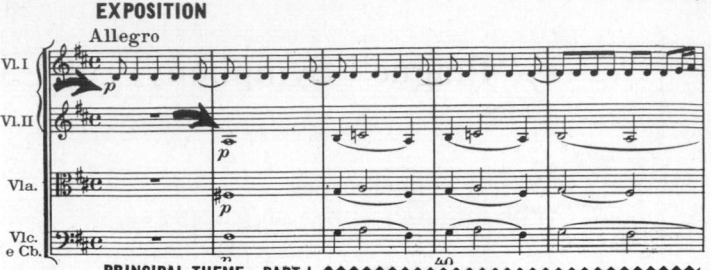

EXPOSITION

Allegro

PRINCIPAL THEME—PART I 〰〰〰〰〰〰〰〰

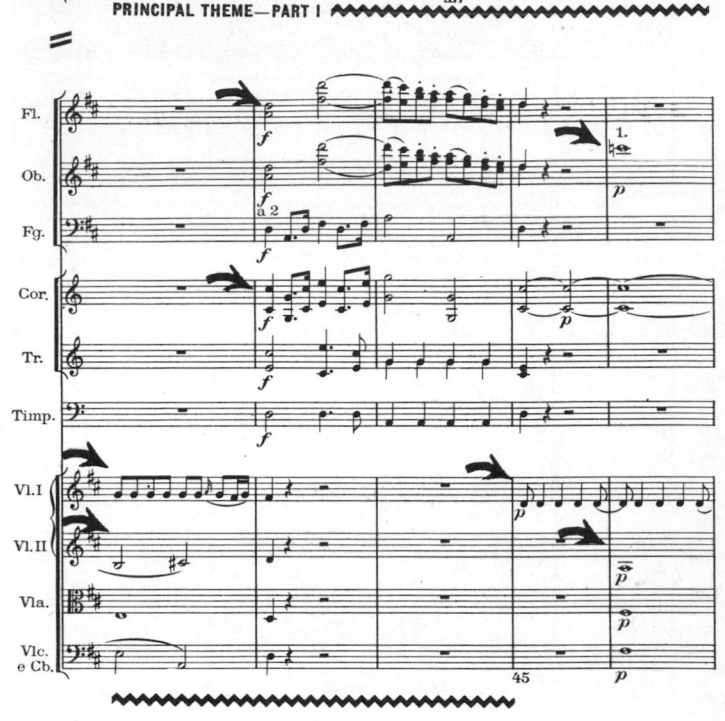

BRIDGE PASSAGE 〰〰

45

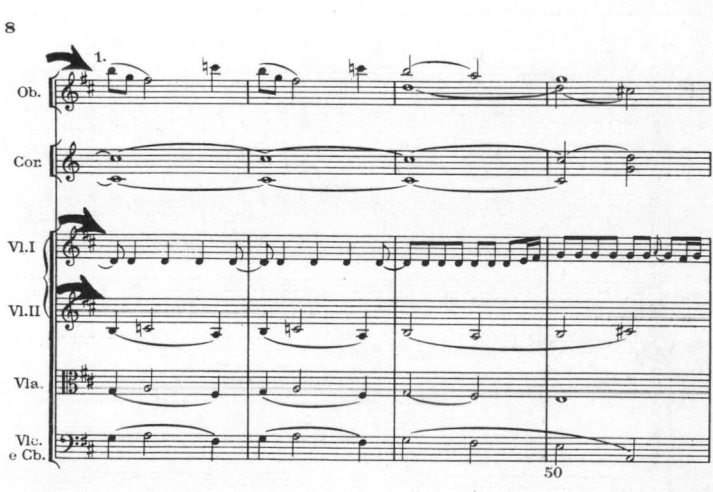

PRINCIPAL THEME—PART II 〰〰〰〰〰〰〰〰

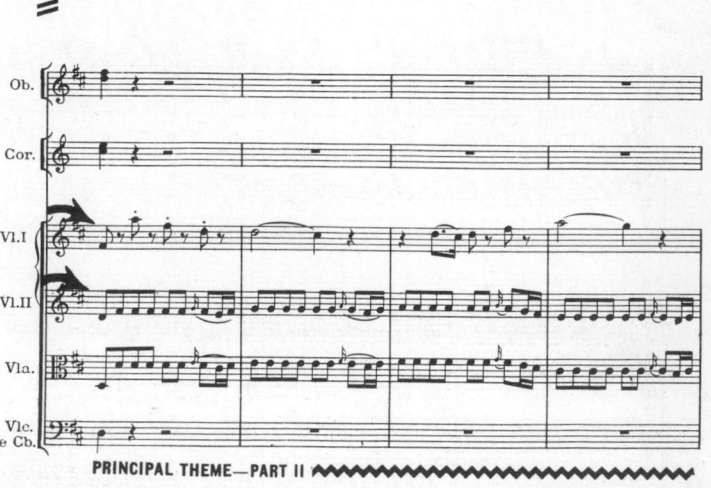

50

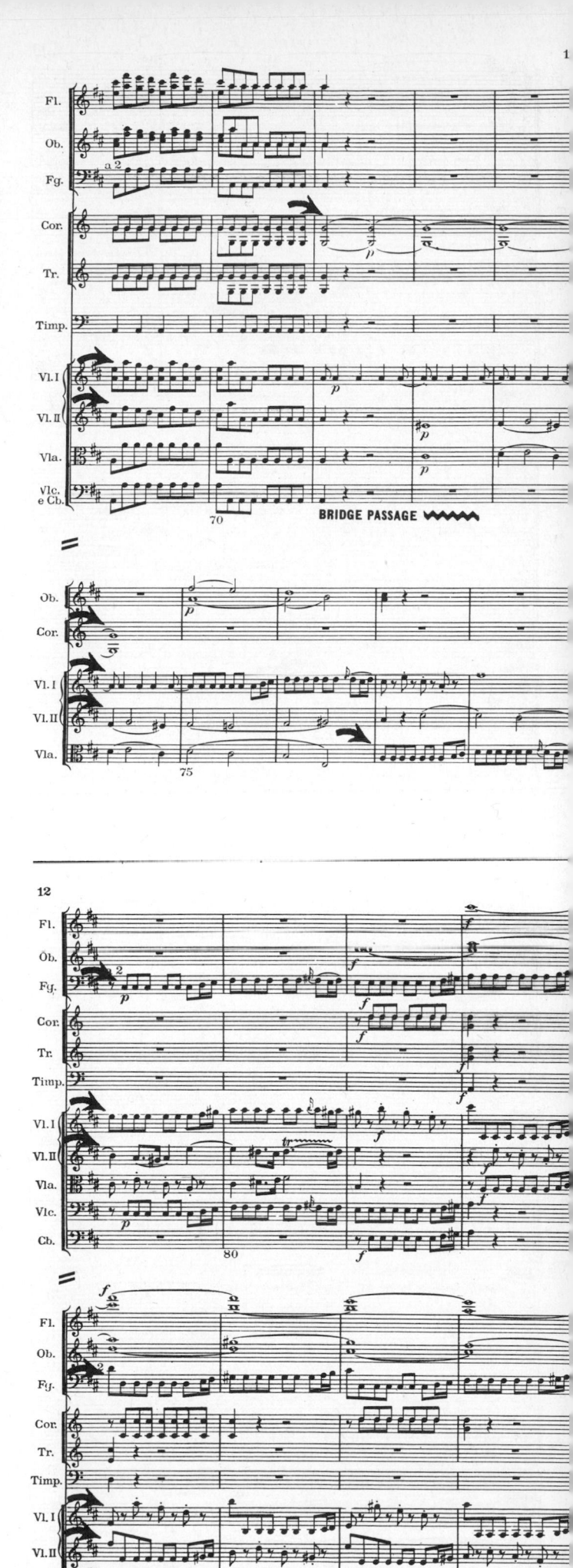

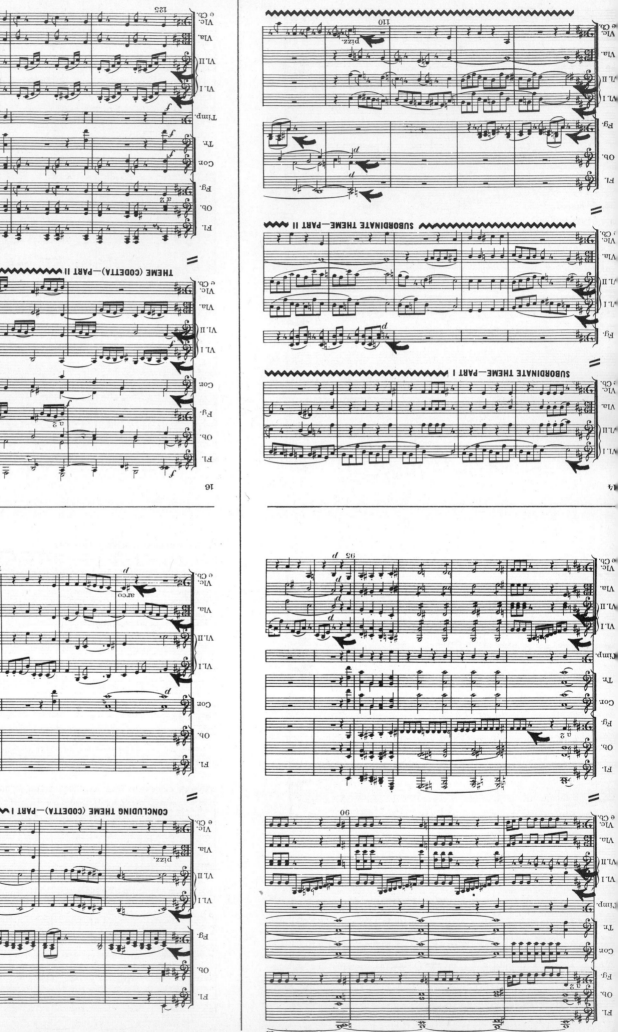

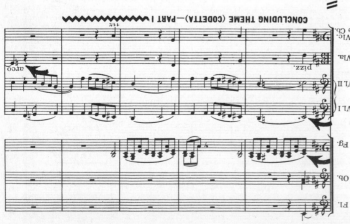

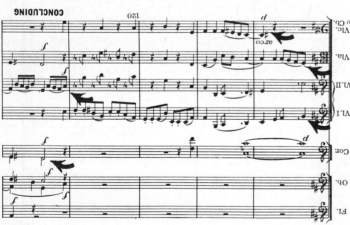

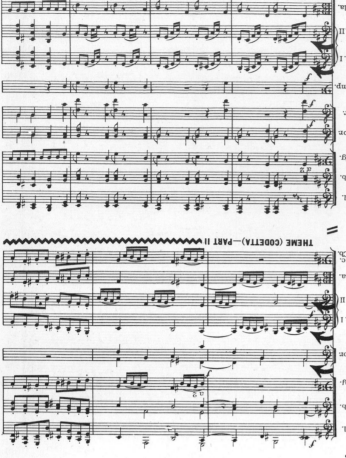

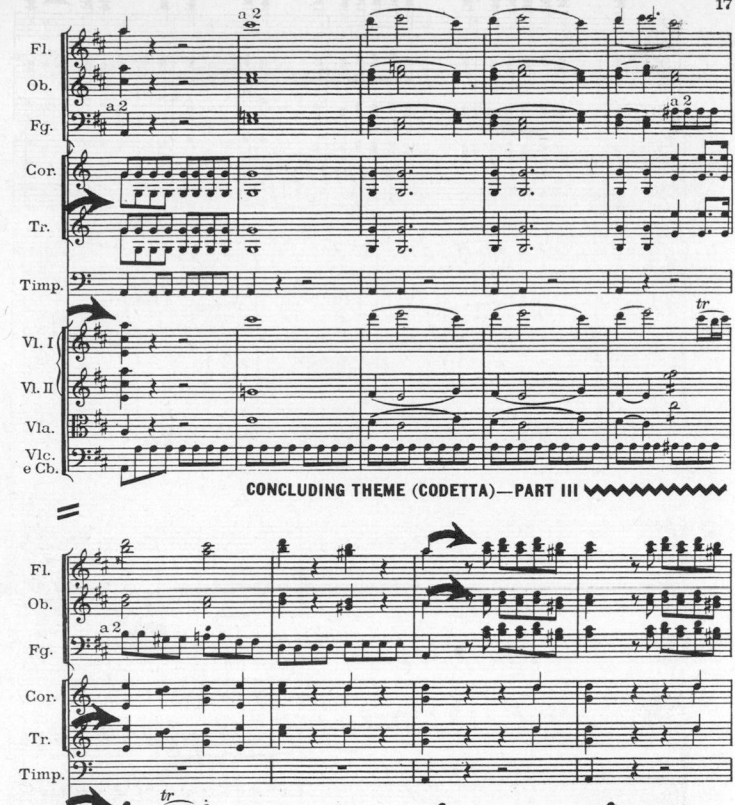
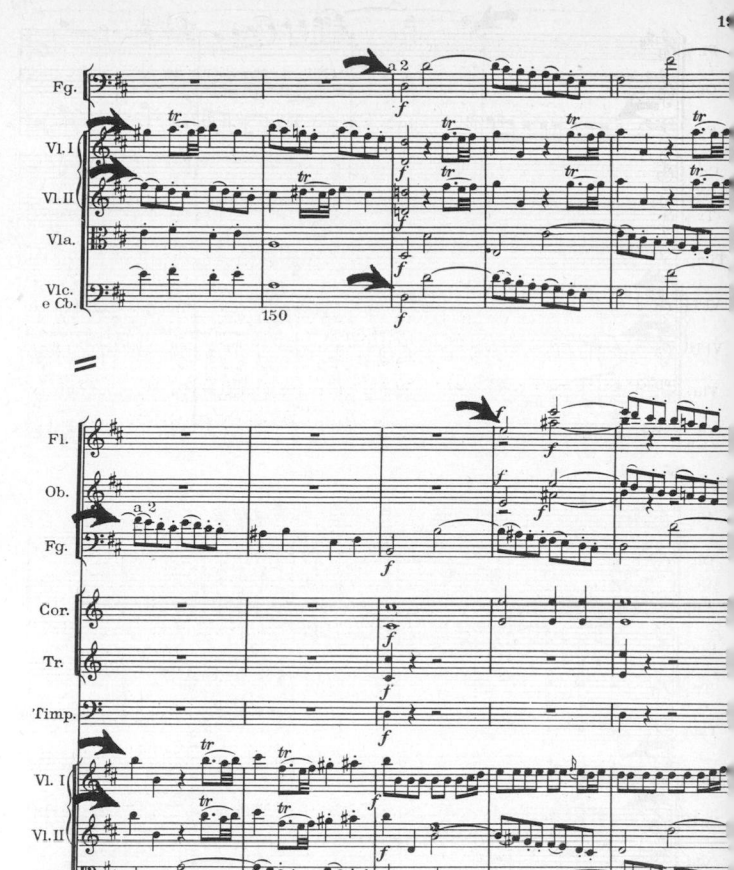
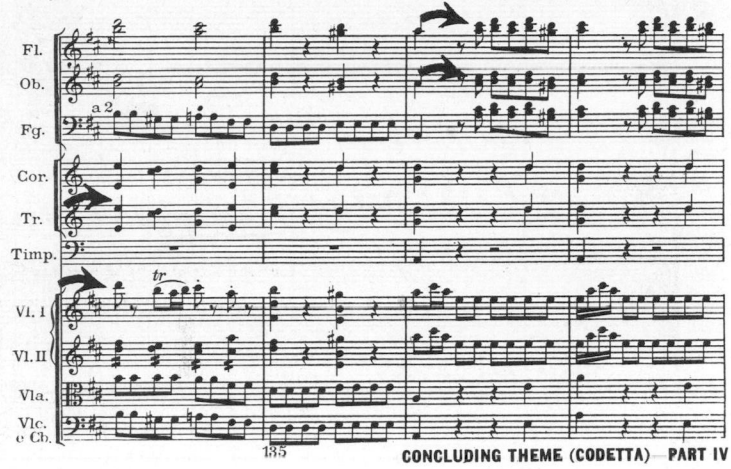
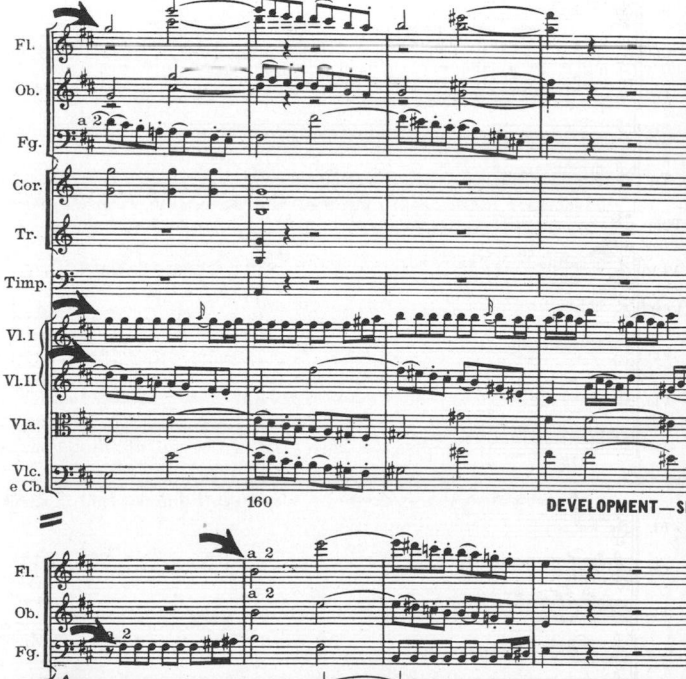
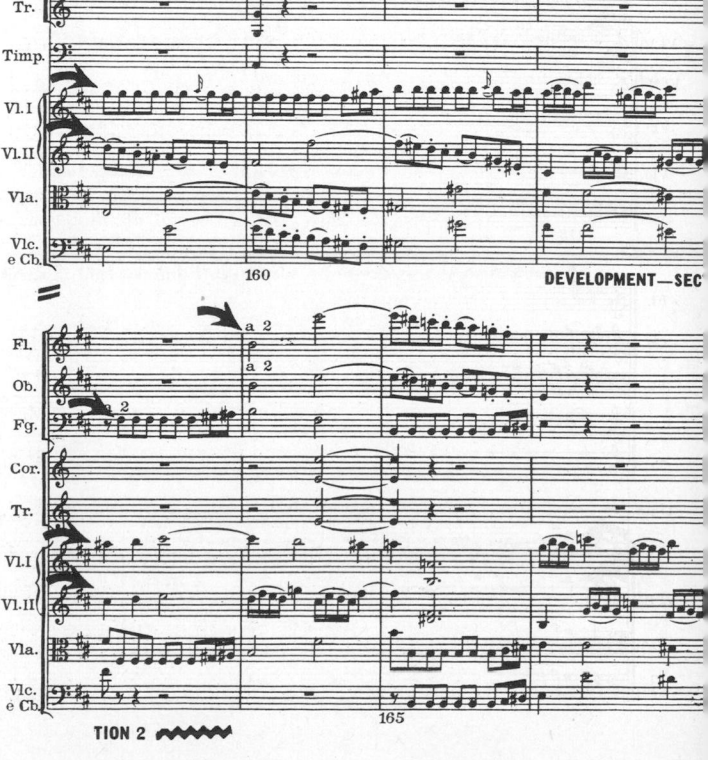

170

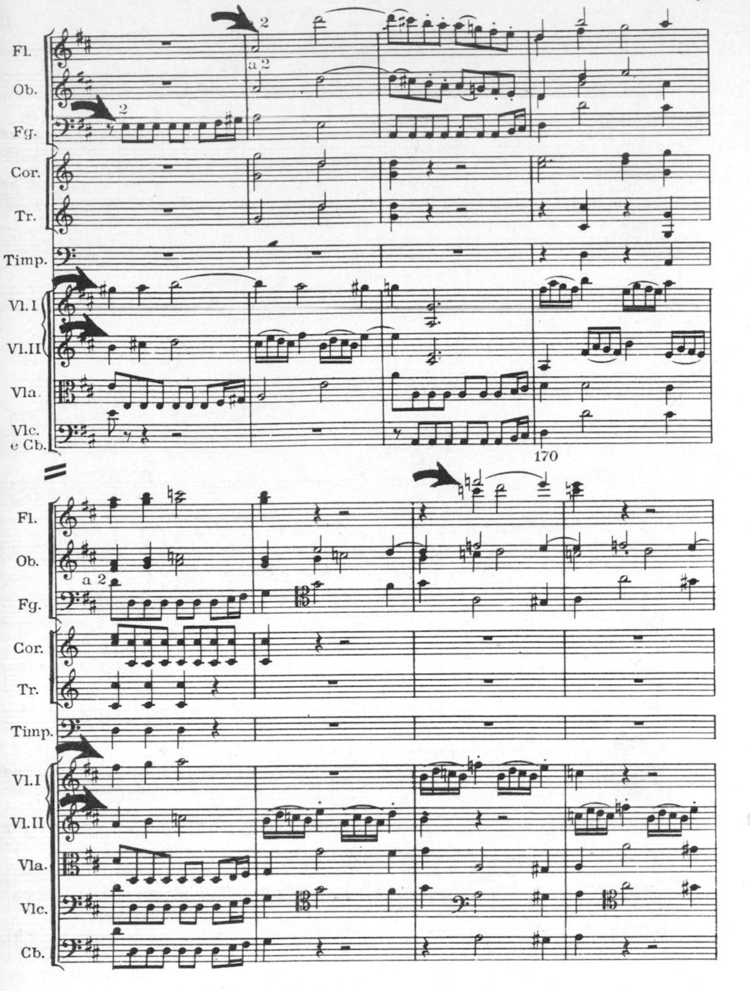

185

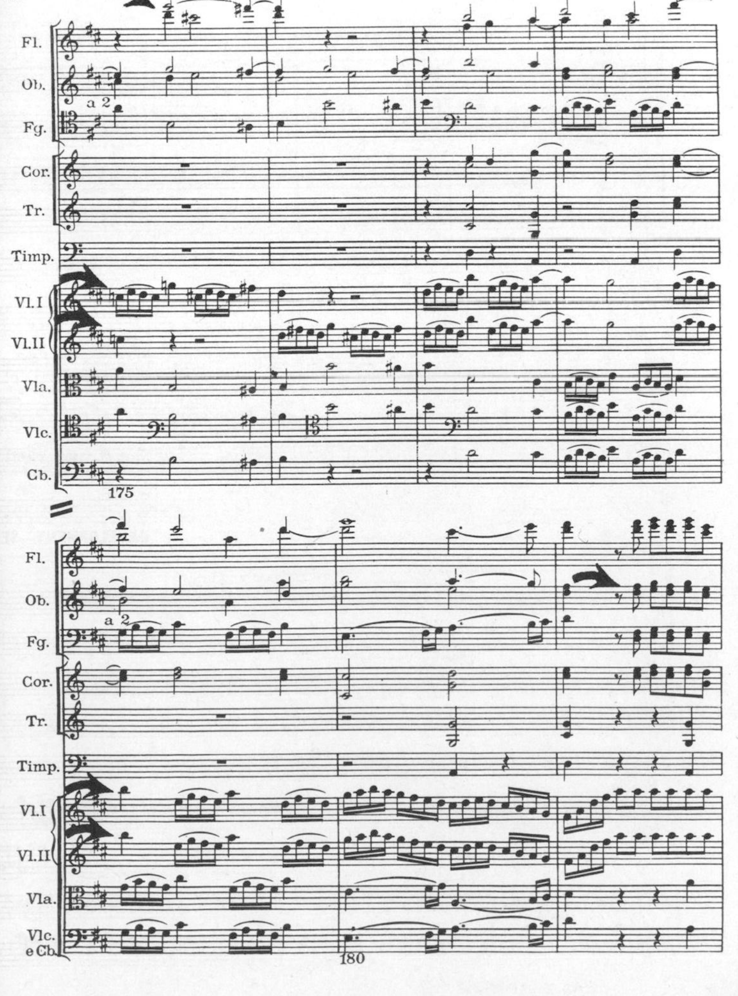

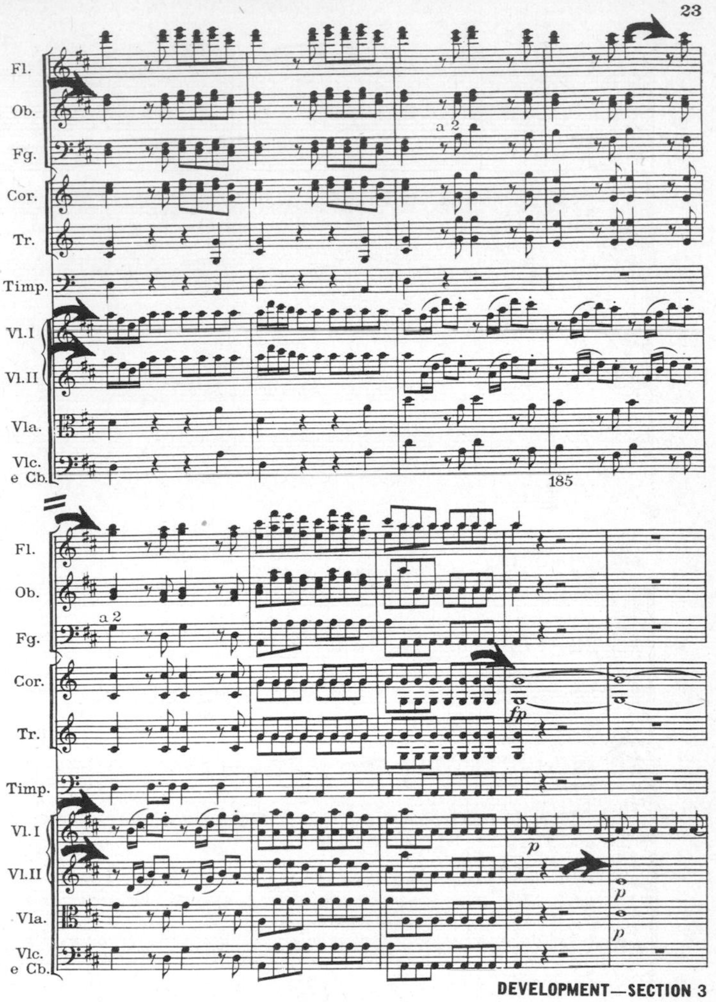

DEVELOPMENT—SECTION 3

175

195

180

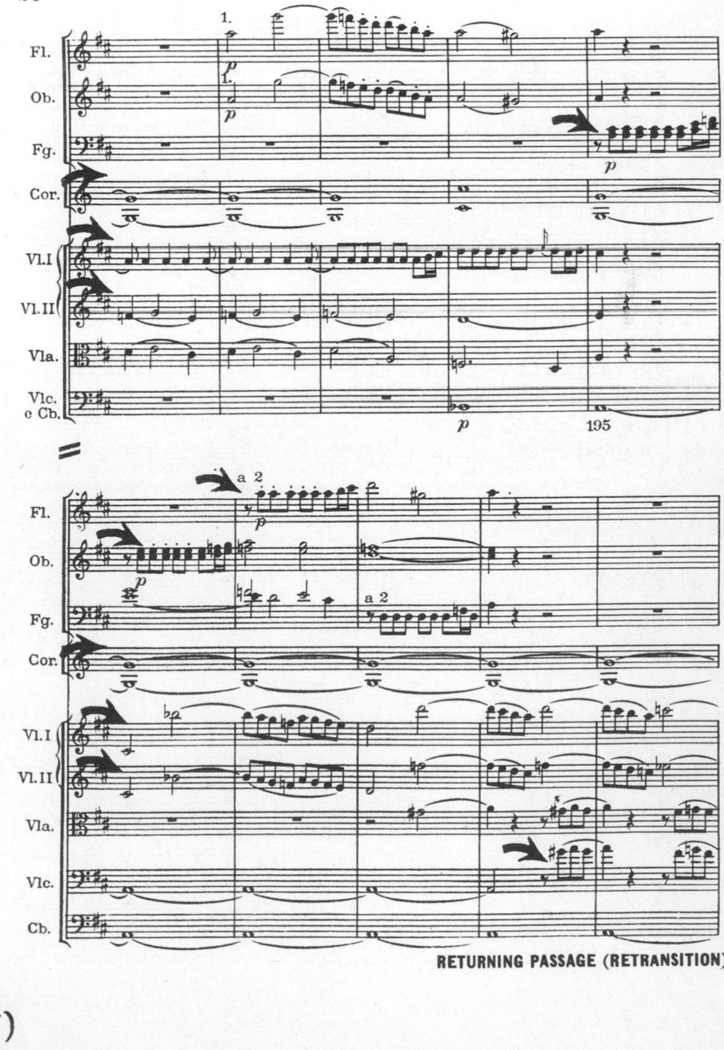

RETURNING PASSAGE (RETRANSITION)

25

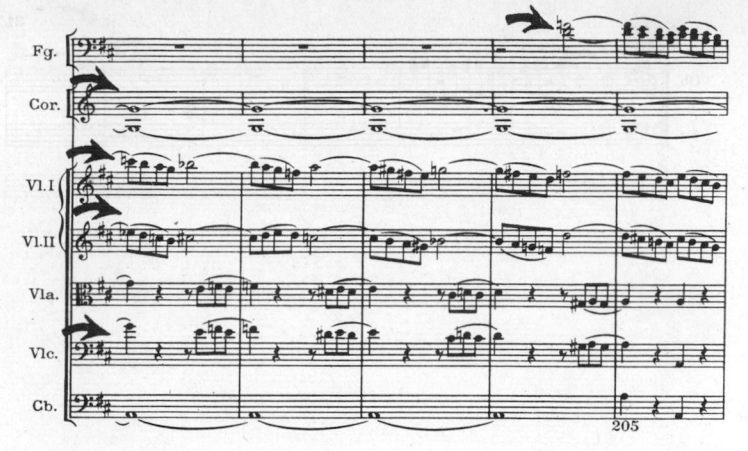

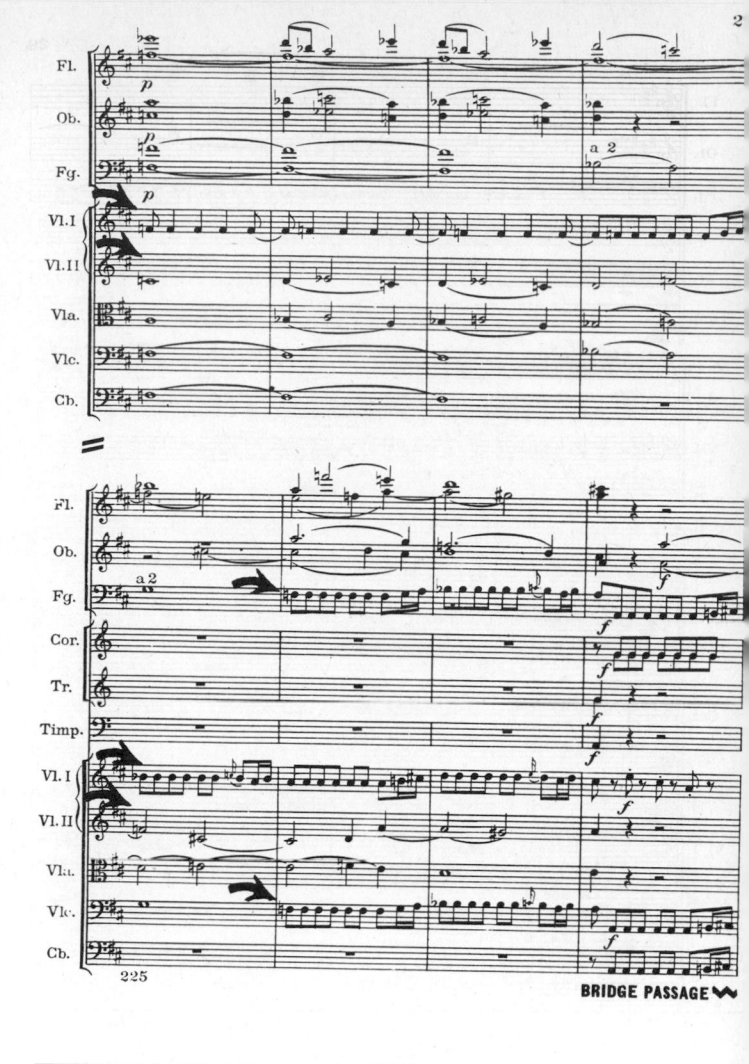

RECAPITULATION

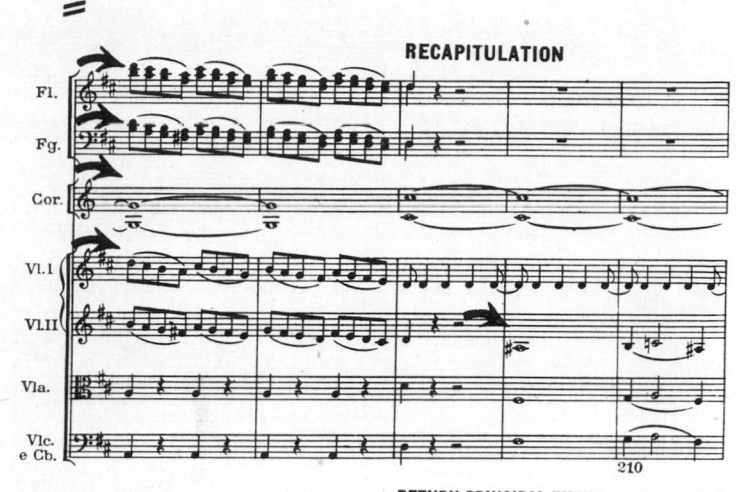

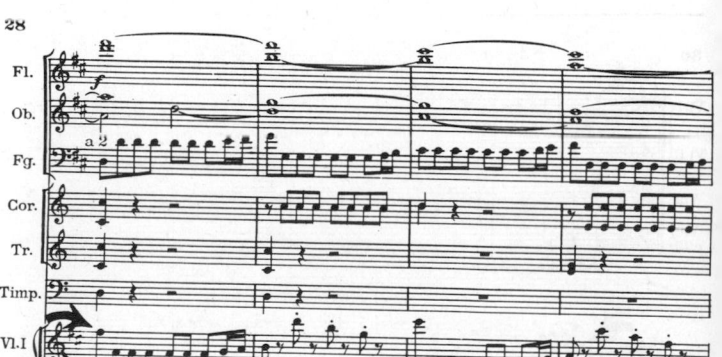

RETURN PRINCIPAL THEME—PART I 〰〰

BRIDGE PASSAGE 〰

26

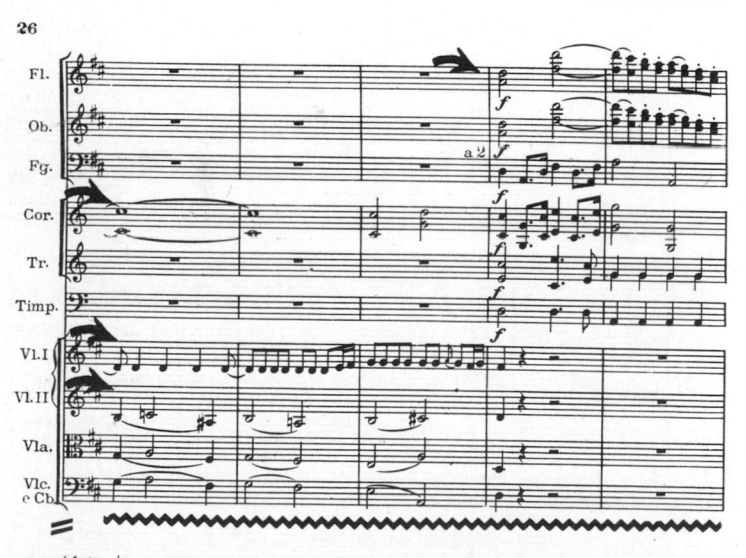

28

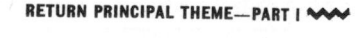

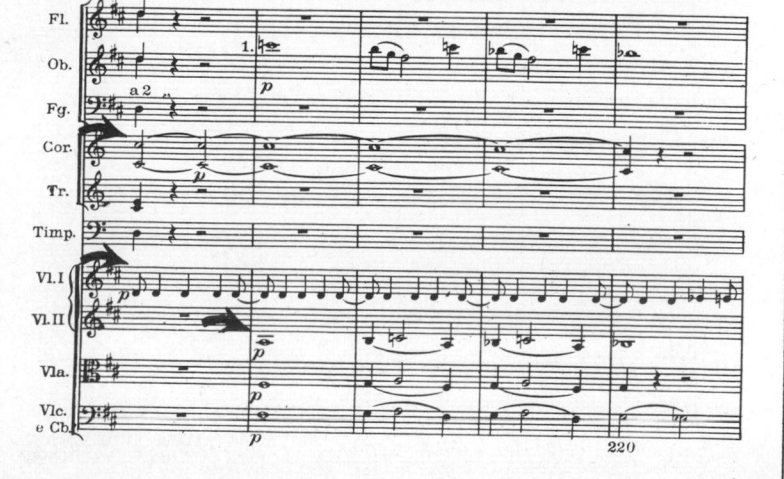

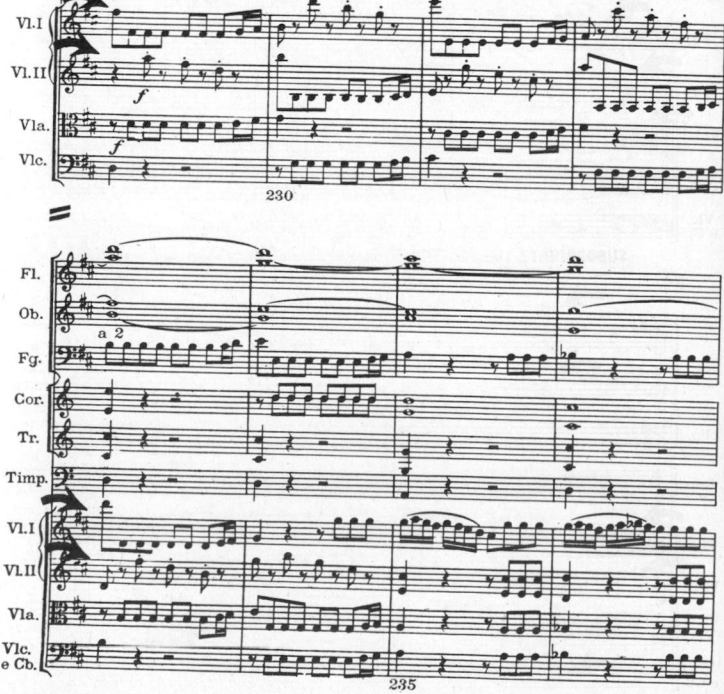

(168)

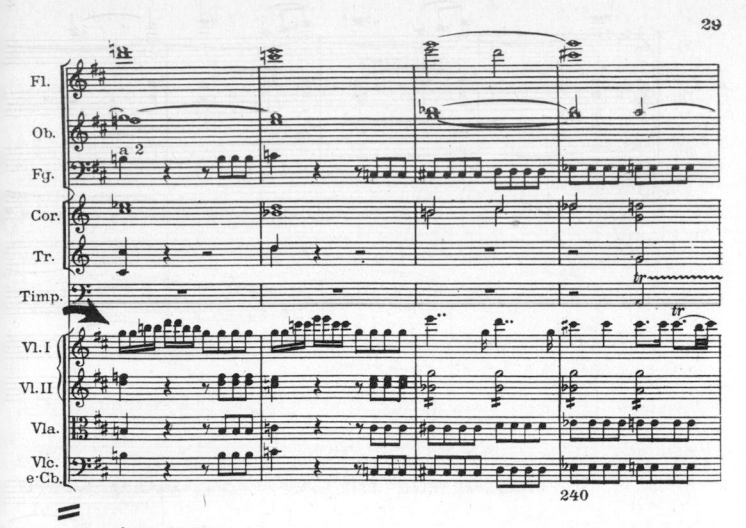

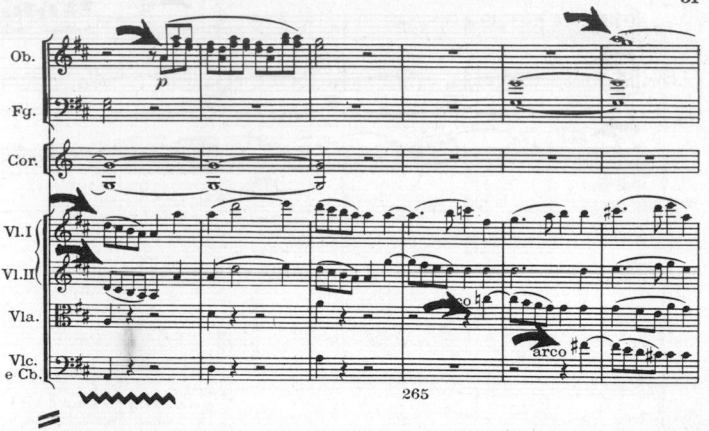

240

RETURN SUBORDINATE THEME—PART I

RETURN CONCLUDING THEME (CODETTA)—

265

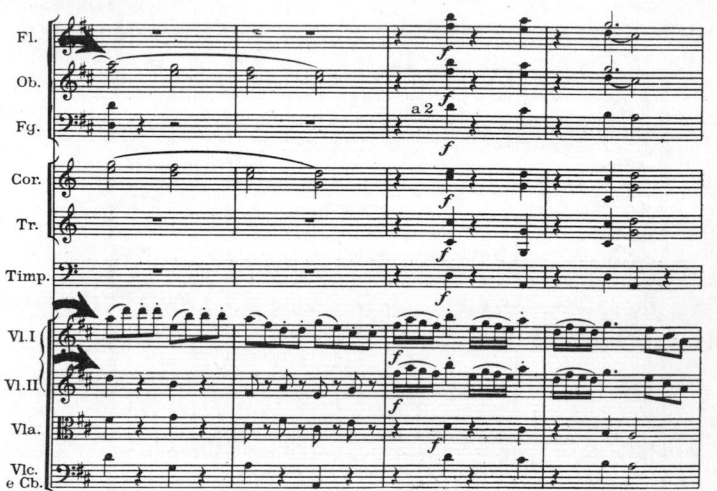

RETURN

SUBORDINATE THEME—PART II

RETURN CONCLUDING THEME (CODETTA)—PART I

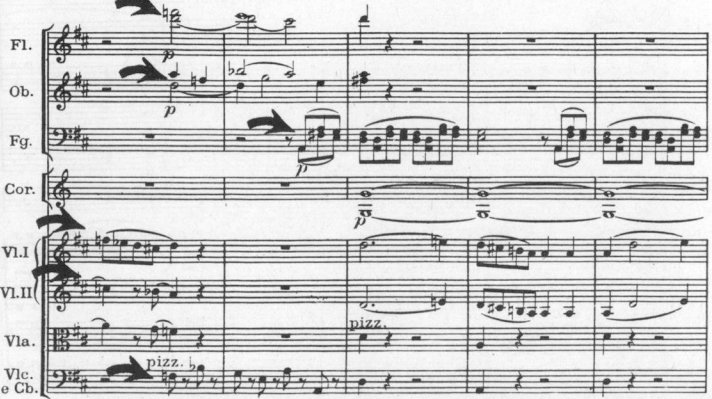

PART II

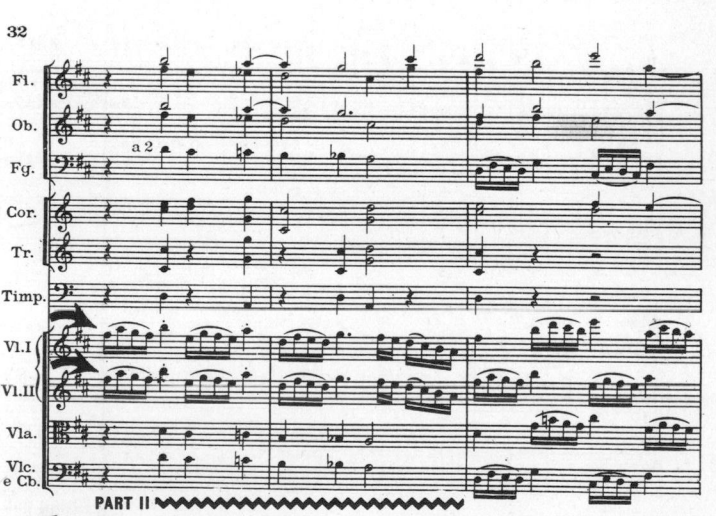

275

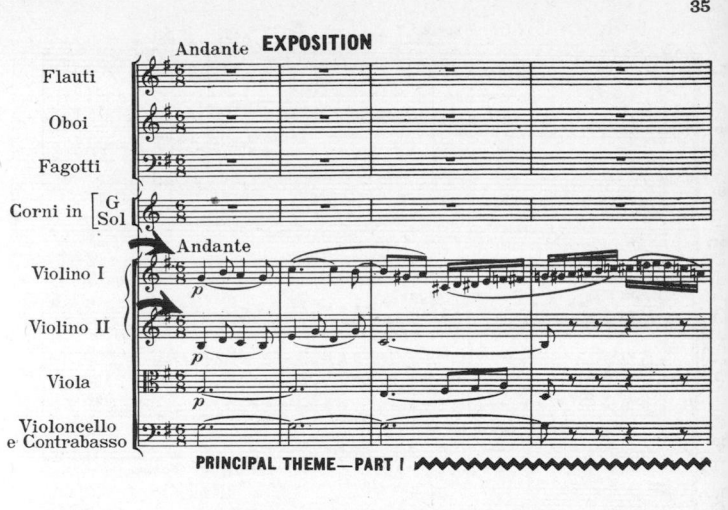

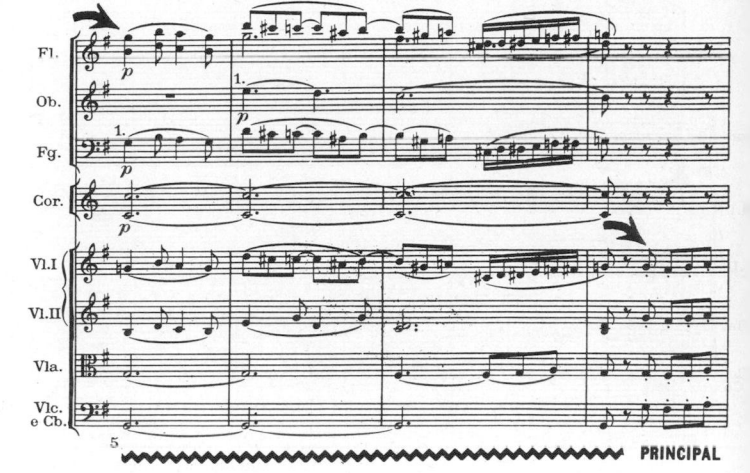

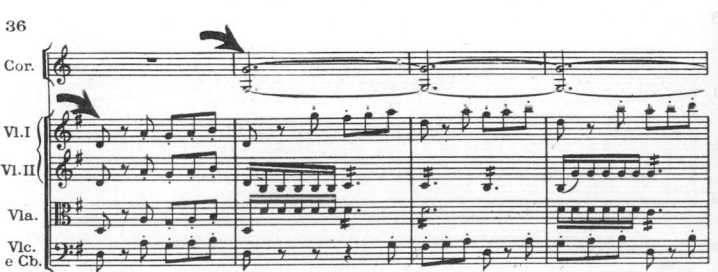

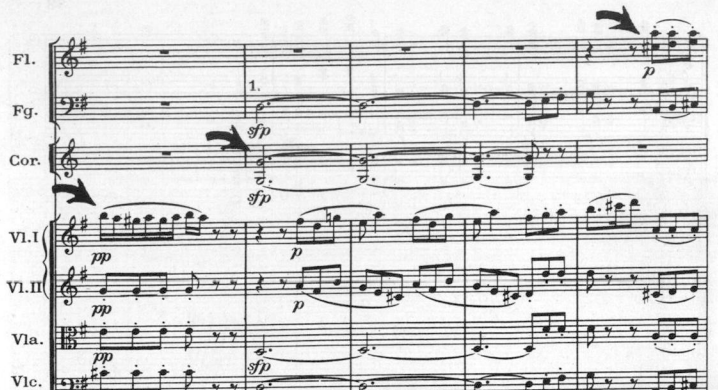

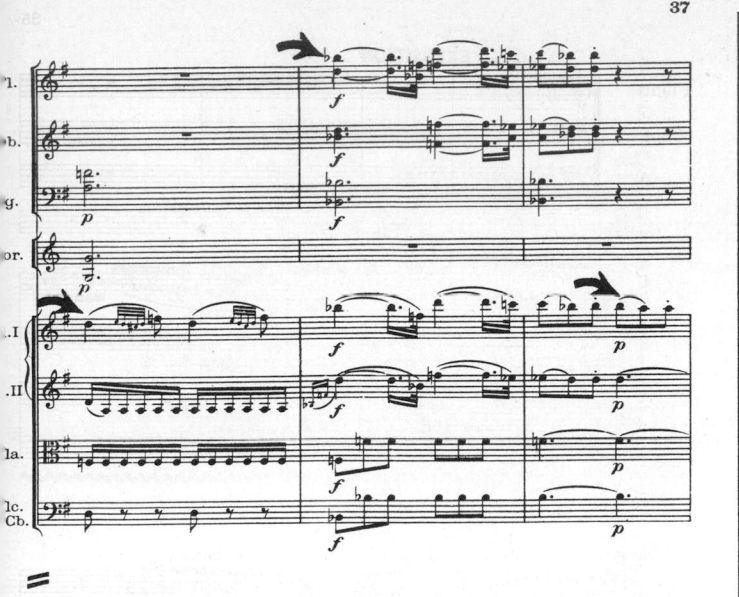

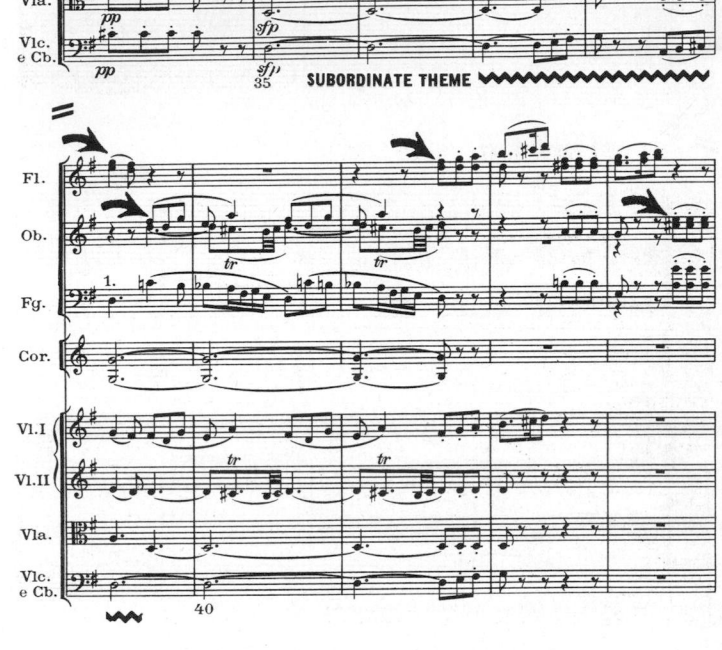

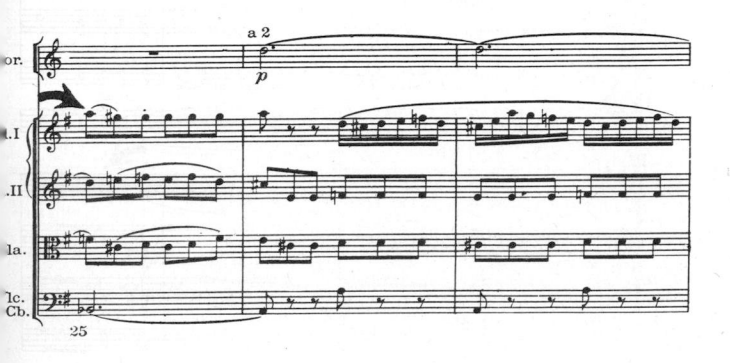

SUBORDINATE THEME 〰〰〰〰〰〰〰

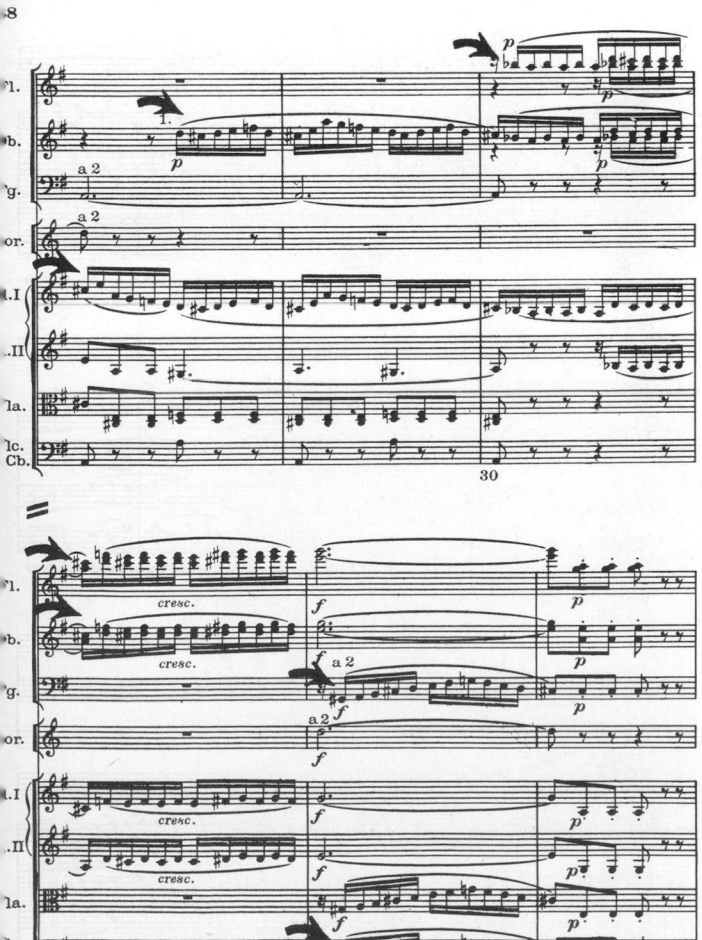

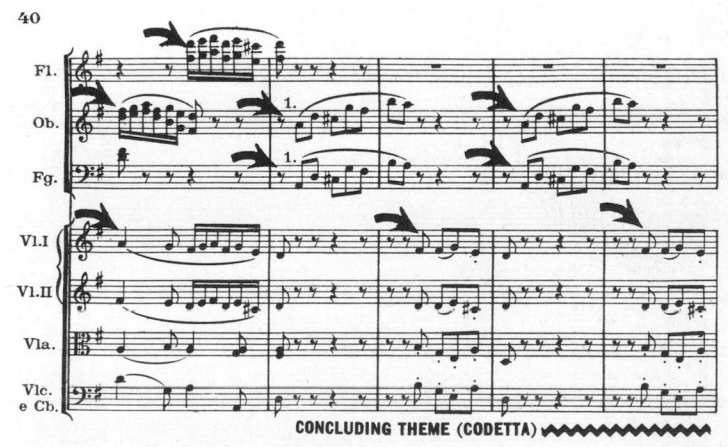

CONCLUDING THEME (CODETTA) 〰〰〰〰〰〰

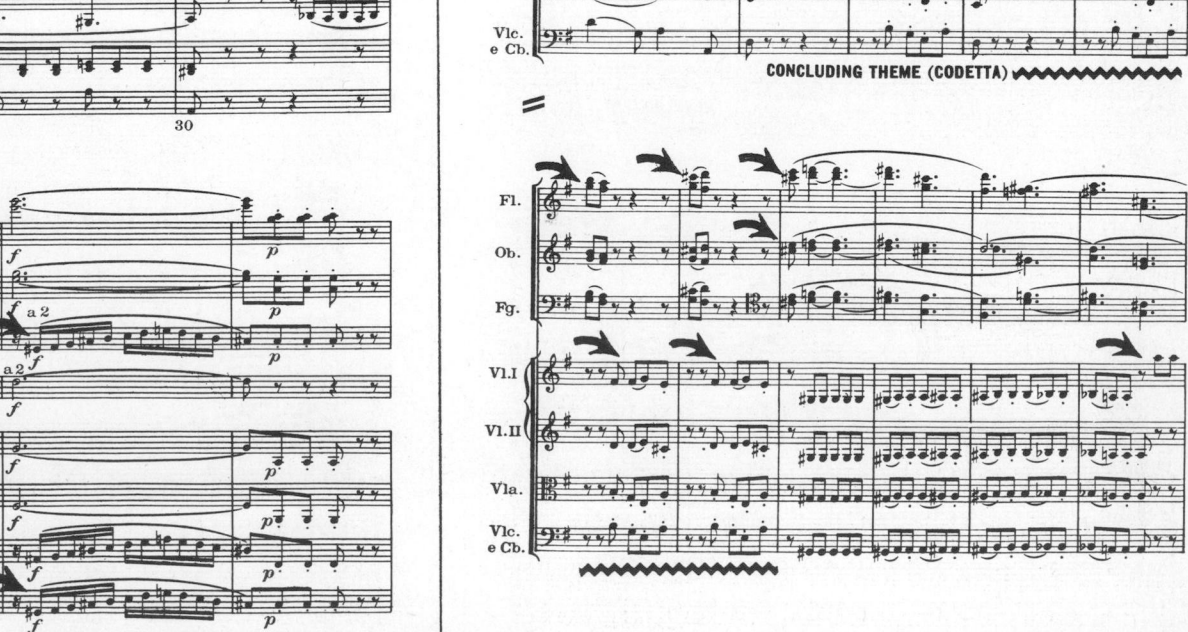

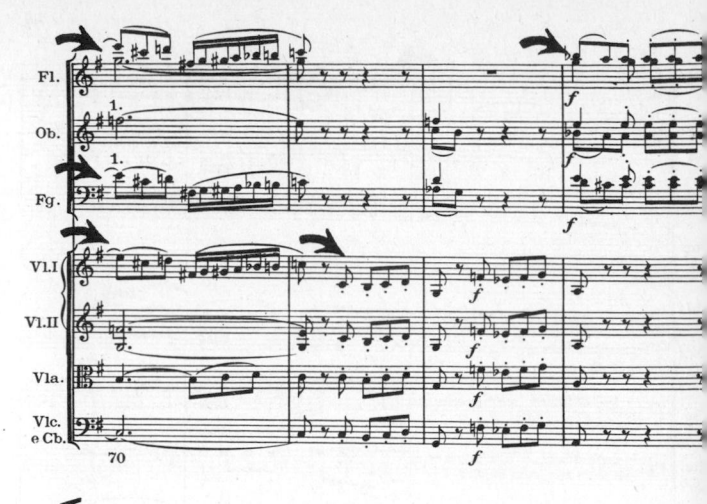

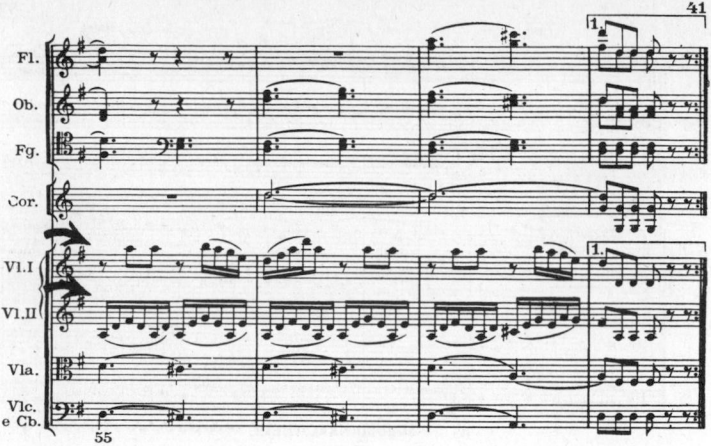

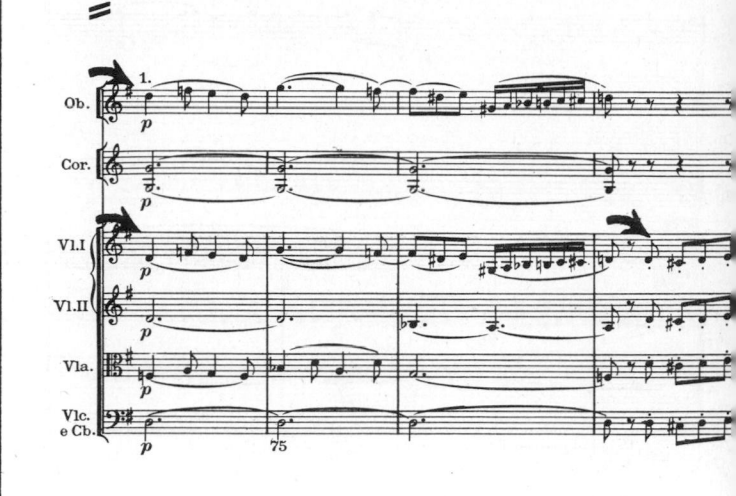

DEVELOPMENT

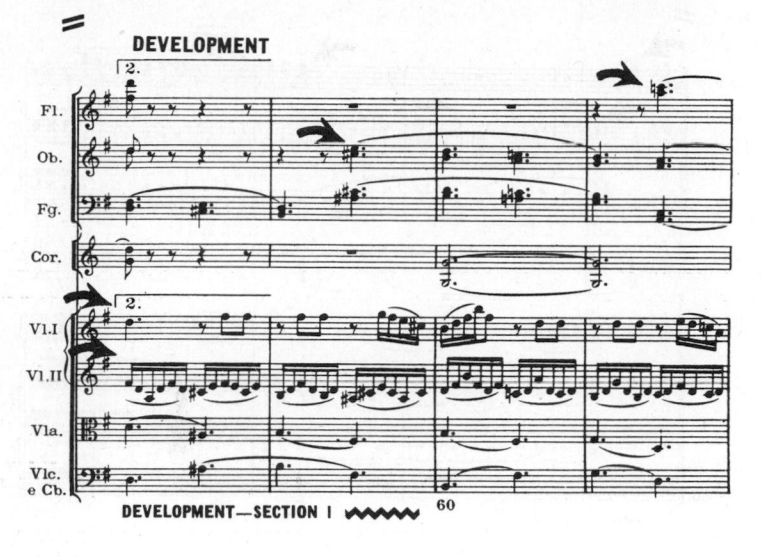

DEVELOPMENT—SECTION I 〰〰〰 60

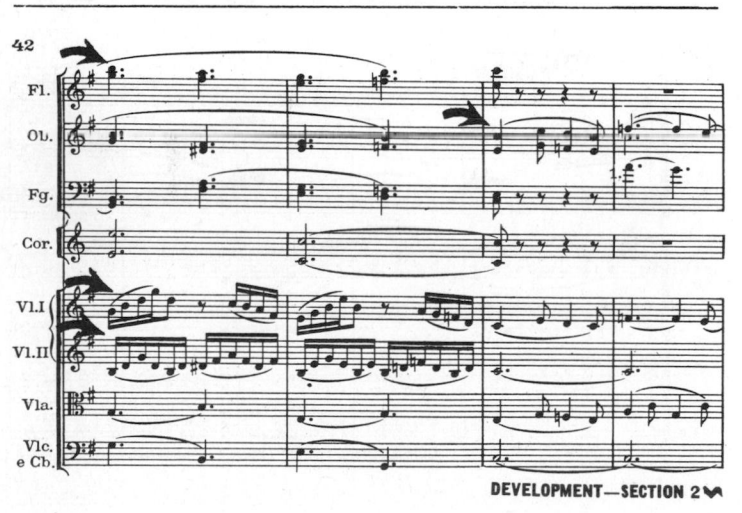

DEVELOPMENT—SECTION 2 〰

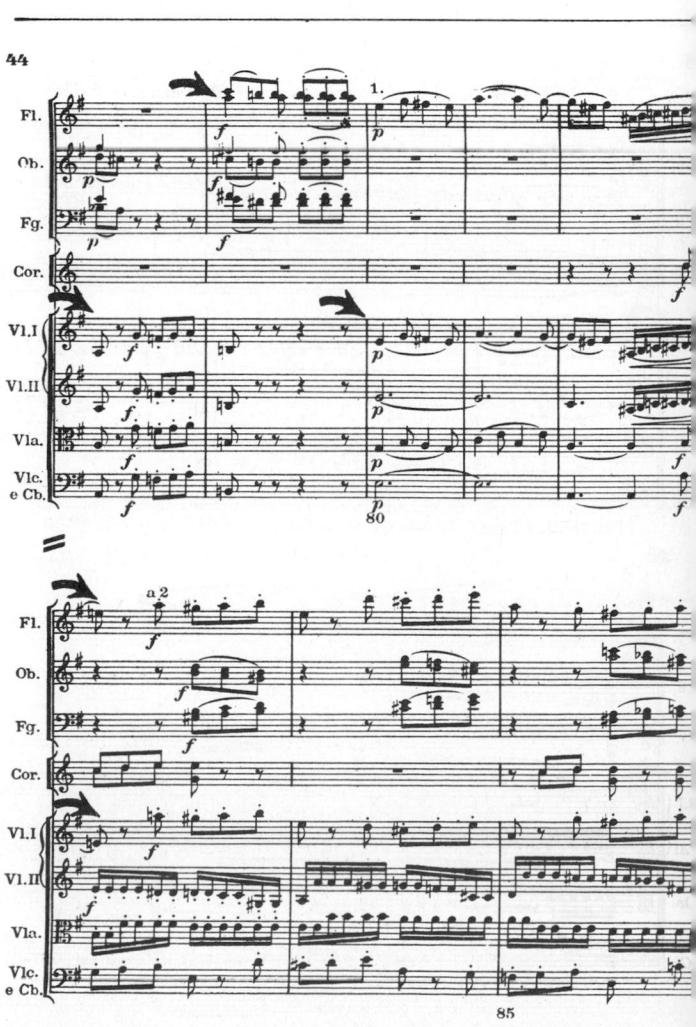

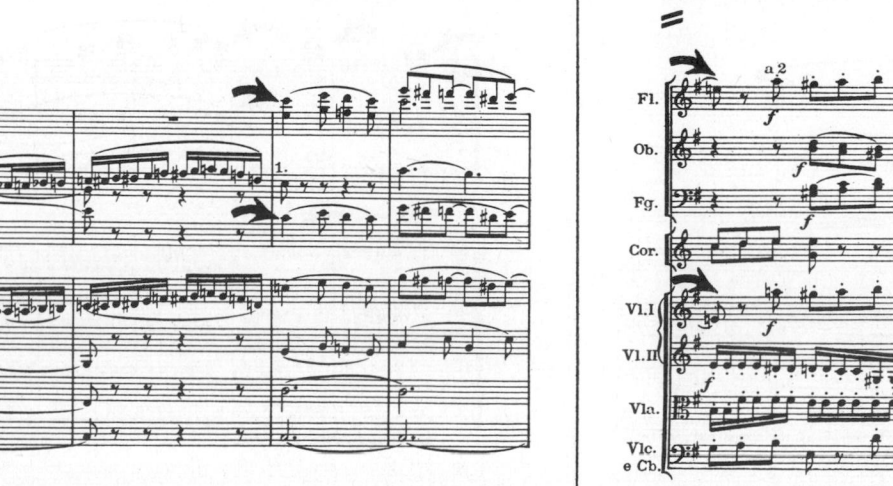

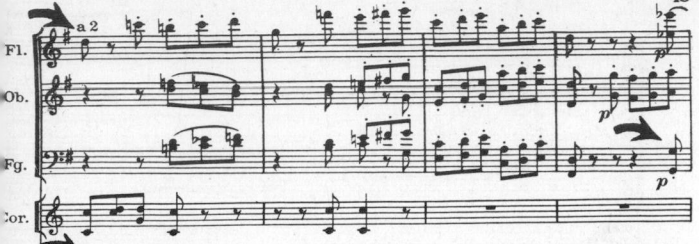

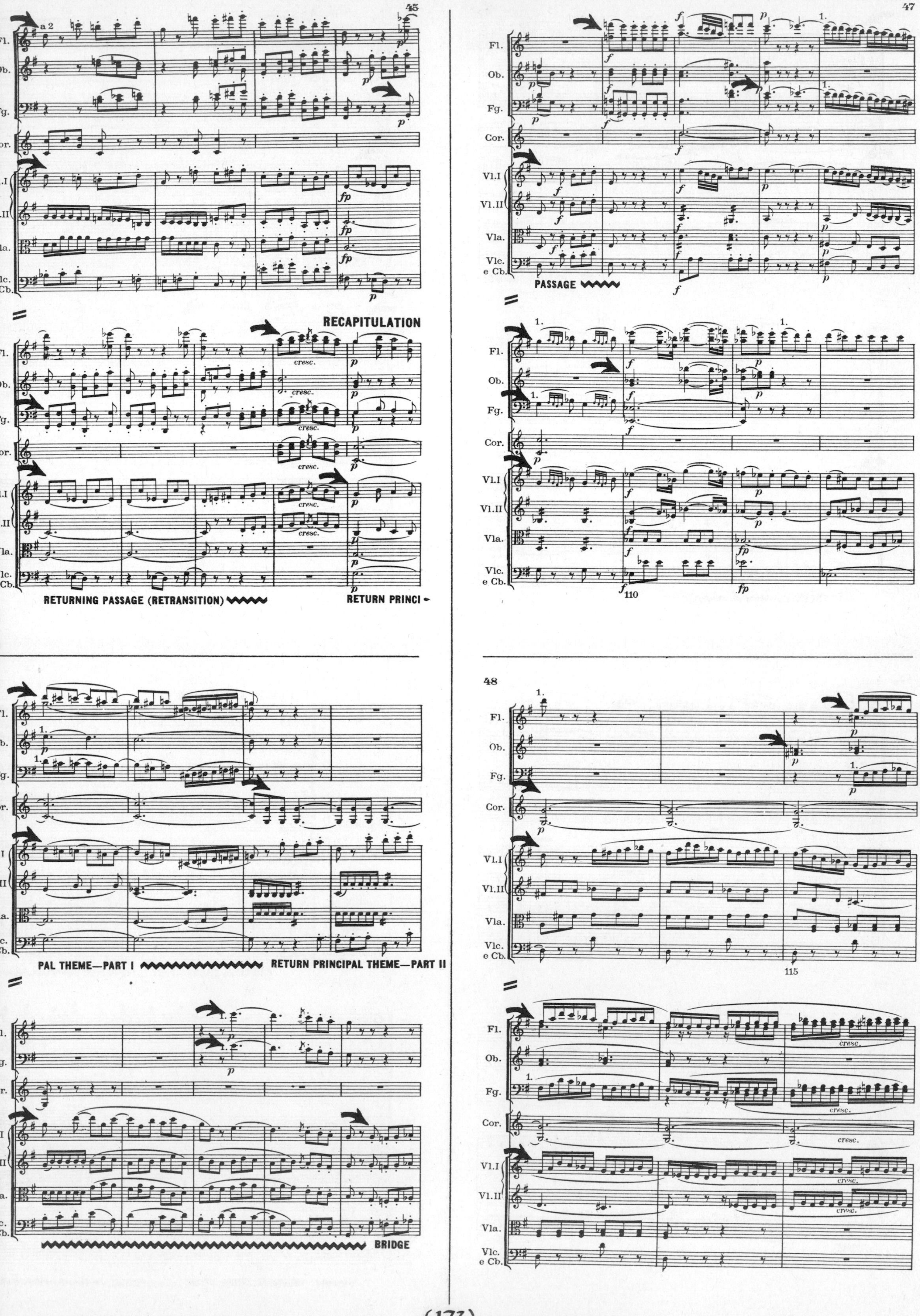

45

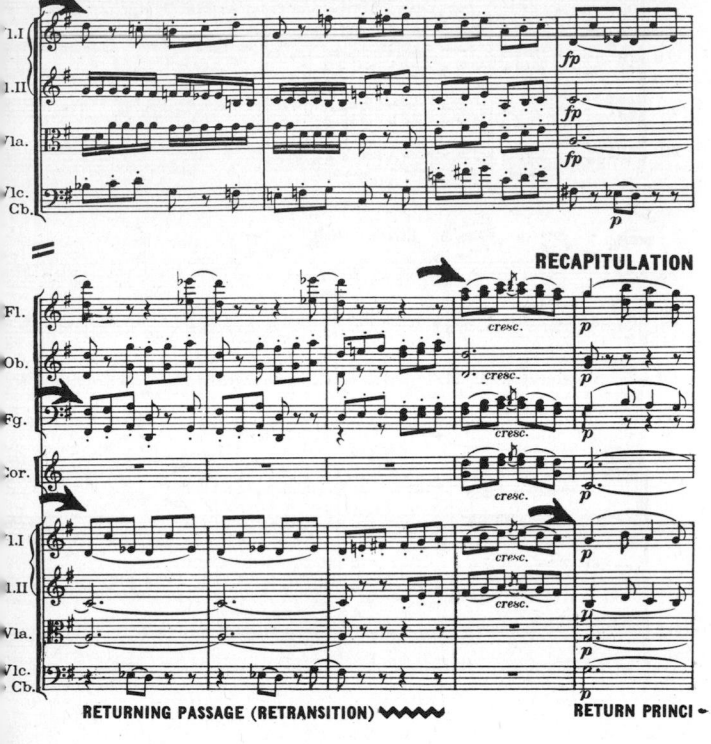

RECAPITULATION

47

RETURNING PASSAGE (RETRANSITION) ~~~~~

RETURN PRINCI-

PASSAGE ~~~~

110

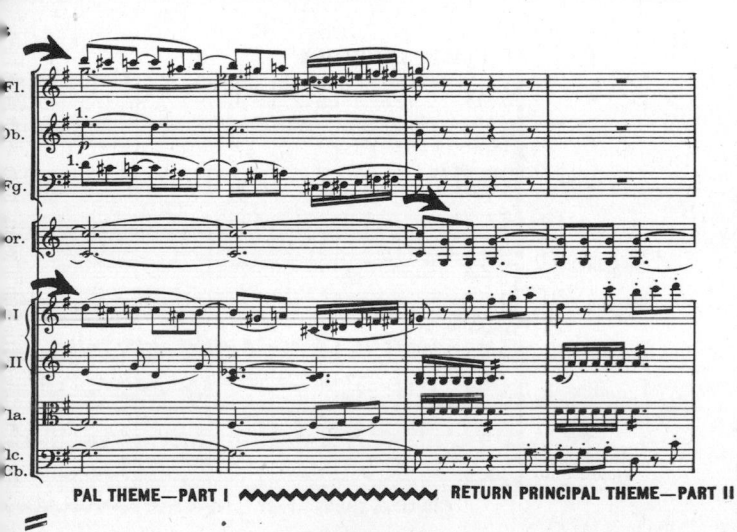

PAL THEME—PART I ~~~~~~~~ RETURN PRINCIPAL THEME—PART II

48

115

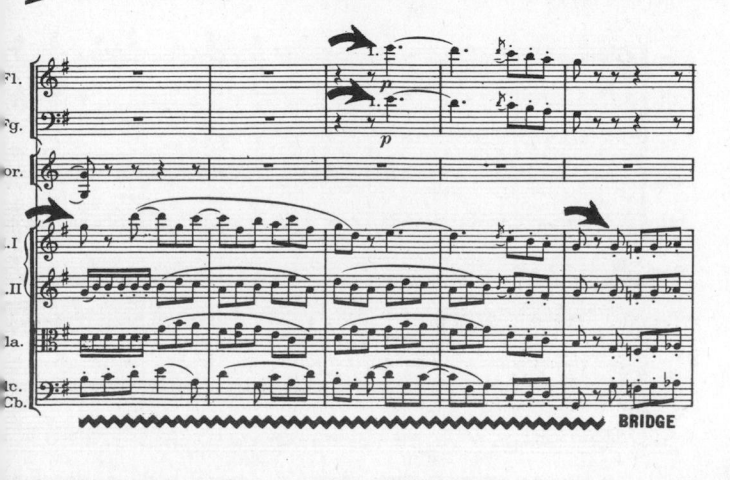

BRIDGE

(173)

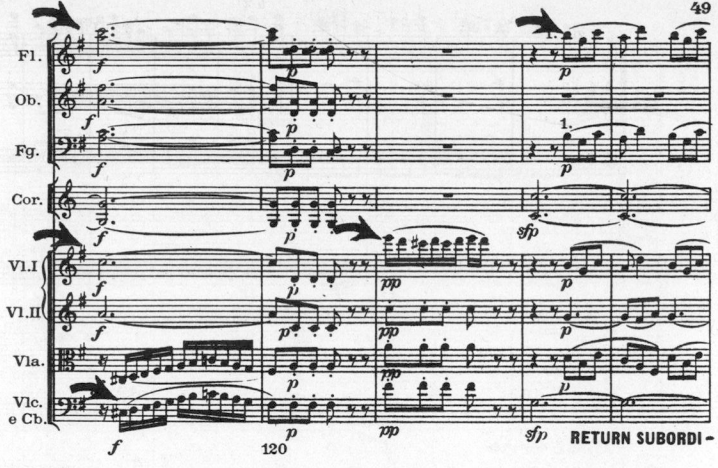

49

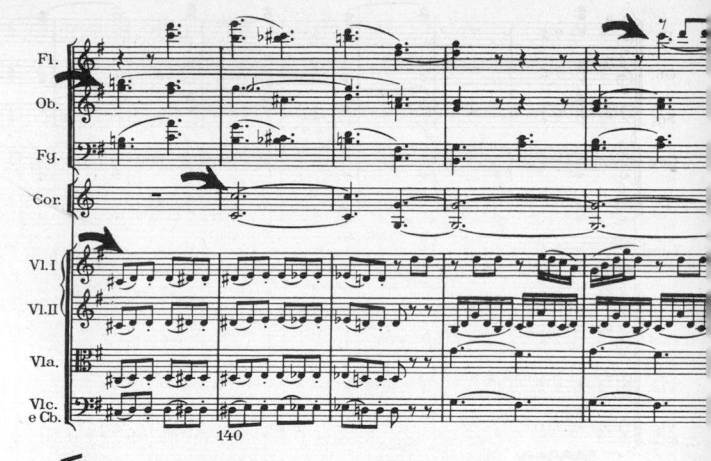

RETURN SUBORDI-

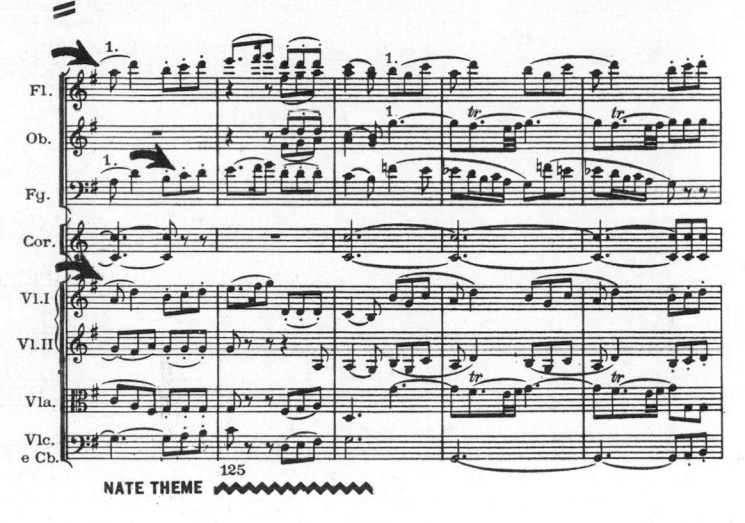

NATE THEME ⌇⌇⌇⌇⌇⌇⌇

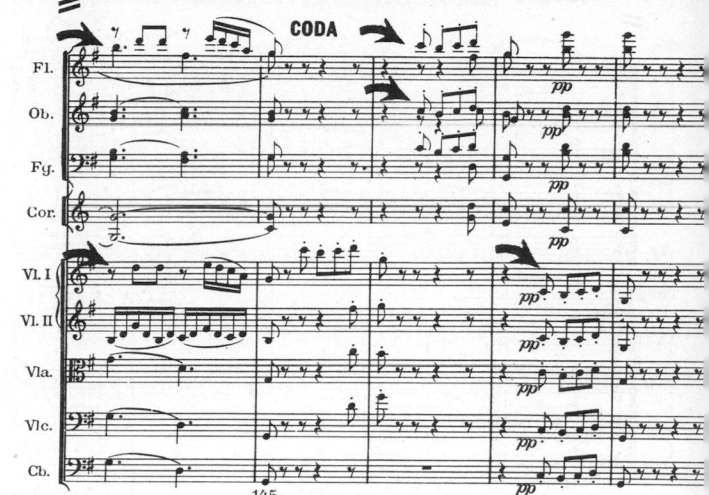

CODA

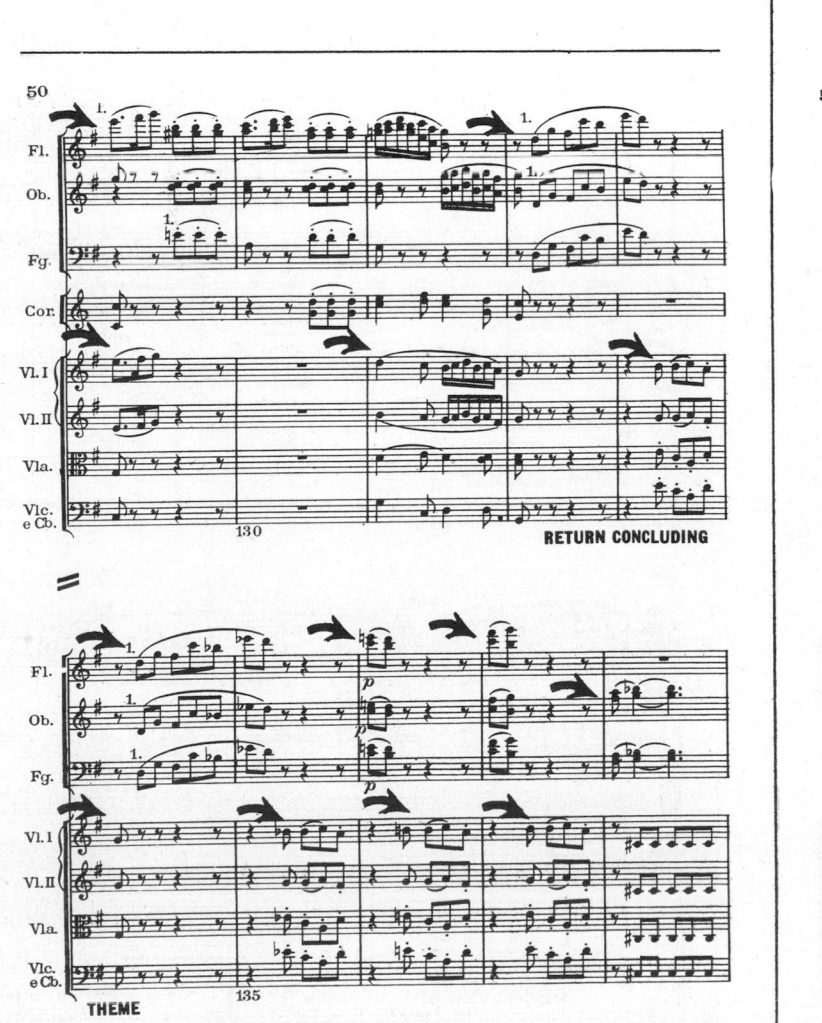

50

RETURN CONCLUDING

THEME

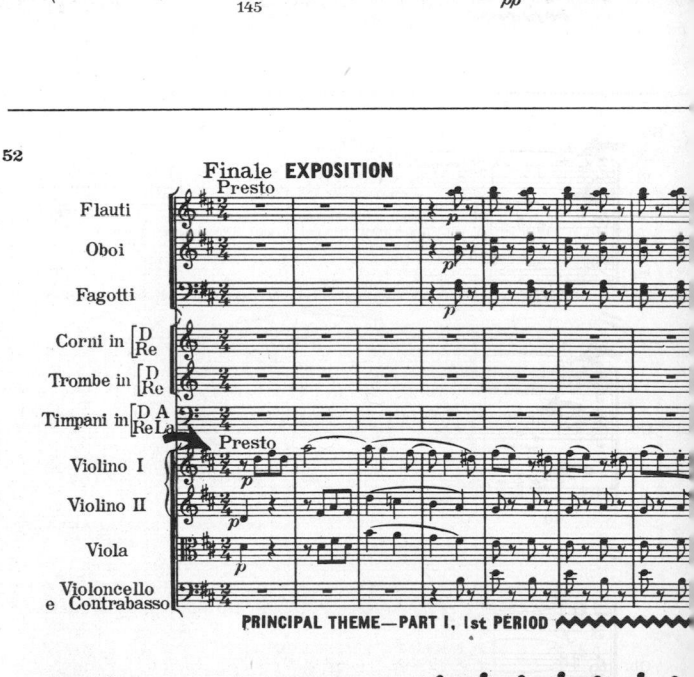

52

Finale EXPOSITION
Presto

Flauti
Oboi
Fagotti
Corni in [D / Re]
Trombe in [D / Re]
Timpani in [D A / Re La]

Presto

Violino I
Violino II
Viola
Violoncello e Contrabasso

PRINCIPAL THEME—PART I, 1st PERIOD ⌇⌇⌇⌇

PRINCIPAL THEME—PART I, 2nd PERIOD ⌇⌇⌇⌇

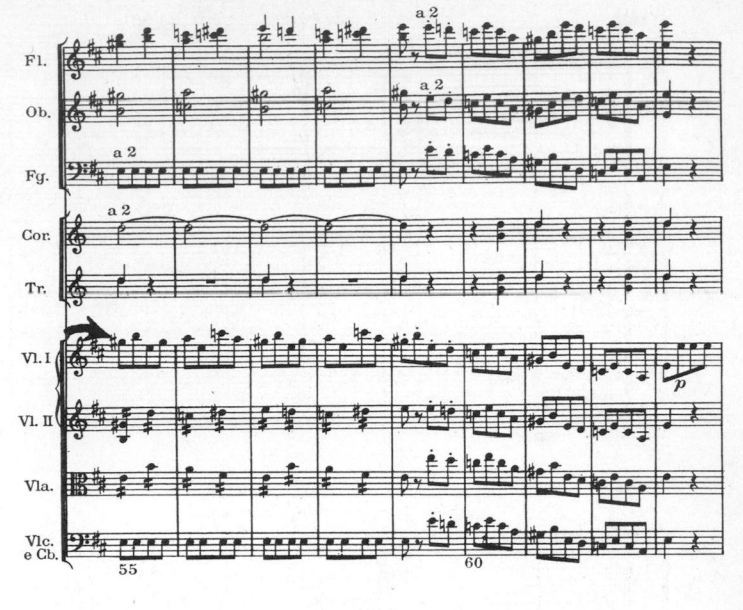

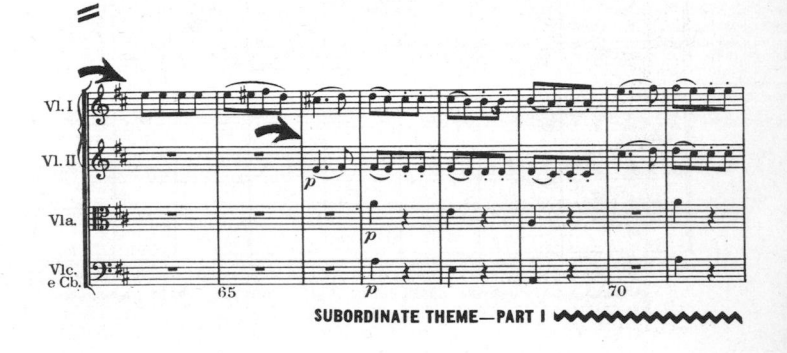

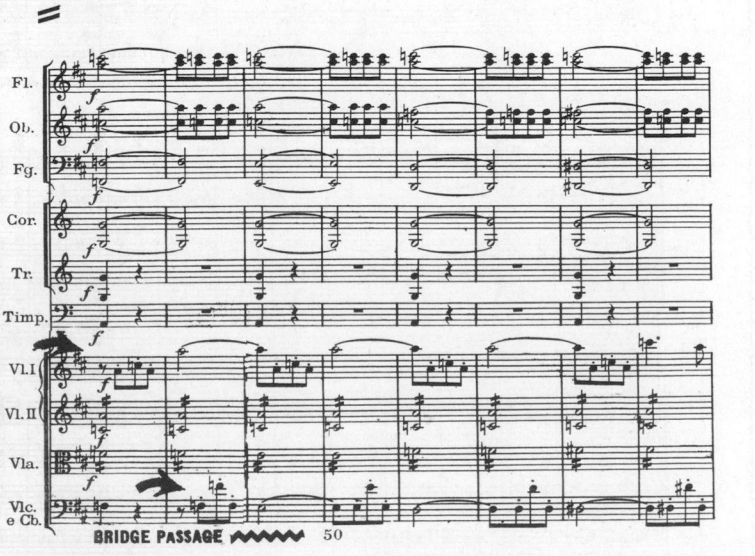

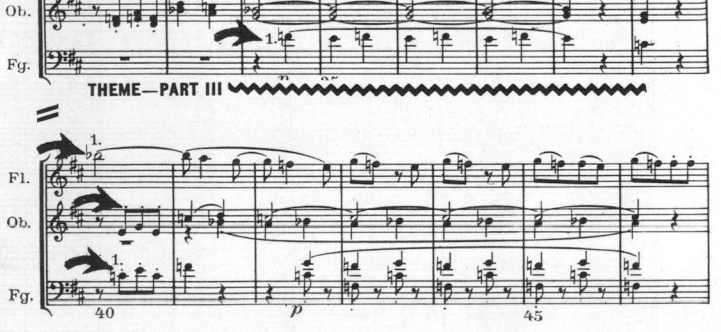

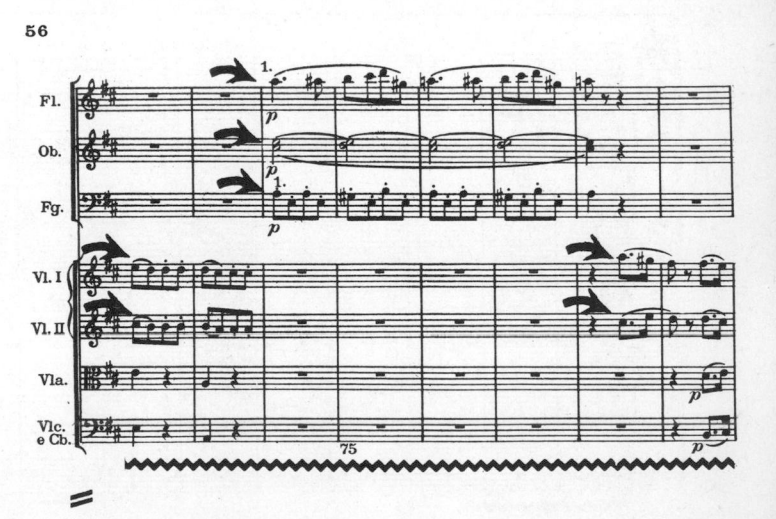

PRINCIPAL THEME—PART II

PRINCIPAL

THEME—PART III

BRIDGE PASSAGE

SUBORDINATE THEME—PART I

SUBORDINATE THEME—PART II

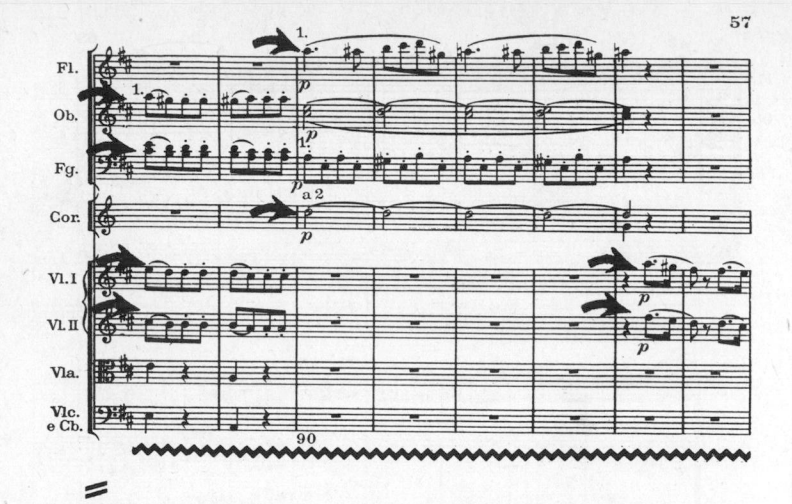

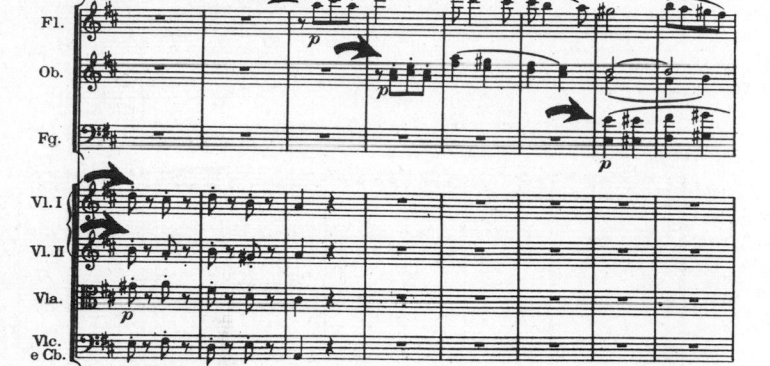

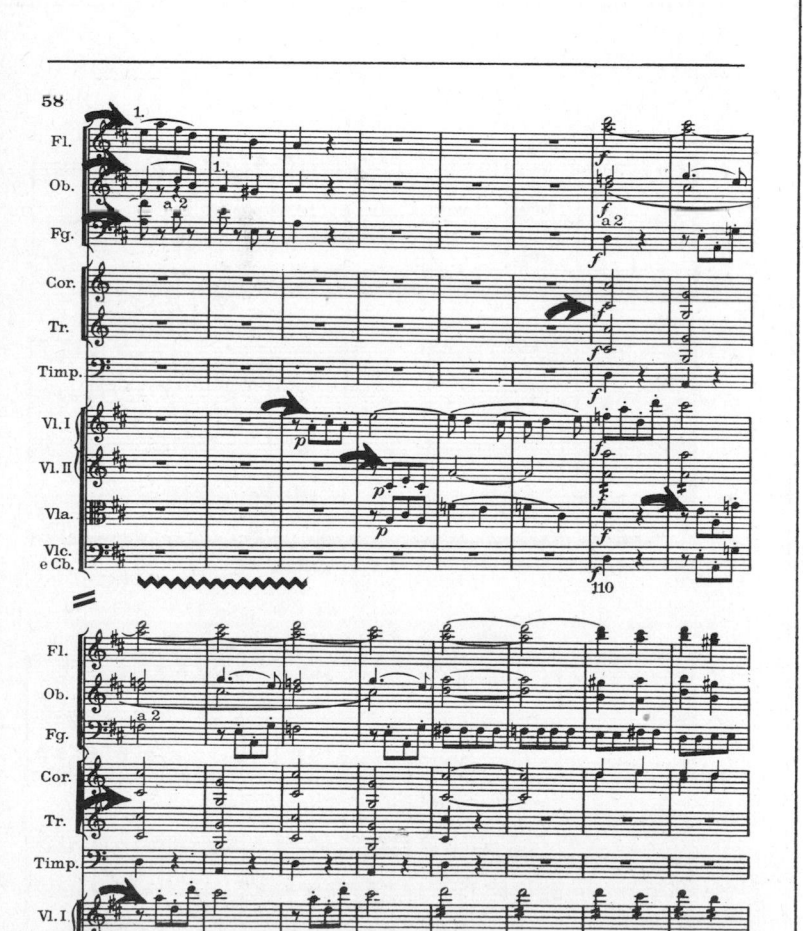

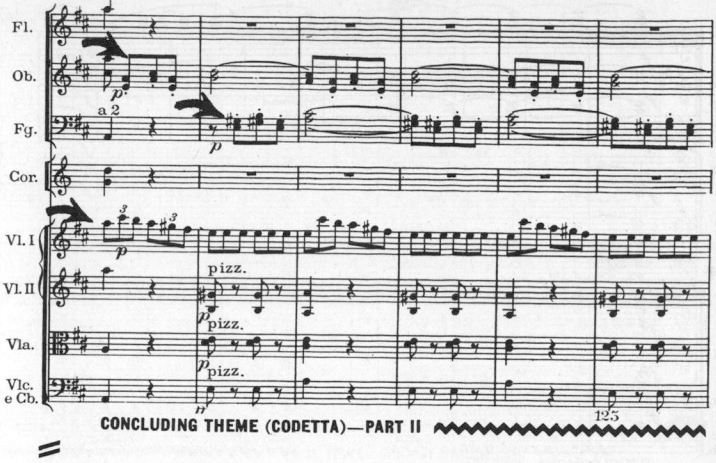

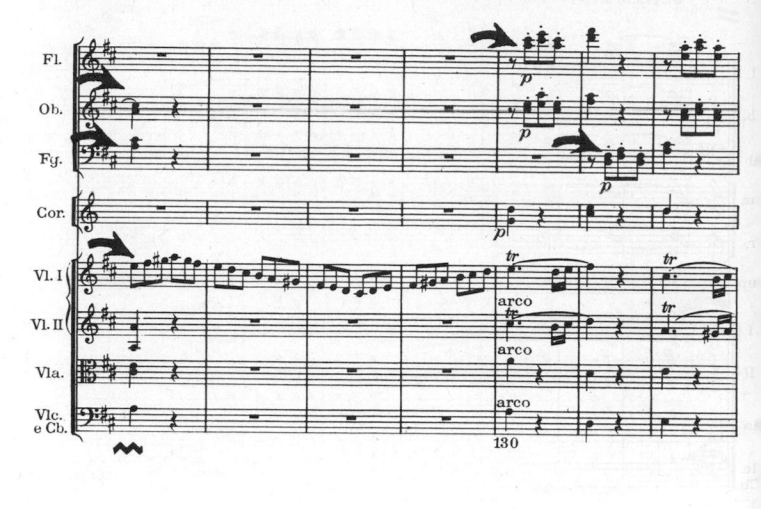

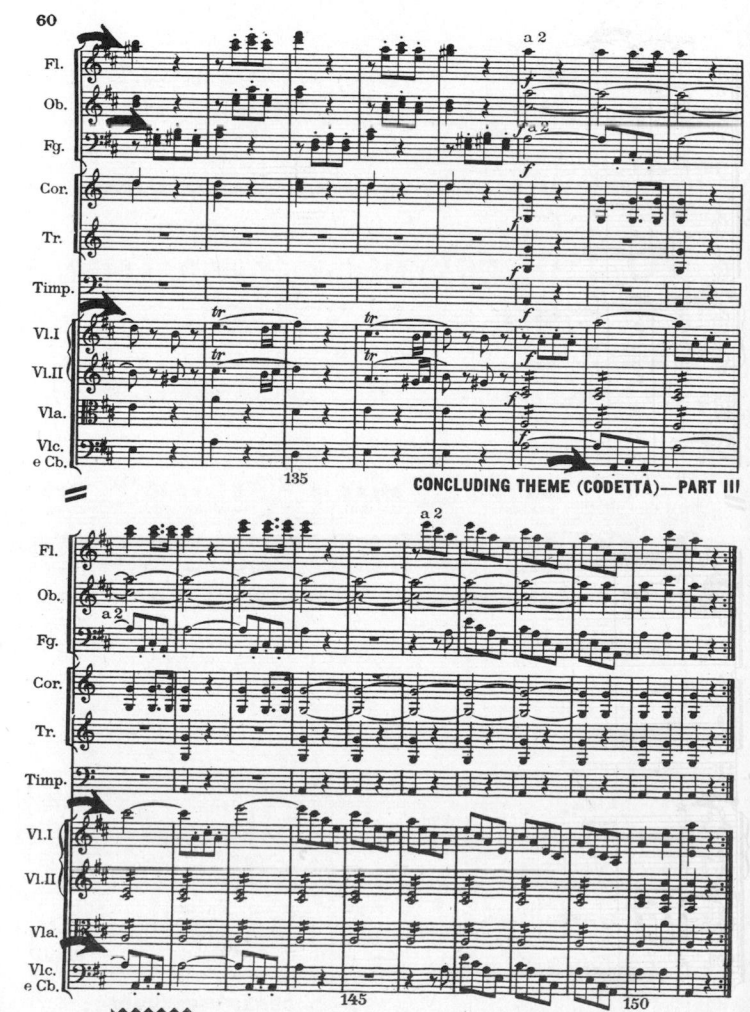

CONCLUDING THEME (CODETTA)—PART I

CONCLUDING THEME (CODETTA)—PART II

CONCLUDING THEME (CODETTA)—PART III

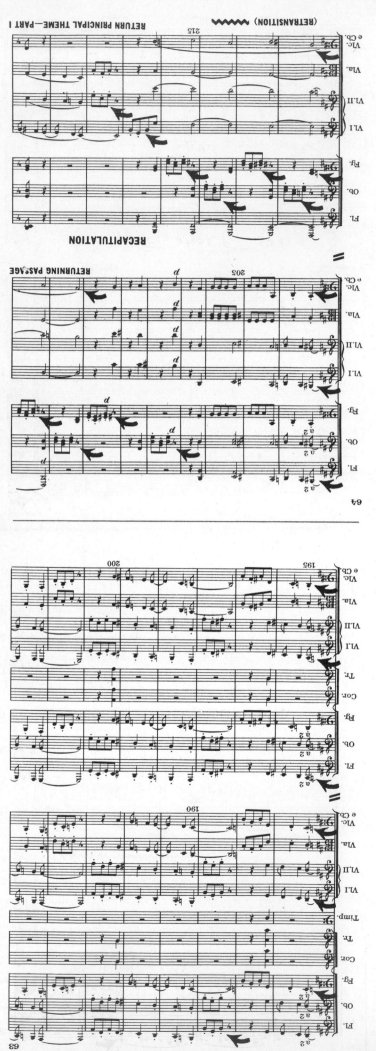

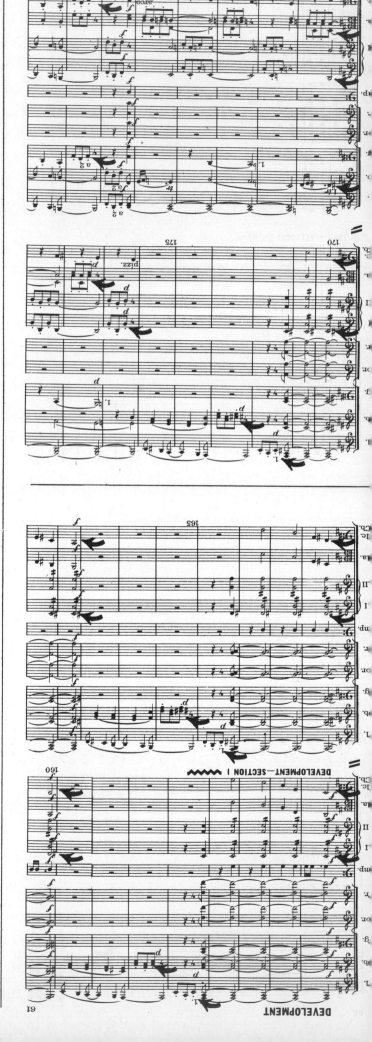

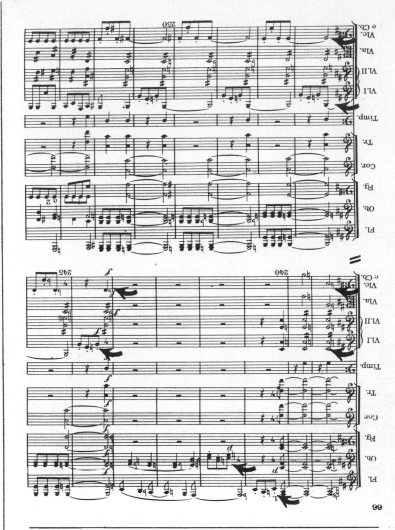
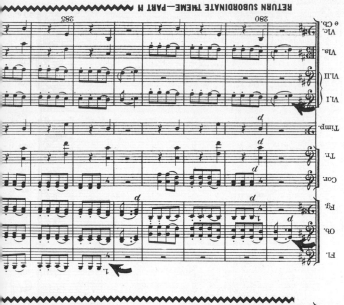
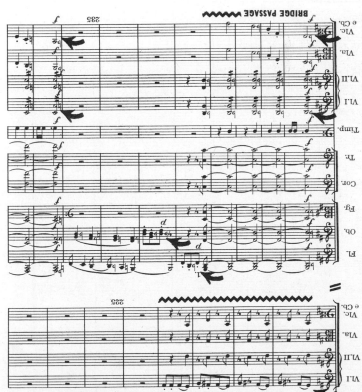
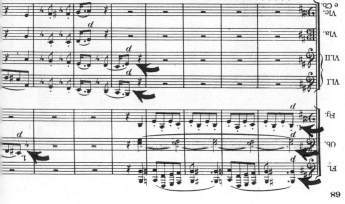
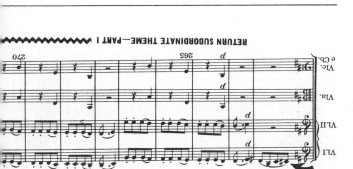
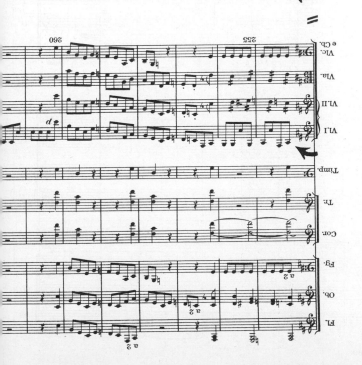
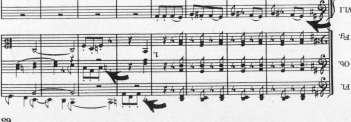

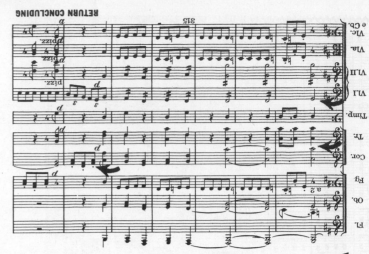
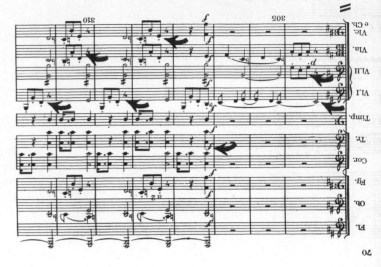
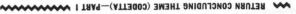
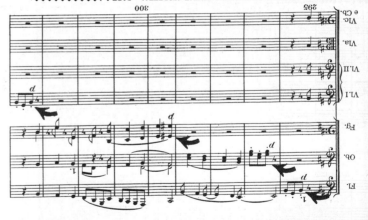
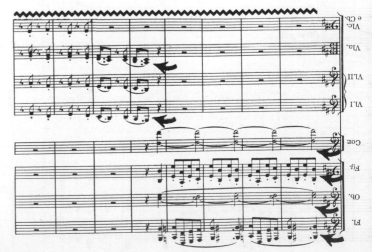
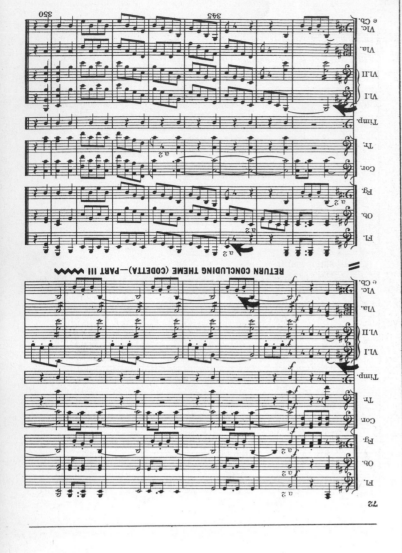
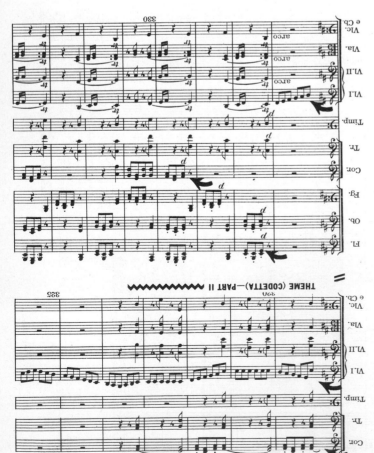

Symphony in Eb Major

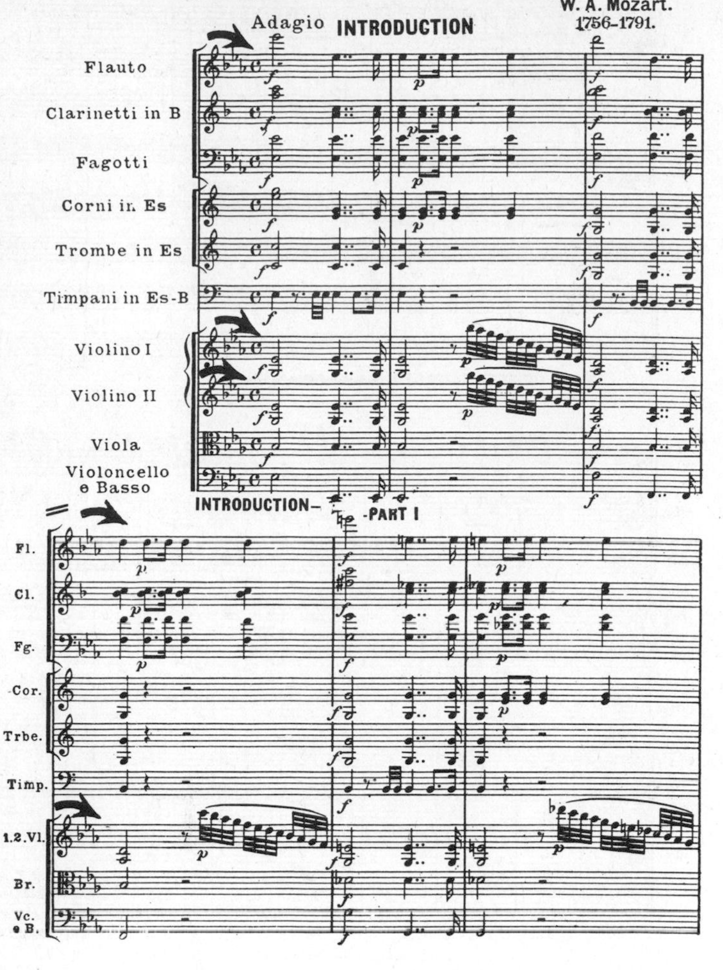

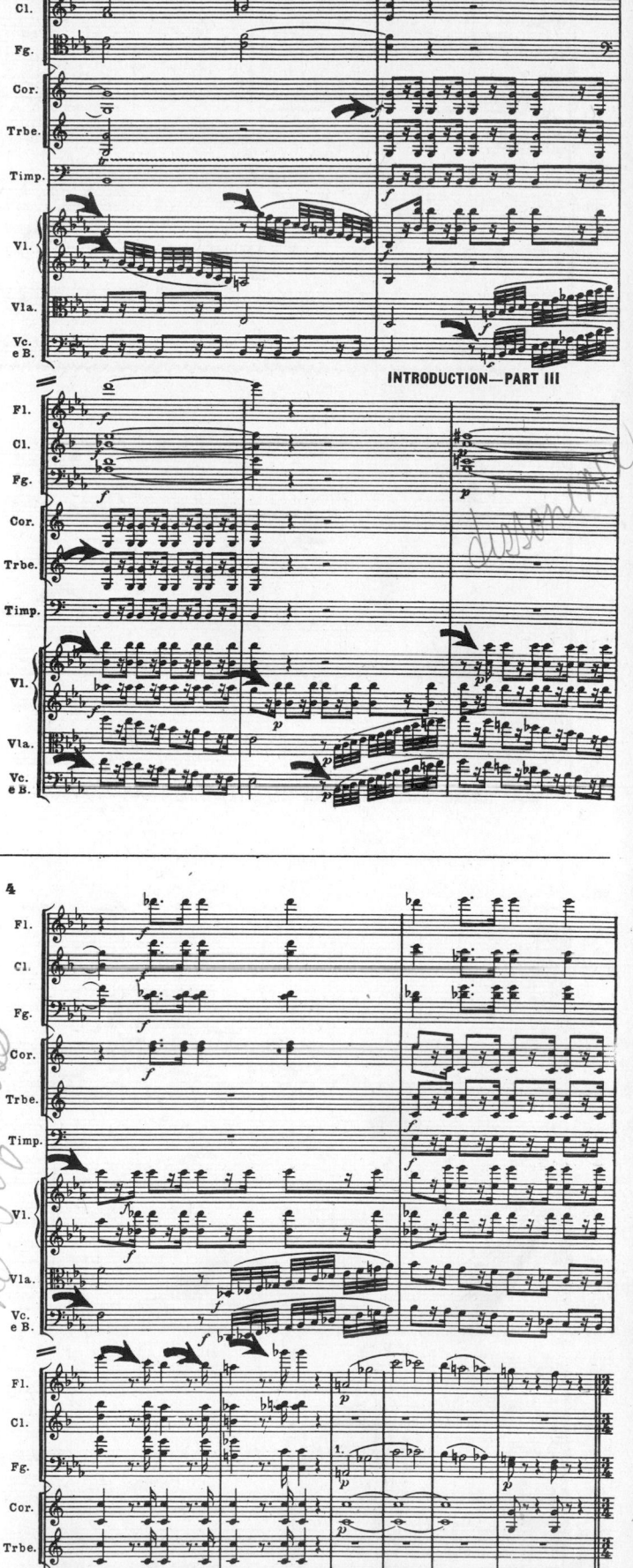

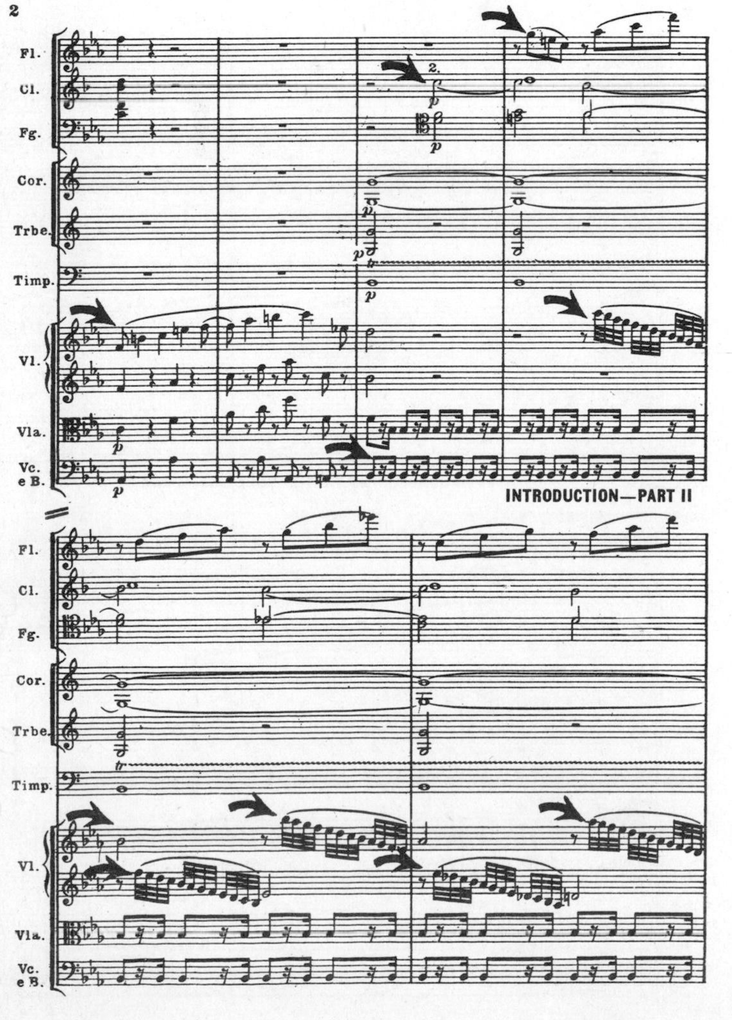

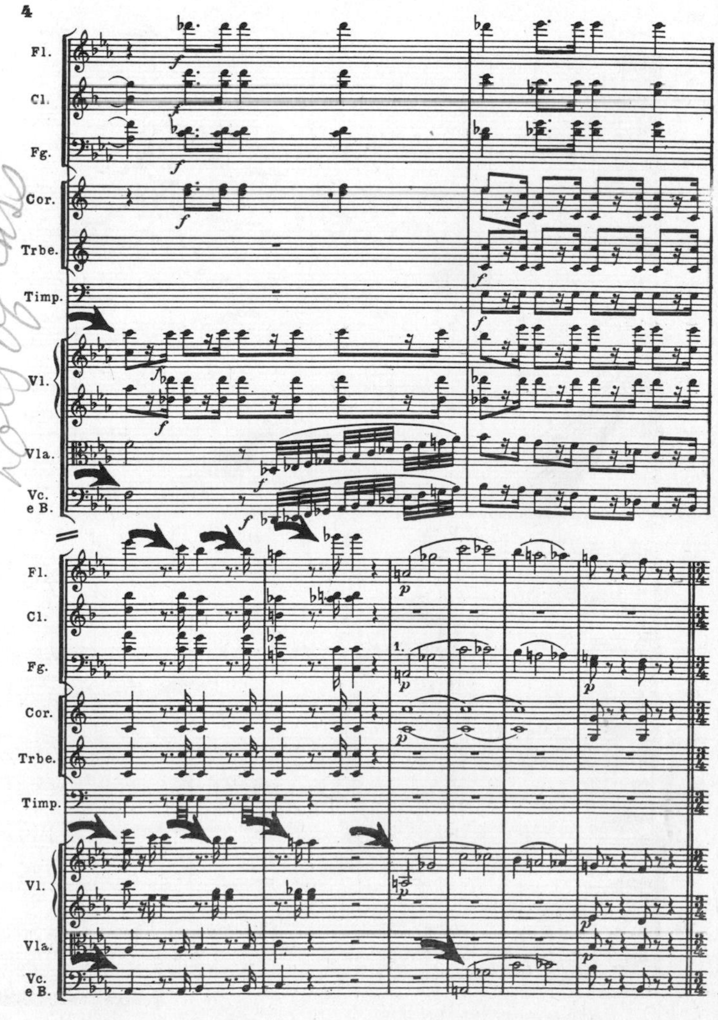

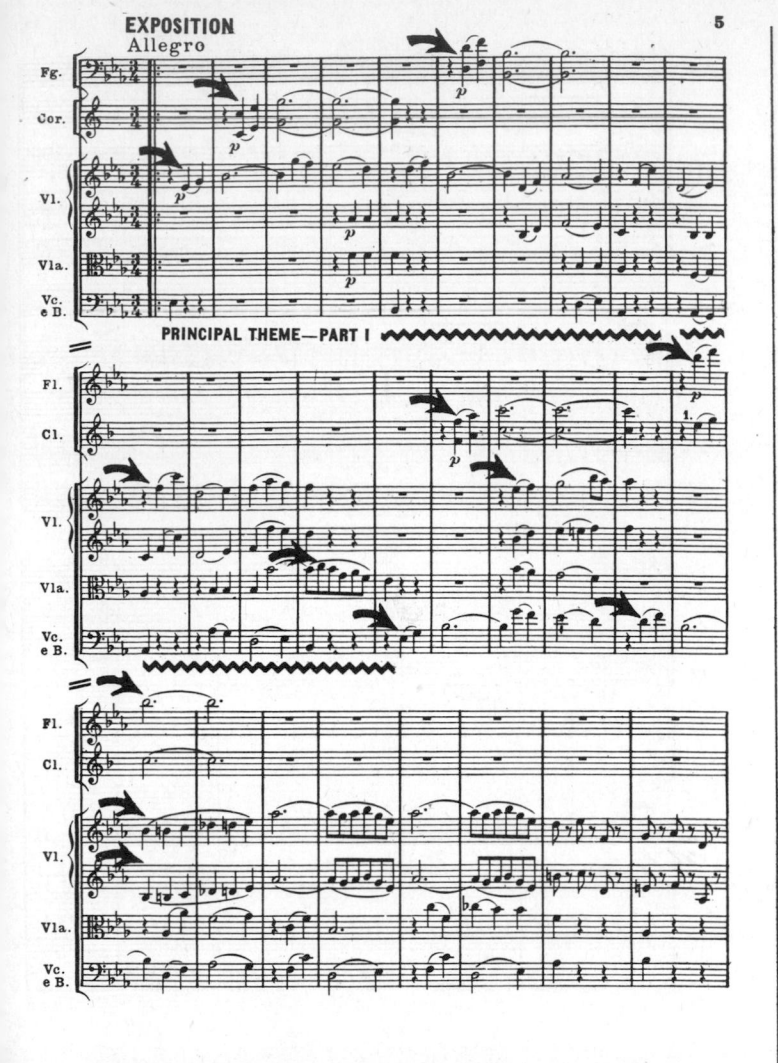

EXPOSITION
Allegro

PRINCIPAL THEME—PART I

BRIDGE PASSAGE

PRINCIPAL THEME—PART II

(181)

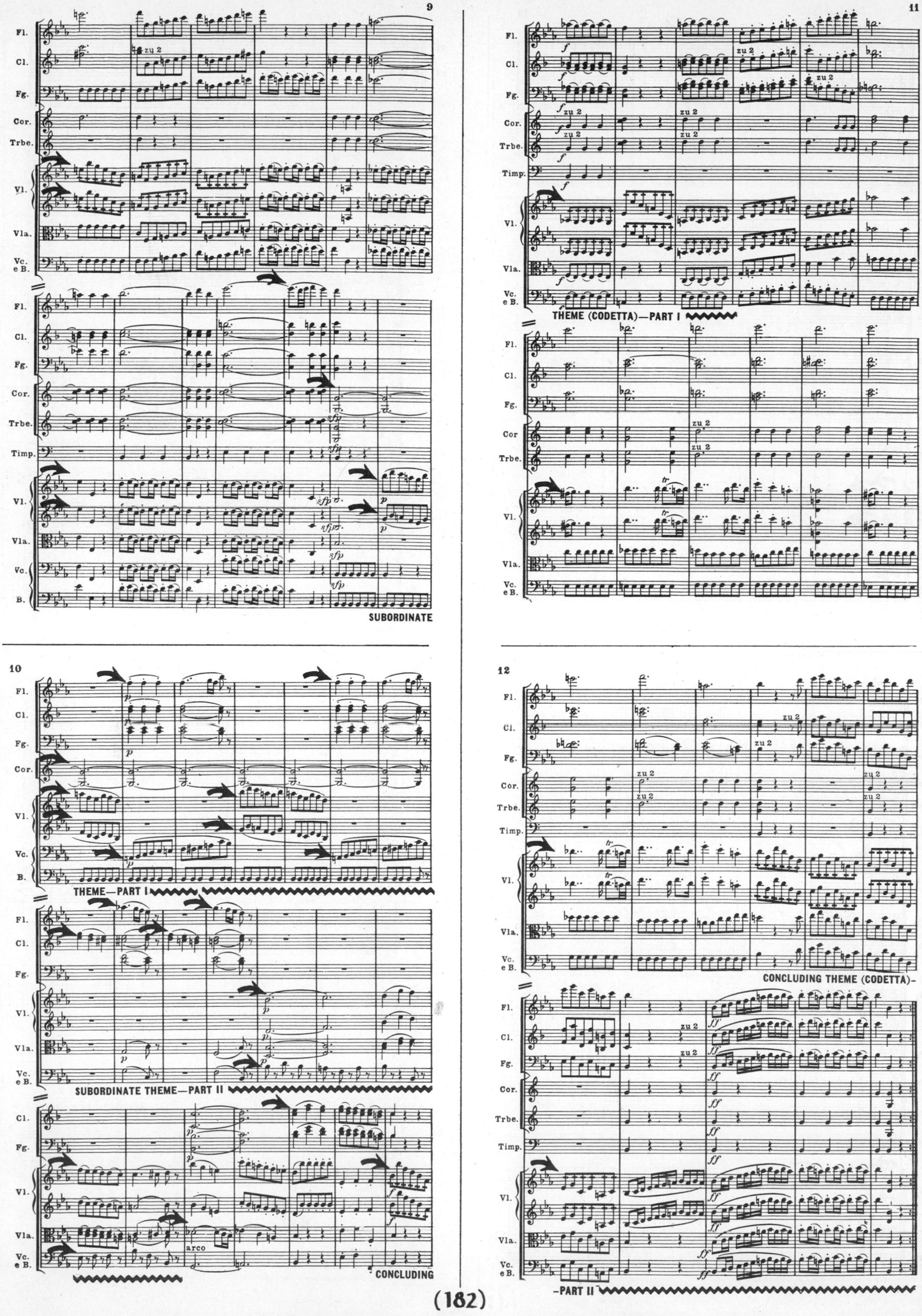
9
11
10
12
SUBORDINATE
THEME (CODETTA)—PART I
THEME—PART I
SUBORDINATE THEME—PART II
CONCLUDING
CONCLUDING THEME (CODETTA)-
-PART II
Fl.
Cl.
Fg.
Cor.
Trbe.
Timp.
Vl.
Vla.
Vc.
B.
Vc. e B.
zu 2
arco

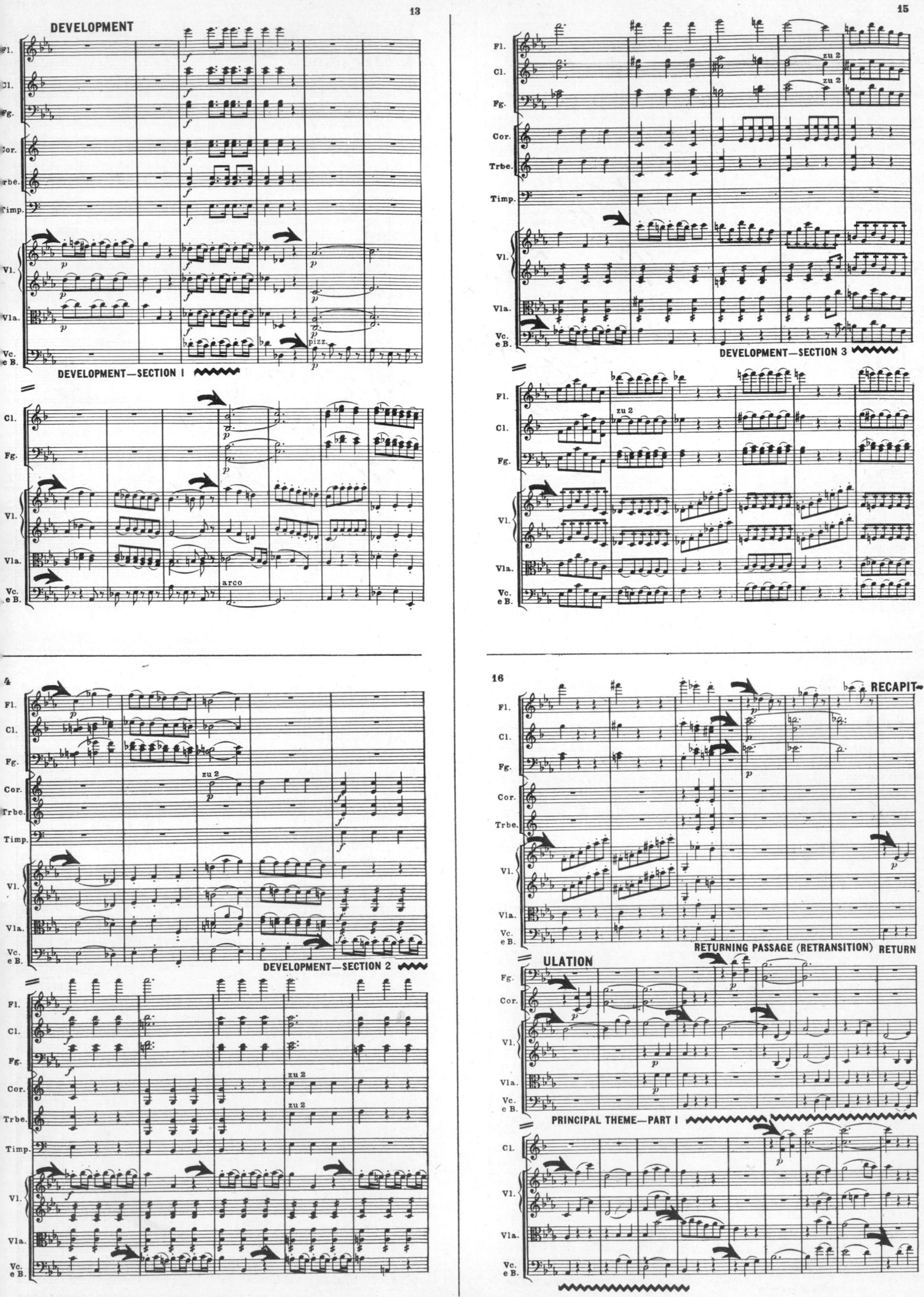

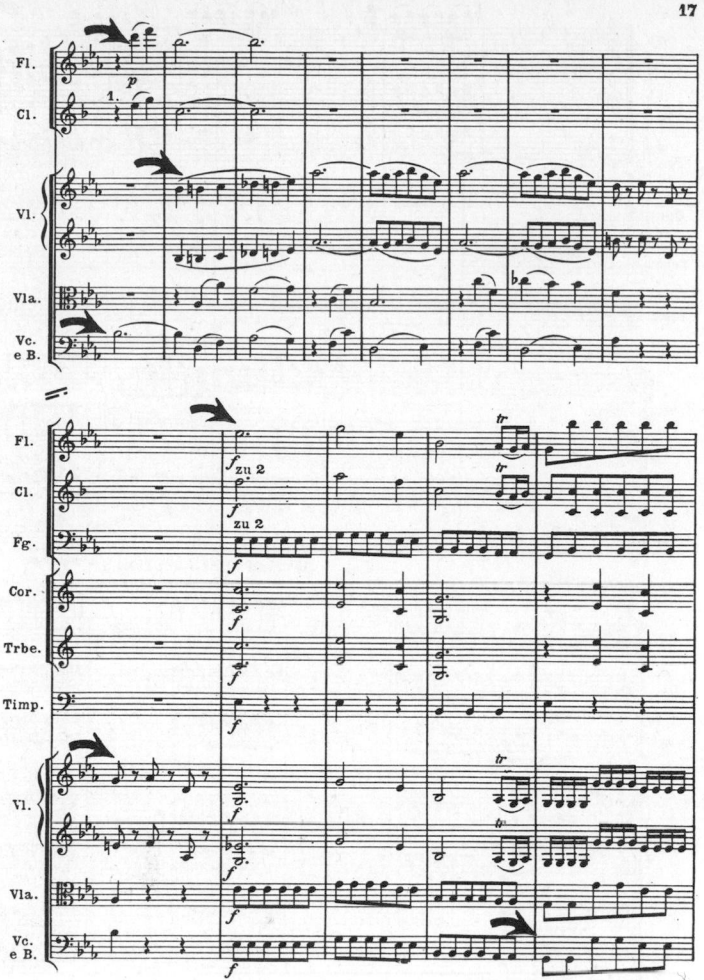

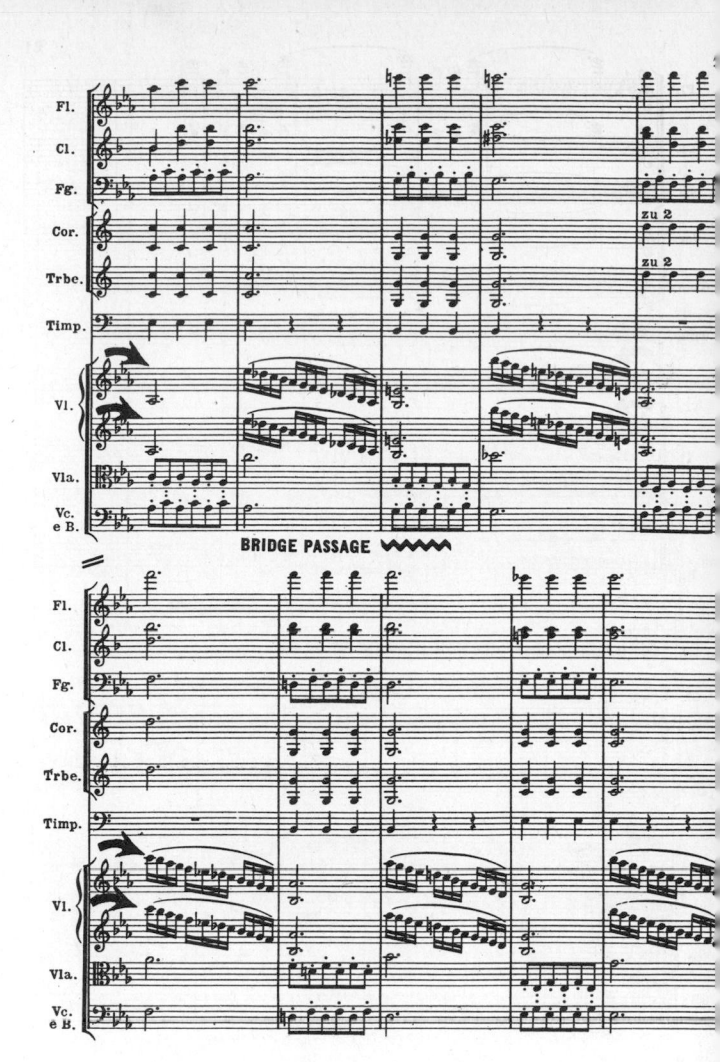

RETURN PRINCIPAL THEME—PART II 〰〰〰〰

BRIDGE PASSAGE 〰〰〰

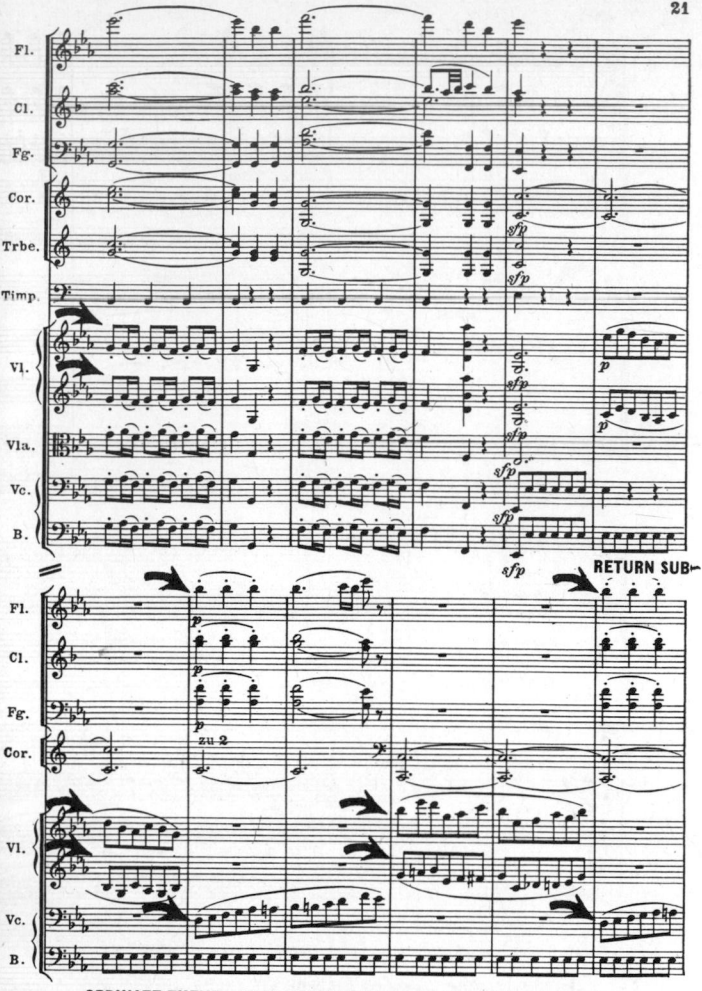

21

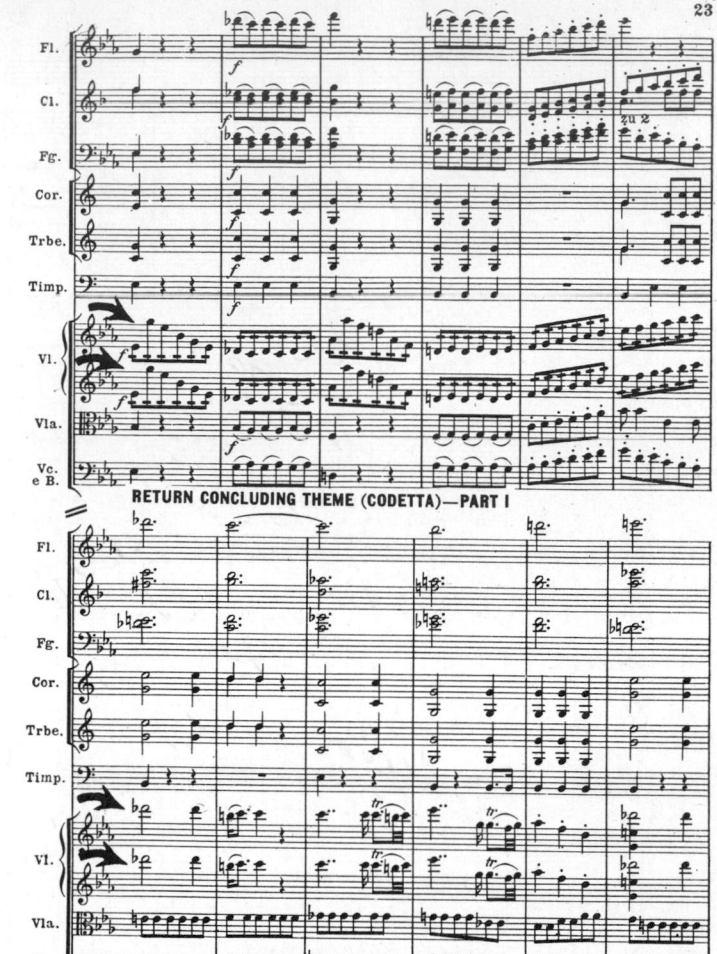

23

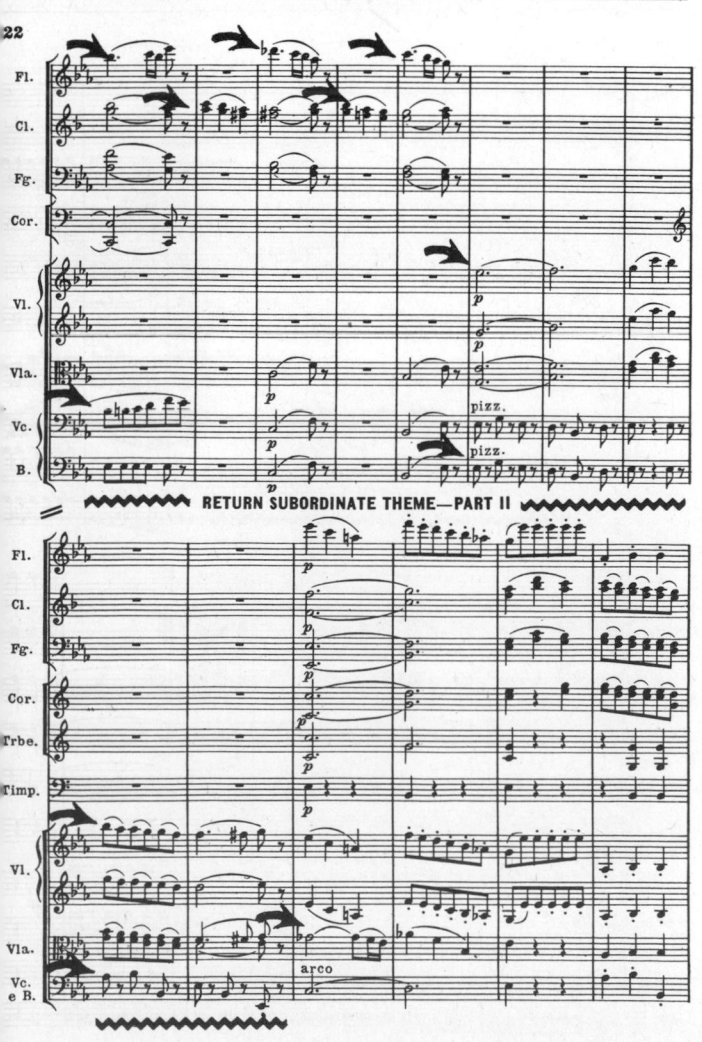

ORDINATE THEME—PART I

RETURN SUB-

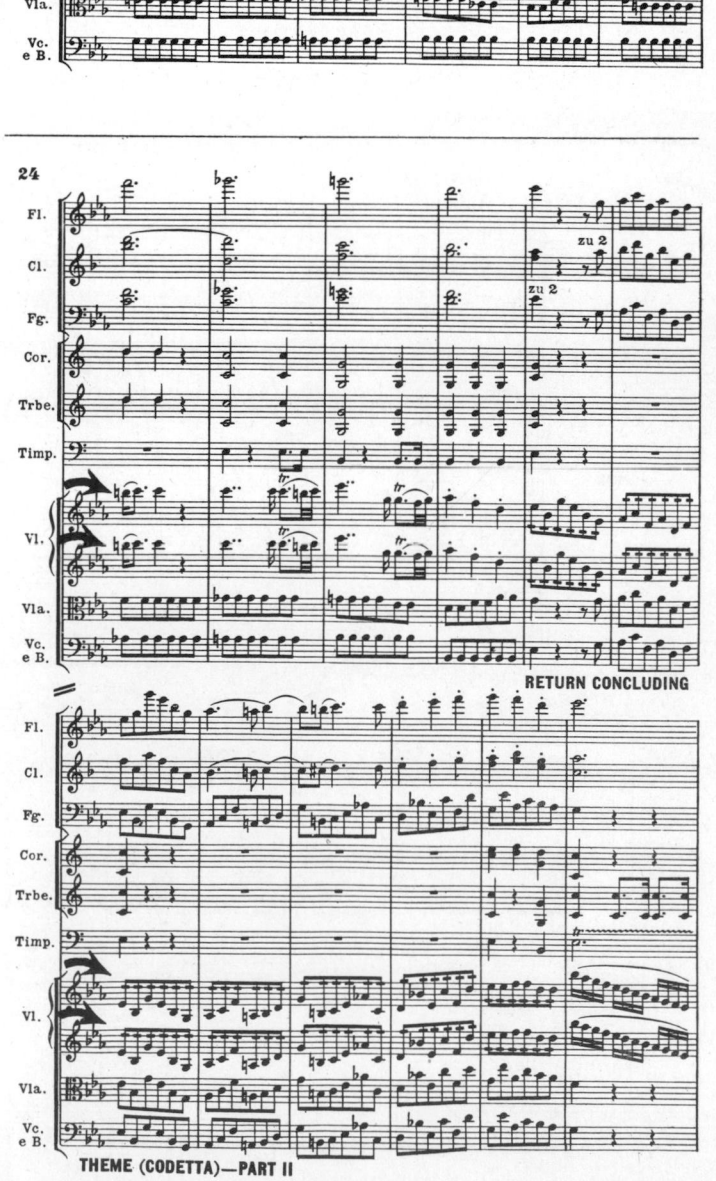

RETURN CONCLUDING THEME (CODETTA)—PART I

22

RETURN SUBORDINATE THEME—PART II

24

RETURN CONCLUDING

THEME (CODETTA)—PART II

(185)

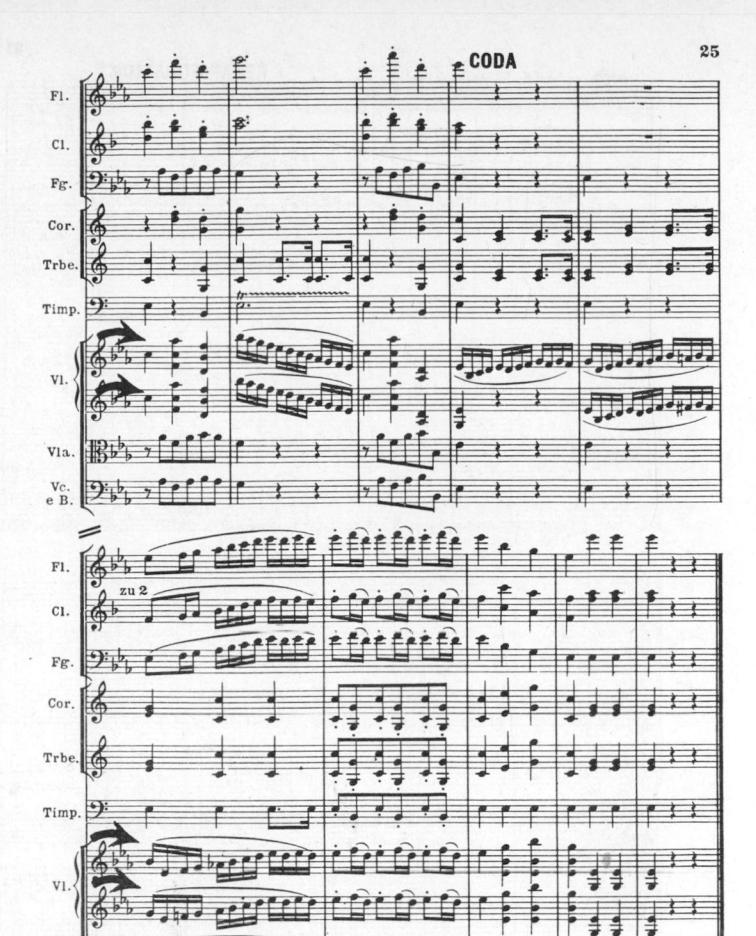

CODA

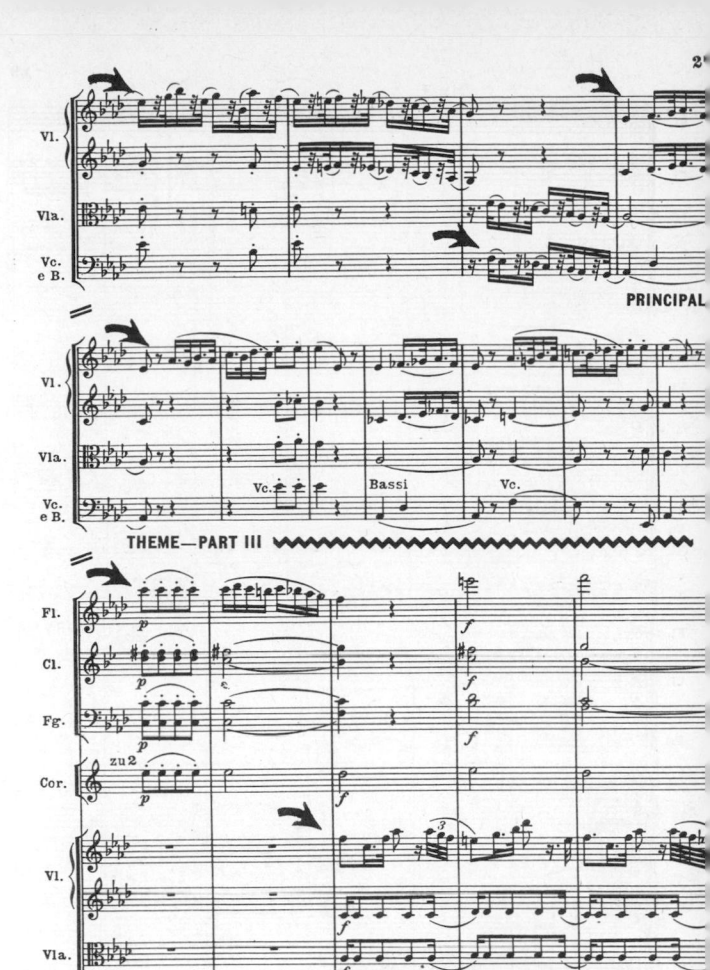

PRINCIPAL

THEME—PART III

BRIDGE PASSAGE ～～～ SUBORDINATE THEME—PART I ～～～

EXPOSITION

Andante

Flauto

Clarinetti in B

Fagotti

Corni in Es

Violino I

Violino II

Viola

Violoncello

Basso

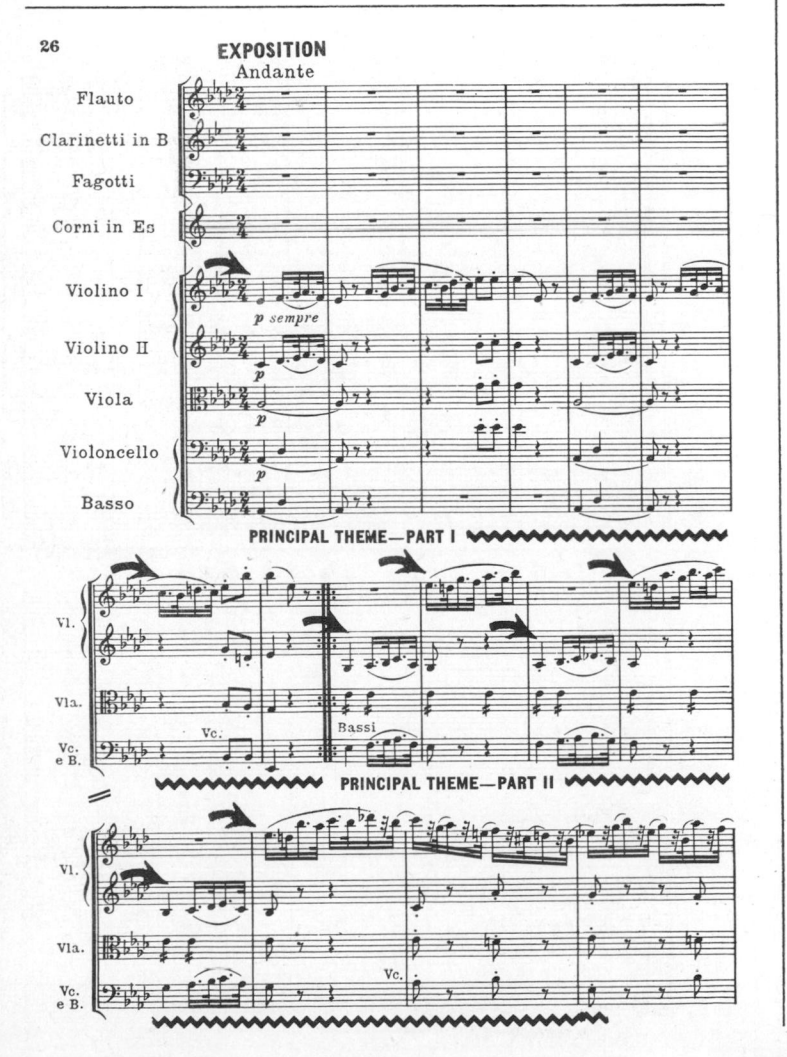

PRINCIPAL THEME—PART I ～～～

PRINCIPAL THEME—PART II ～～～

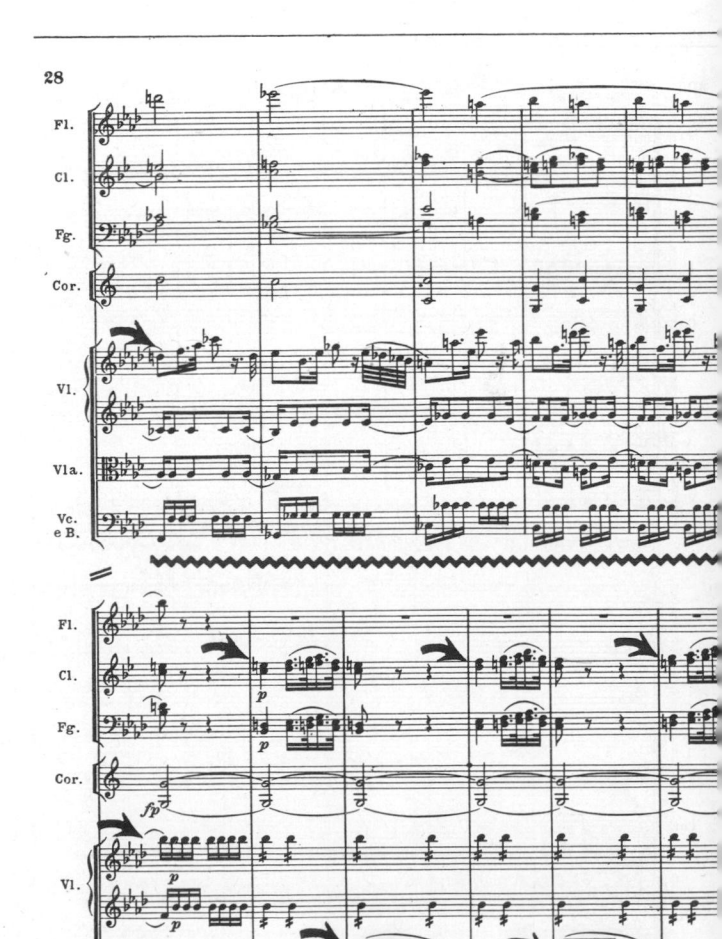

SUBORDINATE THEME—PART II ～～～

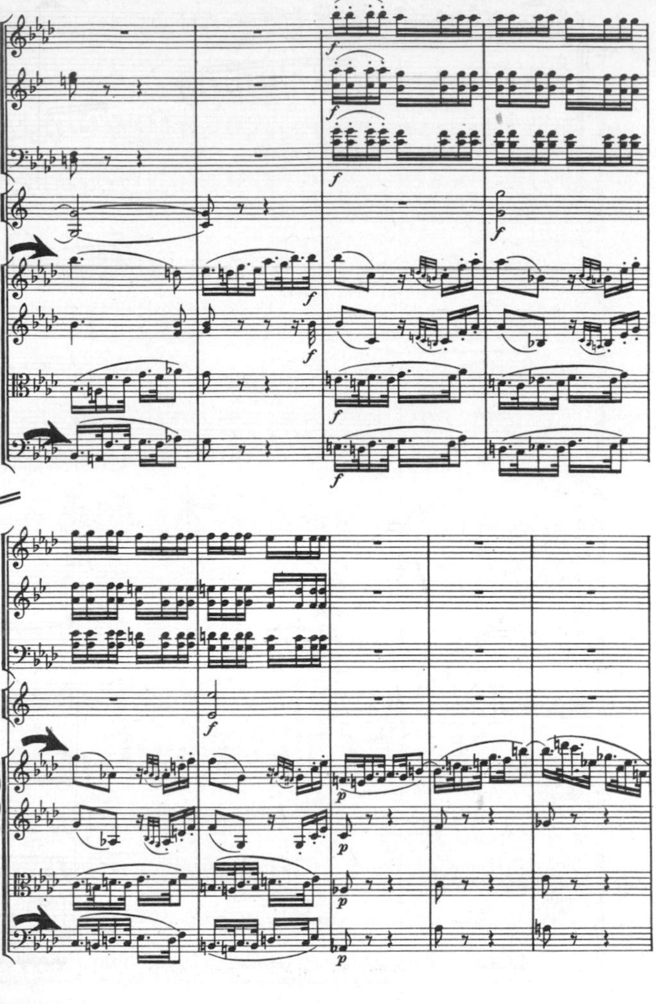

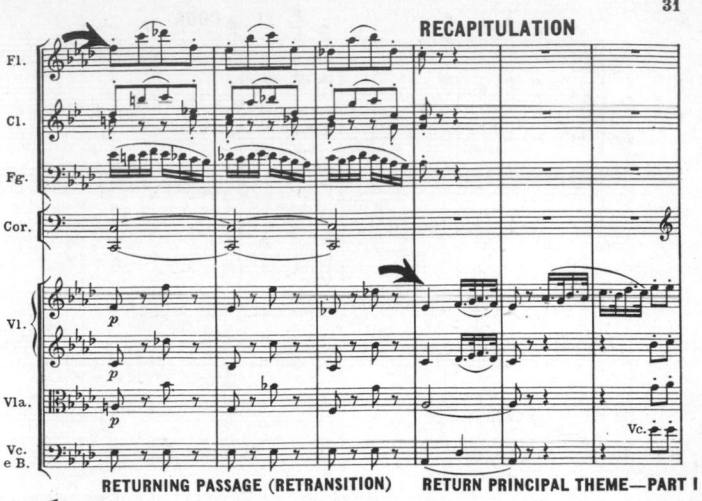

RECAPITULATION

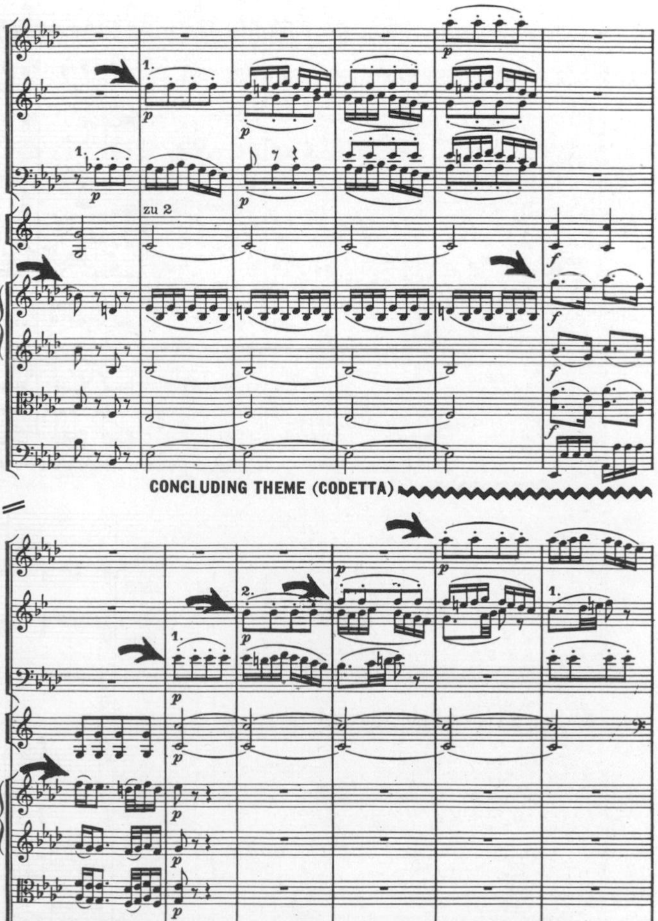

RETURNING PASSAGE (RETRANSITION)   RETURN PRINCIPAL THEME—PART I

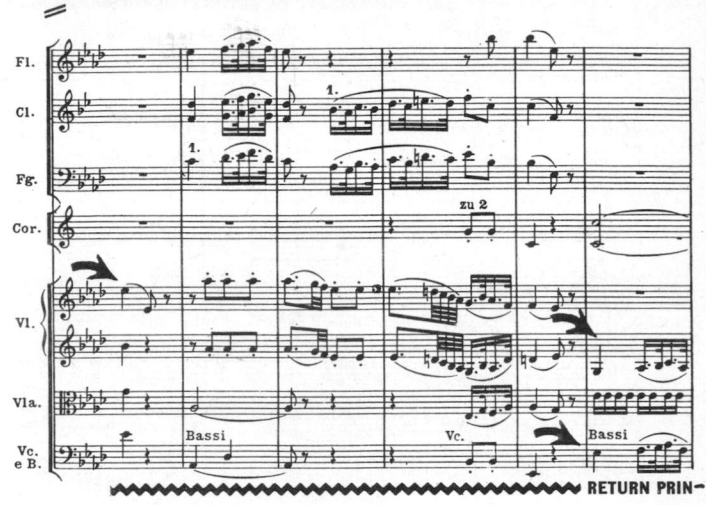

RETURN PRIN—

CONCLUDING THEME (CODETTA) 〜〜〜〜〜〜〜〜

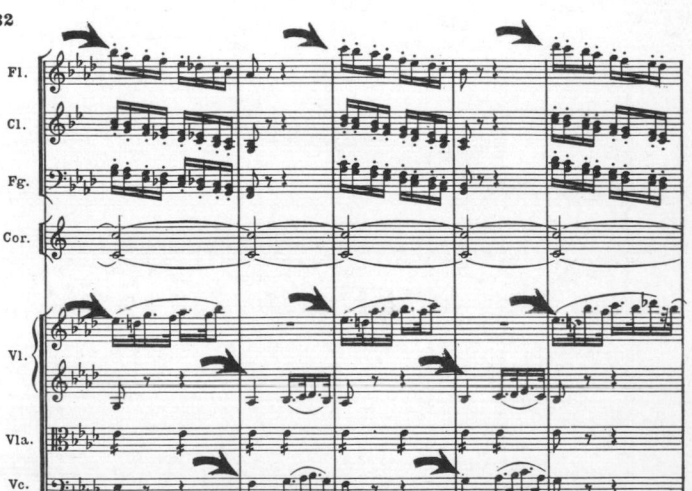

CIPAL THEME—PART II 〜〜〜〜〜

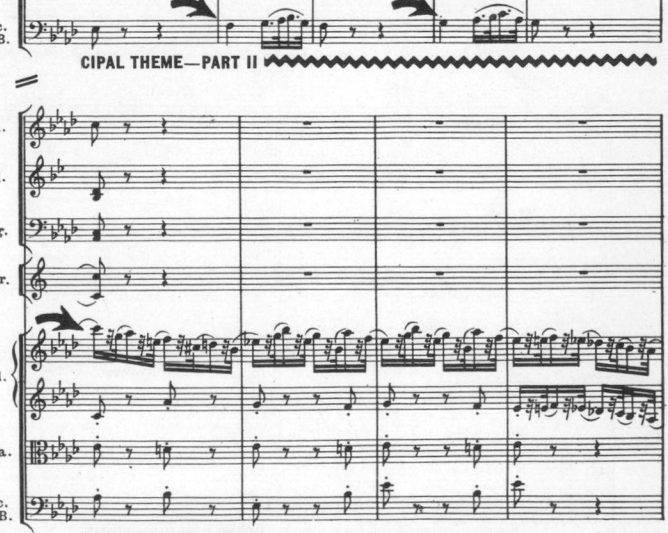

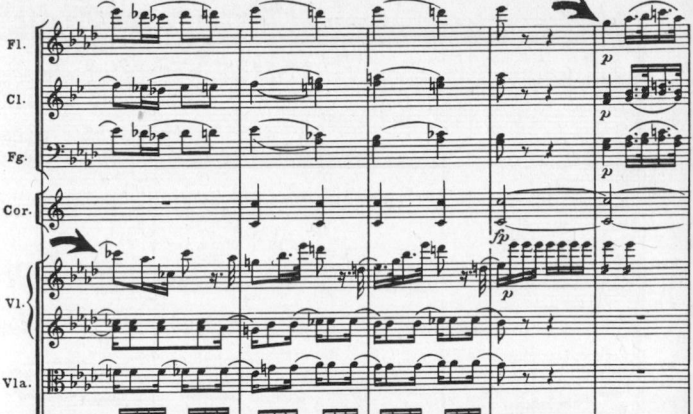

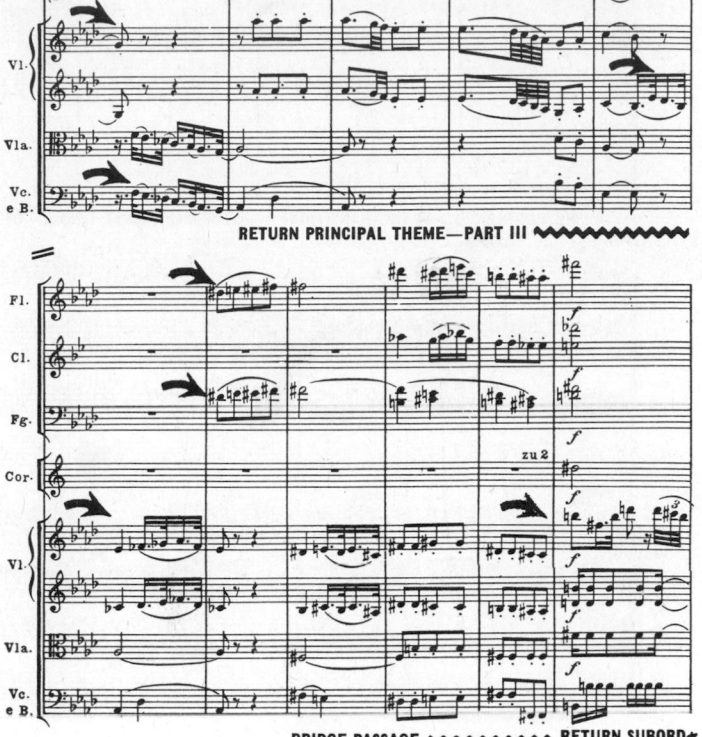

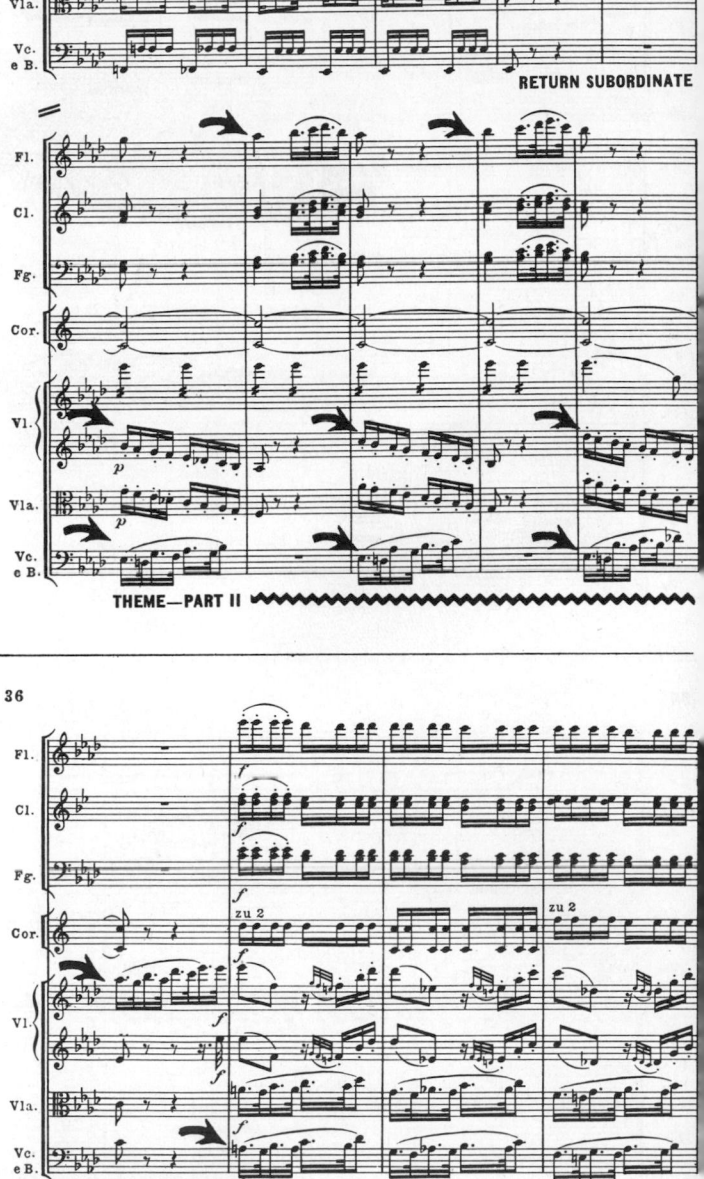

RETURN PRINCIPAL THEME—PART III 〰〰〰〰〰〰

RETURN SUBORDINATE

BRIDGE PASSAGE 〰〰〰〰〰〰〰 RETURN SUBORD.→

THEME—PART II 〰〰〰〰〰〰

INATE THEME—PART I 〰〰〰〰〰〰〰〰〰〰〰

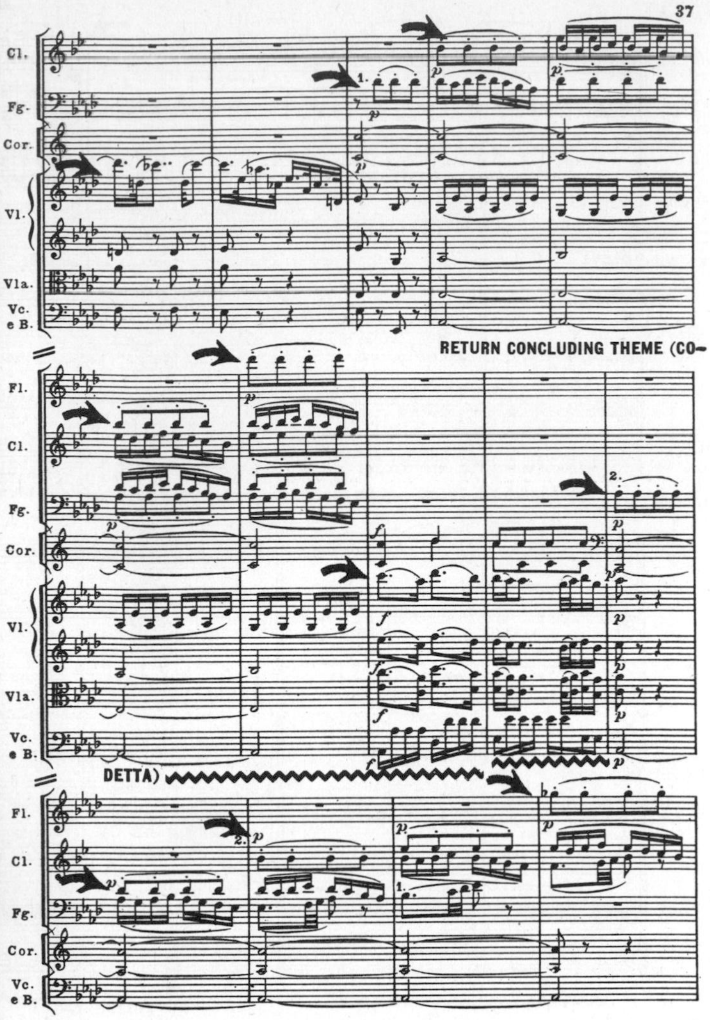

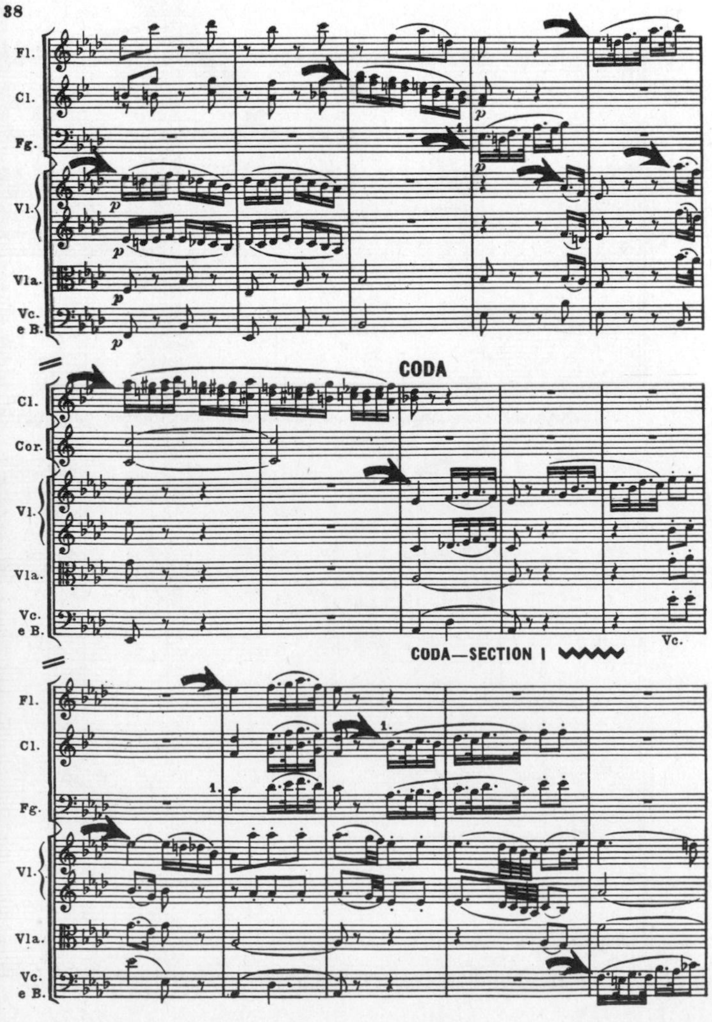

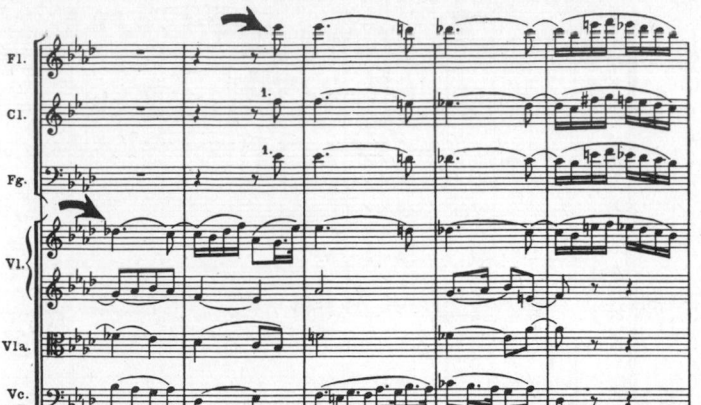
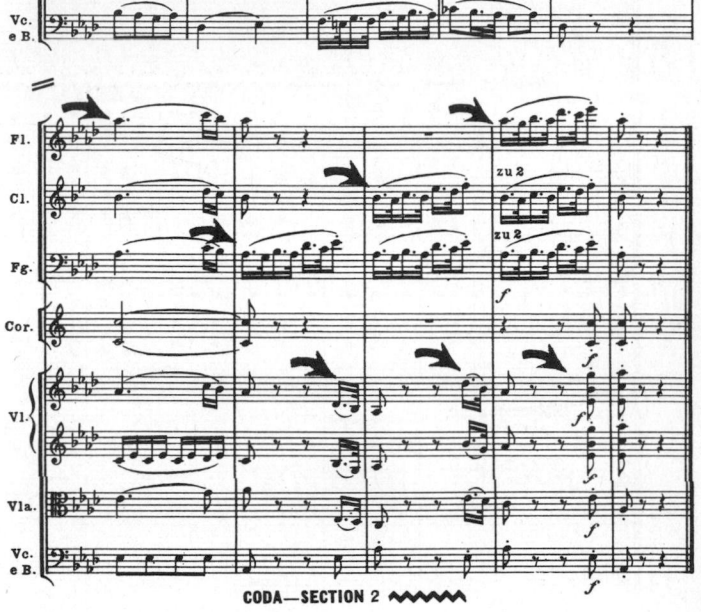
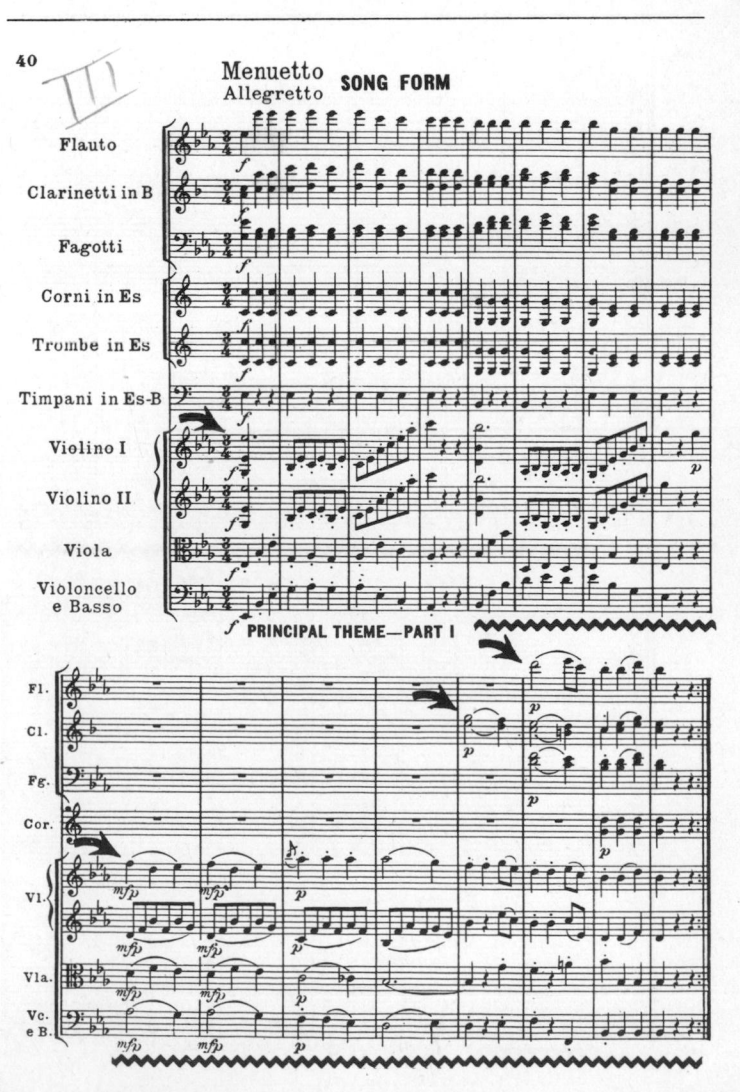

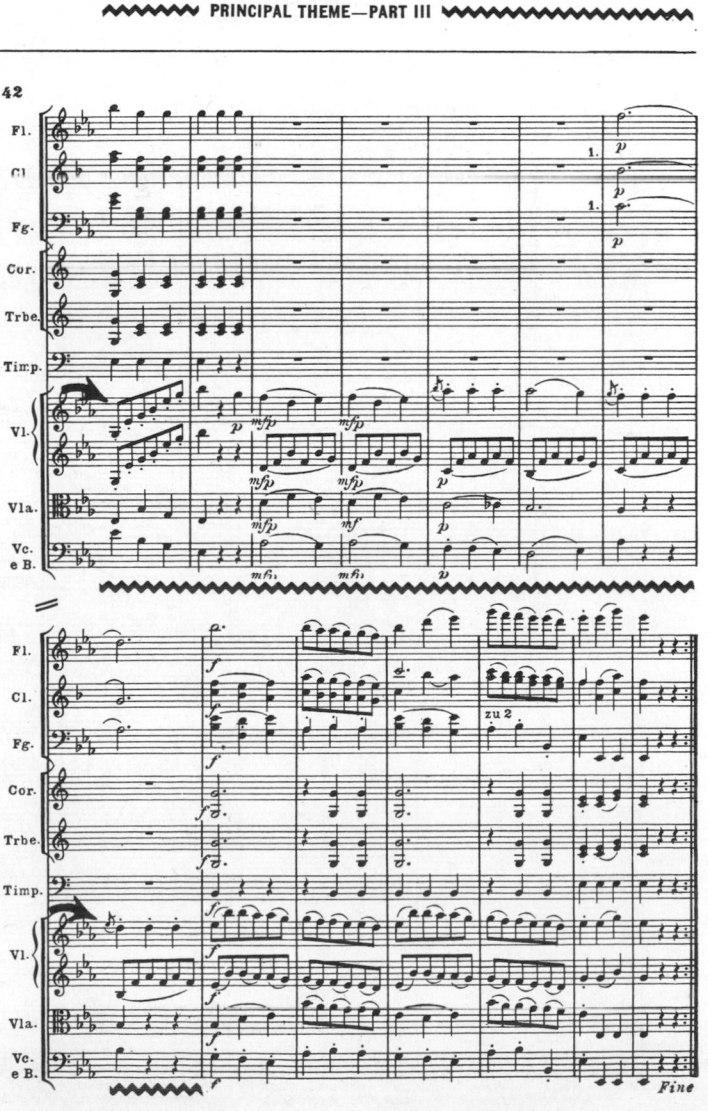

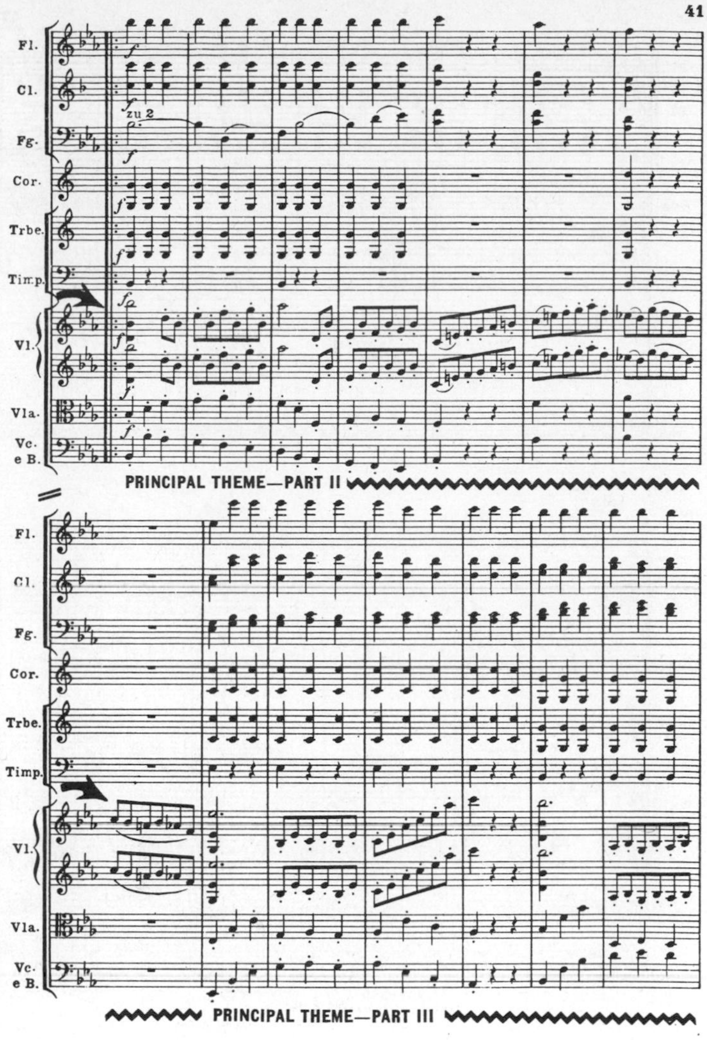
Fl.
Cl.
Fg.
Cor.
Trbe.
Timp.
Vl.
Vla.
Vc. e B.
zu 2
PRINCIPAL THEME—PART II
PRINCIPAL THEME—PART III

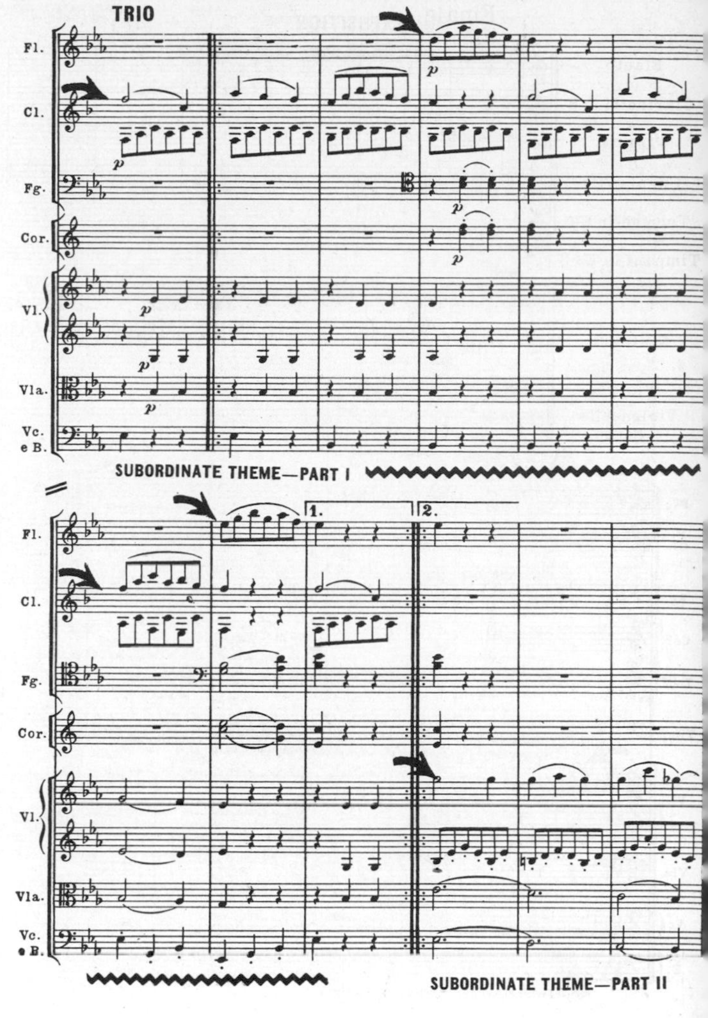
TRIO
Fl.
Cl.
Fg.
Cor.
Vl.
Vla.
Vc. e B.
SUBORDINATE THEME—PART I
1.
2.
SUBORDINATE THEME—PART II

Fl.
Cl.
Fg.
Cor.
Trbe.
Timp.
Vl.
Vla.
Vc. e B.
zu 2
Fine

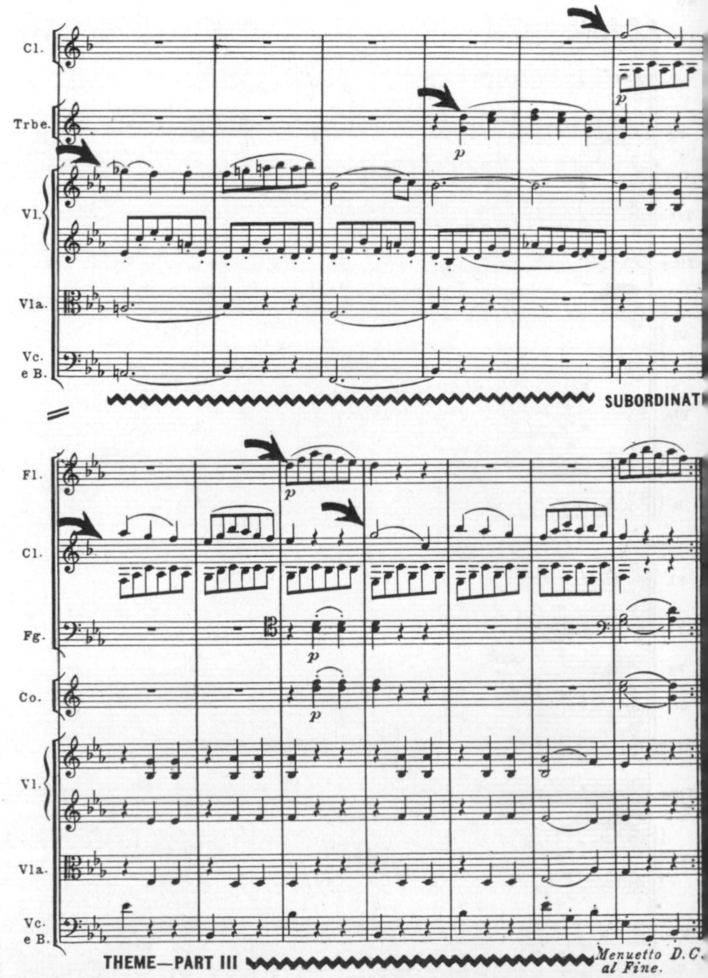
Cl.
Trbe.
Vl.
Vla.
Vc. e B.
SUBORDINAT
Fl.
Cl.
Fg.
Co.
THEME—PART III
Menuetto D.C. al Fine.

45
Finale
Allegro
EXPOSITION
Flauto
Clarinetti in B
Fagotti
Corni in Es
Trombe in Es
Timpani in Es-B
Violino I
Violino II
Viola
Violoncello e Basso
PRINCIPAL THEME—PART I
Fl.
Cl.
Fg.
Cor.
Trbe.
Timp.
Vl.
Vla.
Vc.
B.
zu 2
zu 2

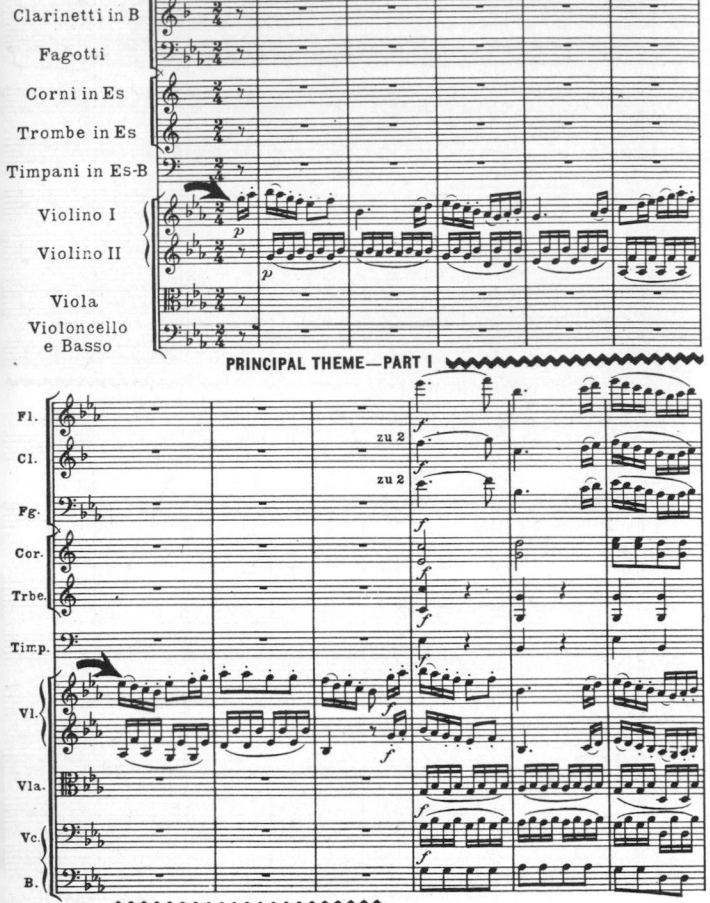

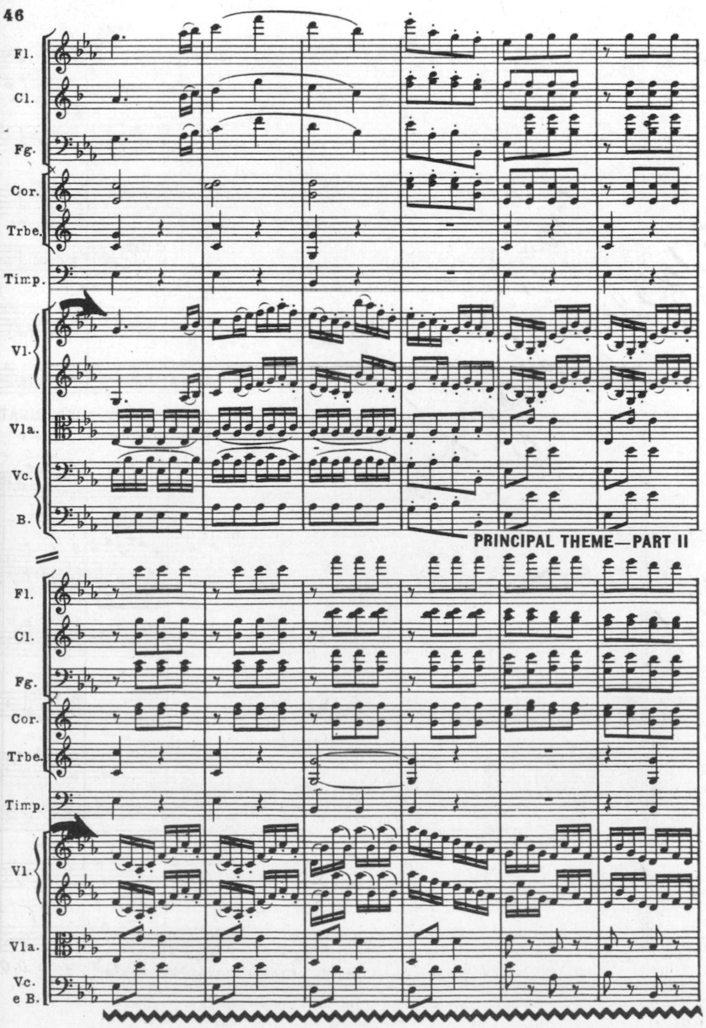
46
Fl.
Cl.
Fg.
Cor.
Trbe.
Timp.
Vl.
Vla.
Vc.
B.
PRINCIPAL THEME—PART II
Fl.
Cl.
Fg.
Cor.
Trbe.
Timp.
Vl.
Vla.
Vc. e B.

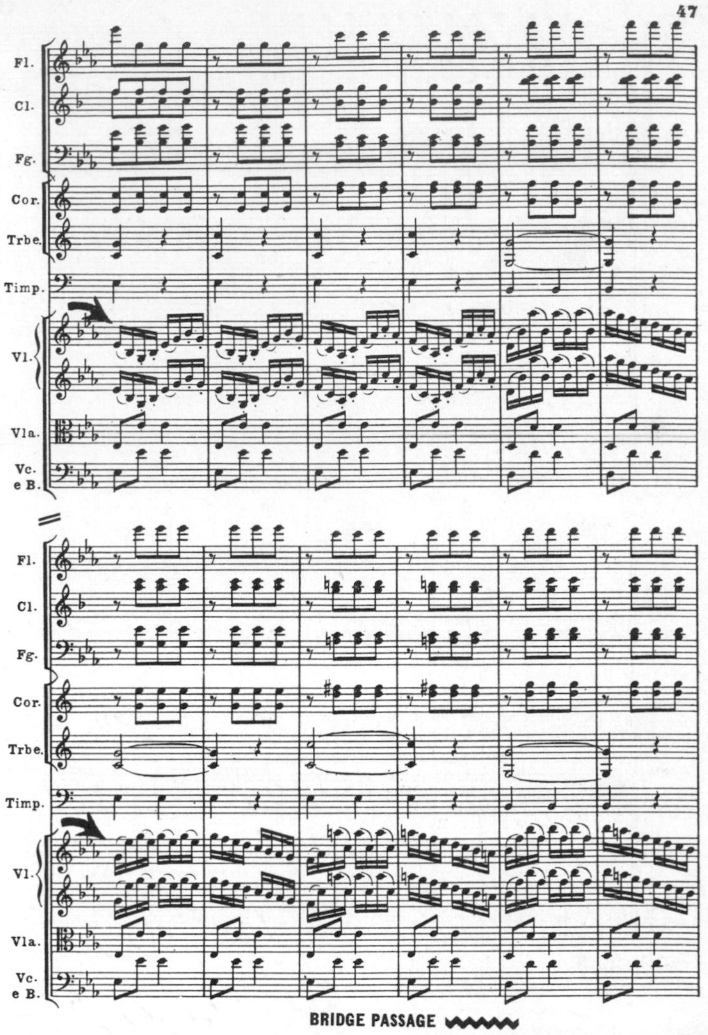
47
Fl.
Cl.
Fg.
Cor.
Trbe.
Timp.
Vl.
Vla.
Vc. e B.
Fl.
Cl.
Fg.
Cor.
Trbe.
Timp.
Vl.
Vla.
Vc. e B.
BRIDGE PASSAGE

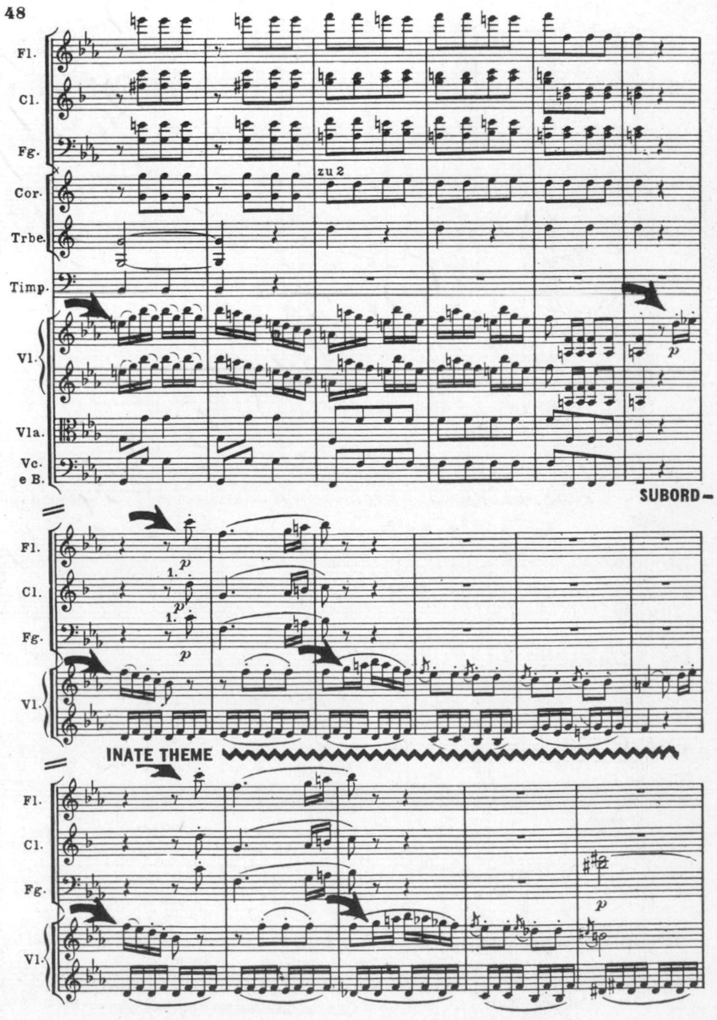
48
Fl.
Cl.
Fg.
Cor.
Trbe.
Timp.
Vl.
Vla.
Vc. e B.
zu 2
SUBORD-
Fl.
Cl.
Fg.
Vl.
INATE THEME
Fl.
Cl.
Fg.
Vl.

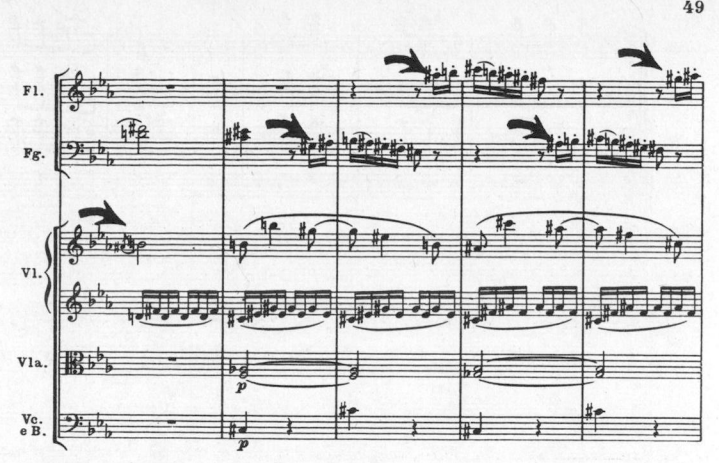

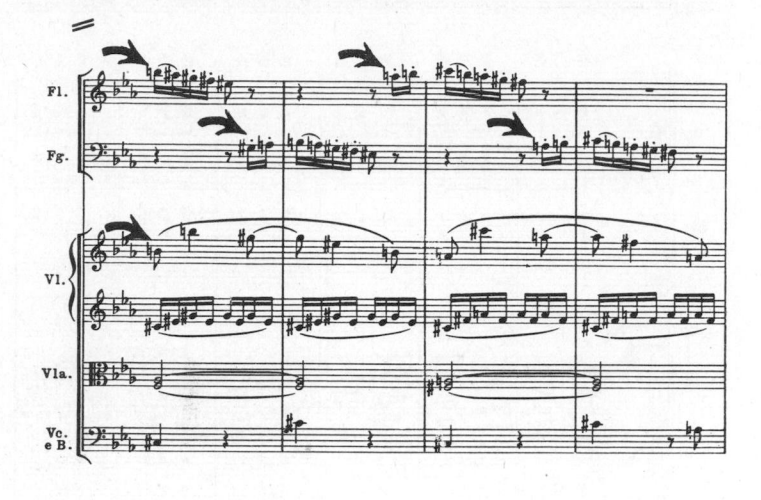

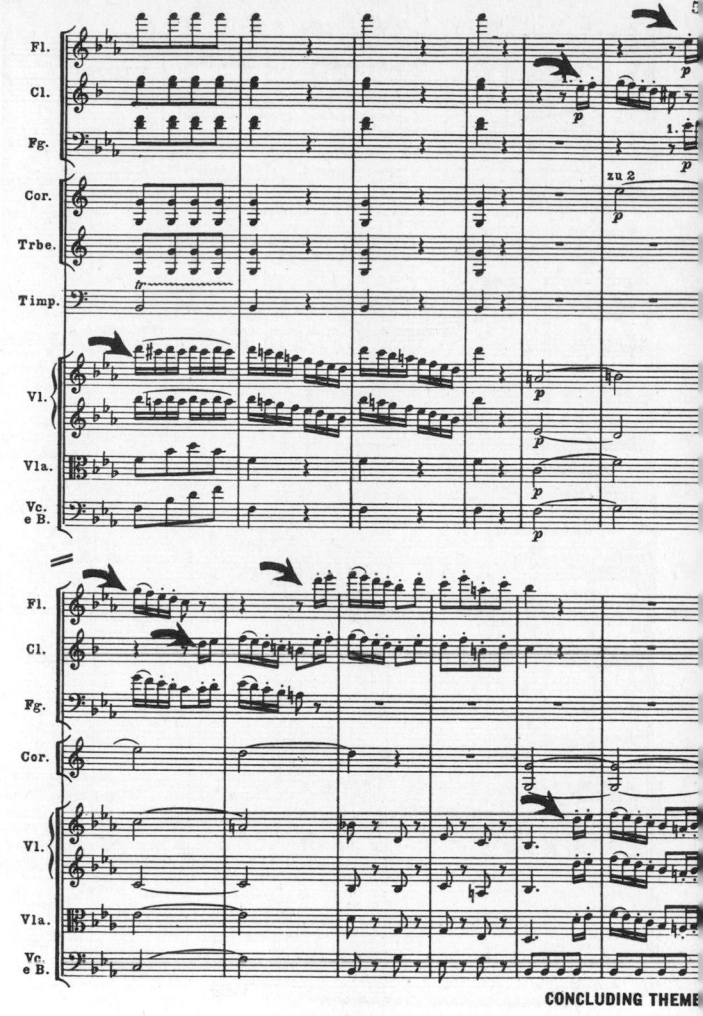

CONCLUDING THEME

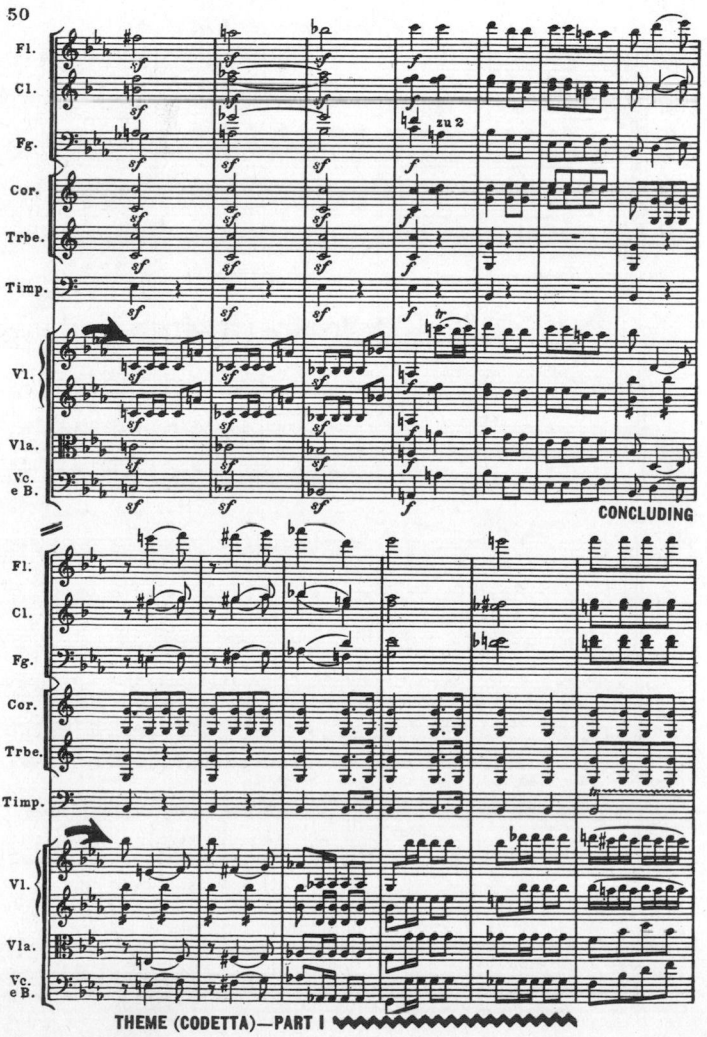

THEME (CODETTA)—PART I

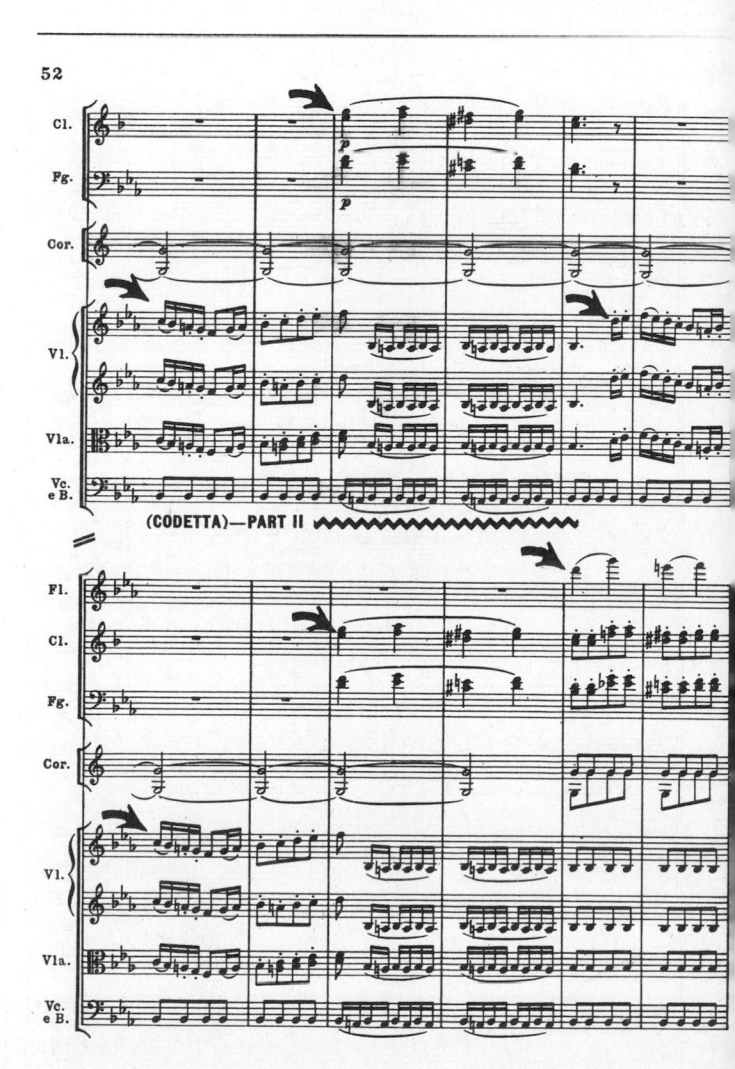

CONCLUDING

(CODETTA)—PART II

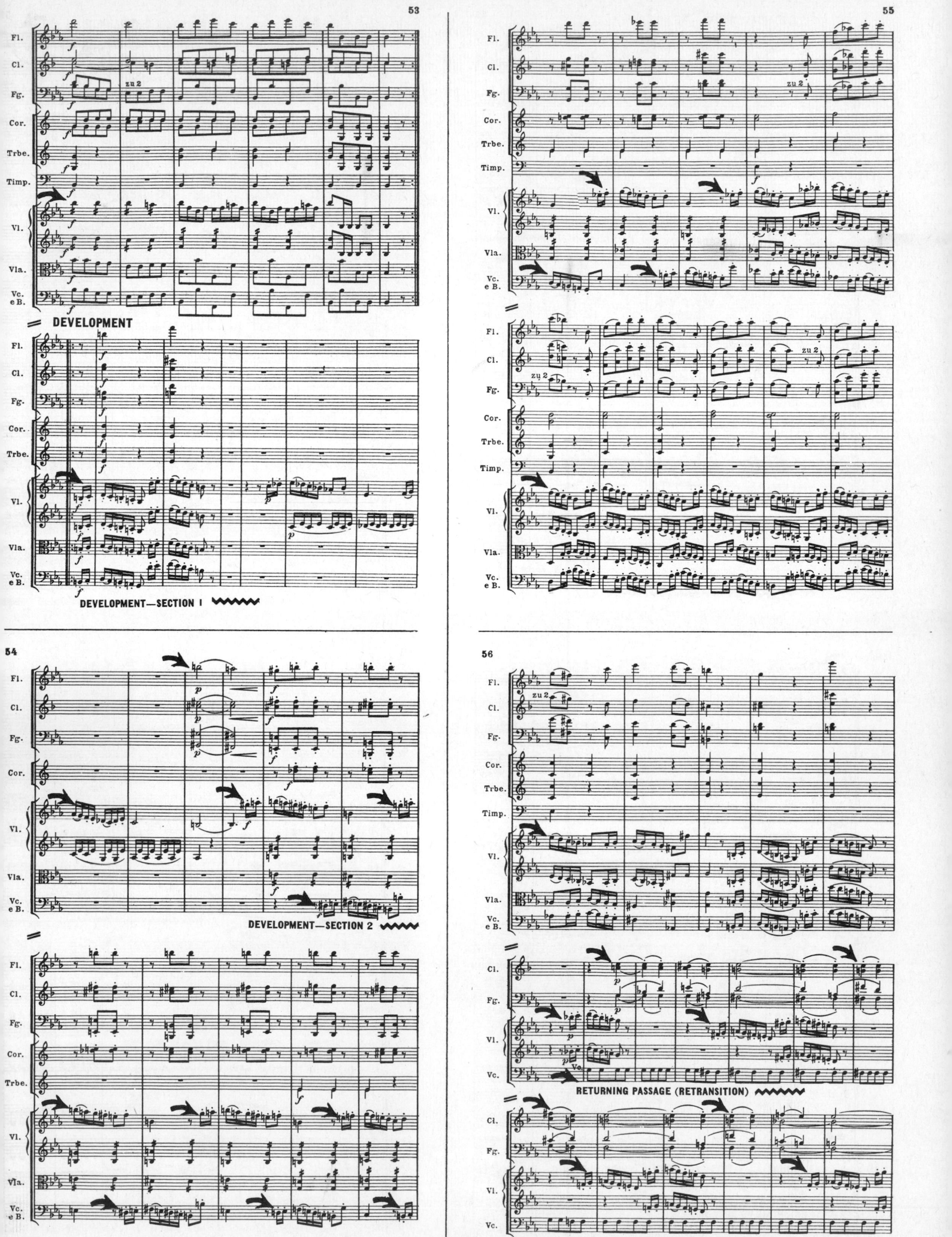
53
DEVELOPMENT
DEVELOPMENT—SECTION I
55
54
DEVELOPMENT—SECTION 2
56
RETURNING PASSAGE (RETRANSITION)
Fl.
Cl.
Fg.
Cor.
Trbe.
Timp.
Vl.
Vla.
Vc. e B.
Vc.
zu 2

RECAPITULATION

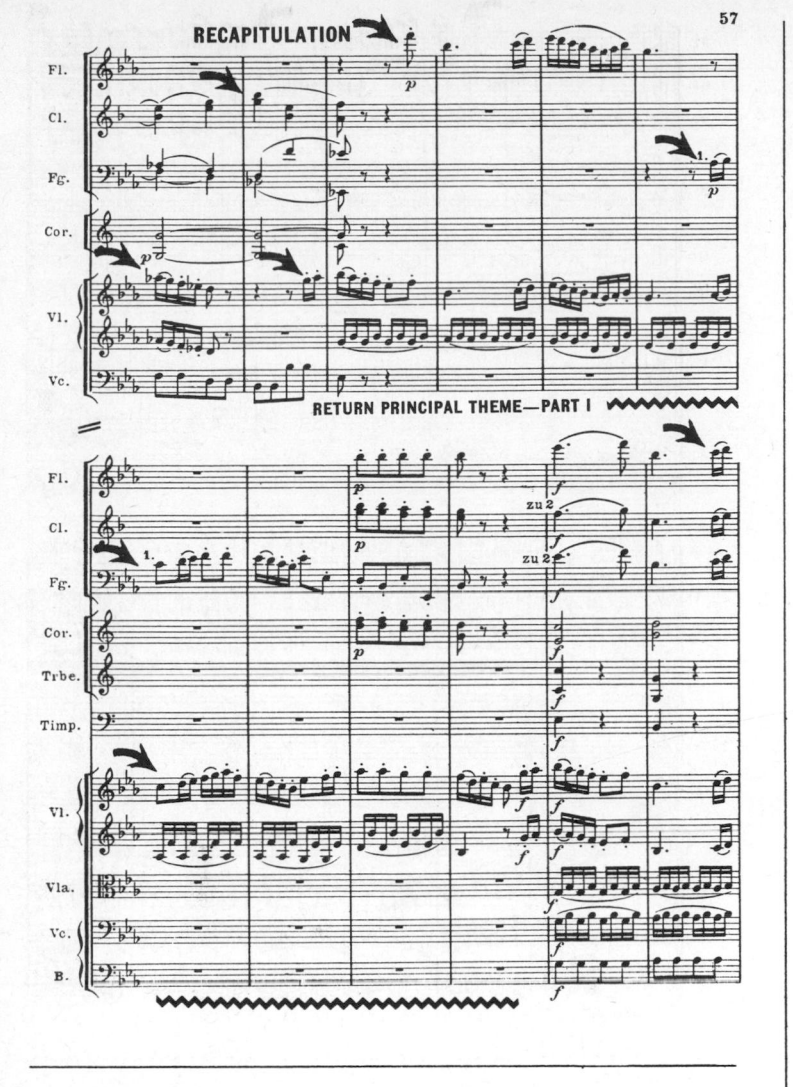

RETURN PRINCIPAL THEME—PART I

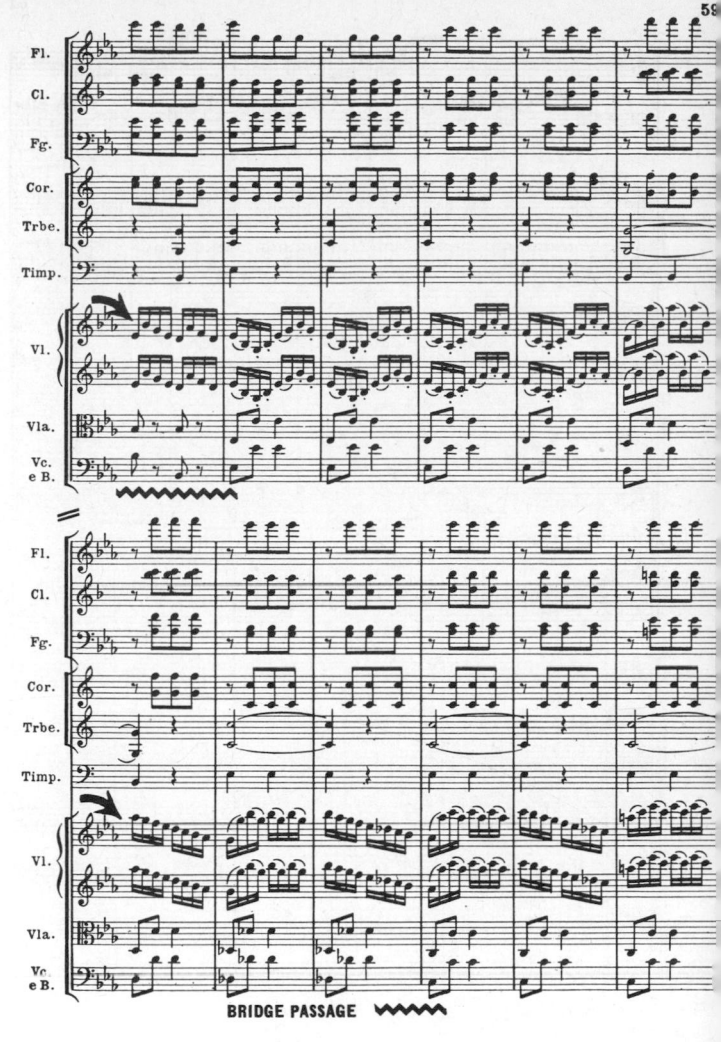

BRIDGE PASSAGE

RETURN PRIN-

CIPAL THEME—PART II

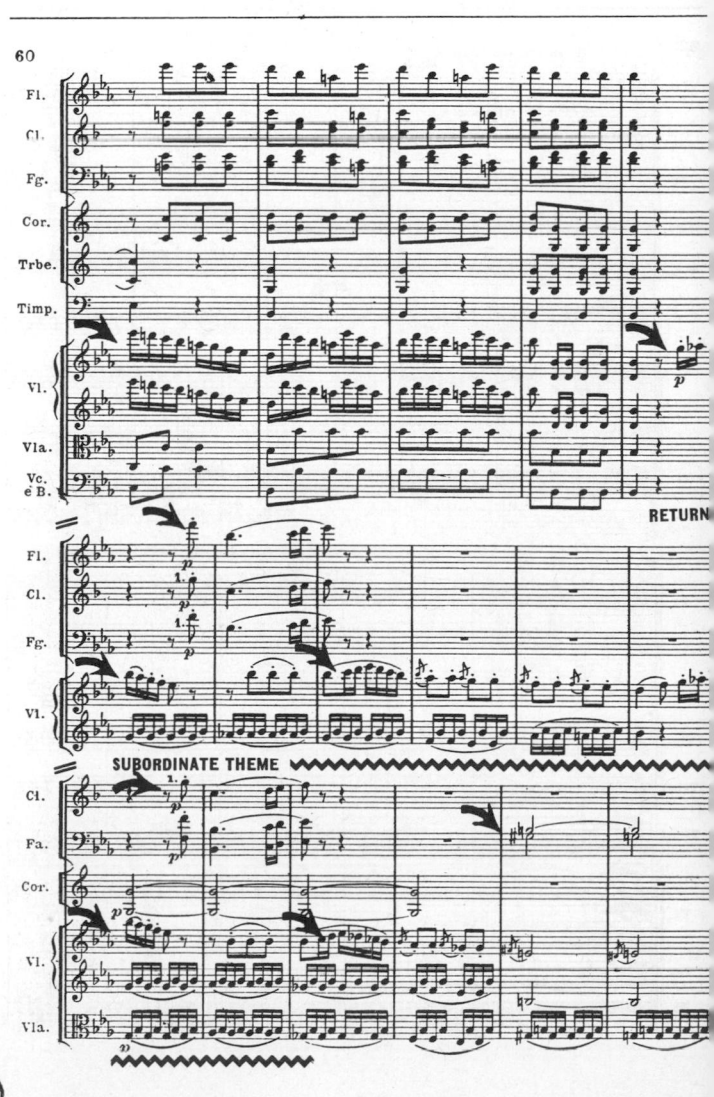

RETURN

SUBORDINATE THEME

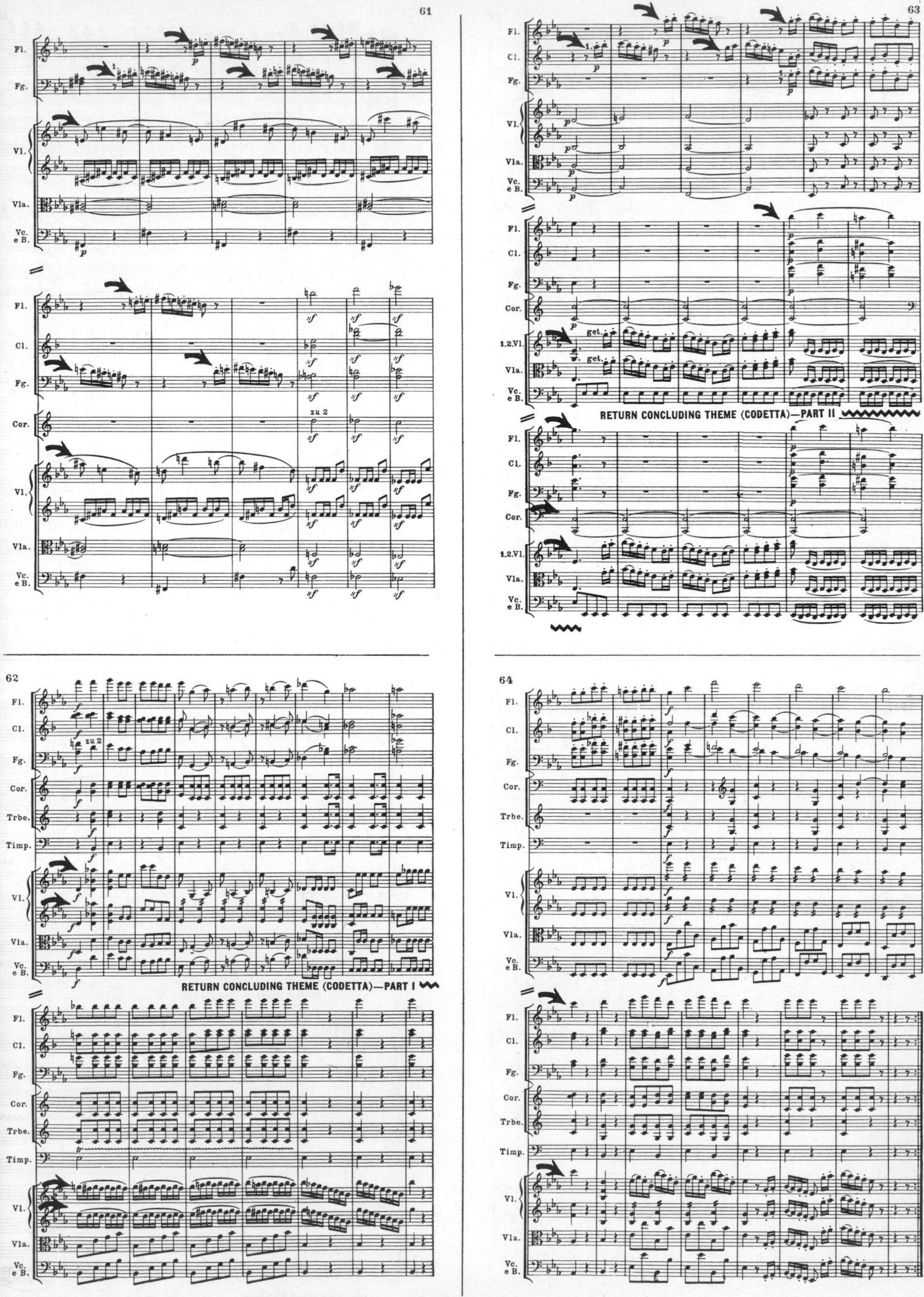

Symphony in G Minor

W.A.Mozart
1756-1791

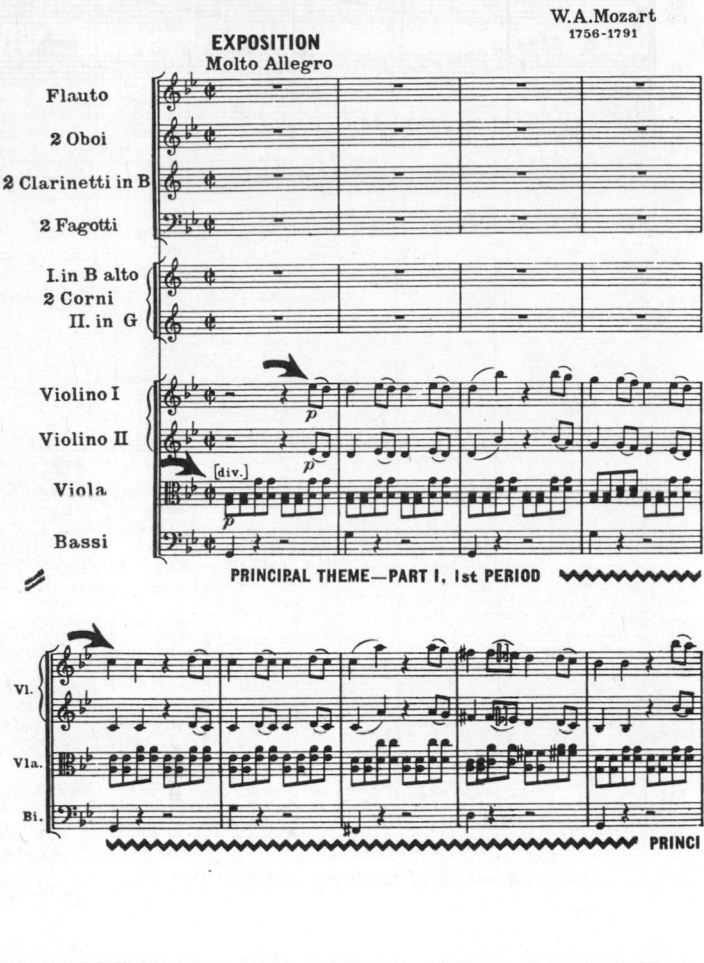

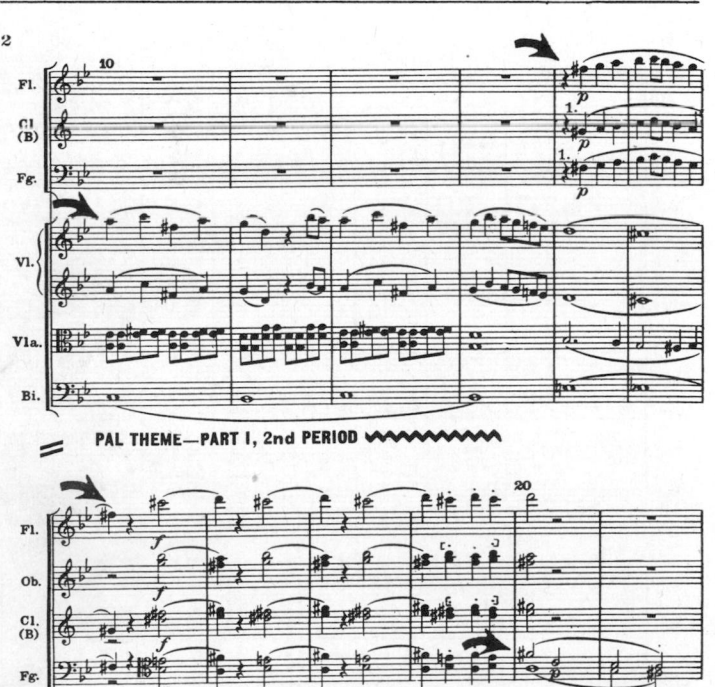

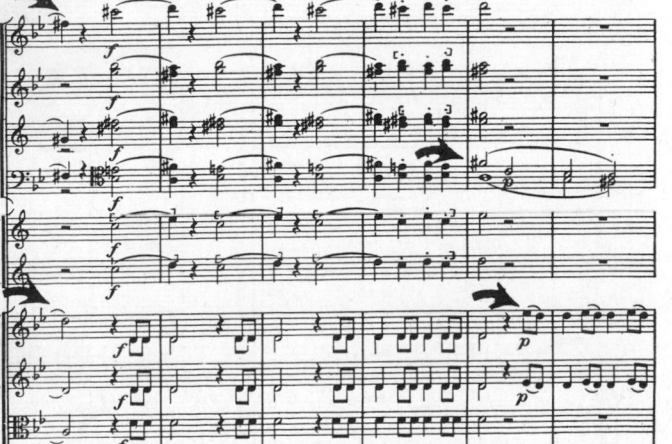

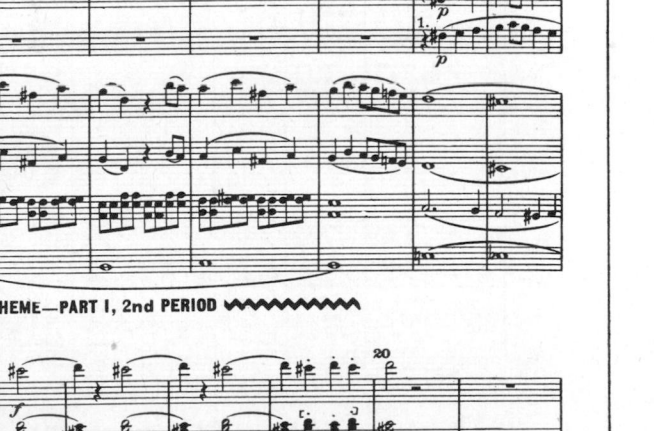

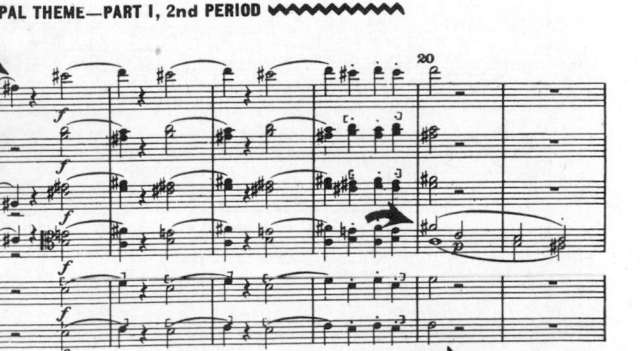

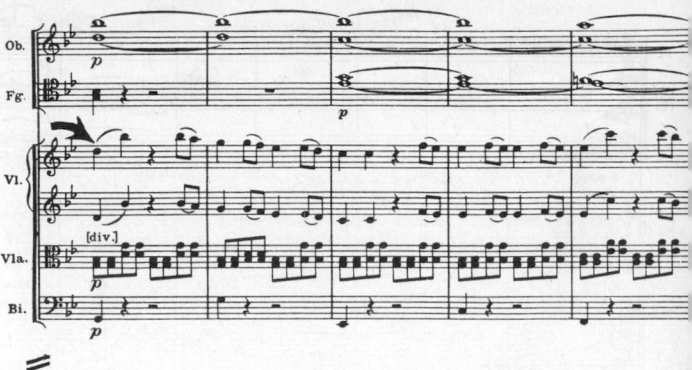

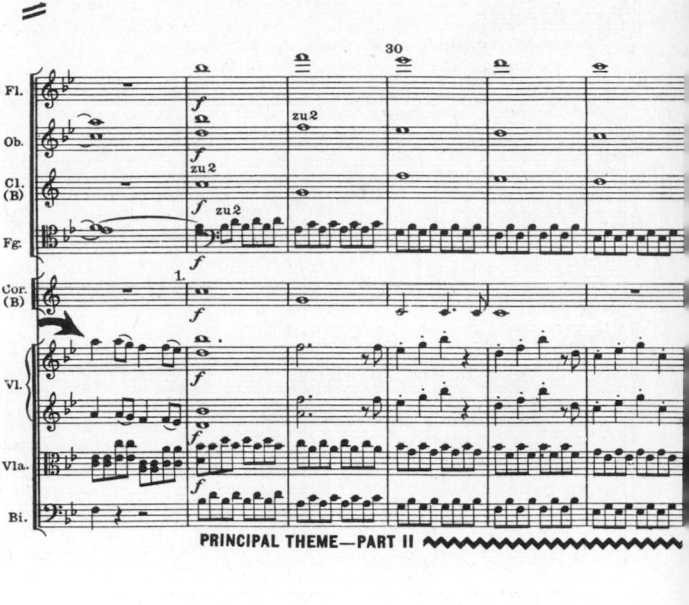

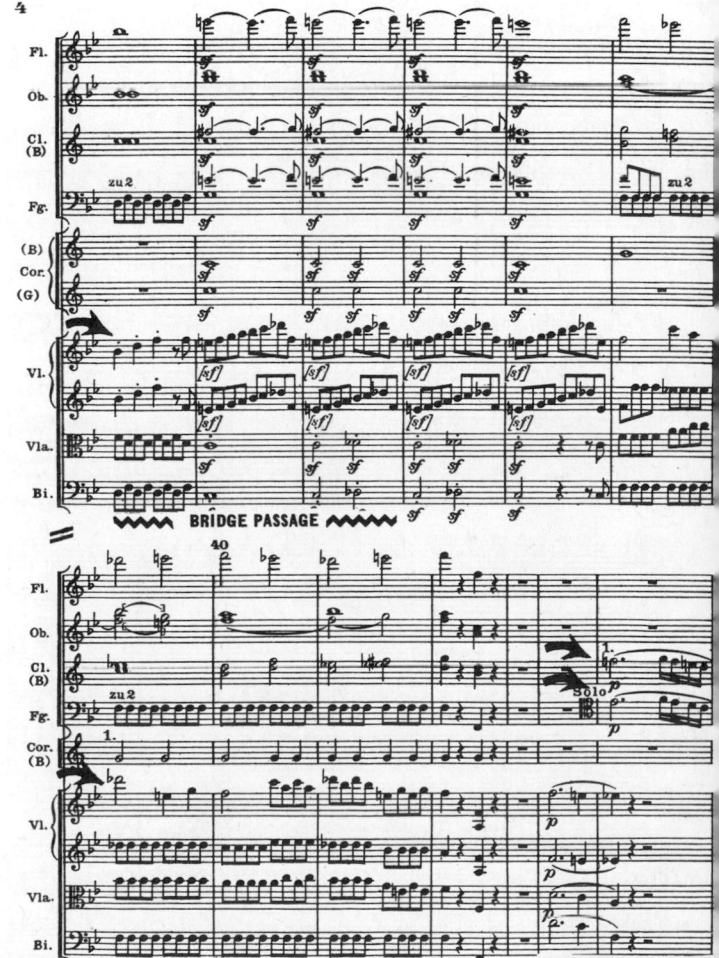

(196)

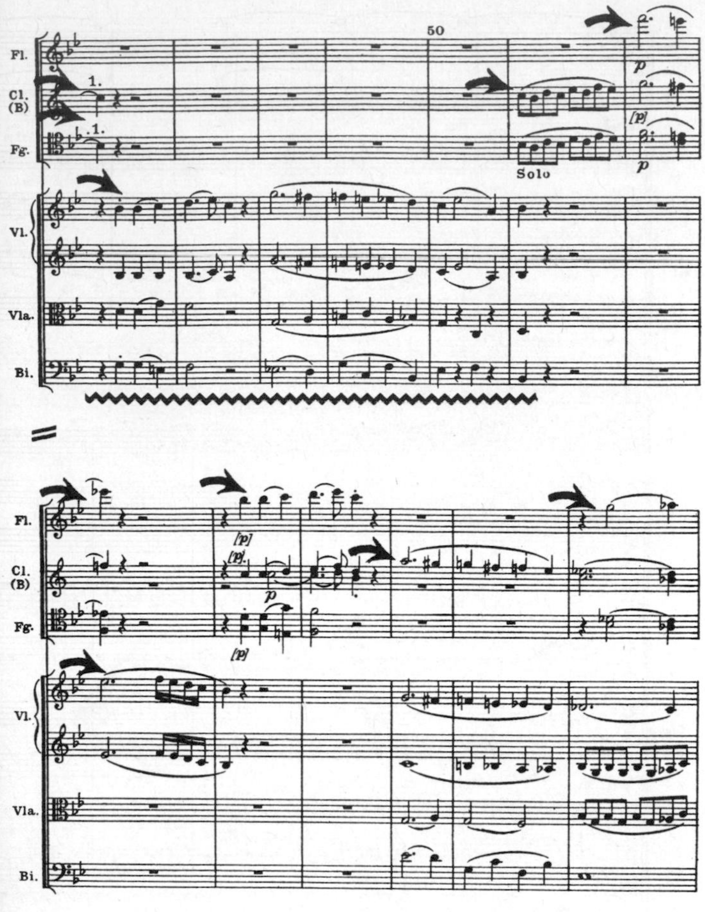

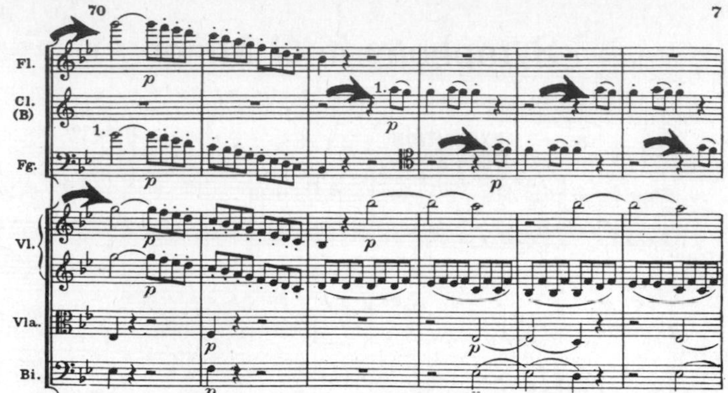

CONCLUDING THEME (CODETTA)—PART I

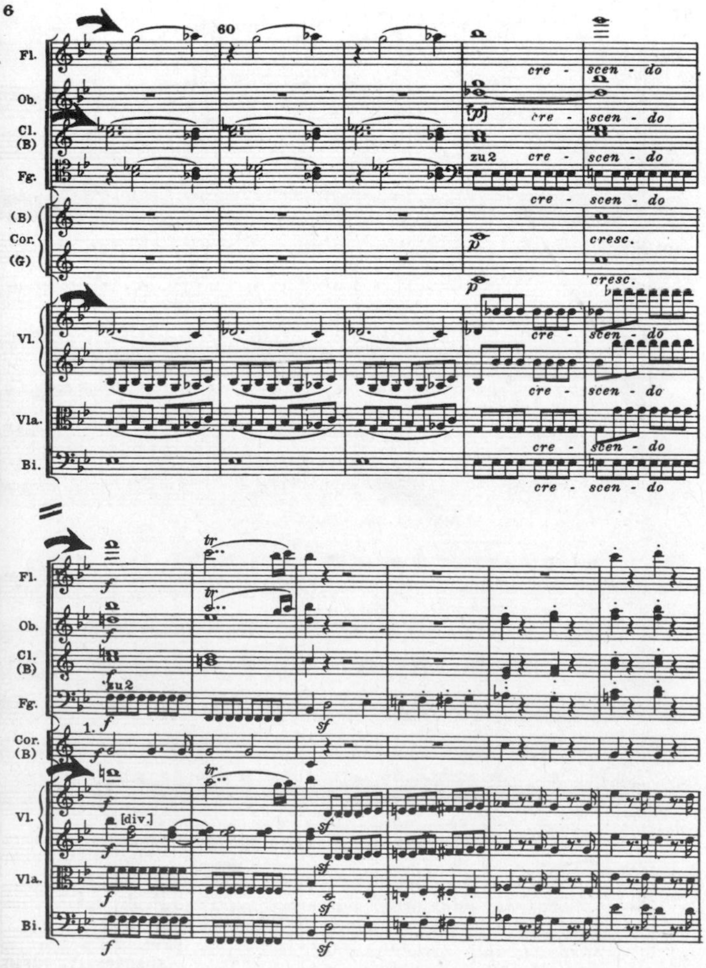

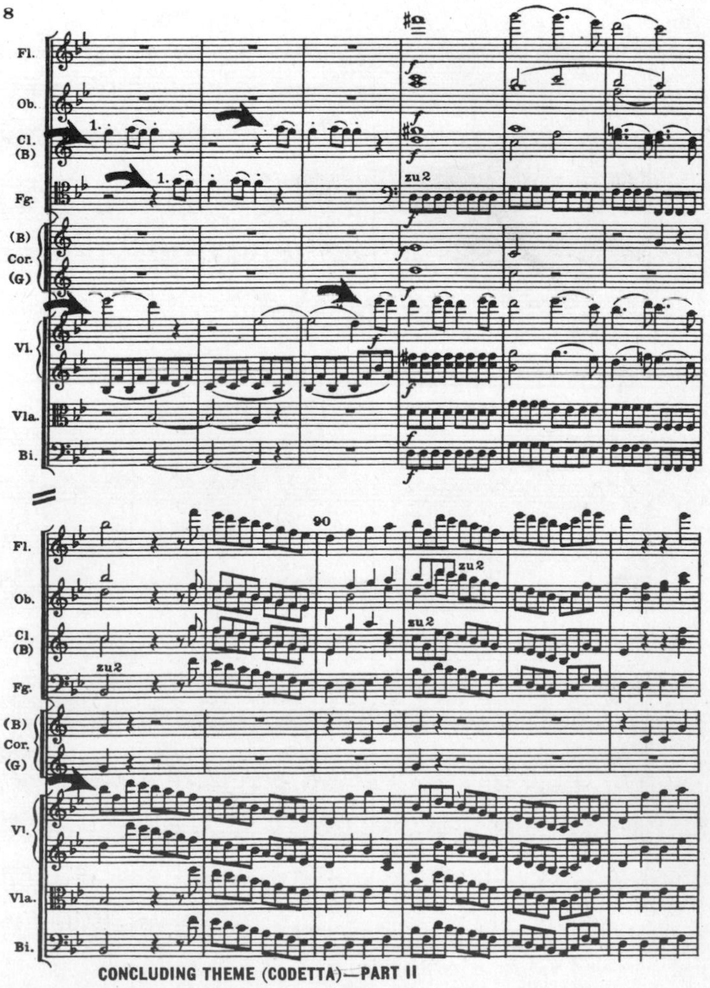

CONCLUDING THEME (CODETTA)—PART II

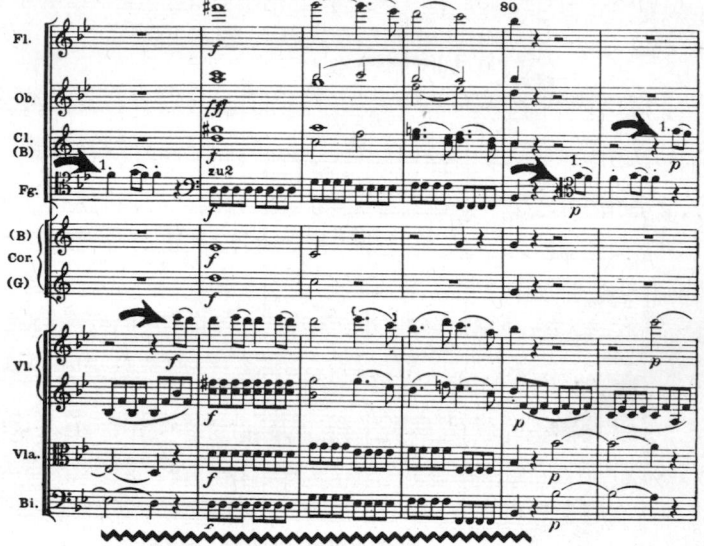

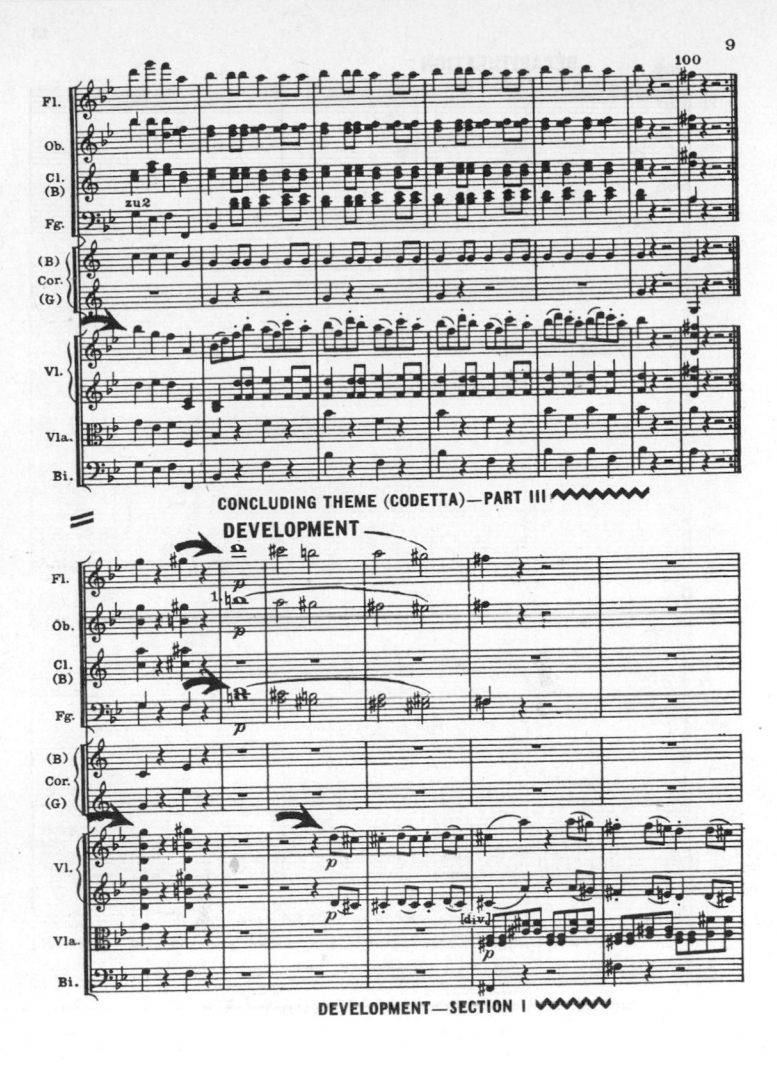

CONCLUDING THEME (CODETTA)—PART III 〰〰〰

DEVELOPMENT

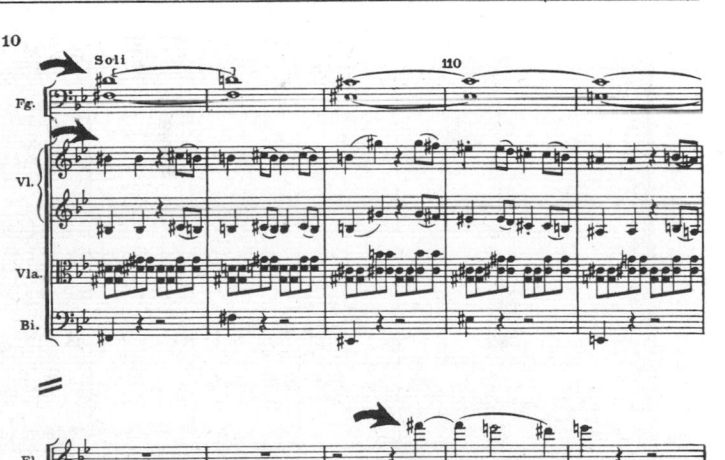

DEVELOPMENT—SECTION 1 〰〰〰

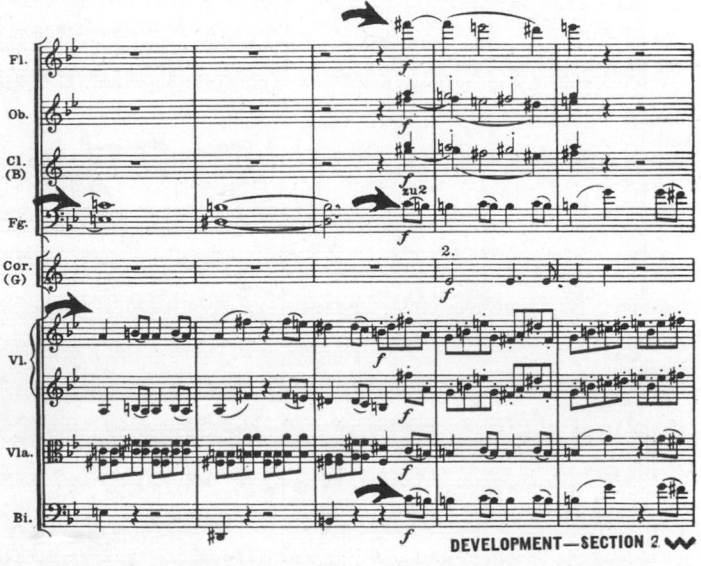

DEVELOPMENT—SECTION 2 〰

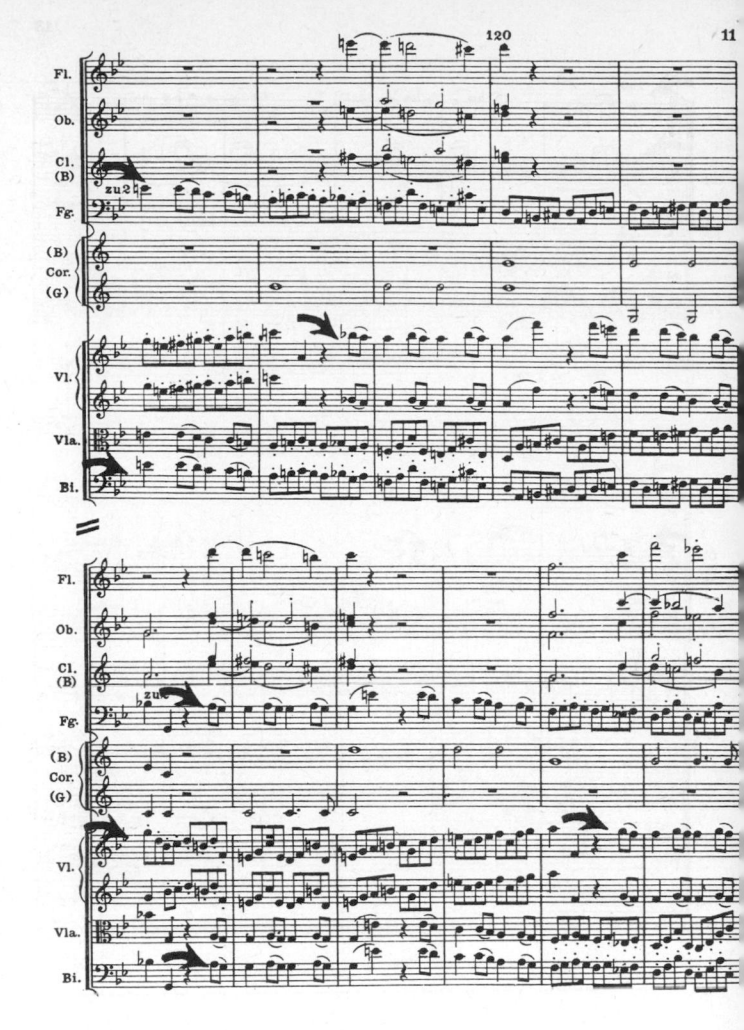

DEVELOPMENT—SECTIO

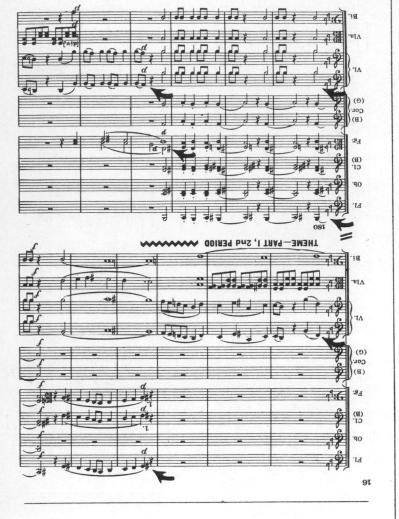
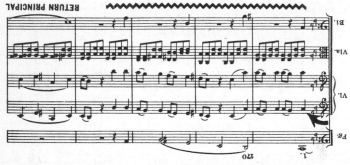
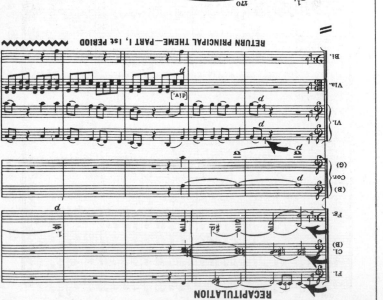
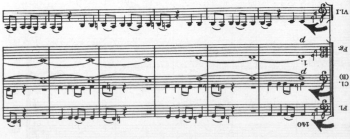

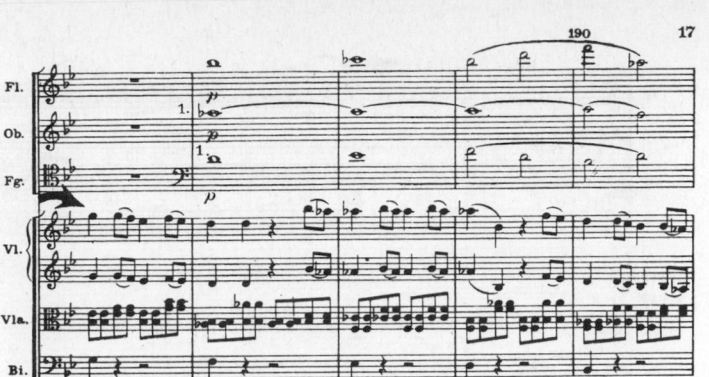

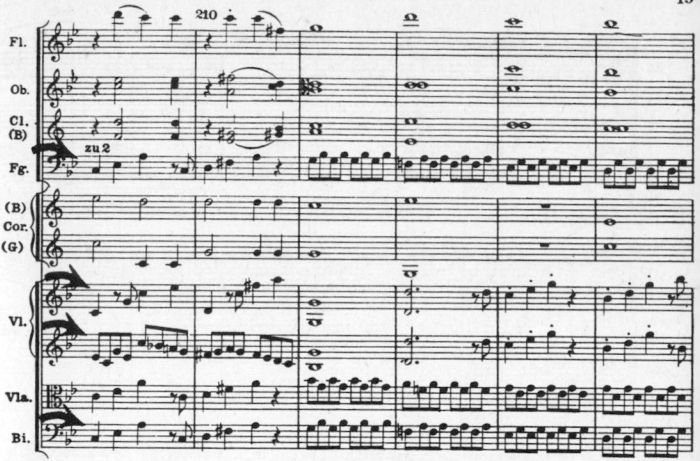

RETURN PRINCIPAL THEME—PART II ∿∿∿∿∿∿∿∿∿∿∿

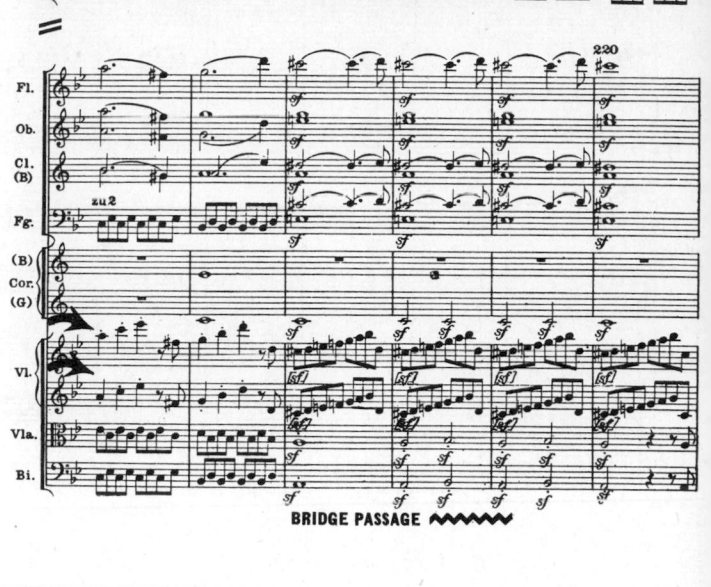

BRIDGE PASSAGE ∿∿∿∿∿

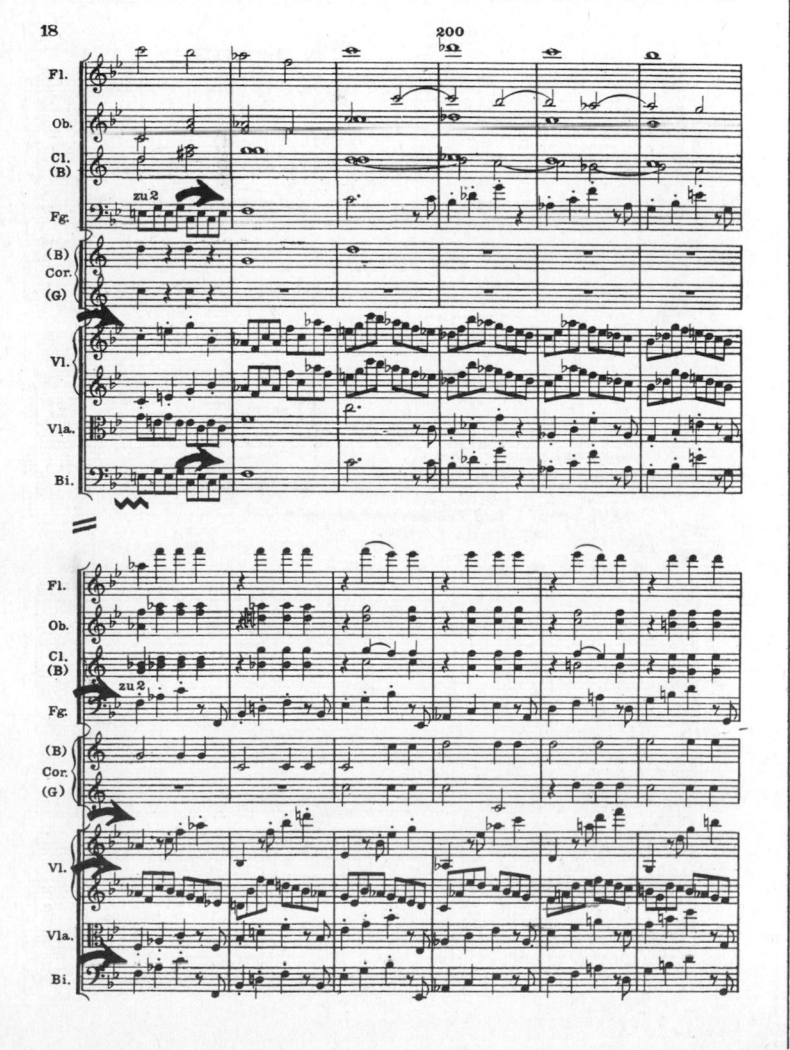

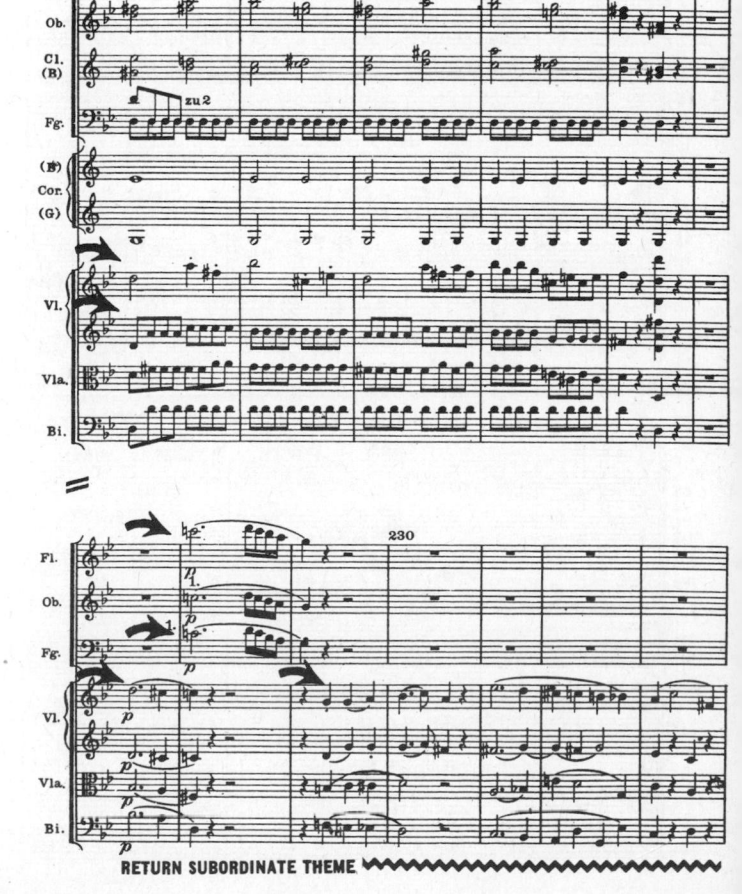

RETURN SUBORDINATE THEME ∿∿∿∿∿∿∿∿∿∿∿

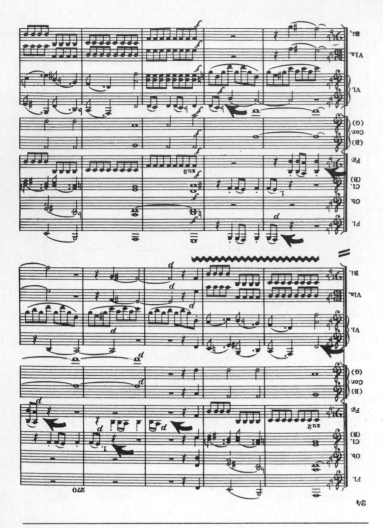
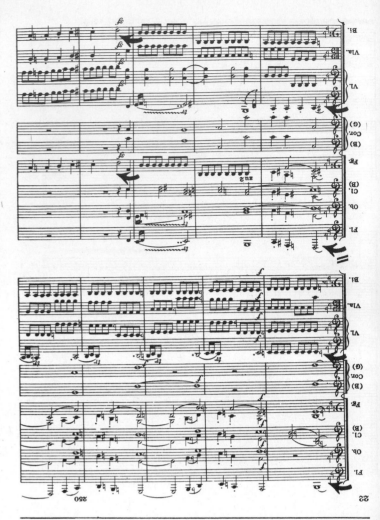
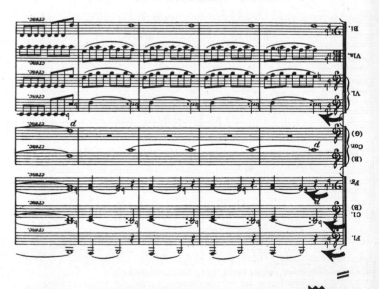
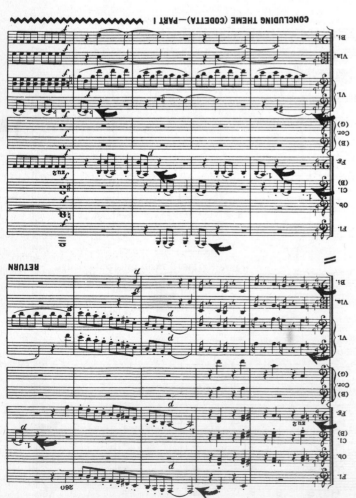
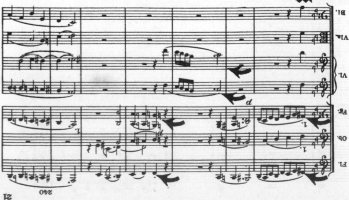

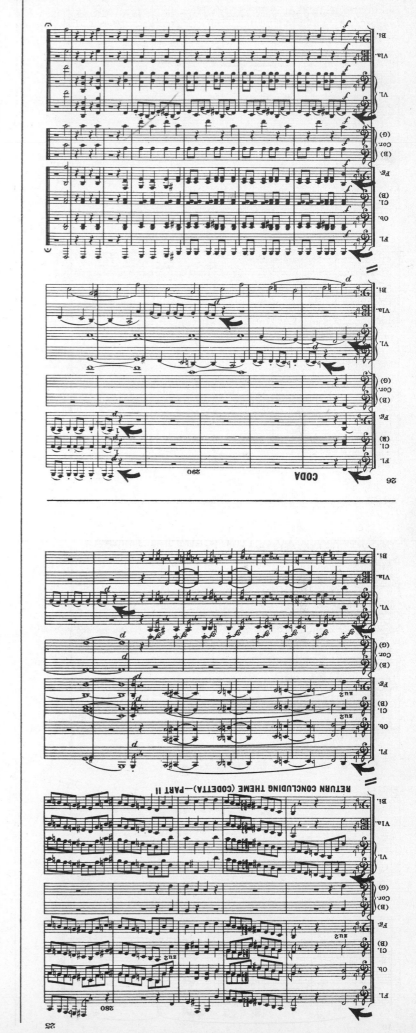
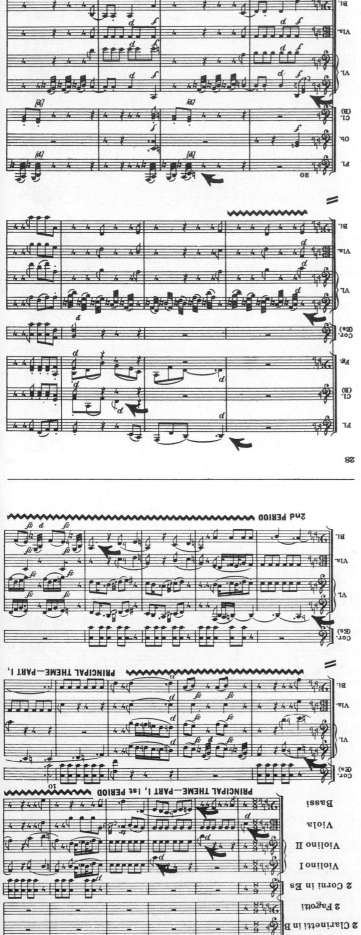

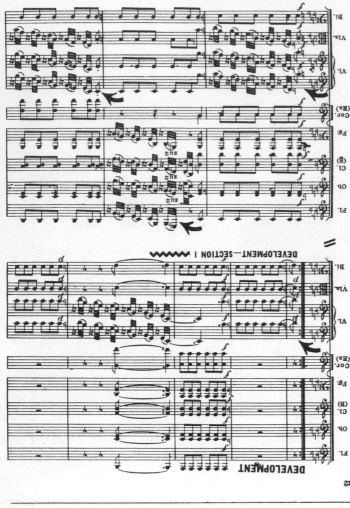

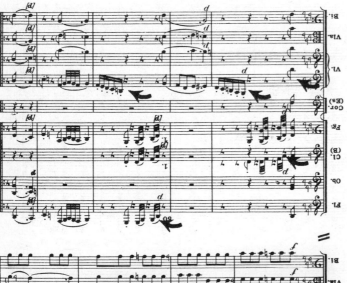

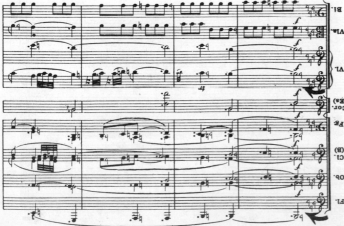

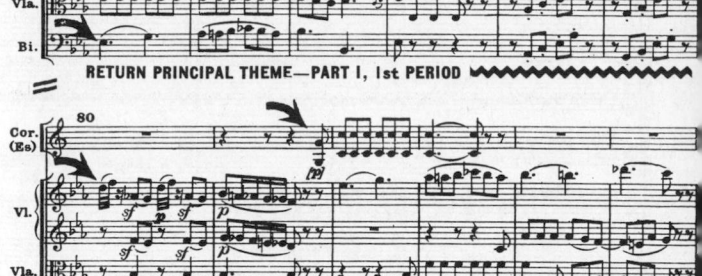

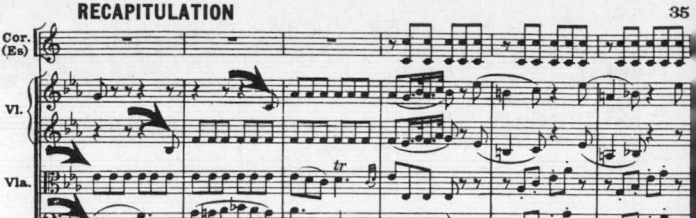

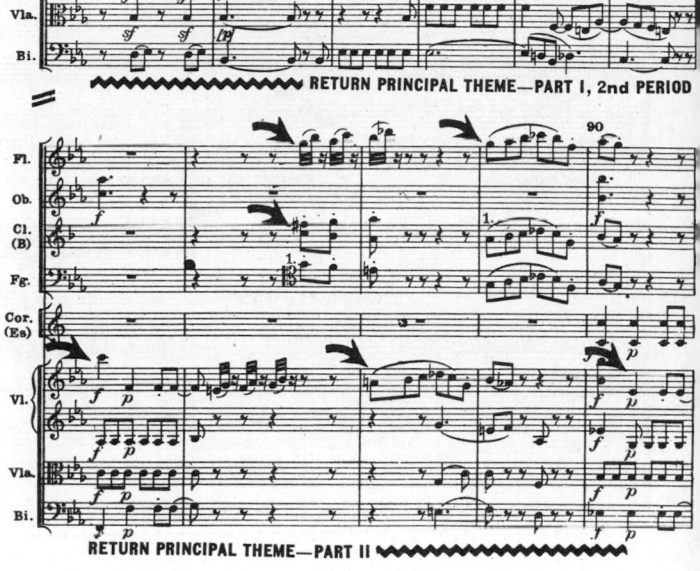

RETURN PRINCIPAL THEME—PART I, 1st PERIOD ～～～

RETURN PRINCIPAL THEME—PART I, 2nd PERIOD

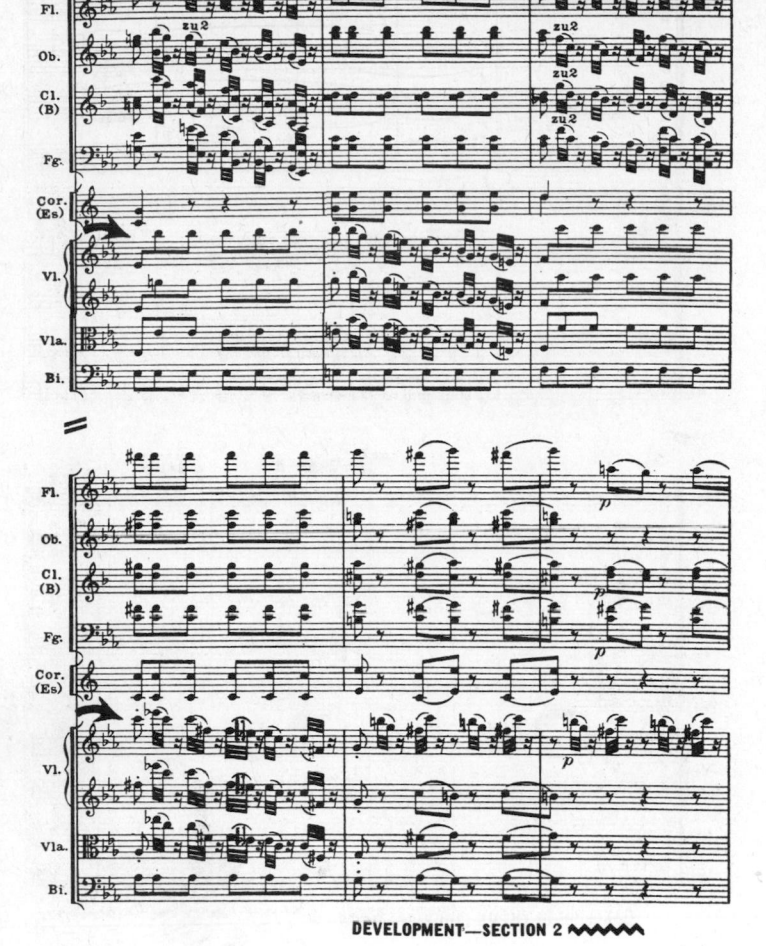

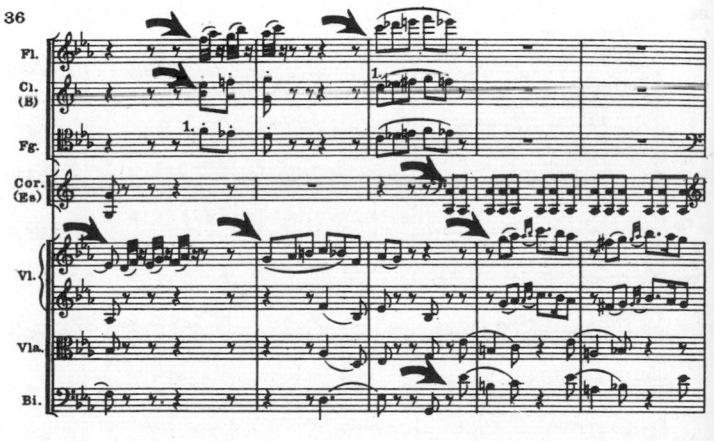

DEVELOPMENT—SECTION 2 ～～～

RETURN PRINCIPAL THEME—PART II ～～～

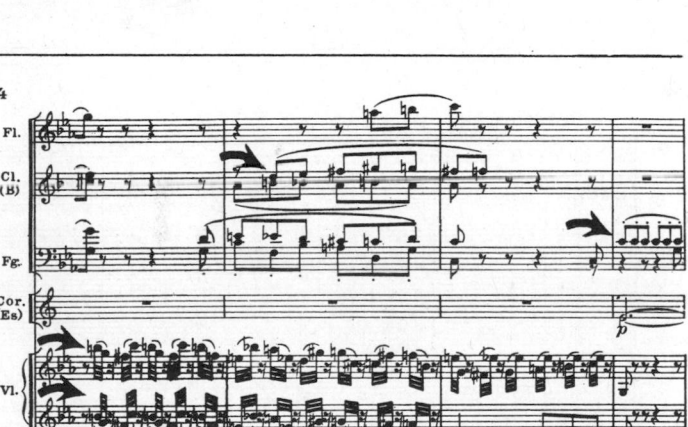

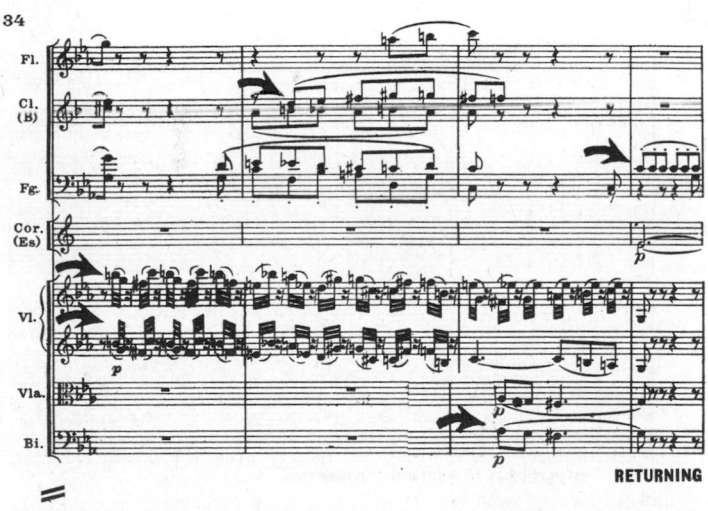

RETURNING

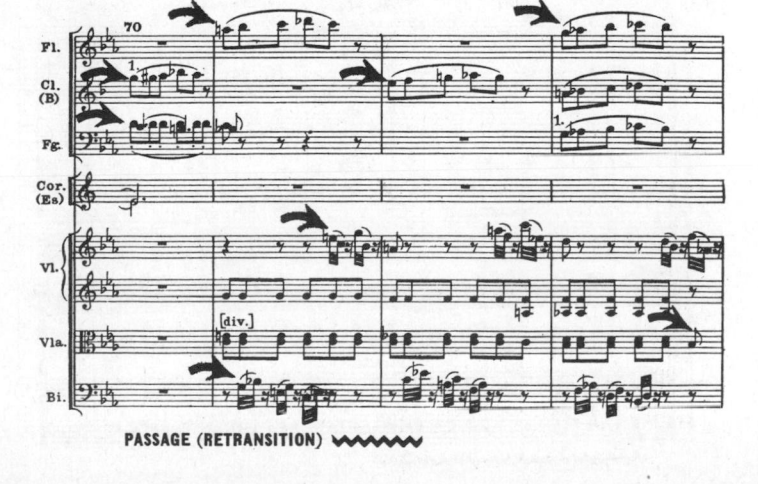

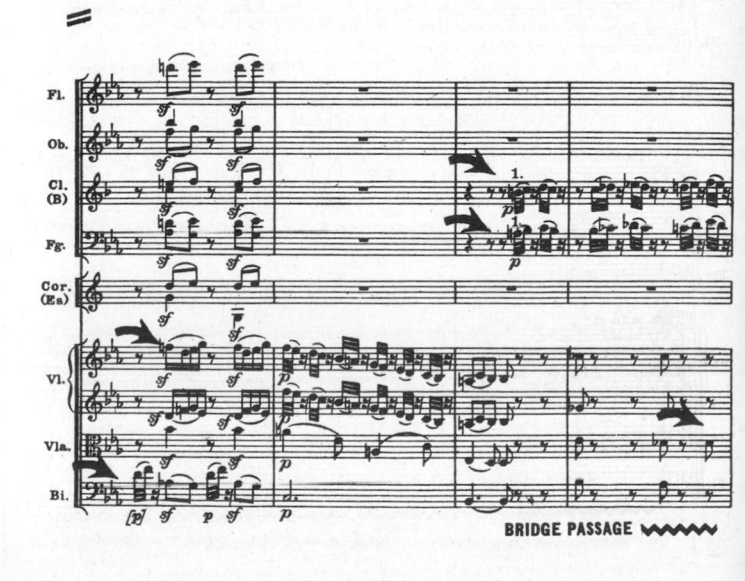

PASSAGE (RETRANSITION) ～～～

BRIDGE PASSAGE ～～～

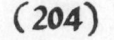

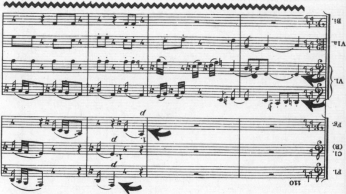
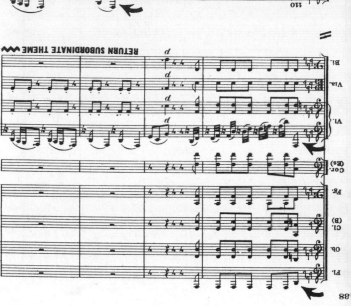
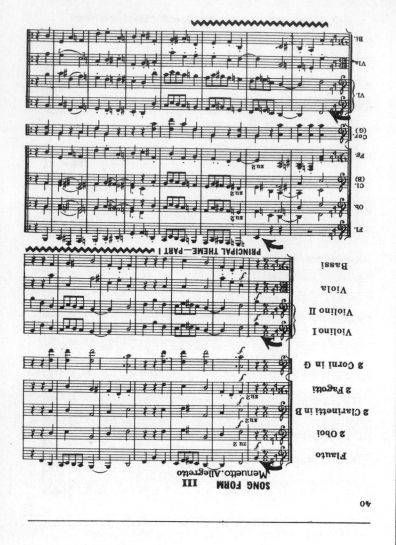
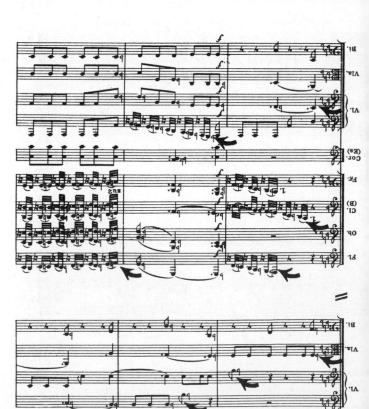
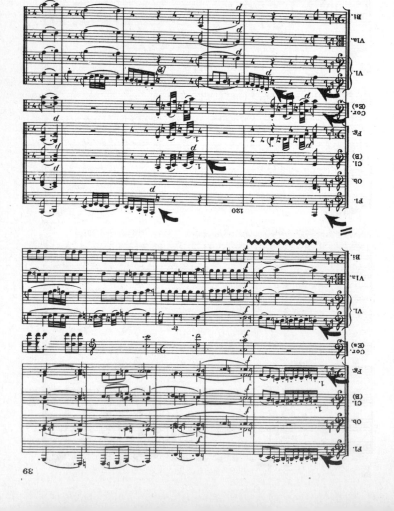

41
PRINCIPAL THEME—PART II
PRINCIPAL
42
THEME—PART III
CONCLUDING THEME (CODETTA)
[Fine]
43
TRIO
SUBORDINATE THEME—PART I
44
SUBORDINATE THEME—PART II
SUBORDINATE THEME—PART III
CONCLUDING THEME (CODETTA)
D.C. Menuetto

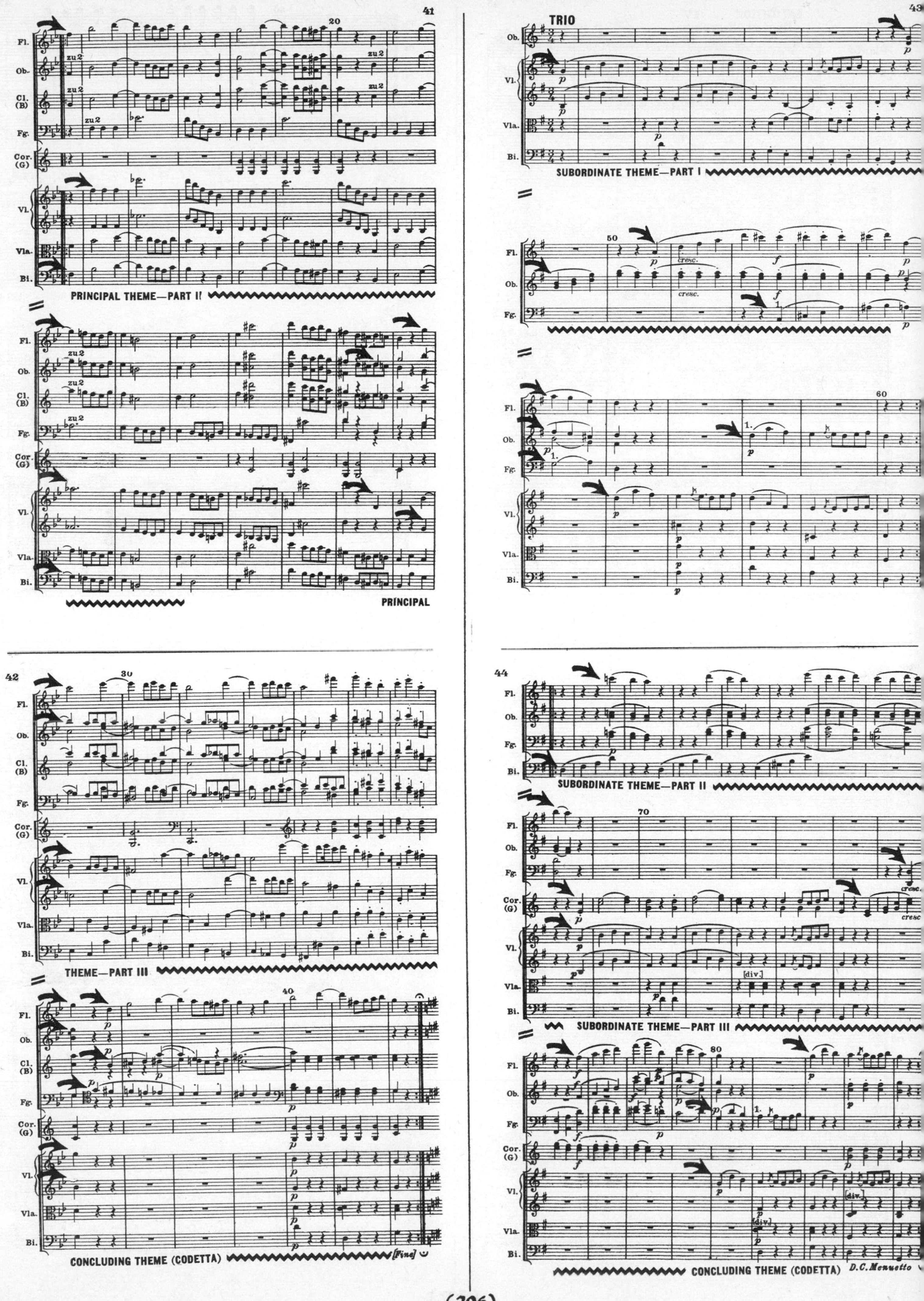

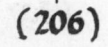

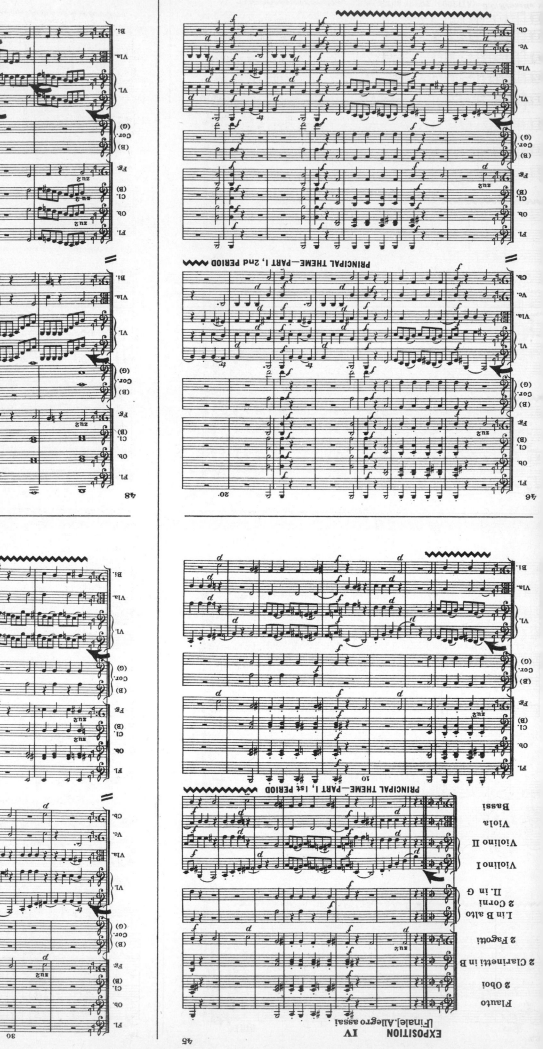

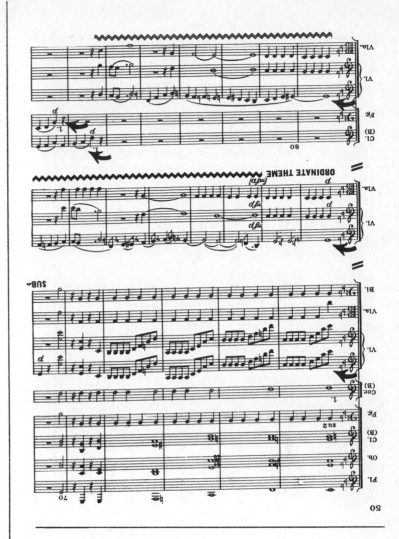
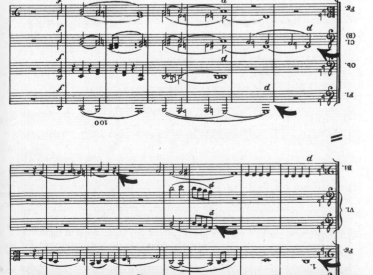

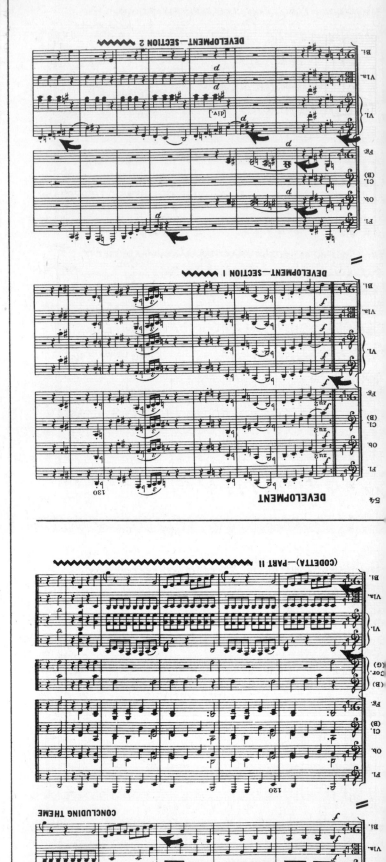
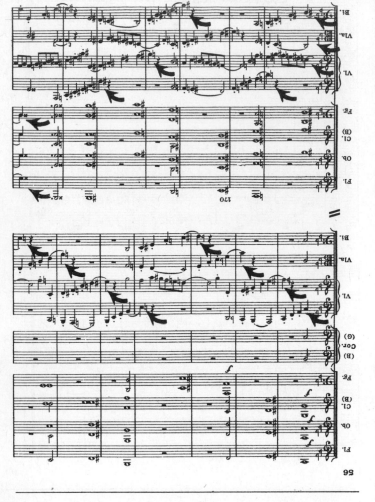
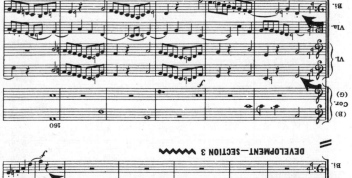
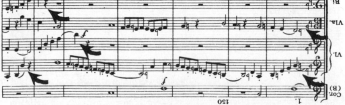
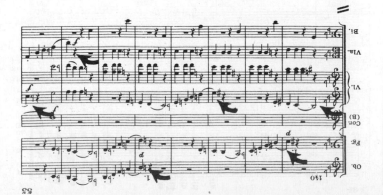

57

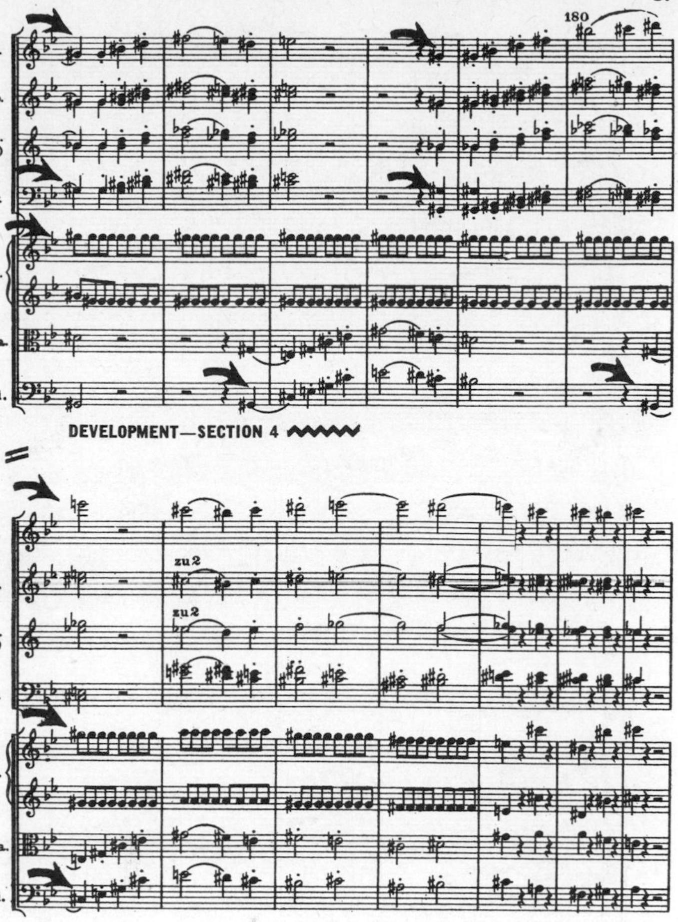

180
Fl.
Ob.
Cl. (B)
Fg.
Vl.
Vla.
Bi.
DEVELOPMENT—SECTION 4
zu 2

5

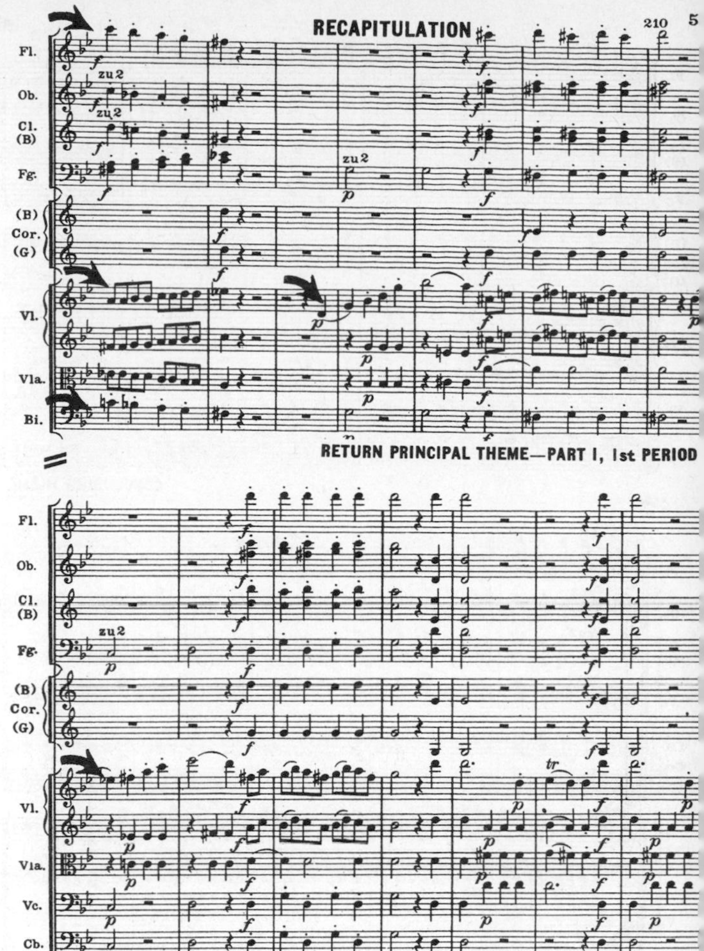

RECAPITULATION
210
Fl.
Ob.
Cl. (B)
Fg.
(B) Cor. (G)
Vl.
Vla.
Bi.
zu 2
RETURN PRINCIPAL THEME—PART I, 1st PERIOD
Vc.
Cb.
tr
RETURN PRINCIPAL THEME—PART

58

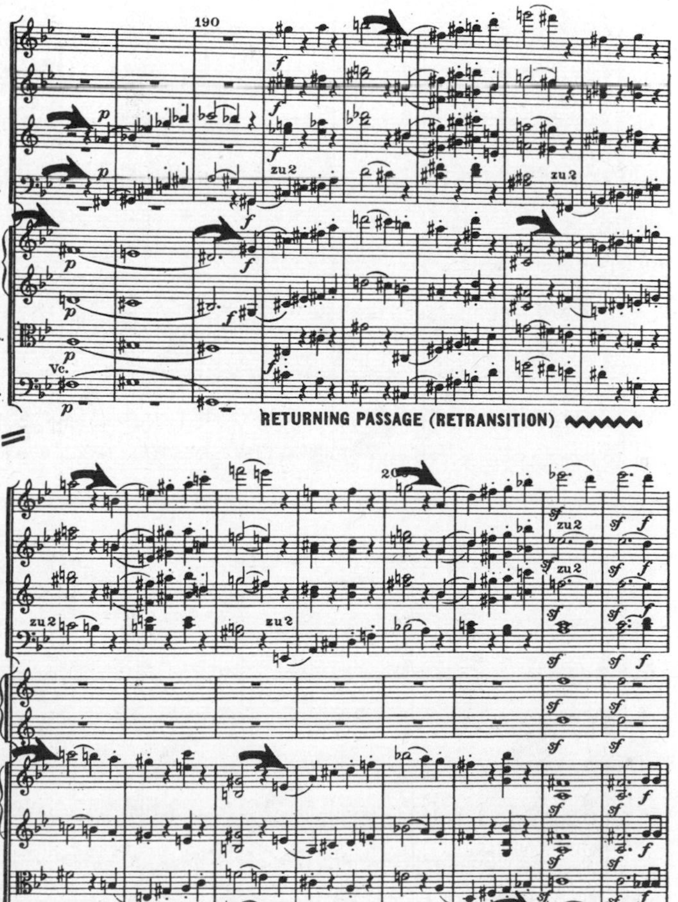

190
Fl.
Ob
Cl. (B)
Fg.
Vl.
Vla.
Vc.
Bi.
zu 2
RETURNING PASSAGE (RETRANSITION)
200
(B) Cor. (G)

60

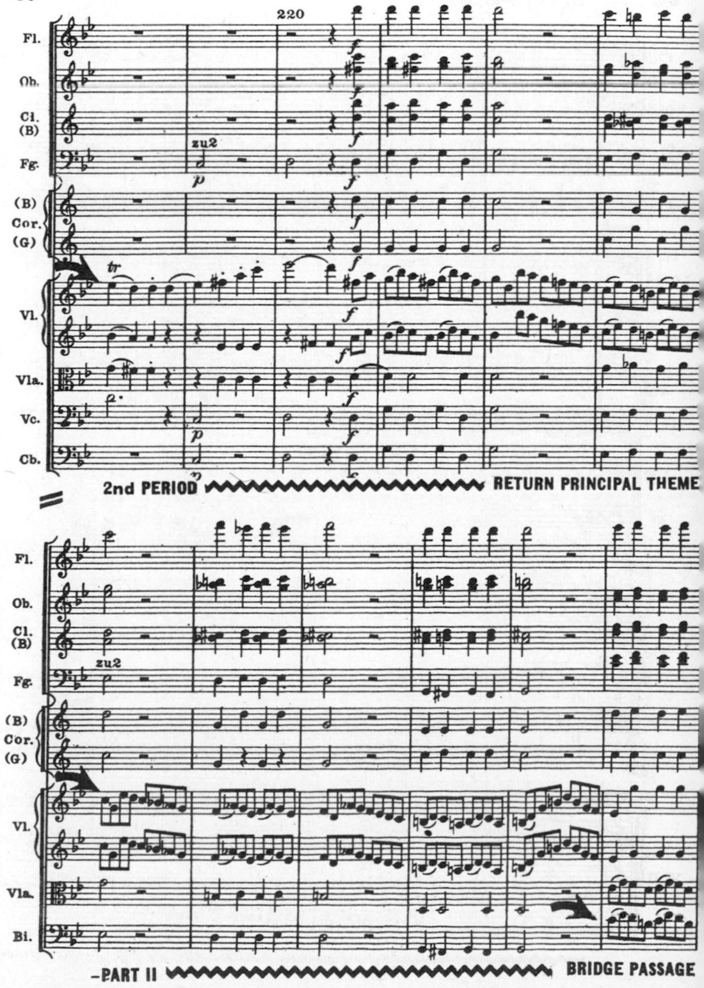

220
Fl.
Ob.
Cl. (B)
Fg.
(B) Cor. (G)
Vl.
Vla.
Vc.
Cb.
zu 2
tr
2nd PERIOD
RETURN PRINCIPAL THEME
-PART II
BRIDGE PASSAGE

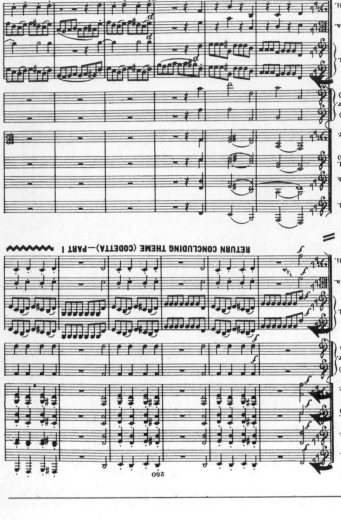

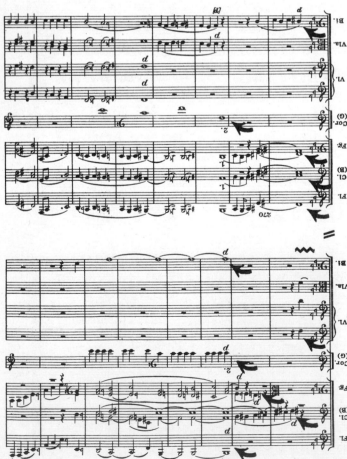

65

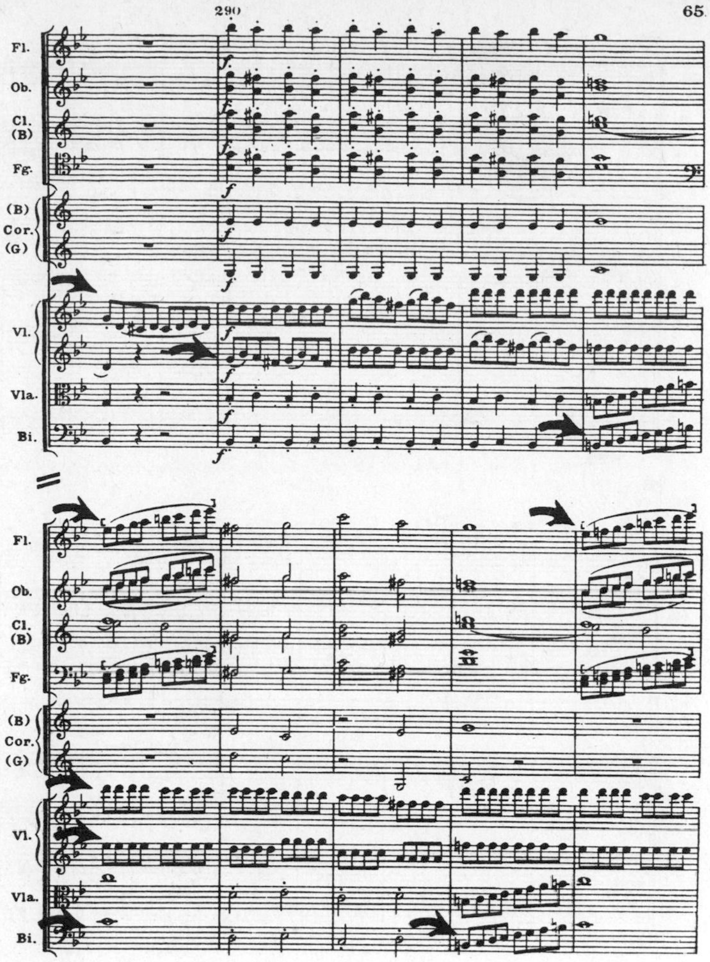
Fl.
Ob.
Cl. (B)
Fg.
(B) Cor. (G)
Vl.
Vla.
Bi.
290

66

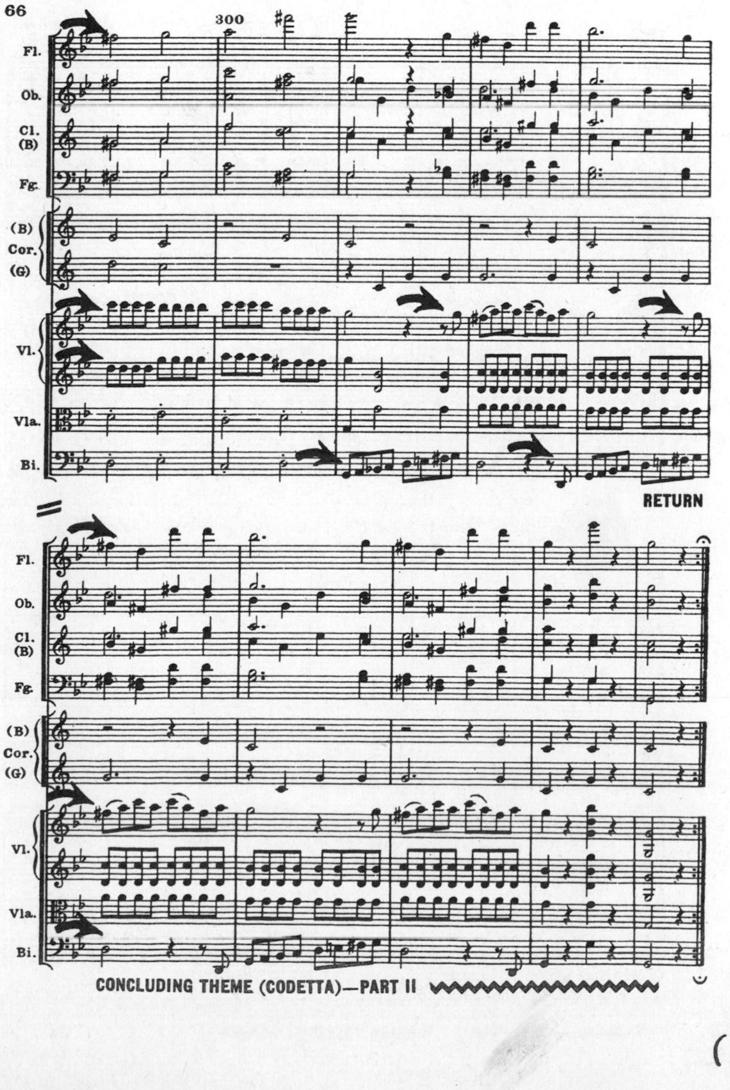
Fl.
Ob.
Cl. (B)
Fg.
(B) Cor. (G)
Vl.
Vla.
Bi.
300
RETURN
CONCLUDING THEME (CODETTA)—PART II

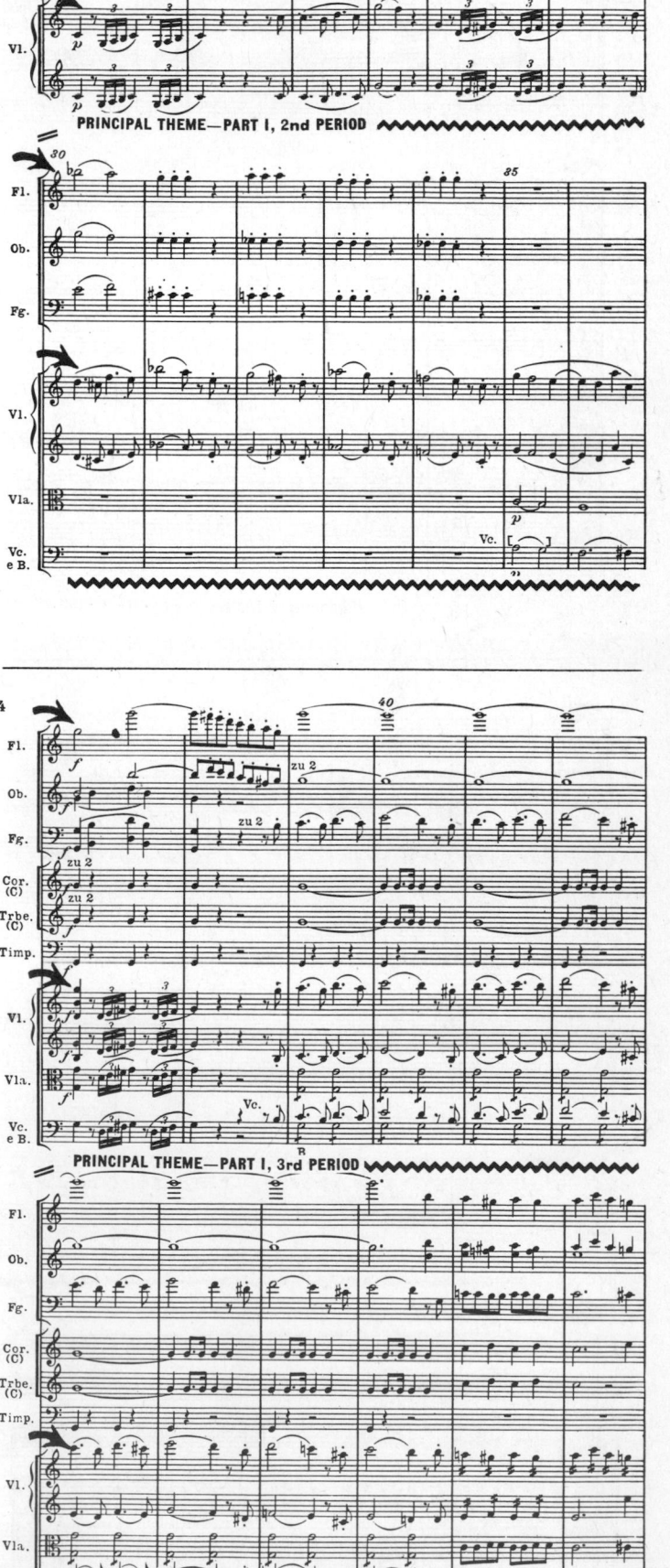

"Jupiter" Symphony

W. A. Mozart
1756-1791

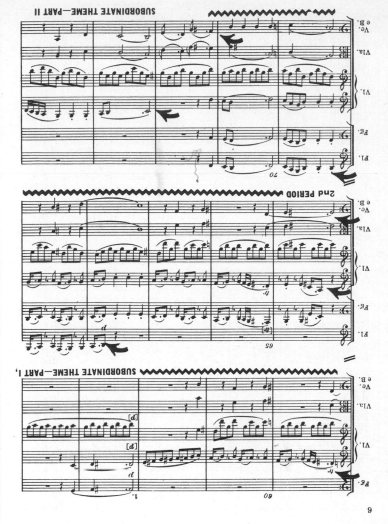

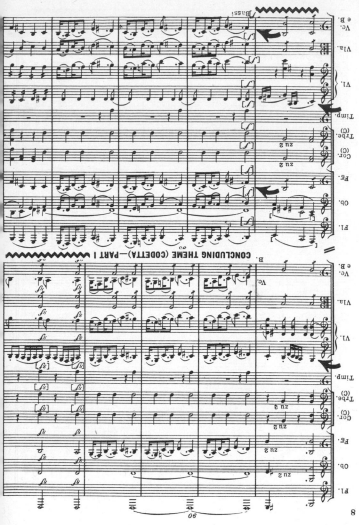

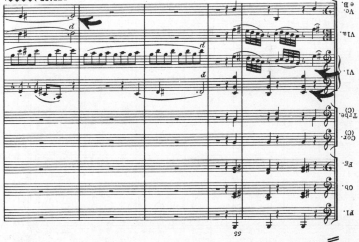

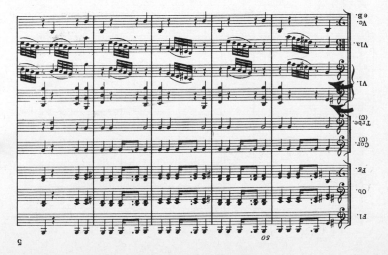

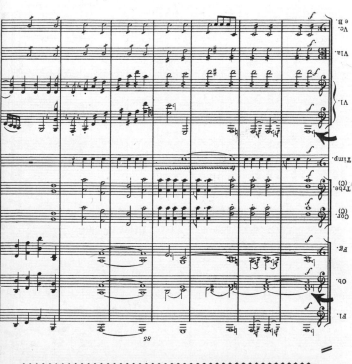

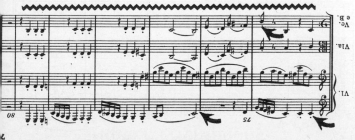

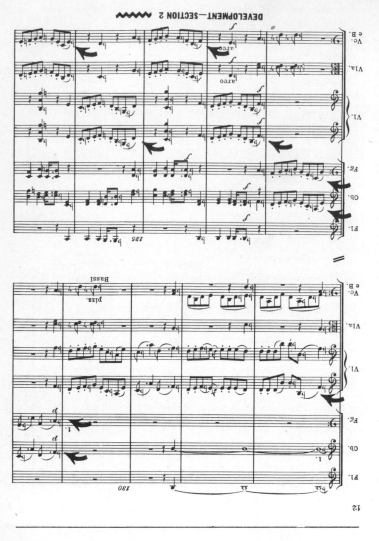

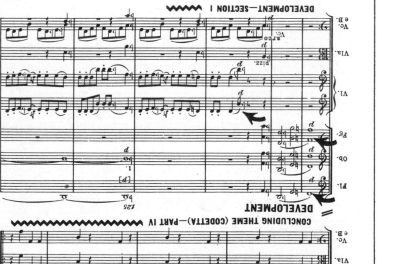

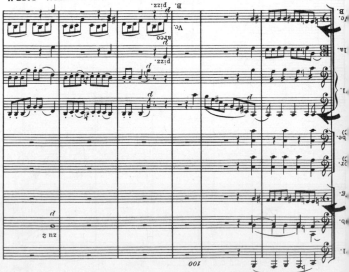

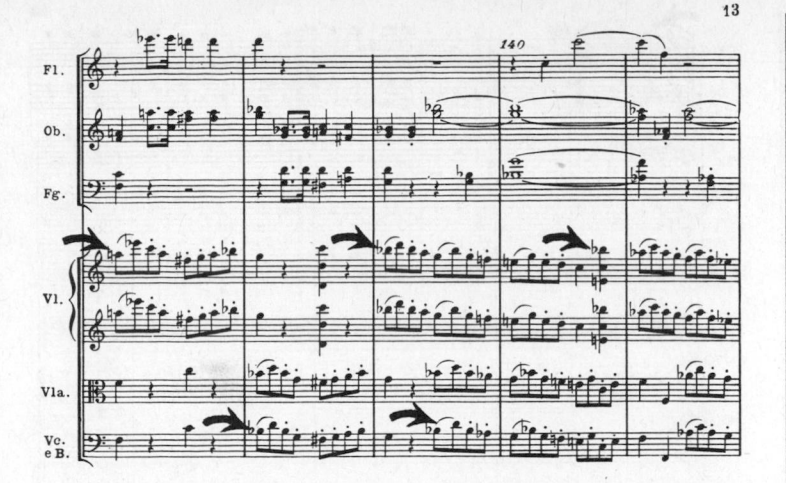

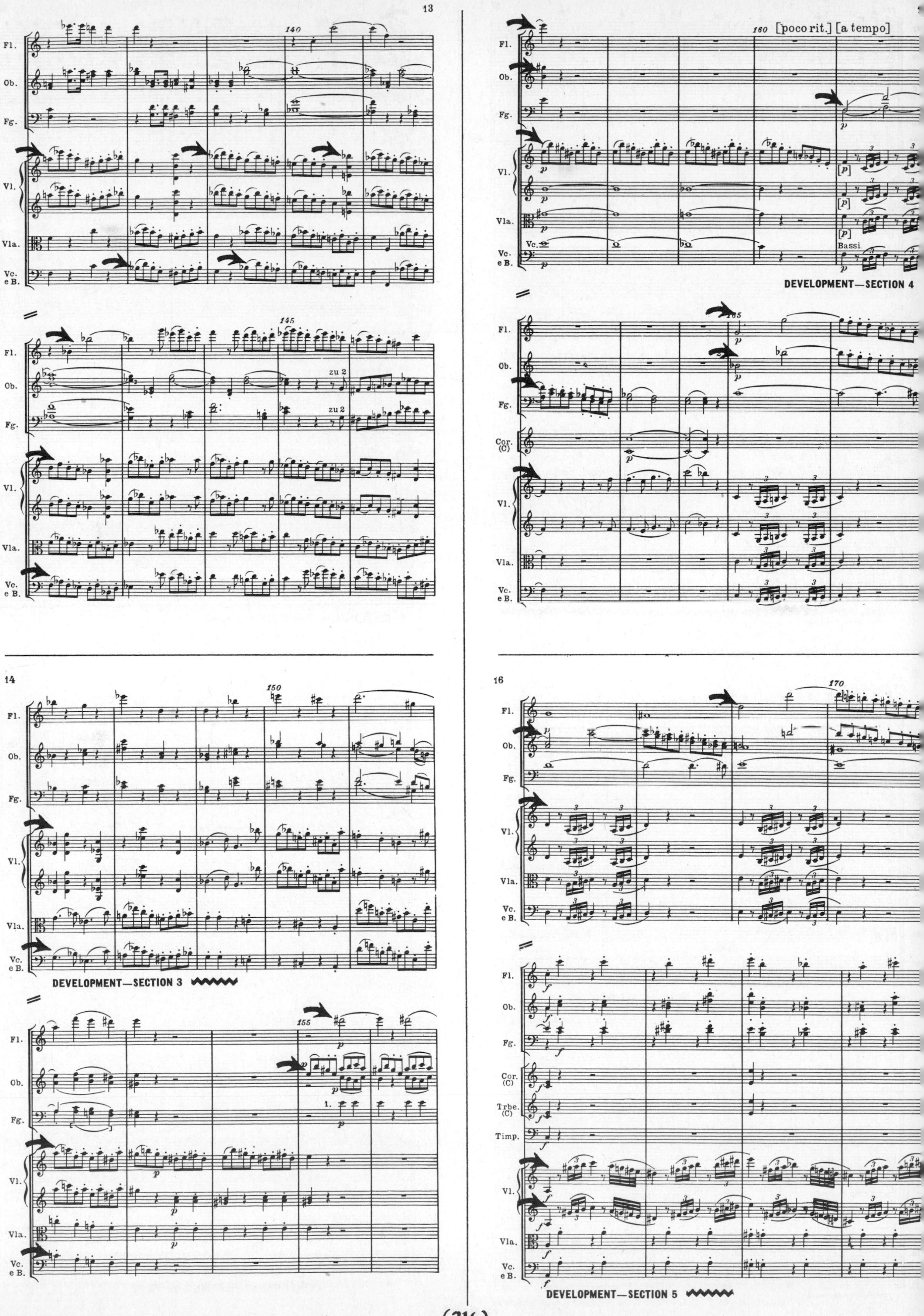

160 [poco rit.] [a tempo]

DEVELOPMENT—SECTION 4

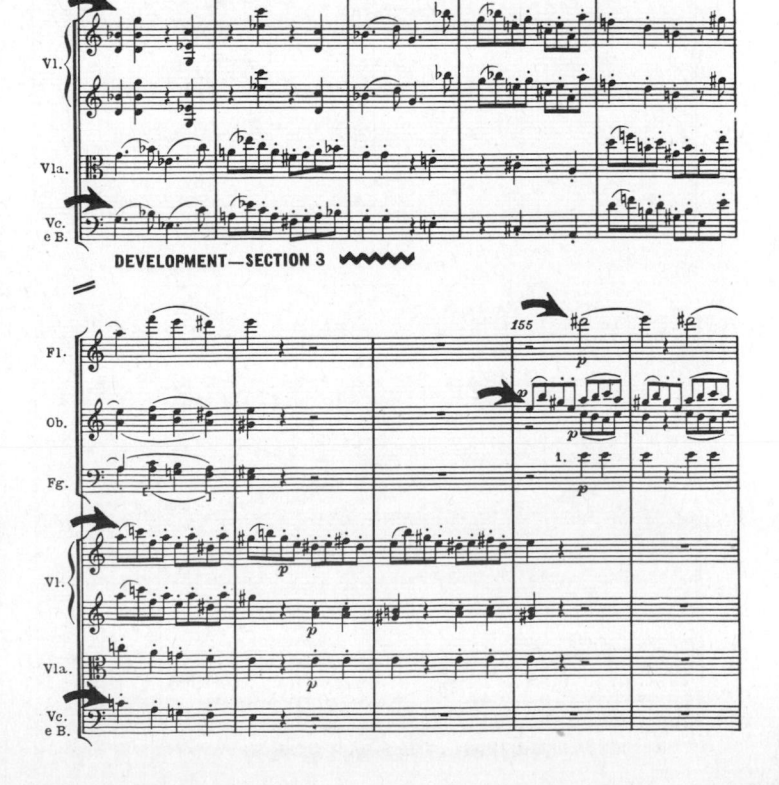

DEVELOPMENT—SECTION 3 〰〰

DEVELOPMENT—SECTION 5 〰〰〰

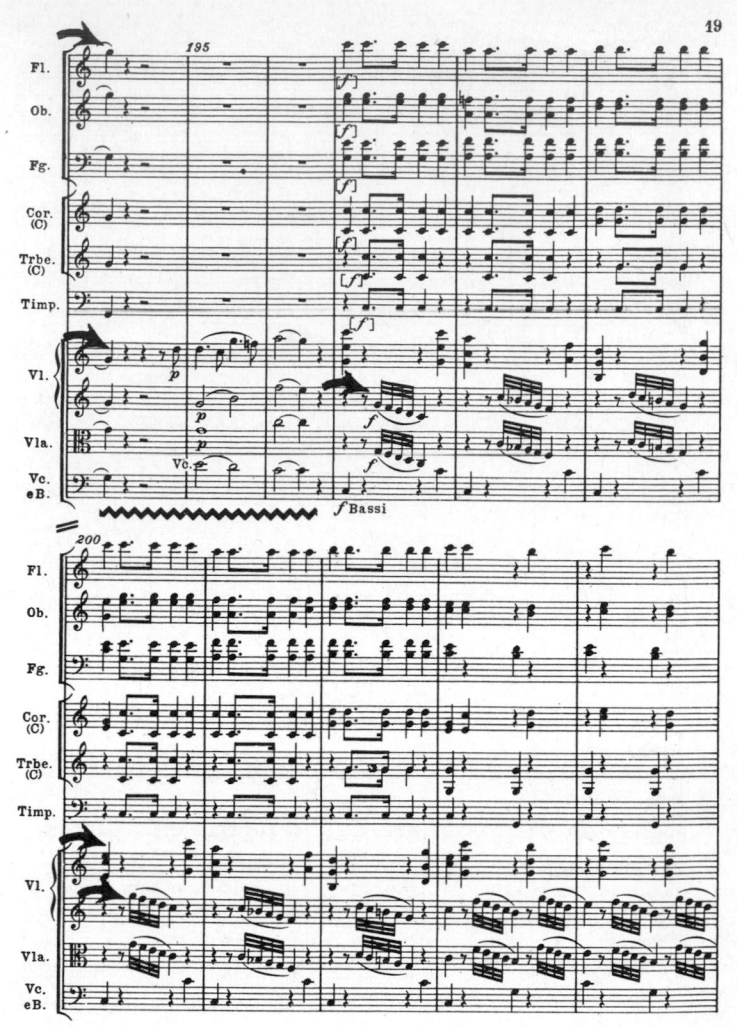

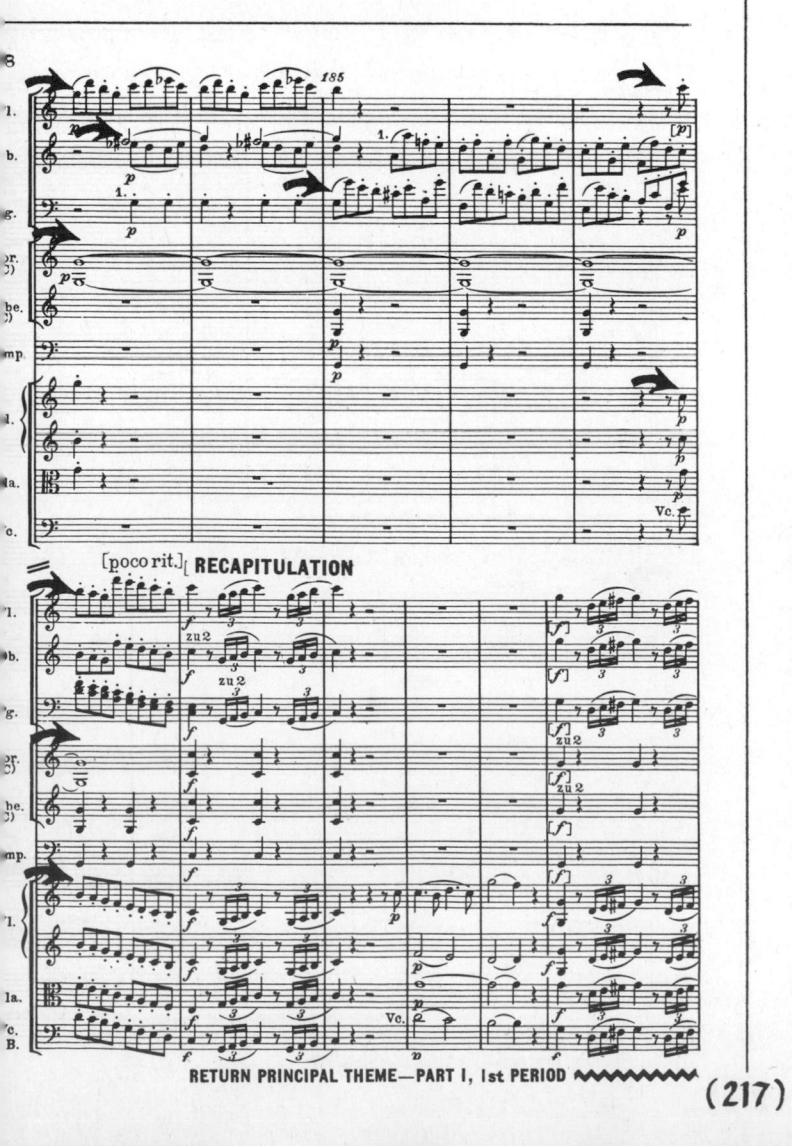

RETURNING PASSAGE (RETRANSITION) ∿∿∿∿

[poco rit.] [RECAPITULATION

RETURN PRINCIPAL THEME—PART I, 1st PERIOD ∿∿∿∿∿

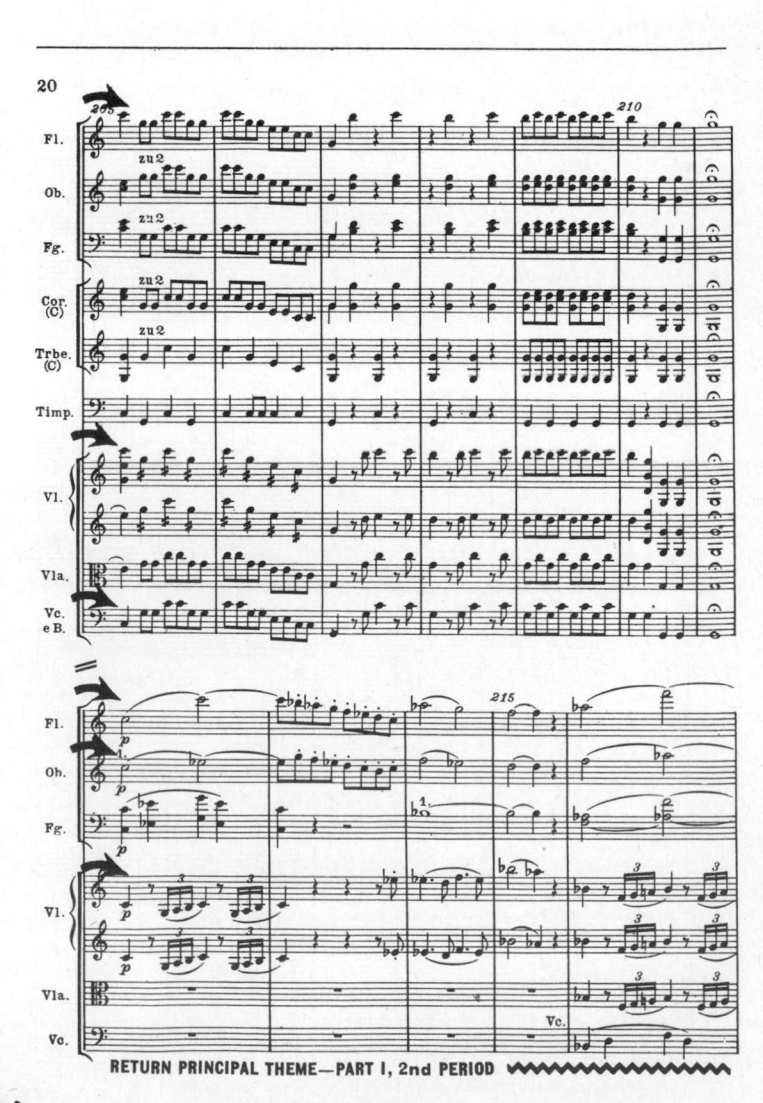

RETURN PRINCIPAL THEME—PART I, 2nd PERIOD ∿∿∿∿∿∿

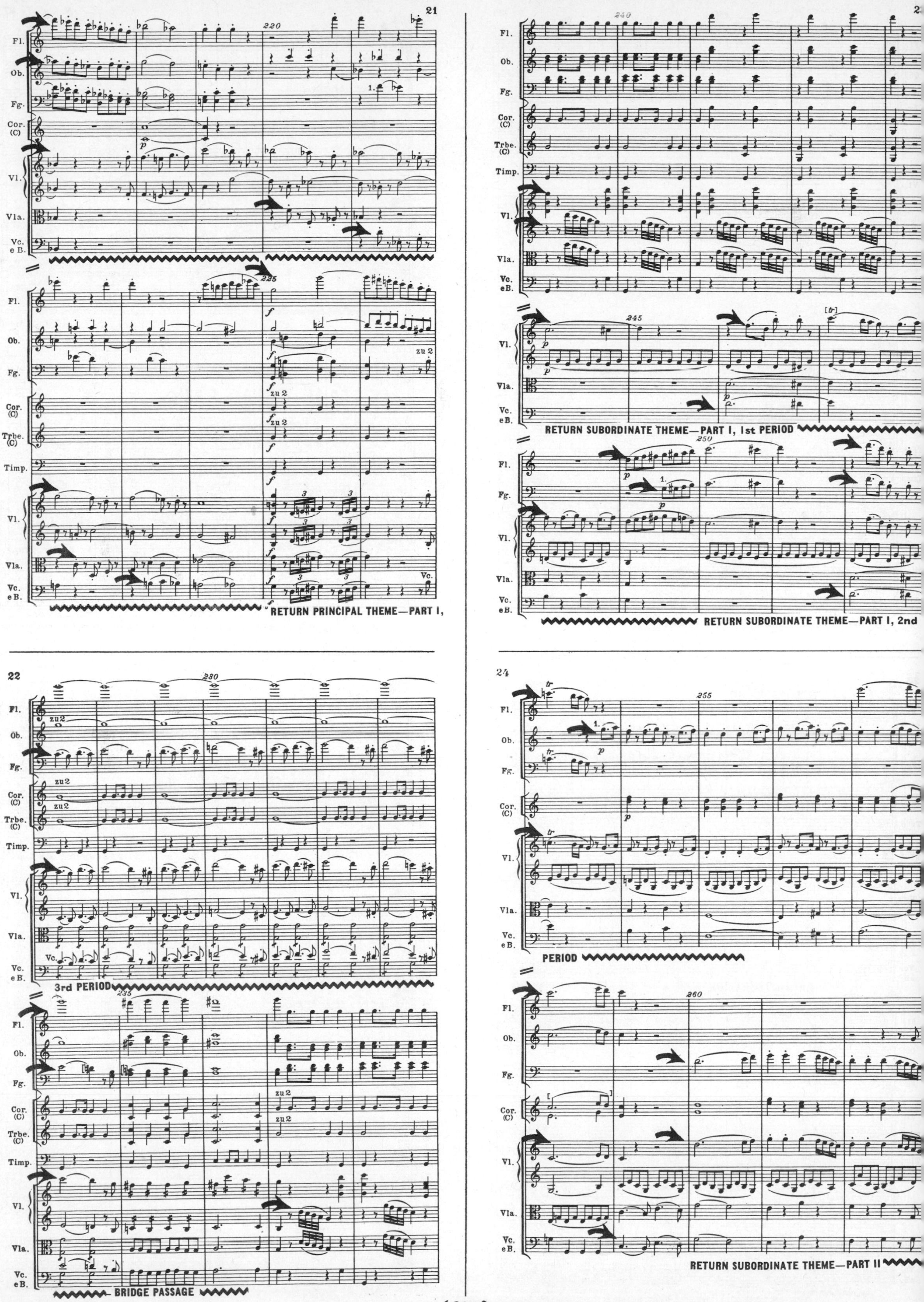
21
22
24
Fl.
Ob.
Fg.
Cor. (C)
Trbe. (C)
Timp.
Vl.
Vla.
Vc. e B.
RETURN PRINCIPAL THEME—PART I,
3rd PERIOD
BRIDGE PASSAGE
RETURN SUBORDINATE THEME—PART I, 1st PERIOD
RETURN SUBORDINATE THEME—PART I, 2nd
PERIOD
RETURN SUBORDINATE THEME—PART II

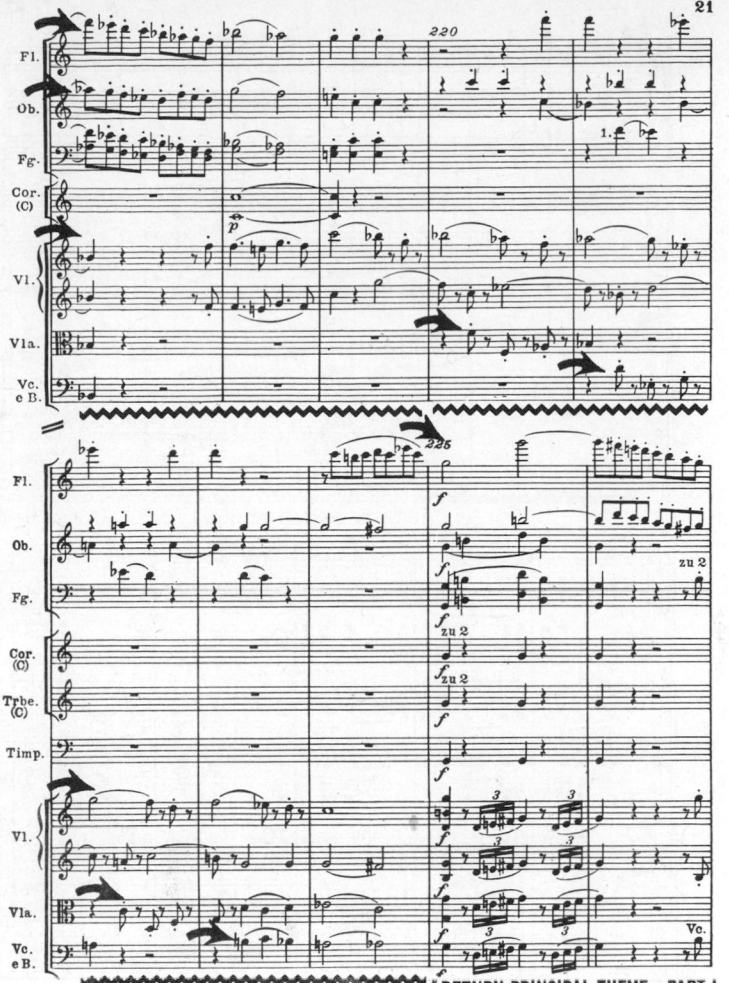

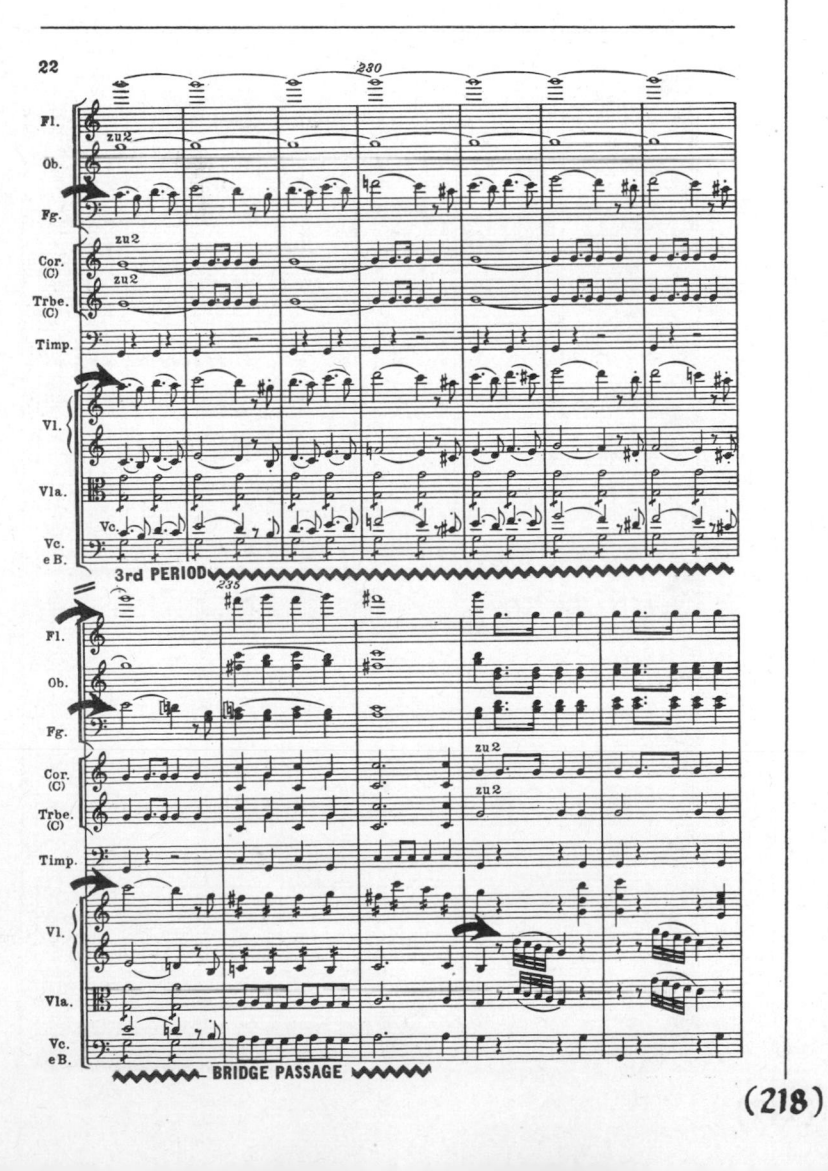

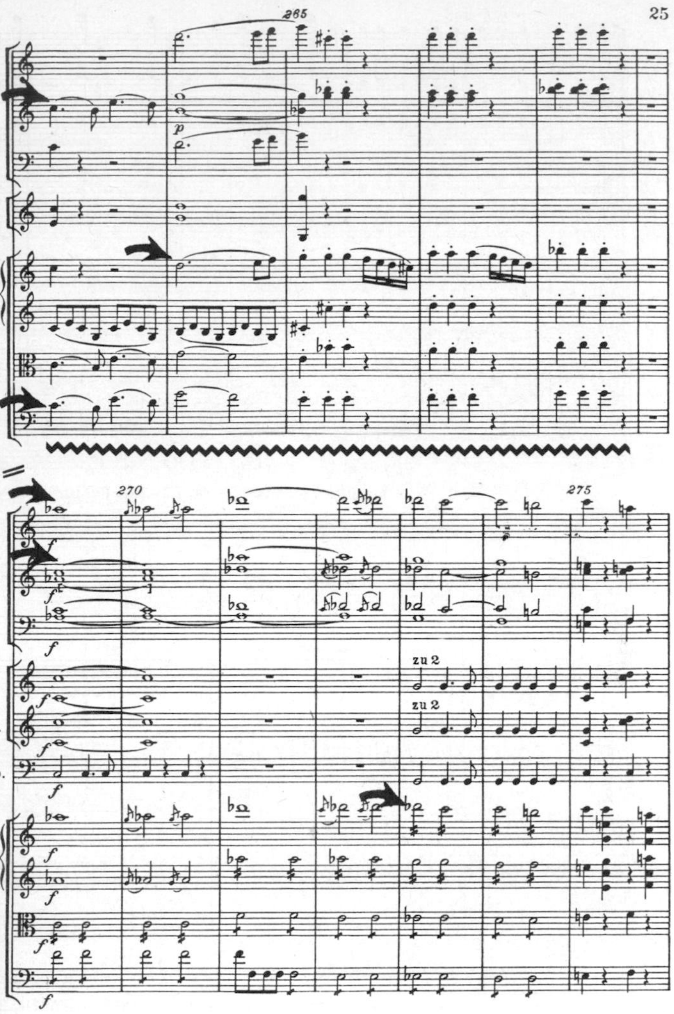

Fl.
Ob.
Fg.
Cor. (C)
Trbe. (C)
Timp.
Vl.
Vla.
Vc. e B.
zu 2

Fl.
Ob.
Fg.
Cor. (C)
Trbe. (C)
Timp.
Vl.
Vla.
Vc. e B.
pizz.
RETURN CONCLUDING THEME (CODETTA)—PART II
Bassi

Fl.
Ob.
Fg.
Cor. (C)
Trbe. (C)
Timp.
Vl.
Vla.
Vc. e B.
RETURN CONCLUDING THEME (CODETTA)—PART I
zu 2

Fl.
Ob.
Fg.
Cor. (C)
Trbe. (C)
Timp.
Vl.
Vla.
Vc. e B.
zu 2
arco
RETURN CONCLUDING THEME (CODETTA)—
PART III

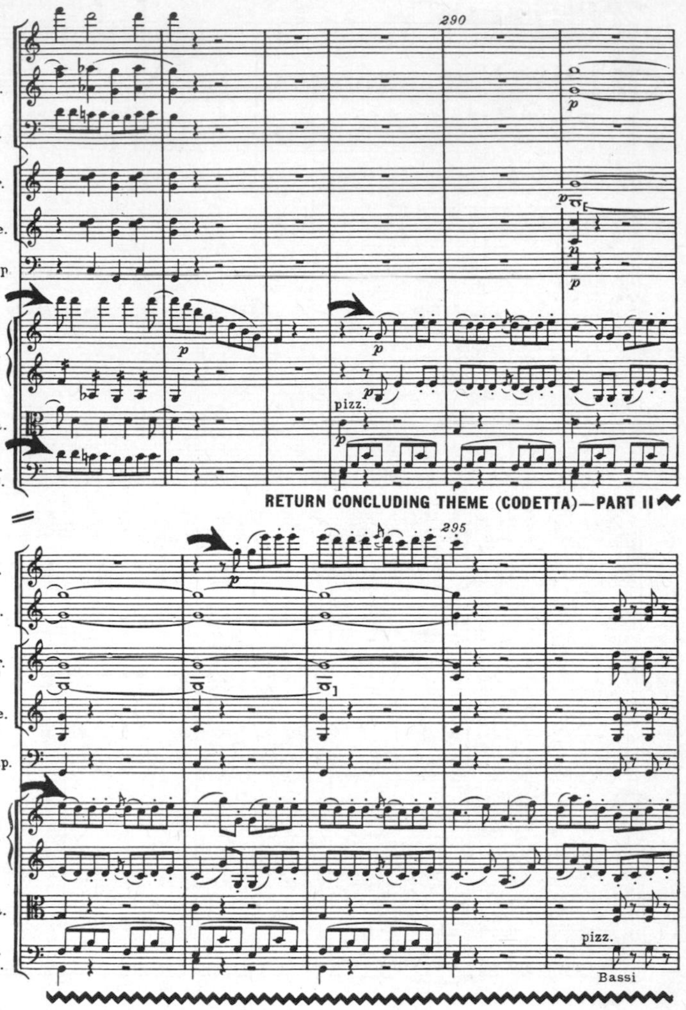

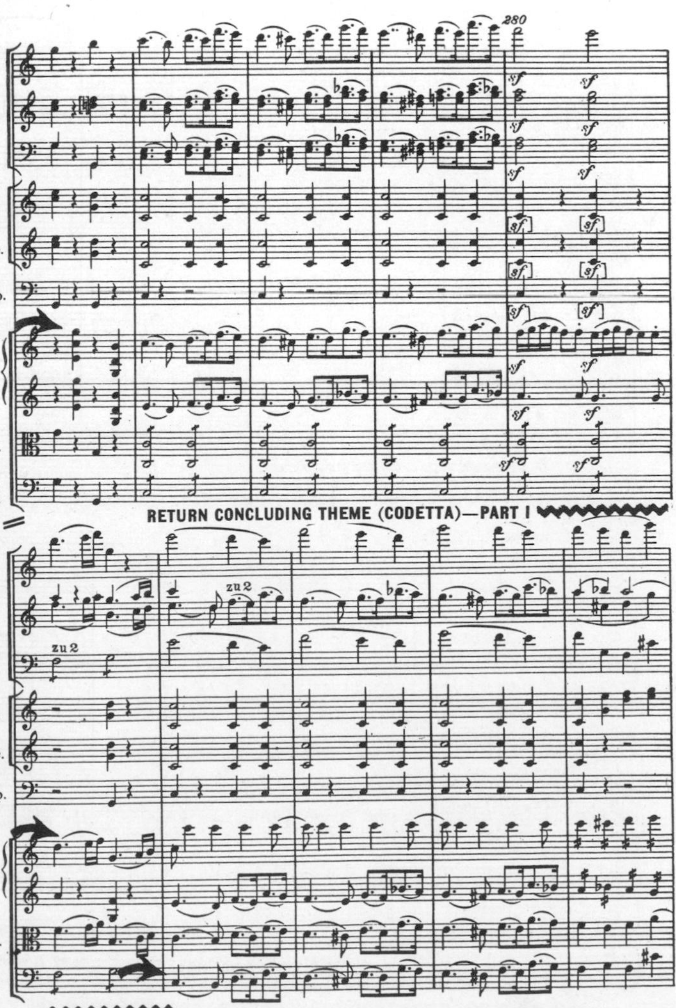

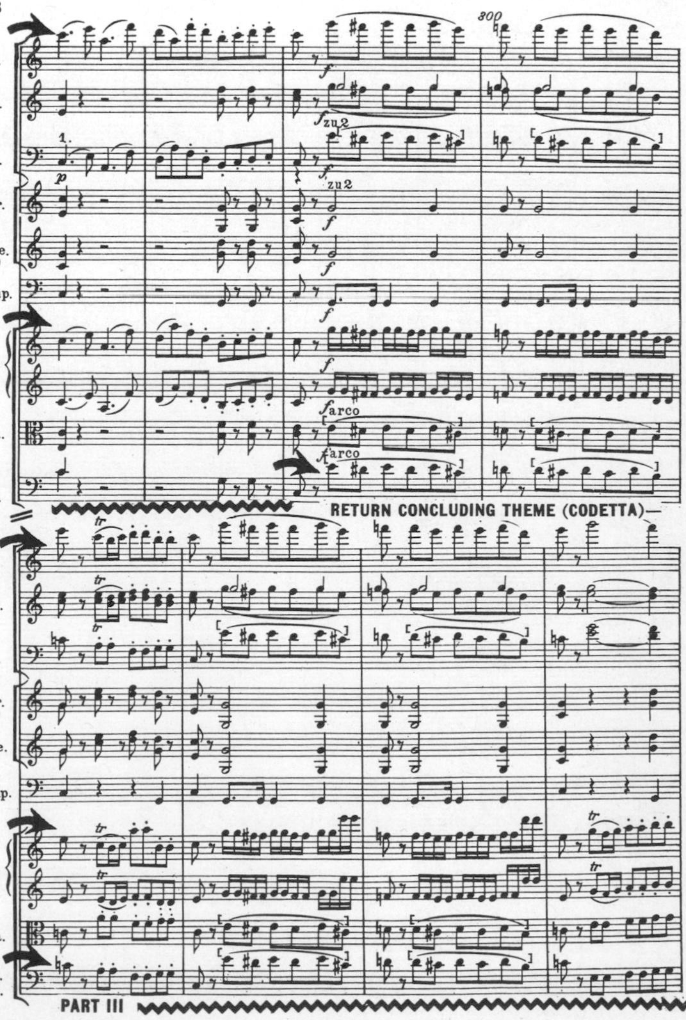

29

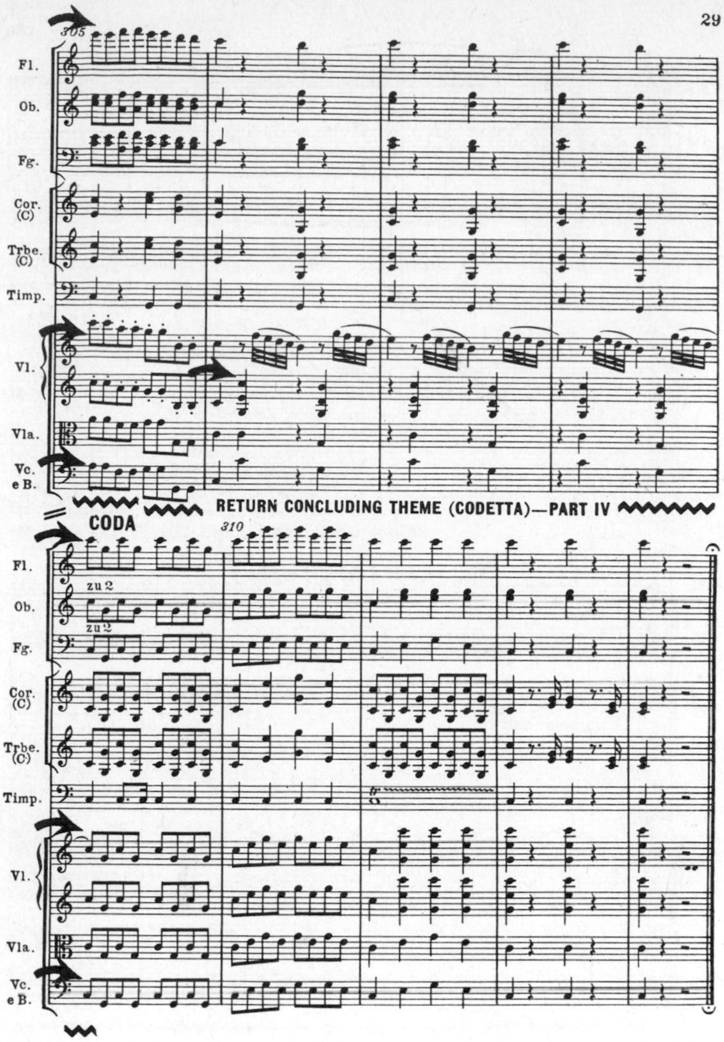

3

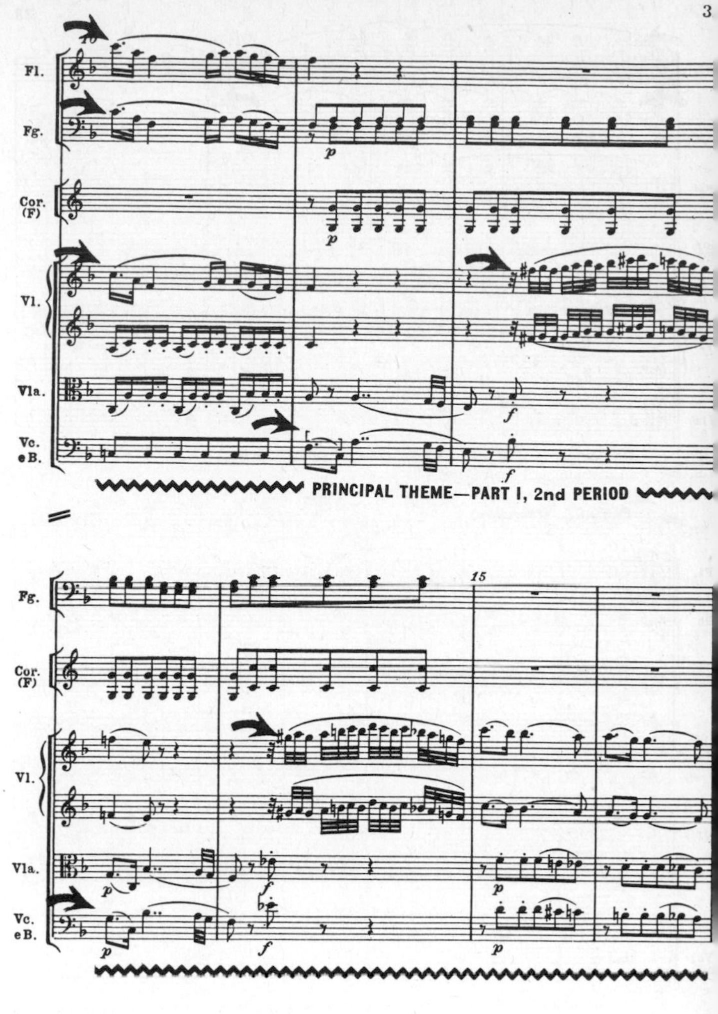

30

EXPOSITION II

Andante cantabile

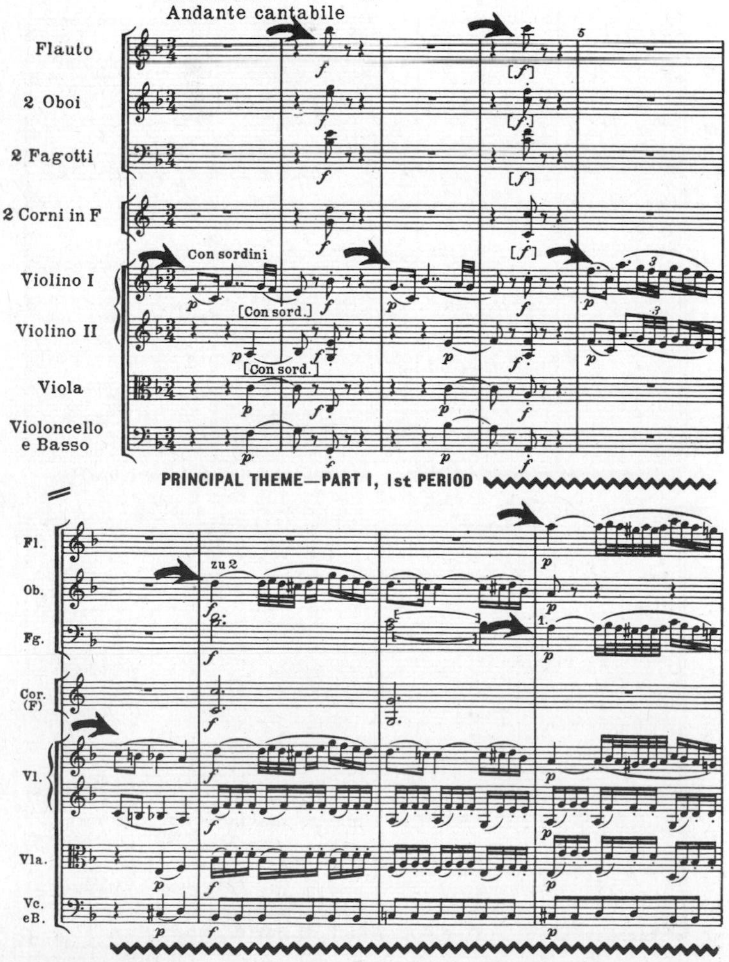

32

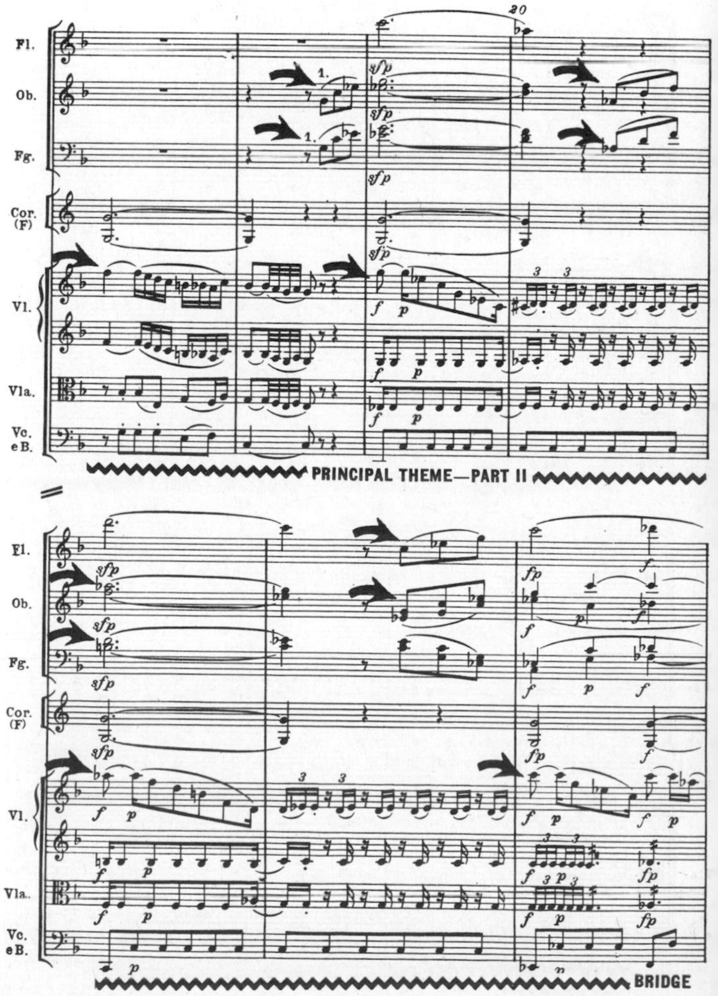

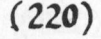

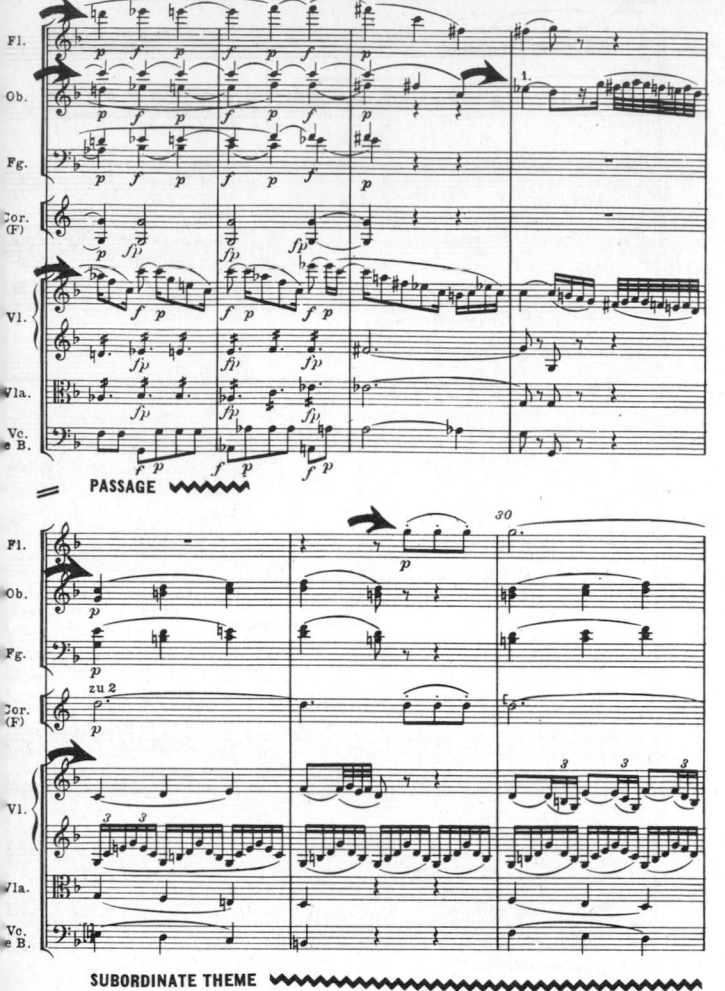

PASSAGE

SUBORDINATE THEME

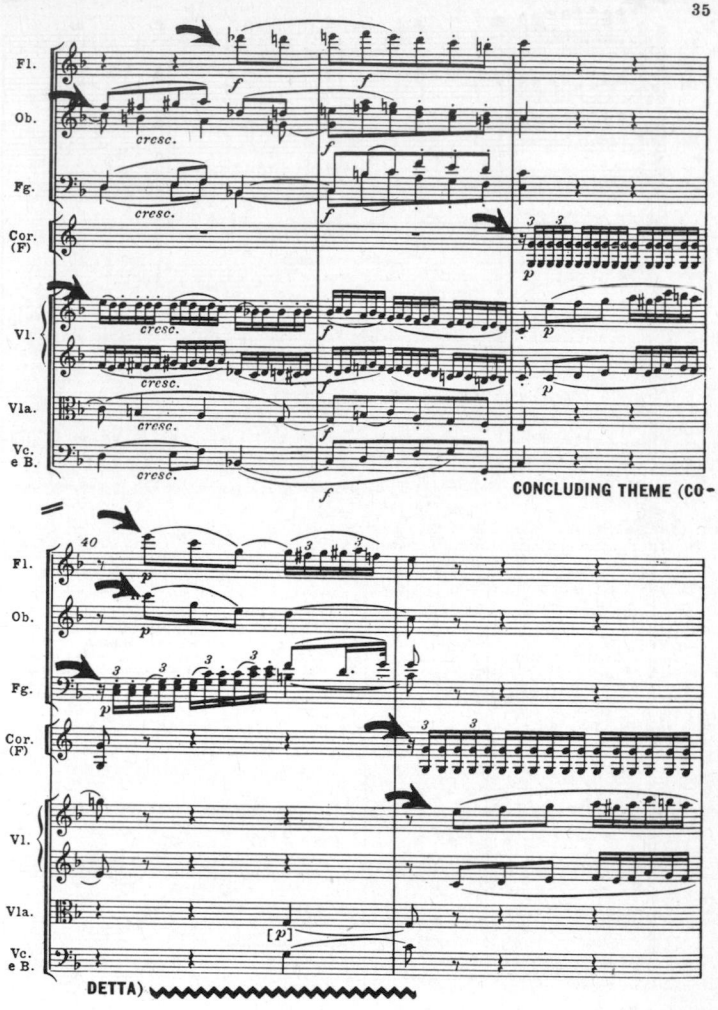

CONCLUDING THEME (CO-

DETTA)

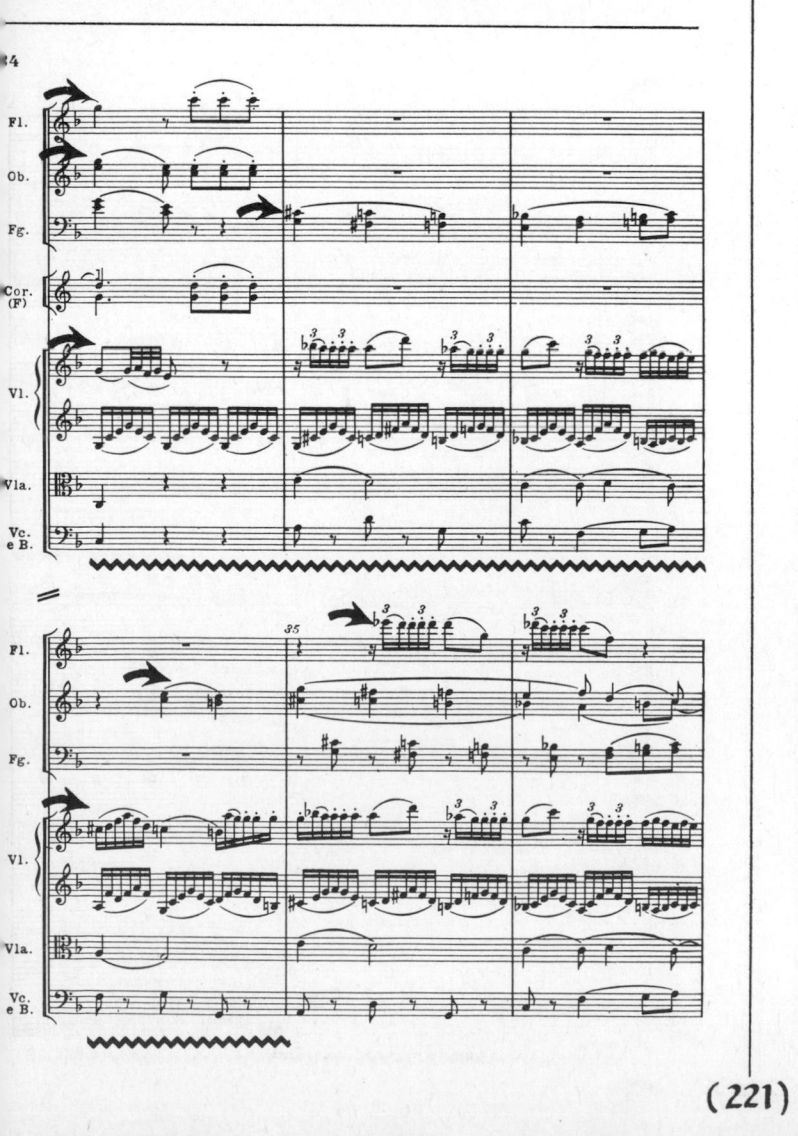

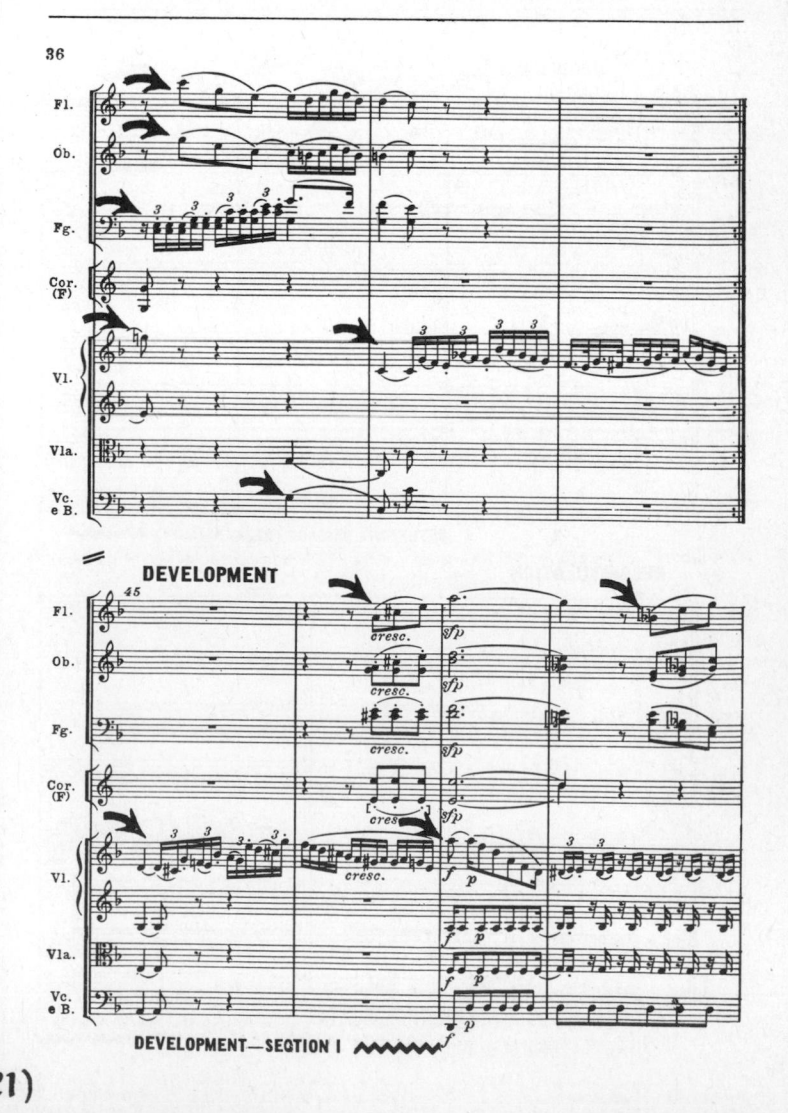

DEVELOPMENT

DEVELOPMENT—SECTION I

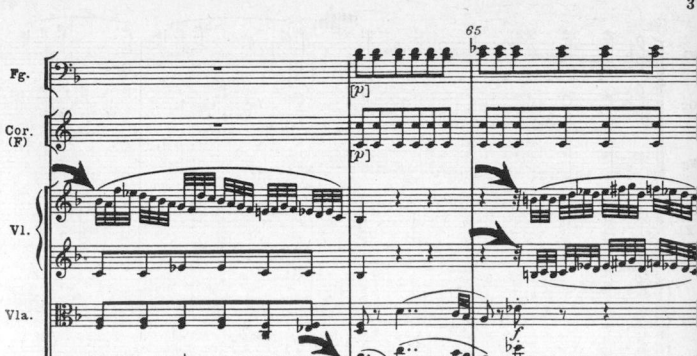

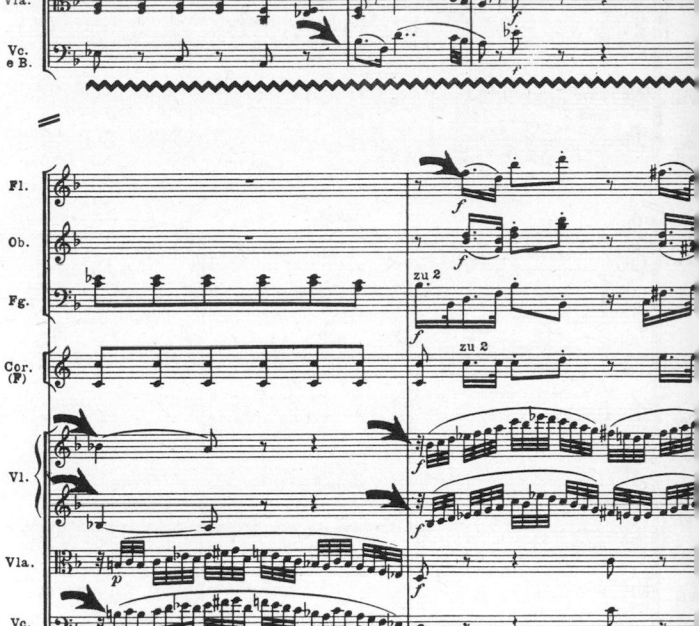

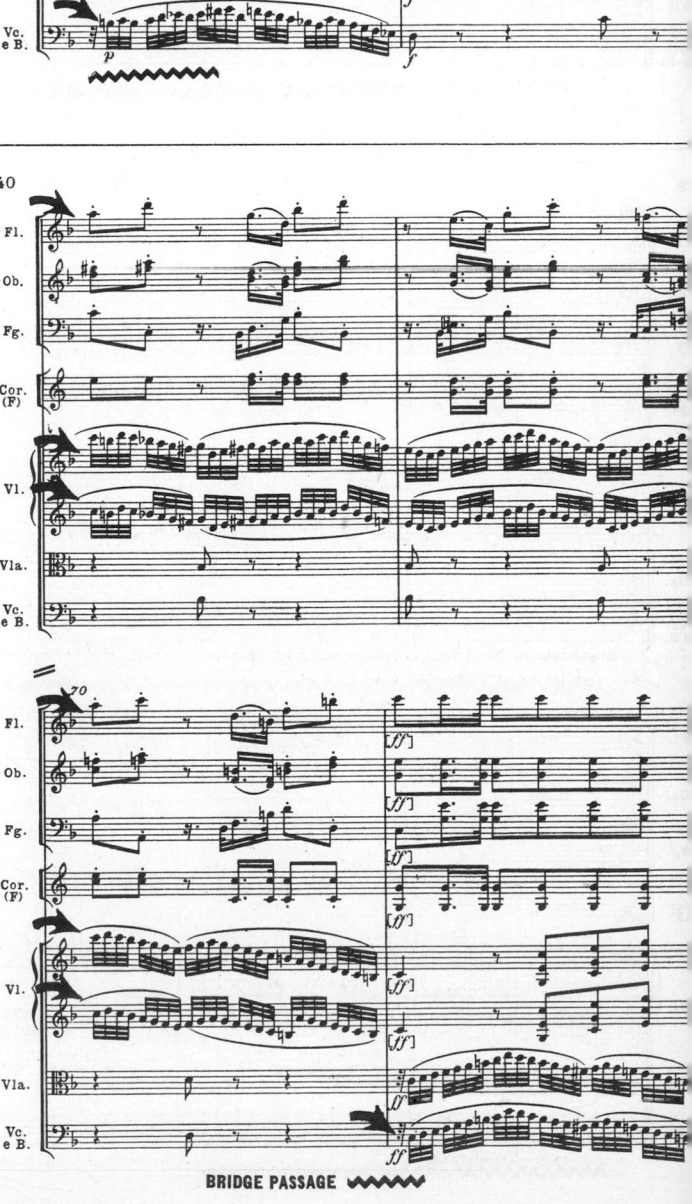

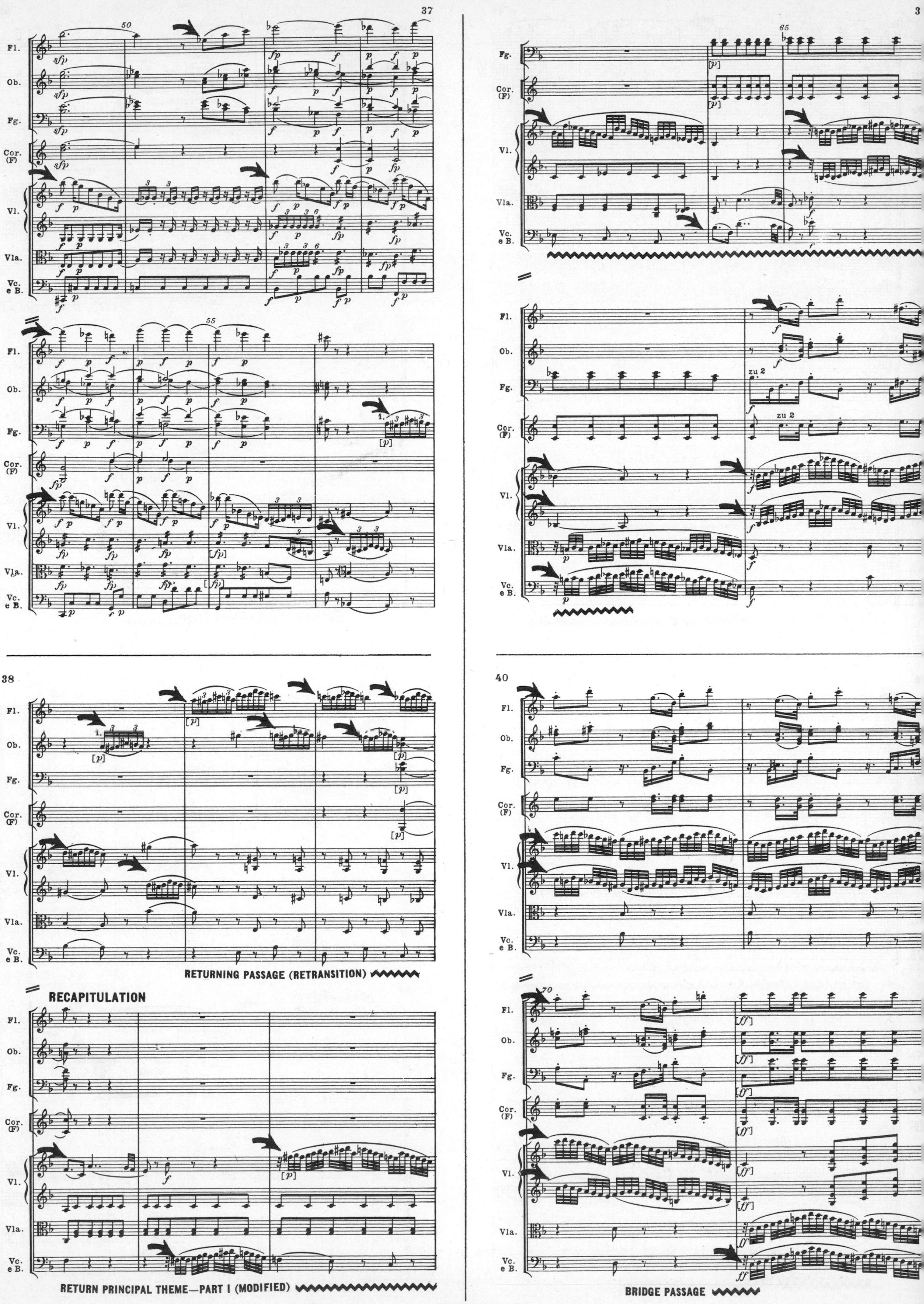
37
Fl.
Ob.
Fg.
Cor. (F)
Vl.
Vla.
Vc. e B.
50
55
65
zu 2
38
RETURNING PASSAGE (RETRANSITION)
RECAPITULATION
RETURN PRINCIPAL THEME—PART I (MODIFIED)
40
70
BRIDGE PASSAGE

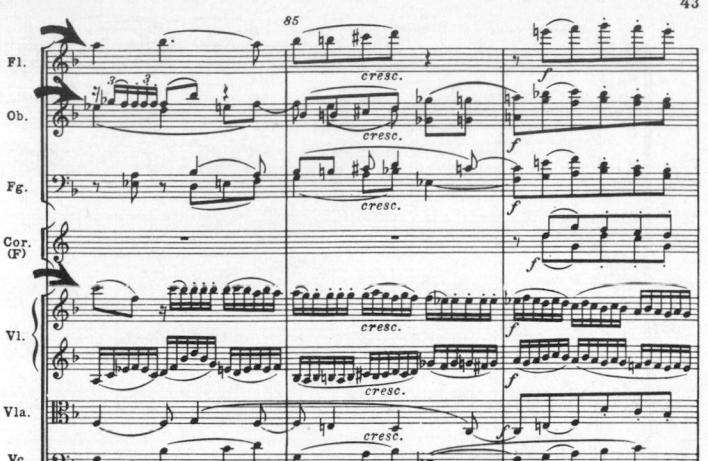

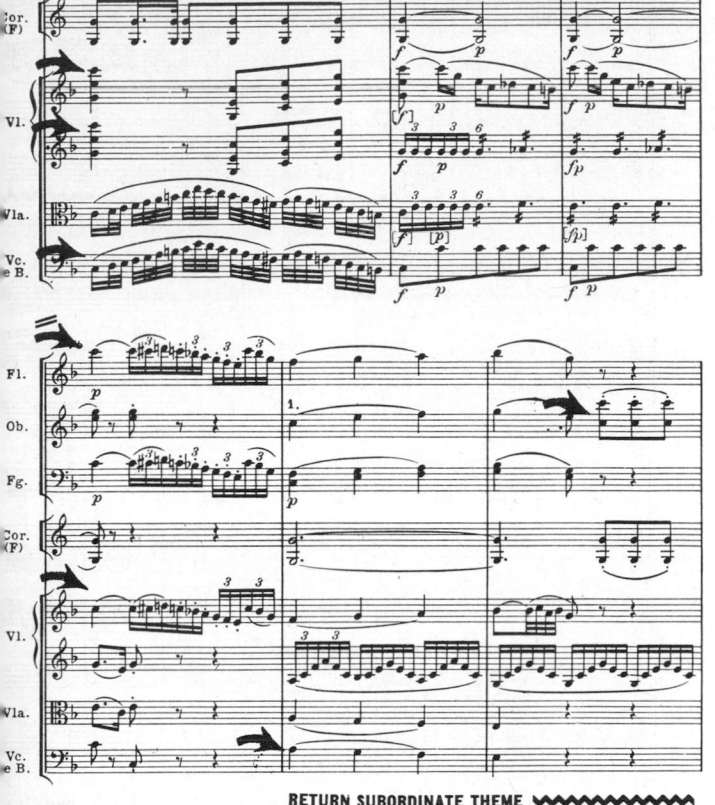

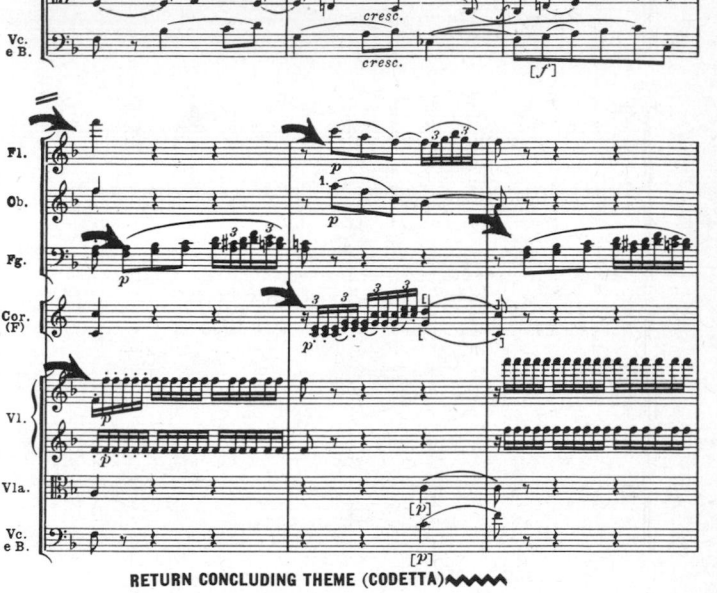

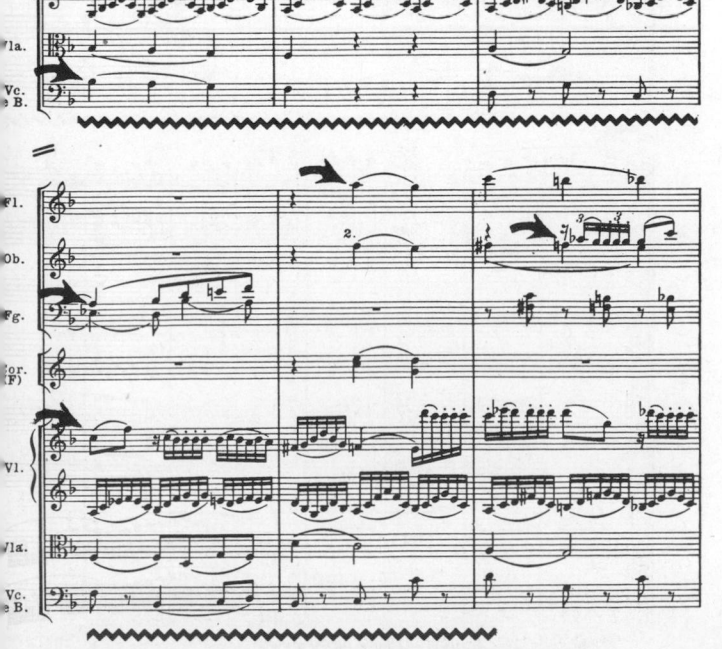

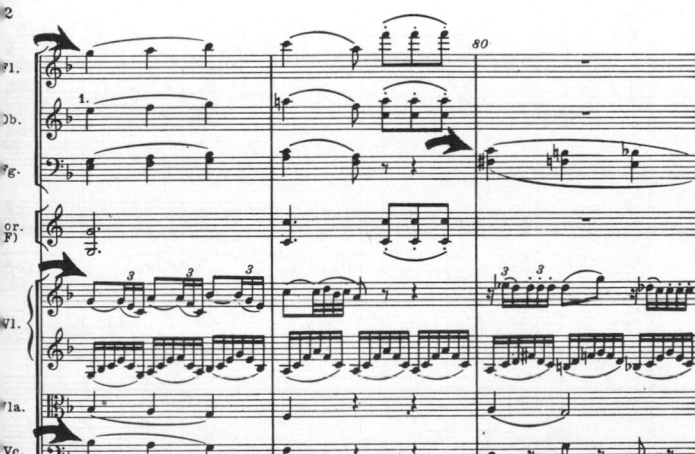

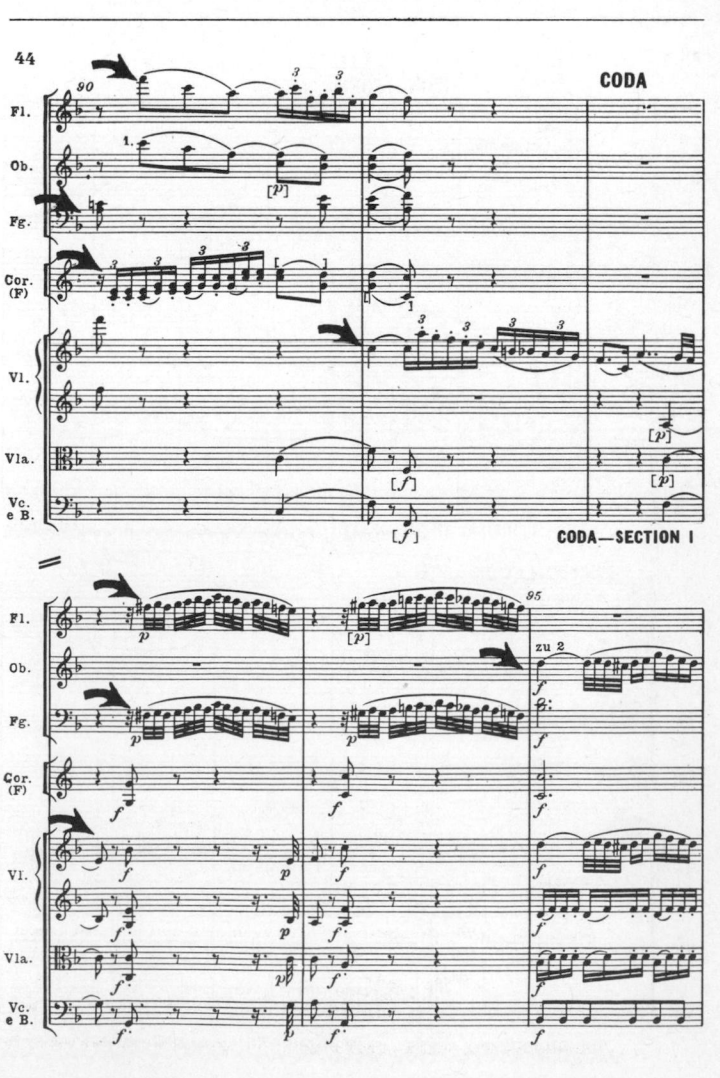

RETURN SUBORDINATE THEME ∿∿∿∿∿∿∿

RETURN CONCLUDING THEME (CODETTA) ∿∿∿

CODA

CODA—SECTION I

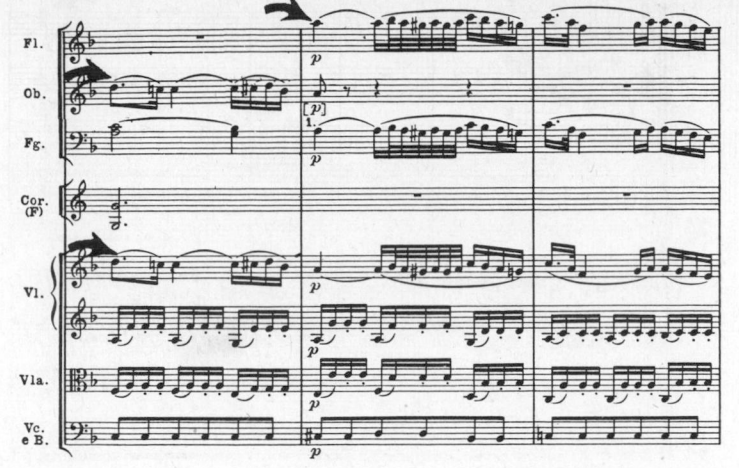

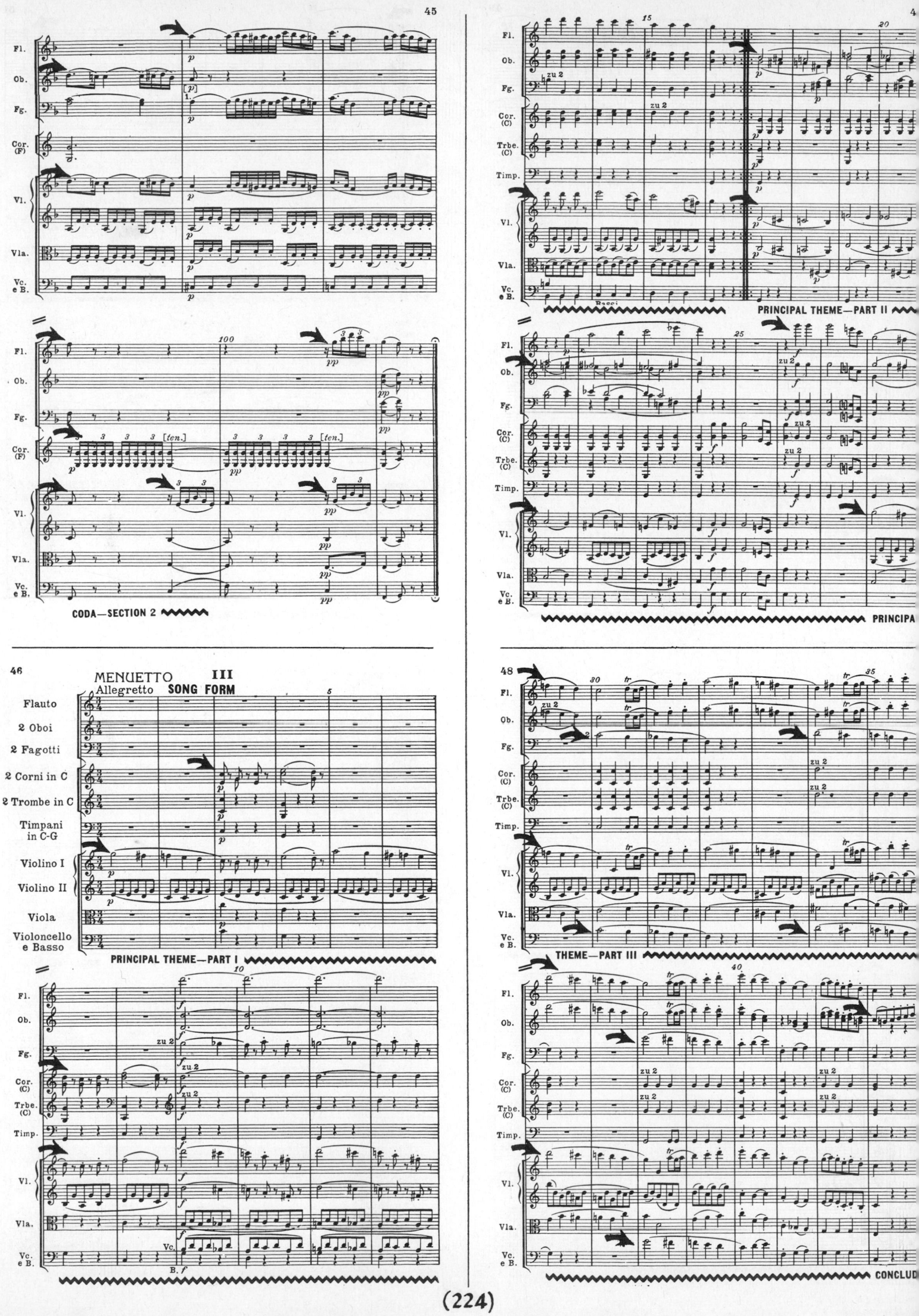

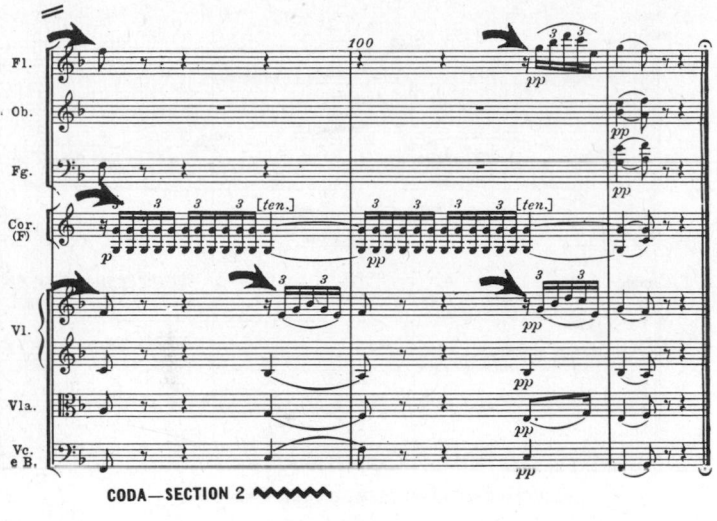

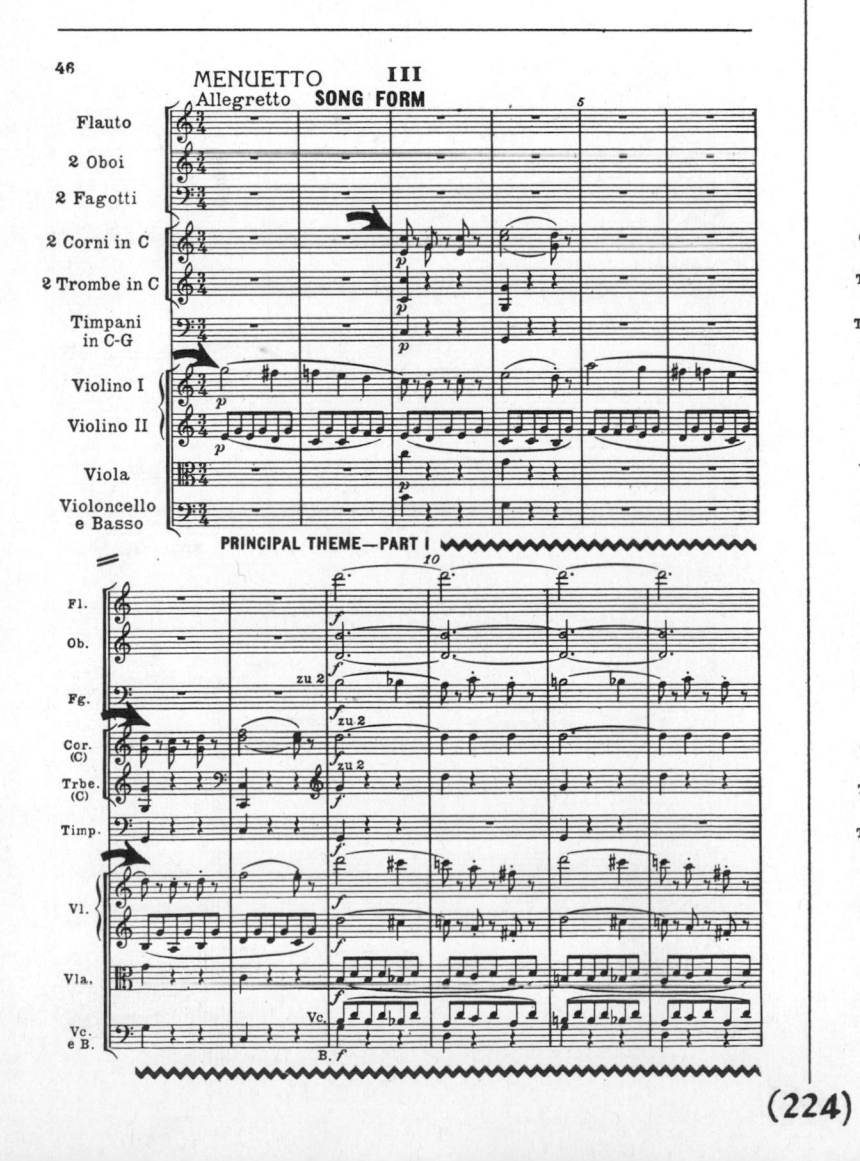

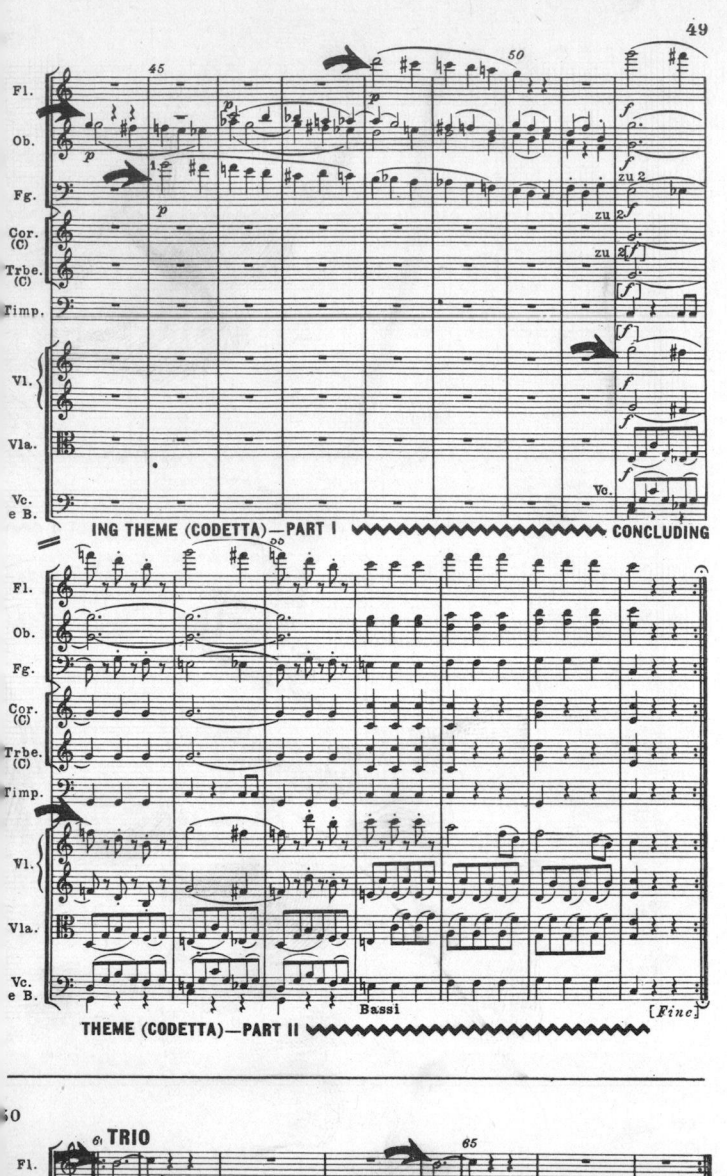

ING THEME (CODETTA)—PART I 〰〰〰〰〰〰〰〰〰〰 CONCLUDING

THEME (CODETTA)—PART II 〰〰〰〰〰〰〰〰〰〰〰〰〰

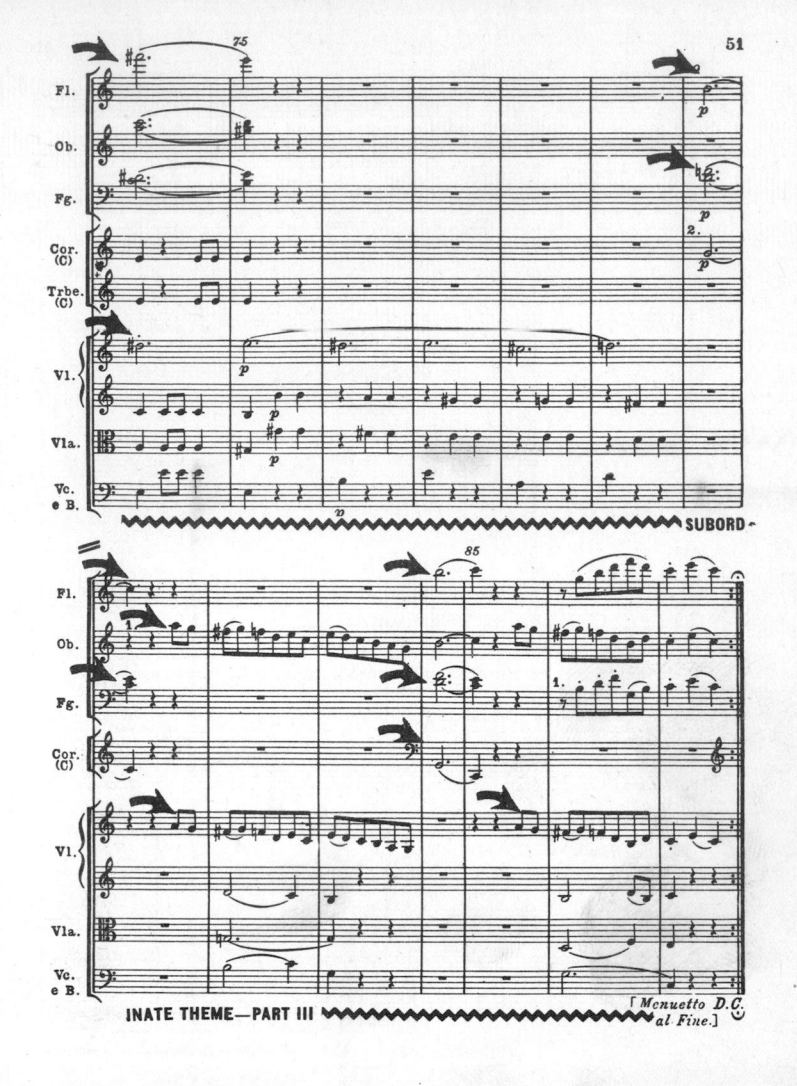

SUBORD-

INATE THEME—PART III 〰〰〰〰〰〰〰 [Menuetto D.C.
al Fine.]

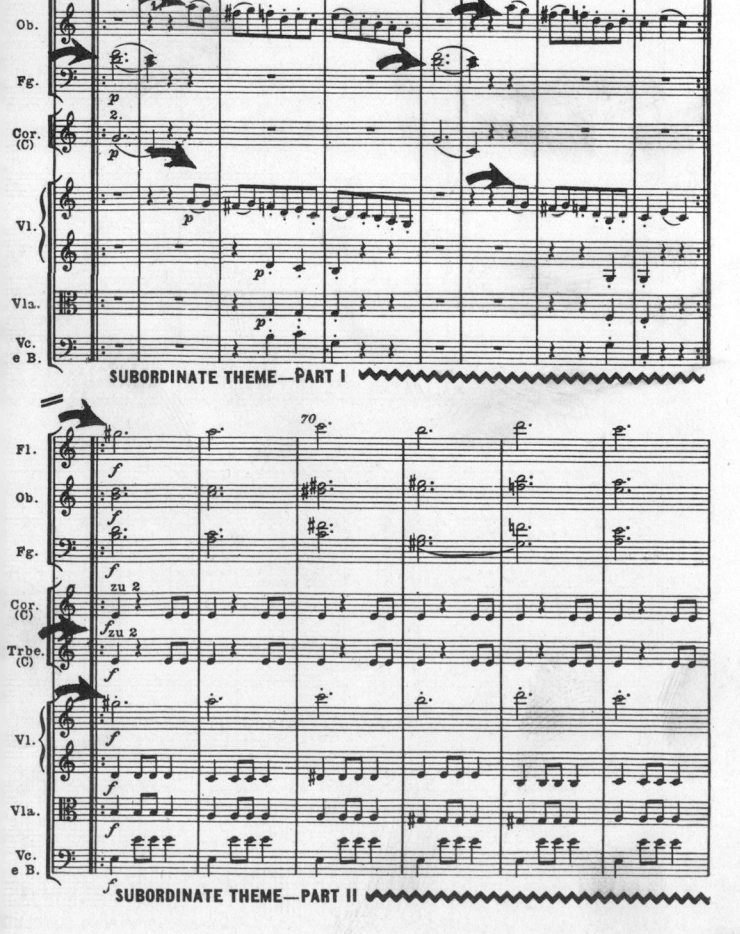

TRIO

SUBORDINATE THEME—PART I 〰〰〰〰〰〰〰

SUBORDINATE THEME—PART II 〰〰〰〰〰〰〰〰

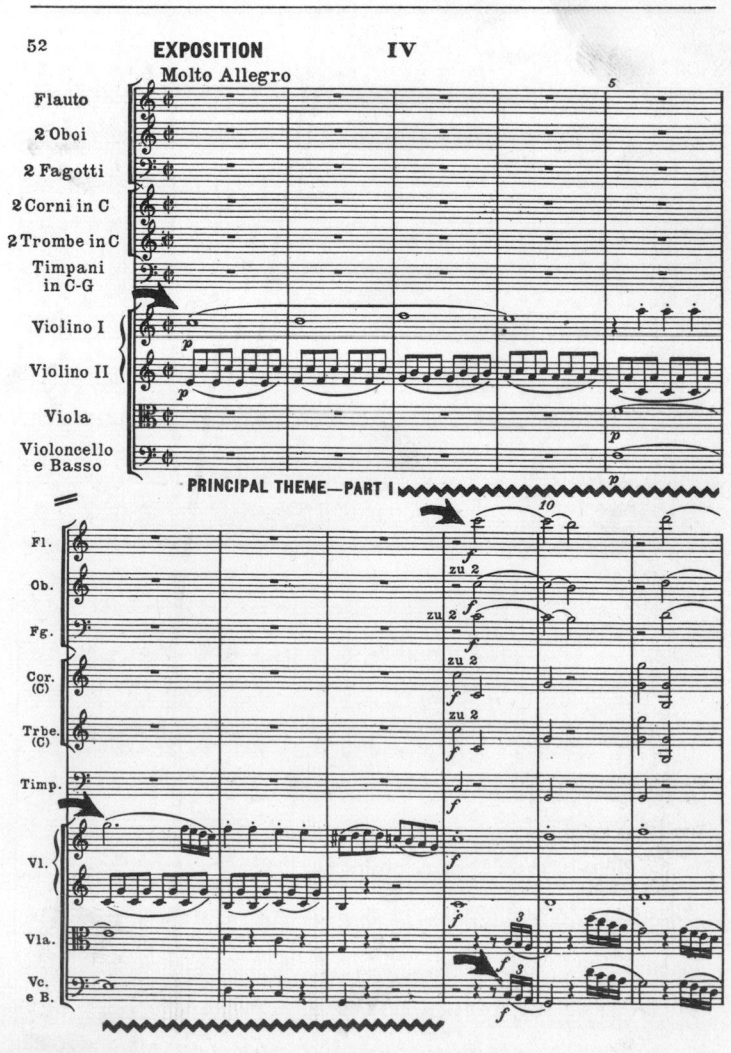

EXPOSITION   IV

Molto Allegro

Flauto

2 Oboi

2 Fagotti

2 Corni in C

2 Trombe in C

Timpani
in C-G

Violino I

Violino II

Viola

Violoncello
e Basso

PRINCIPAL THEME—PART I 〰〰〰〰〰〰〰〰

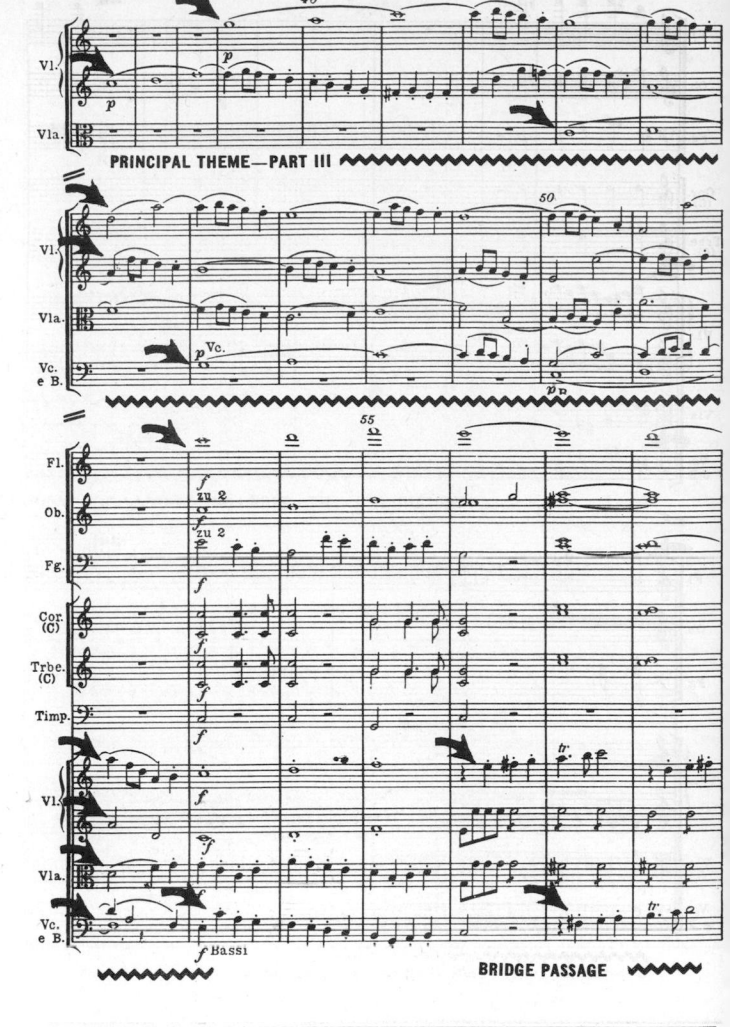

PRINCIPAL THEME—PART III ∿∿∿∿∿∿∿

PRINCIPAL THEME—PART II ∿∿∿∿∿∿∿

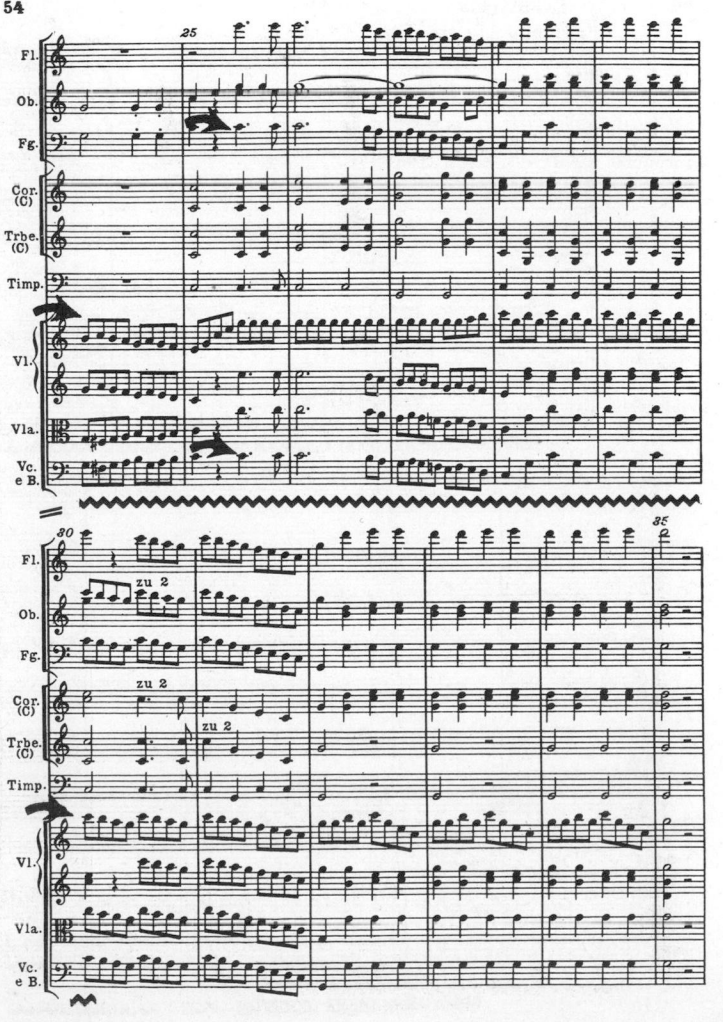

BRIDGE PASSAGE ∿∿∿∿∿

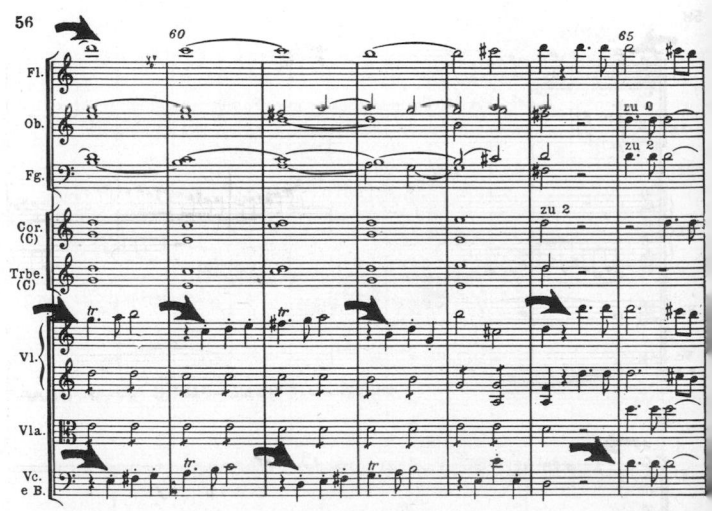

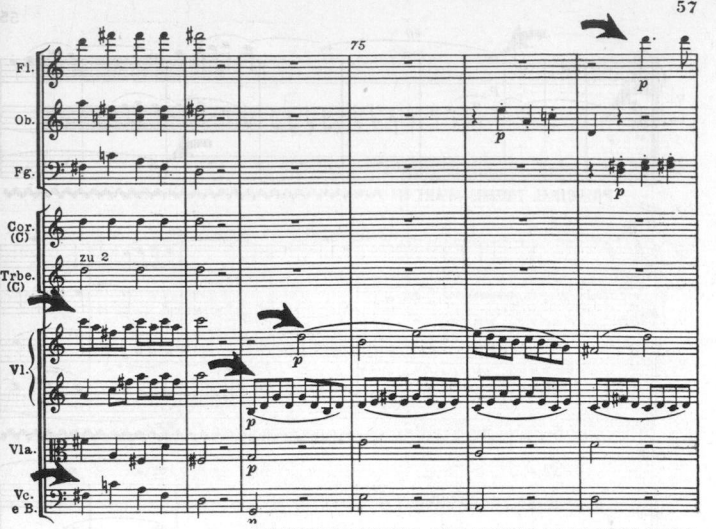

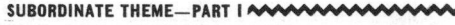

SUBORDINATE THEME—PART I

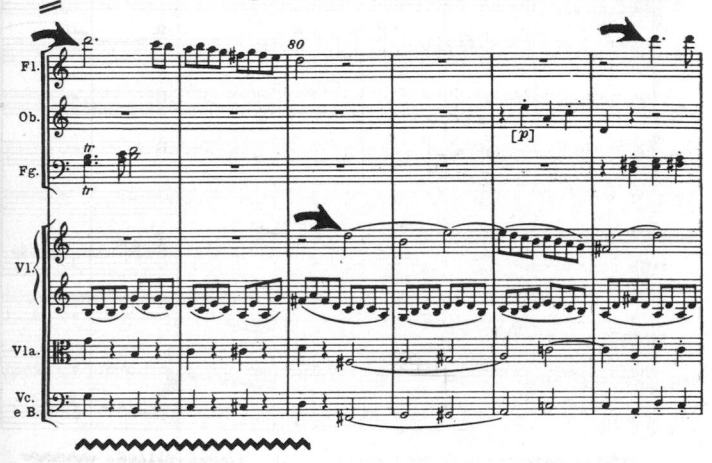

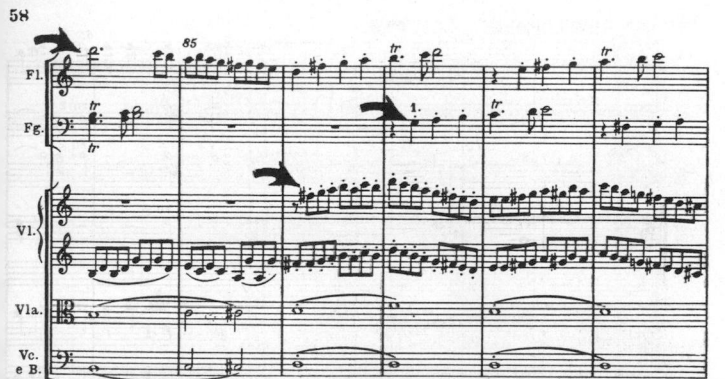

SUBORDINATE THEME—PART II

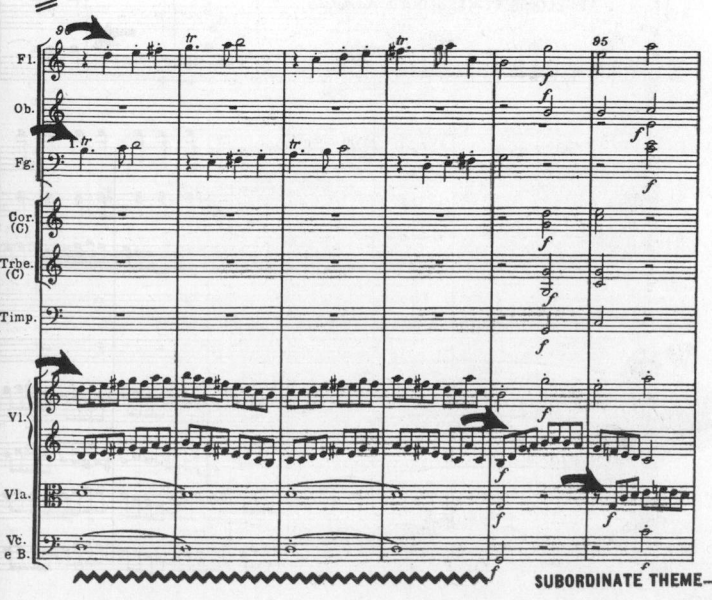

SUBORDINATE THEME—

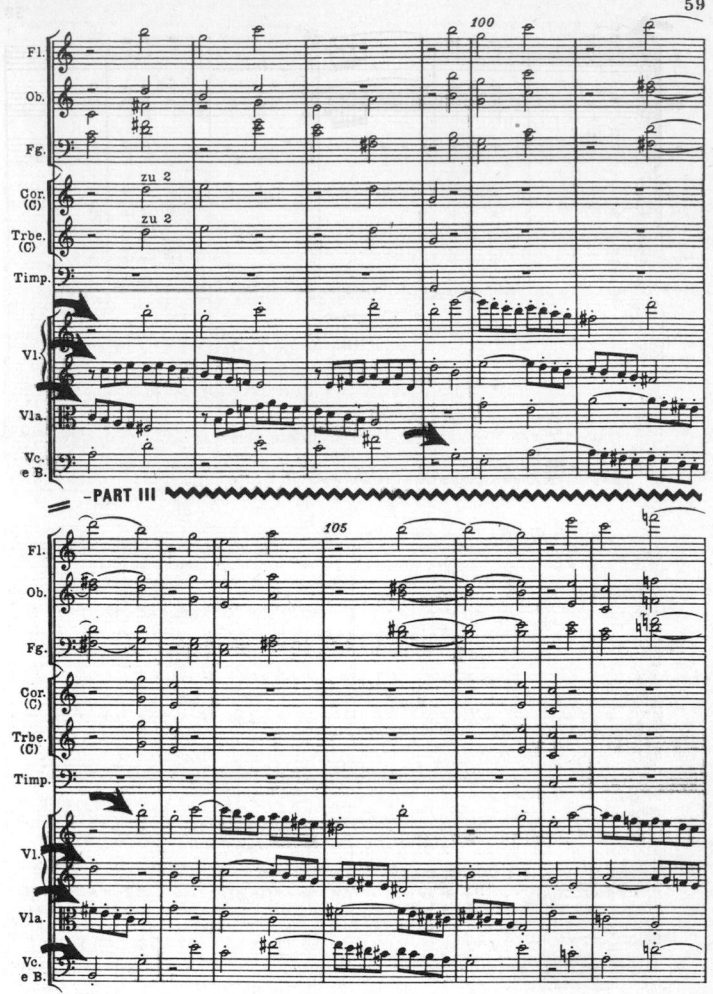

—PART III

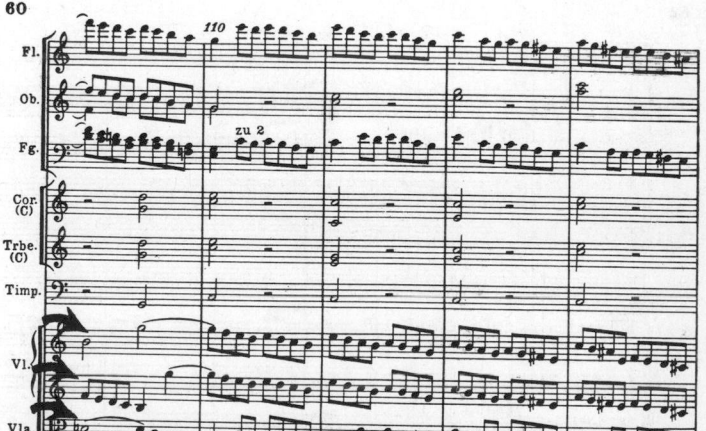

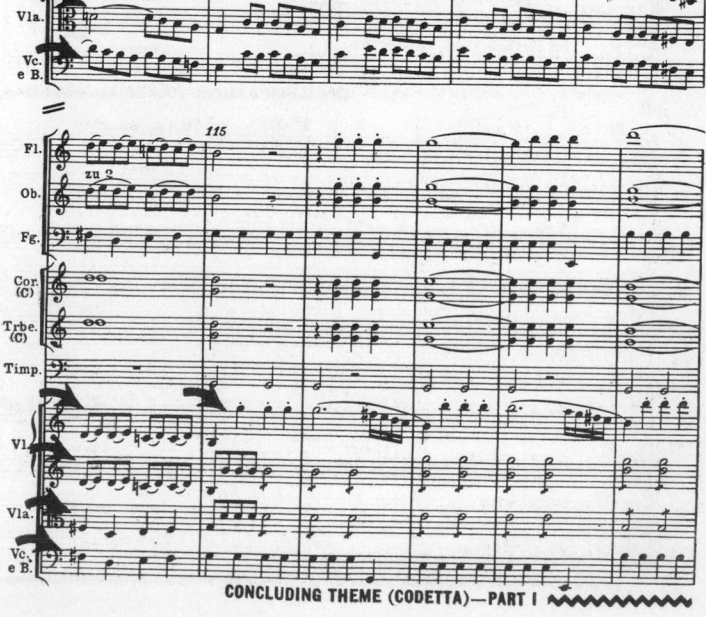

CONCLUDING THEME (CODETTA)—PART I

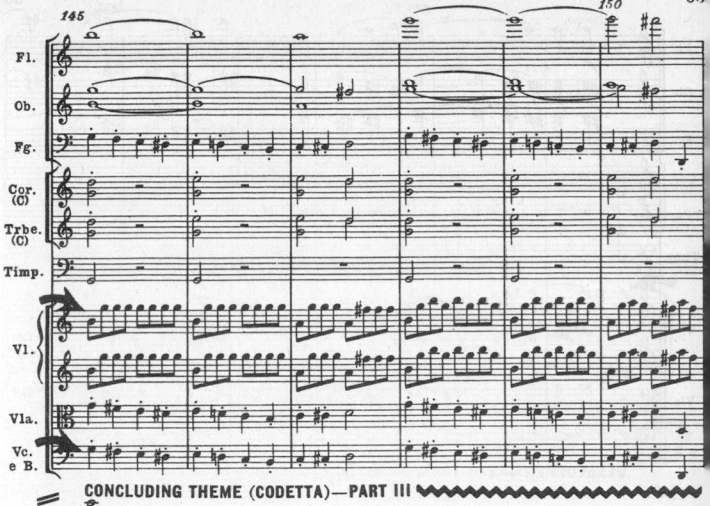

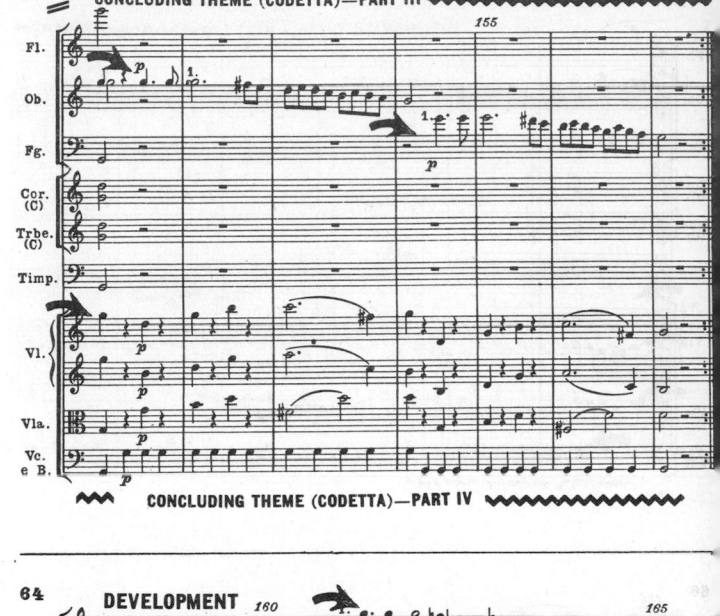

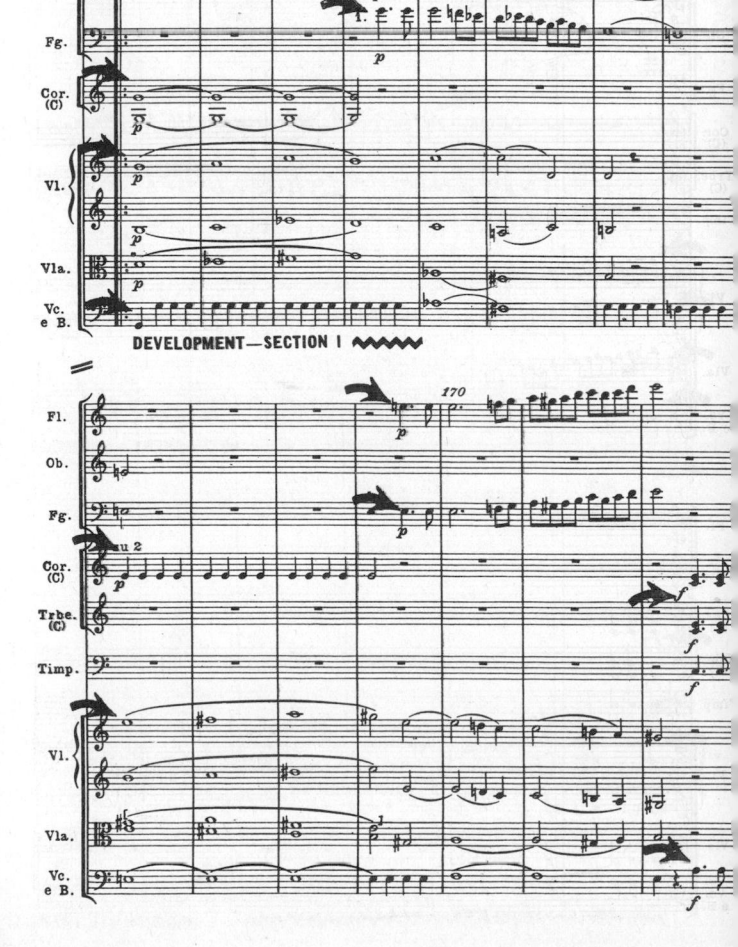

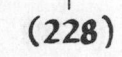
(228)

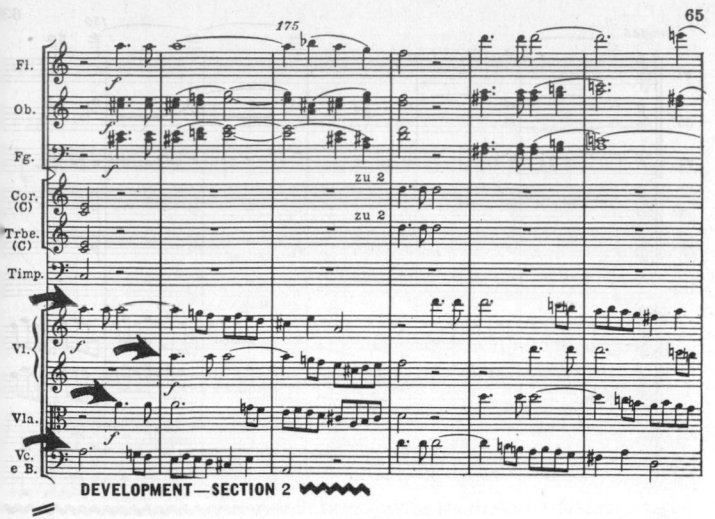

DEVELOPMENT—SECTION 2 〰〰

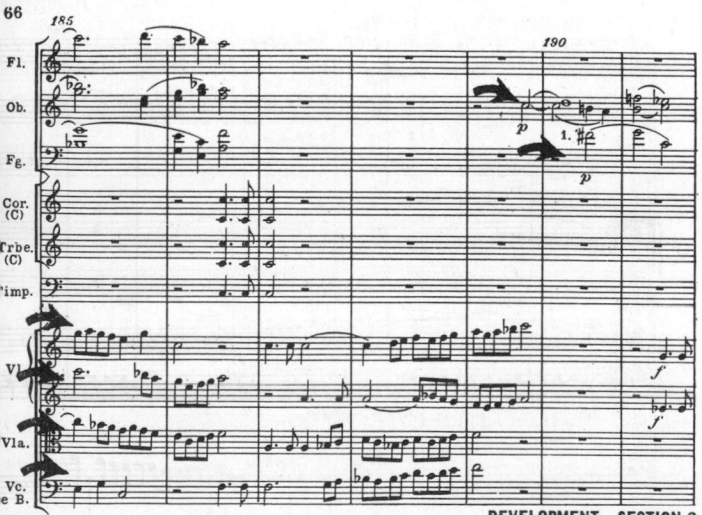

DEVELOPMENT—SECTION 3

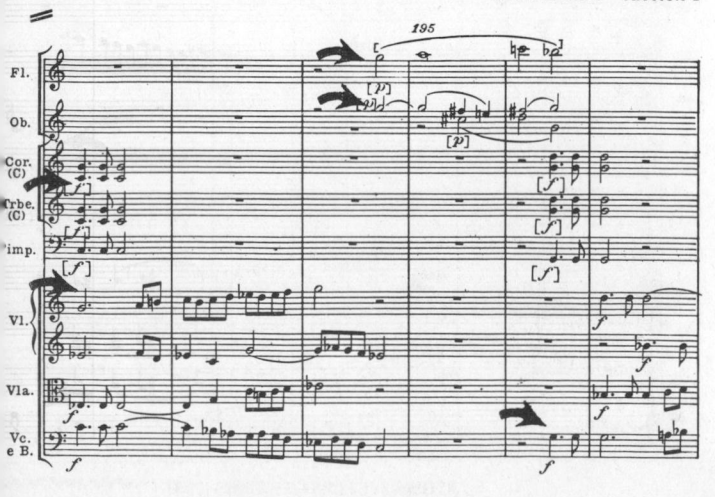

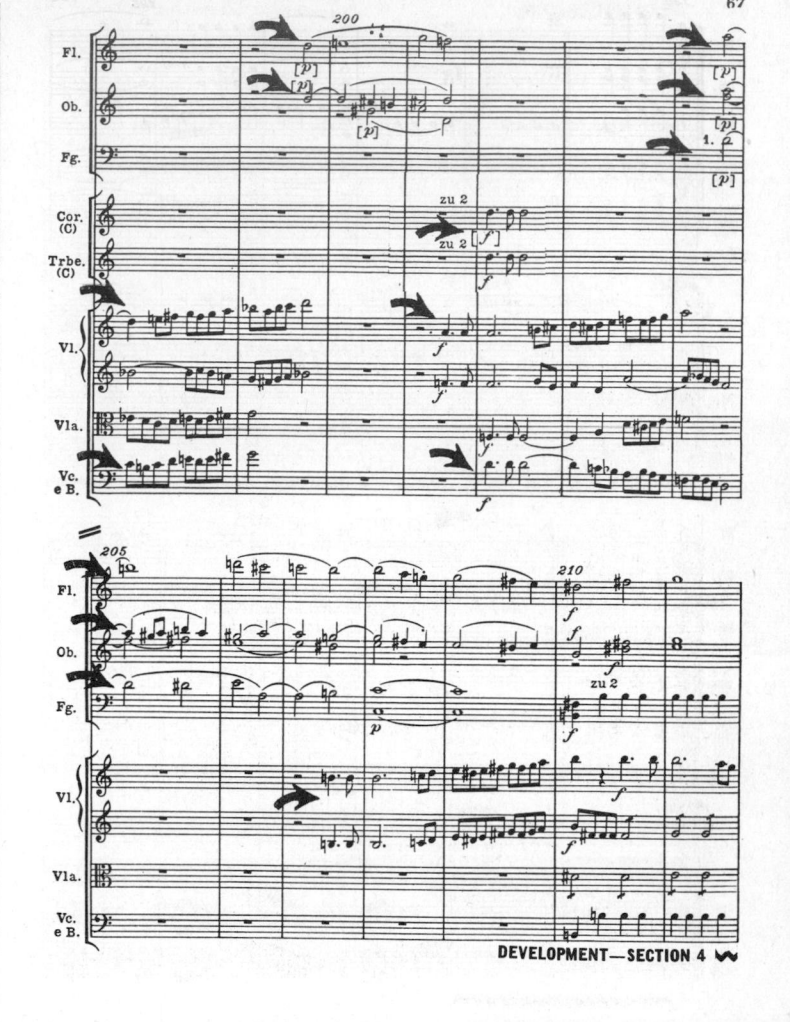

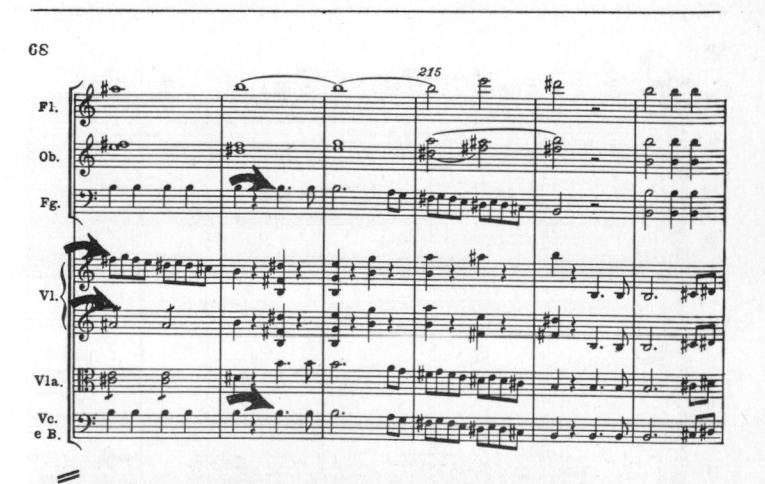

DEVELOPMENT—SECTION 4 〰

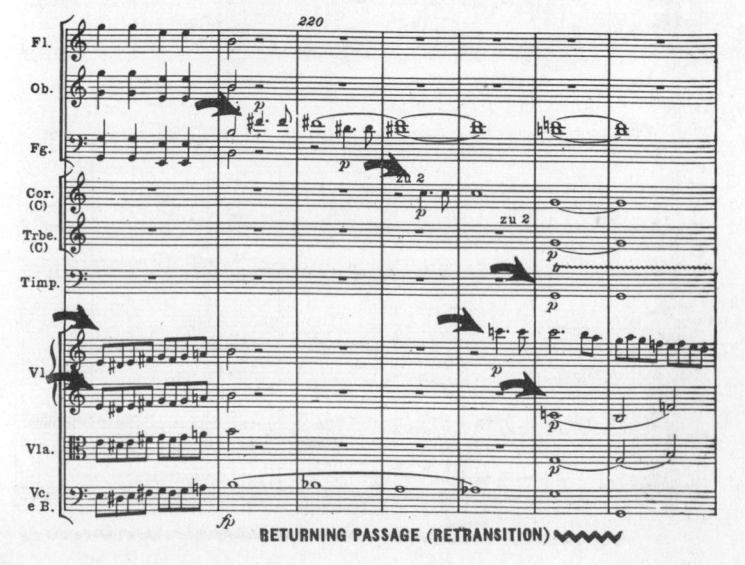

BETURNING PASSAGE (RETRANSITION) 〰〰

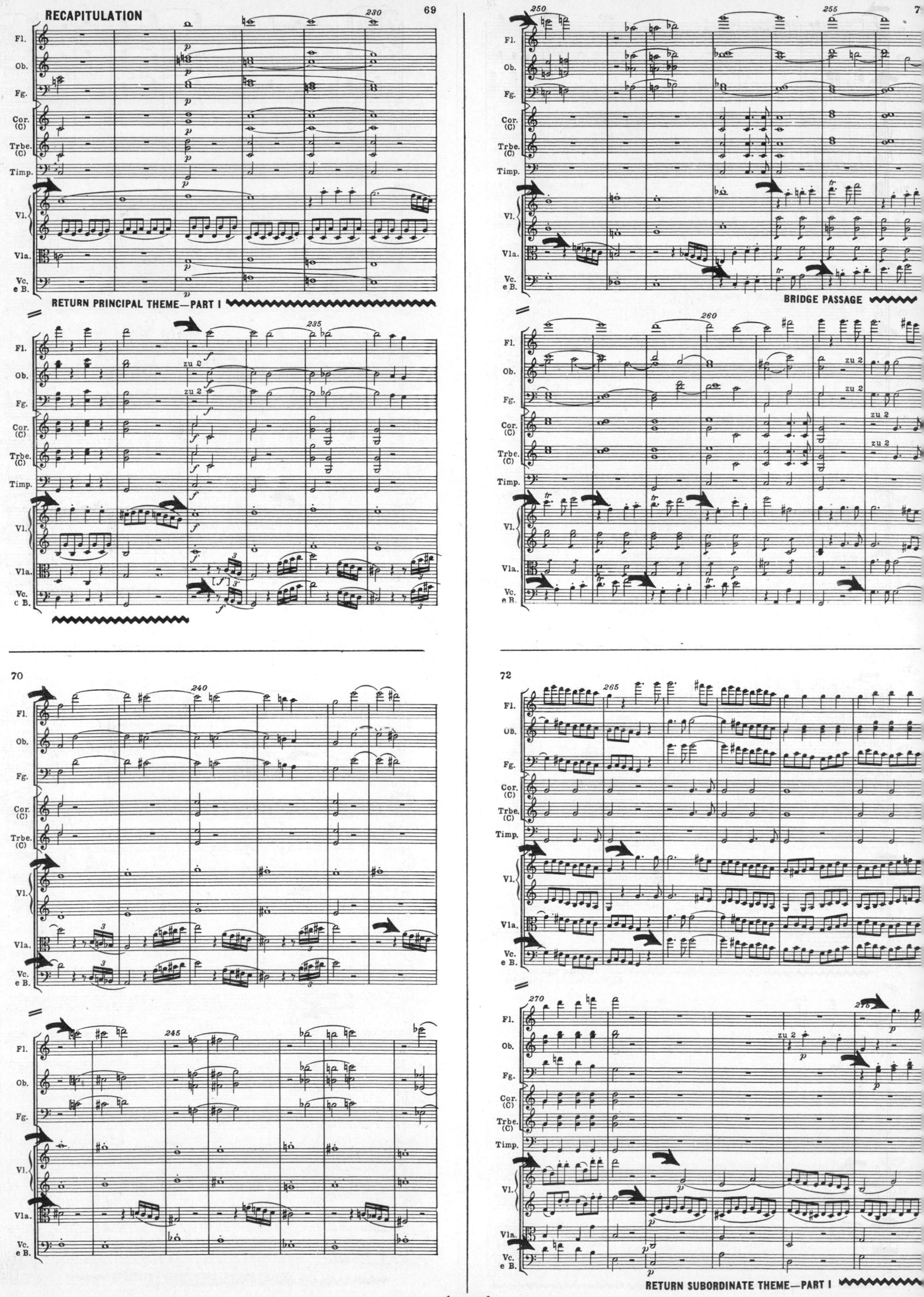

RECAPITULATION

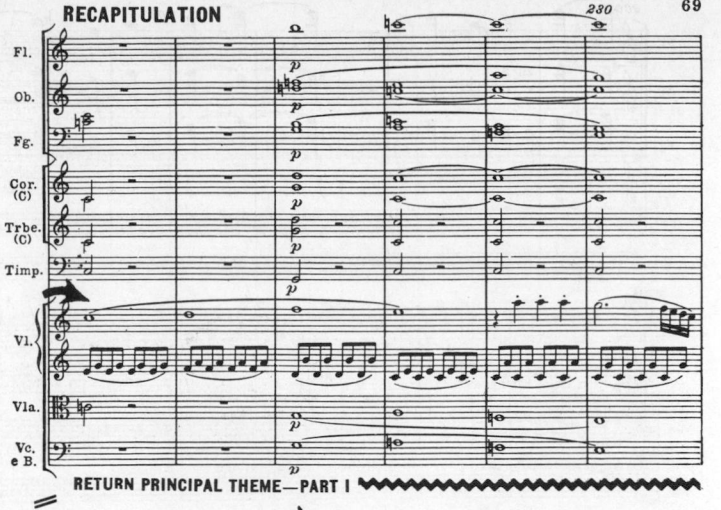

RETURN PRINCIPAL THEME—PART I 〰〰〰〰〰〰〰

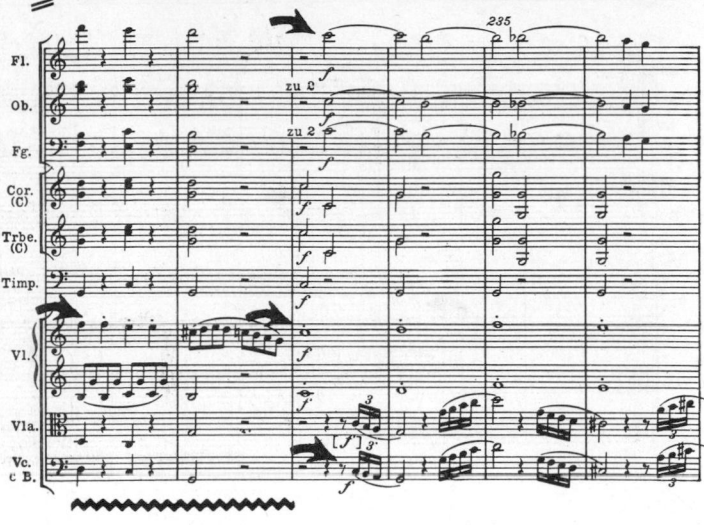

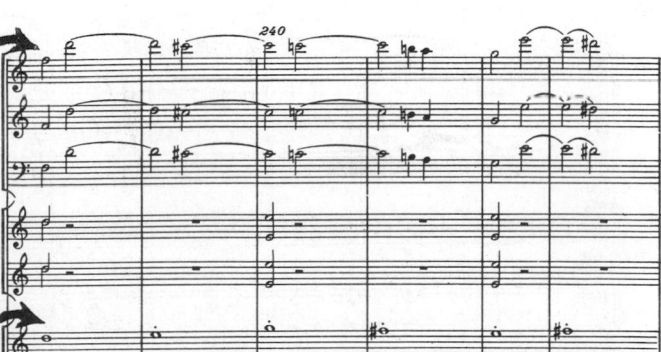

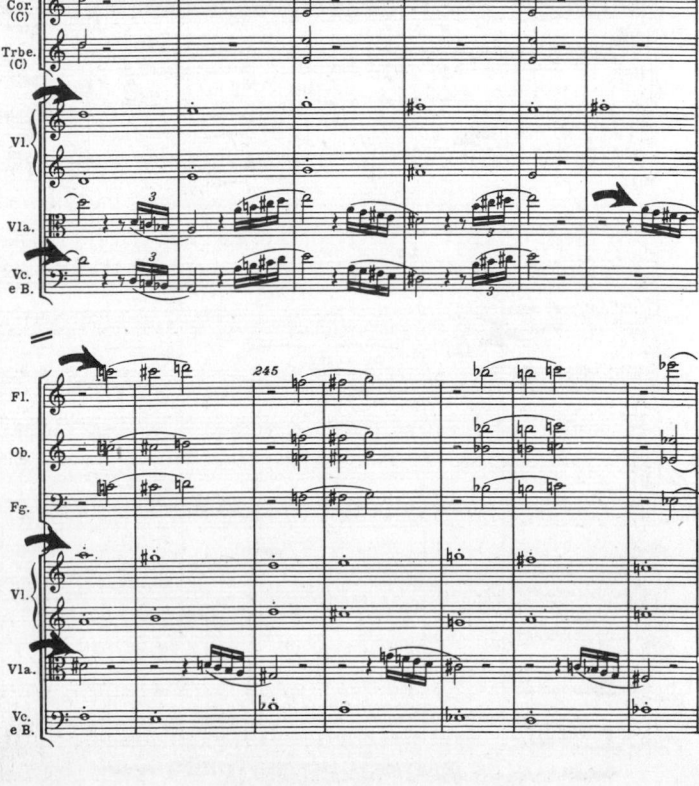

BRIDGE PASSAGE 〰〰

RETURN SUBORDINATE THEME—PART I 〰〰〰〰〰

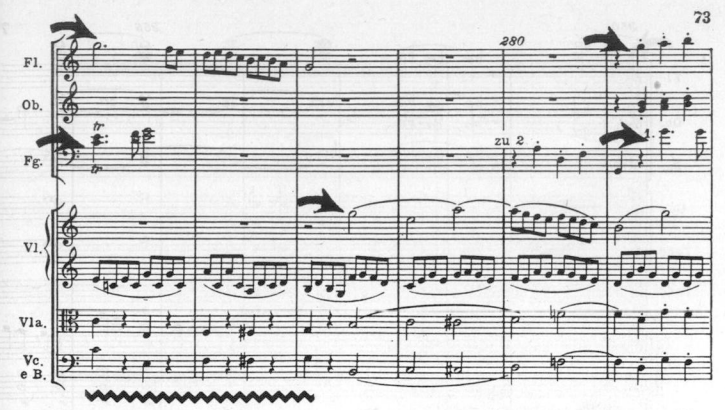

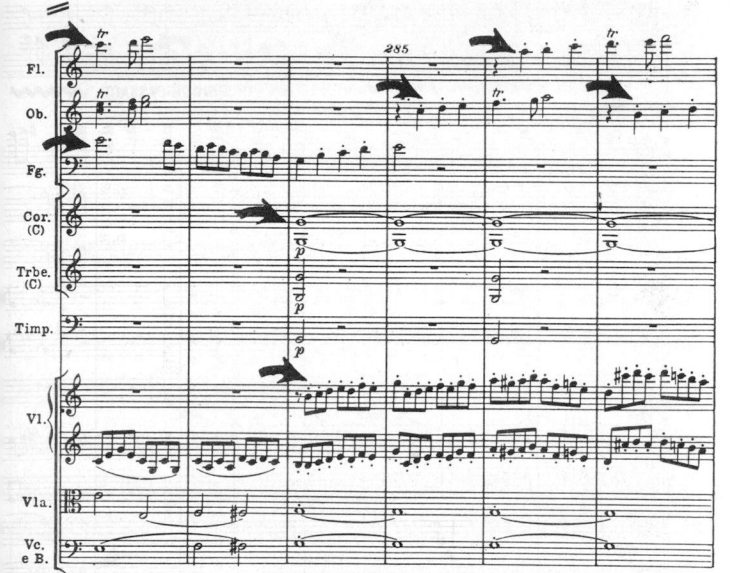

RETURN SUBORDINATE THEME—PART II ∿∿∿∿∿

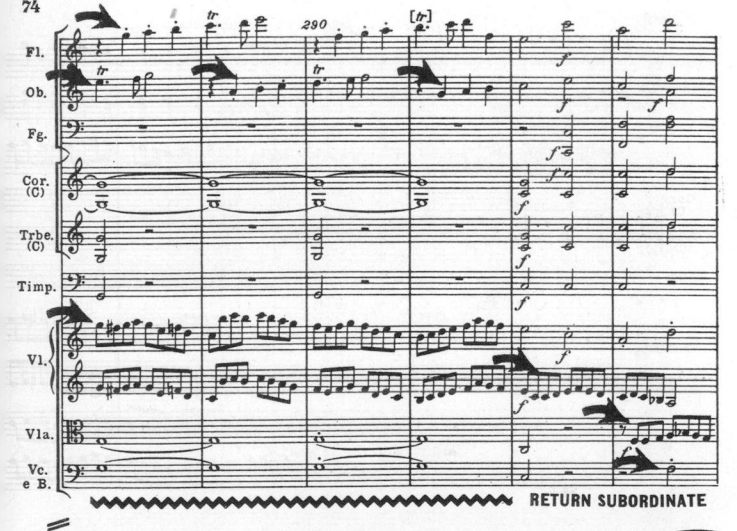

RETURN SUBORDINATE

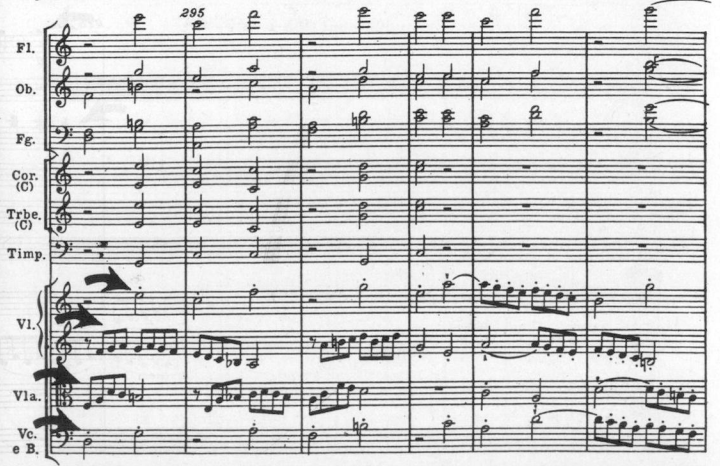

THEME—PART III ∿∿∿∿∿∿∿∿∿∿∿∿∿∿∿∿∿∿∿∿∿∿∿∿∿∿∿∿

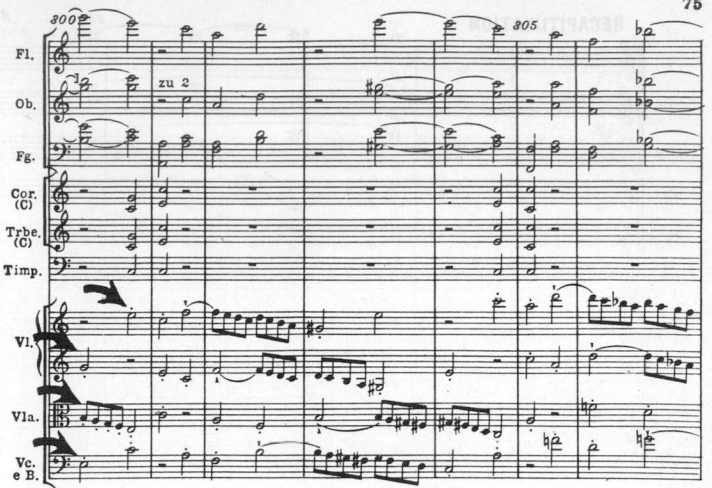

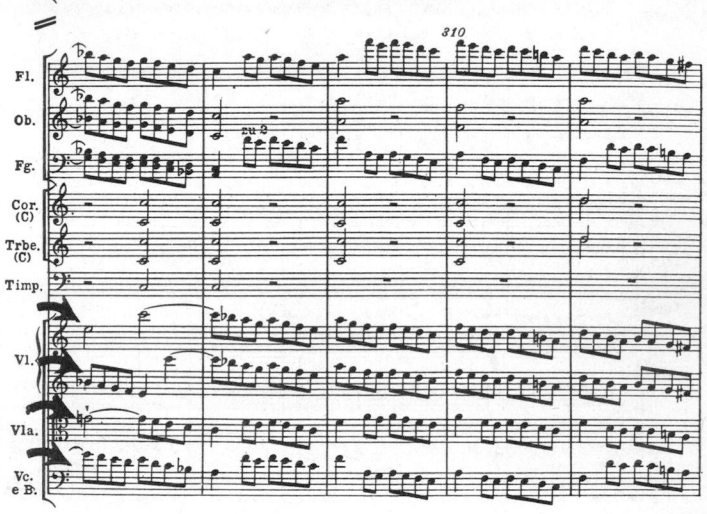

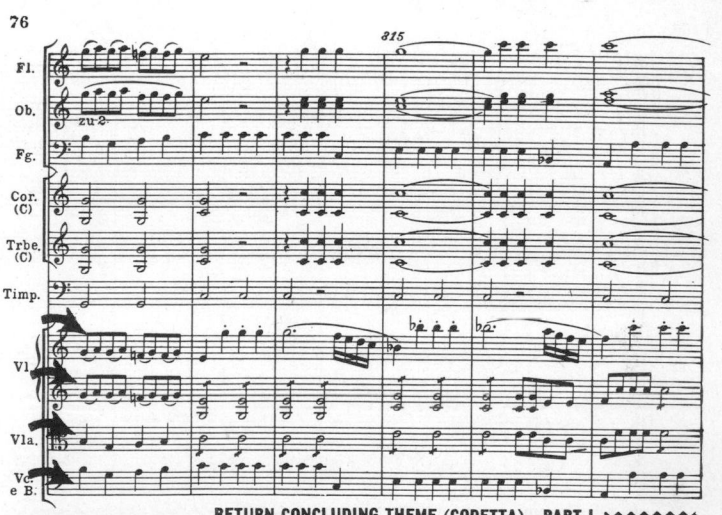

RETURN CONCLUDING THEME (CODETTA)—PART I ∿∿∿∿∿∿

77

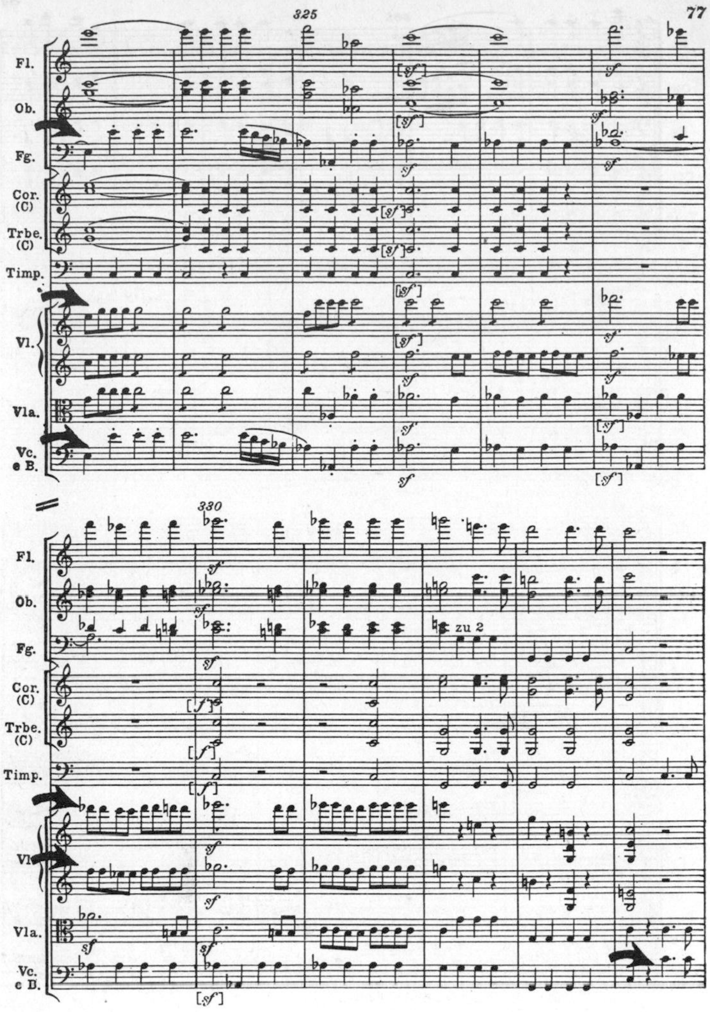
325
330
Fl.
Ob.
Fg.
Cor. (C)
Trbe. (C)
Timp.
Vl.
Vla.
Vc. e B.
zu 2

79

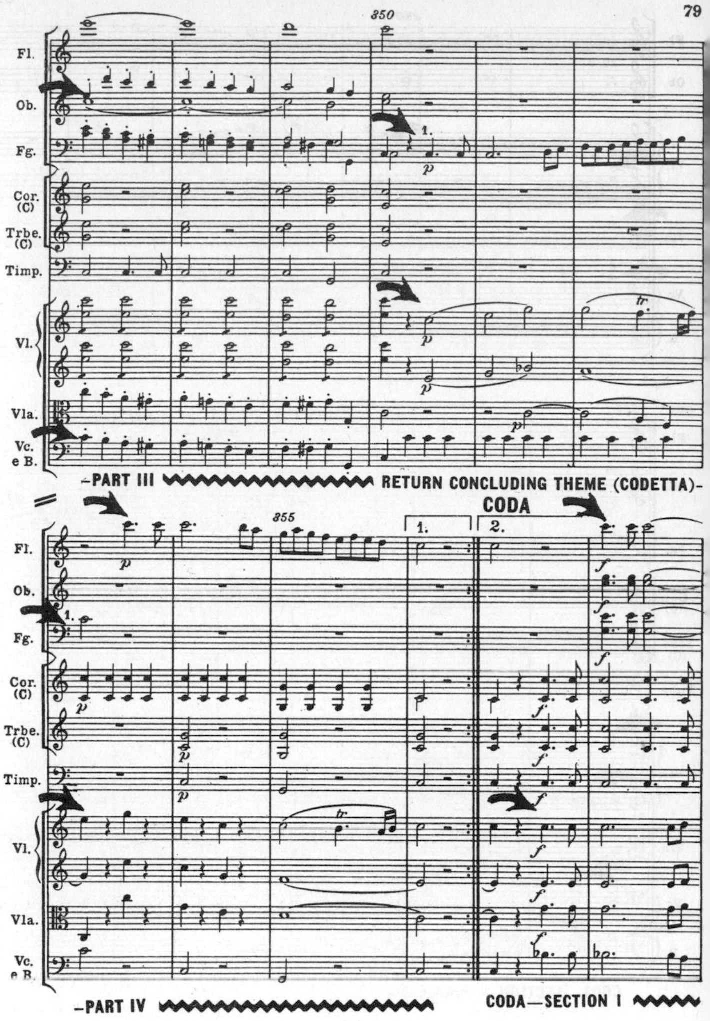
350
355
Fl.
Ob.
Fg.
Cor. (C)
Trbe. (C)
Timp.
Vl.
Vla.
Vc. e B.
–PART III
RETURN CONCLUDING THEME (CODETTA)–
CODA
1.
2.
–PART IV
CODA—SECTION I

78

835
340
345
zu 2
Fl.
Ob.
Fg.
Cor. (C)
Trbe. (C)
Timp.
Vl.
Vla.
Vc. e B.
RETURN CONCLUDING THEME (CODETTA)—PART II
RETURN CONCLUDING THEME (CODETTA)–

80

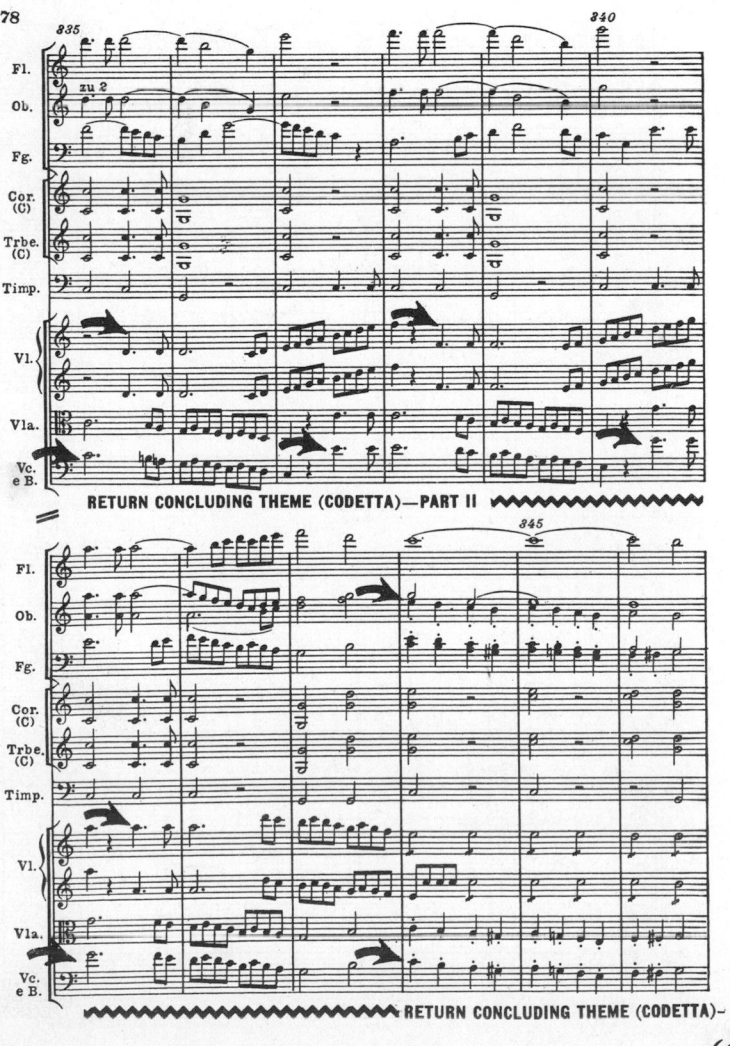

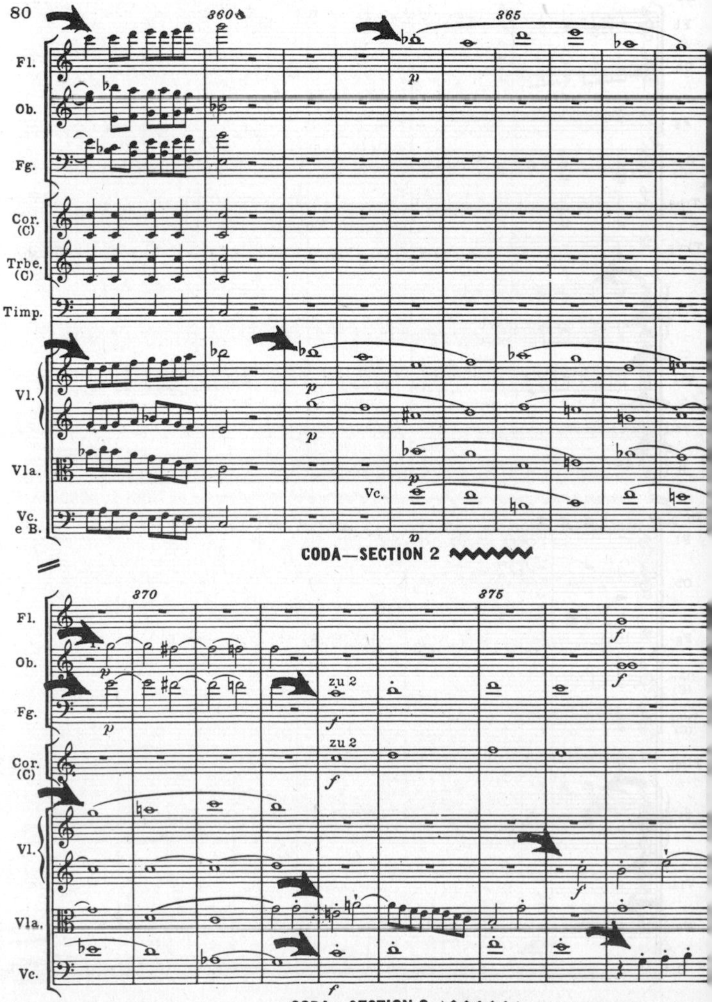
360
365
370
375
Fl.
Ob.
Fg.
Cor. (C)
Trbe. (C)
Timp.
Vl.
Vla.
Vc. e B.
Vc.
zu 2
CODA—SECTION 2
CODA—SECTION 3

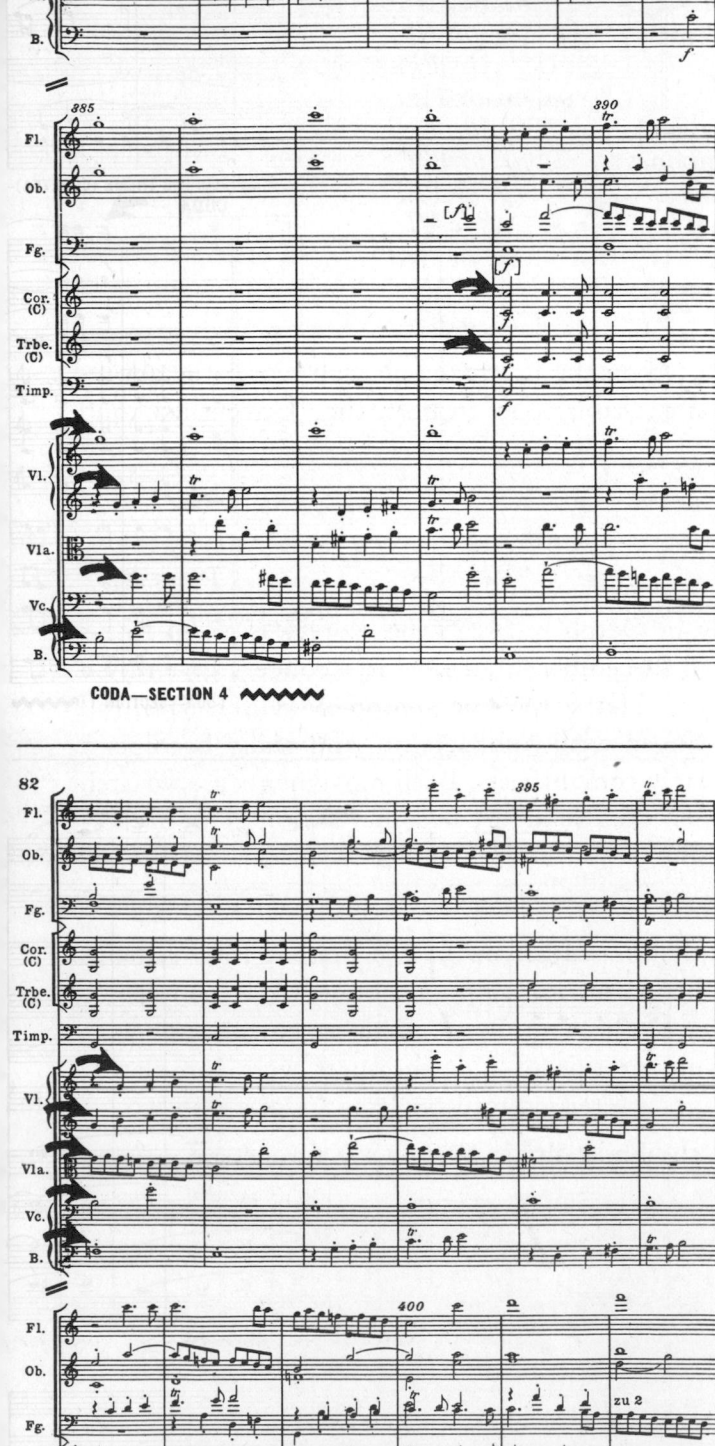
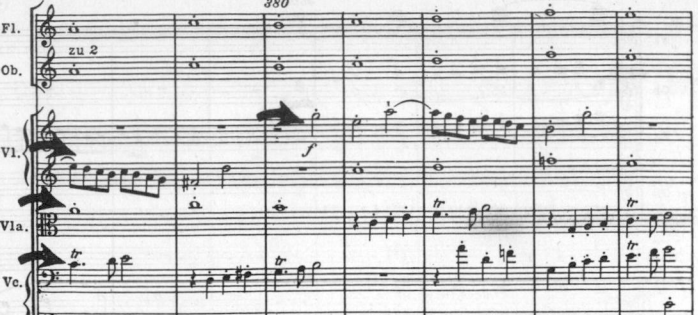

81

83

380

405

CODA—SECTION 5 〰〰〰

385   390

410

CODA—SECTION 4 〰〰〰

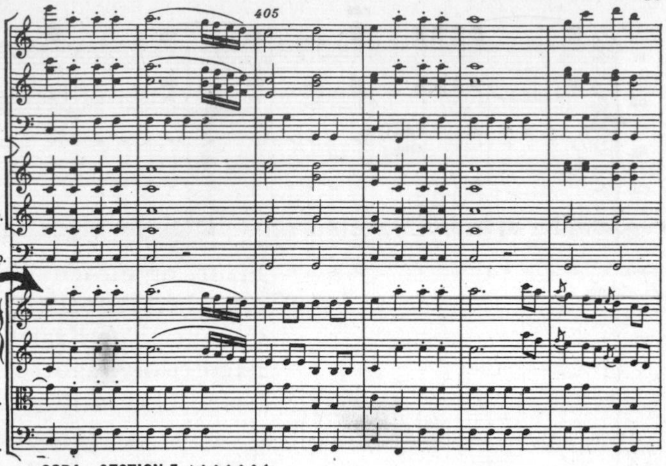

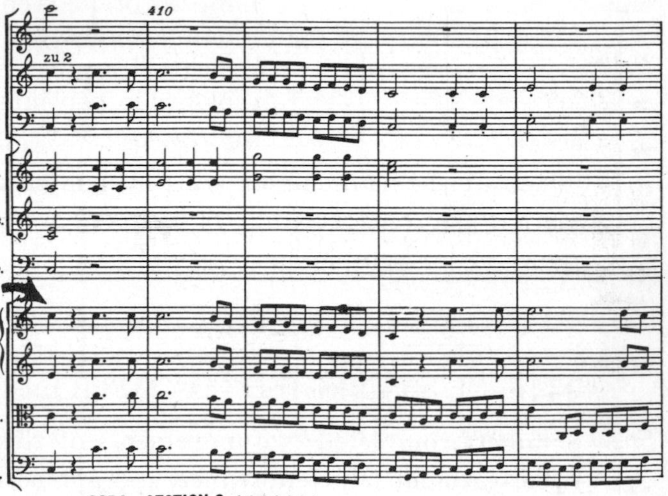

CODA—SECTION 6 〰〰〰

82

84

395   415

400   420

[Fine]

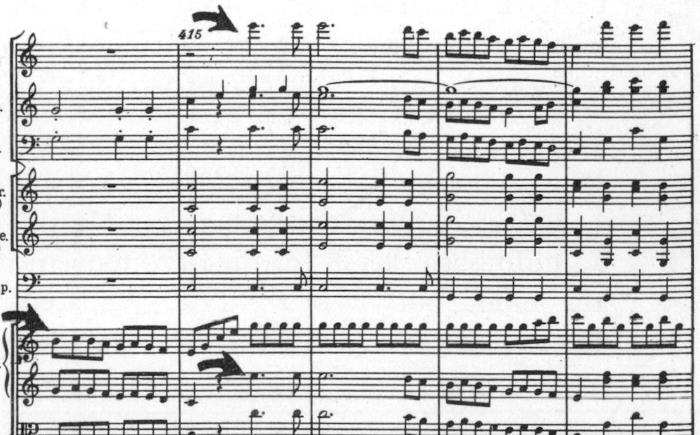

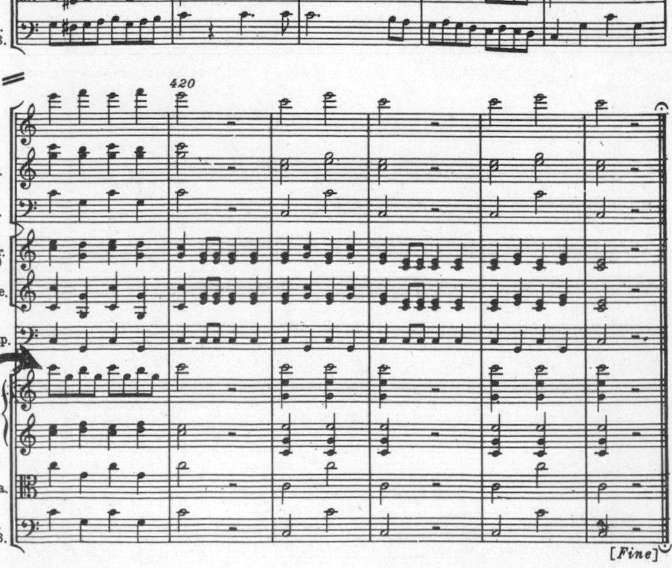

HISTORICAL AND CRITICAL COMMENT ON
SCHUBERT SYMPHONIES

The symphonies of Franz Peter Schubert were scored for the following instruments:

Flauti or Flöten (Flutes)	*Fl.*
Oboi or Hoboen (Oboes)	*Ob.* or *Hb.*
Clarinetti or Klarinetten (Clarinets)	*Cl.* or *Kl.*
Fagotti or Fagotte (Bassoons)	*Fg.*
Corni or Hörner (Horns)	*Cor.* or *Hr.*
Trombe or Trompeten (Trumpets)	*Tbe.* or *Tr.*
Tromboni or Posaunen (Trombones)	*Tbni.* or *Pos.*
Timpani or Pauken (Tympani)	*Timp.* or *Pk.*
Violini (Violins)	*Vl.*
Violi or Bratschen (Violas)	*Vla.* or *Br.*
Violoncello or Violoncelli	*Vc.*
Contrabasso or Kontrabässe	*Cb.* or *Kb.*

These are the names under which the instruments are listed on the first page of each score; the abbreviation used on succeeding pages follows. Schubert uses the trombones in both the "Unfinished" and the C Major Symphonies.

THE "UNFINISHED" SYMPHONY   Page 237

Schubert completed two movements of this symphony in October, 1822; the score was given to his friend, Anselm Hüttenbrenner, and not performed until December 17, 1865, at a concert given by a musical society in Vienna, under the direction of Johann Herbeck. The symphony differs from all other Schubert works of this kind in that it is deeply tinged with romanticism, and really becomes a bridge between the works of the late classicists and the early romanticists. Both movements are written in polyphonic style, but the instrumentation is so unusual that Schubert becomes a pioneer in orchestral tone painting for everyone who studies this score closely.

Why Schubert did not complete this symphony is a question which up to the present time remains unanswered. The Gesellschaft der Musikfreunde of Vienna has in its possession what is apparently an unfinished sketch for the third movement (*Scherzo*) of this symphony. This fragment ends with the middle portion of the Trio. Apparently the instrumentation of nine measures were completed; these measures, and also the three piano manuscript pages are reproduced on Page 235.

This symphony is recorded by Leopold Stokowski and the Philadelphia Symphony Orchestra.

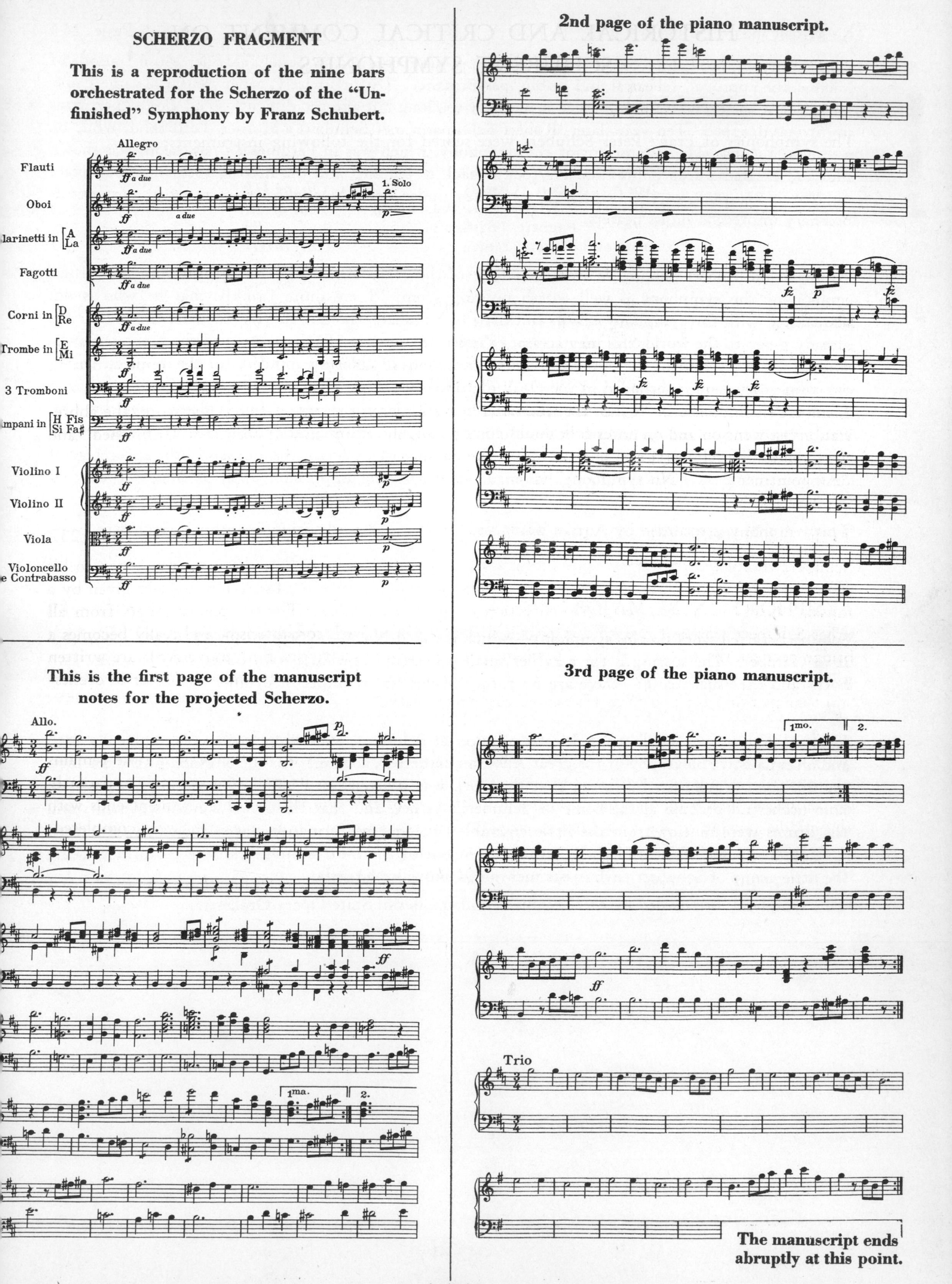

SCHERZO FRAGMENT

This is a reproduction of the nine bars orchestrated for the Scherzo of the "Unfinished" Symphony by Franz Schubert.

2nd page of the piano manuscript.

This is the first page of the manuscript notes for the projected Scherzo.

3rd page of the piano manuscript.

The manuscript ends abruptly at this point.

(235)

SYMPHONY IN C MAJOR Page 253

This symphony was completed in March, 1828, and submitted to the Gesselschaft der Musikfreunde of Vienna for approval, rehearsal and public performance. Unfortunately, when rehearsal time came, members of the orchestra pronounced it not only too long but also too difficult, so all idea of performing it was dropped. Ten years later, Robert Schumann met Schubert's brother, Ferdinand, while on a visit to Vienna. The manuscript of the symphony, which was in Ferdinand's possession, was shown him and created a deep impression. He took it back to Leipzig, and the first performance took place on March 21, 1839, in the Leipzig Gewandhaus under Felix Mendelssohn, creating a most extraordinary impression on its hearers.

At that time Robert Schumann was the editor of the *Neue Zeitschrift Für Musik*, and his critical opinion of this symphony is well worth quoting from: "I say quite frankly that he who is not acquainted with this symphony knows but little of Schubert, though, in view of what the master has already given to the world, this may appear exaggerated praise. Herein is revealed the finest technical skill, life in every fibre of the music, the finest gradations of coloring and care for the minutest detail; the whole structure is shrouded in the cloak of romanticism which has now become familiar to us in Schubert's compositions. It has, too, the same heavenly length as, say, a four-volume novel by Jean Paul, who went on and on and never could come to an end. How gratifying to the ear is this wealth of invention in Schubert; and how we dread the coming to a close in the works of others, for fear of disappointment! . . . No symphony has made such a strong impression upon us since the days of Beethoven".

This symphony is recorded by Adrian Boult and the British Broadcasting Symphony Orchestra.

SYMPHONY IN Bb MAJOR Page 320

Schubert started work on this symphony—which is called No. 5—in September, 1816, and completed it in October. The scoring is for a rather small orchestra—one flute, two oboes, two bassoons, two horns and the usual strings—there are no parts for clarinet, trumpet or drums.

Heinrich Kreissle von Hellborn, a devoted admirer of Schubert, who wrote both a biographical sketch and an exhaustive biography of the great Austrian composer, accounts for the omission of the clarinet, trumpet and drum parts by saying that the work was written for a circle of amateurs who used to hold orchestral practise at the home of Schubert's father, and that these two wind instruments and the drums were missing from the little ensemble. Its first performance was supposed to have been given at the home of Otto Hadwig, a member of one of the theatre orchestras, the performers being the little group of Schubert enthusiasts mentioned above by Kreissle.

This symphony is recorded by Dr. Leo Blech and the Berlin State Opera Orchestra.

Unfinished Symphony

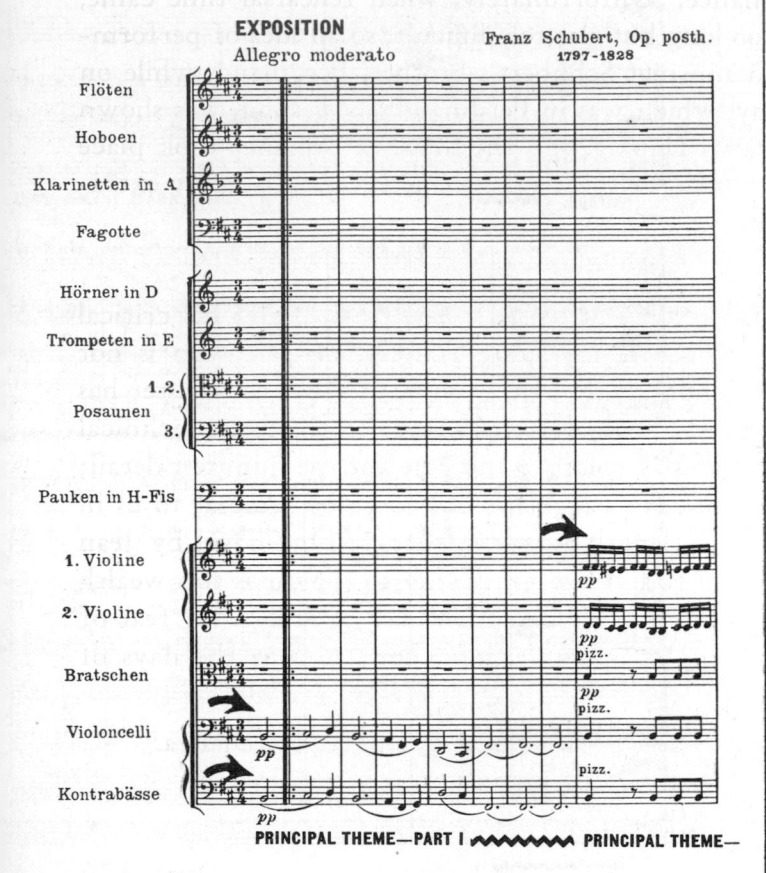

EXPOSITION
Allegro moderato

Franz Schubert, Op. posth.
1797-1828

Flöten
Hoboen
Klarinetten in A
Fagotte
Hörner in D
Trompeten in E
1.2. Posaunen 3.
Pauken in H-Fis
1. Violine
2. Violine
Bratschen
Violoncelli
Kontrabässe

PRINCIPAL THEME—PART I ∿∿∿∿∿ PRINCIPAL THEME—

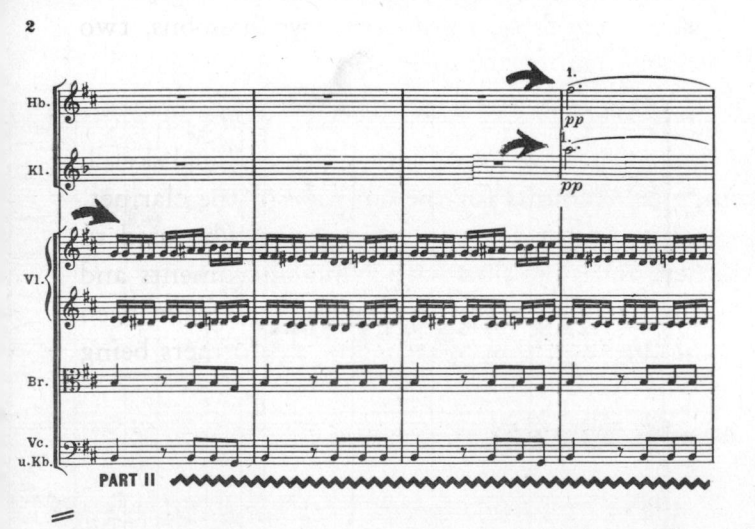

PART II ∿∿∿∿∿∿∿∿∿∿∿∿∿∿∿∿∿∿∿∿∿∿∿

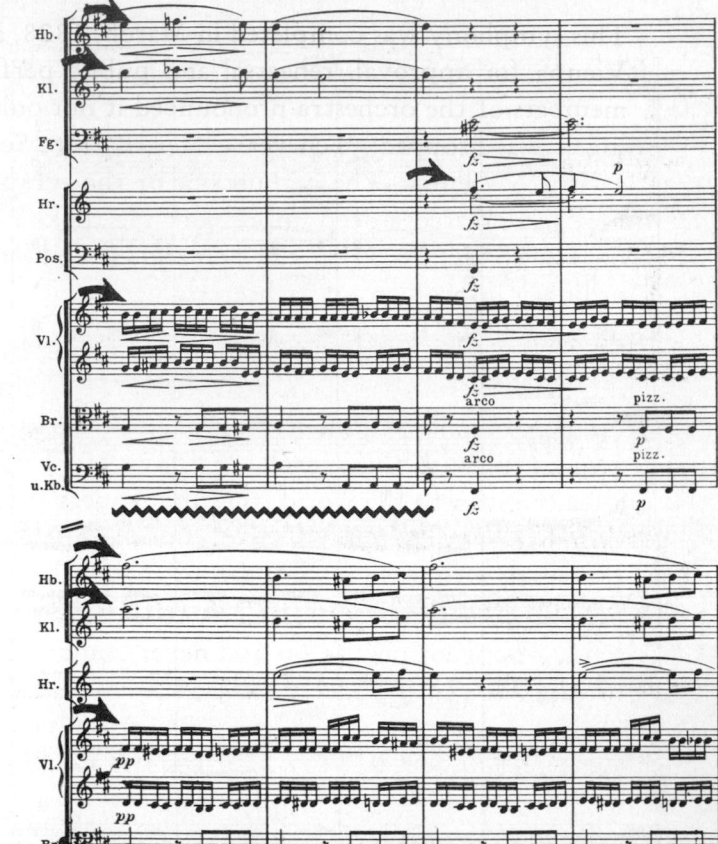

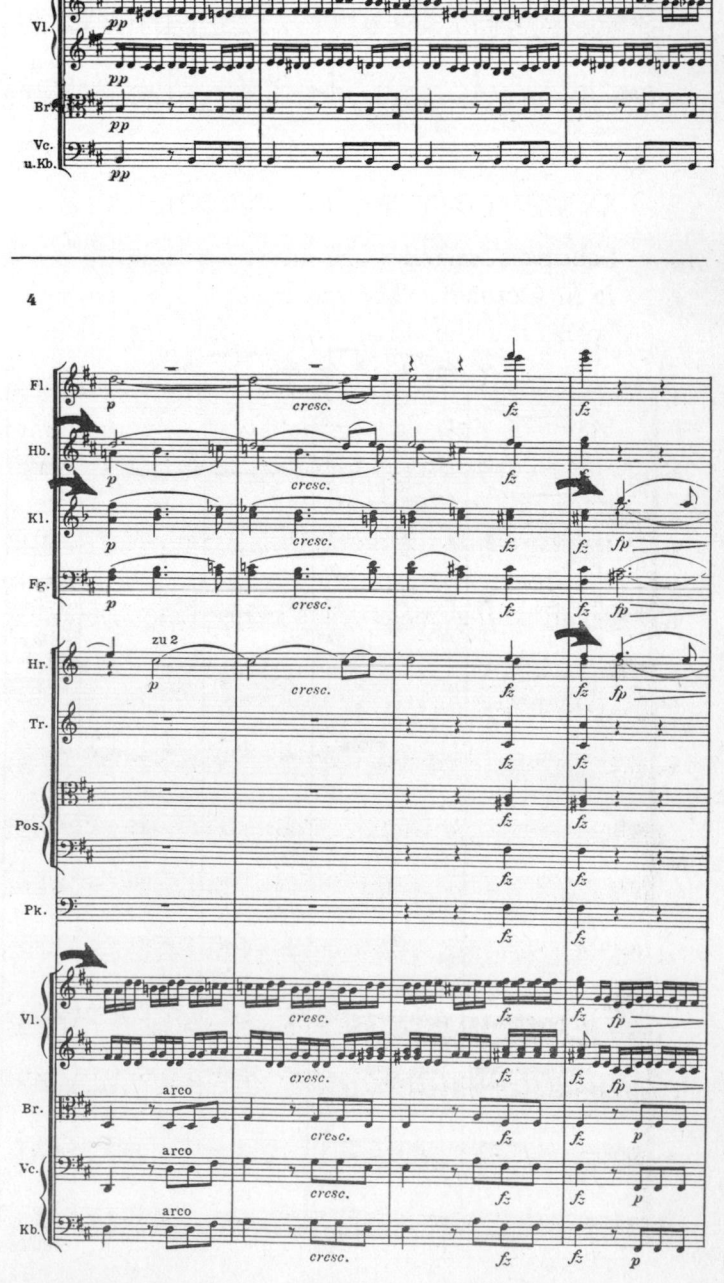

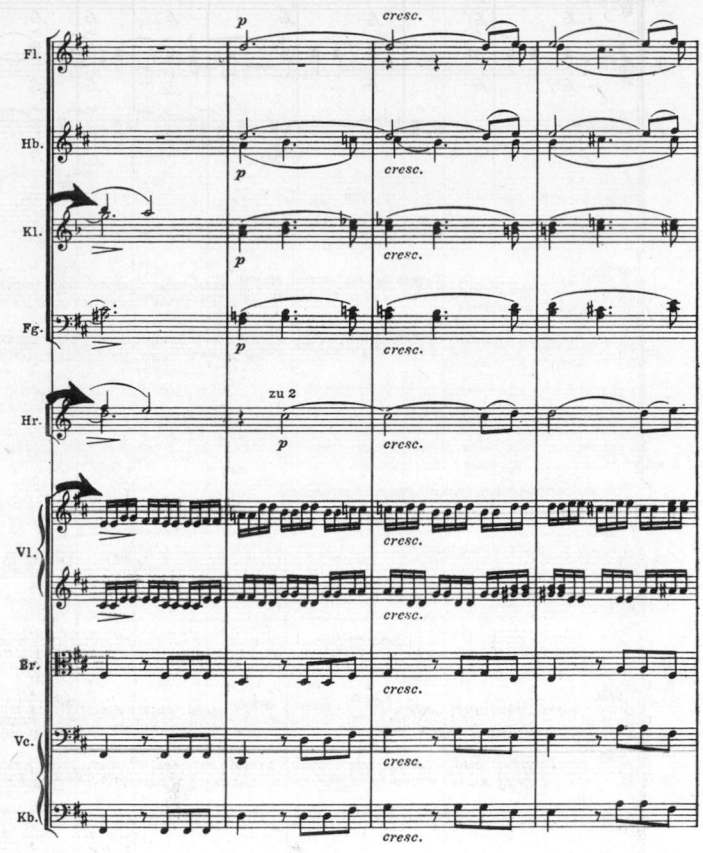

5

Fl.
Hb.
Kl.
Fg.
Hr.
Vl.
Br.
Vc.
Kb.
cresc.
zu 2

7

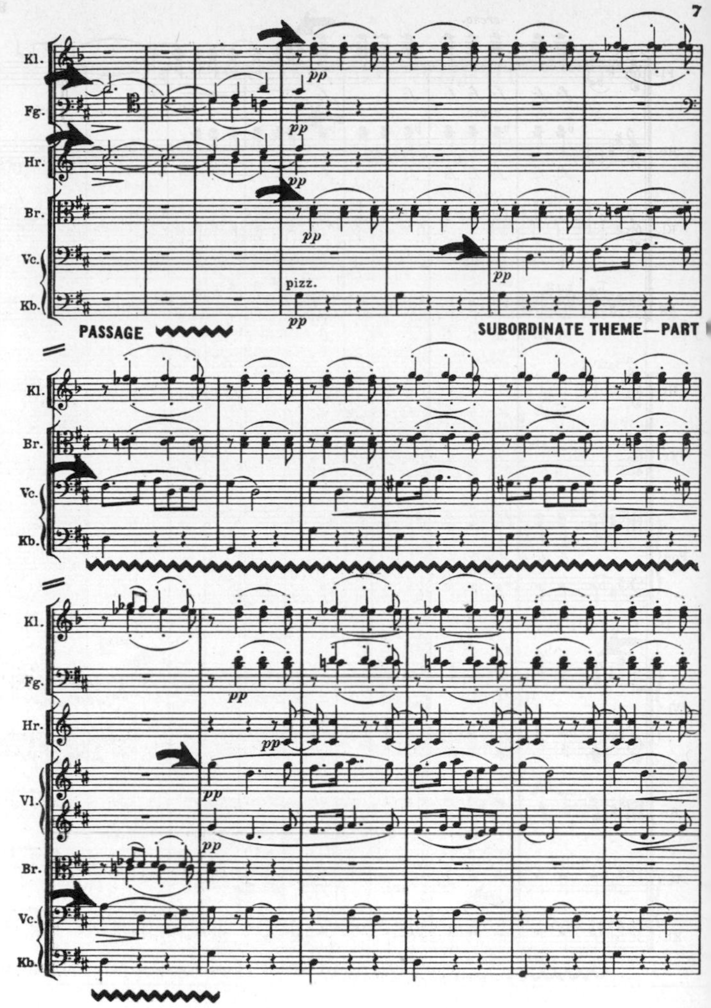
Kl.
Fg.
Hr.
Br.
Vc.
Kb.
pizz.
PASSAGE
SUBORDINATE THEME—PART I
Vl.

6

Fl.
Hb.
Kl.
Fg.
Hr.
Tr.
Pos.
Pk.
Vl.
Br.
Vc. u. Kb.
BRIDGE

8

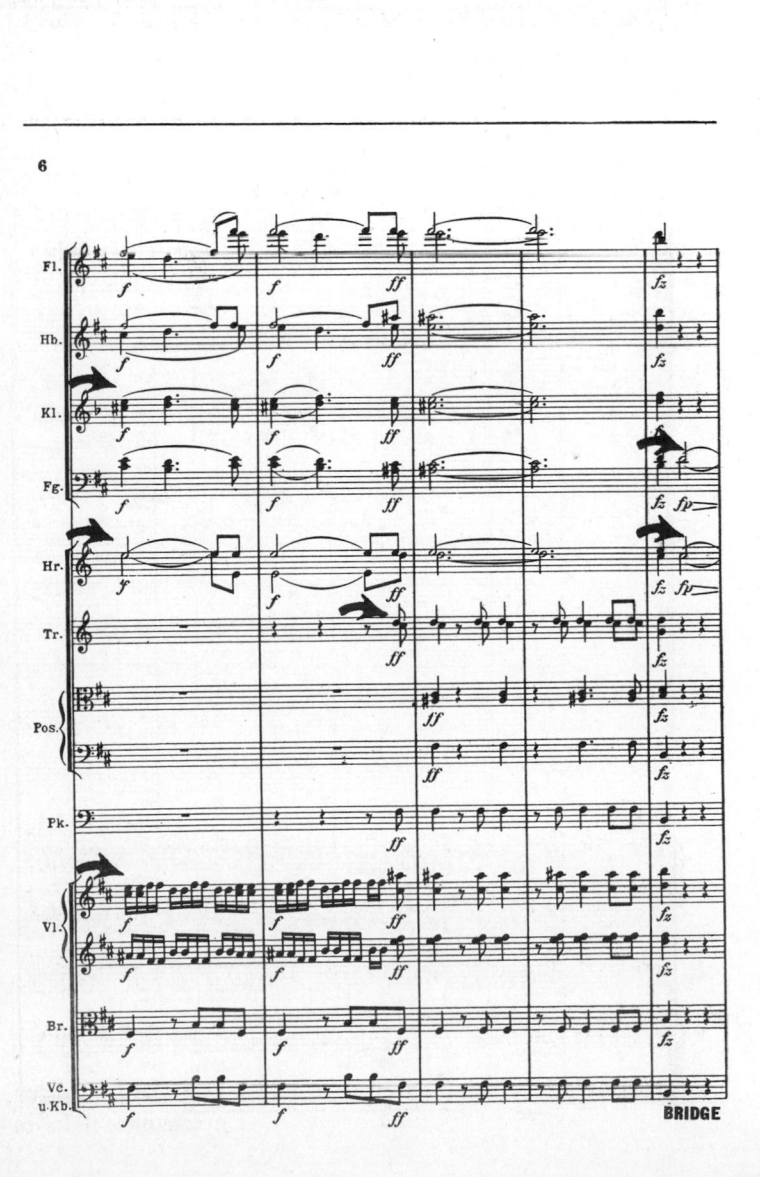

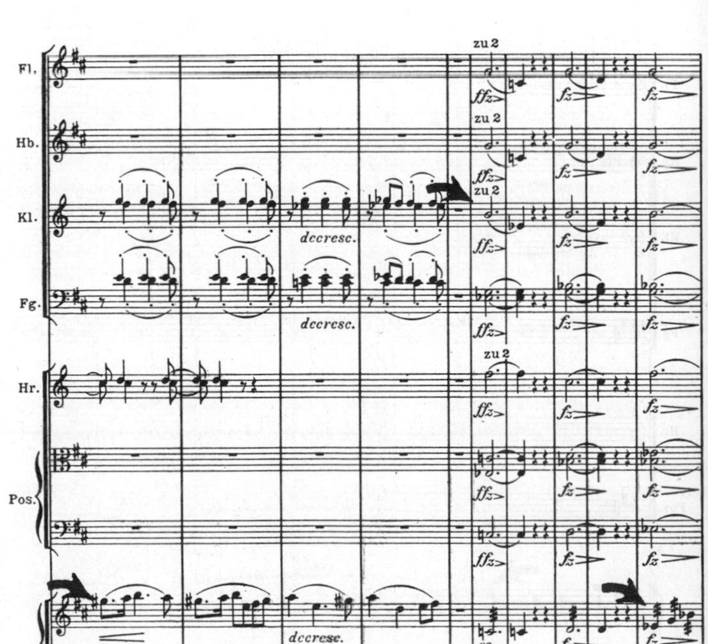
Fl.
Hb.
Kl.
Fg.
Hr.
Pos.
Vl.
Br.
Vc.
Kb.
zu 2
decresc.
arco
SUBORDINATE THEME—PART II

9

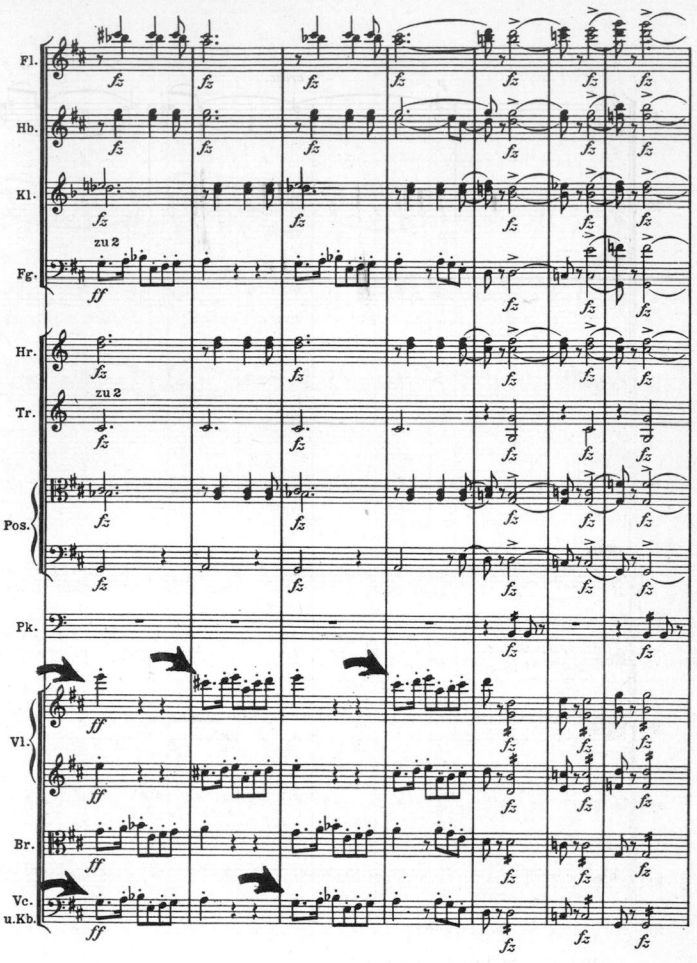

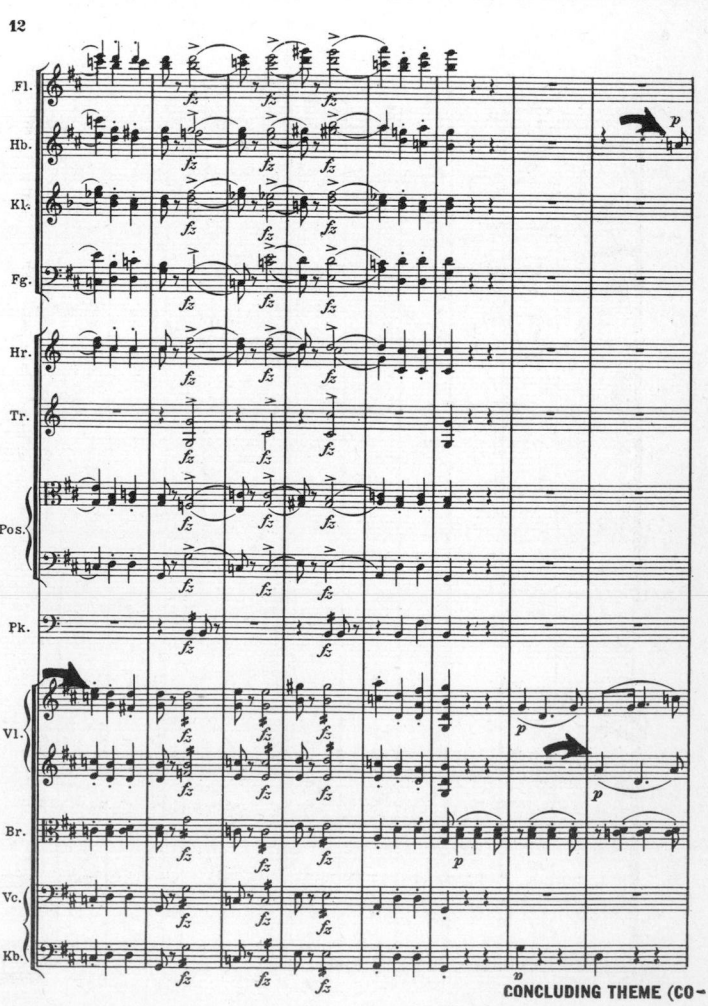

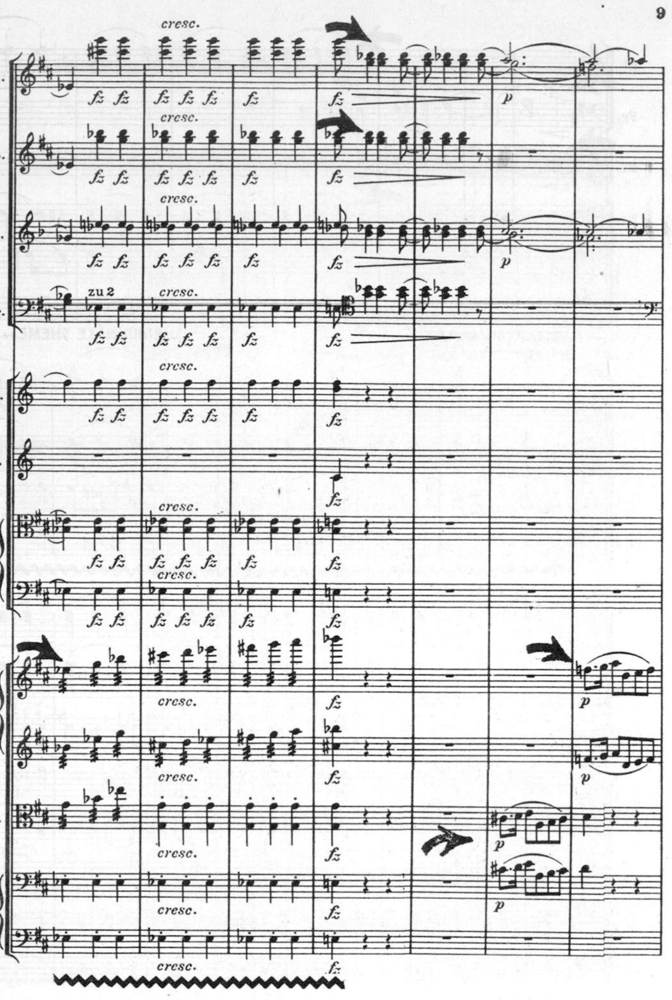

11

10

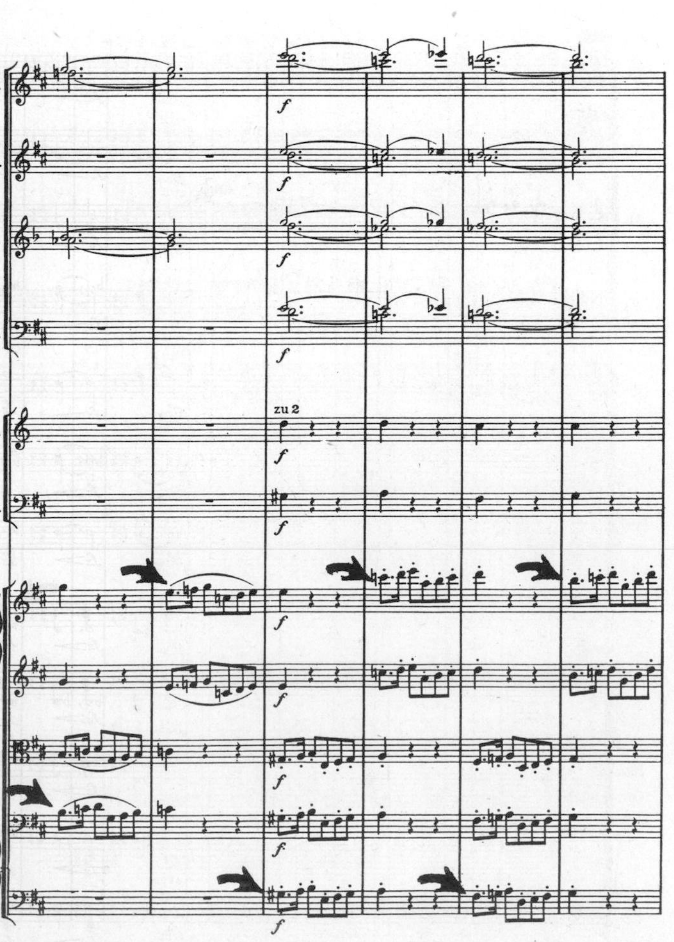

12

CONCLUDING THEME (CO-

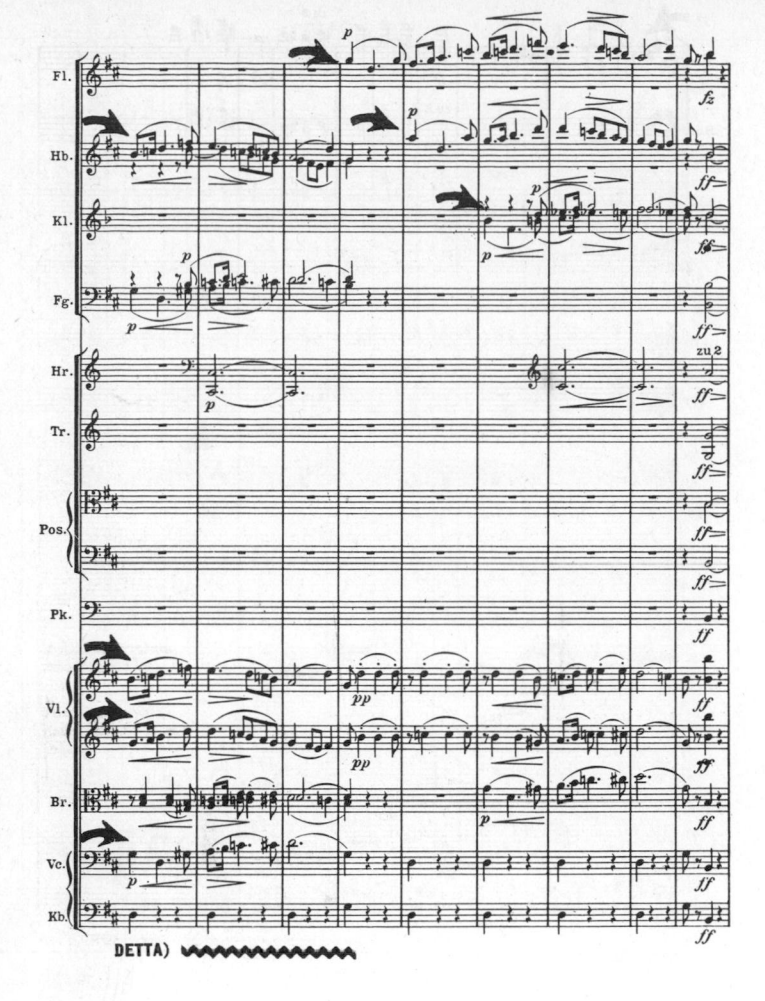

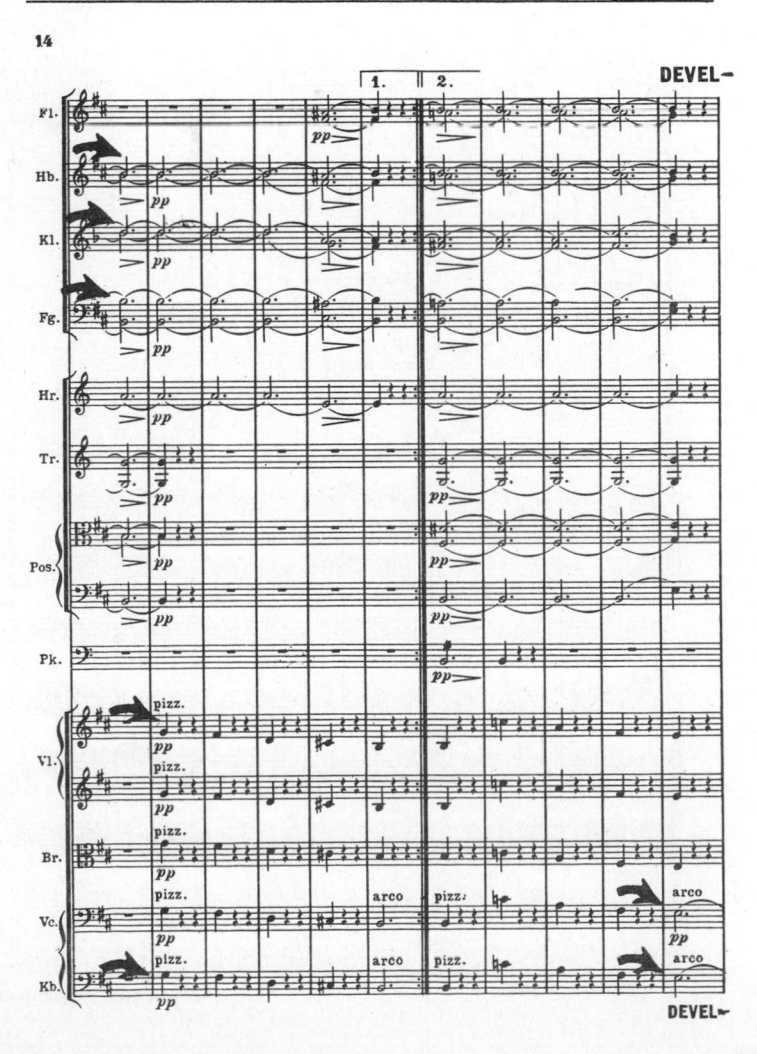

OPMENT

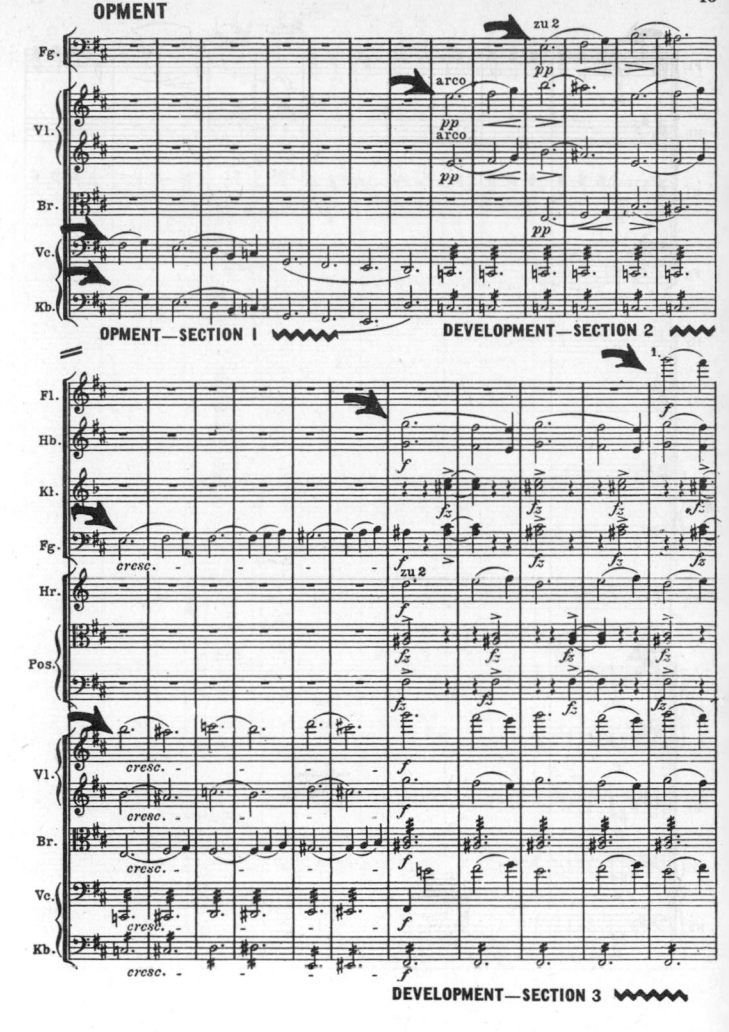

DEVEL-

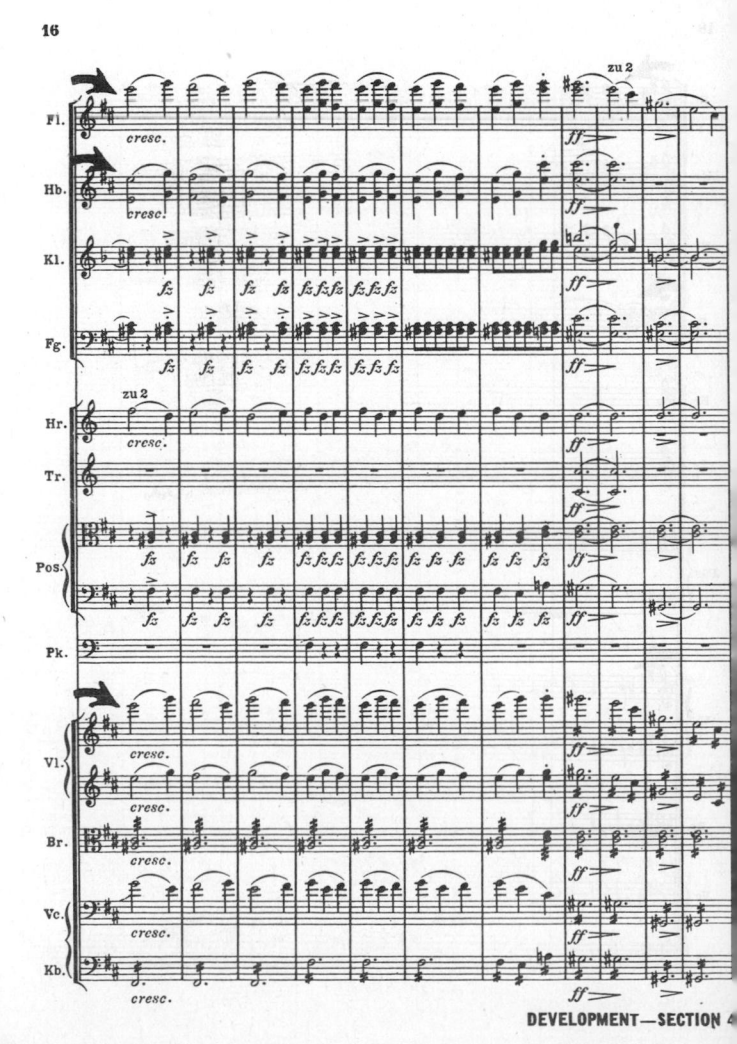

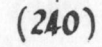

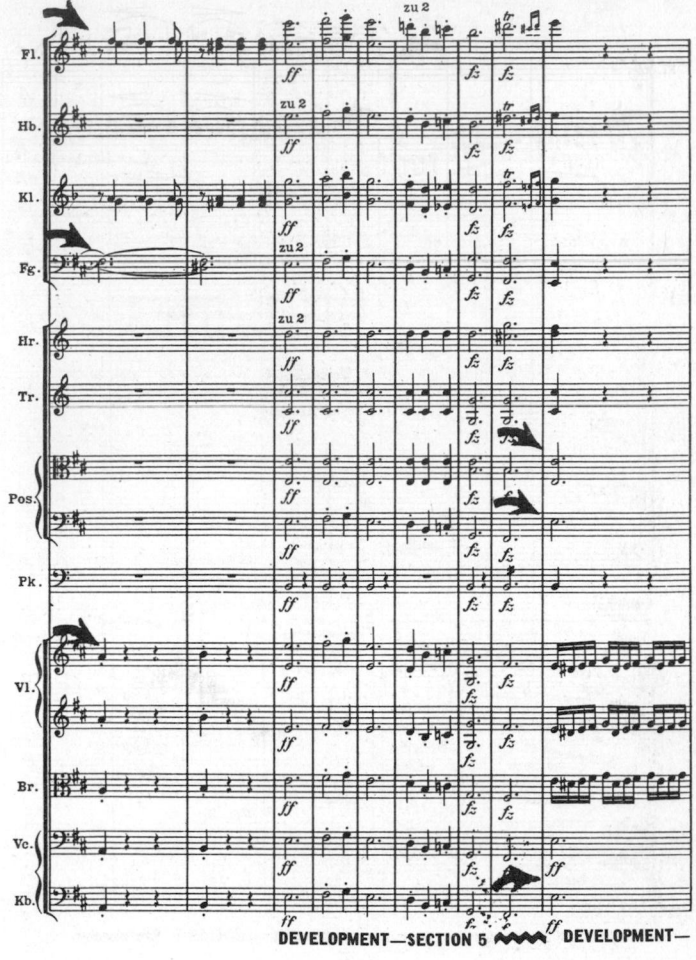

17

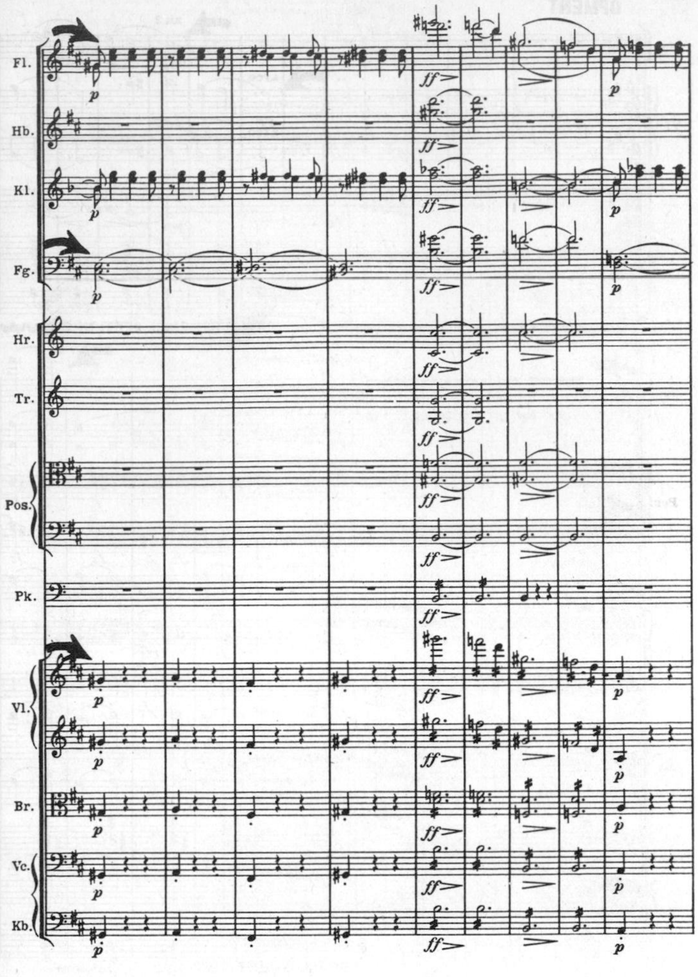
Fl.
Hb.
Kl.
Fg.
Hr.
Tr.
Pos.
Pk.
Vl.
Br.
Vc.
Kb.
p
ff

19

Fl.
Hb.
Kl.
Fg.
Hr.
Tr.
Pos.
Pk.
Vl.
Br.
Vc.
Kb.
zu 2
tr.
ff
fz
DEVELOPMENT—SECTION 5
DEVELOPMENT—

18

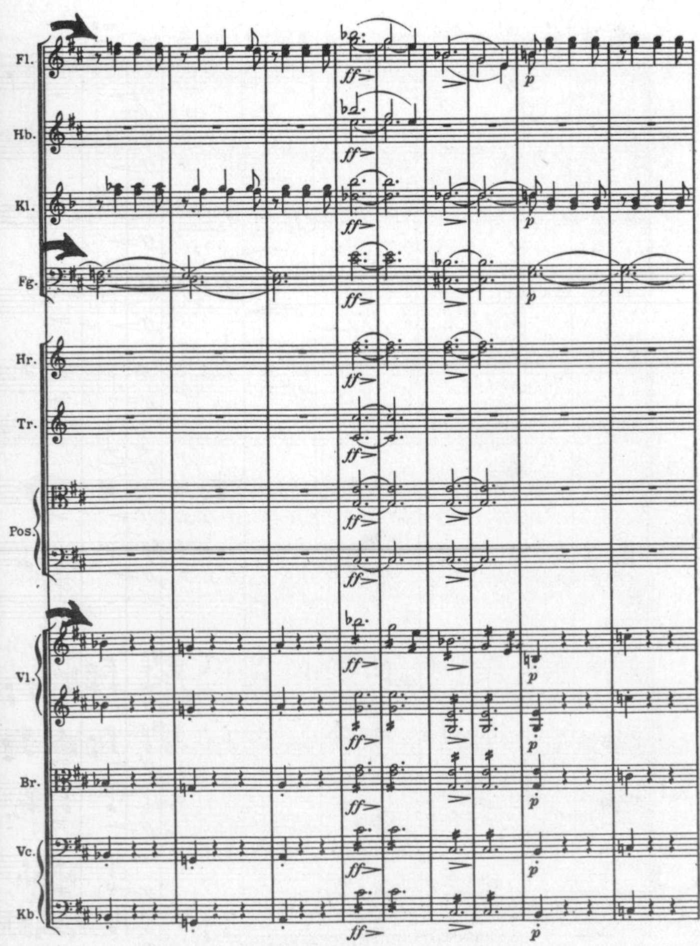
Fl.
Hb.
Kl.
Fg.
Hr.
Tr.
Pos.
Vl.
Br.
Vc.
Kb.
p
ff

20

Fl.
Hb.
Kl.
Fg.
Hr.
Tr.
Pos.
Pk.
Vl.
Br.
Vc.
Kb.
zu 2
SECTION 6

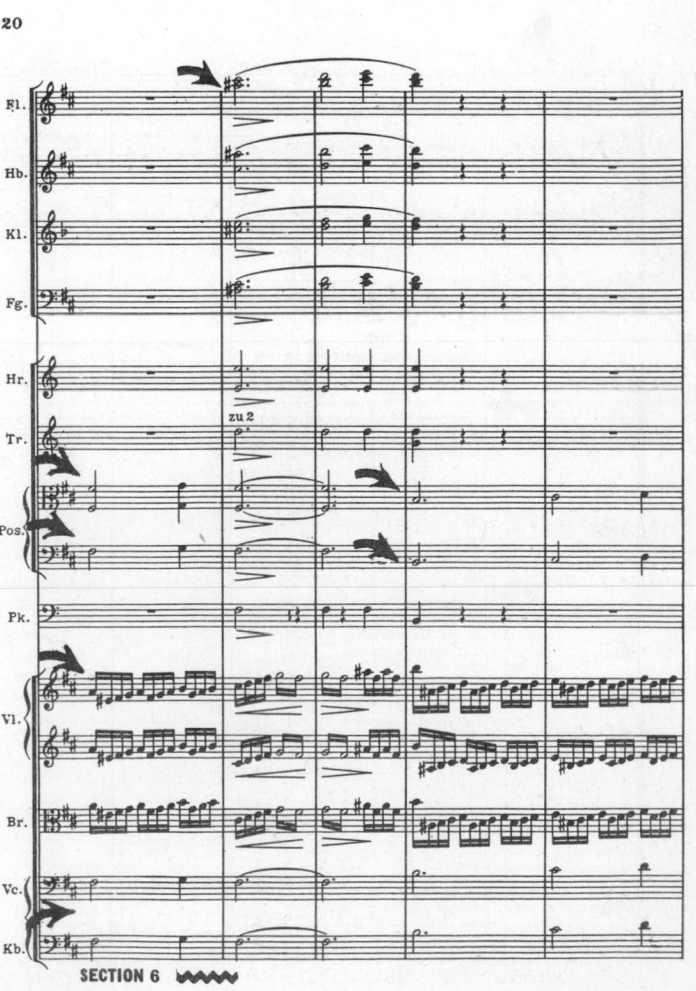

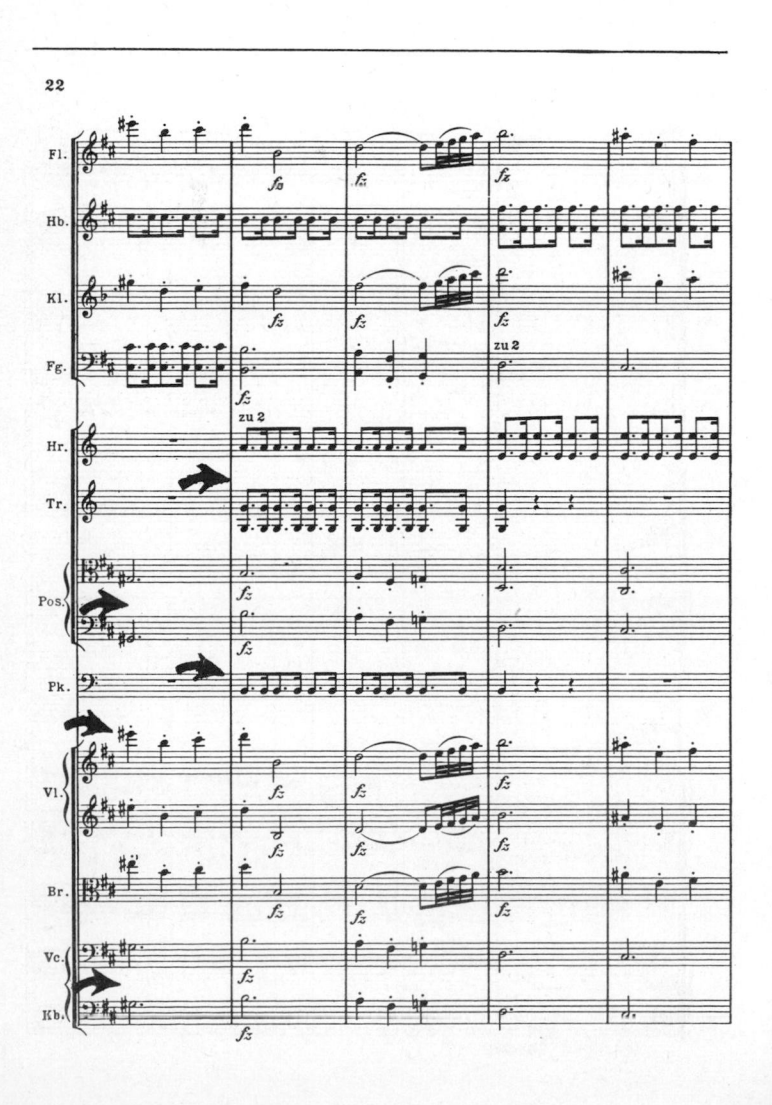

21

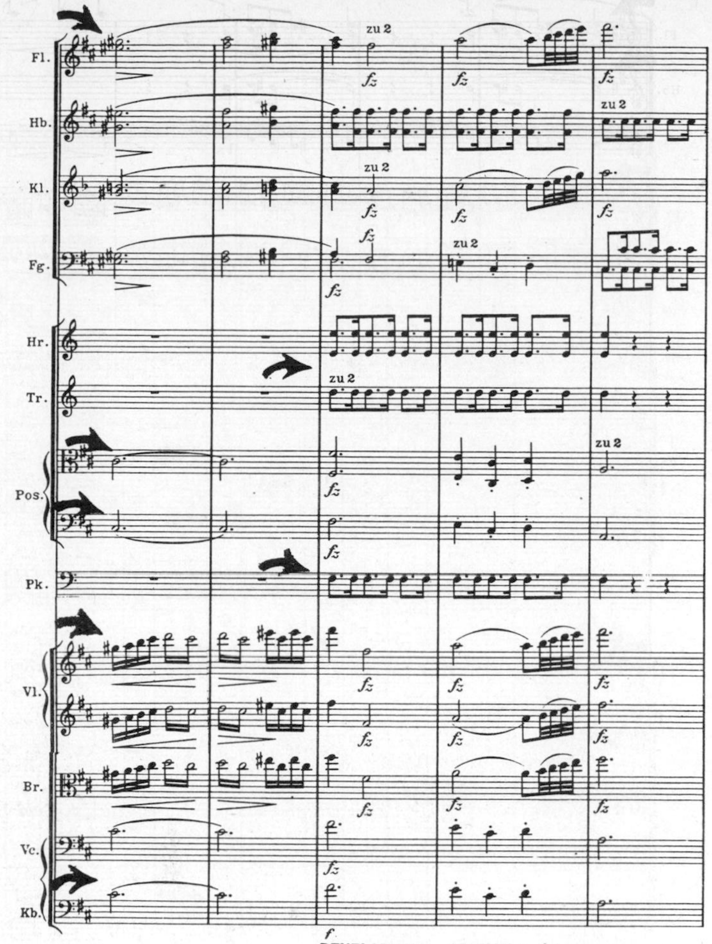

DEVELOPMENT—SECTION 7

23

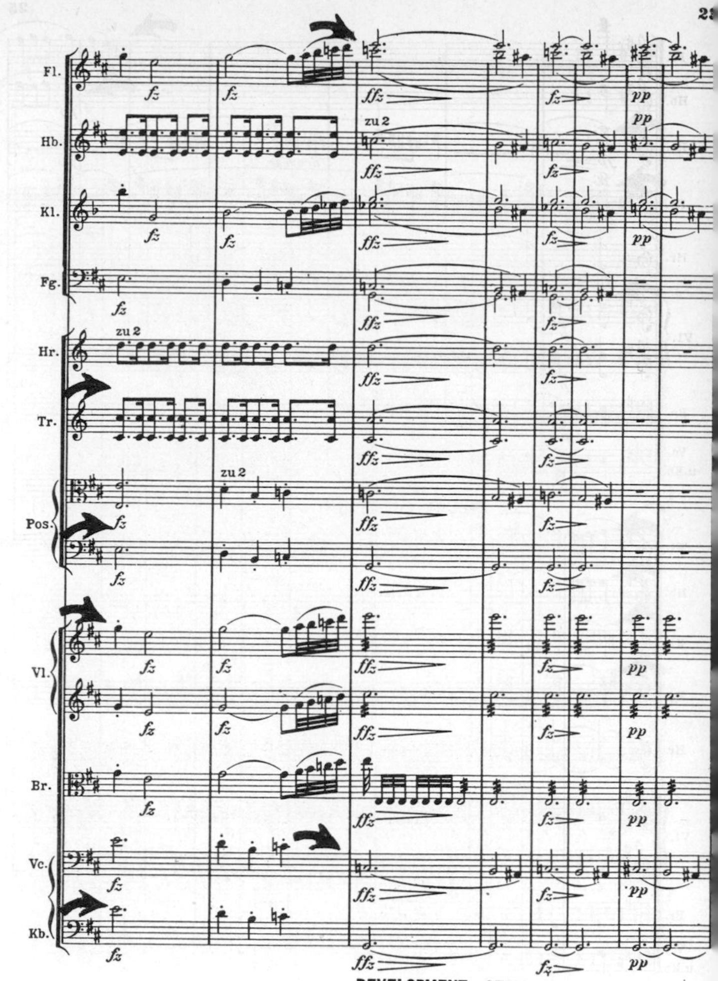

DEVELOPMENT—SECTION 8

22

24

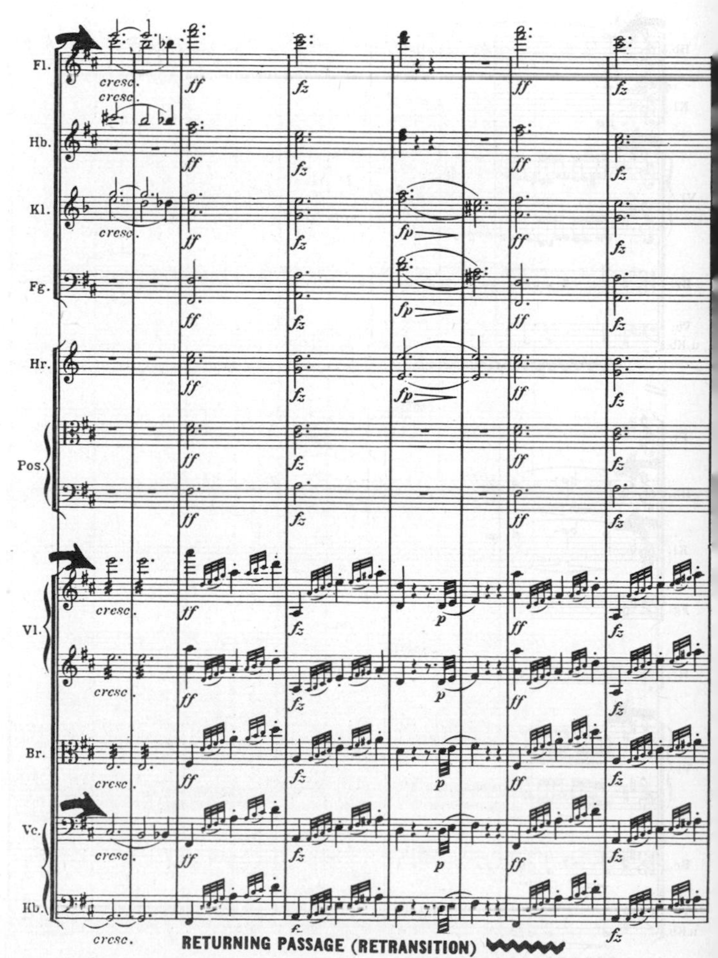

RETURNING PASSAGE (RETRANSITION)

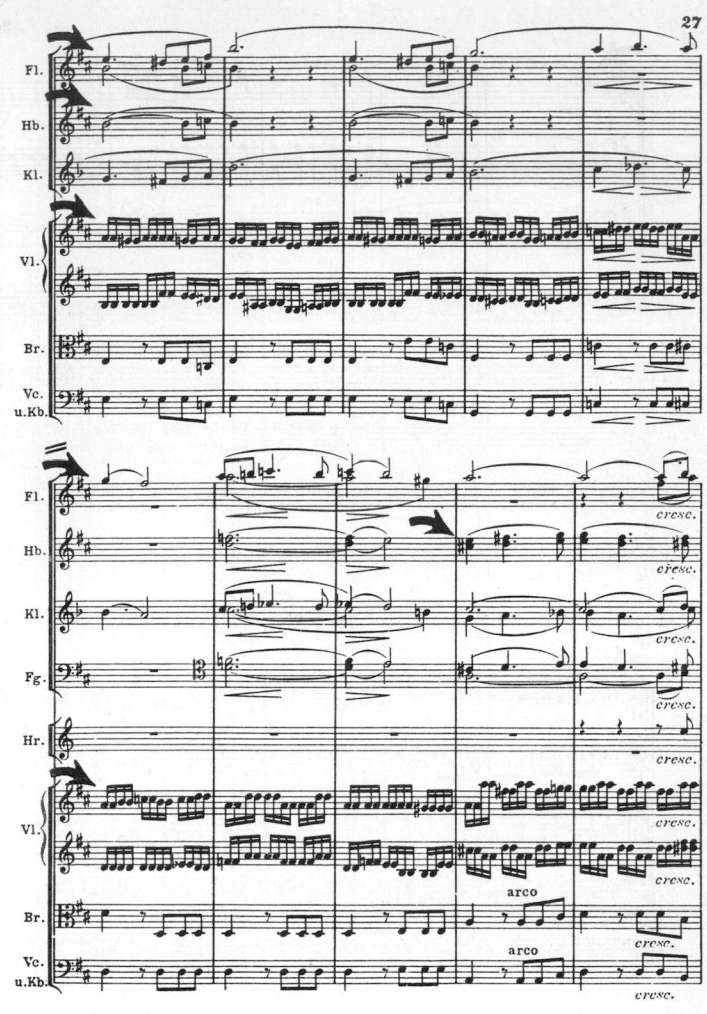

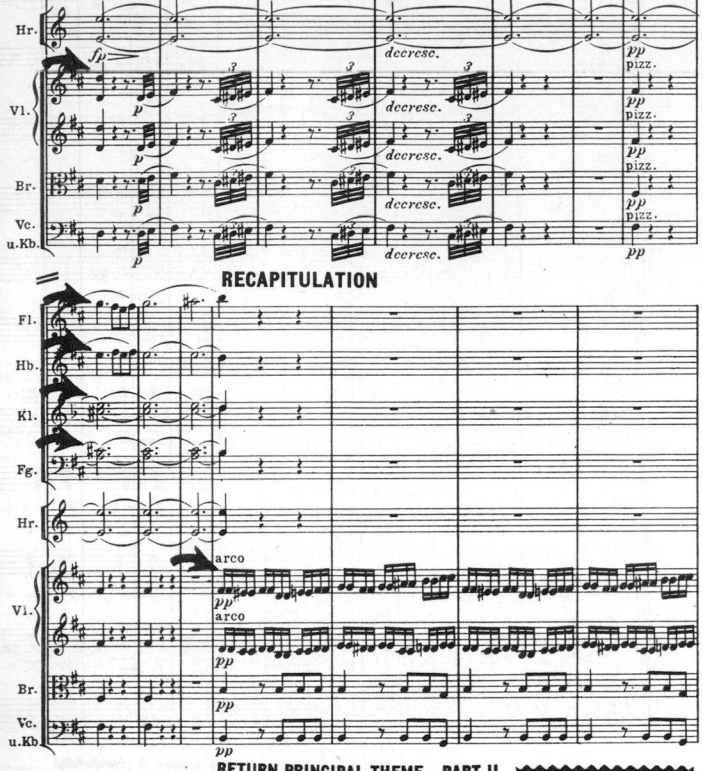

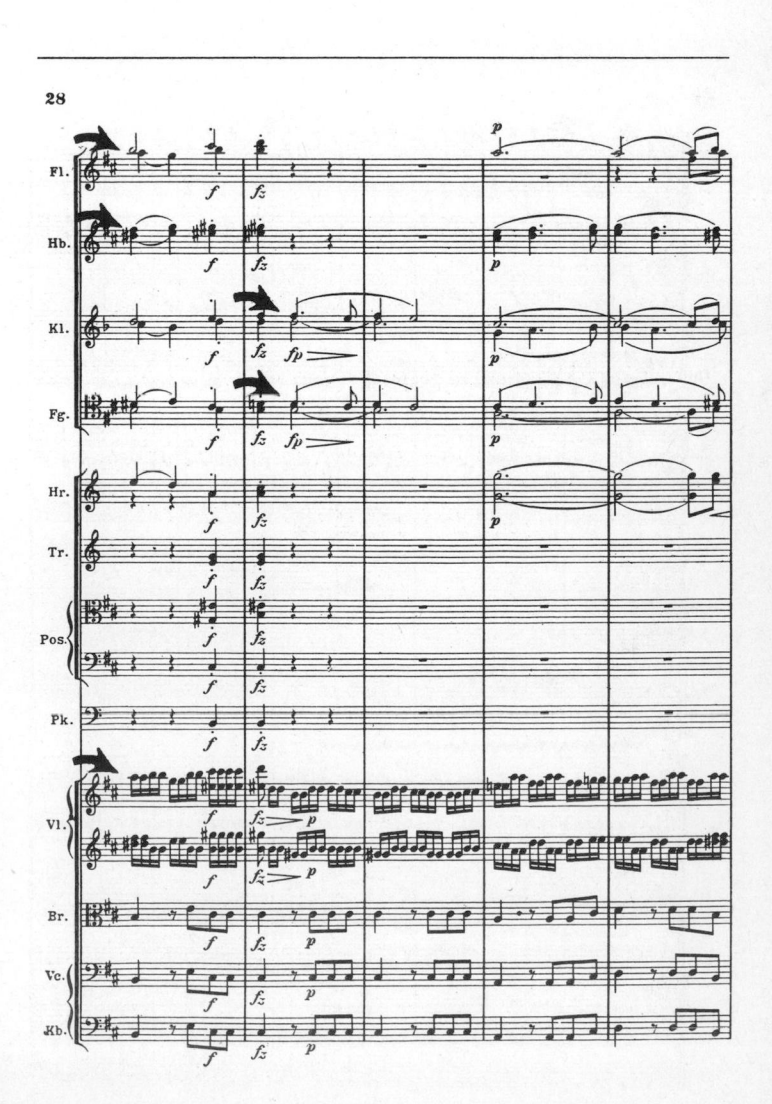

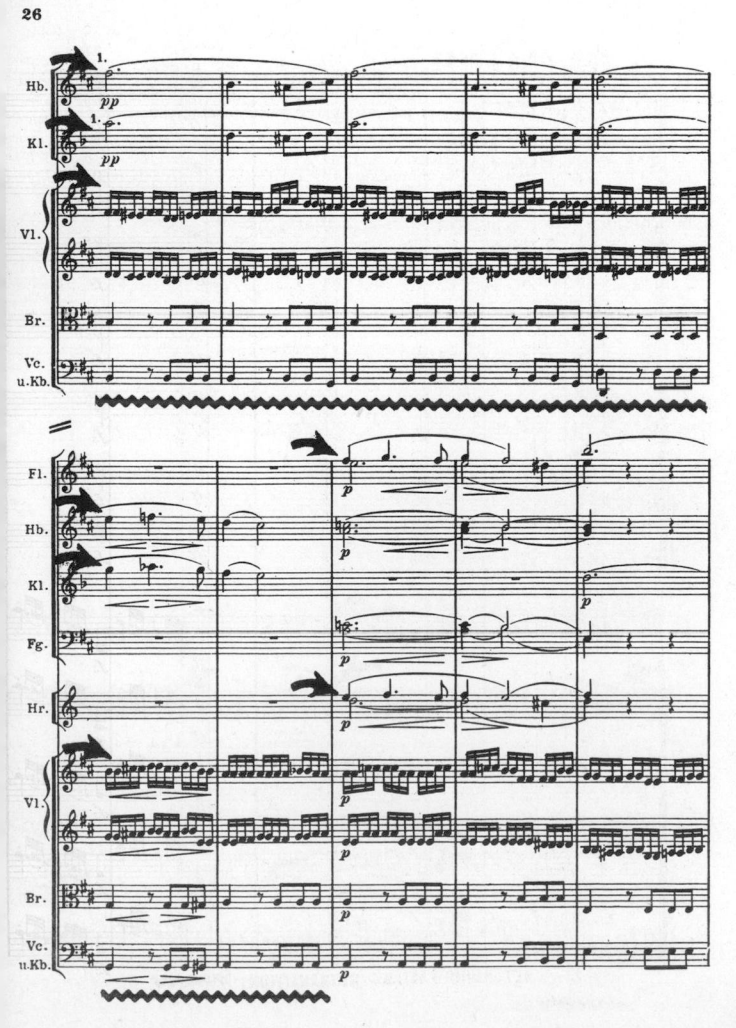

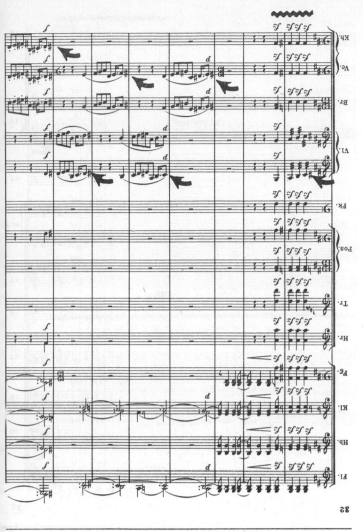

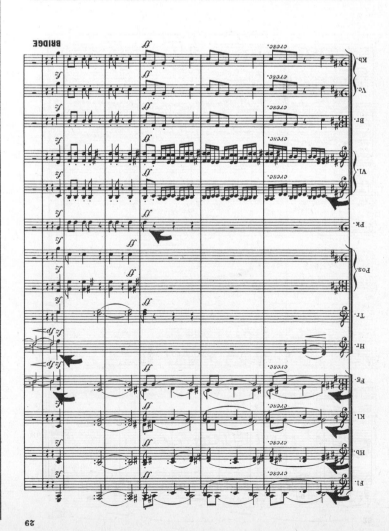

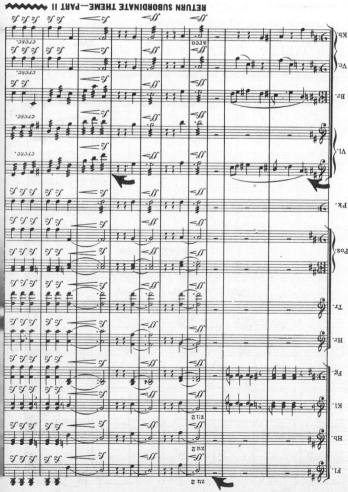

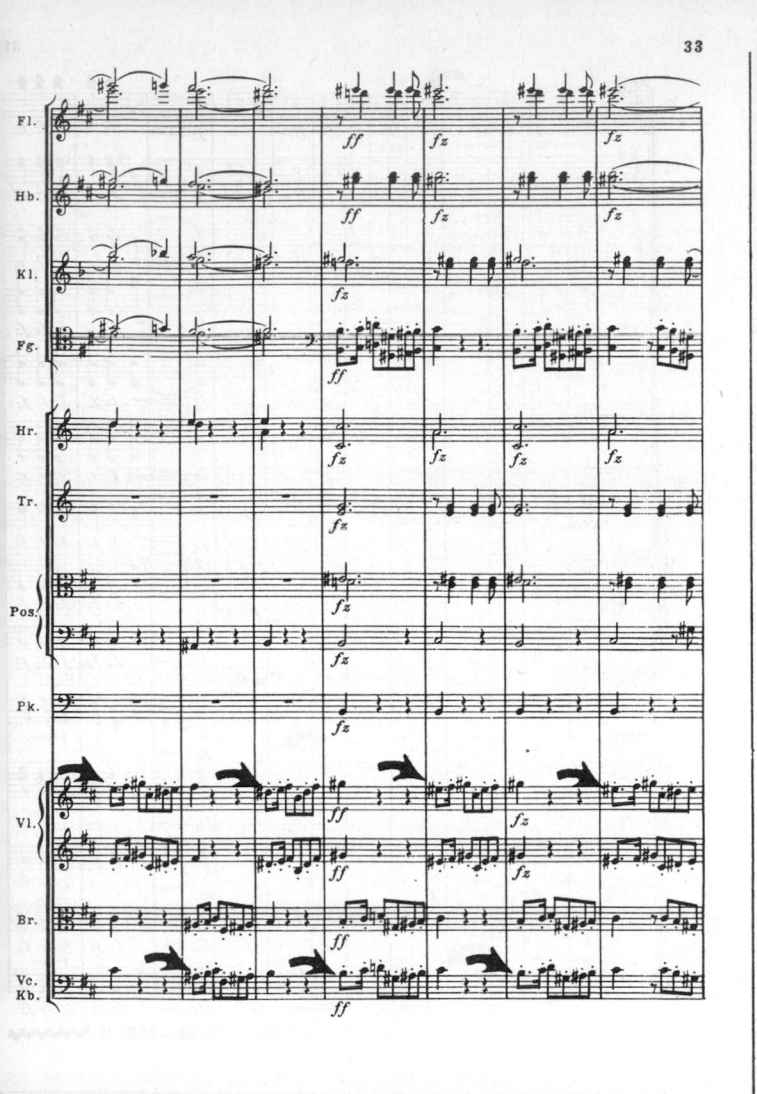

33

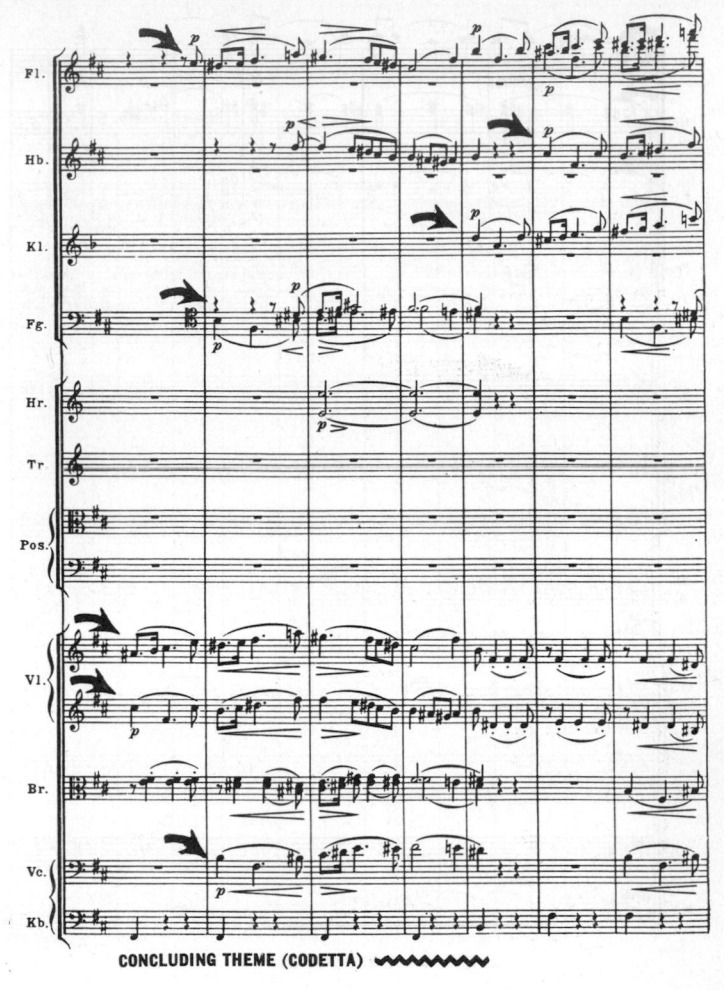

35

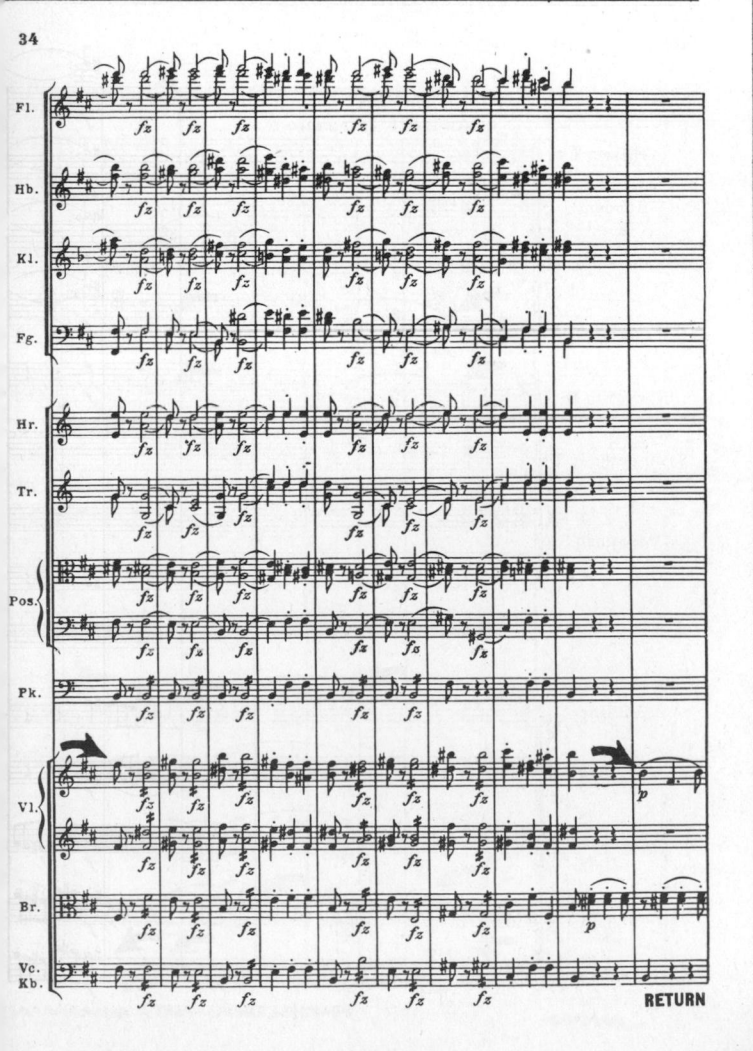

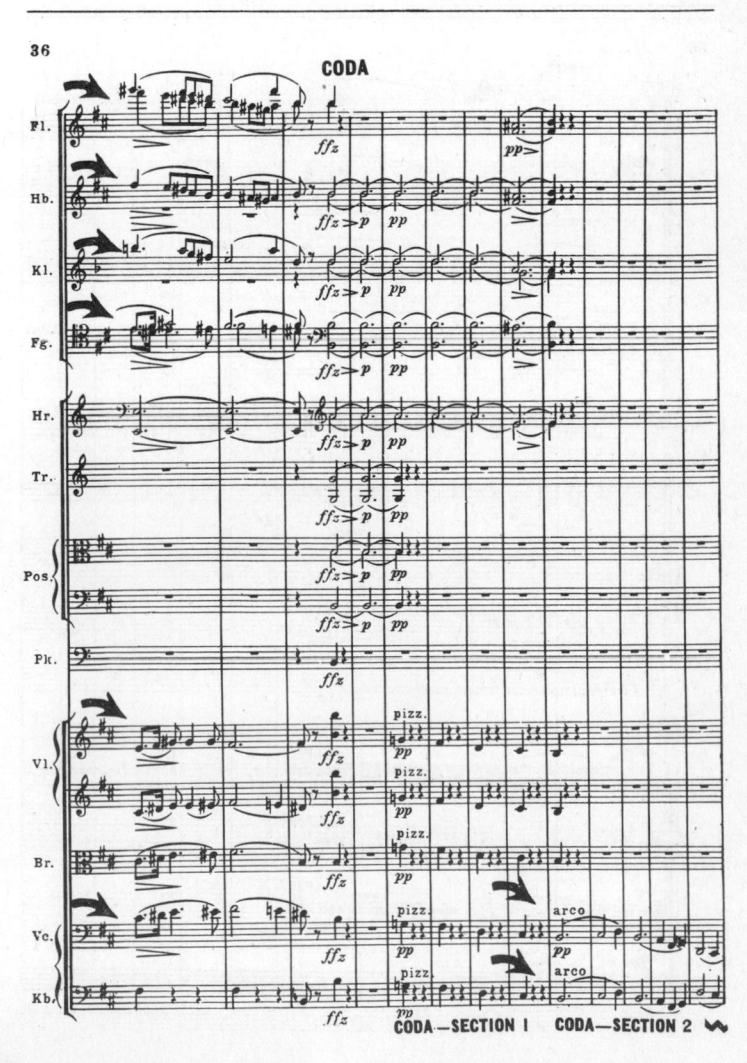

(245)

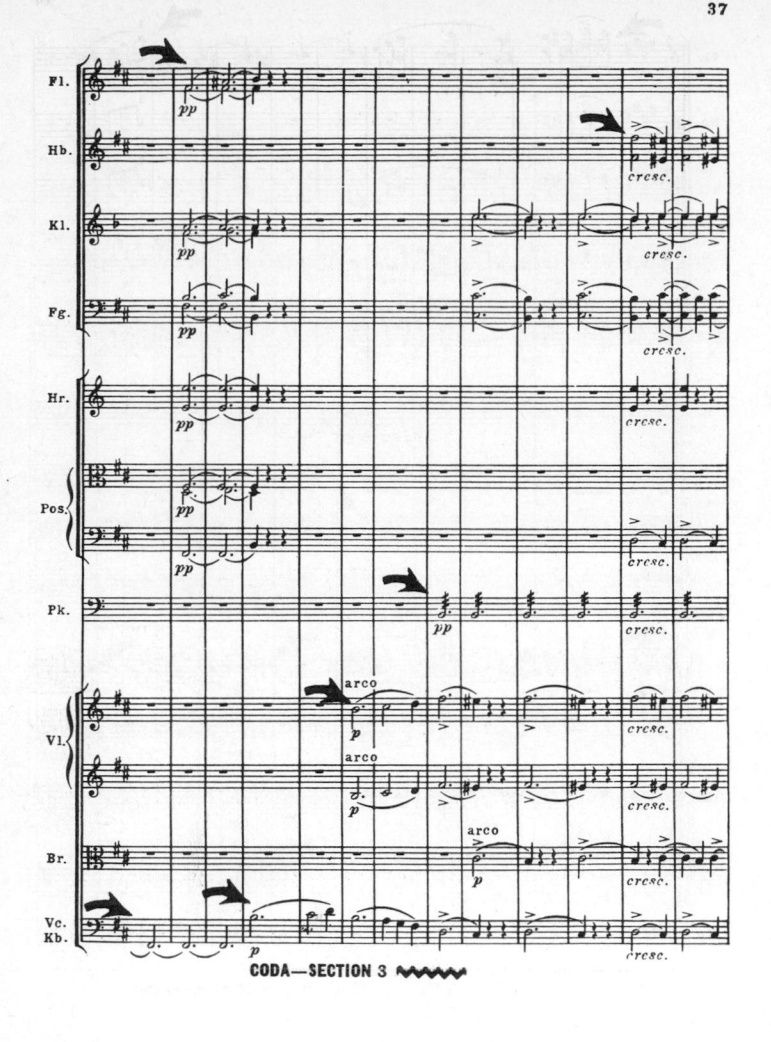

CODA—SECTION 3 〰〰〰

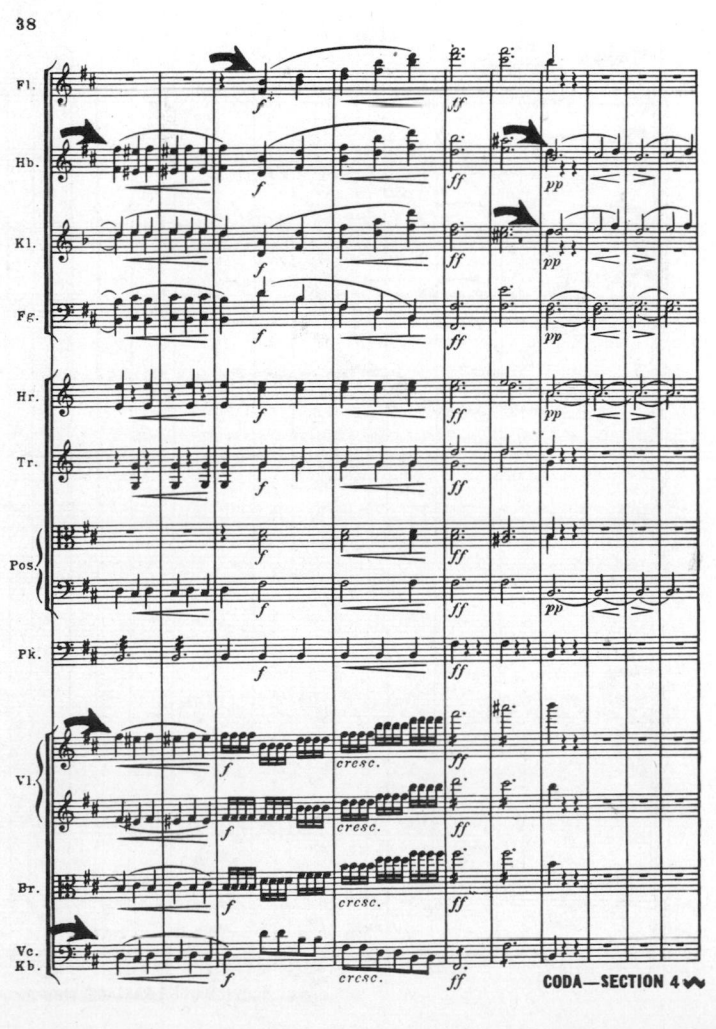

CODA—SECTION 4 〰

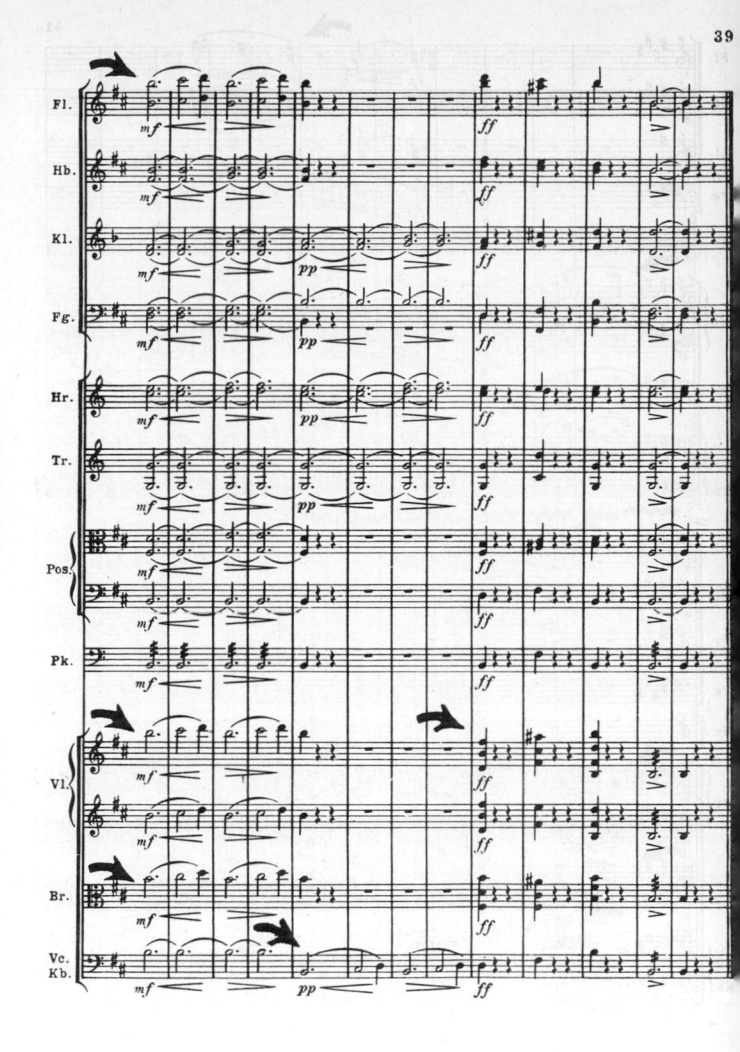

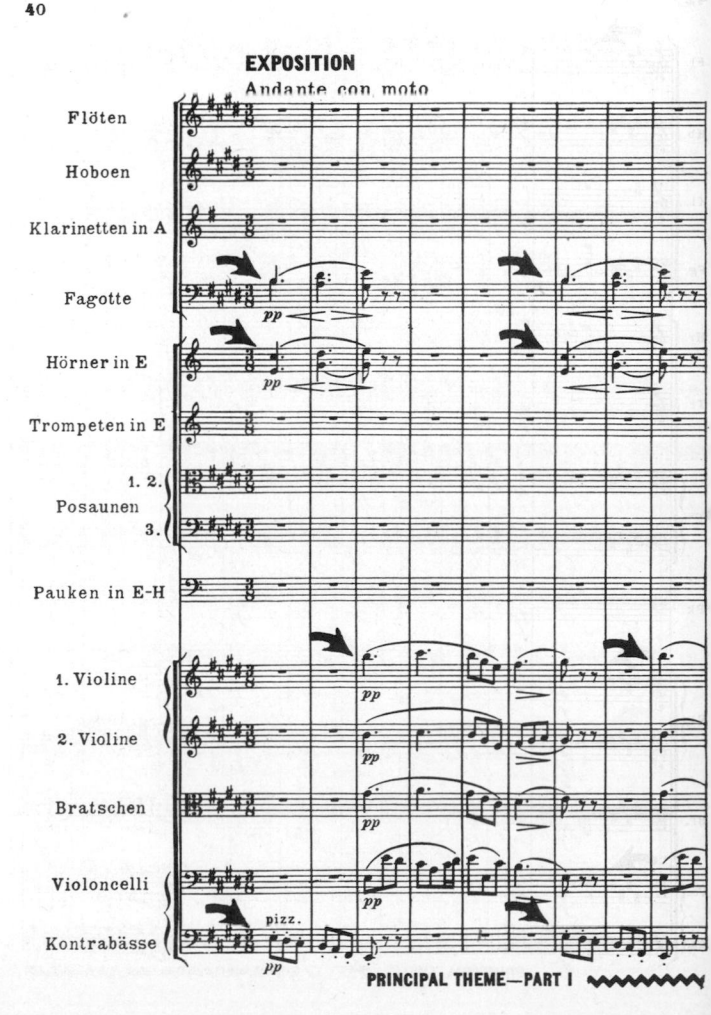

PRINCIPAL THEME—PART I 〰〰〰〰

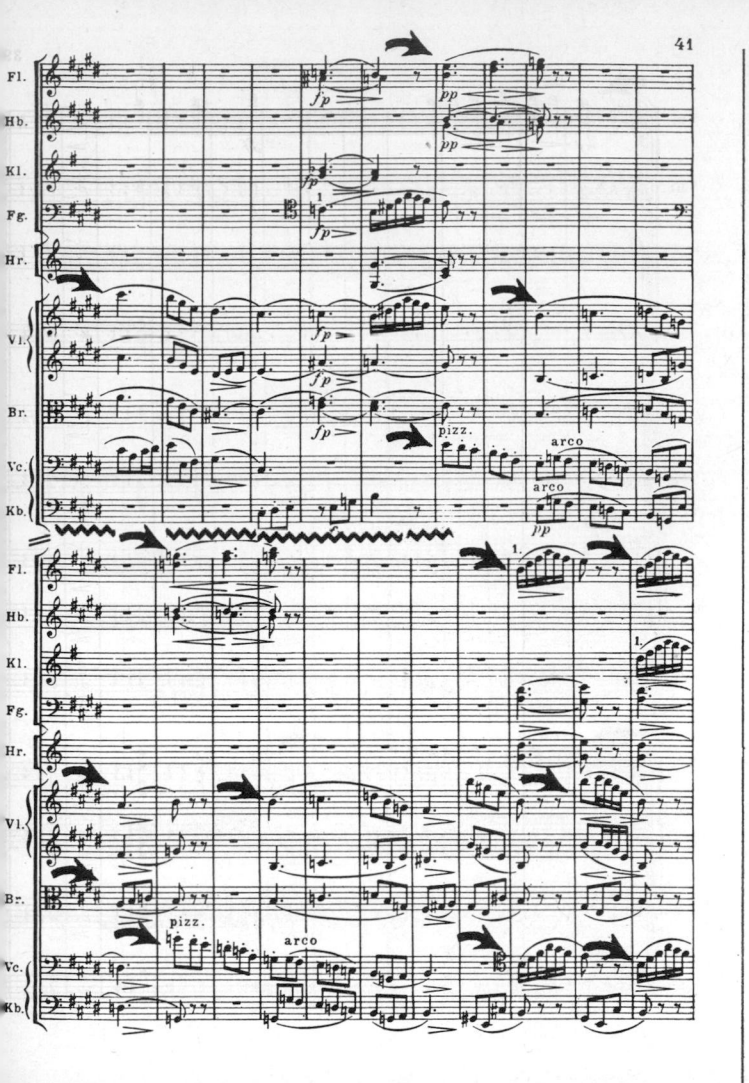

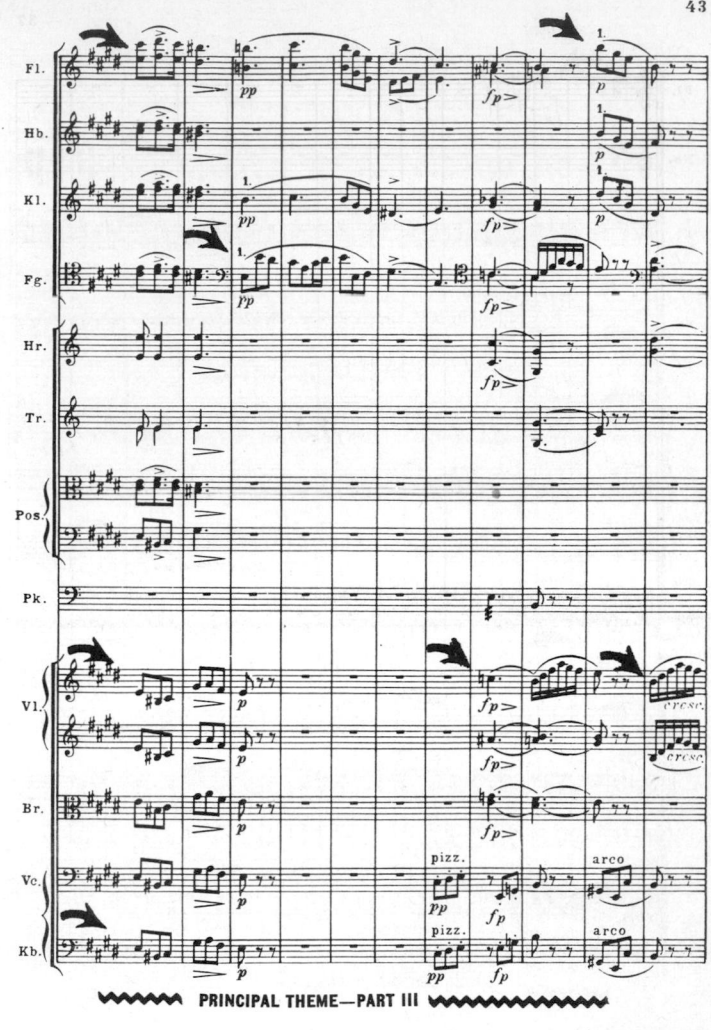

PRINCIPAL THEME—PART III ∿∿∿∿

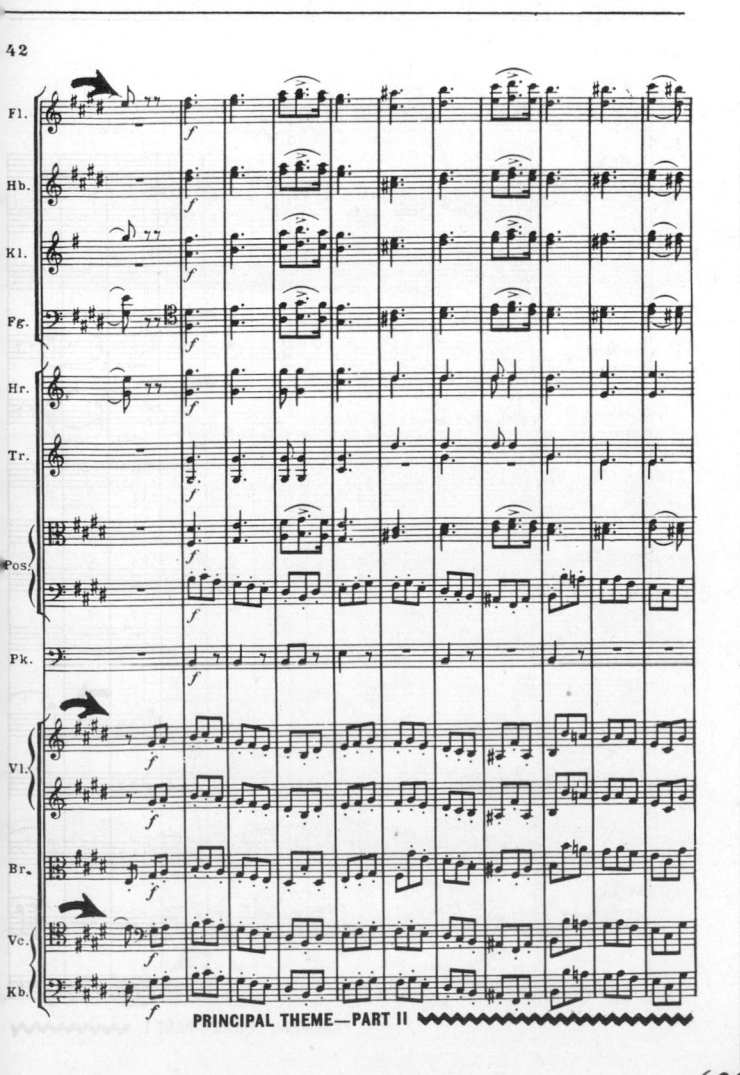

PRINCIPAL THEME—PART II ∿∿∿∿∿

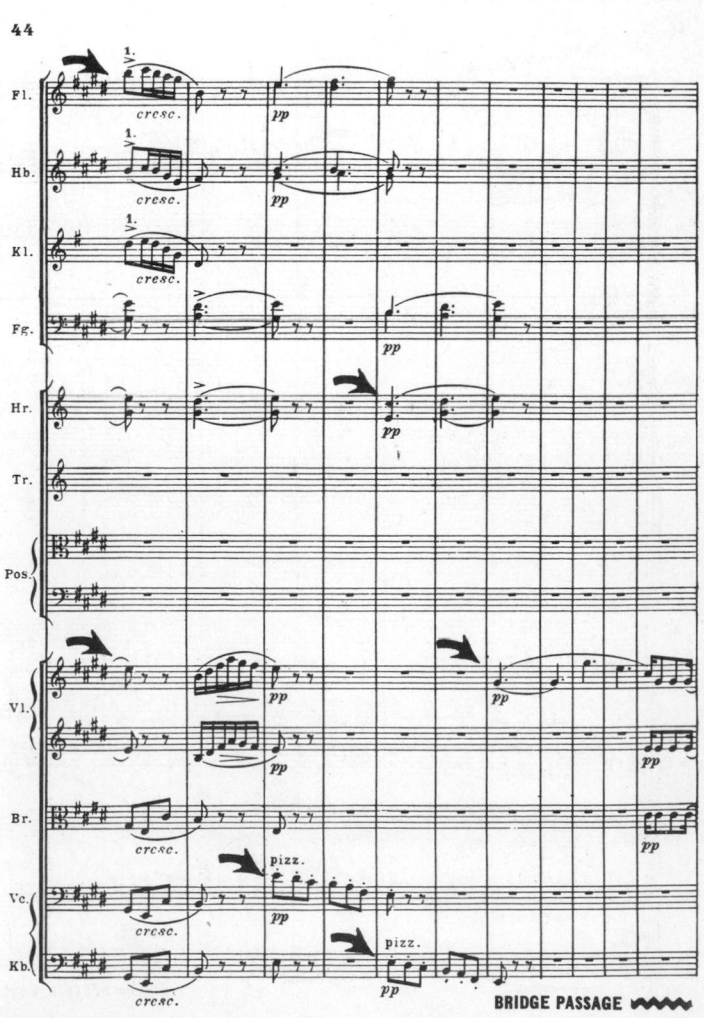

BRIDGE PASSAGE ∿∿∿

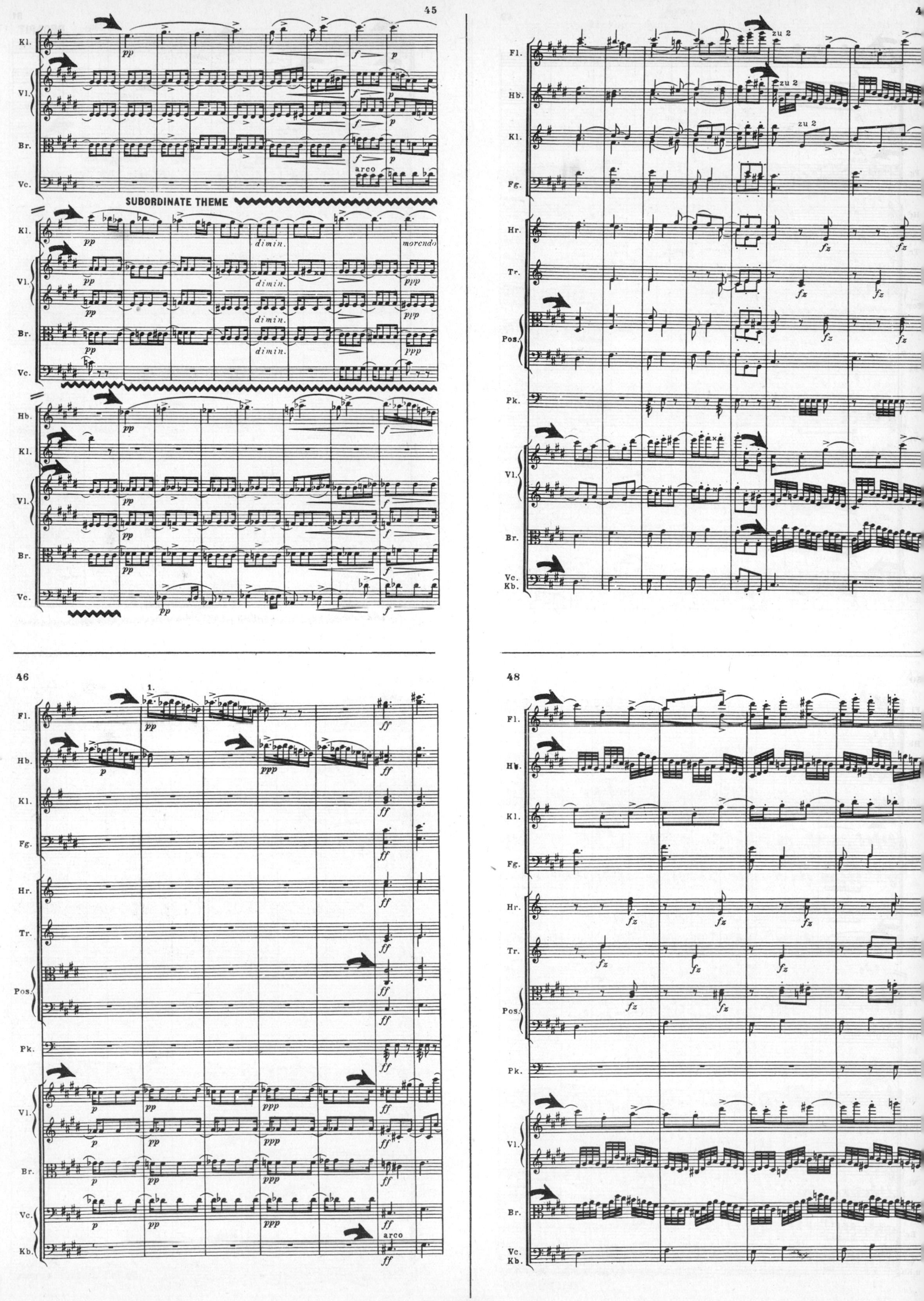
45
SUBORDINATE THEME
Kl.
Vl.
Br.
Vc.
Hb.
pp
p
f
ppp
dimin.
morendo
arco
46
Fl.
Hb.
Kl.
Fg.
Hr.
Tr.
Pos.
Pk.
Vl.
Br.
Vc.
Kb.
1.
ff
zu 2
fz
48

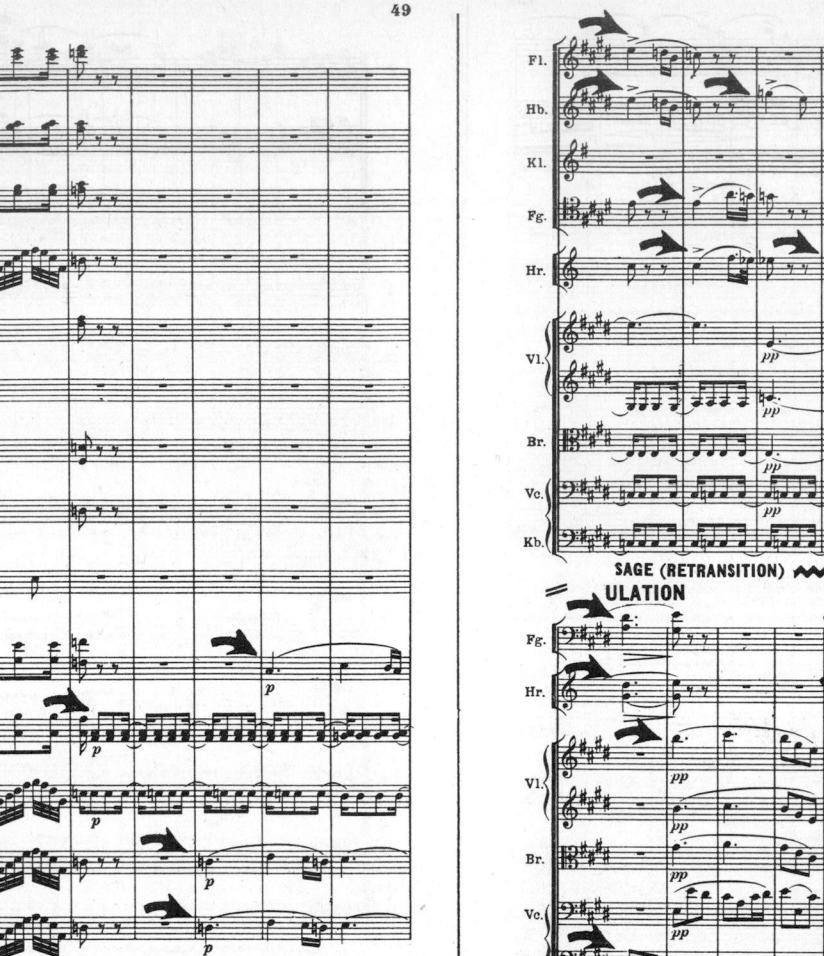

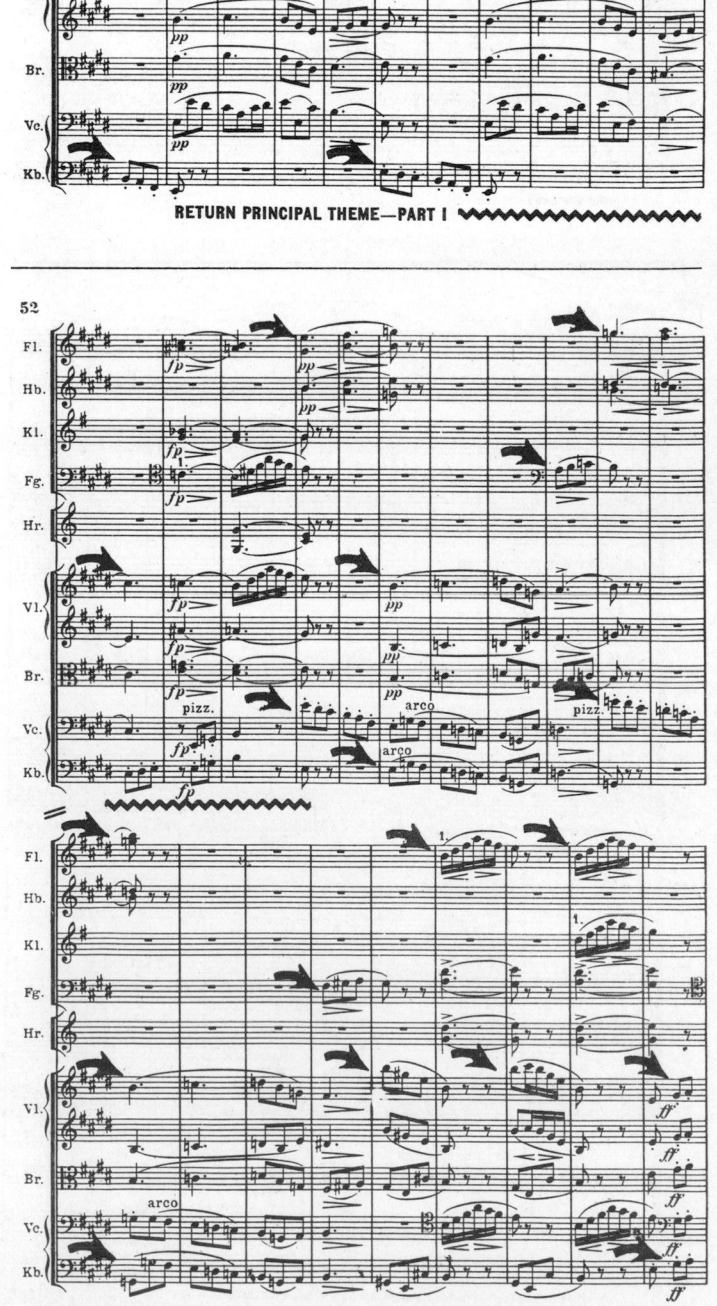

SAGE (RETRANSITION) 〜〜〜〜

ULATION

RETURN PRINCIPAL THEME—PART I 〜〜〜〜〜〜〜〜〜〜

50

52

RETURNING PAS ~

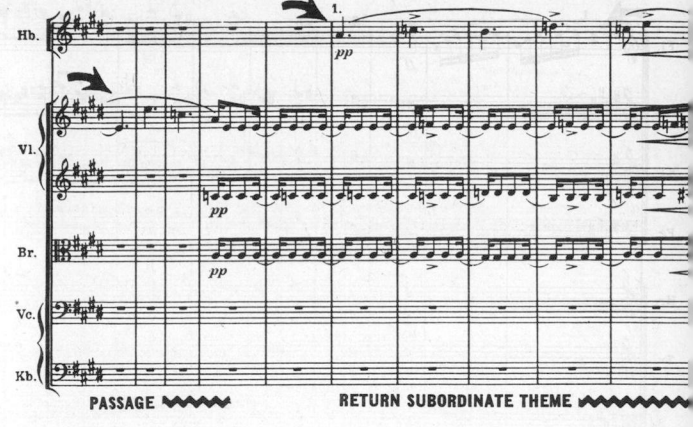

RETURN PRINCIPAL THEME—PART II ∿∿∿∿∿∿∿∿∿∿

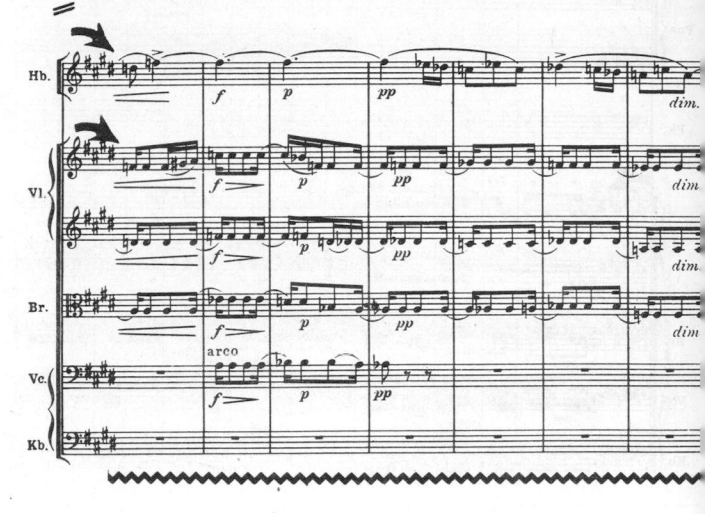

RETURN PRINCIPAL THEME—PART III ∿∿∿∿∿

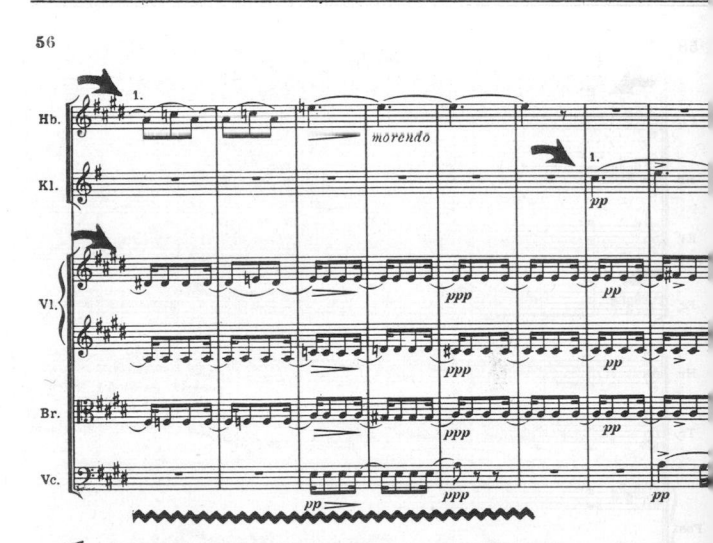

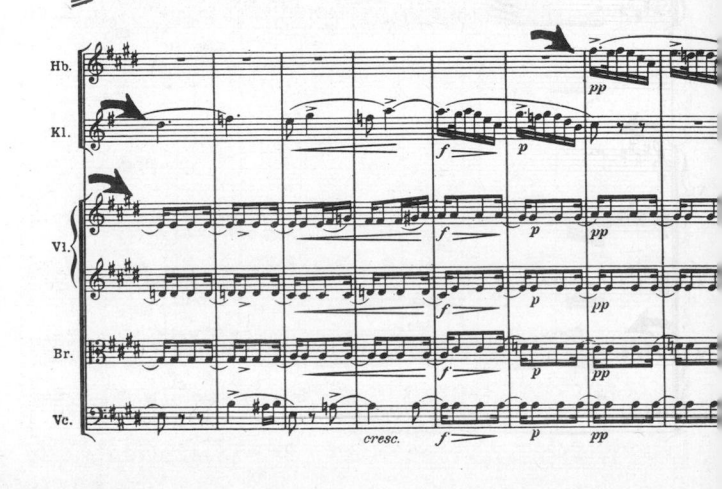

BRIDGE

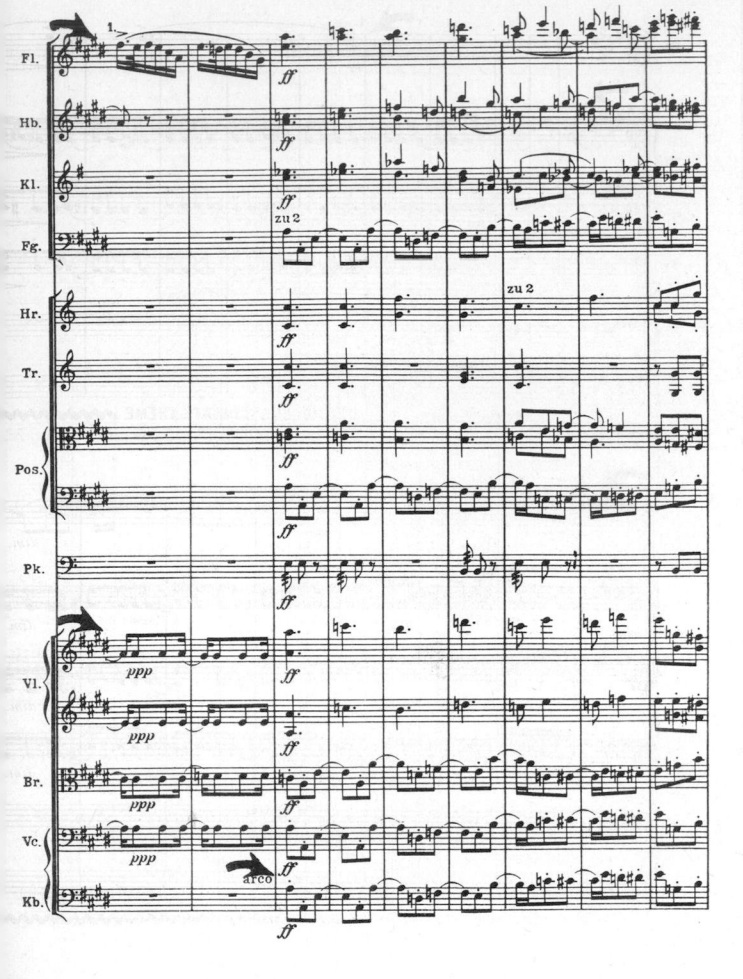

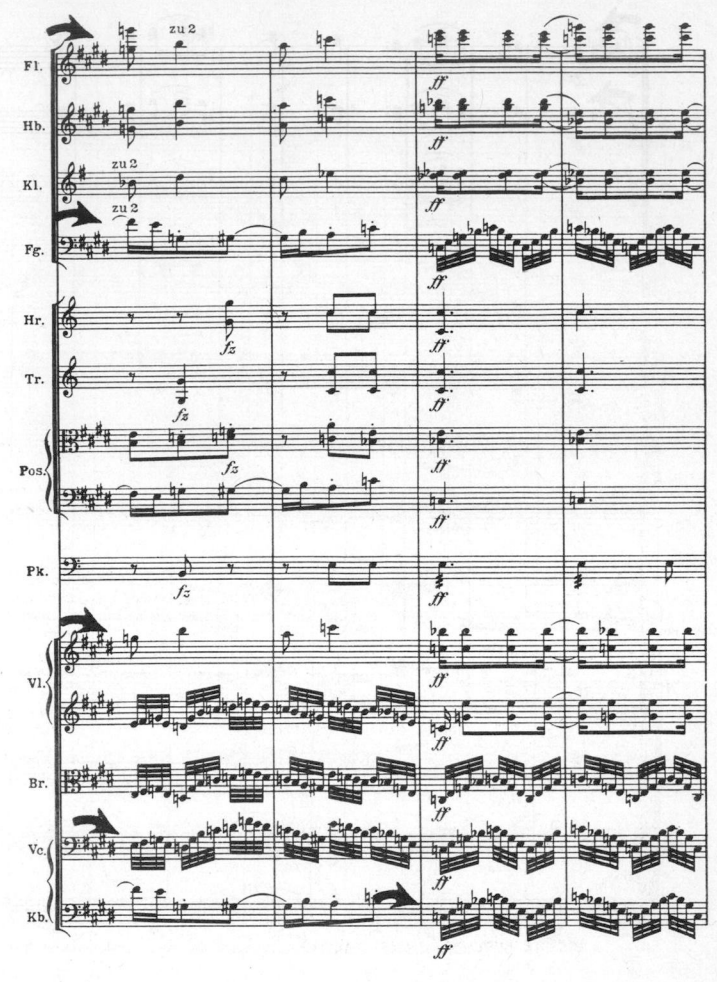

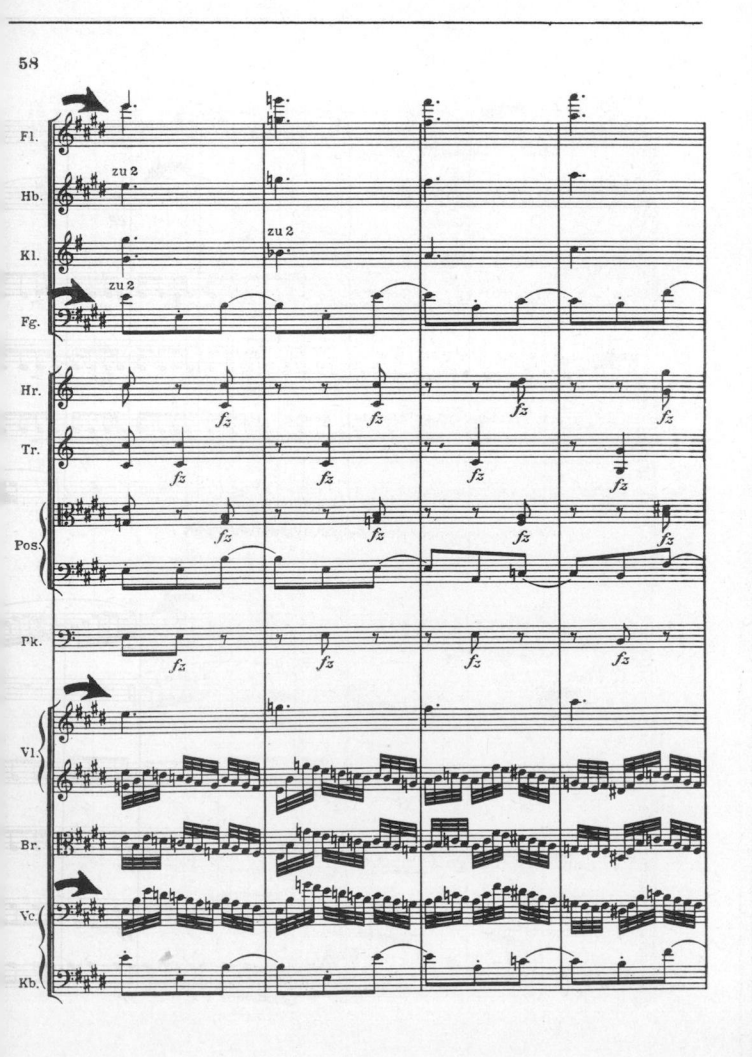

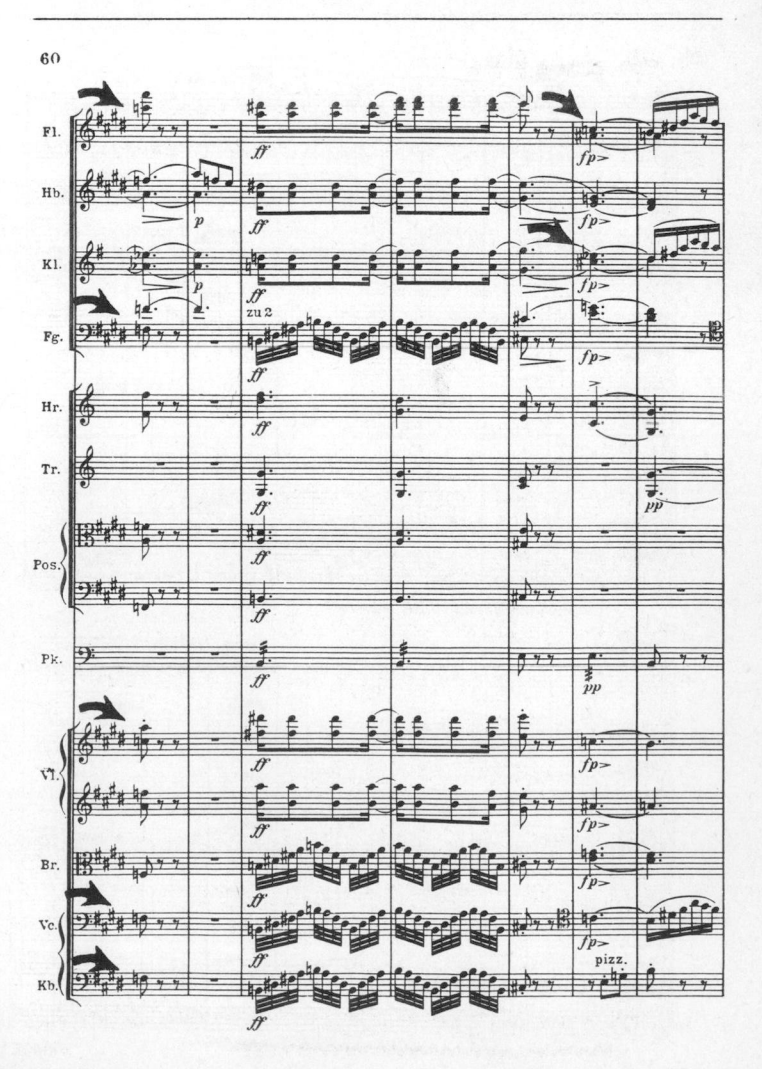

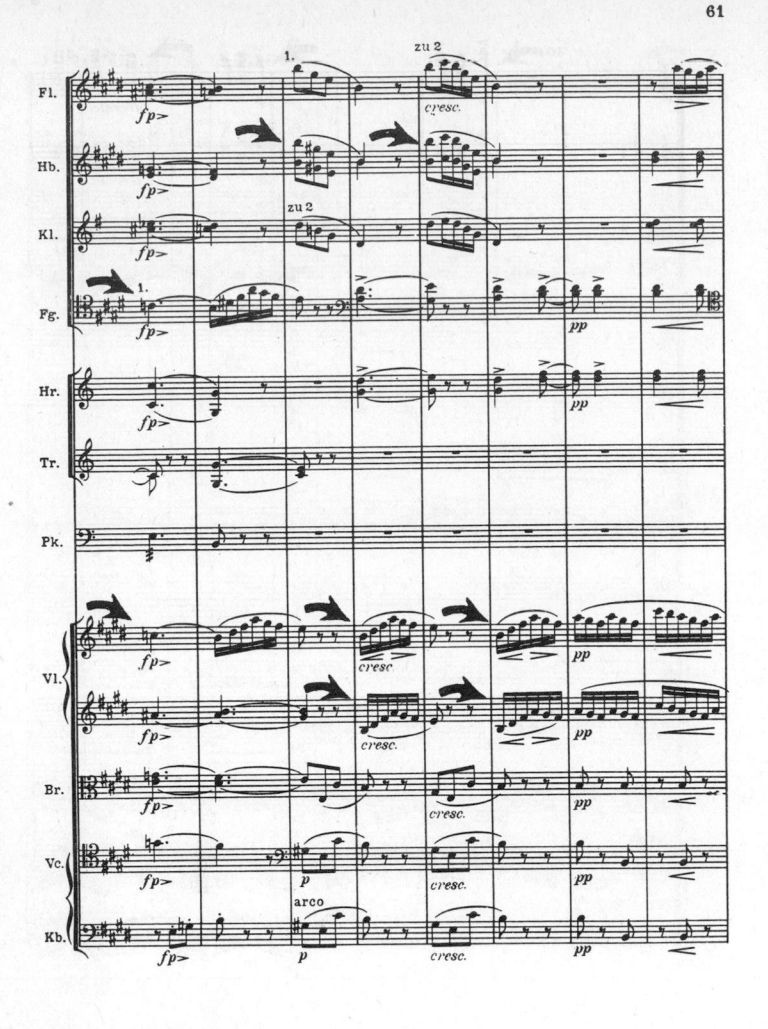

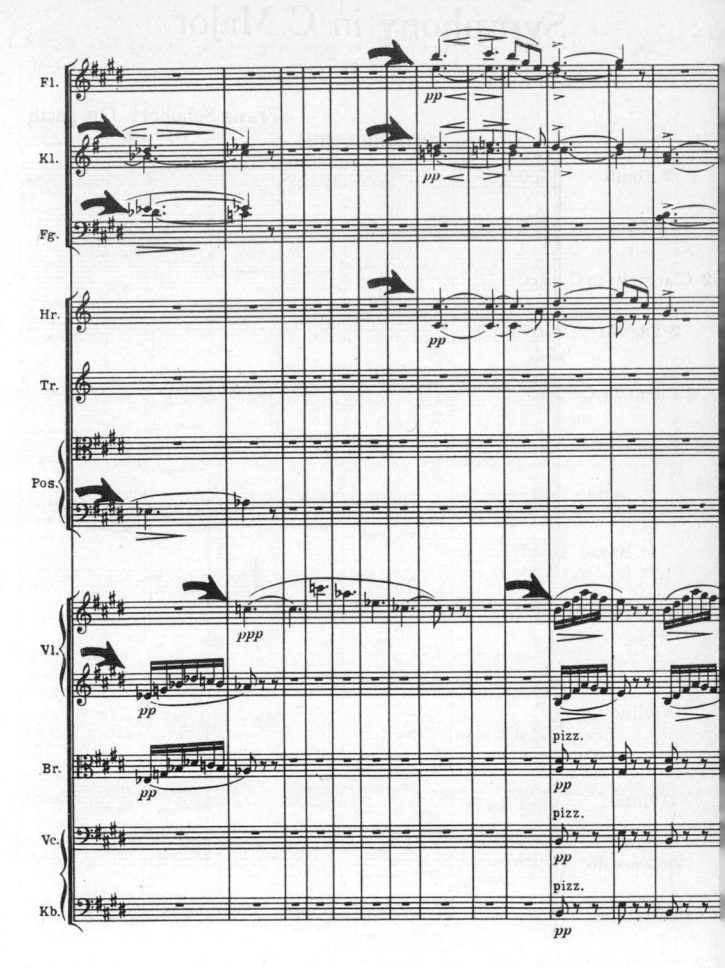

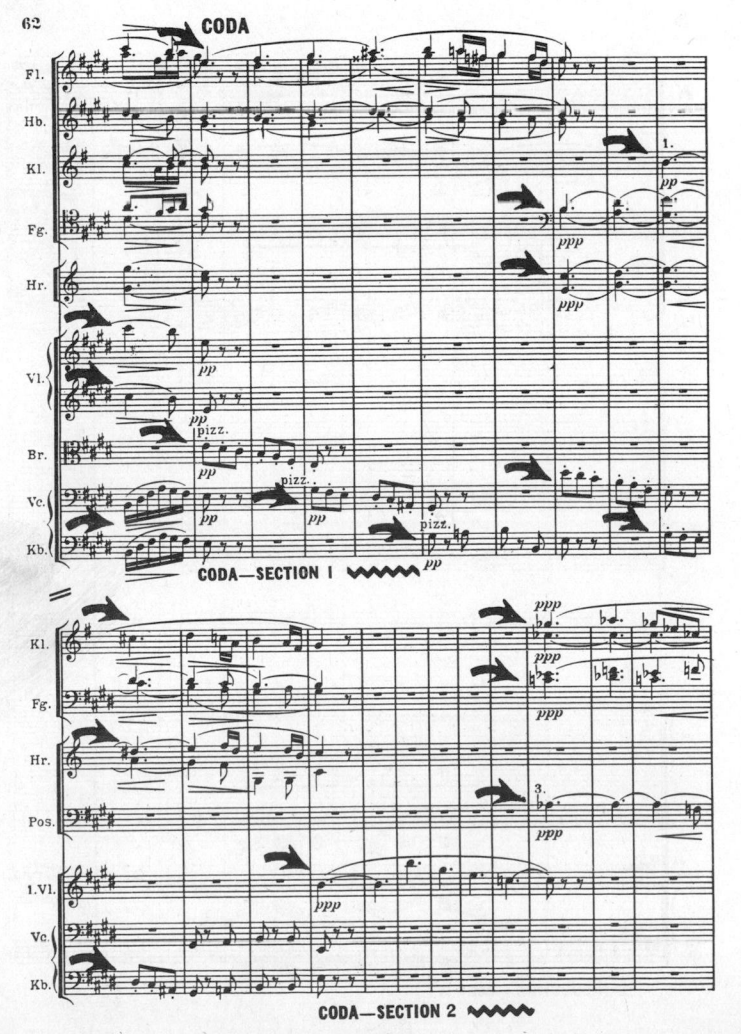

CODA—SECTION 1 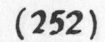 *pp*

CODA—SECTION 2

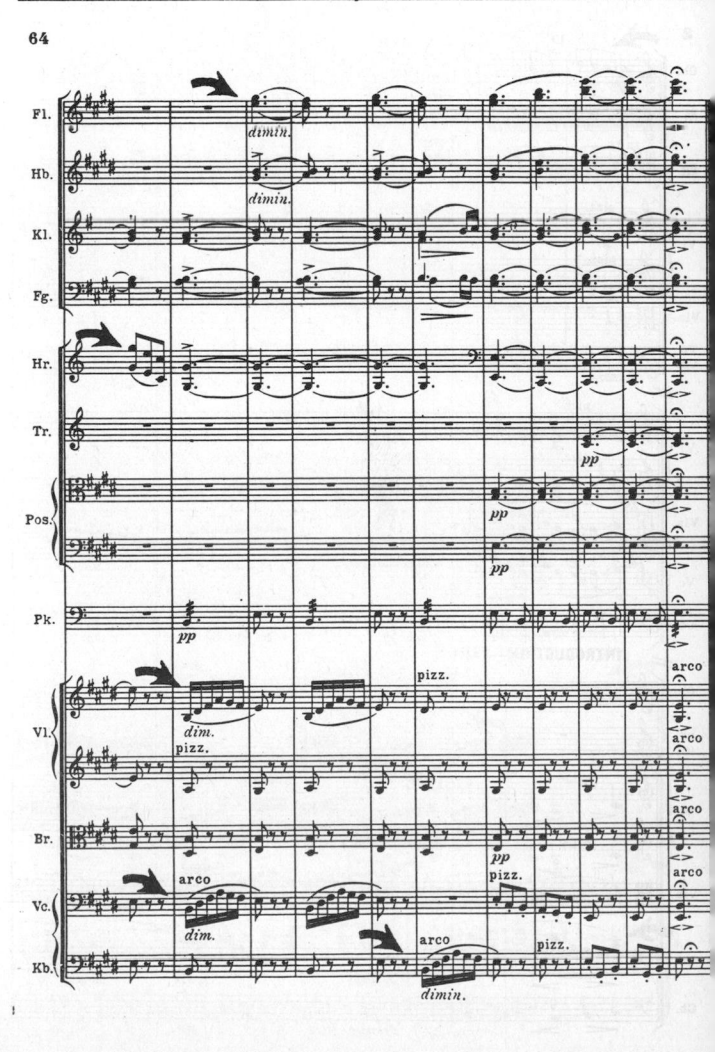

Symphony in C Major

I

Franz Schubert, Op. posth.
1797-1828

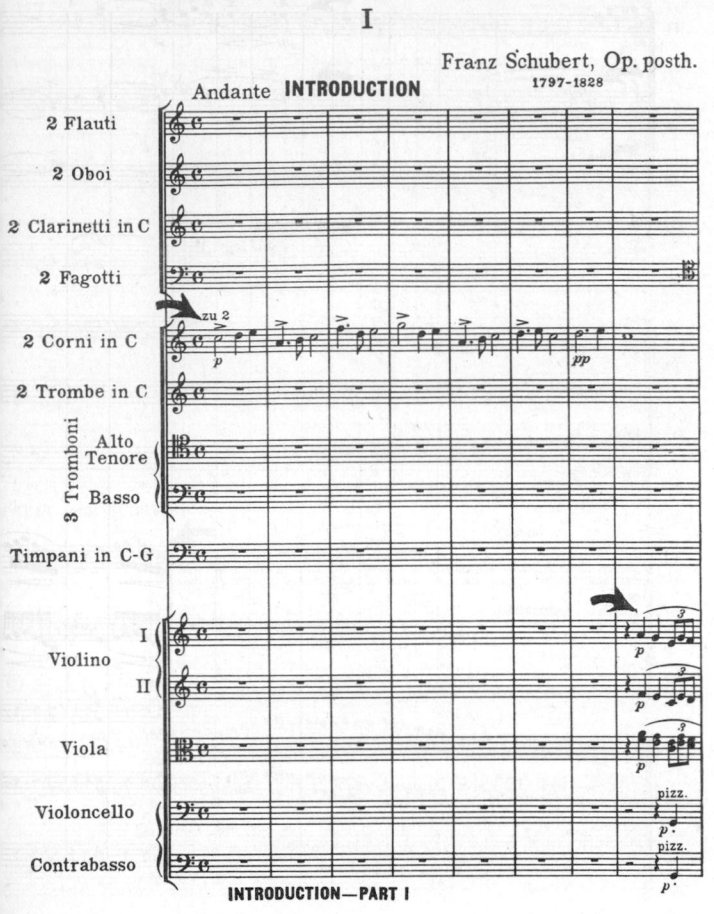

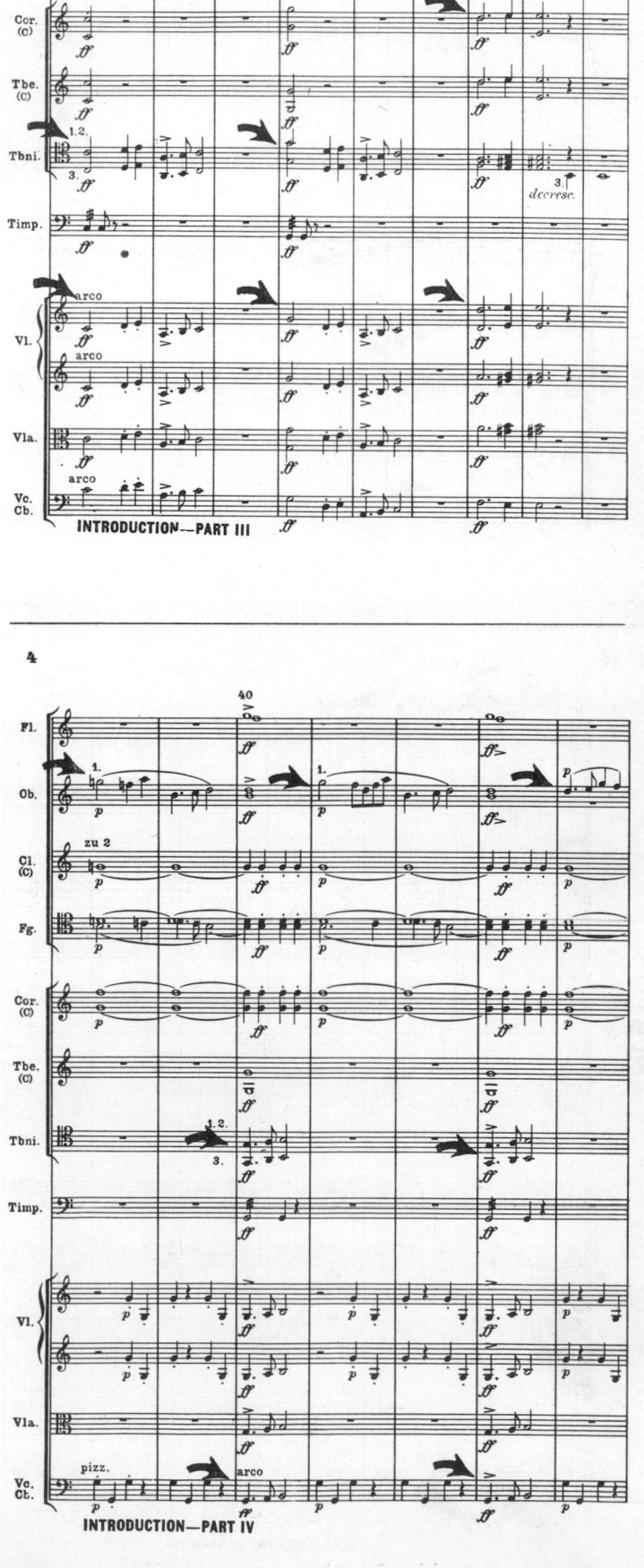

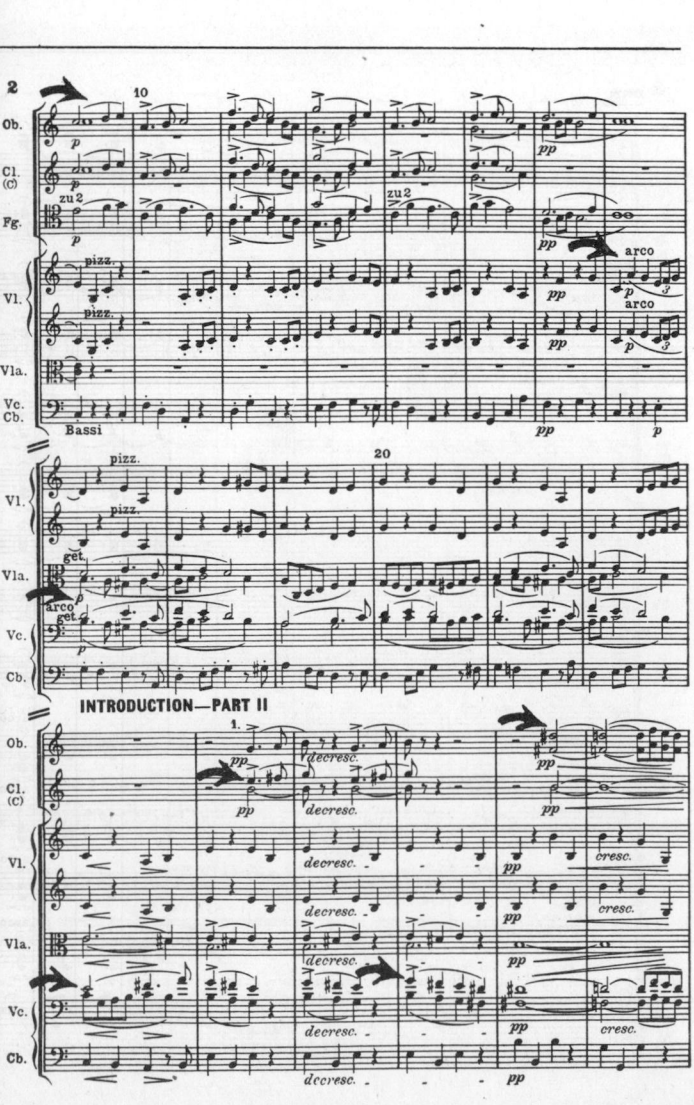

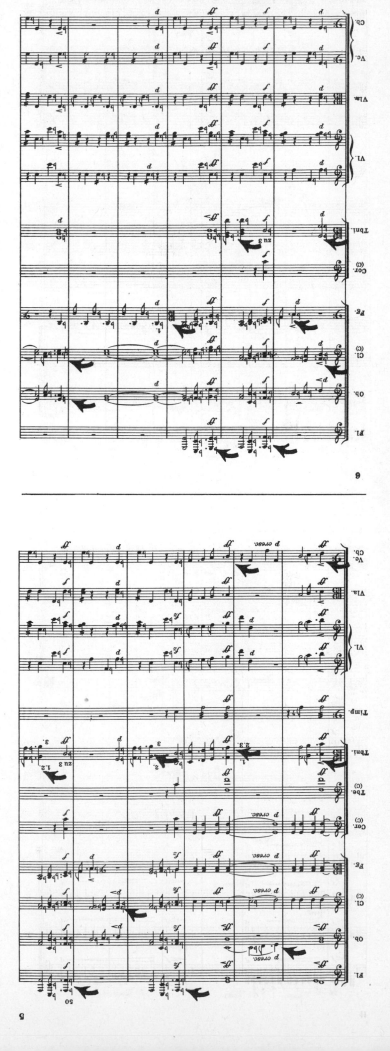

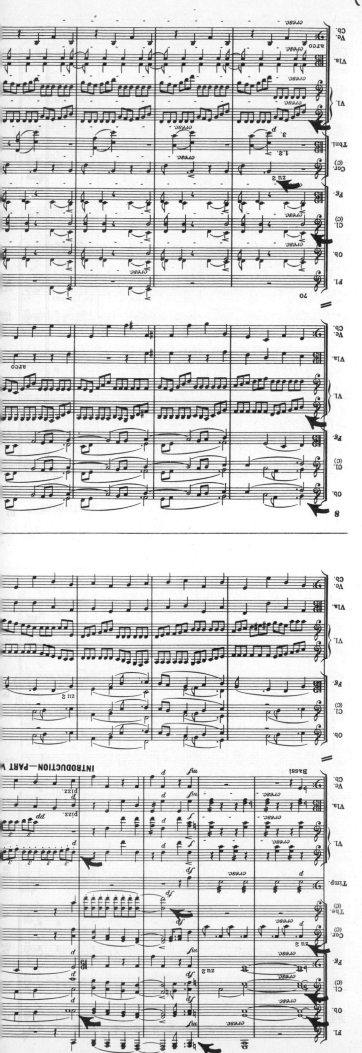

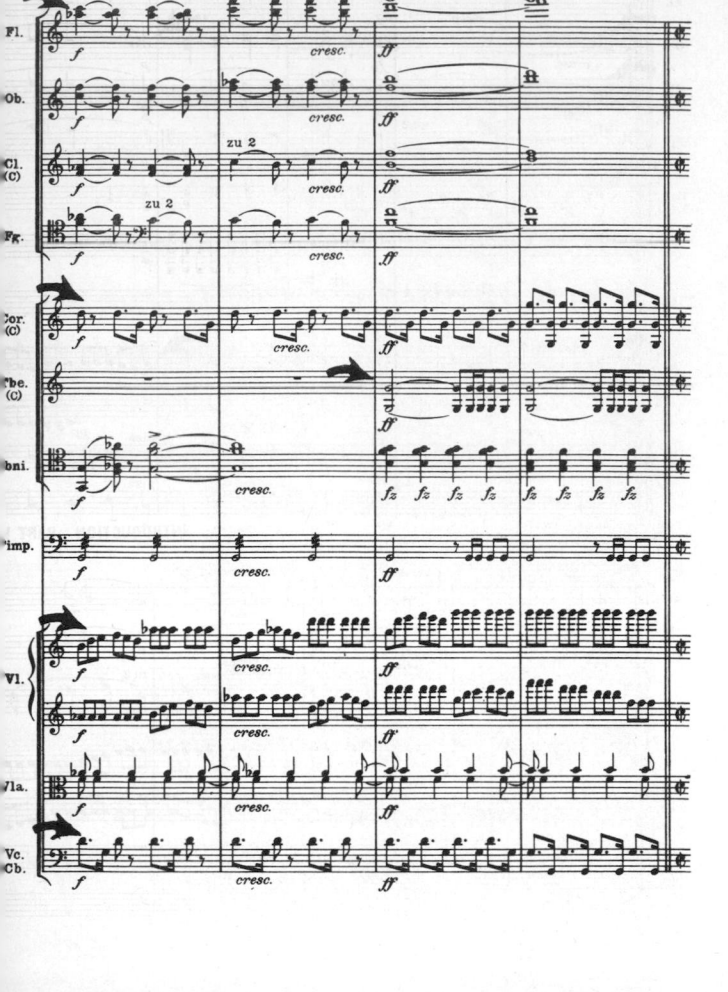

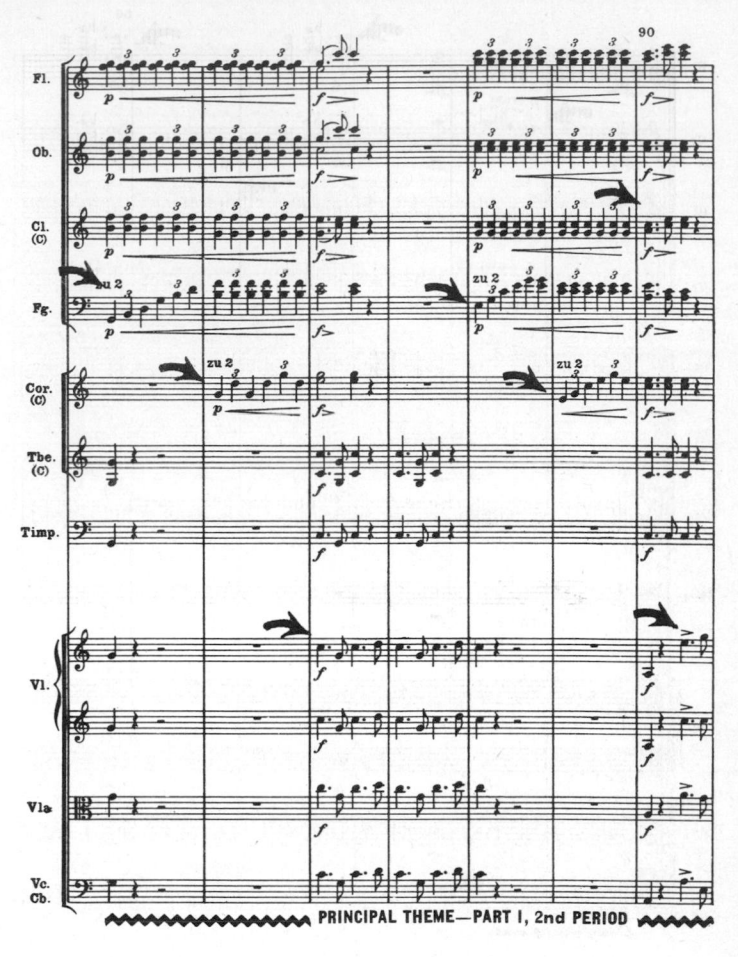

PRINCIPAL THEME—PART I, 2nd PERIOD

EXPOSITION

Allegro ma non troppo

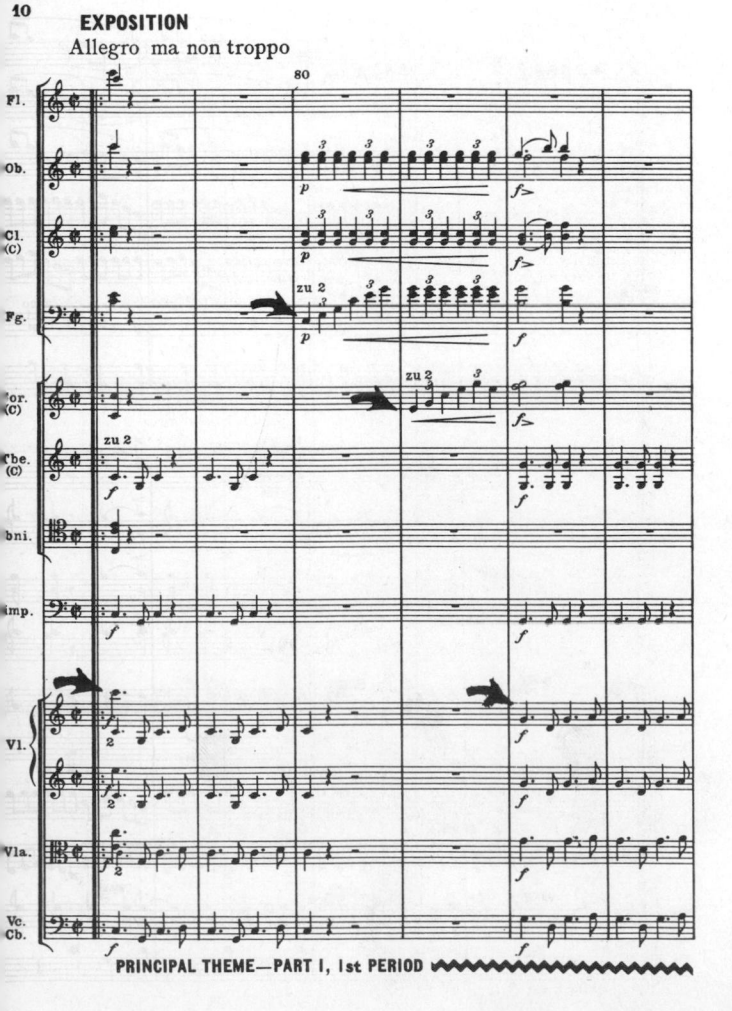

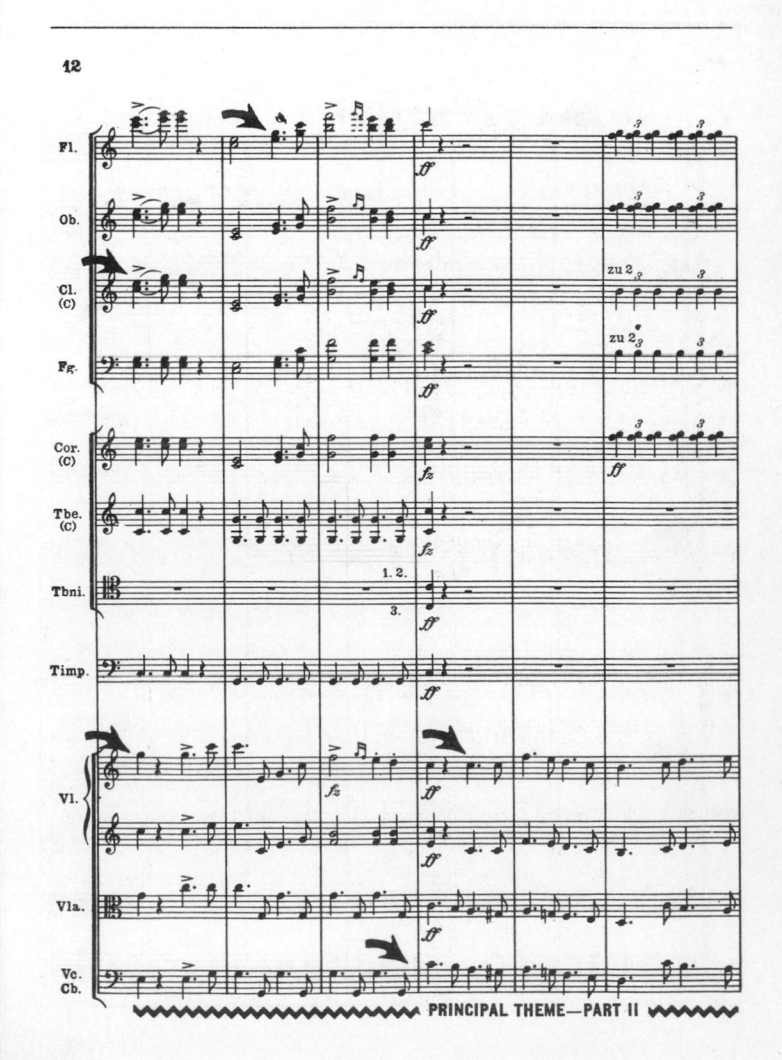

PRINCIPAL THEME—PART I, 1st PERIOD

PRINCIPAL THEME—PART II

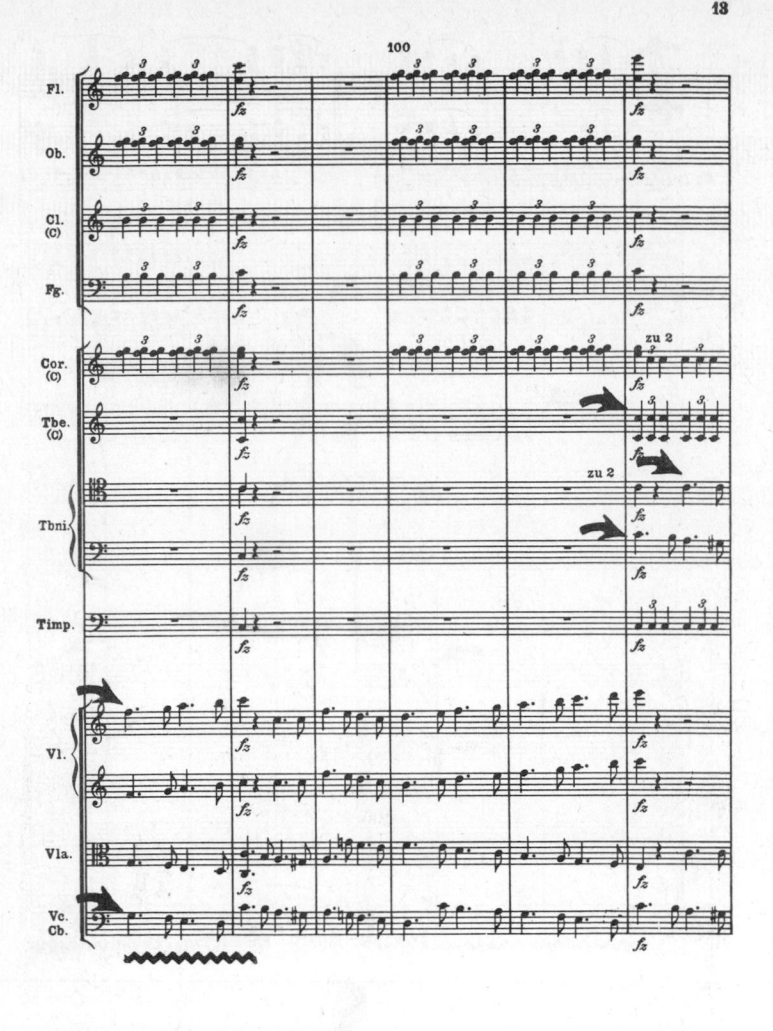

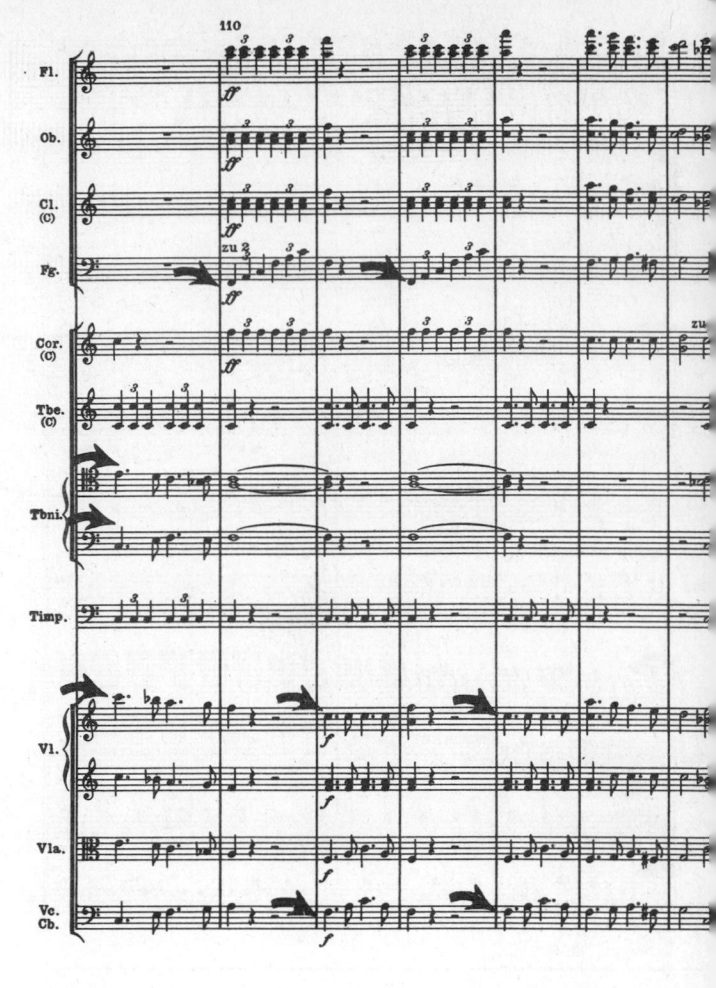

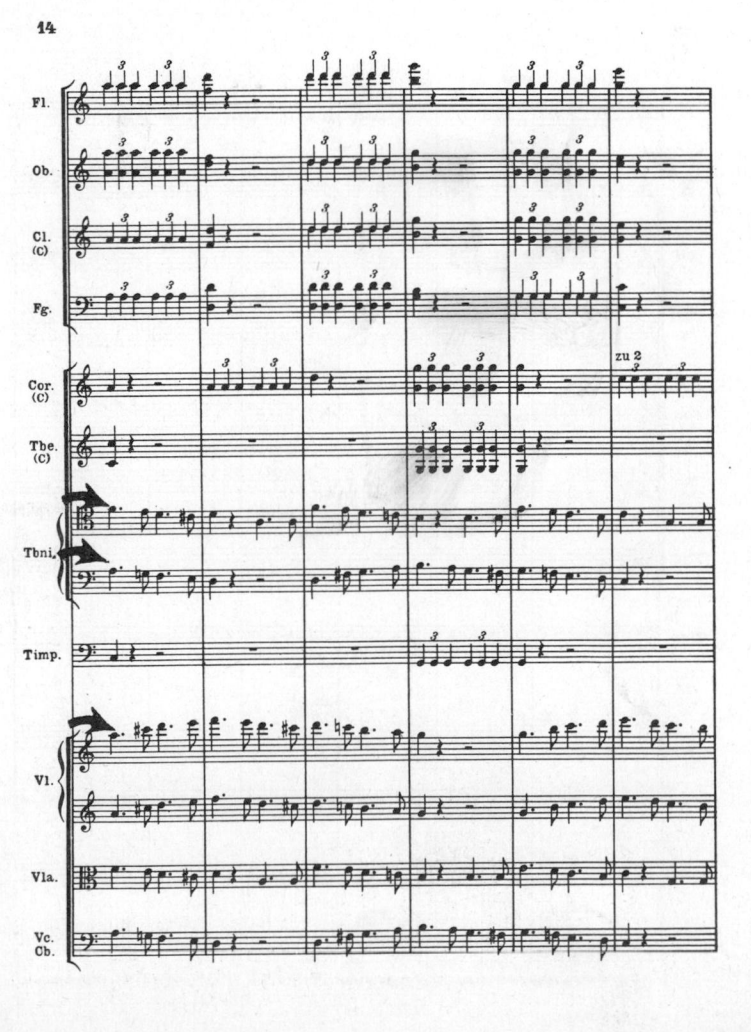

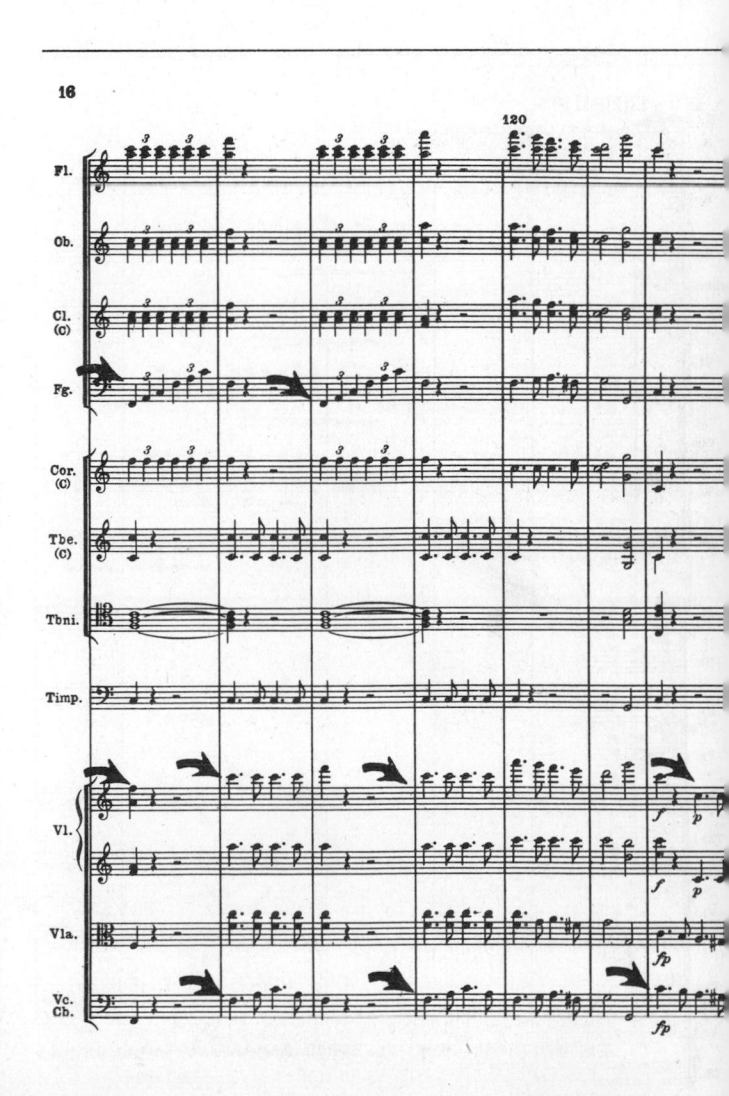

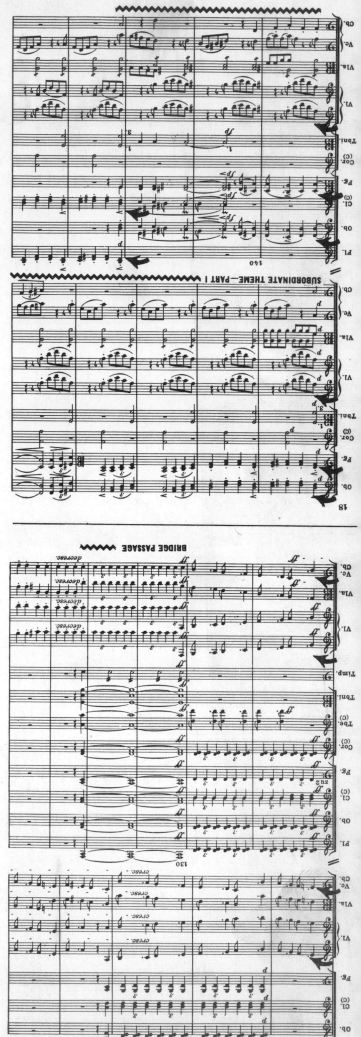

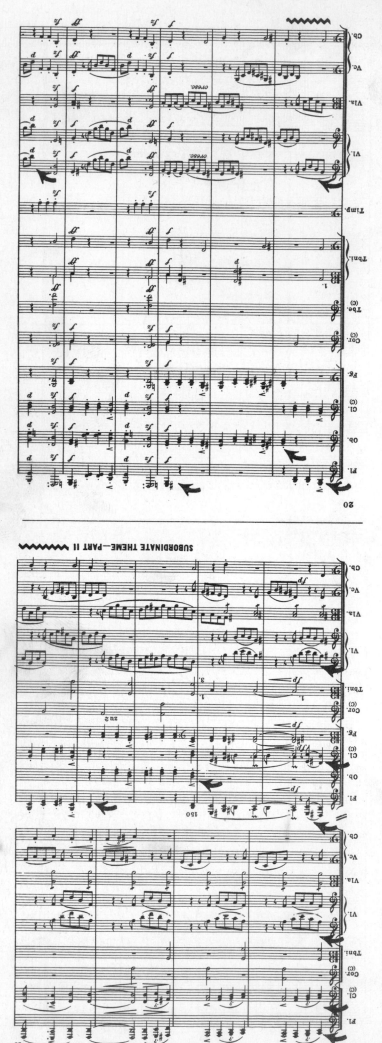

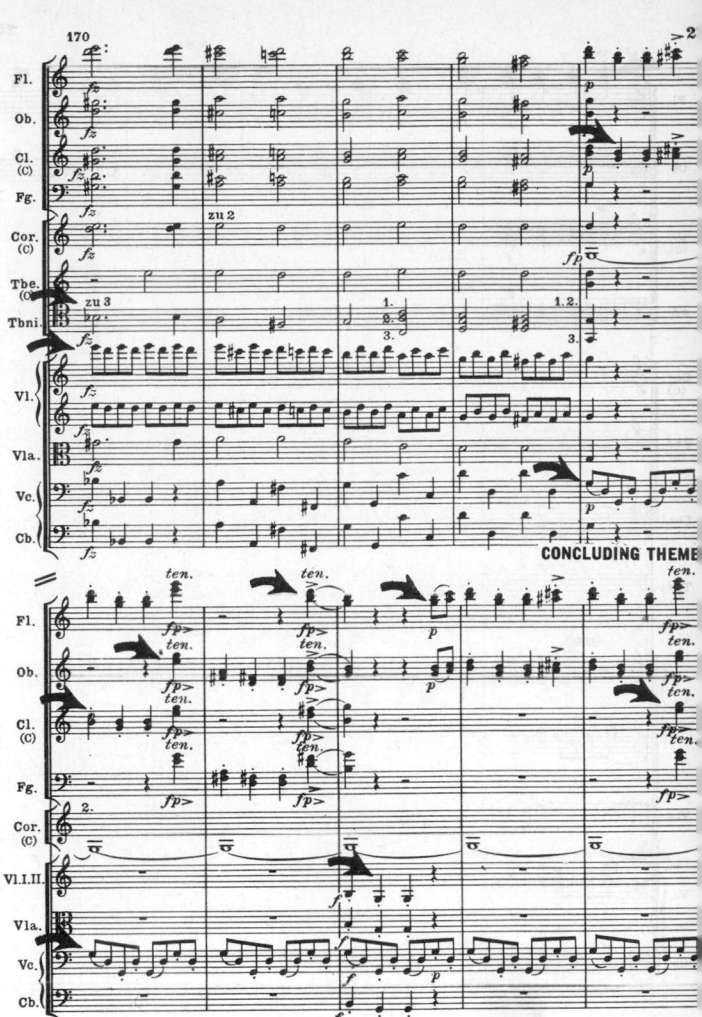

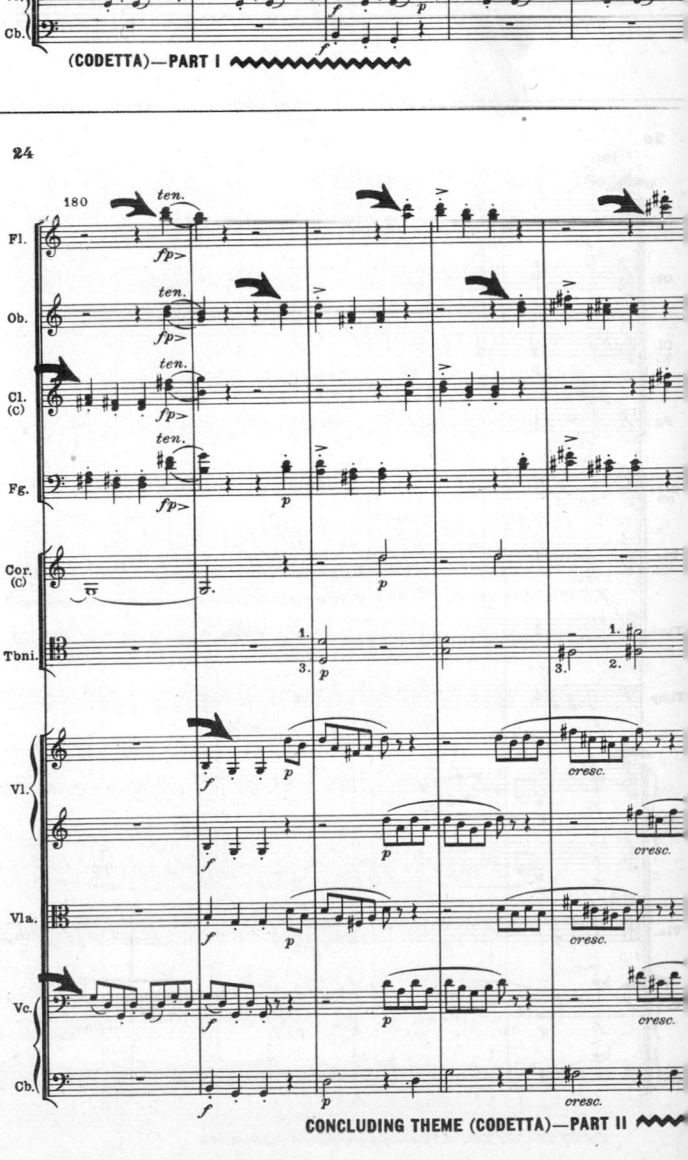

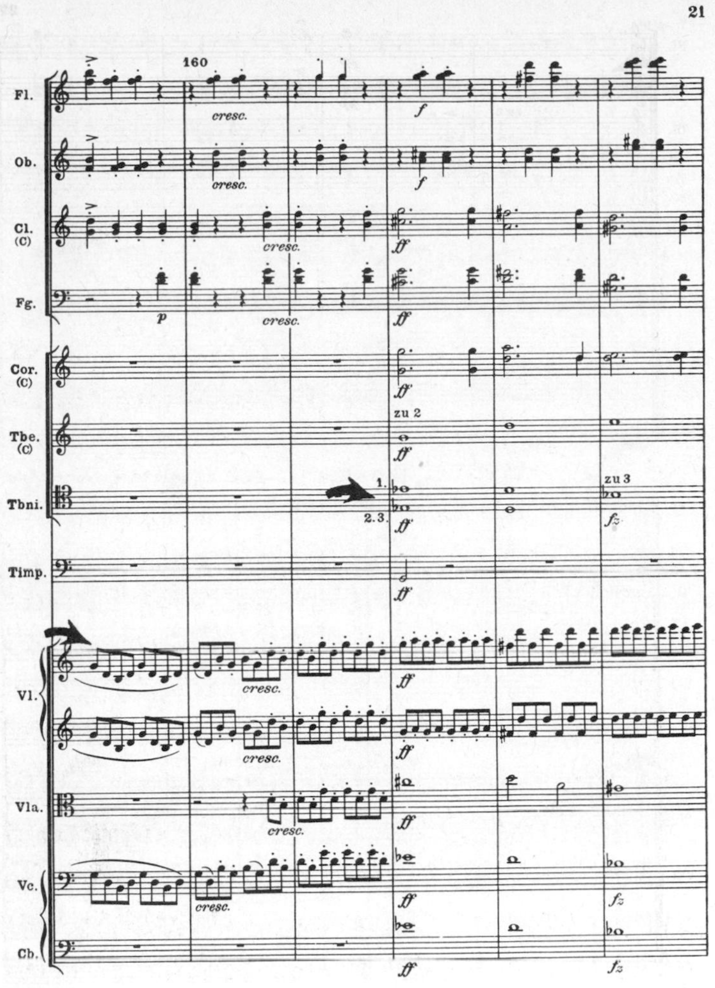
21
160
Fl.
Ob.
Cl. (C)
Fg.
Cor. (C)
Tbe. (C)
Tbni.
Timp.
Vl.
Vla.
Vc.
Cb.
cresc.
zu 2
zu 3

170
Fl.
Ob.
Cl. (C)
Fg.
Cor. (C)
Tbe. (C)
Tbni.
Vl.
Vla.
Vc.
Cb.
zu 2
zu 3
CONCLUDING THEME
ten.
Vl.I.II.
(CODETTA)—PART I

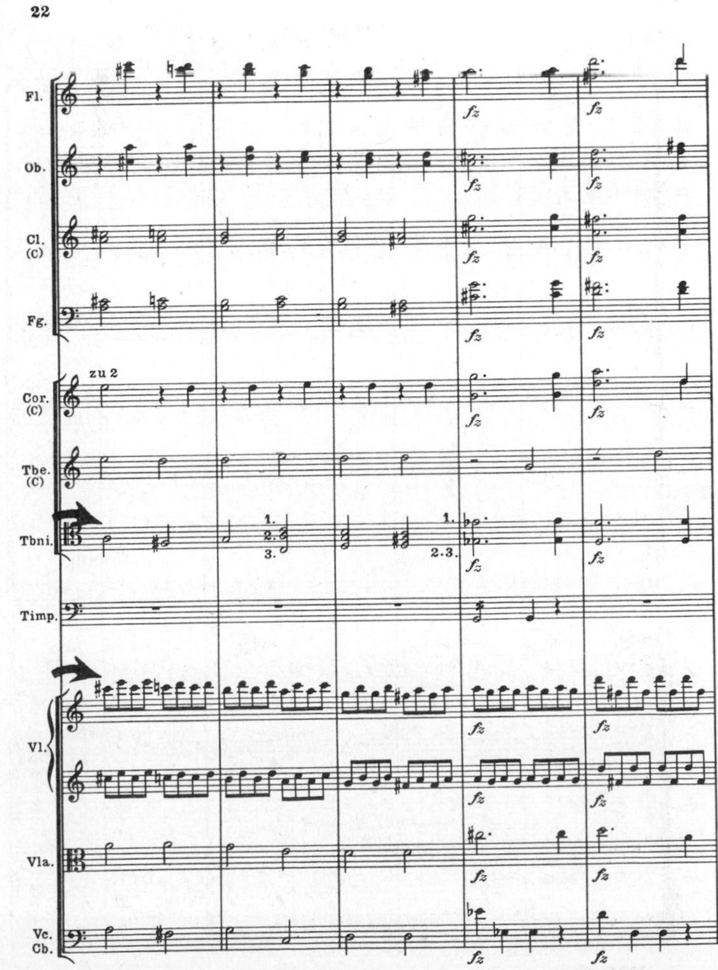
22
Fl.
Ob.
Cl. (C)
Fg.
Cor. (C)
Tbe. (C)
Tbni.
Timp.
Vl.
Vla.
Vc. Cb.
zu 2

24
180
Fl.
Ob.
Cl. (C)
Fg.
Cor. (C)
Tbni.
Vl.
Vla.
Vc.
Cb.
ten.
cresc.
CONCLUDING THEME (CODETTA)—PART II

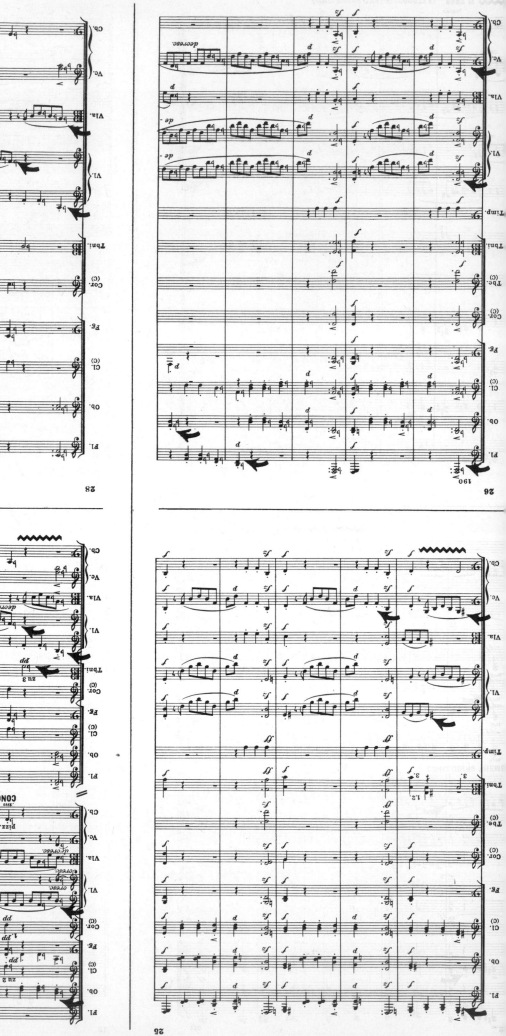
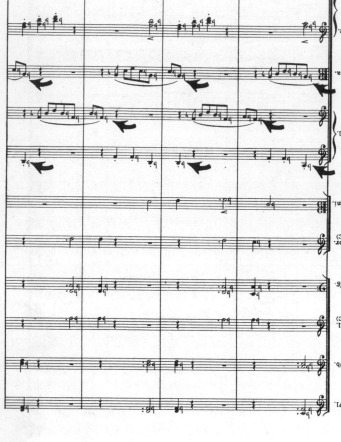
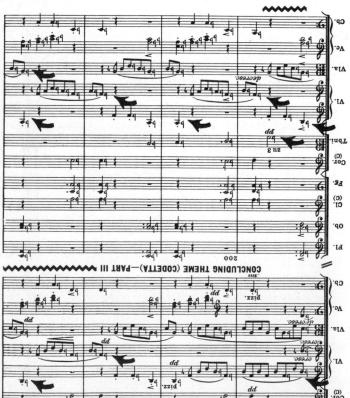

(259)

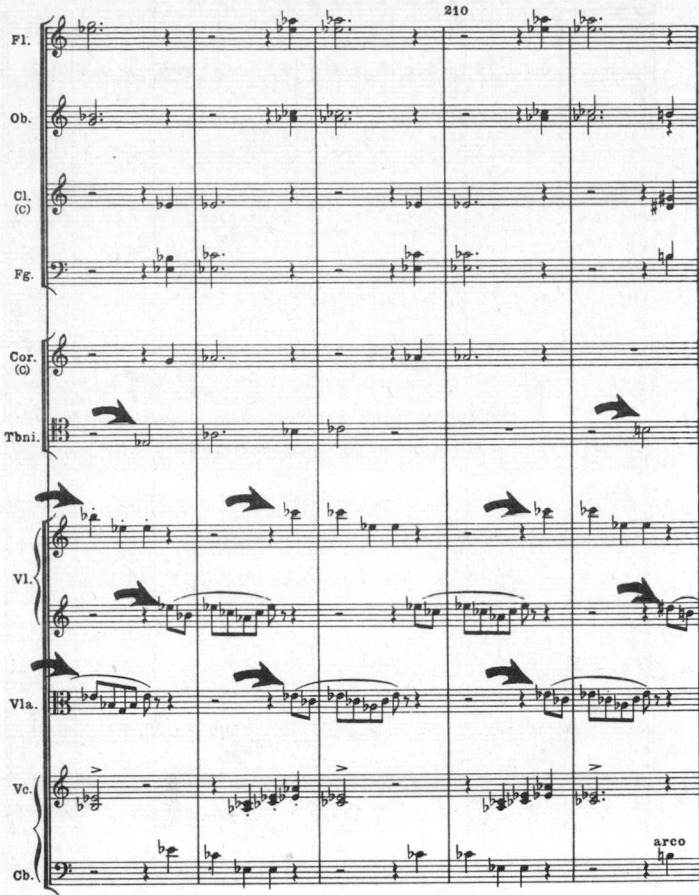

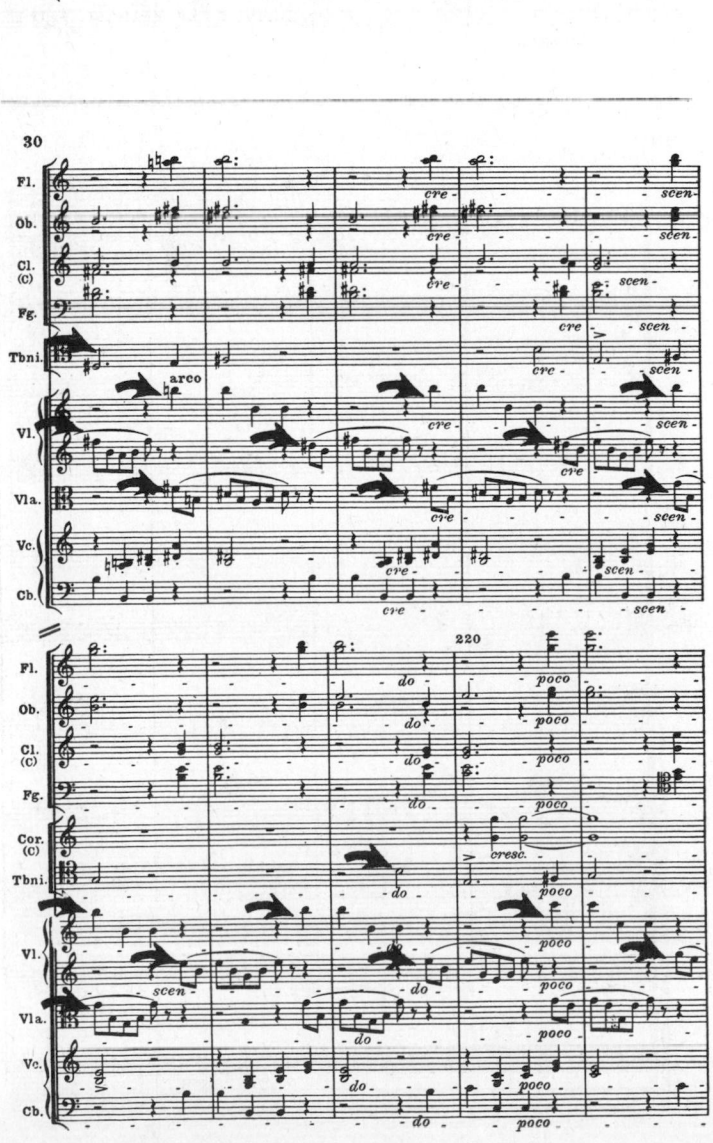

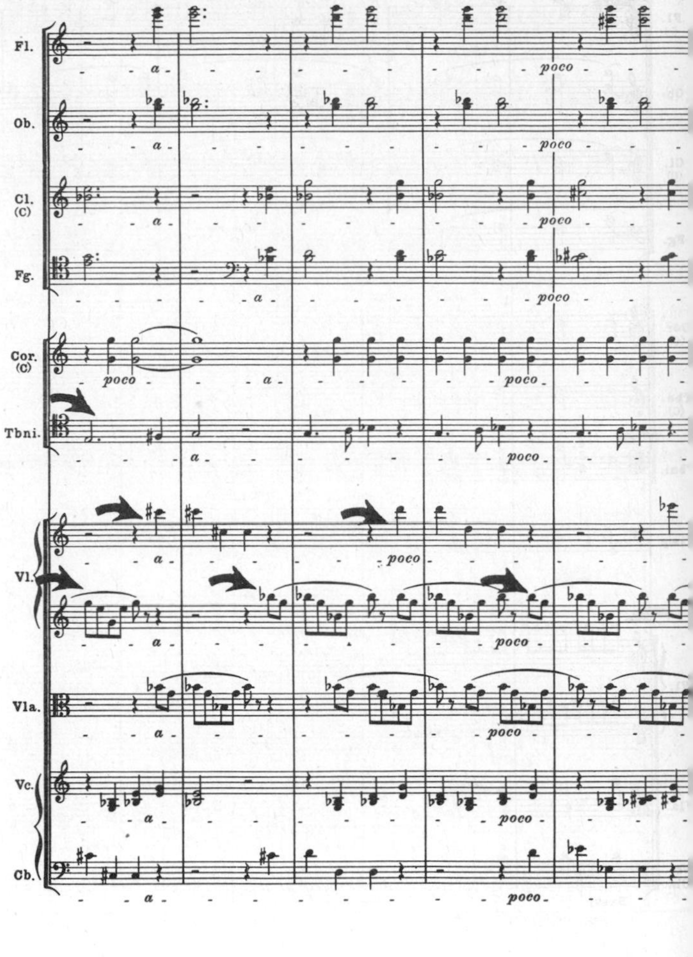

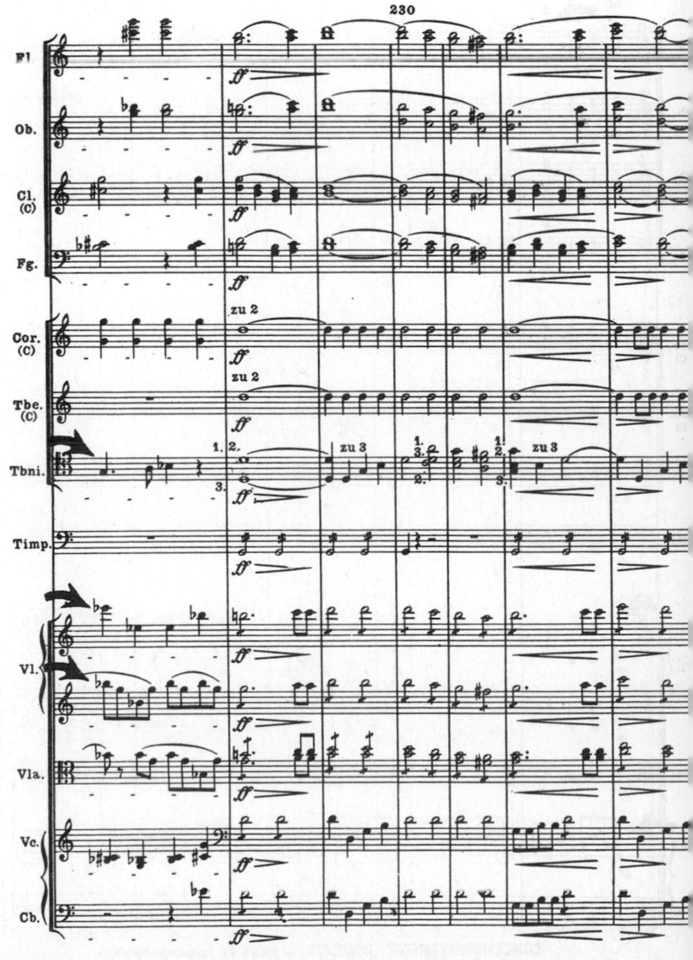

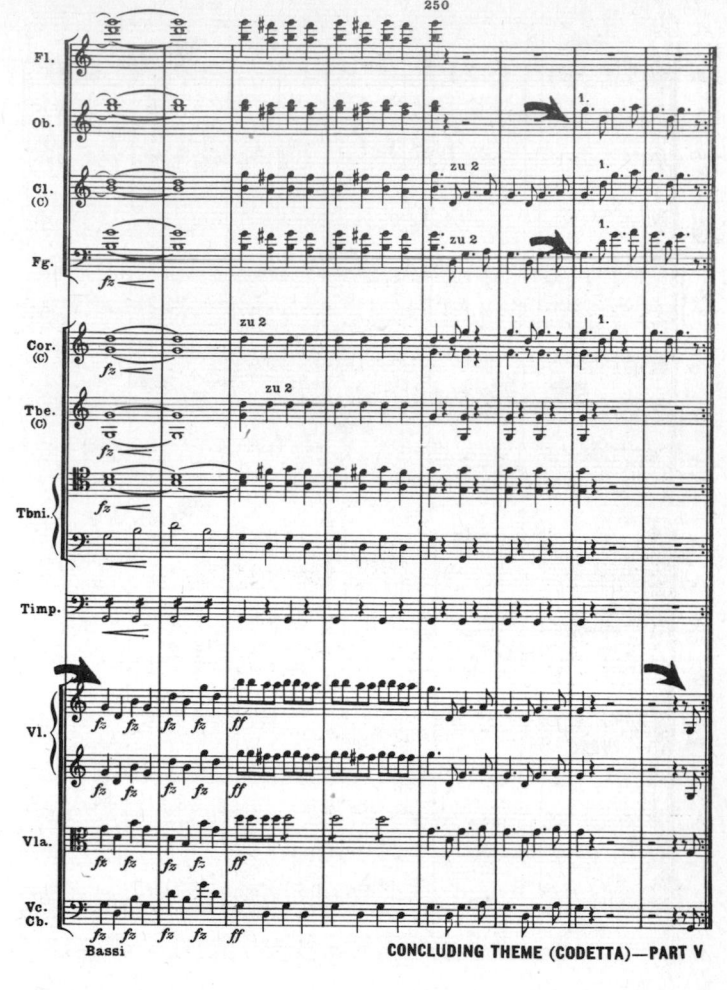

250

CONCLUDING THEME (CODETTA)—PART V

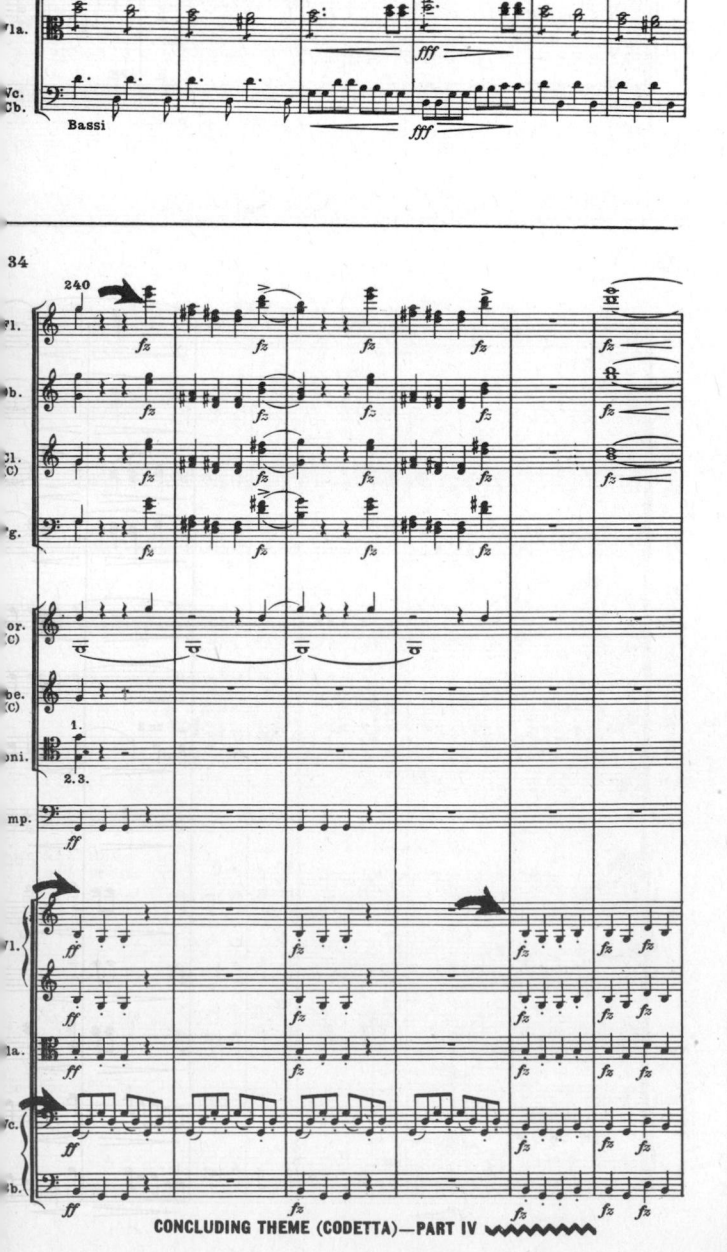

240

CONCLUDING THEME (CODETTA)—PART IV 〰〰〰

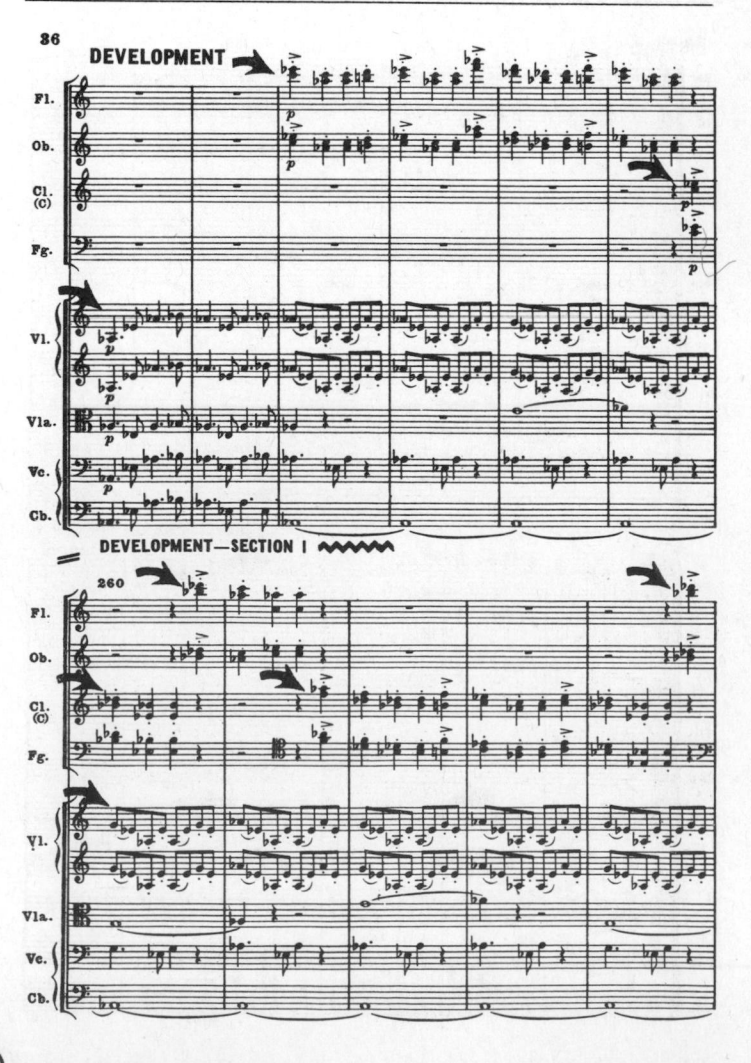

DEVELOPMENT

DEVELOPMENT—SECTION I 〰〰〰

260

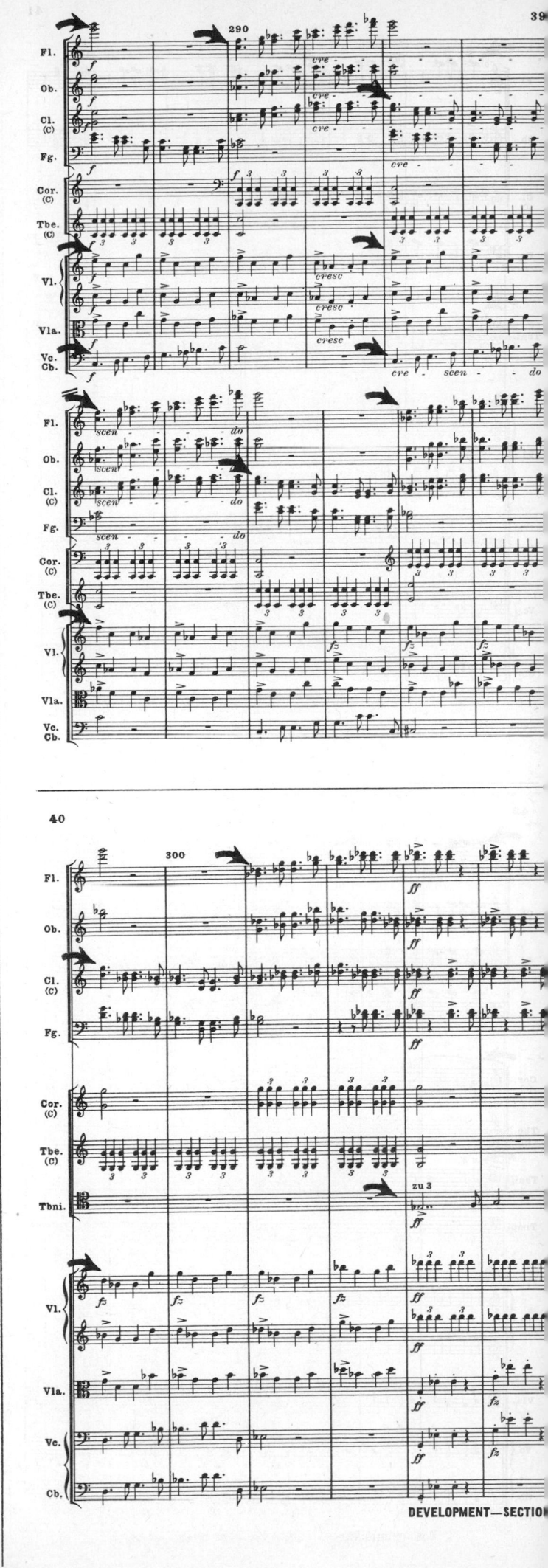

DEVELOPMENT—SECTION 2

DEVELOPMENT—SECTION 3

DEVELOPMENT—SECTION

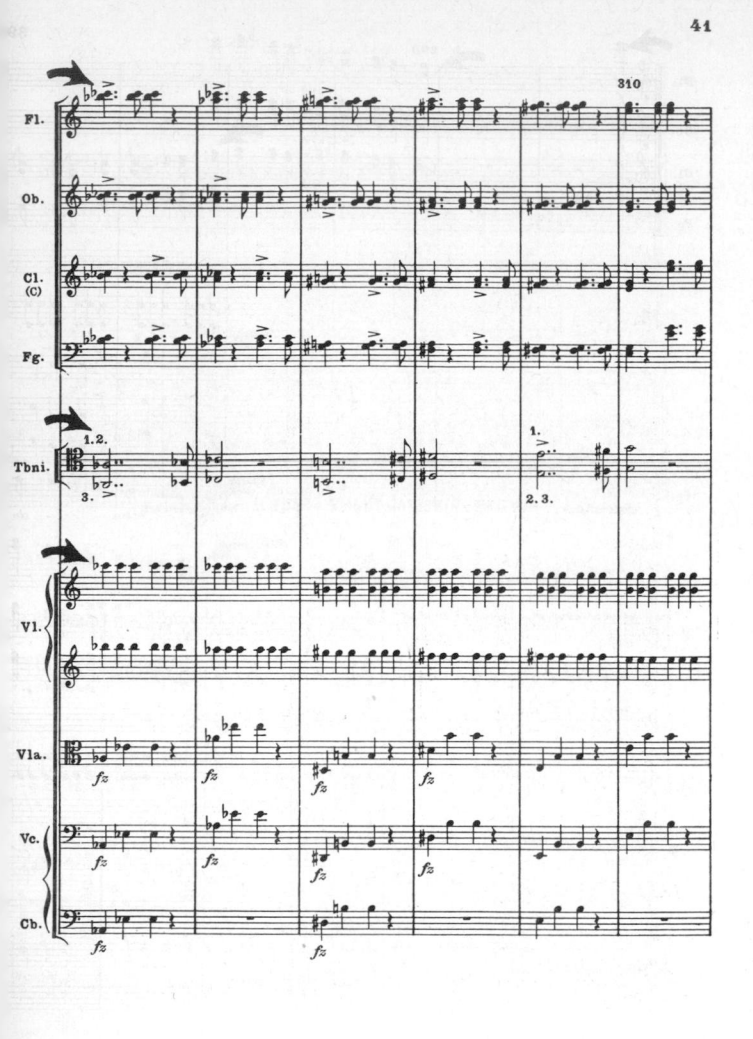

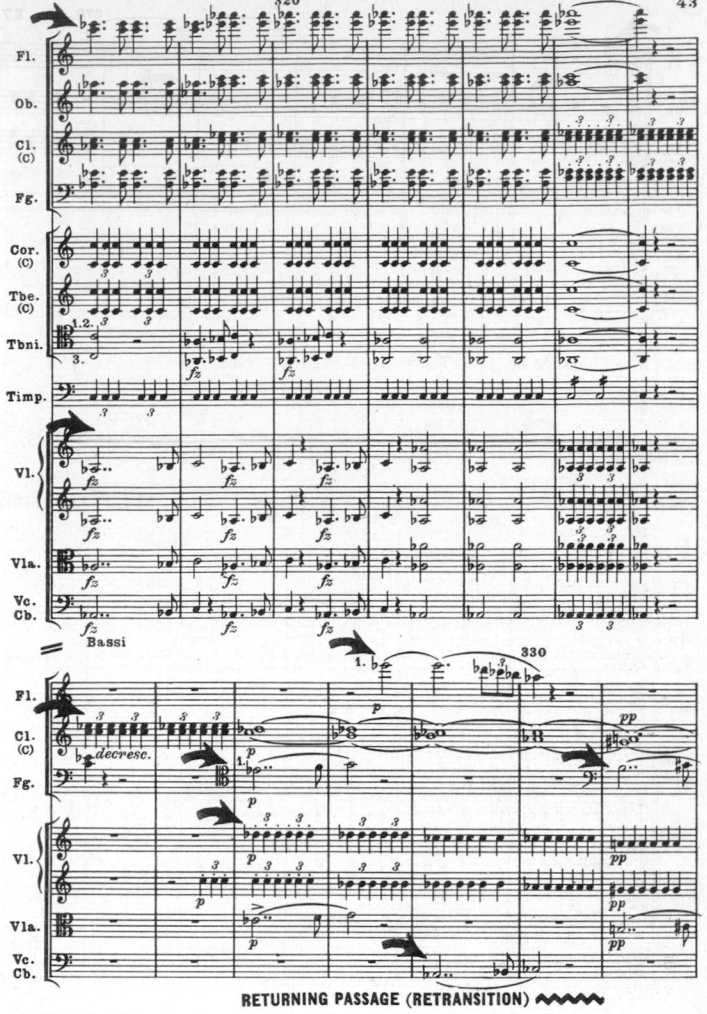

RETURNING PASSAGE (RETRANSITION) ∿∿∿∿

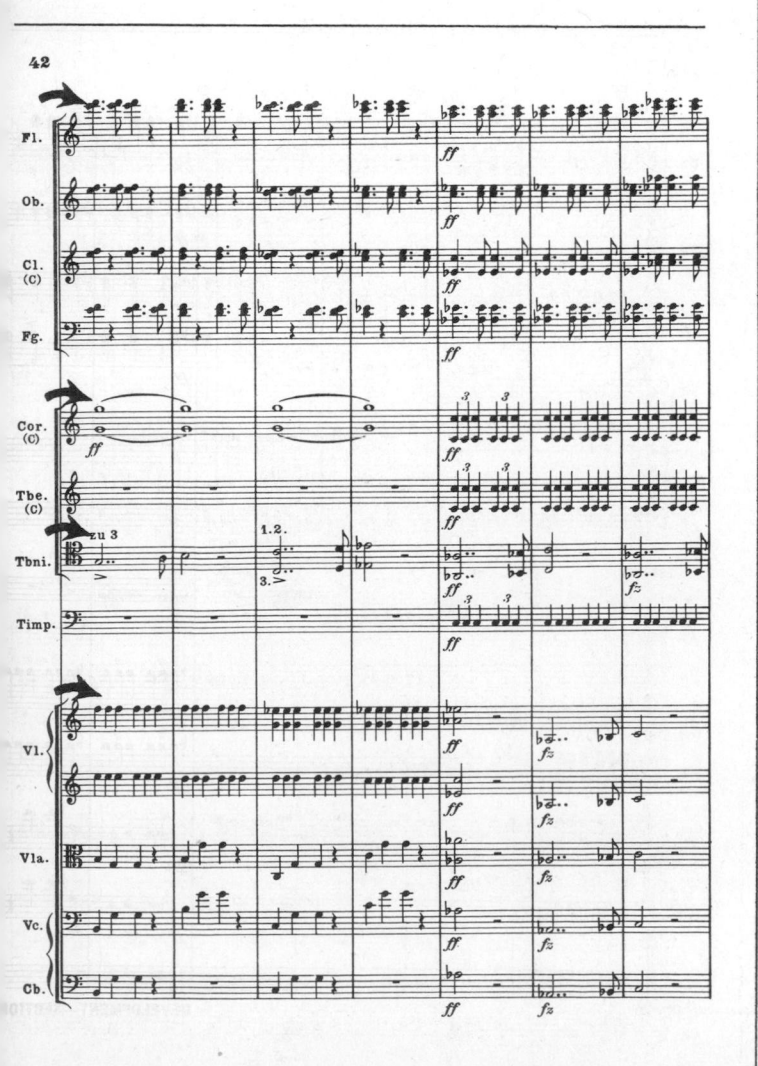

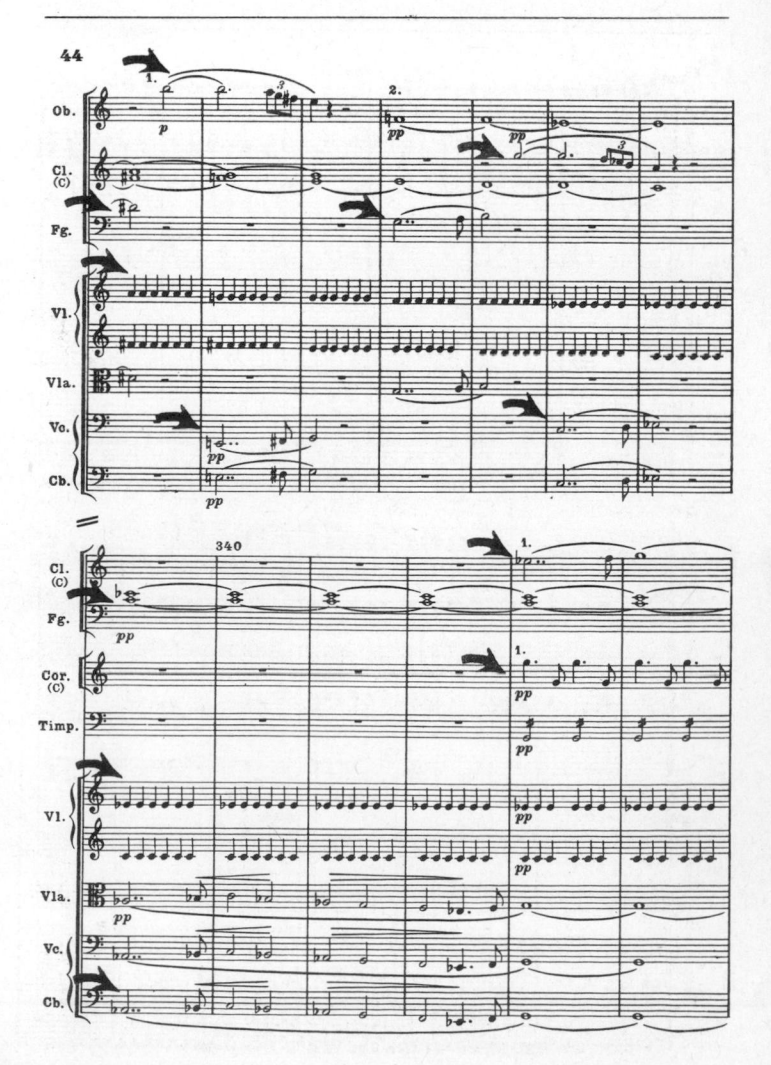

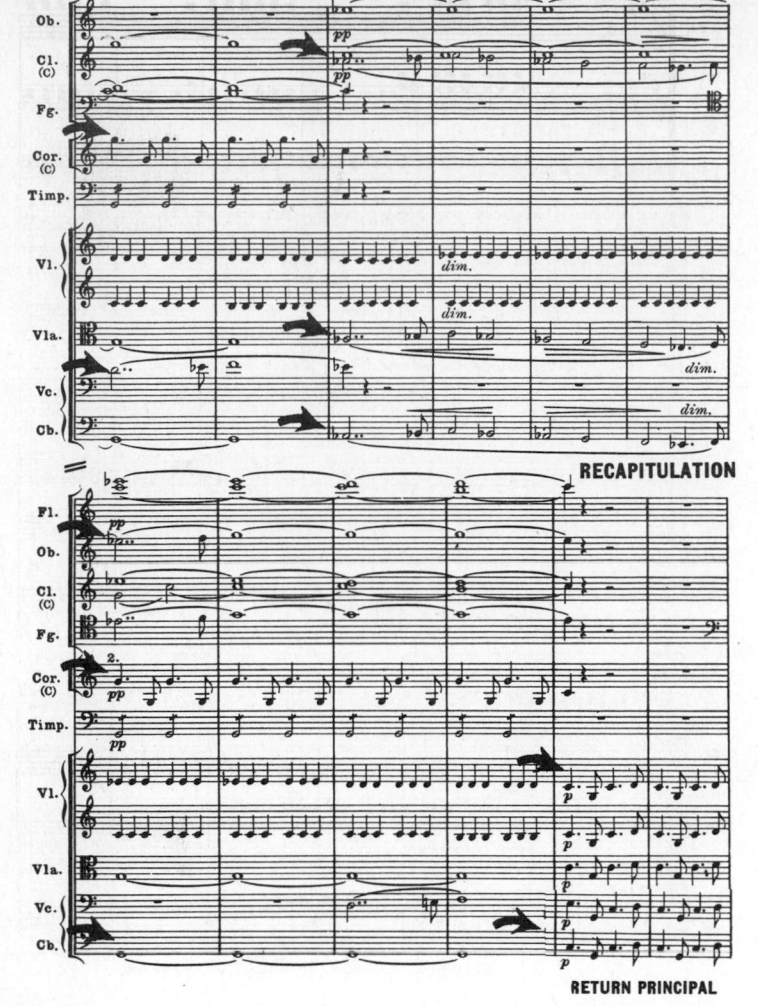

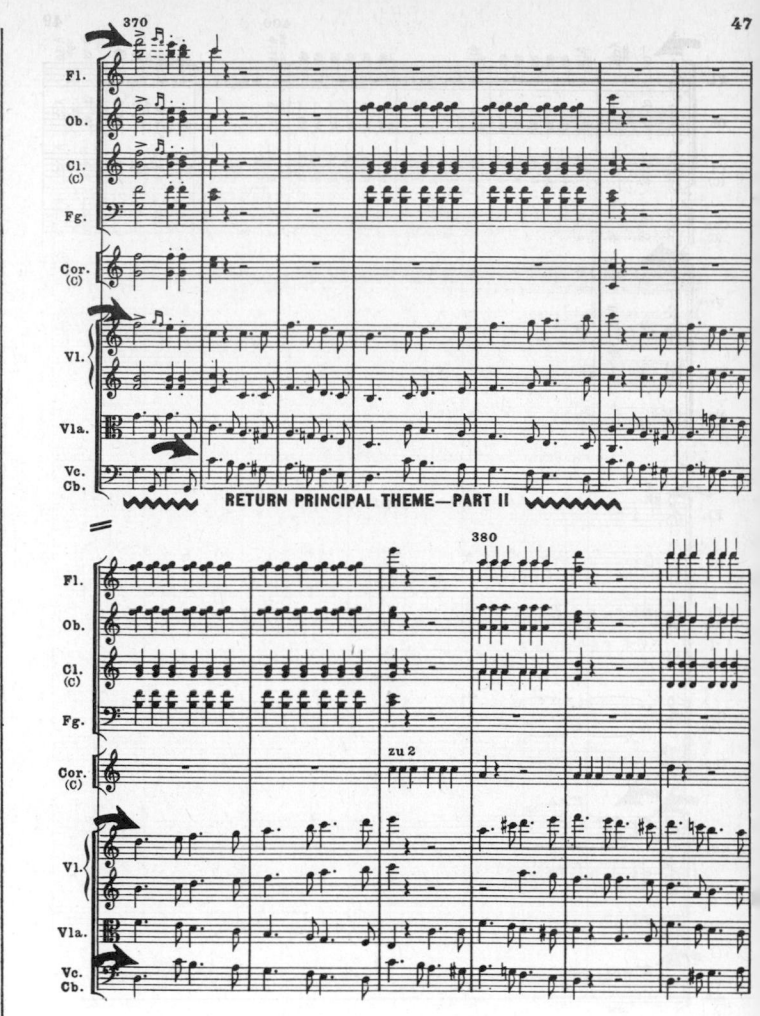

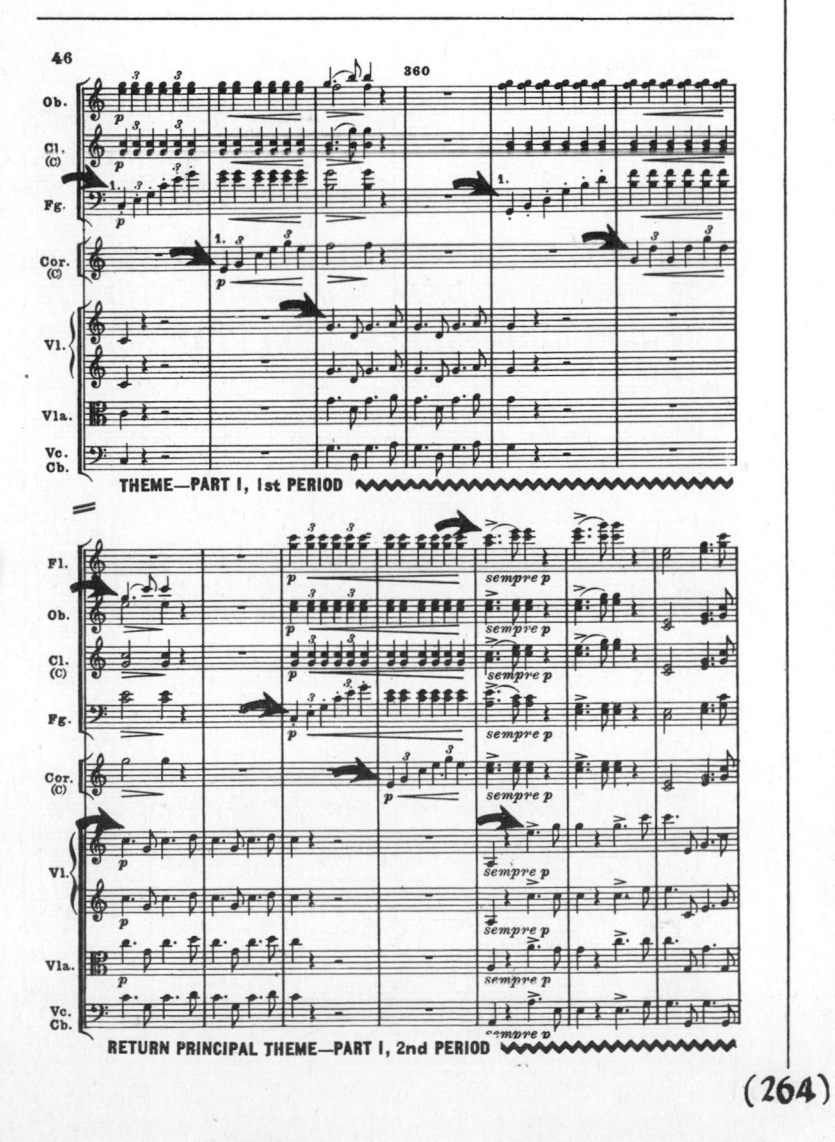

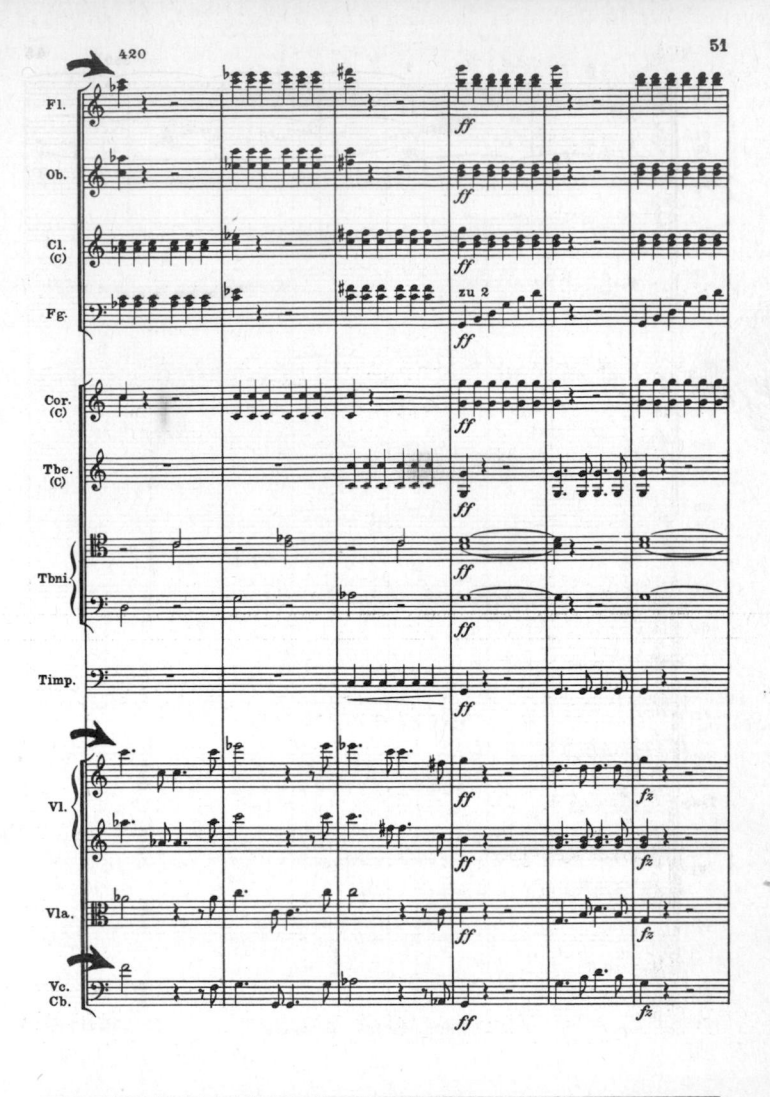

53

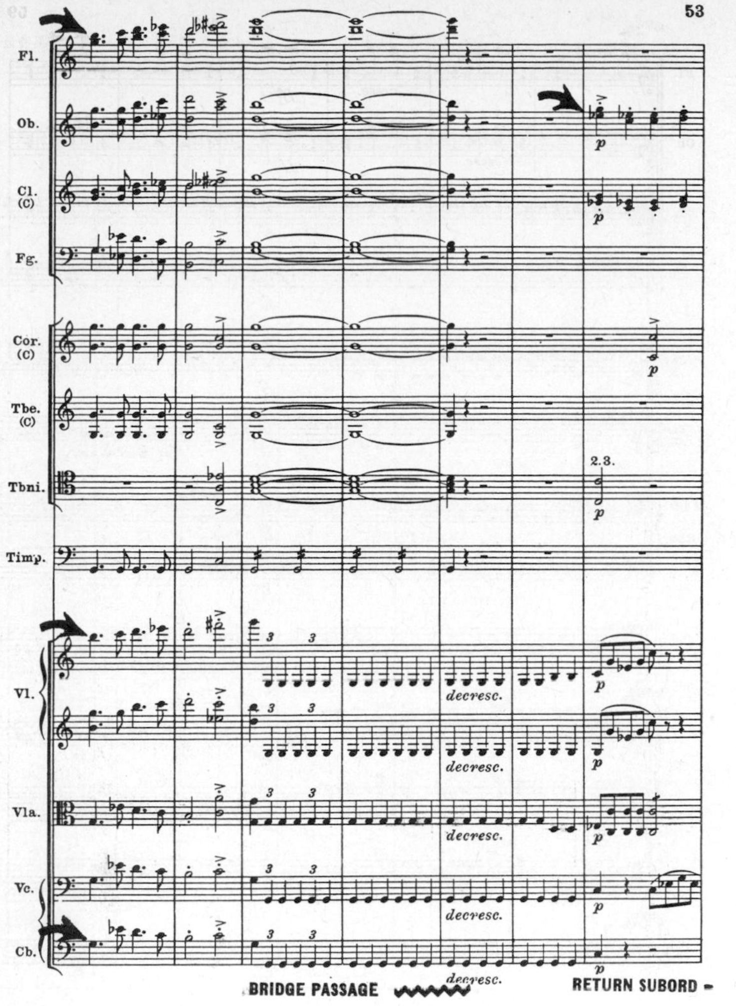
Fl.
Ob.
Cl. (C)
Fg.
Cor. (C)
Tbe. (C)
Tbni.
Timp.
Vl.
Vla.
Vc.
Cb.
2.3.
decresc.
BRIDGE PASSAGE
RETURN SUBORD -

55

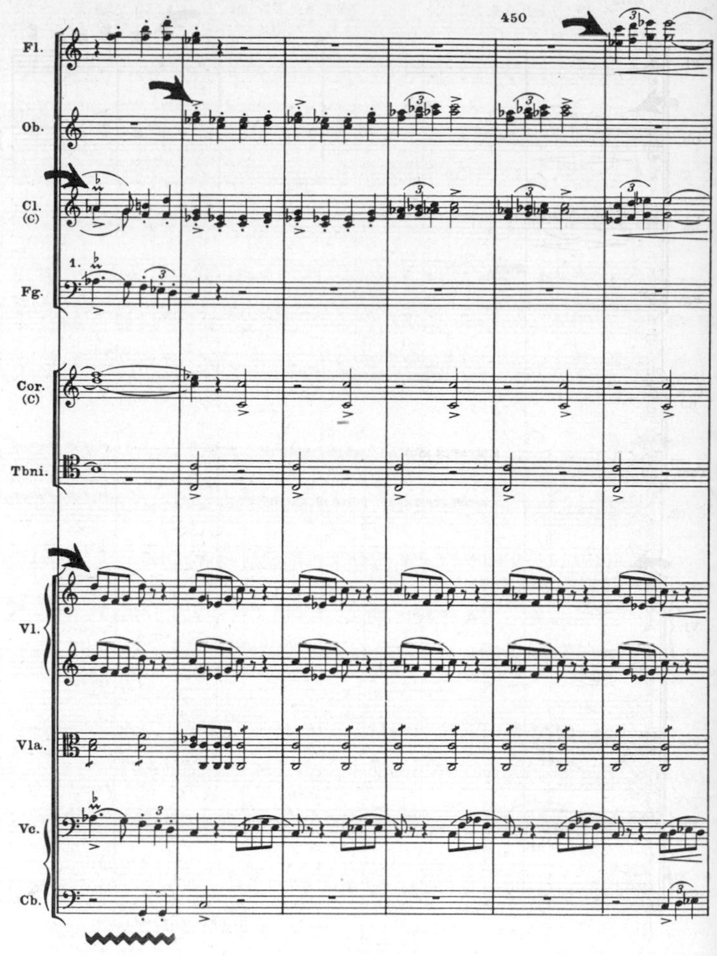
450
Fl.
Ob.
Cl. (C)
Fg.
Cor. (C)
Tbni.
Vl.
Vla.
Vc.
Cb.

54

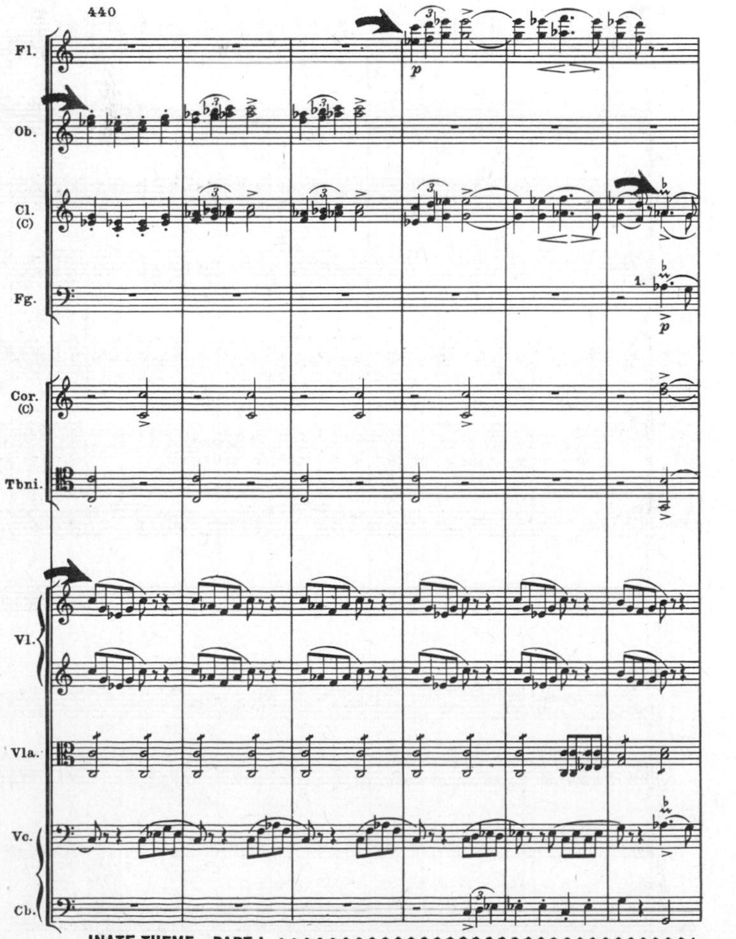
440
Fl.
Ob.
Cl. (C)
Fg.
Cor. (C)
Tbni.
Vl.
Vla.
Vc.
Cb.
INATE THEME—PART I

56

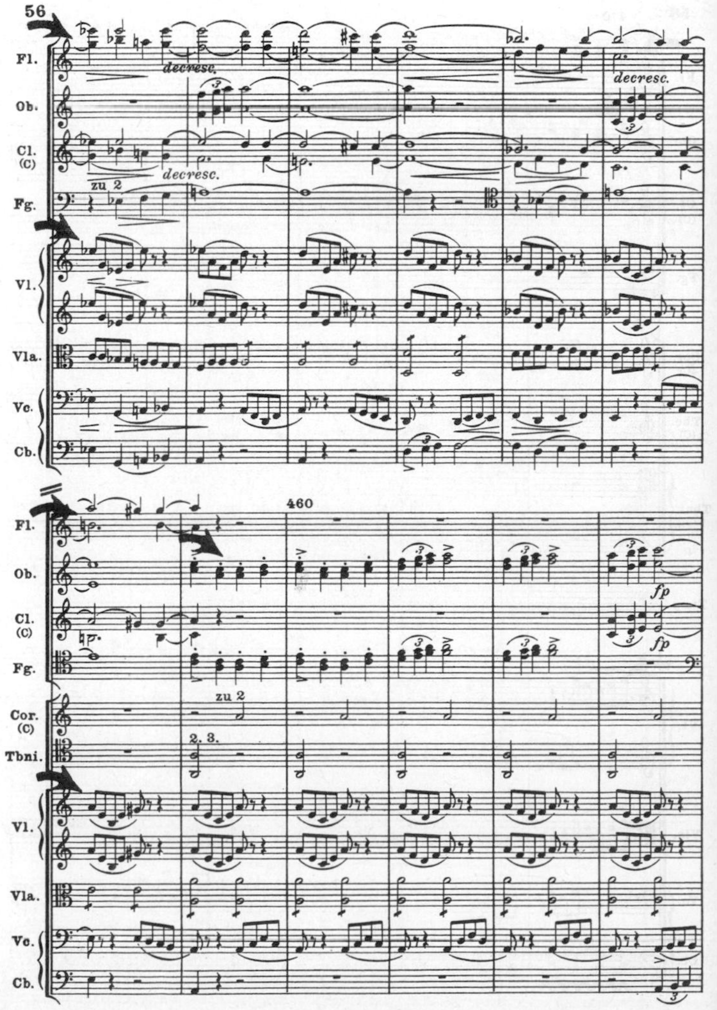
Fl.
Ob.
Cl. (C)
Fg.
Vl.
Vla.
Vc.
Cb.
decresc.
zu 2
460
Cor. (C)
Tbni.
2. 3.
fp

57

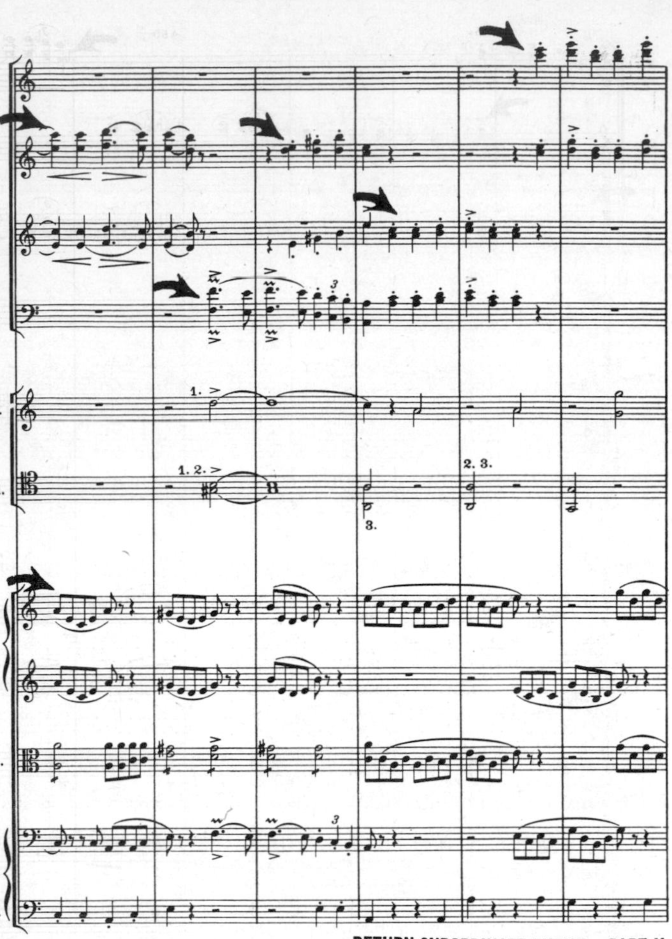

RETURN SUBORDINATE THEME— PART II

58

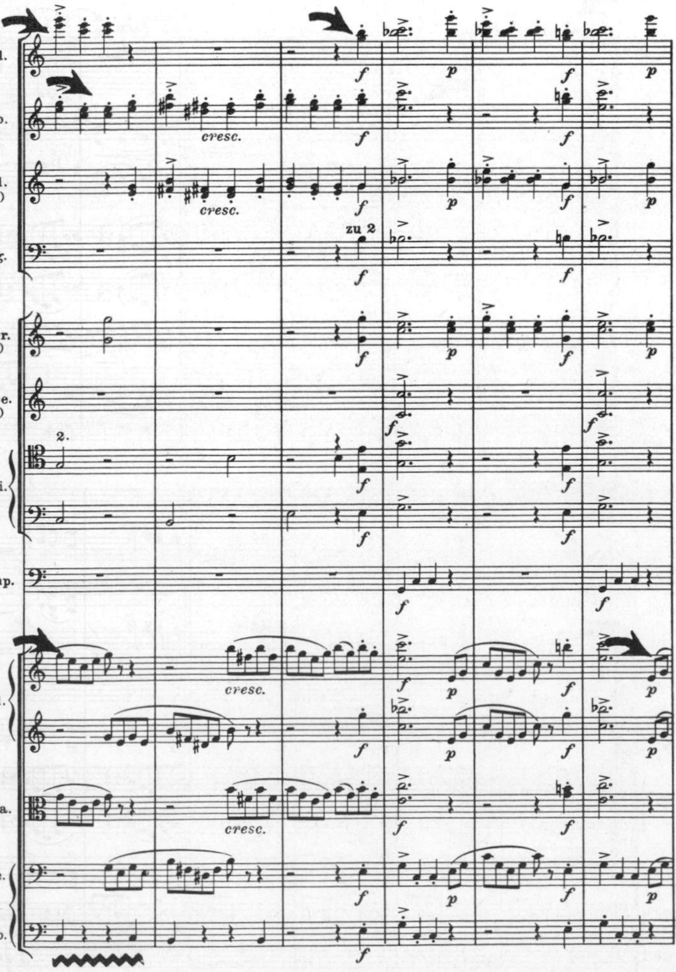

59

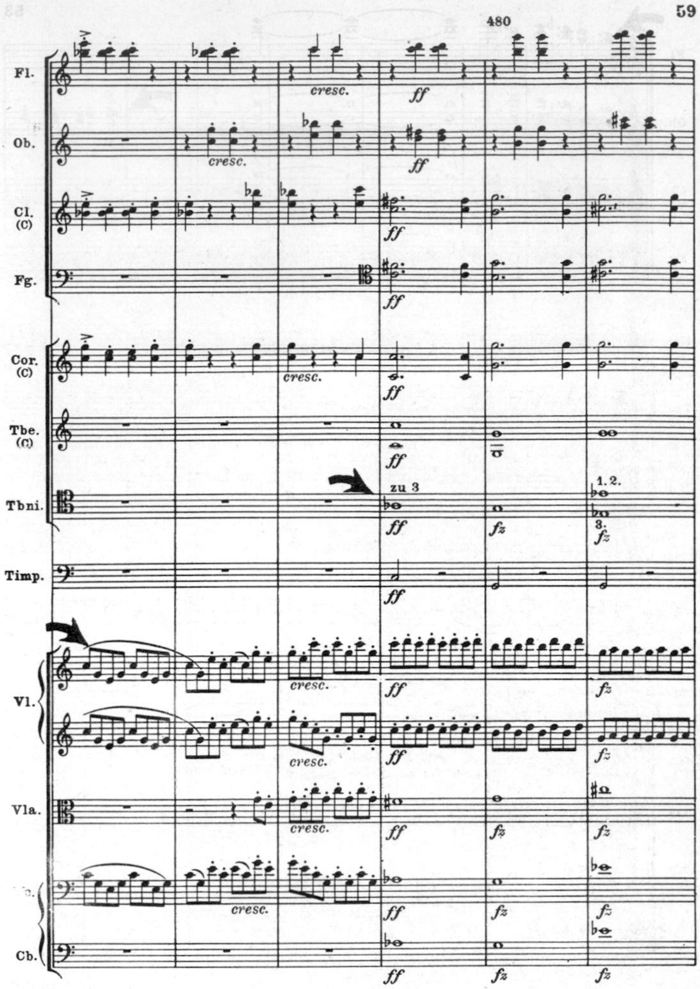

60

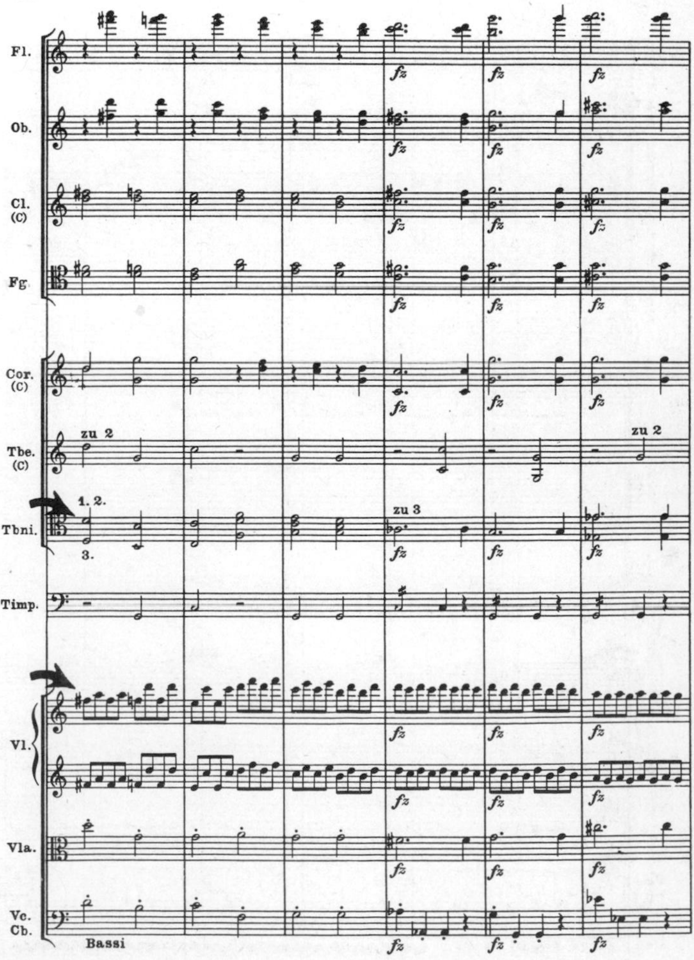

(267)

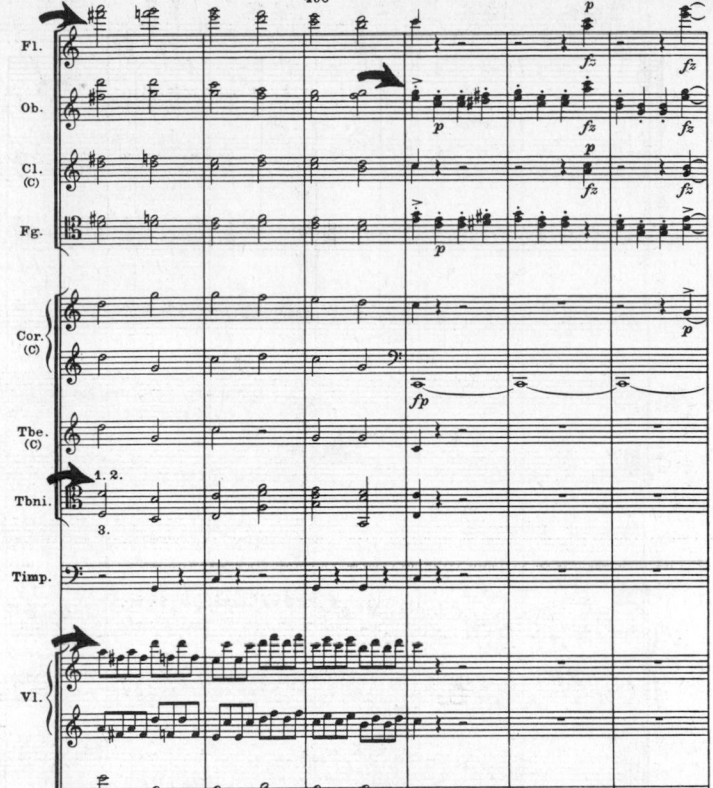

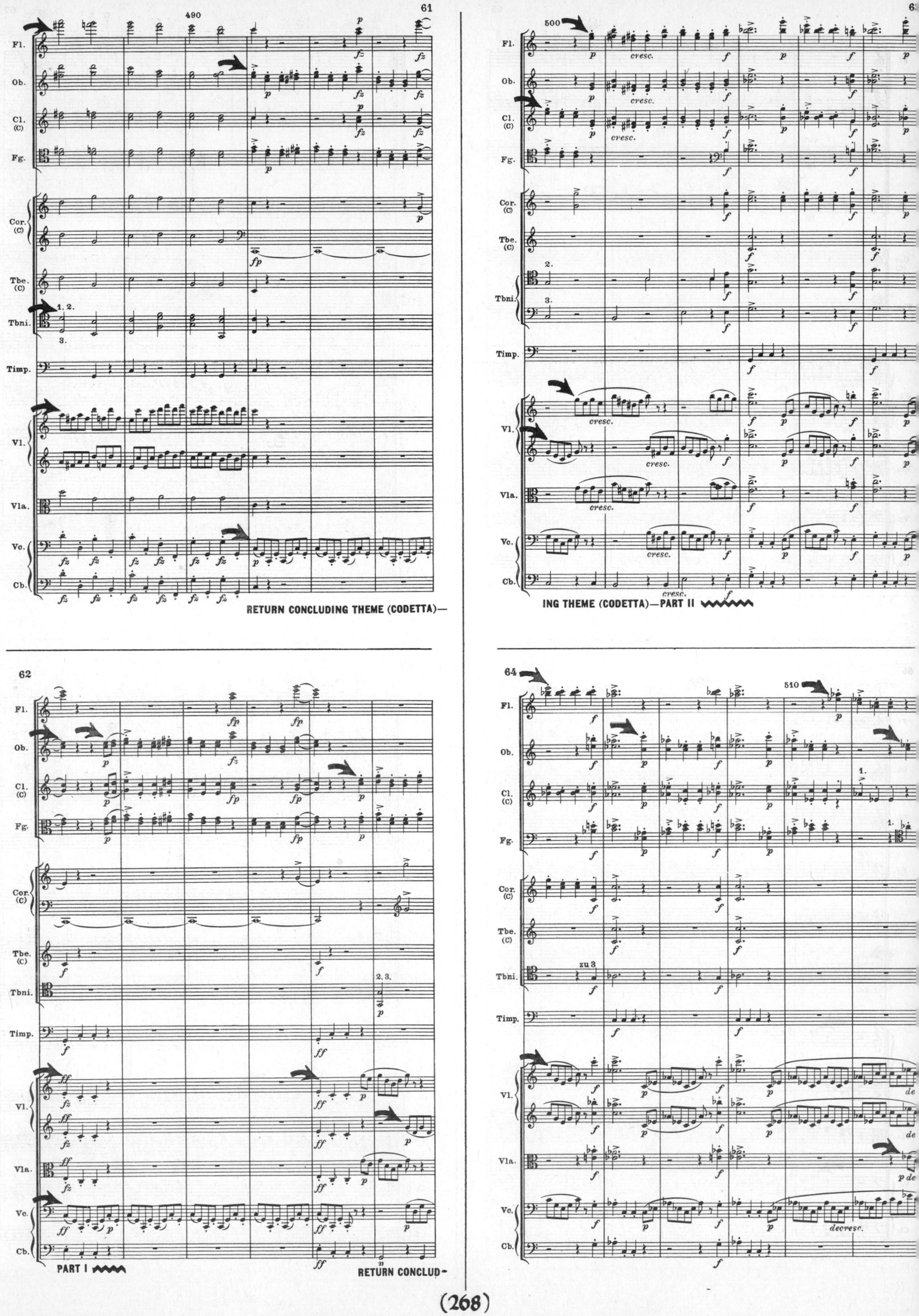

61

RETURN CONCLUDING THEME (CODETTA)—

63

ING THEME (CODETTA)—PART II ∿∿∿

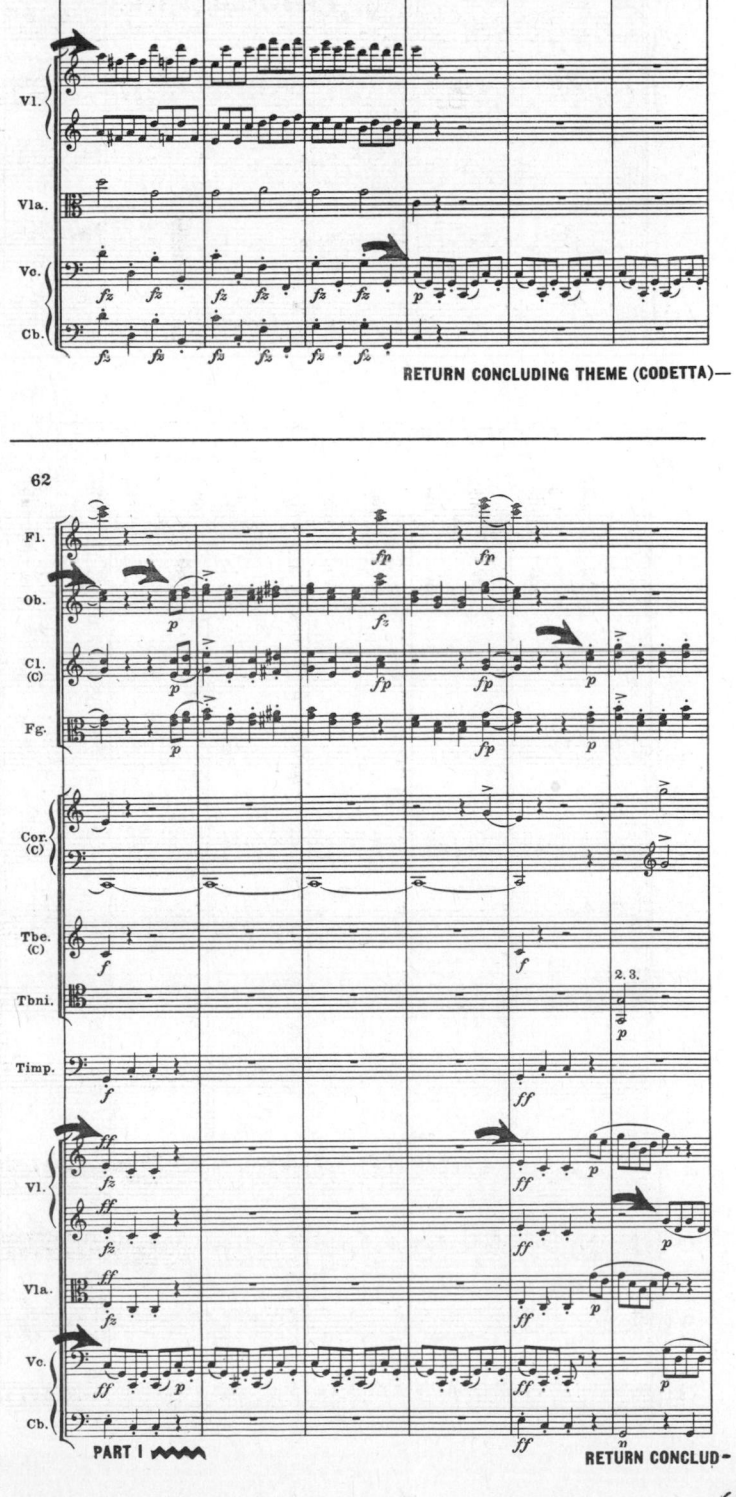

62

PART I ∿∿∿

RETURN CONCLUD-

64

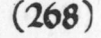

(268)

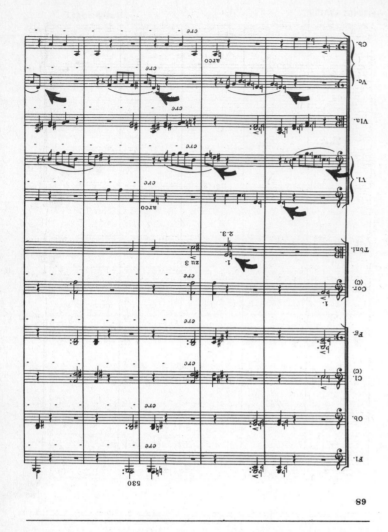

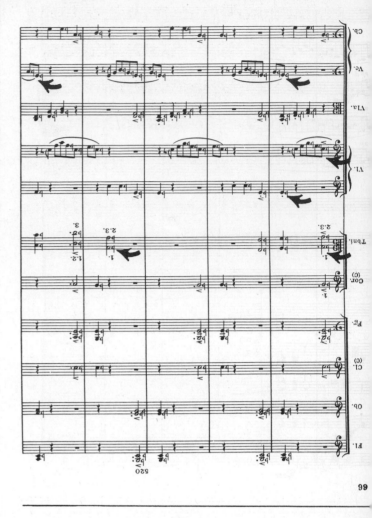

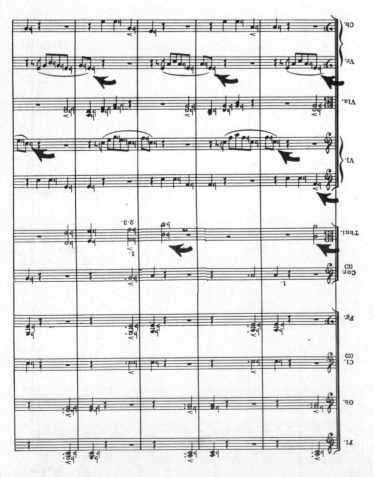

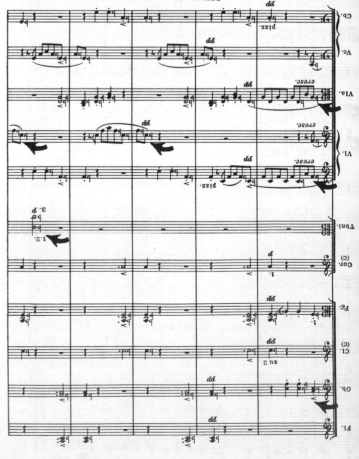

RETURN CONCLUDING THEME (CODETTA)—PART III

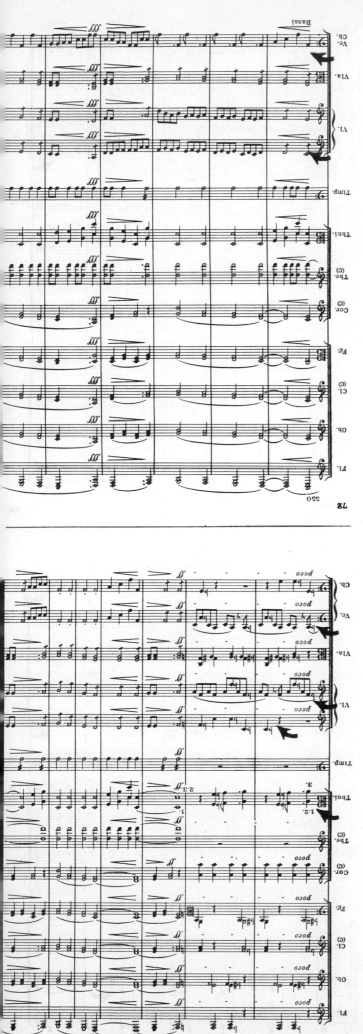
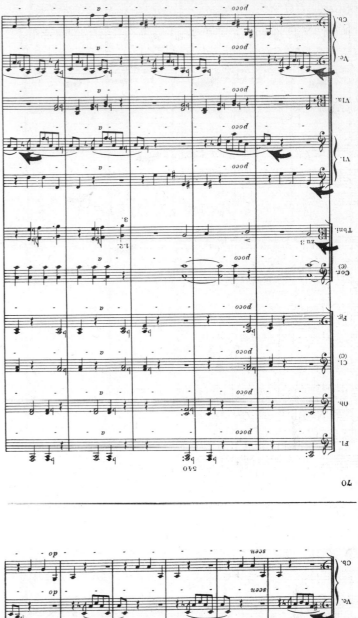
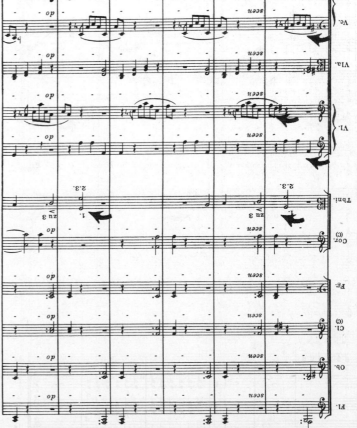

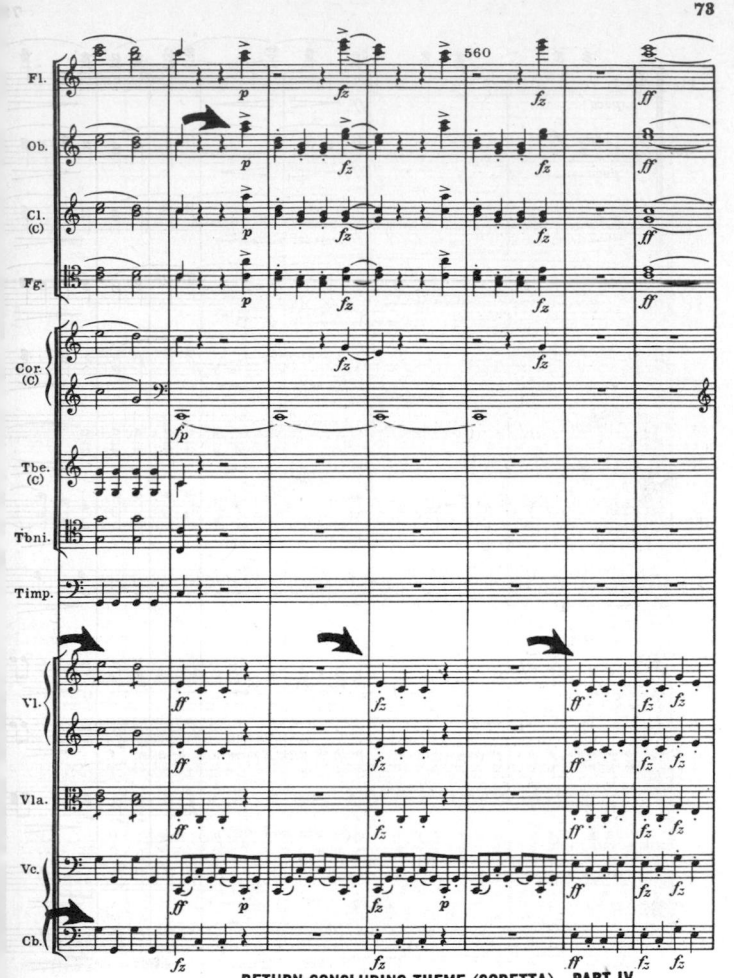

73
560
Fl.
Ob.
Cl. (C)
Fg.
Cor. (C)
Tbe. (C)
Tbni.
Timp.
Vl.
Vla.
Vc.
Cb.
RETURN CONCLUDING THEME (CODETTA)—PART IV

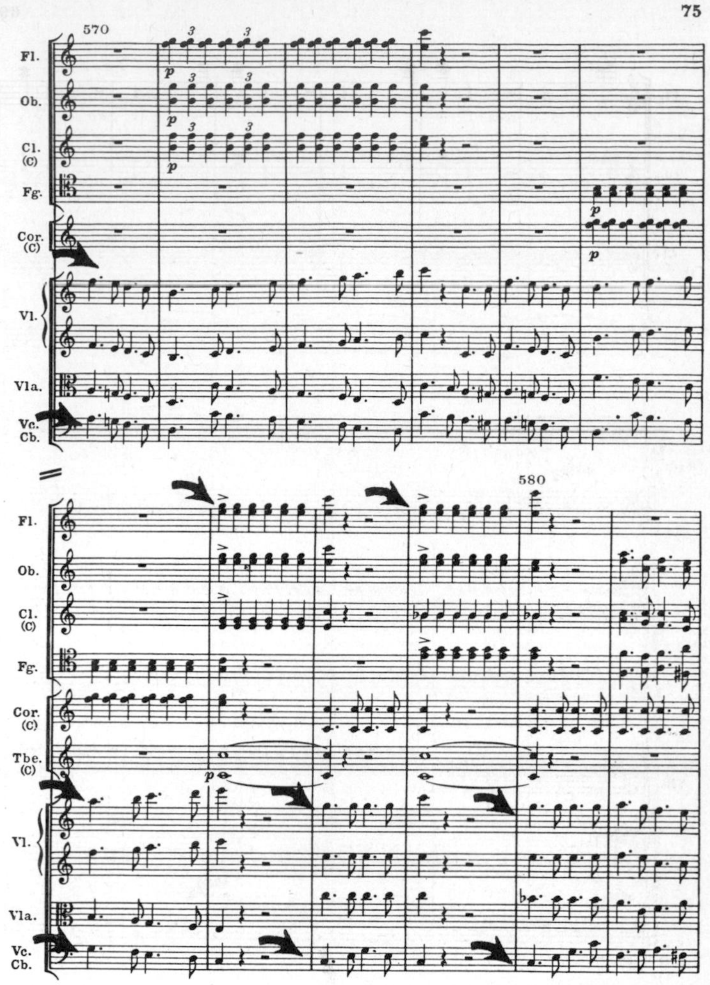
75
570
580
Fl.
Ob.
Cl. (C)
Fg.
Cor. (C)
Tbe. (C)
Vl.
Vla.
Vc. Cb.

74
CODA
Più moto
Fl.
Ob.
Cl. (C)
Fg.
Cor. (C)
Tbe. (C)
Tbni.
Timp.
Vl.
Vla.
Vc. Cb.
Bassi
Più moto
CODA—SECTION I

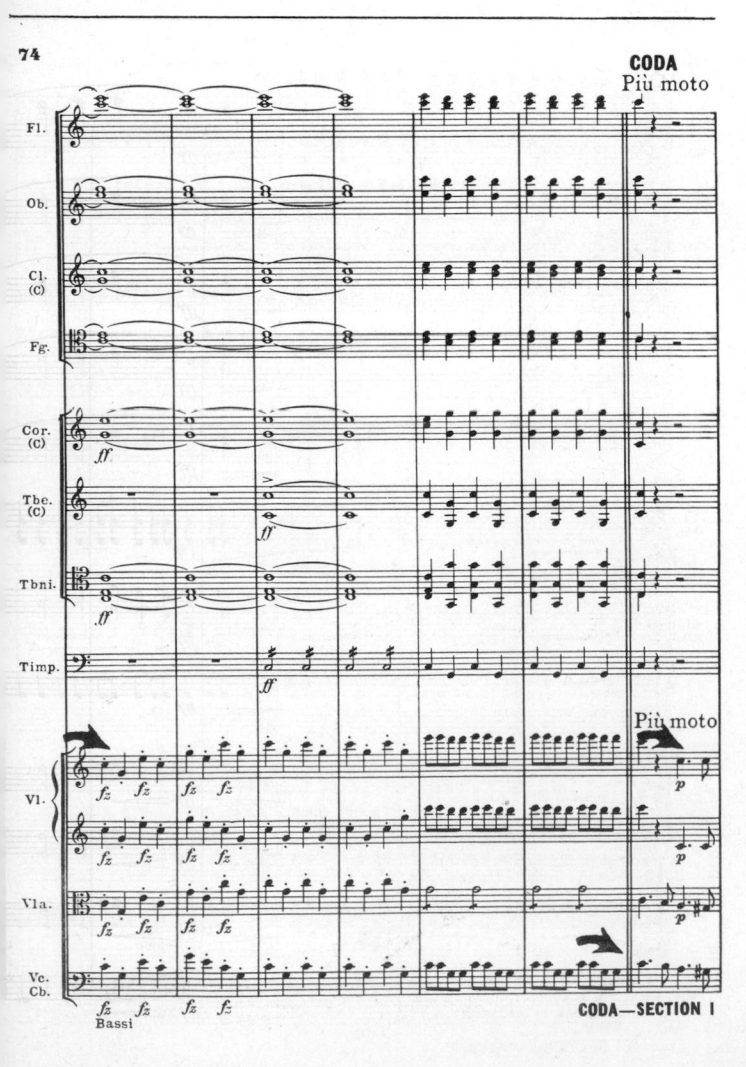

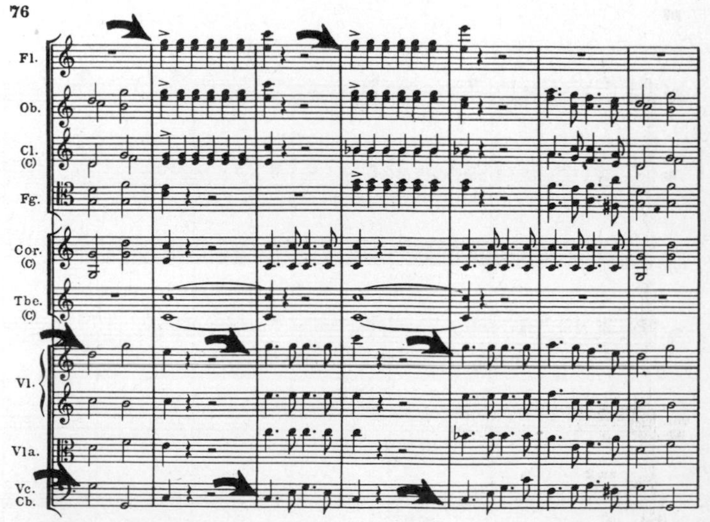
76
590
Fl.
Ob.
Cl. (C)
Fg.
Cor. (C)
Tbe. (C)
Vl.
Vla.
Vc. Cb.
cre
Vc. cre
CODA—SECTION 2

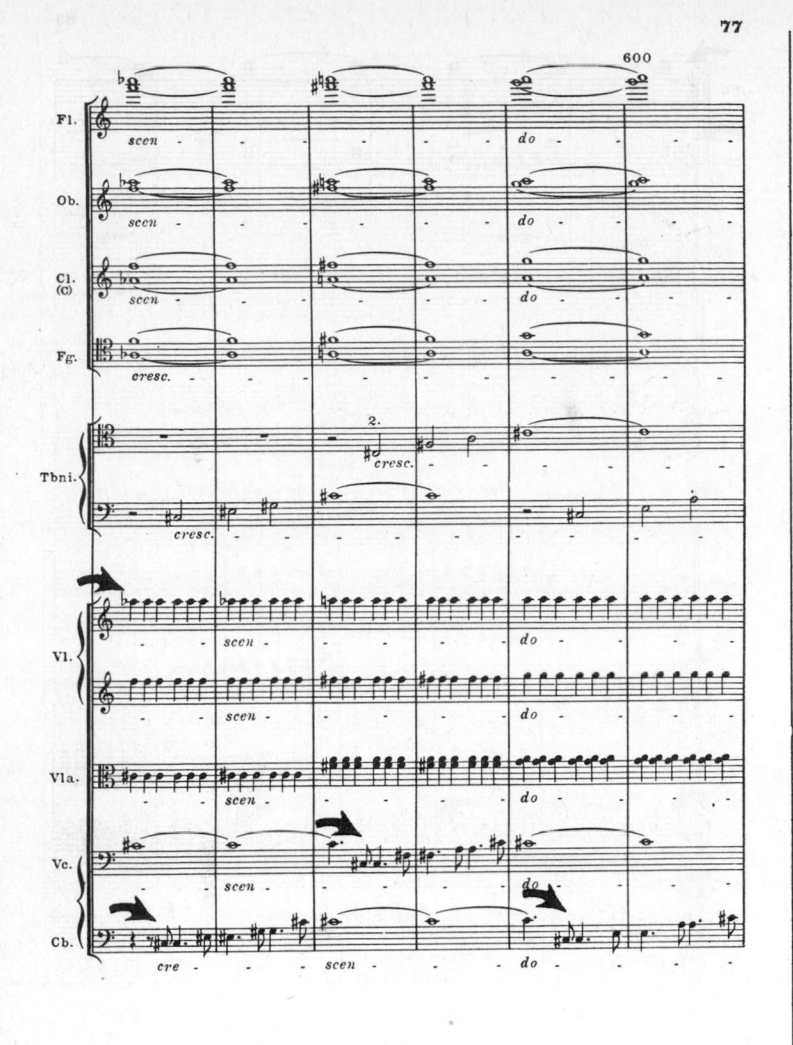
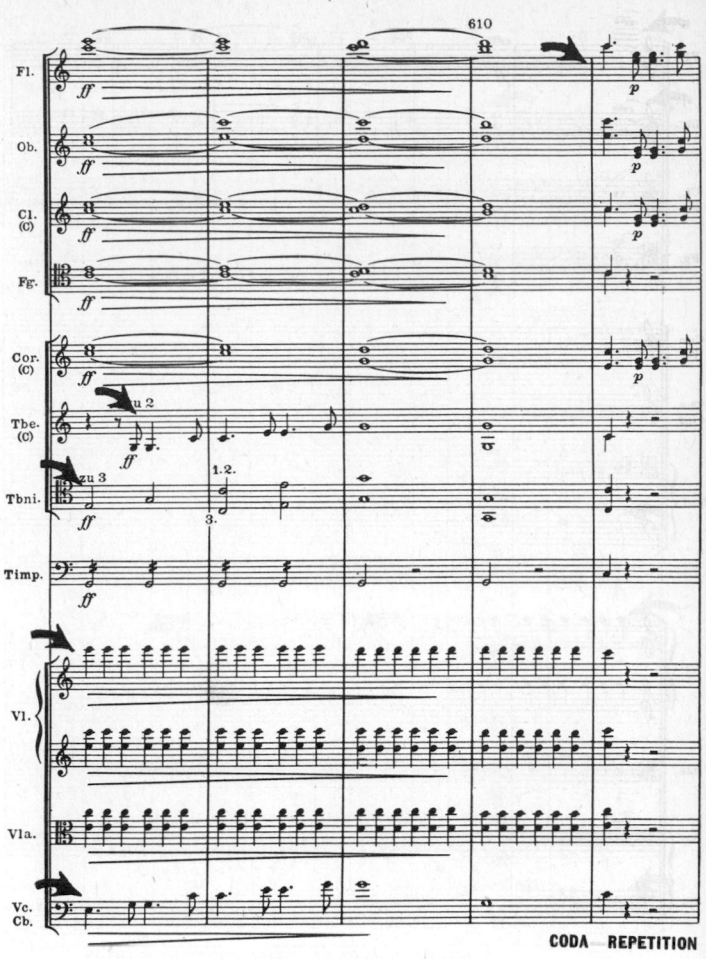
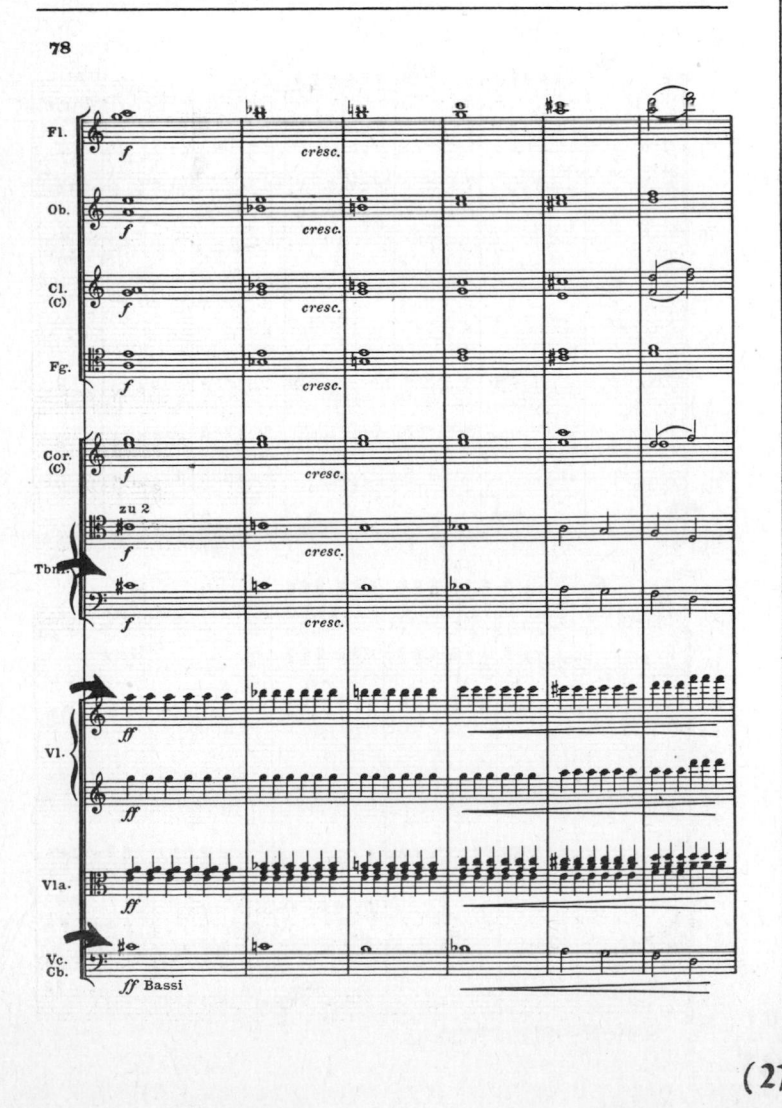
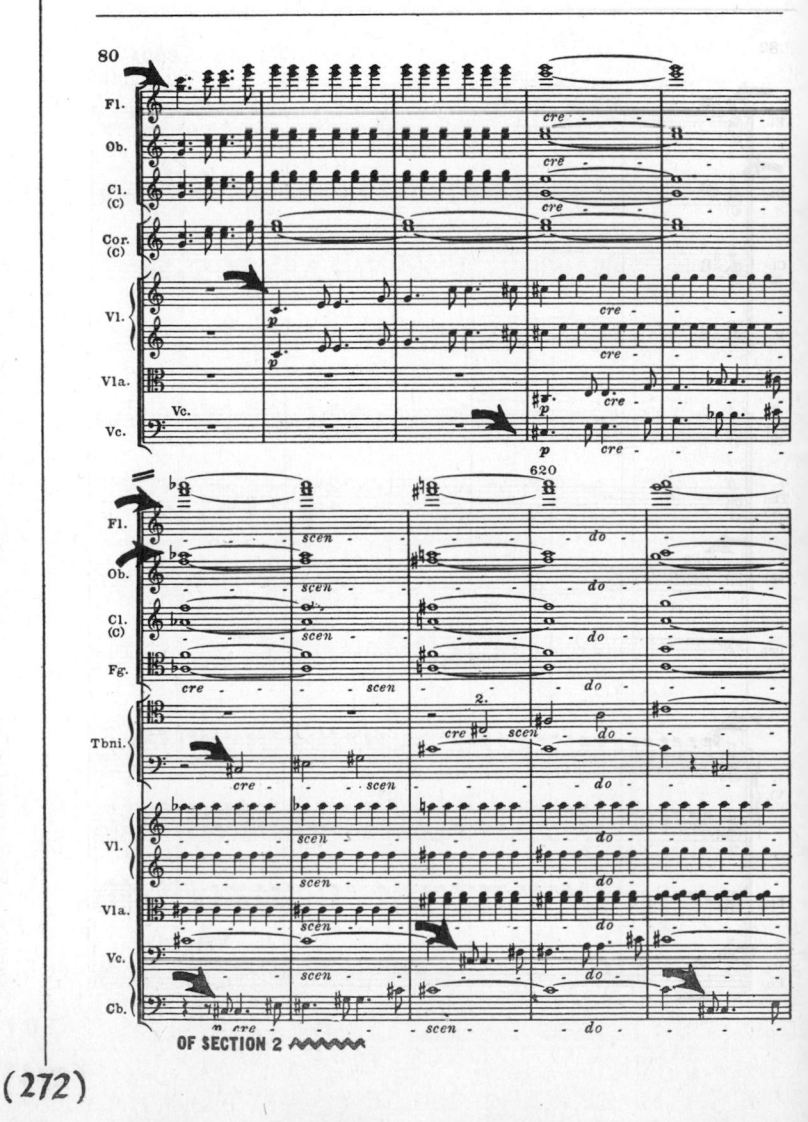

CODA — REPETITION

OF SECTION 2

(272)

81

Fl.
Ob.
Cl. (C)
Fg.
Cor. (C)
Tbe. (C)
Tbni.
Vl.
Vla.
Vc.
Cb.
zu 2
ff

83

Fl.
Ob.
Cl. (C)
Fg.
Cor. (C)
Tbe. (C)
Tbni.
Timp.
Vl.
Vla.
Vc. Cb.
zu 2
zu 3
fz

82

630
Fl.
Ob.
Cl. (C)
Fg.
Cor. (C)
Tbe. (C)
Tbni.
Timp.
Vl.
Vla.
Vc. Cb.
Bassi
zu 2
zu 3
ff

84

640
Fl.
Ob.
Cl. (C)
Fg.
Cor. (C)
Tbe. (C)
Tbni.
Timp.
Vl.
Vla.
Vc. Cb.
zu 2
zu 3
fz

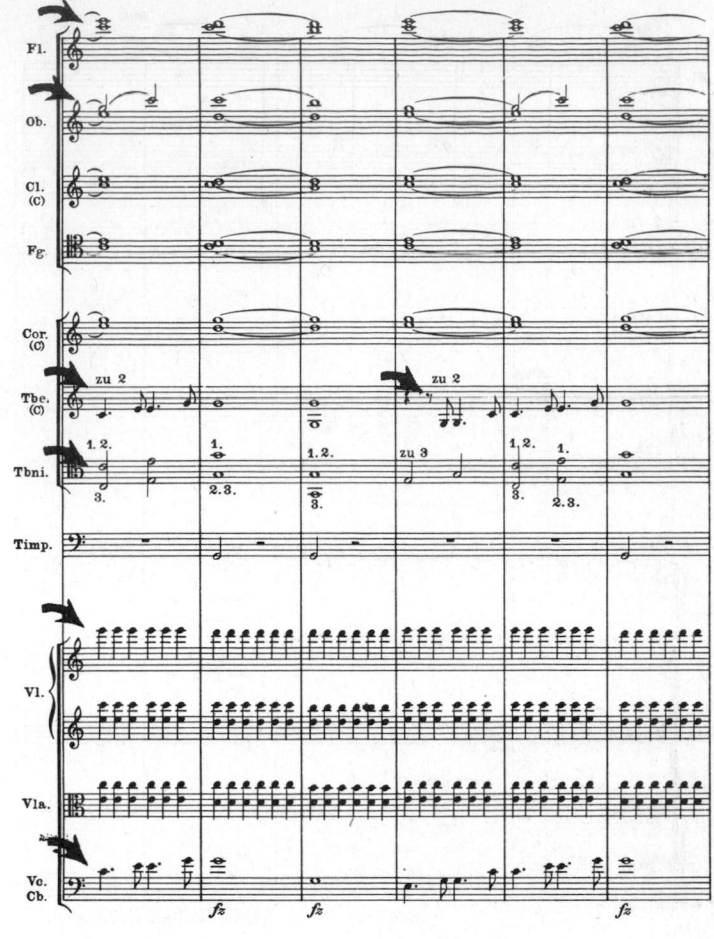

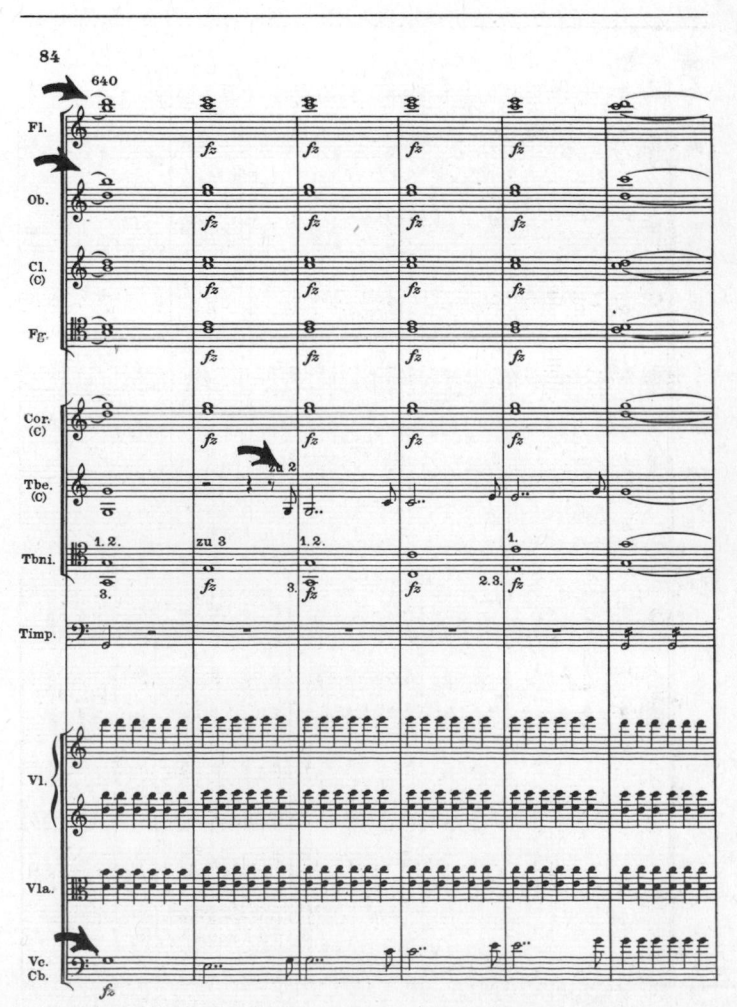

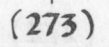

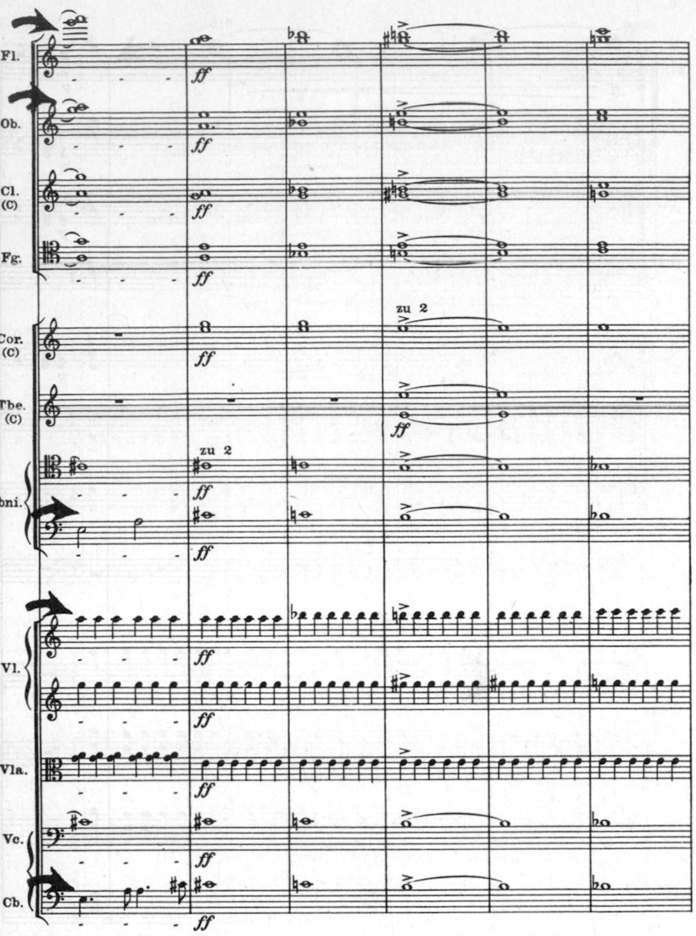

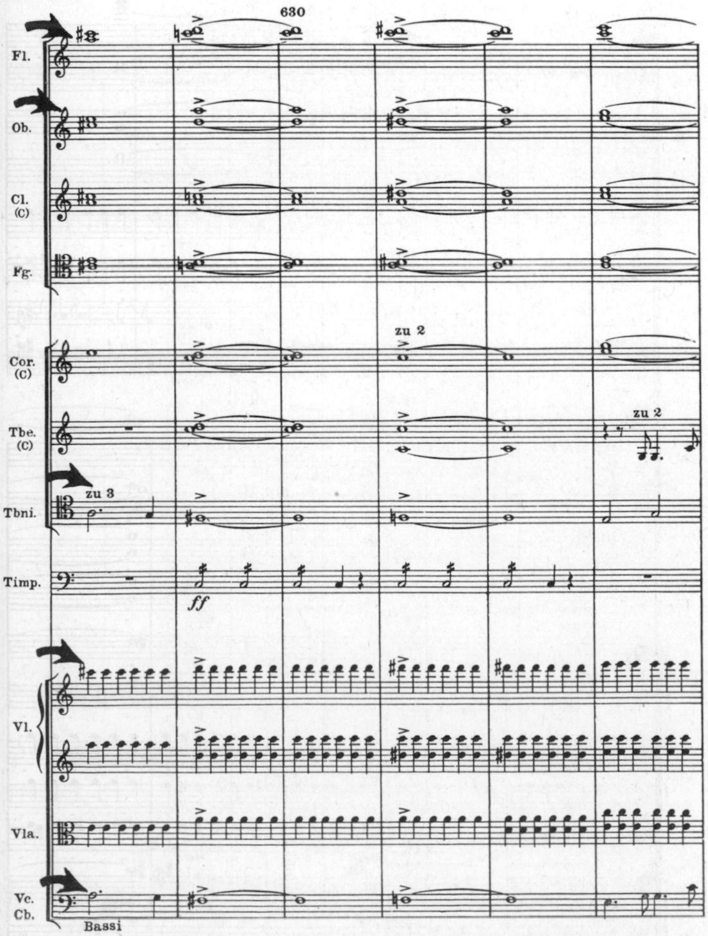

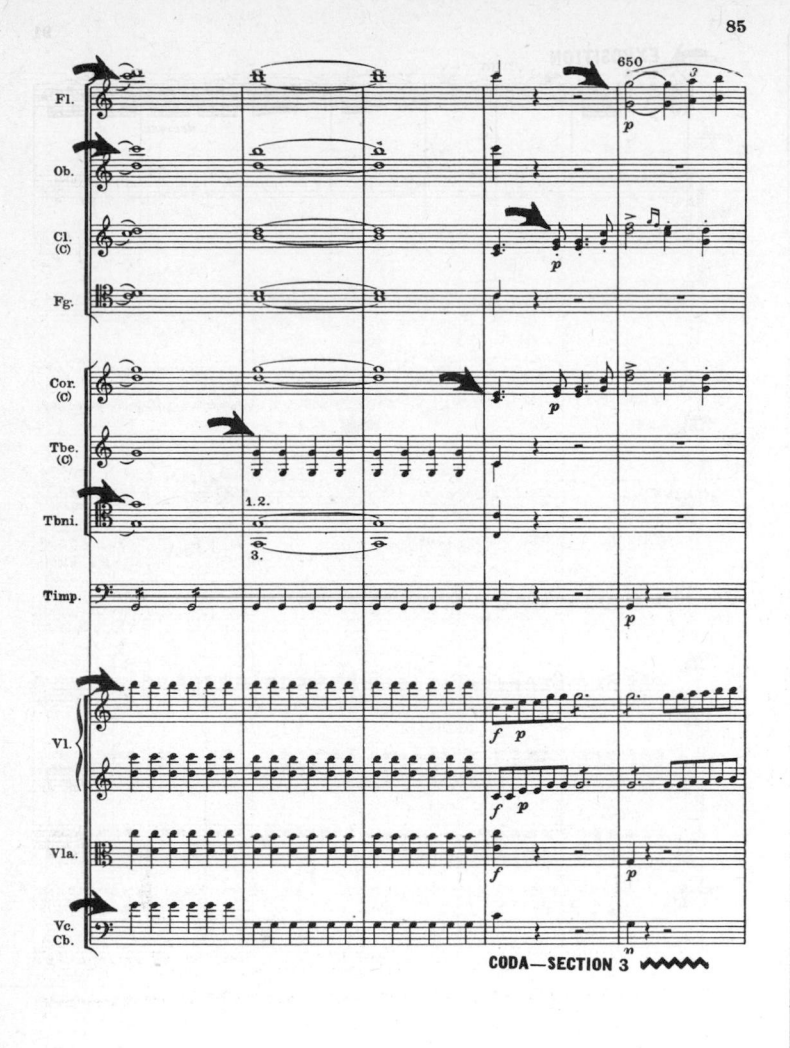

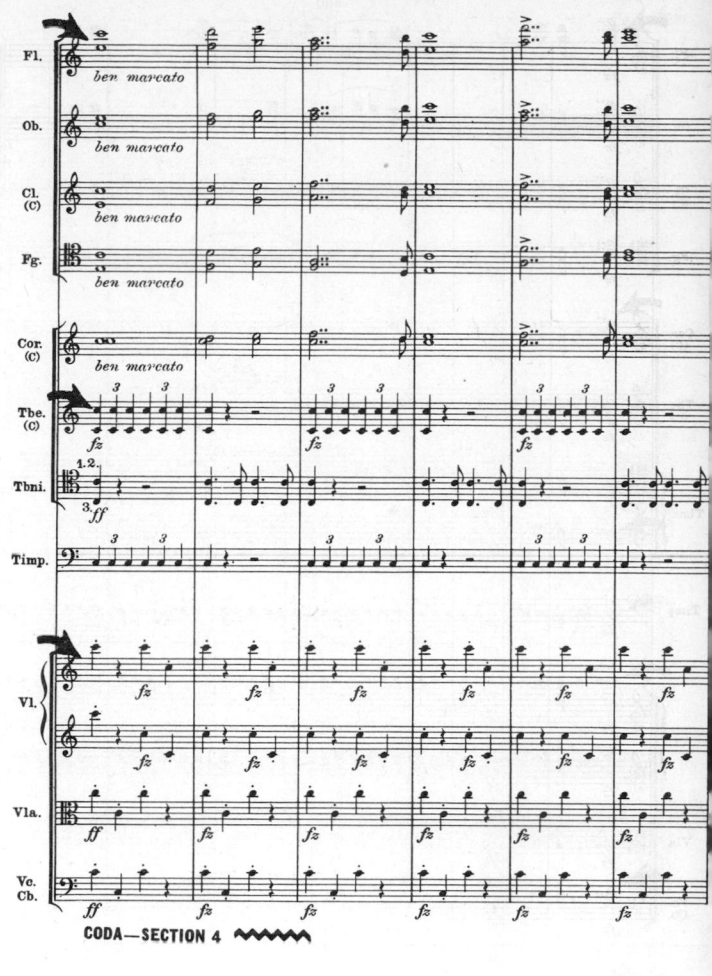

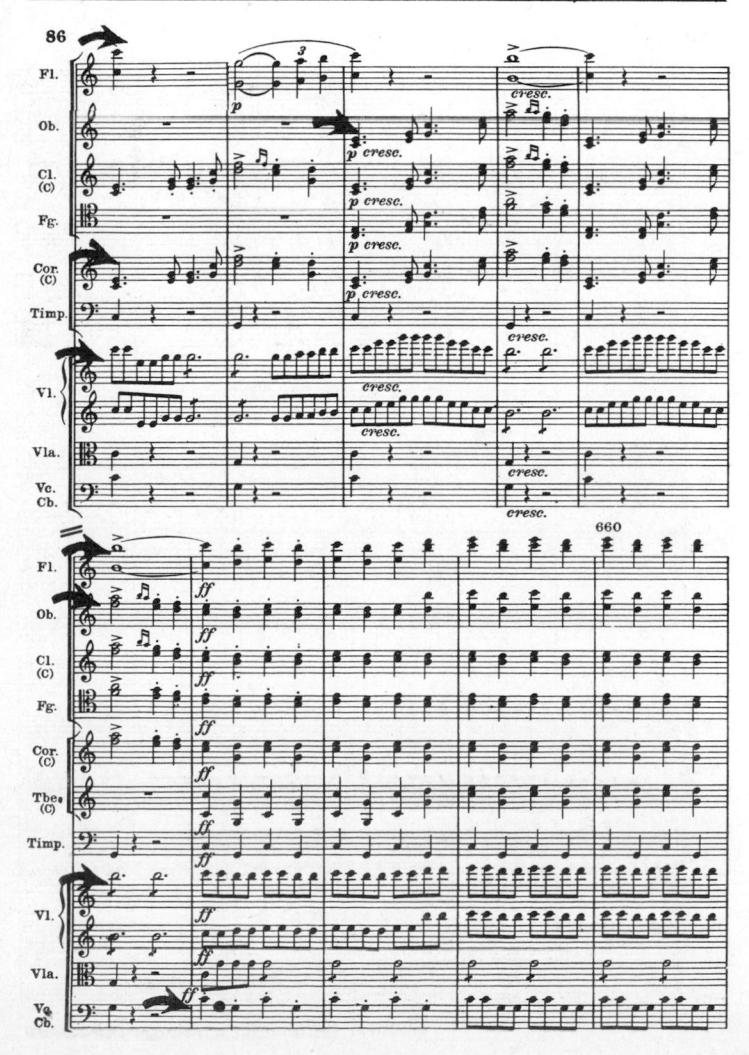

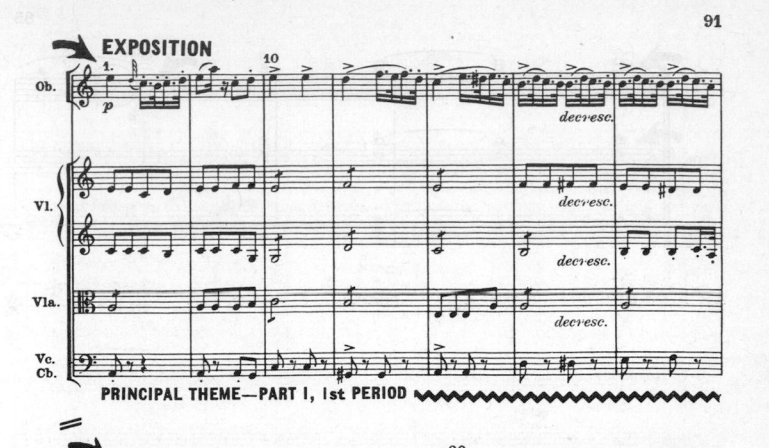

EXPOSITION

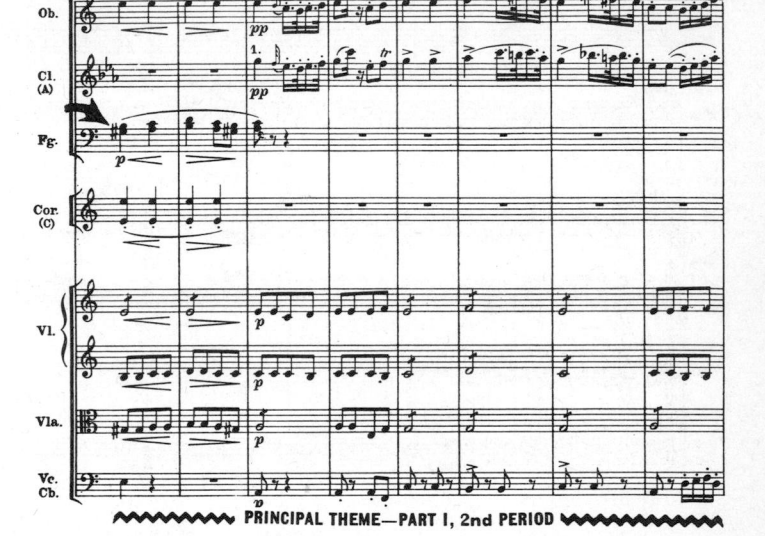

PRINCIPAL THEME—PART I, 1st PERIOD

PRINCIPAL THEME—PART I, 2nd PERIOD

II

INTRODUCTION
Andante con moto

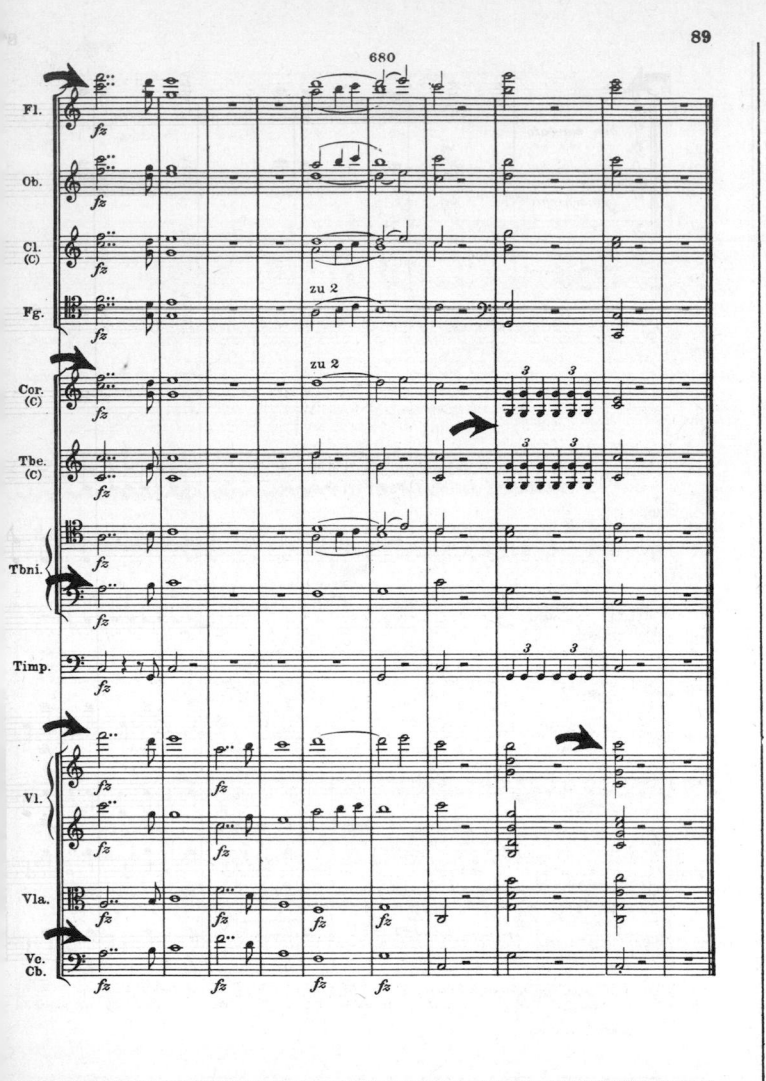

2 Flauti

2 Oboi

2 Clarinetti in A

2 Fagotti

2 Corni in C

2 Trombe in A

3 Tromboni — Alto Tenore — Basso

Timpani in A-F

Violino I

Violino II

Viola

Violoncello

Contrabasso

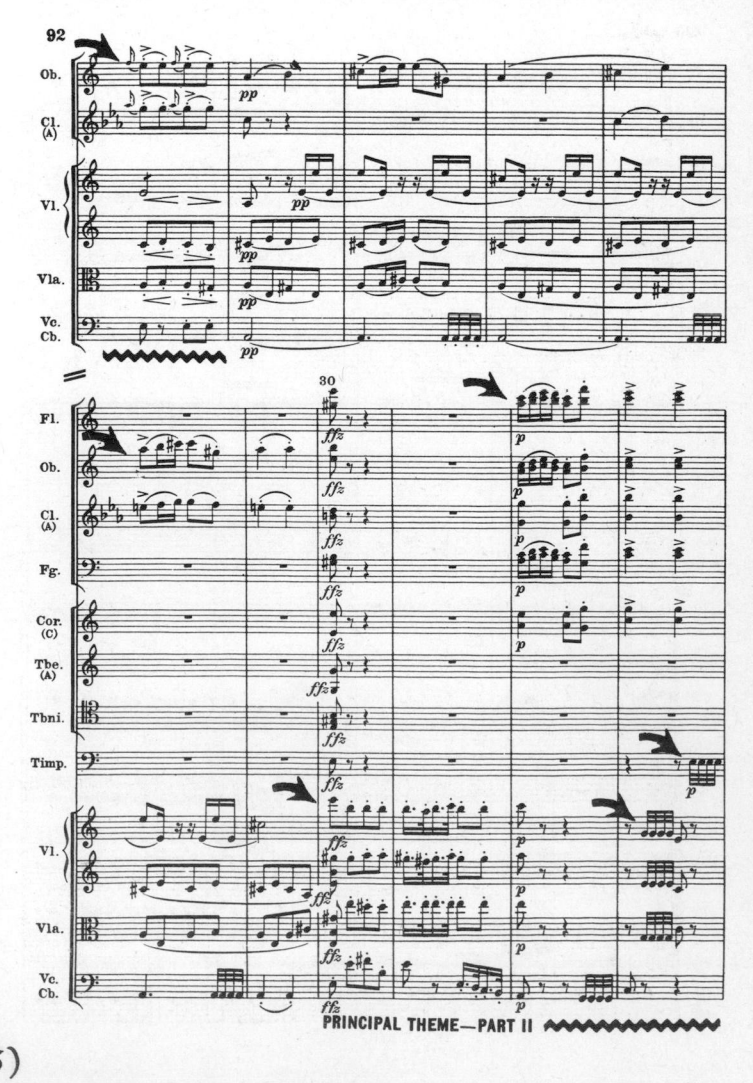

PRINCIPAL THEME—PART II

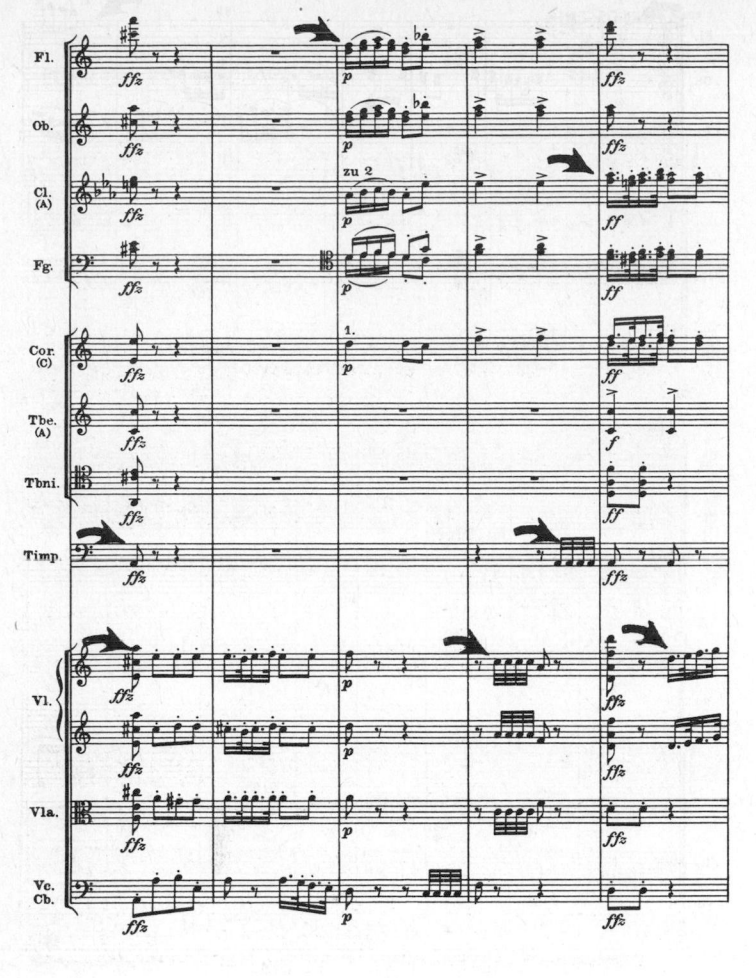

93

Fl.
Ob.
Cl. (A)
Fg.
Cor. (C)
Tbe. (A)
Tbni.
Timp.
Vl.
Vla.
Vc. Cb.
zu 2

95

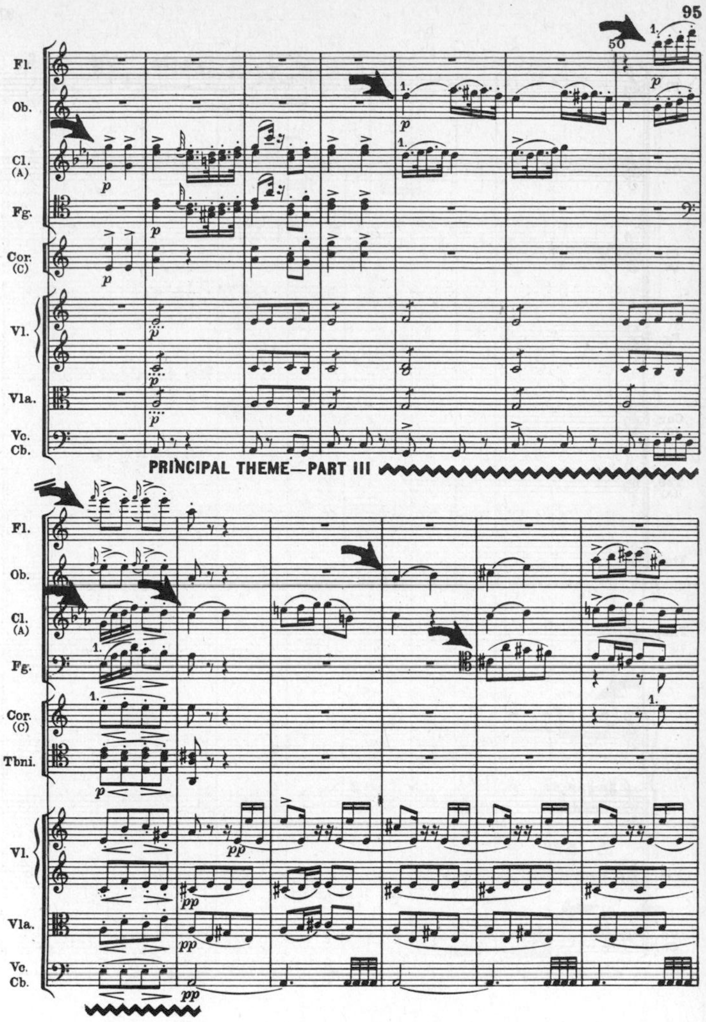
Fl.
Ob.
Cl. (A)
Fg.
Cor. (C)
Vl.
Vla.
Vc. Cb.
PRINCIPAL THEME—PART III
Fl.
Ob.
Cl. (A)
Fg.
Cor. (C)
Tbni.
Vl.
Vla.
Vc. Cb.

94

Fl.
Ob.
Cl. (A)
Fg.
Cor. (C)
Tbe. (A)
Tbni.
Timp.
Vl.
Vla.
Vc. Cb.
zu 2

96

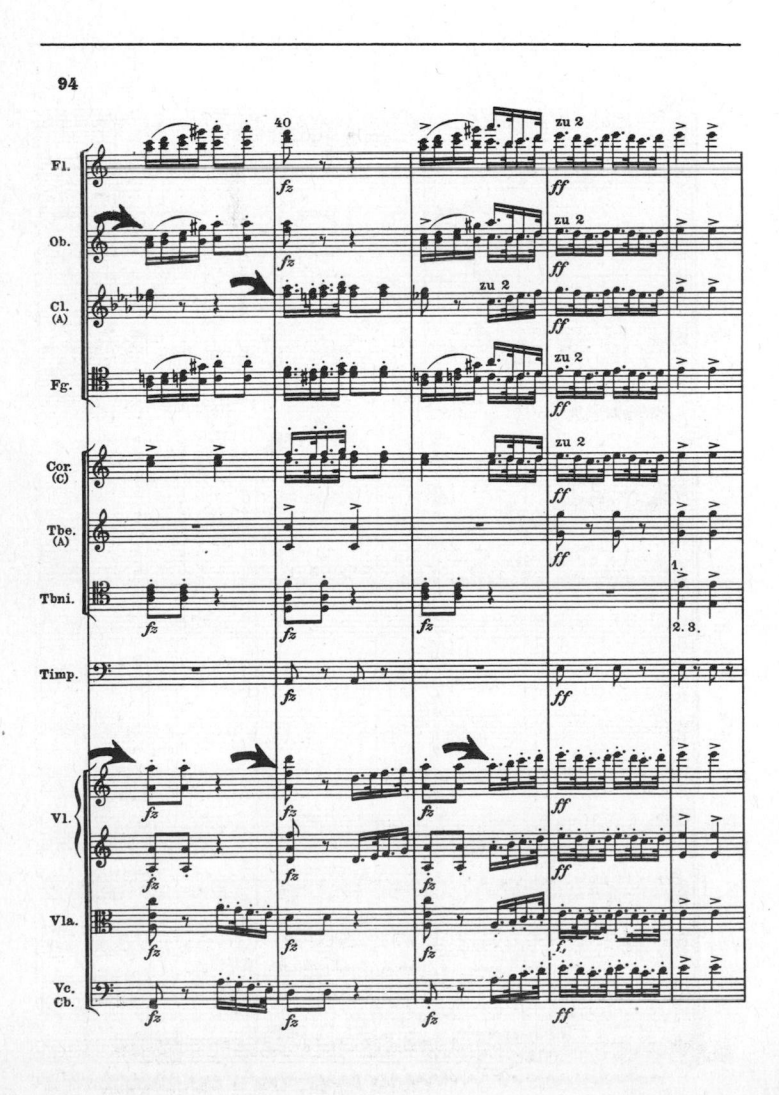

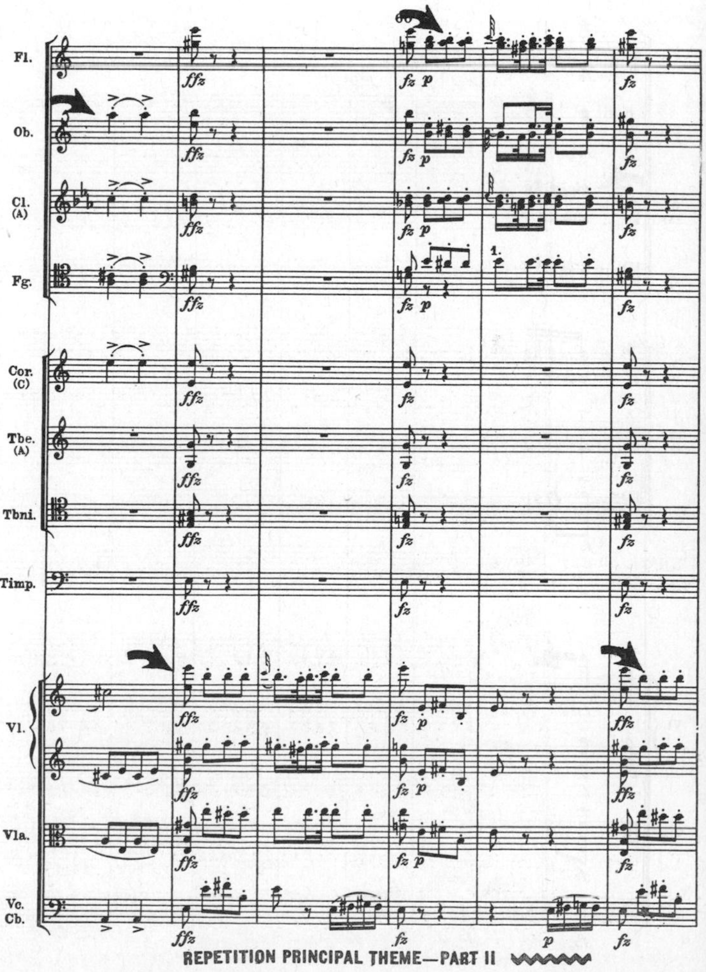
Fl.
Ob.
Cl. (A)
Fg.
Cor. (C)
Tbe. (A)
Tbni.
Timp.
Vl.
Vla.
Vc. Cb.
REPETITION PRINCIPAL THEME—PART II

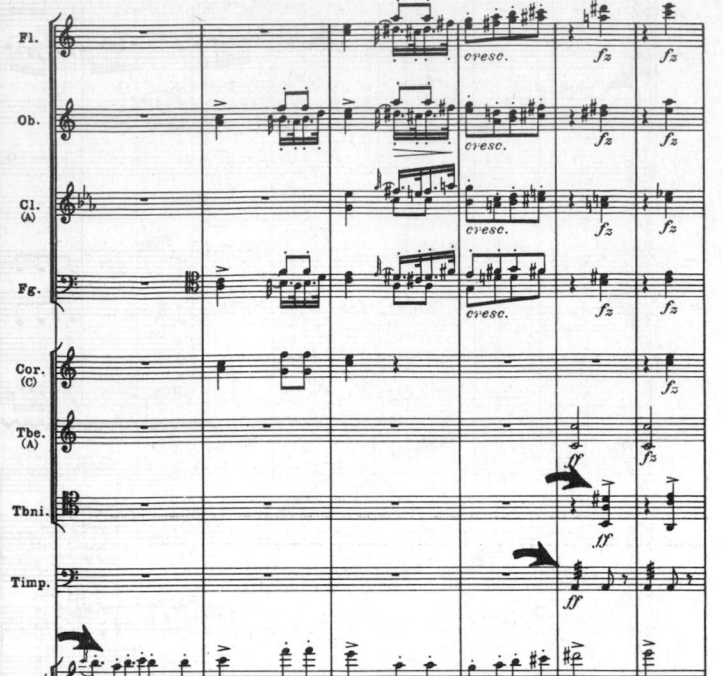

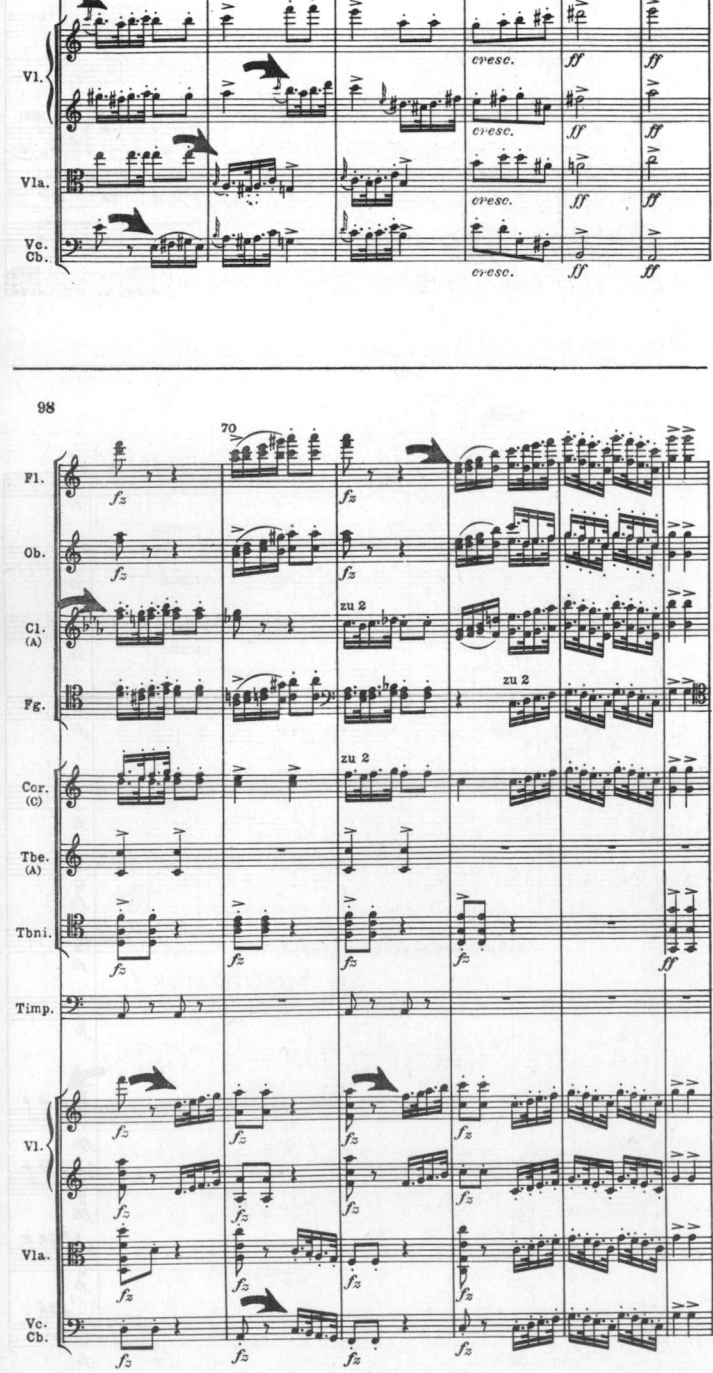

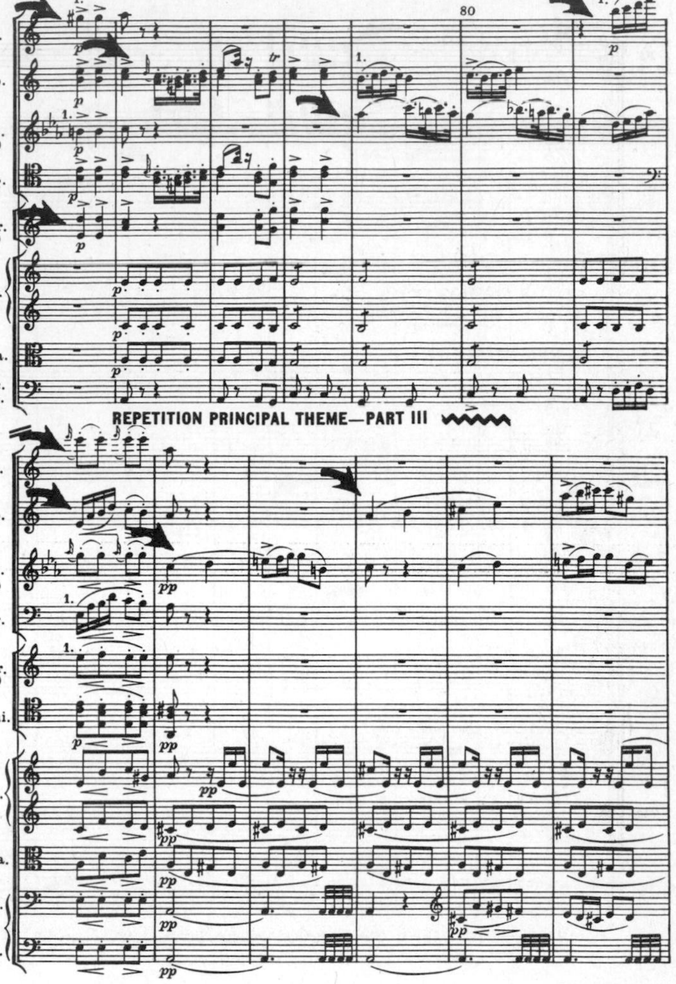

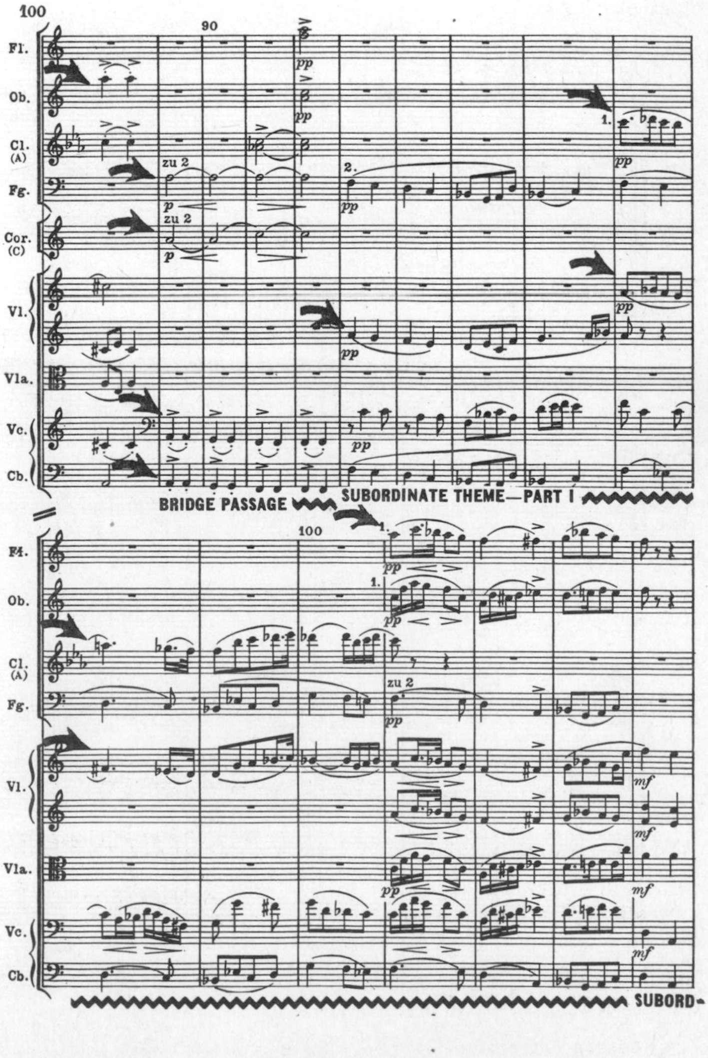

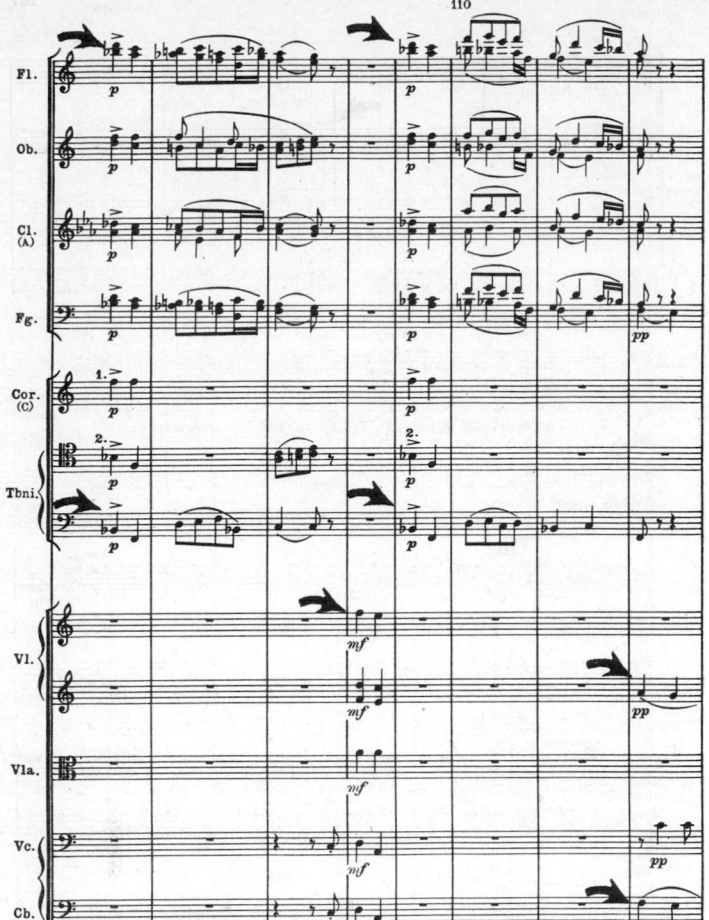

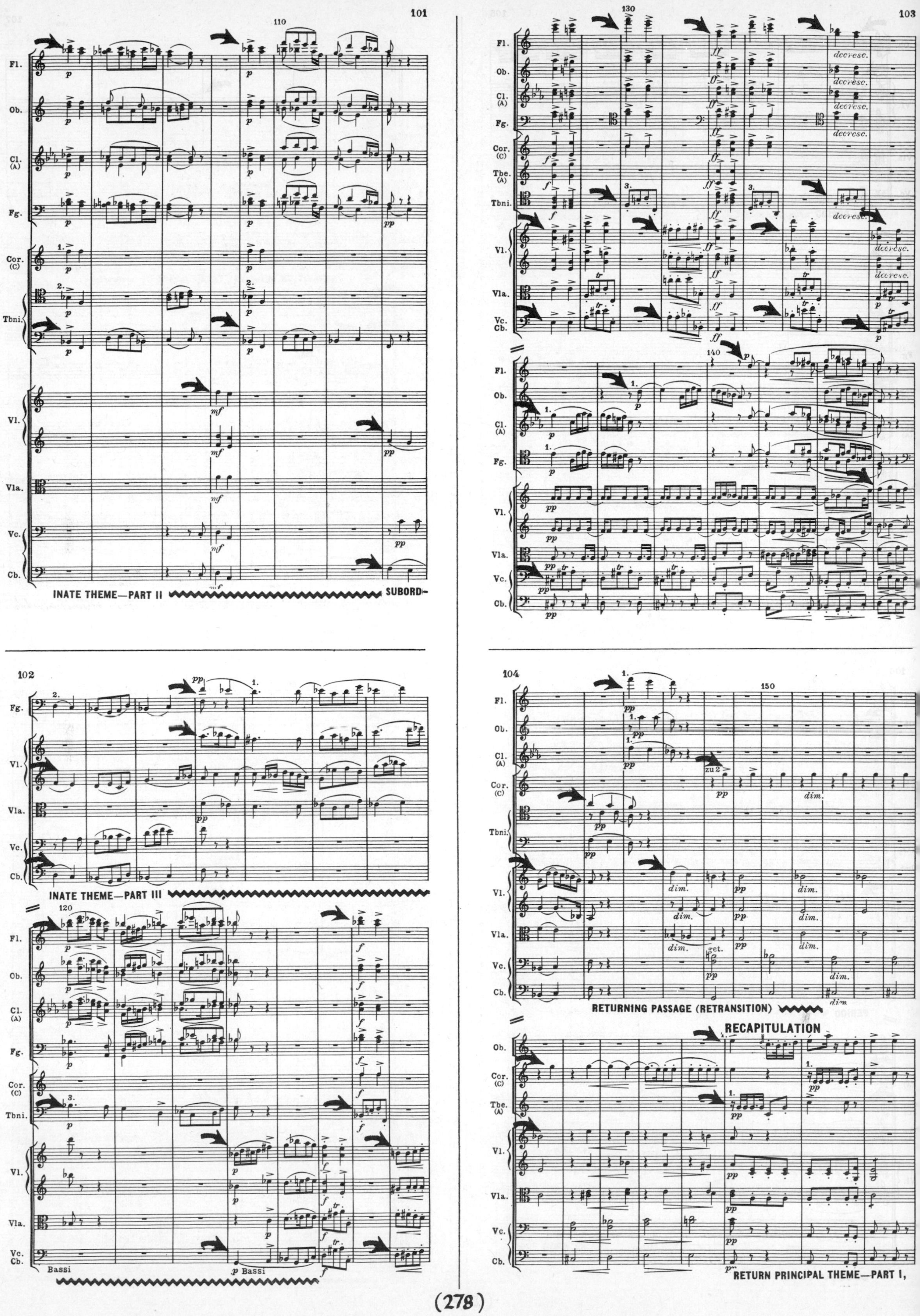

110

130

140

150

INATE THEME—PART II ∿∿∿∿∿∿∿∿∿∿∿∿∿∿∿ SUBORD—

104

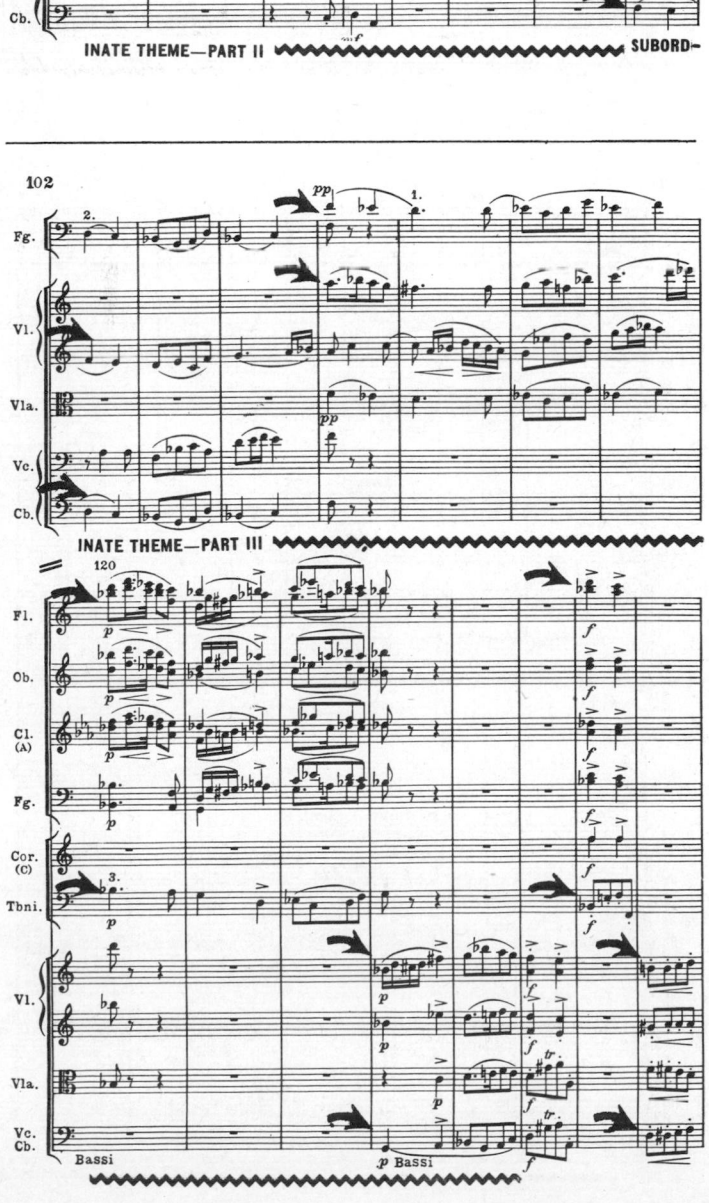

INATE THEME—PART III ∿∿∿∿∿∿∿∿∿∿∿∿∿∿∿∿∿∿∿∿∿∿∿∿∿∿∿∿

120

Bassi ∿∿∿∿∿∿∿∿∿∿∿∿ Bassi

RETURNING PASSAGE (RETRANSITION) ∿∿∿∿

RECAPITULATION

RETURN PRINCIPAL THEME—PART I,

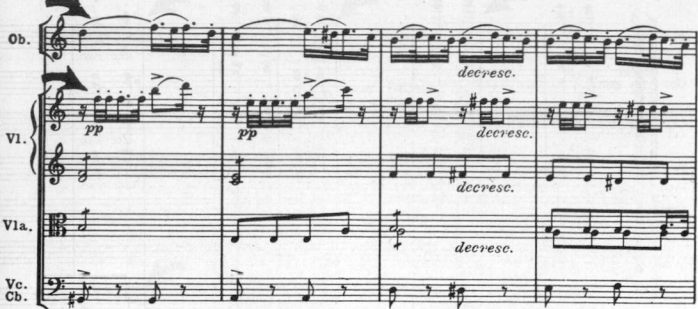

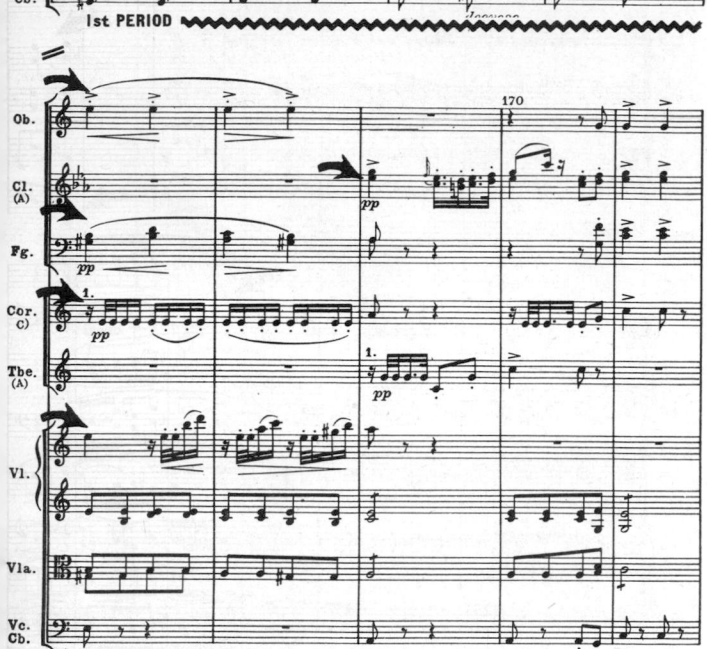

1st PERIOD

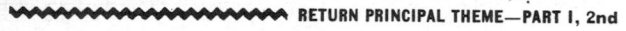

RETURN PRINCIPAL THEME—PART I, 2nd

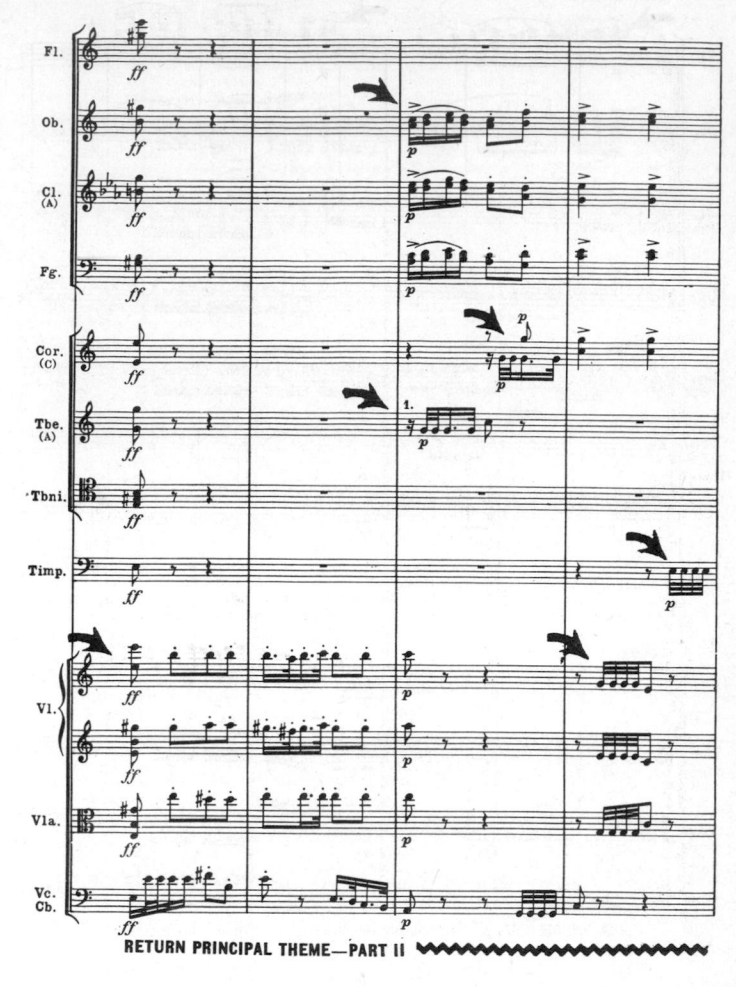

RETURN PRINCIPAL THEME—PART II

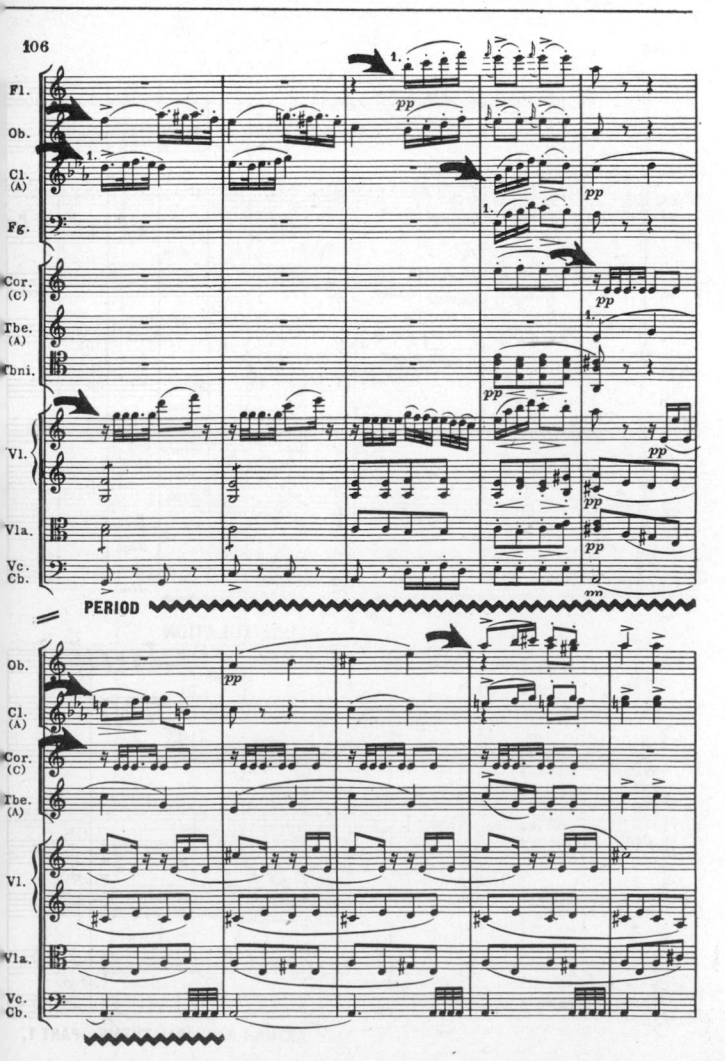

PERIOD

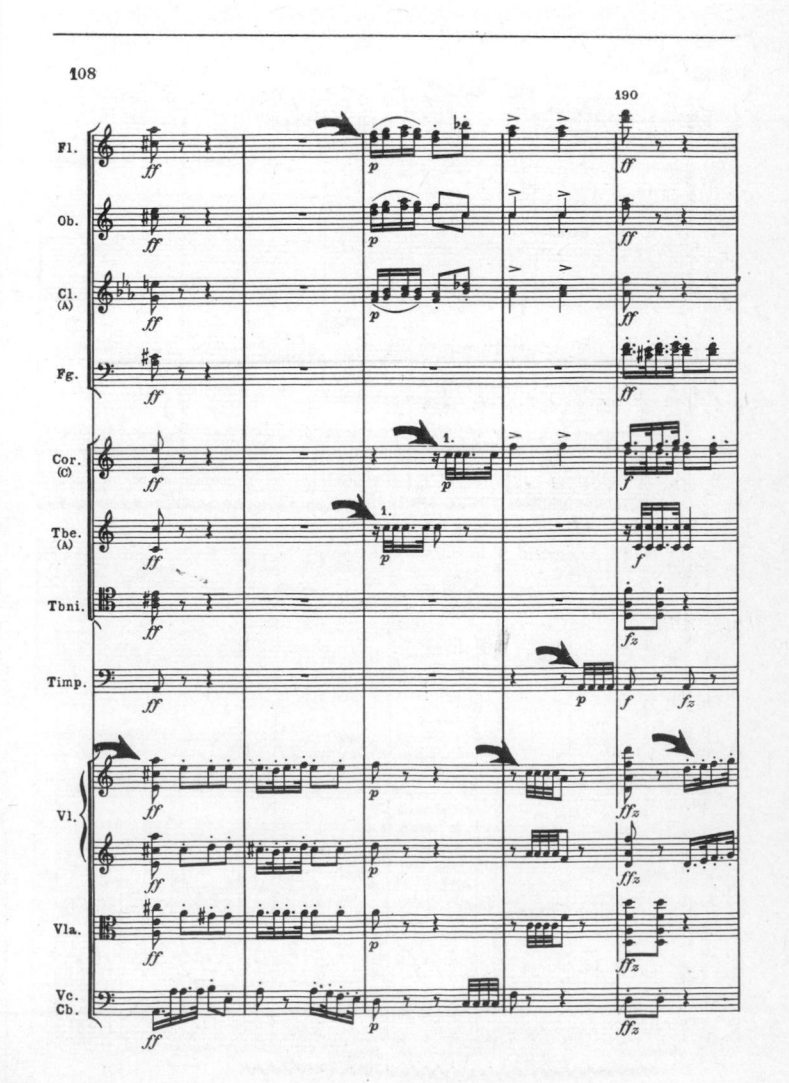

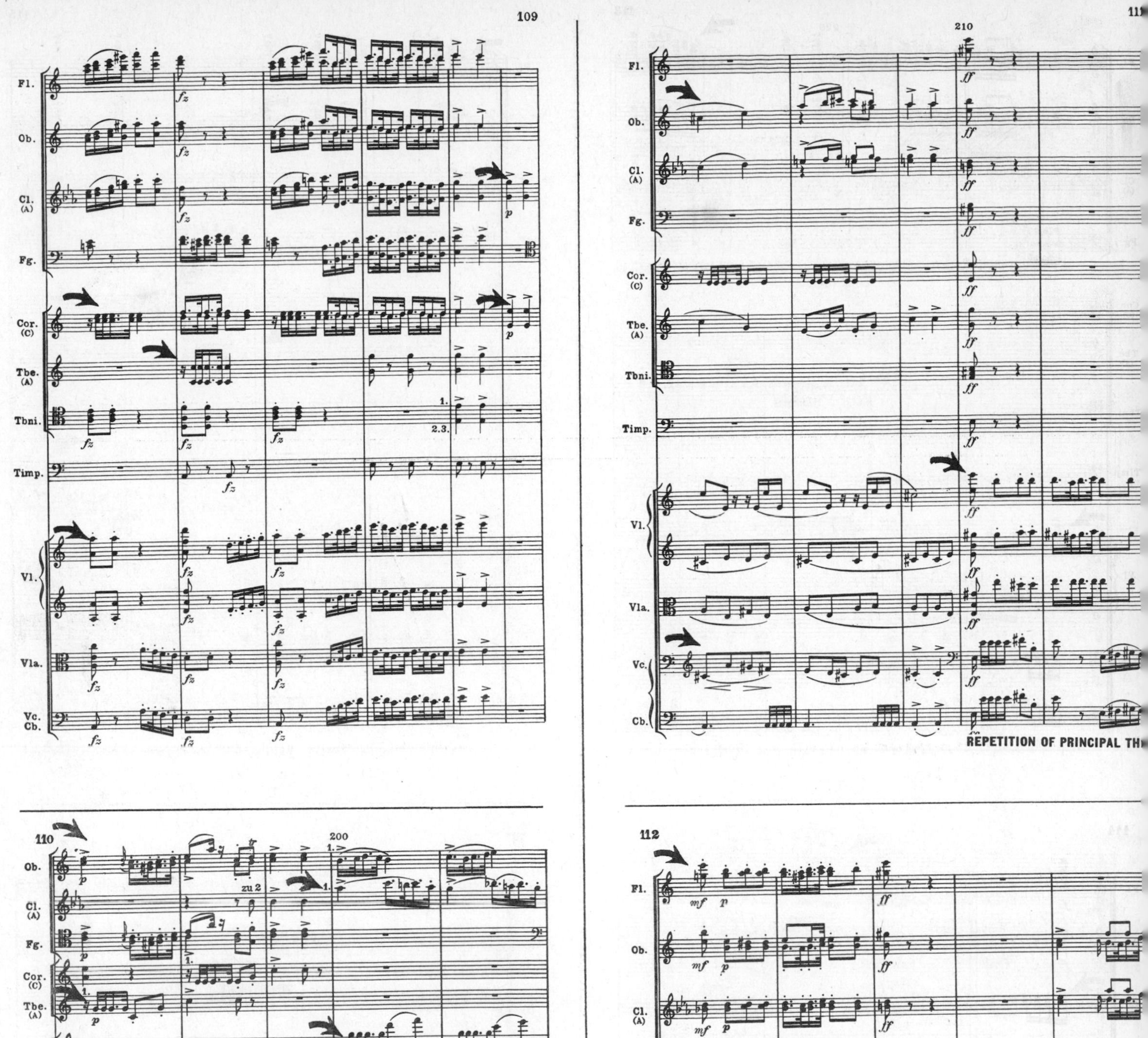

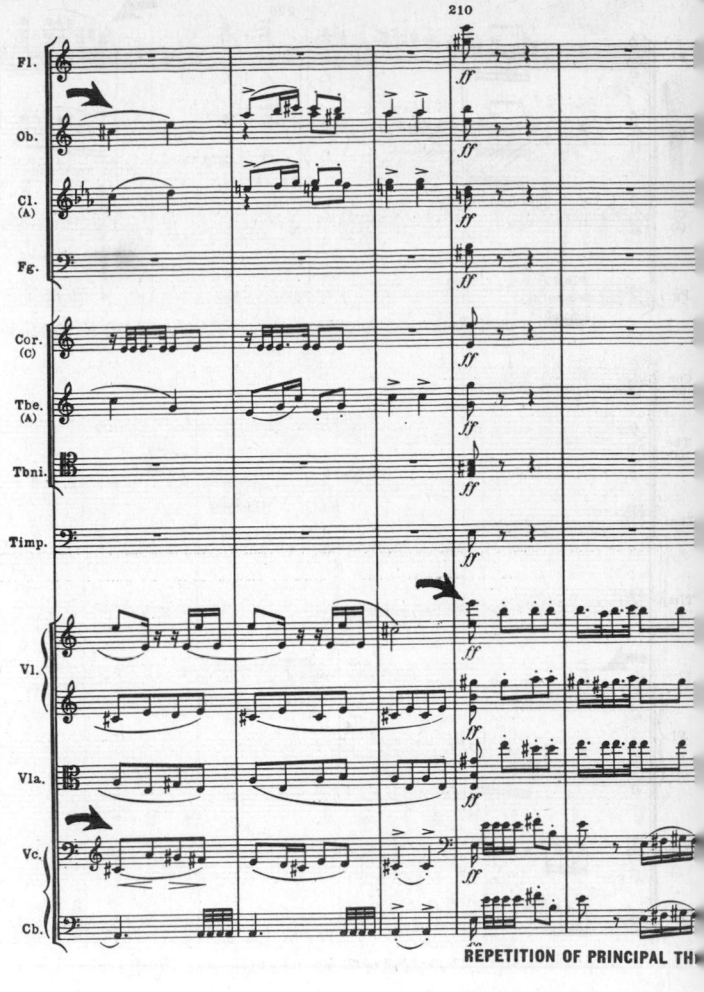

REPETITION OF PRINCIPAL TH

200

RETURN PRINCIPAL THEME—PART III

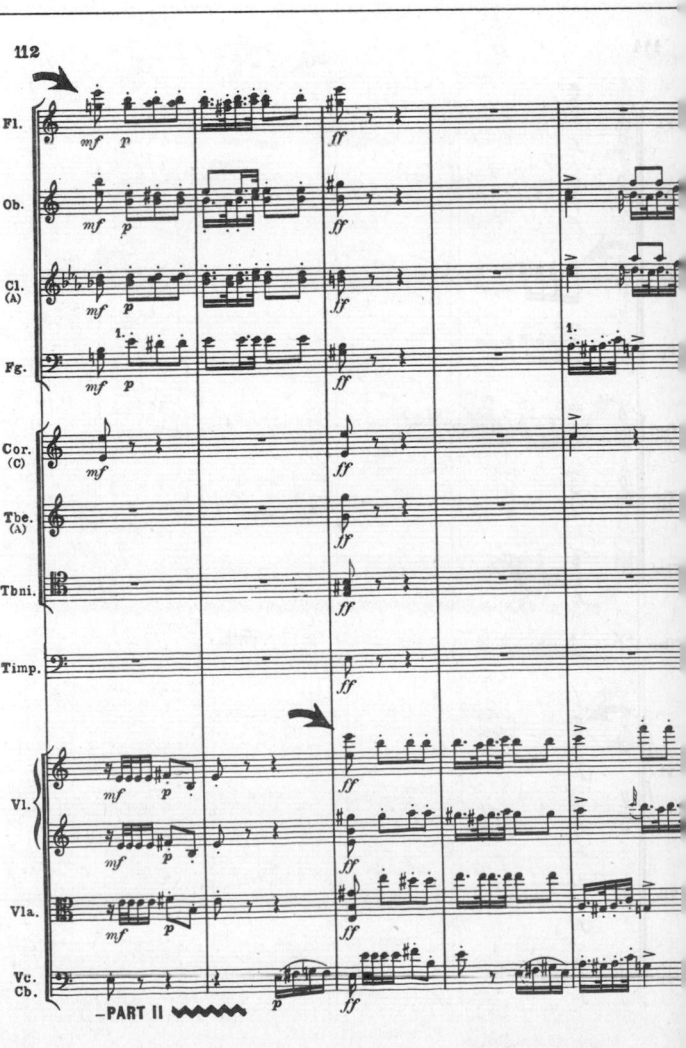

—PART II

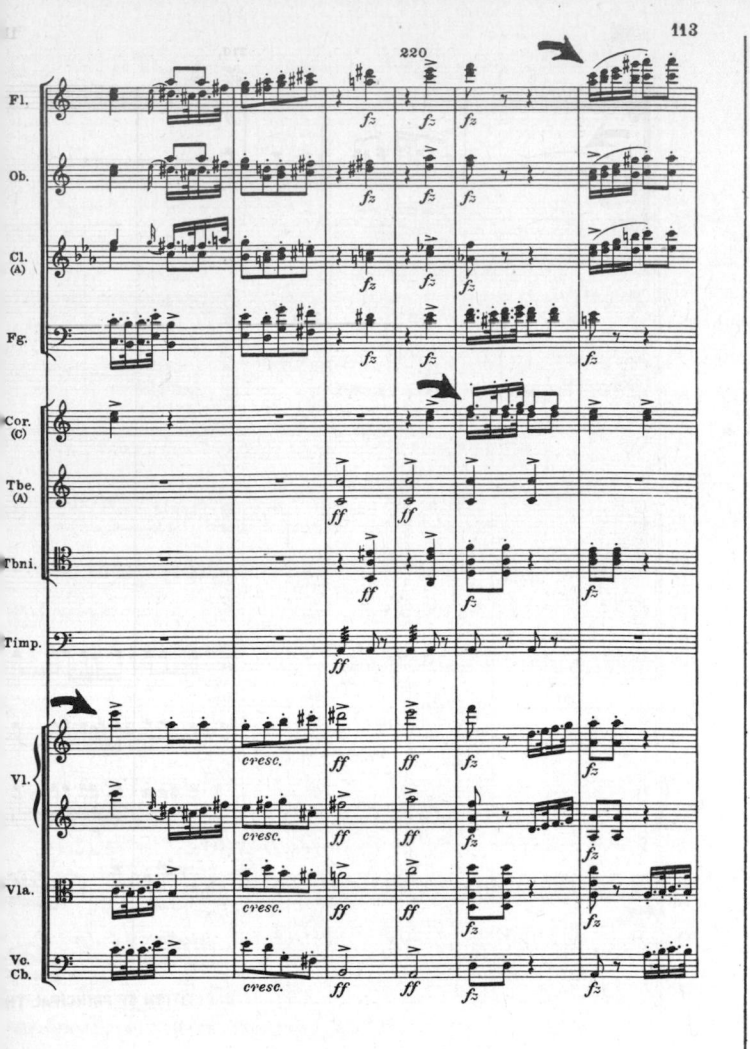

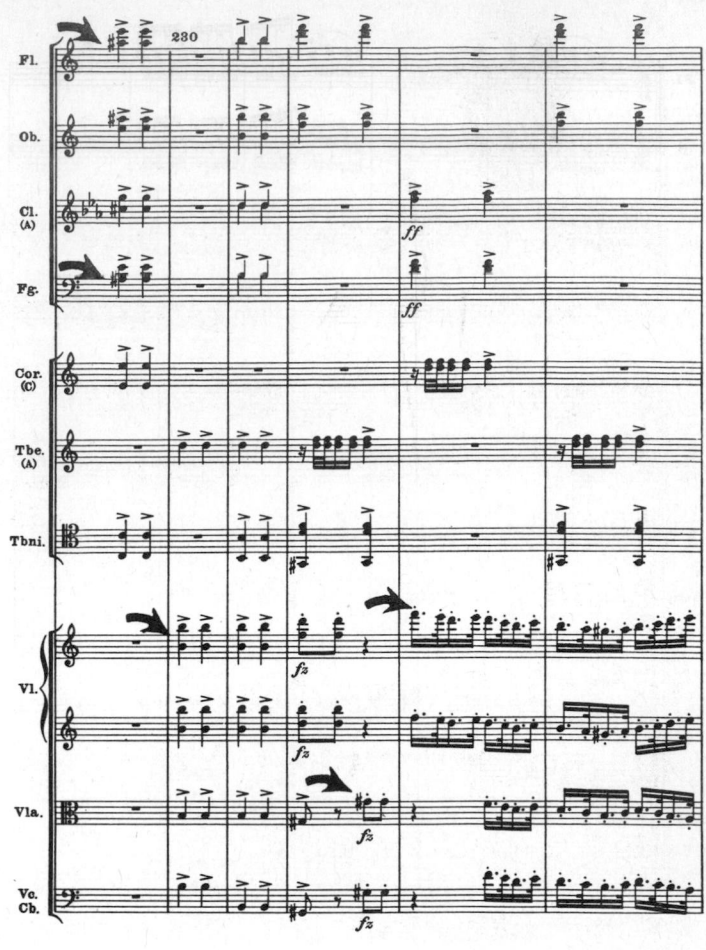

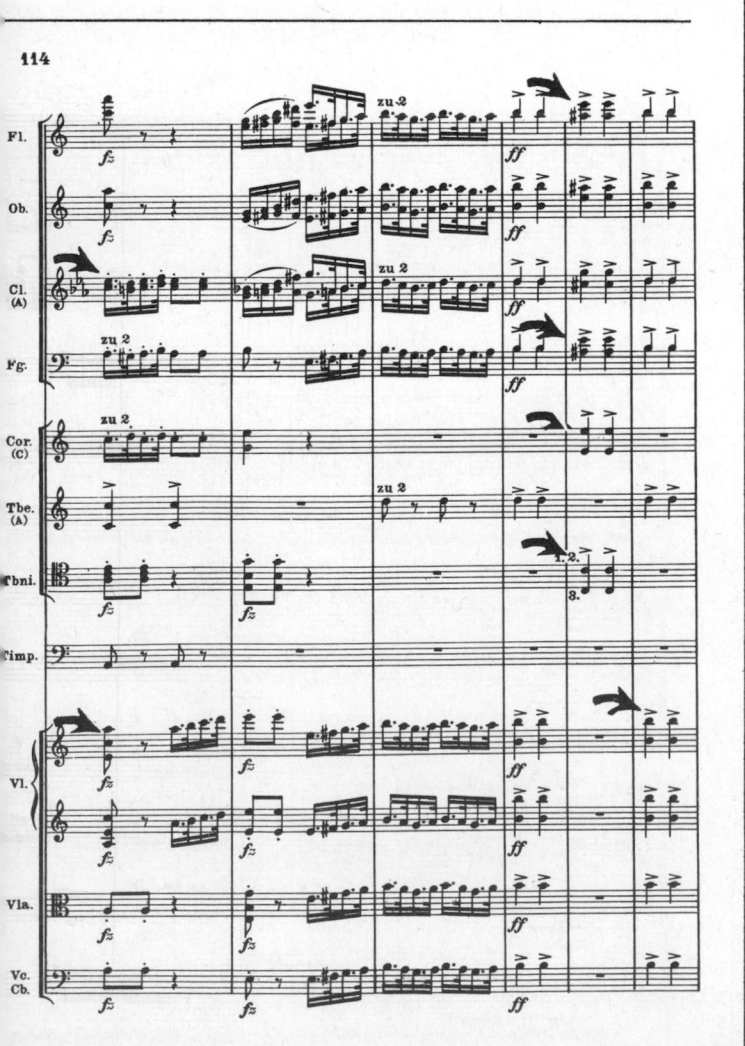

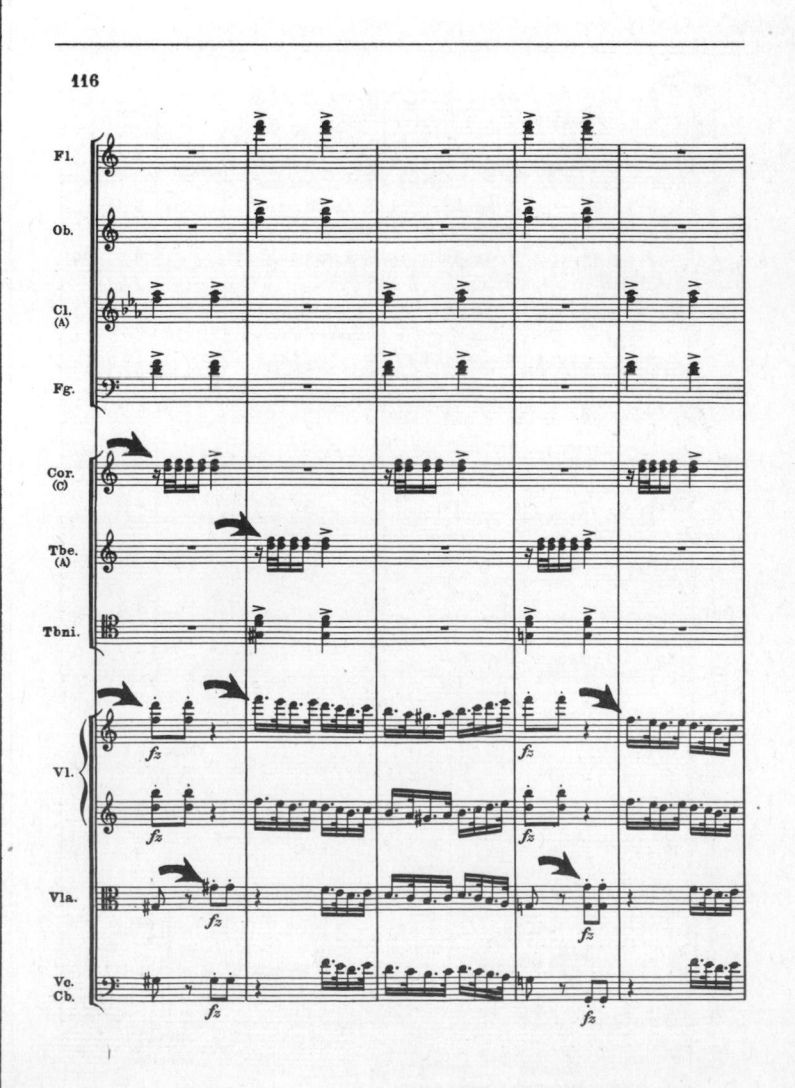

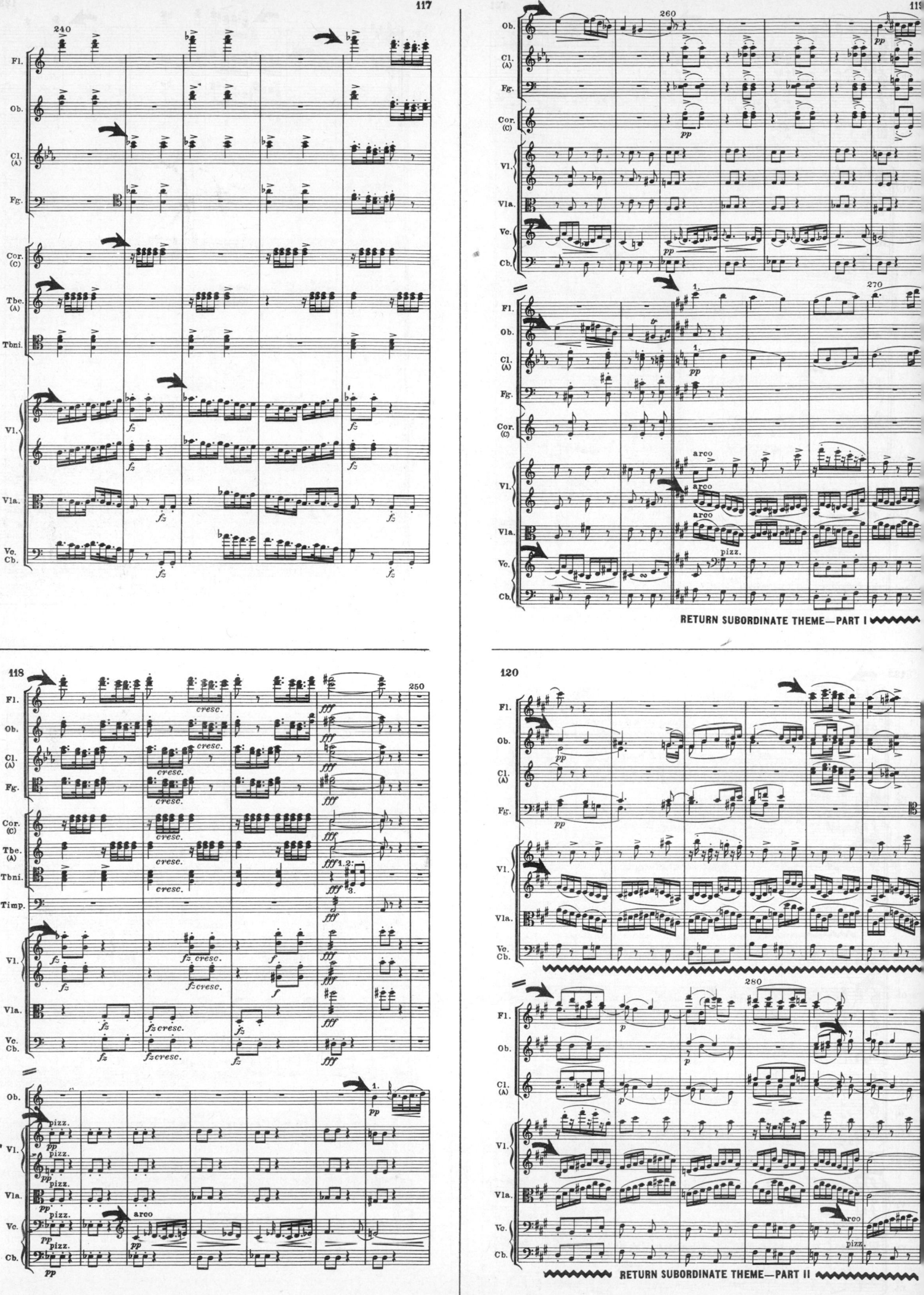

RETURN SUBORDINATE THEME—PART I 〜〜〜〜

RETURN SUBORDINATE THEME—PART II 〜〜〜〜

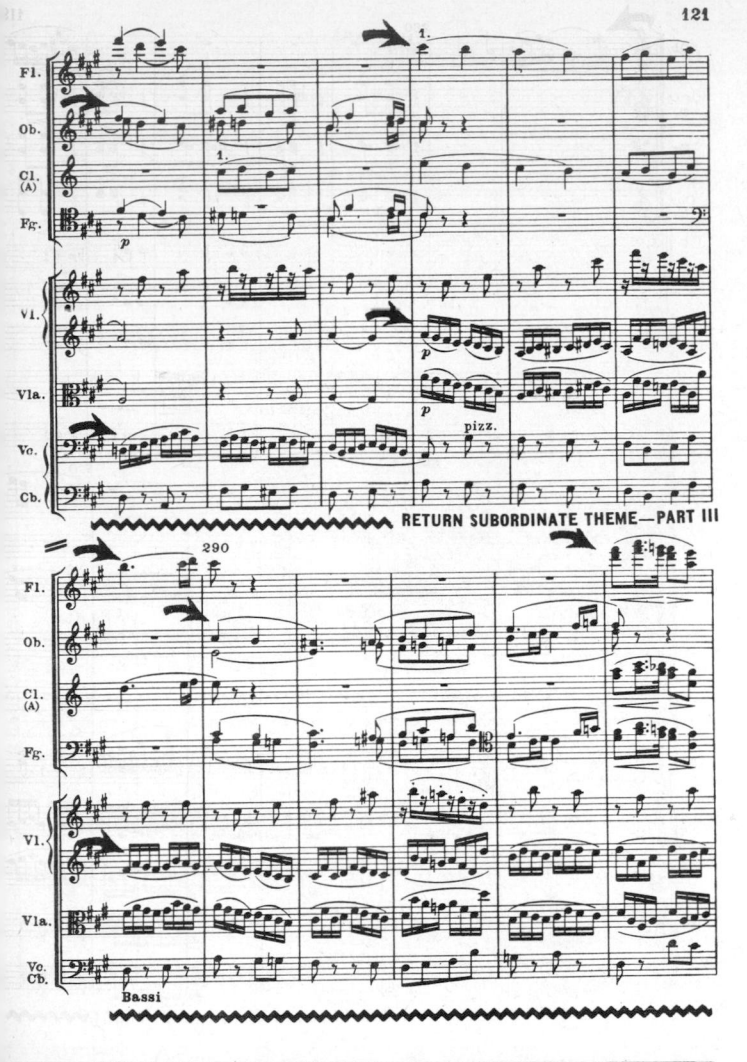

RETURN SUBORDINATE THEME—PART III

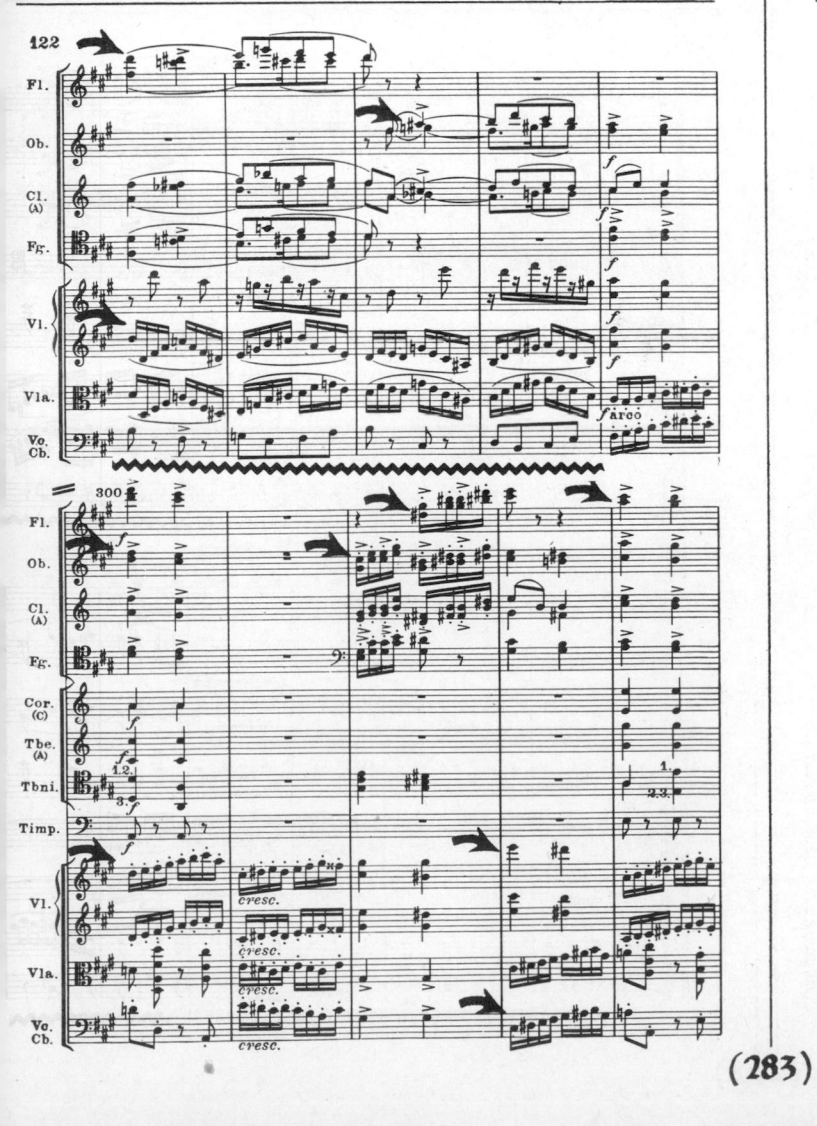

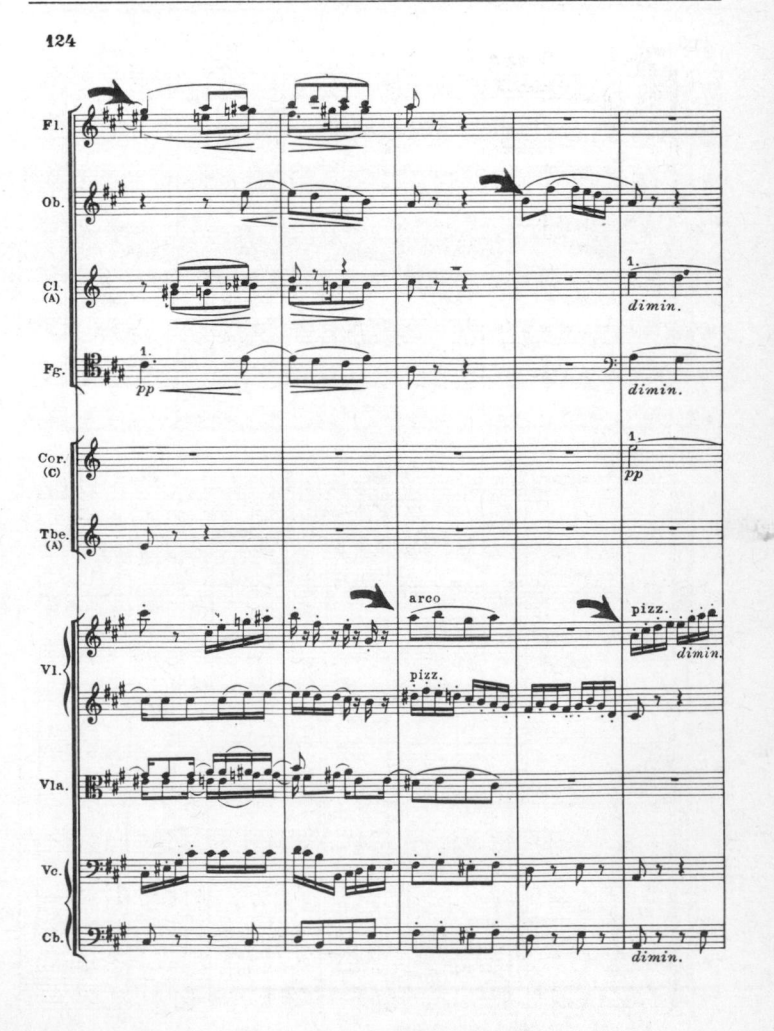

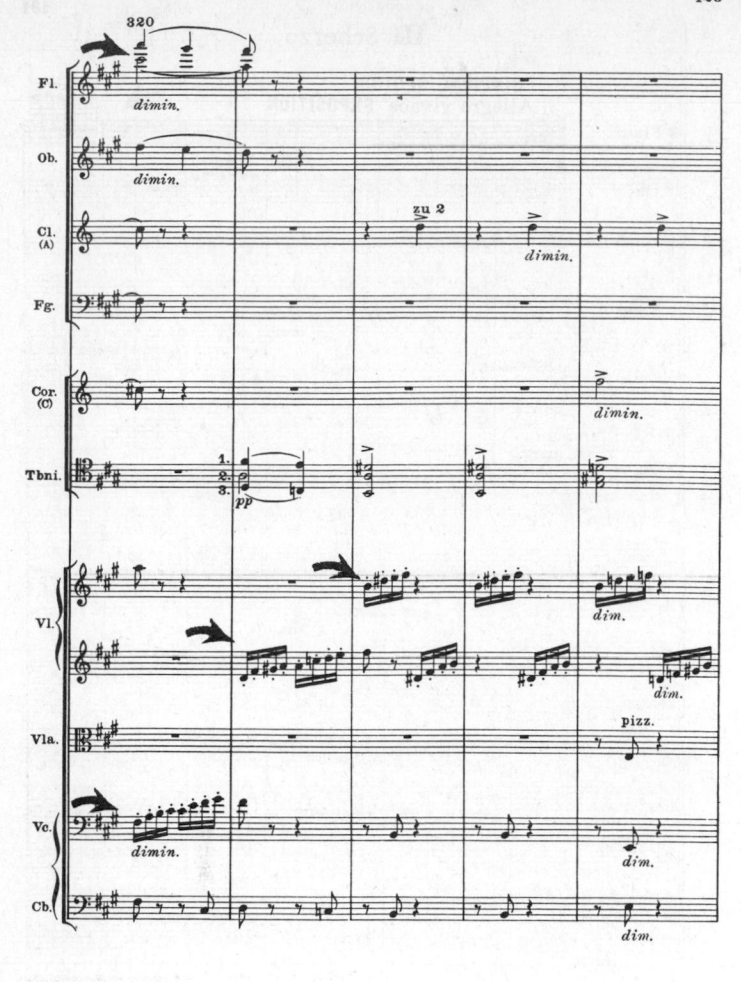

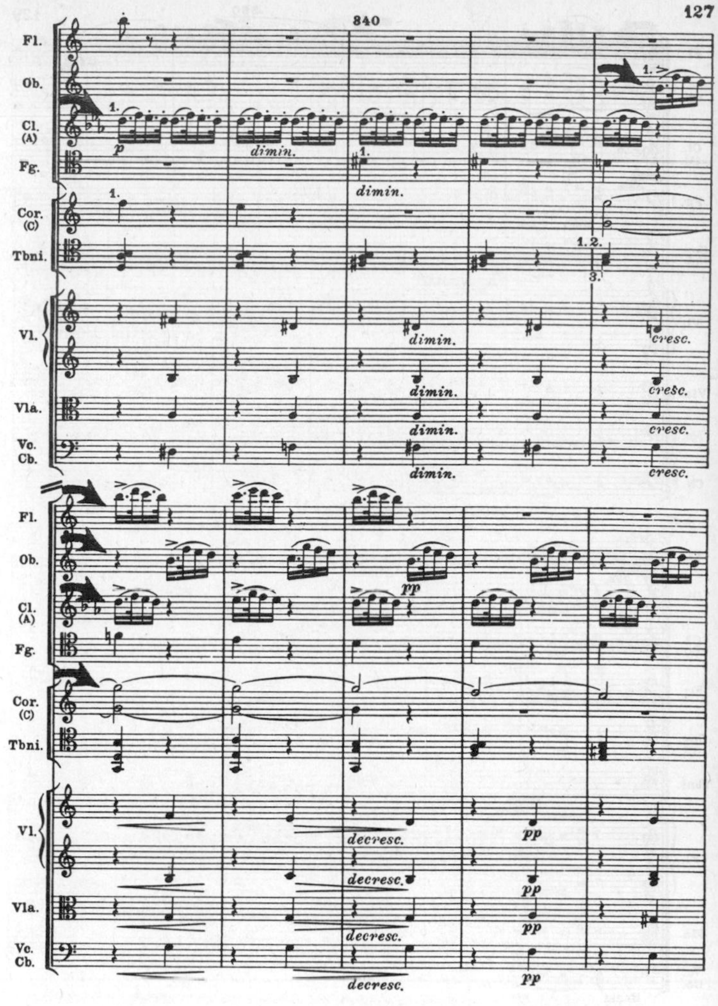

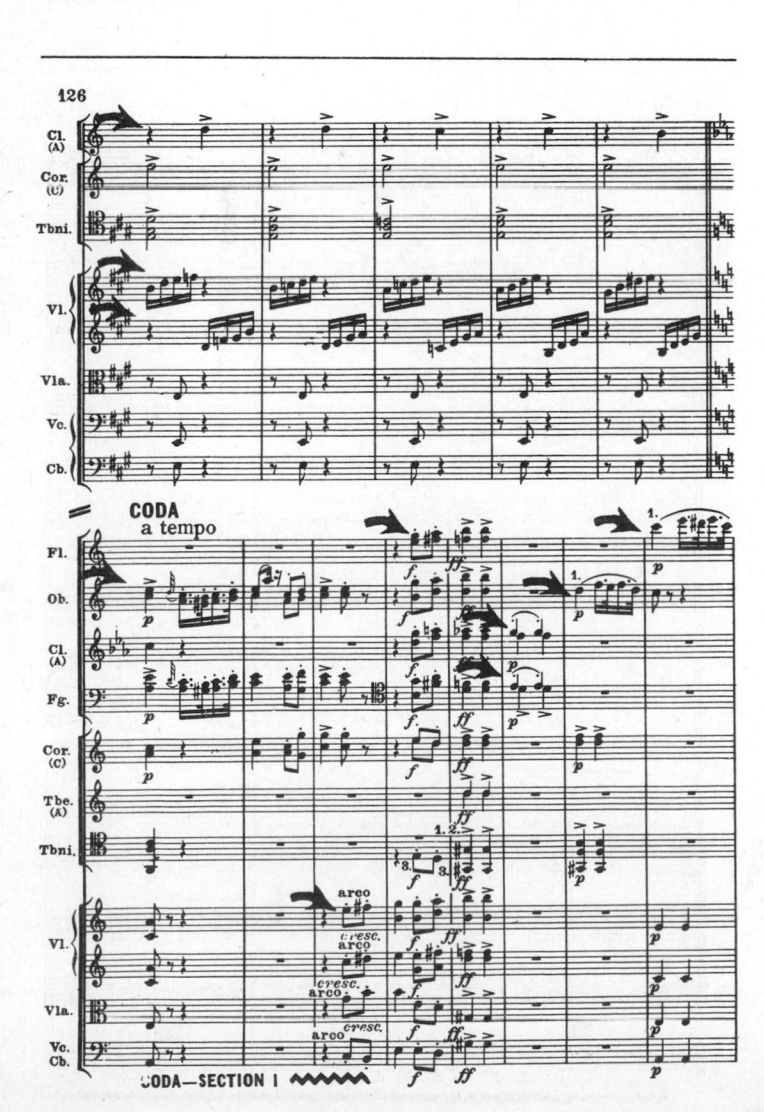

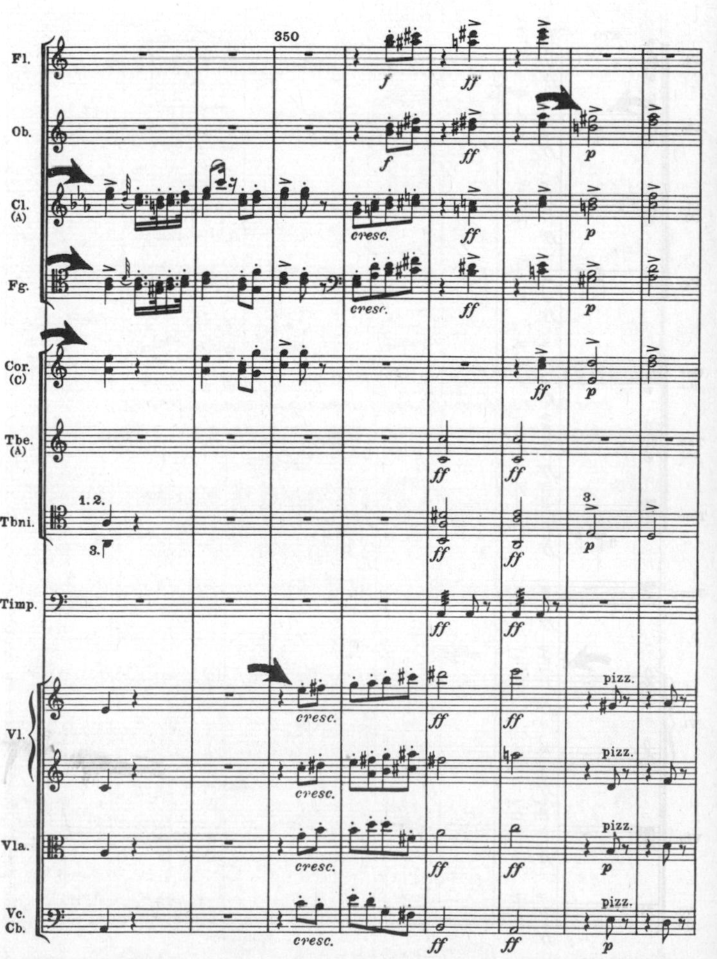

III. Scherzo

PRINCIPAL SECTiON
Allegro vivace EXPOSITION

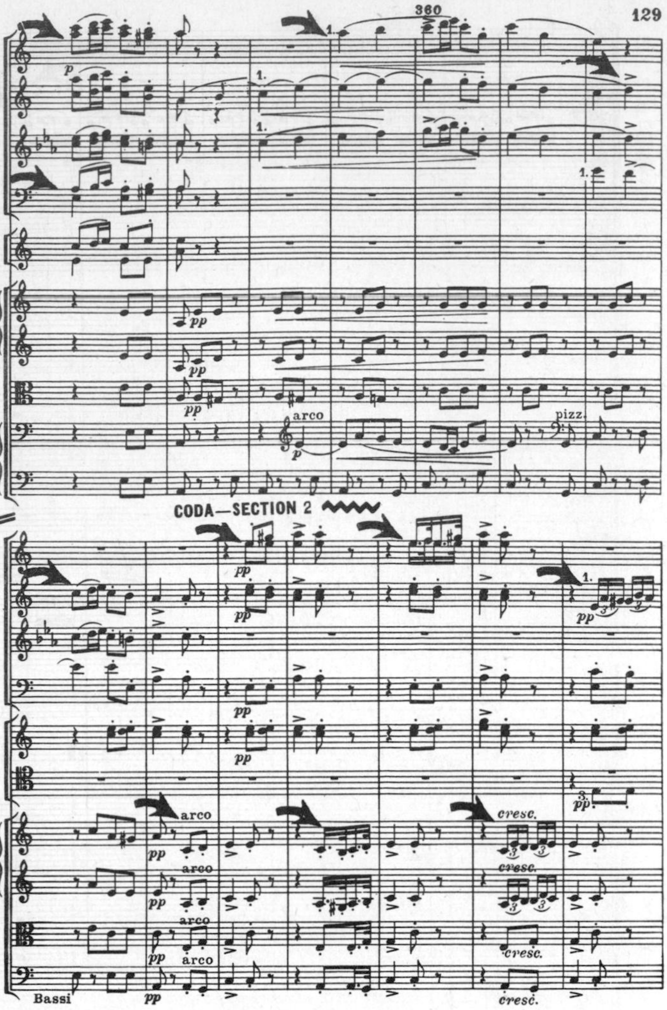

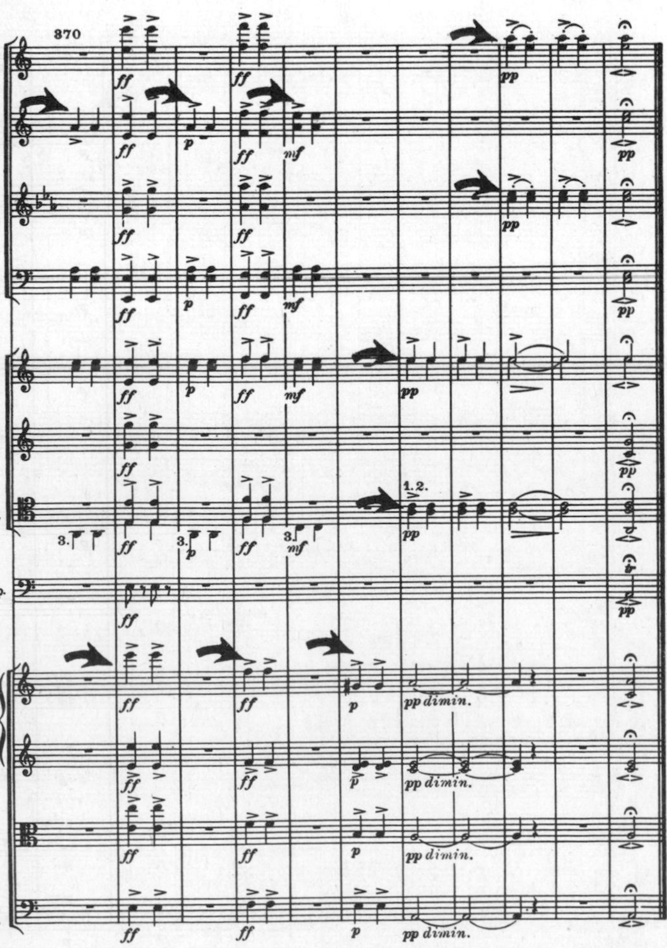

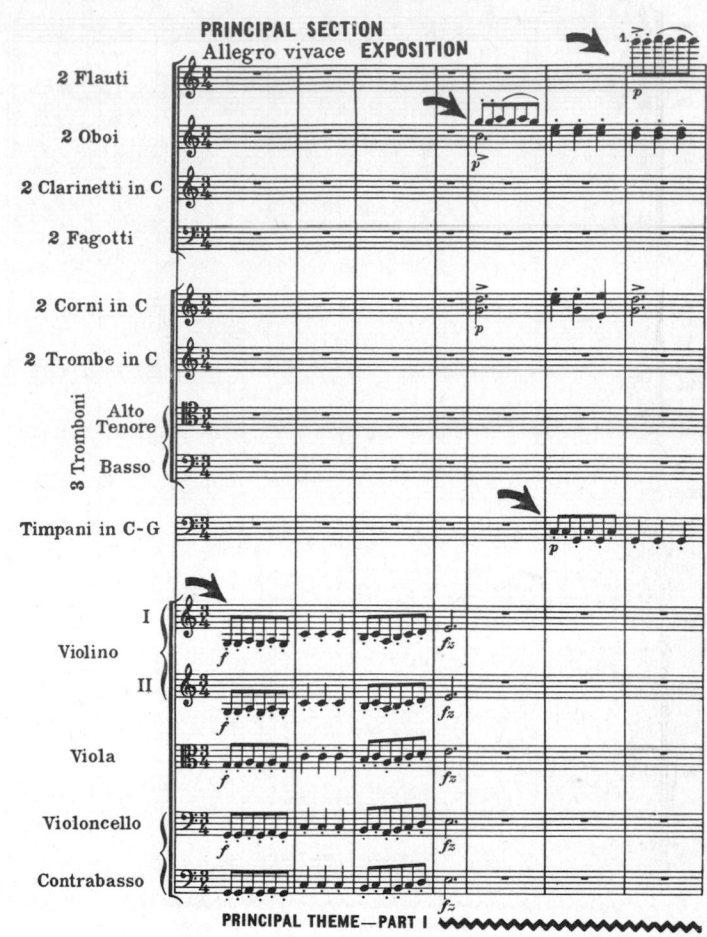

PRINCIPAL THEME—PART I

CODA—SECTION 2

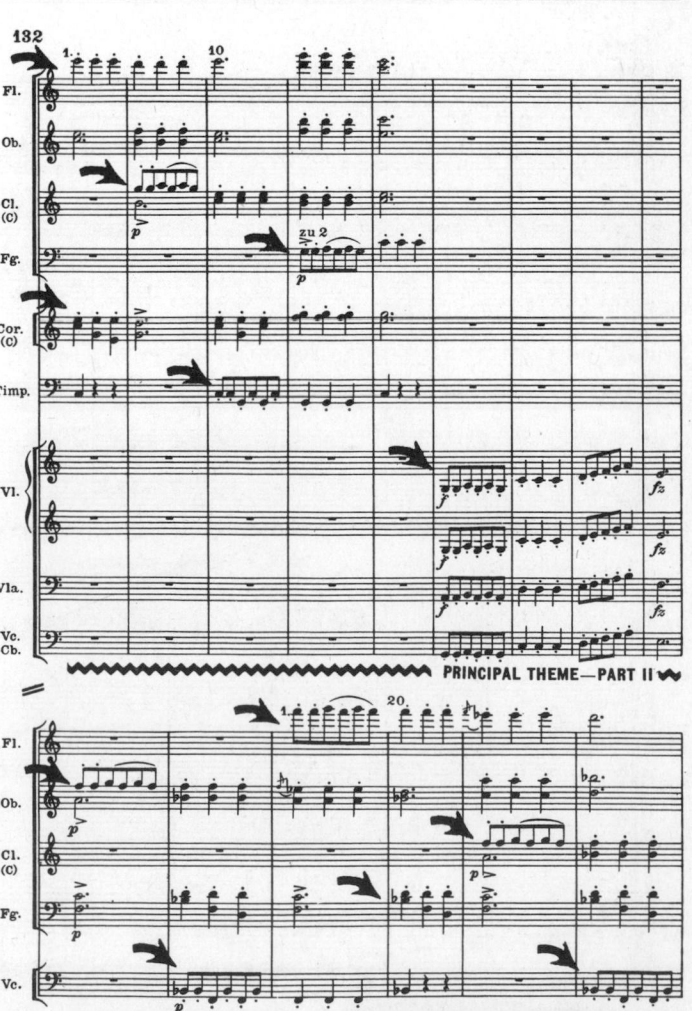

PRINCIPAL THEME—PART II

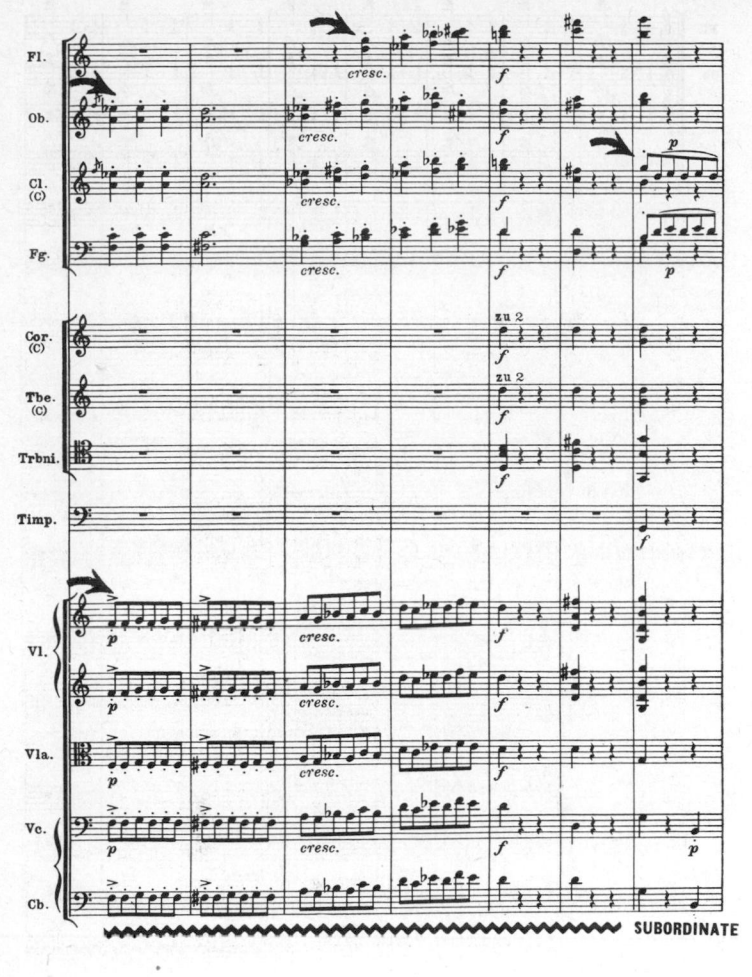

133
Fl.
Ob.
Cl. (C)
Fg.
Cor. (C)
Tbe. (C)
Trbni.
Timp.
Vl.
Vla.
Vc.
Cb.
cresc.
zu 2
SUBORDINATE

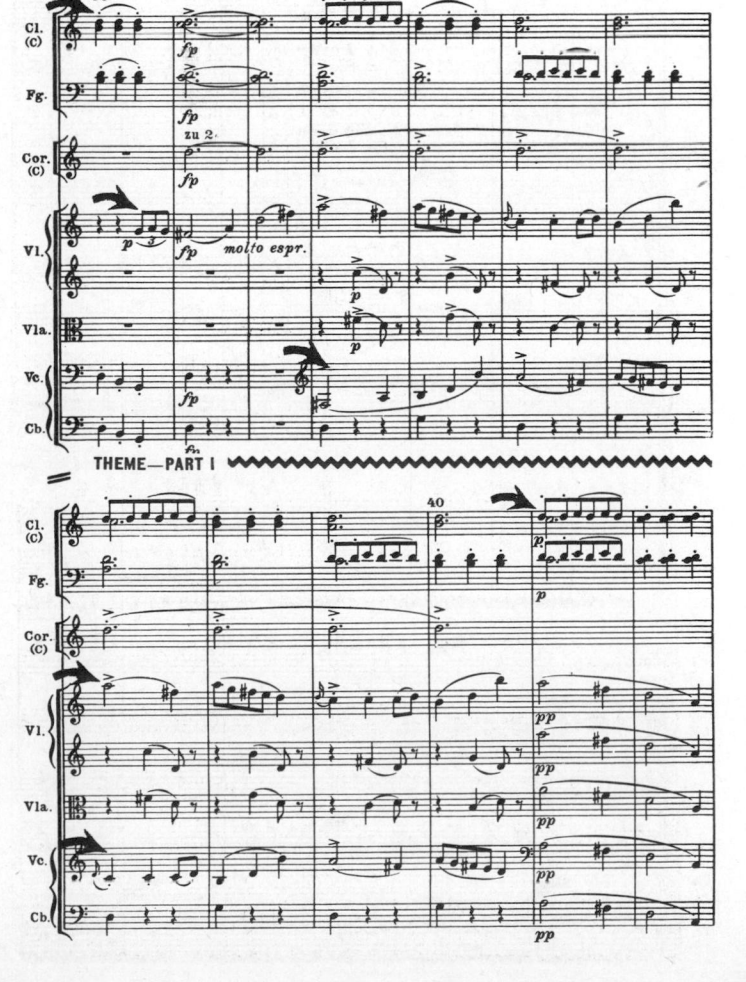

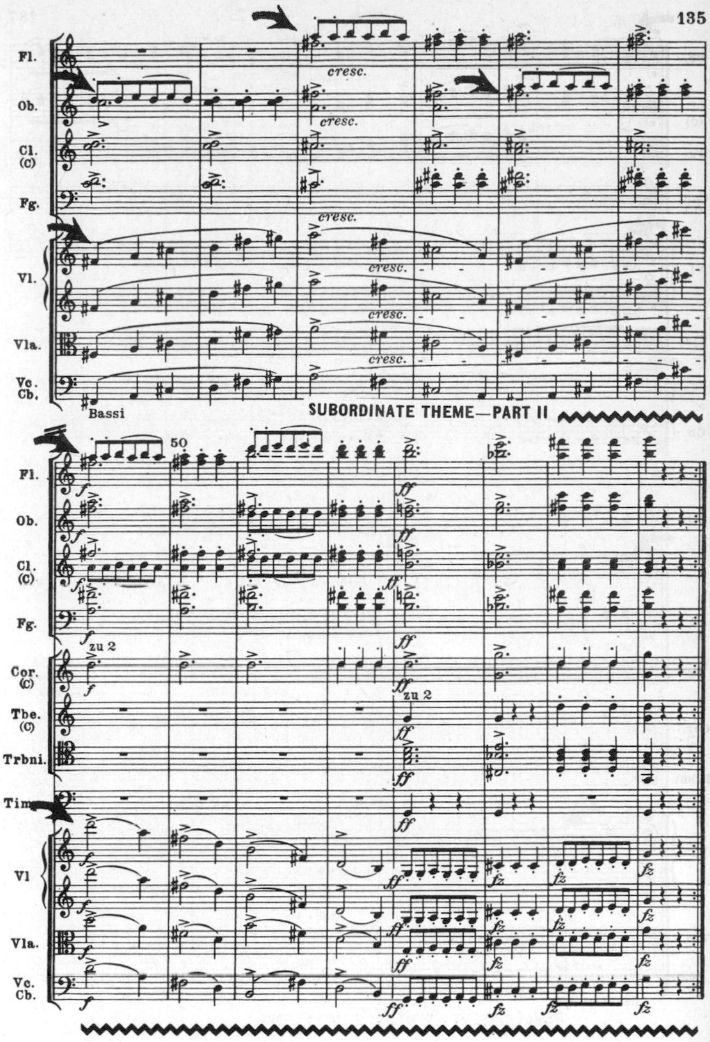
135
Fl.
Ob.
Cl. (C)
Fg.
Vl.
Vla.
Vc. Cb.
cresc.
Bassi
SUBORDINATE THEME—PART II
50
Cor. (C)
Tbe. (C)
Trbni.
Timp.
zu 2

134
30
Cl. (C)
Fg.
Cor. (C)
Vl.
Vla.
Vc.
Cb.
zu 2
molto espr.
THEME—PART I
40

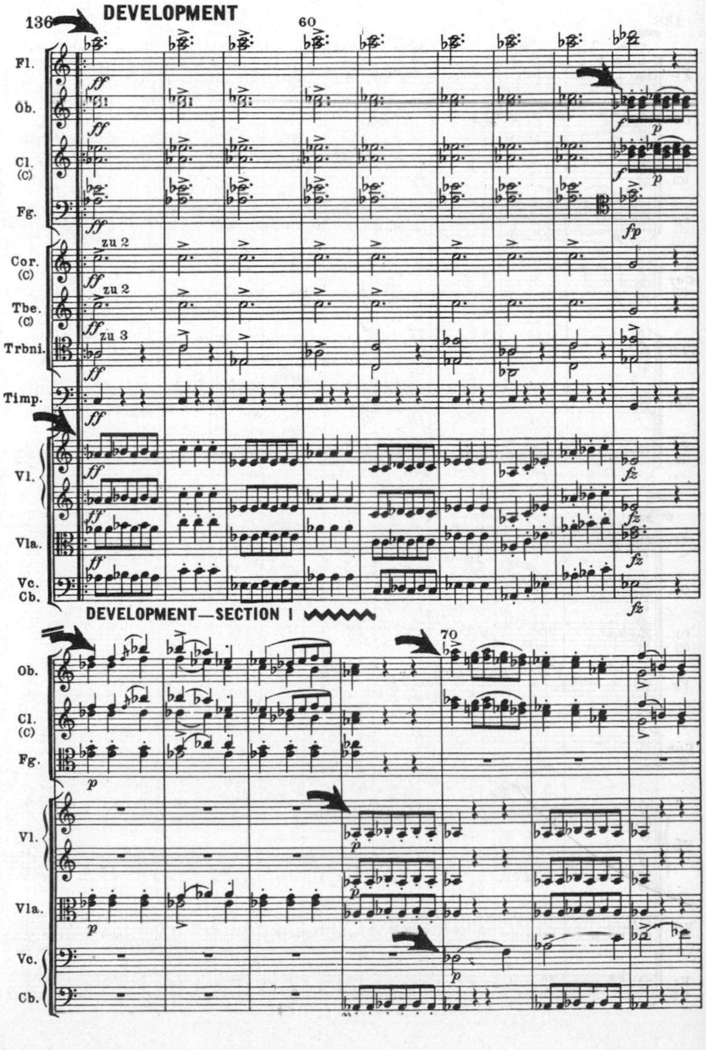
136
DEVELOPMENT
60
Fl.
Ob.
Cl. (C)
Fg.
Cor. (C)
Tbe. (C)
Trbni.
Timp.
Vl.
Vla.
Vc. Cb.
zu 2
zu 3
DEVELOPMENT—SECTION I
70
Vc.
Cb.

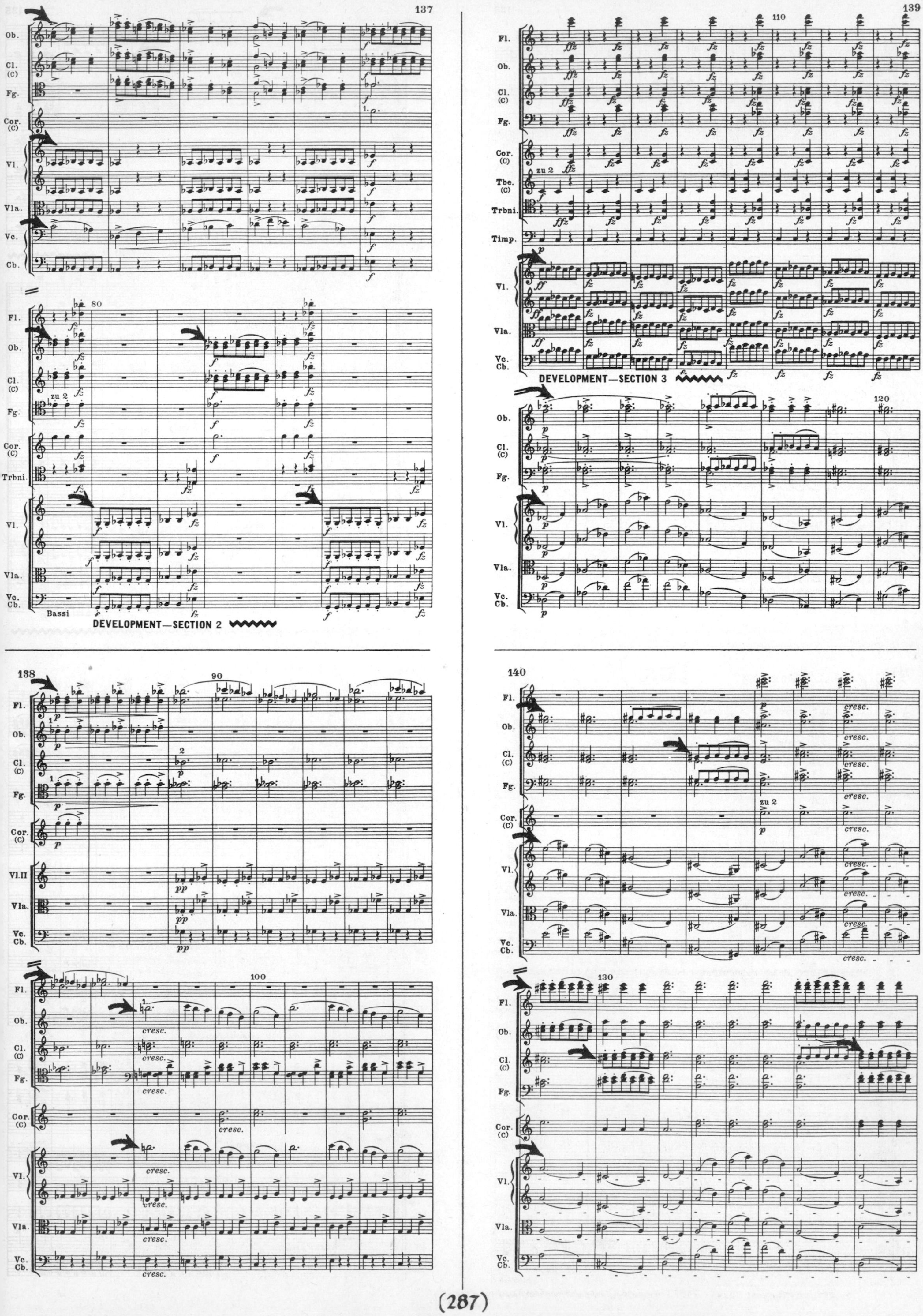

DEVELOPMENT—SECTION 2 〰〰〰〰

DEVELOPMENT—SECTION 3 〰〰〰〰

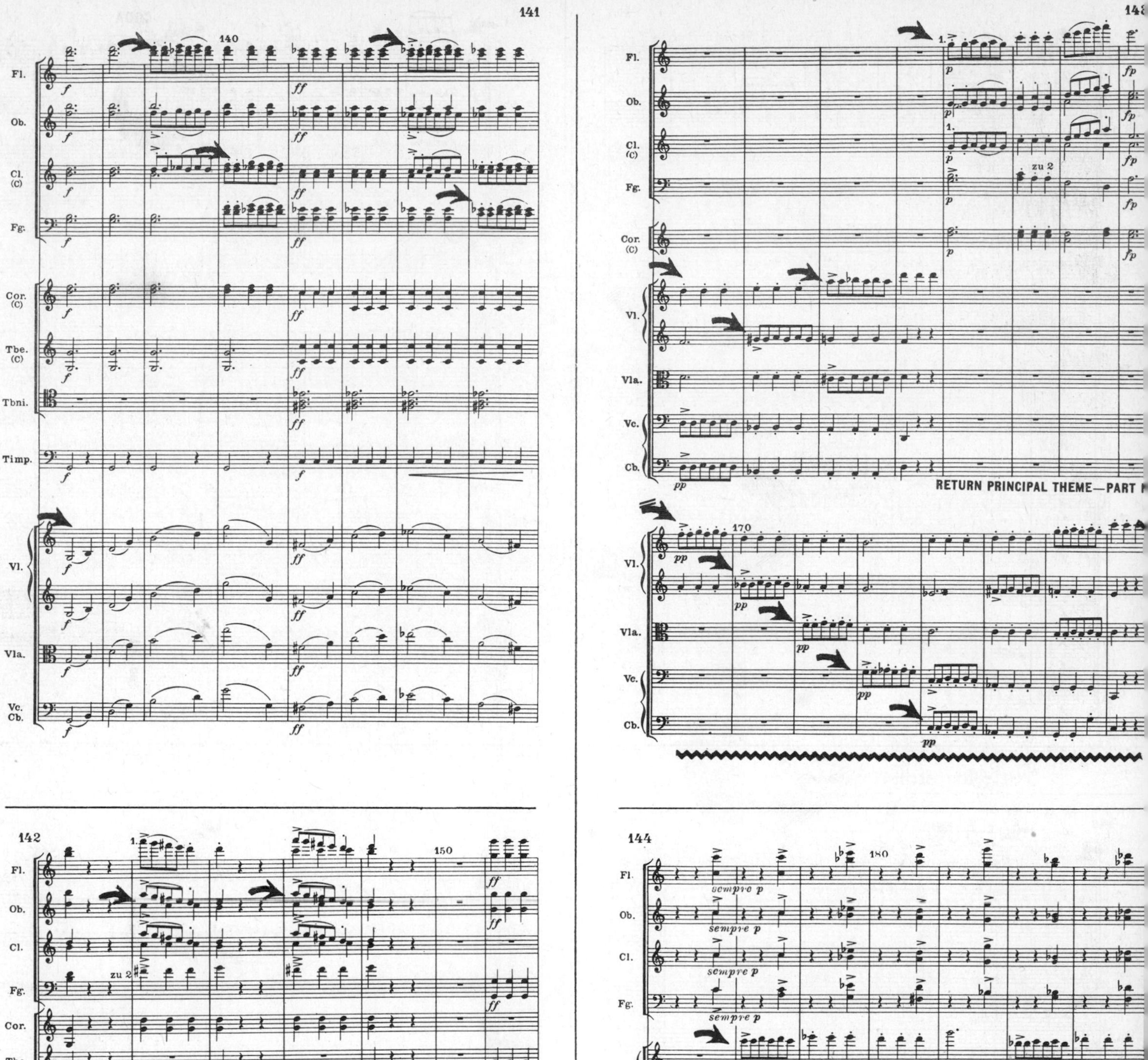

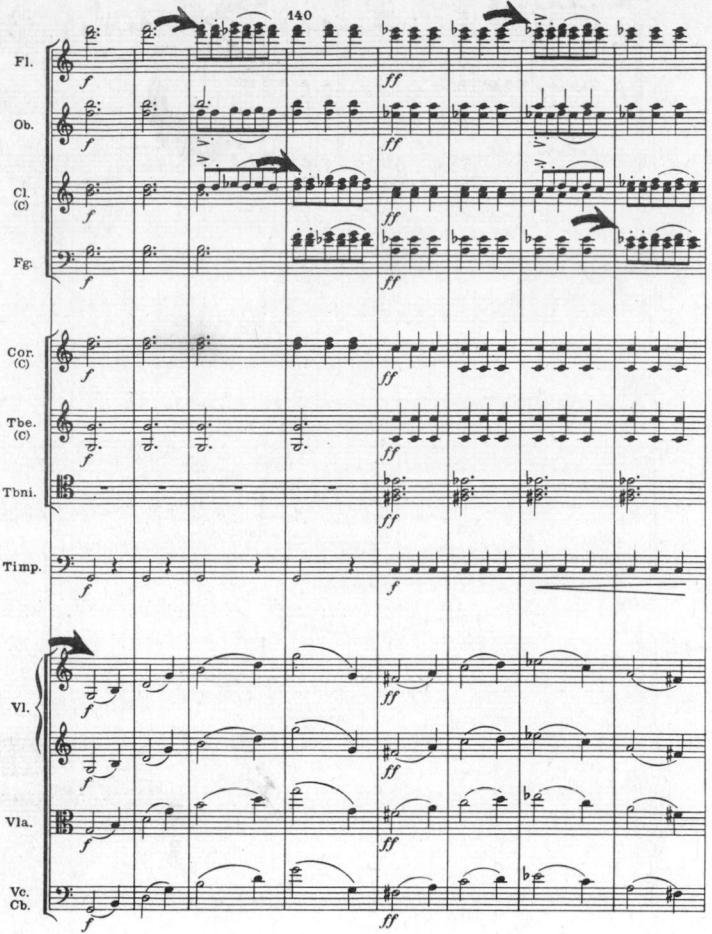

RETURN PRINCIPAL THEME—PART [I]

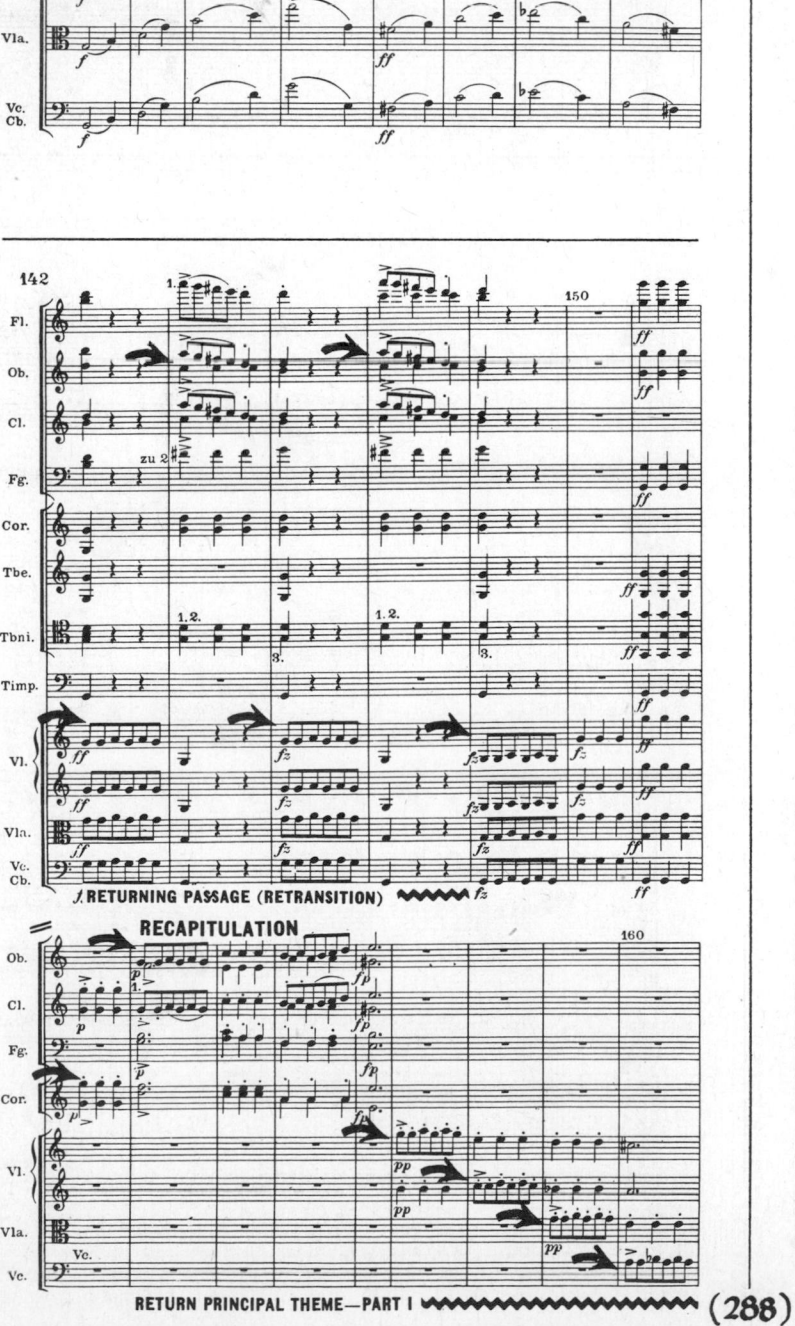

RETURNING PASSAGE (RETRANSITION)

RECAPITULATION

RETURN PRINCIPAL THEME—PART I

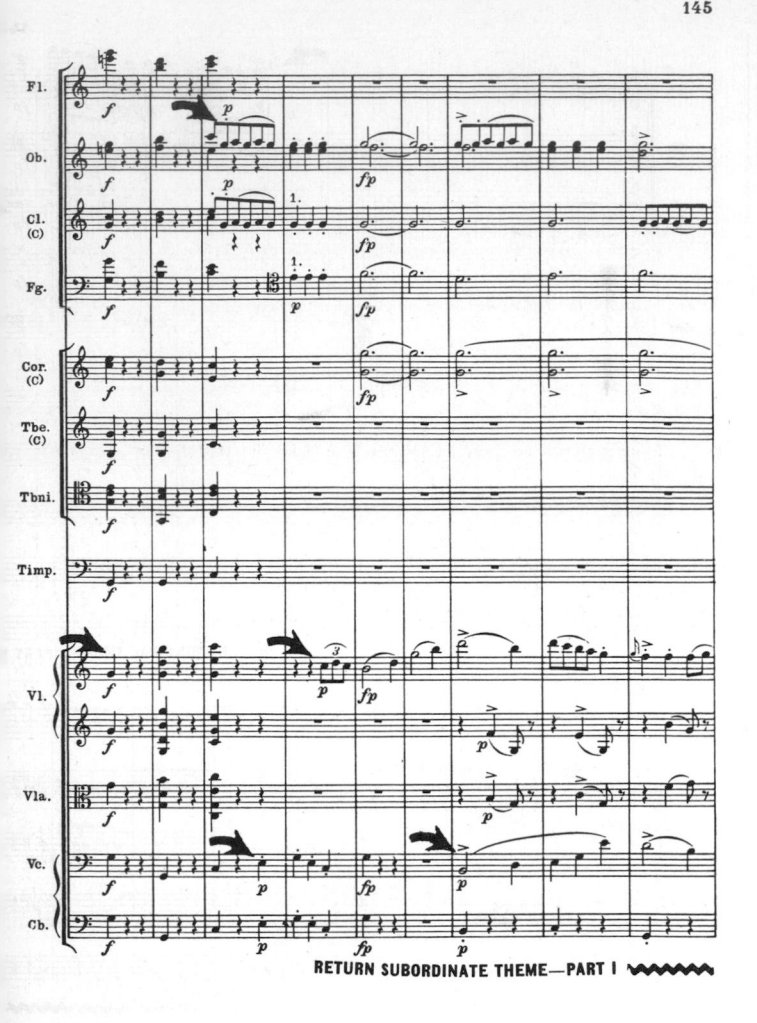

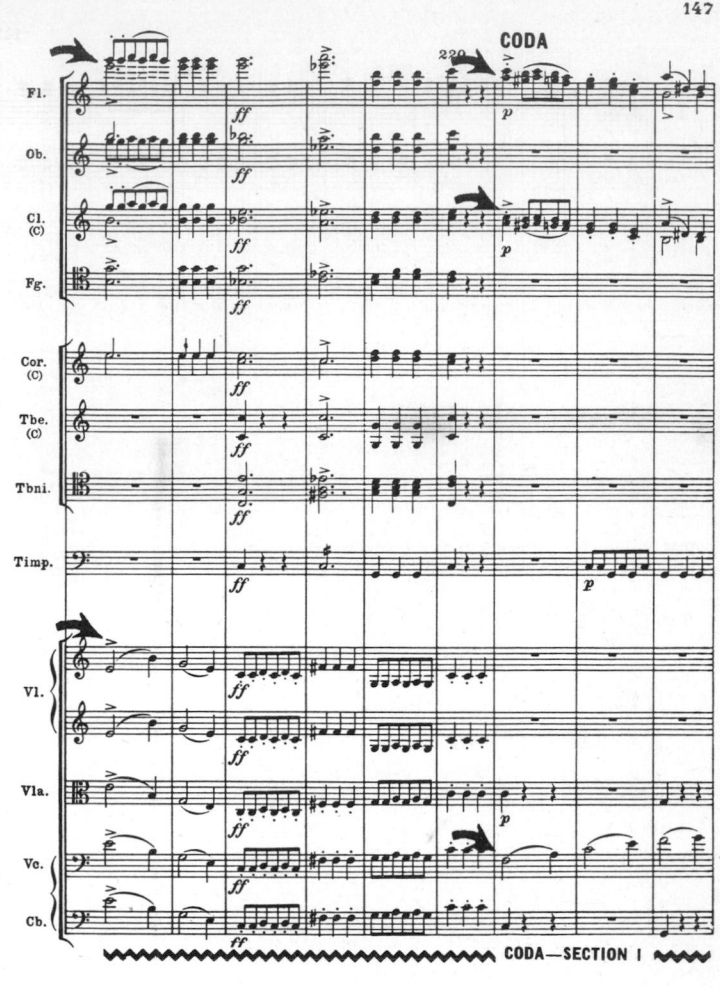

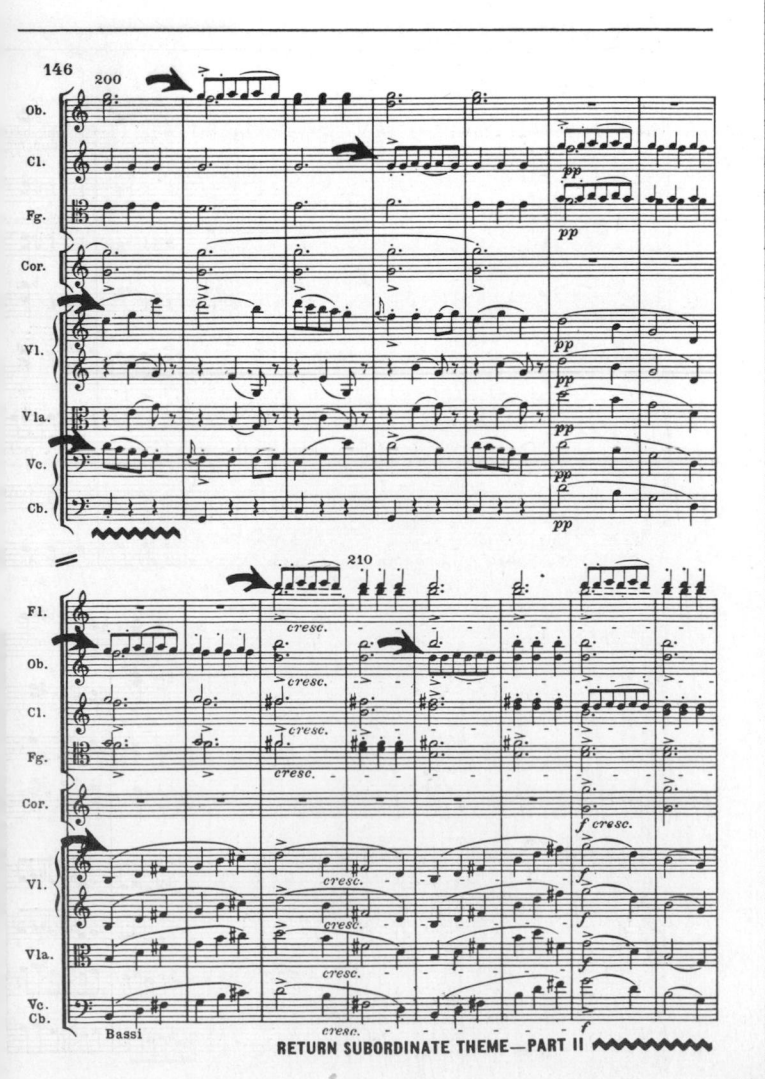

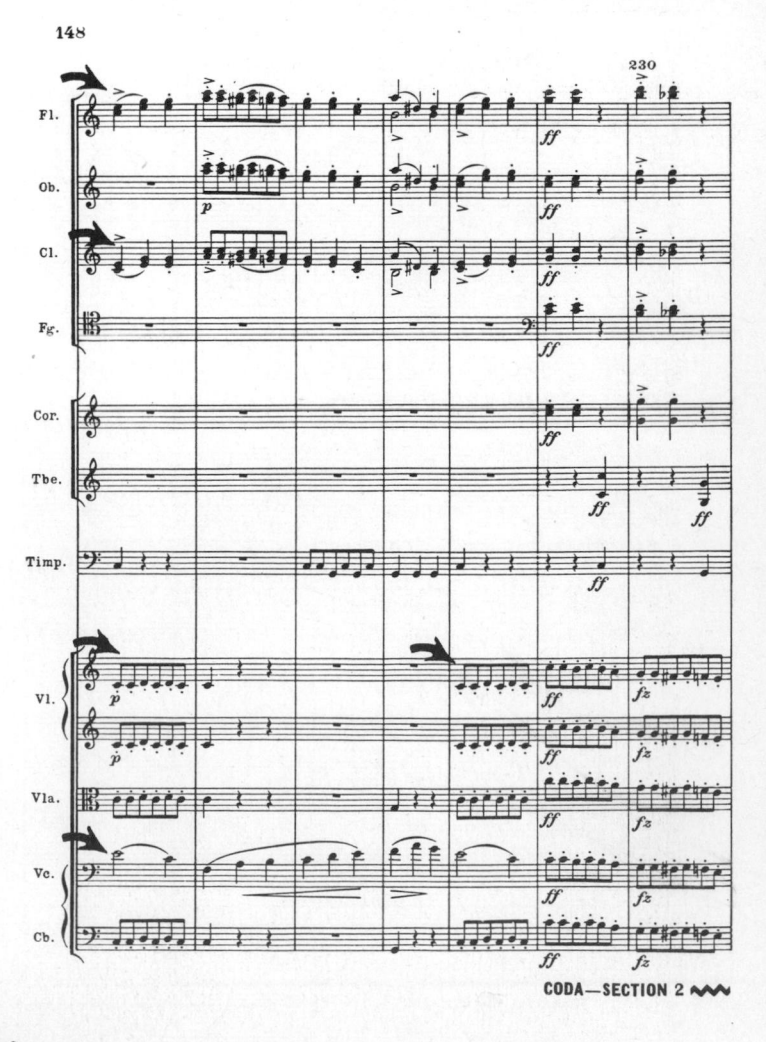

RETURN SUBORDINATE THEME—PART I

CODA—SECTION I

146

148

RETURN SUBORDINATE THEME—PART II

CODA—SECTION 2

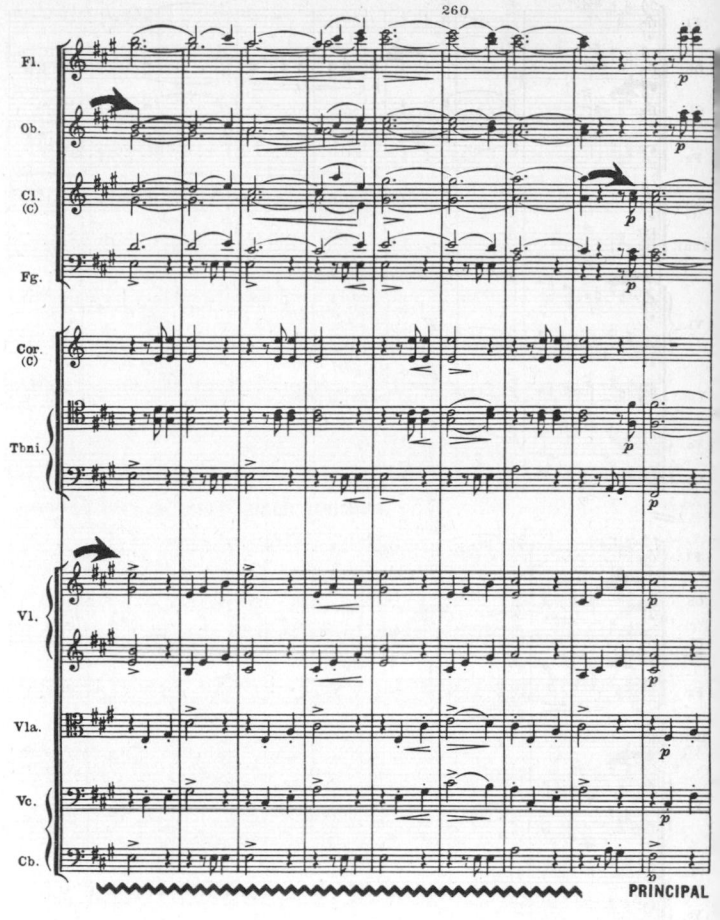

PRINCIPAL

Trio

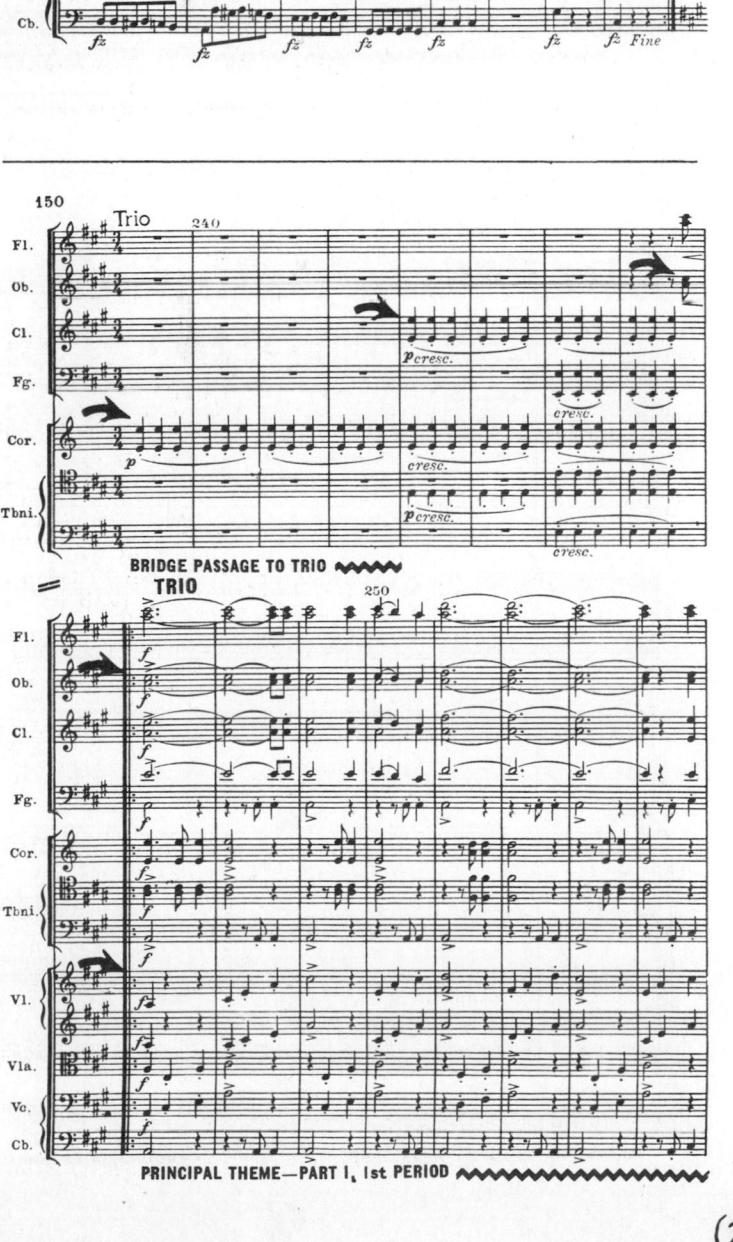

BRIDGE PASSAGE TO TRIO

TRIO

PRINCIPAL THEME—PART I, 1st PERIOD

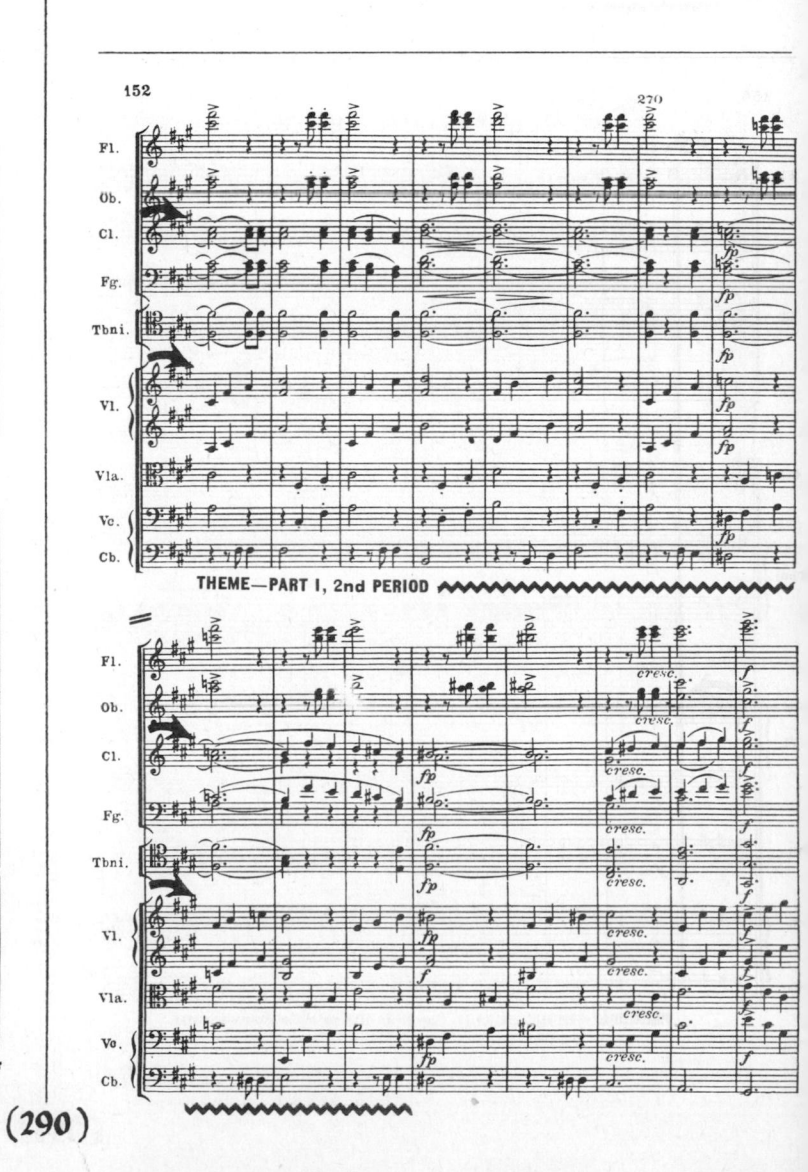

THEME—PART I, 2nd PERIOD

153

280

PRINCIPAL THEME—PART I, 3rd PERIOD 〰〰〰

290

155

310

PRINCIPAL THEME—PART II, 2nd PERIOD 〰〰〰〰〰〰〰〰〰〰

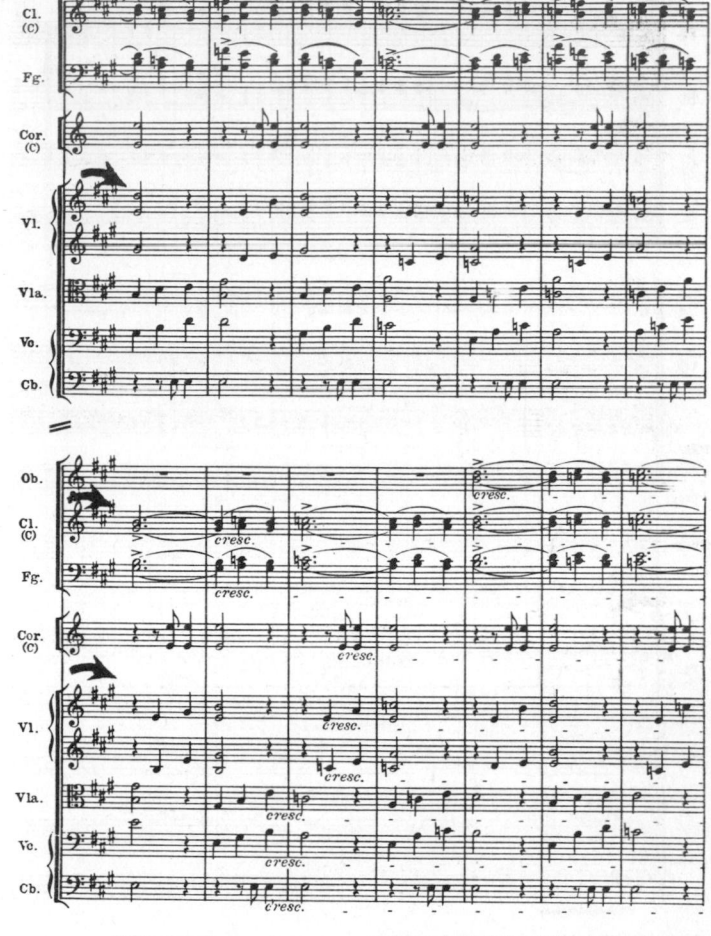

154

300

PRINCIPAL THEME—PART II, 1st PERIOD 〰〰〰〰

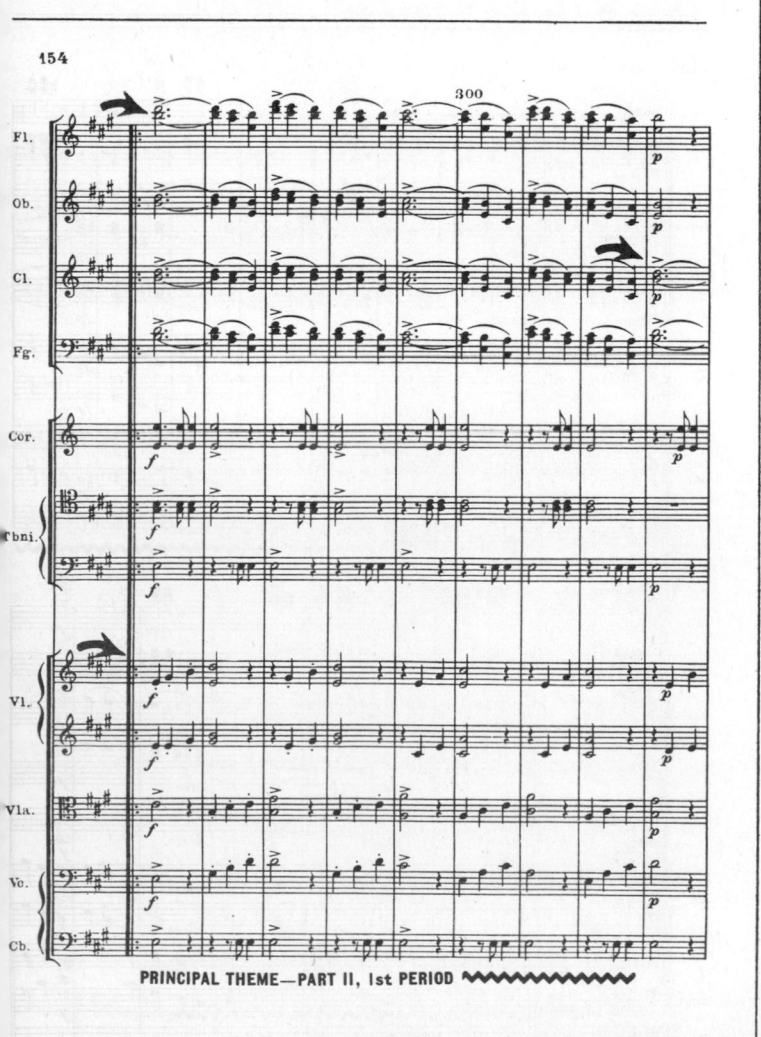

156

320

PRINCIPAL THEME—PART II, 3rd PERIOD 〰〰〰〰〰

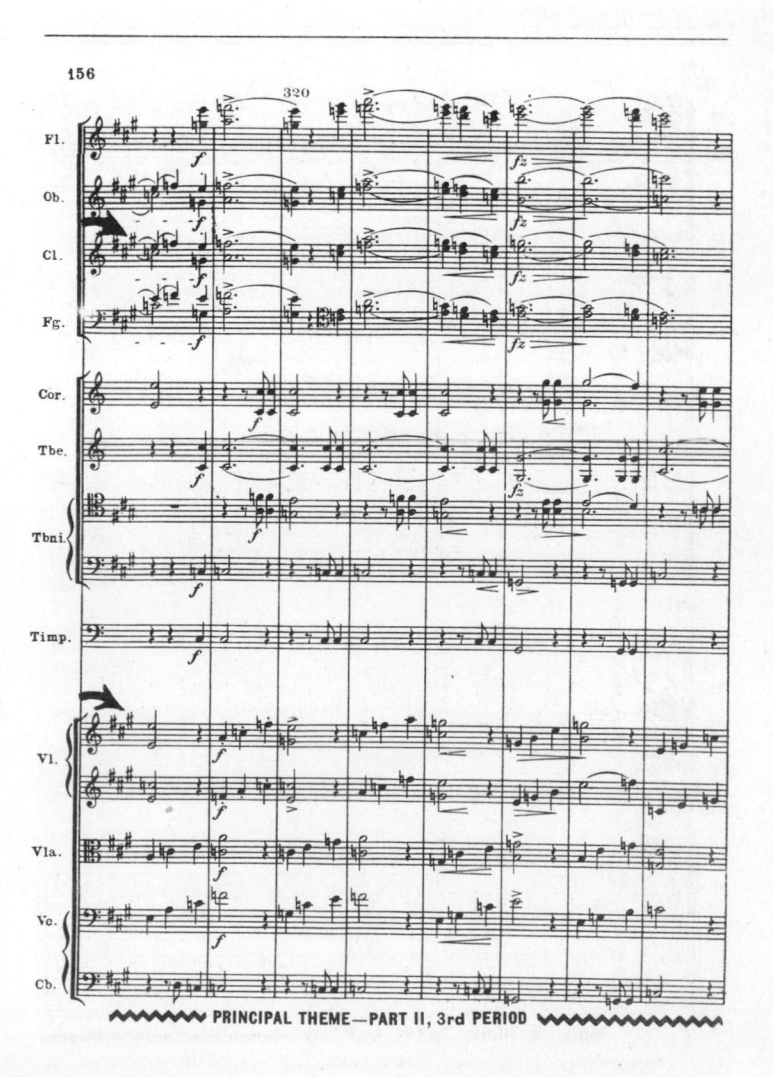

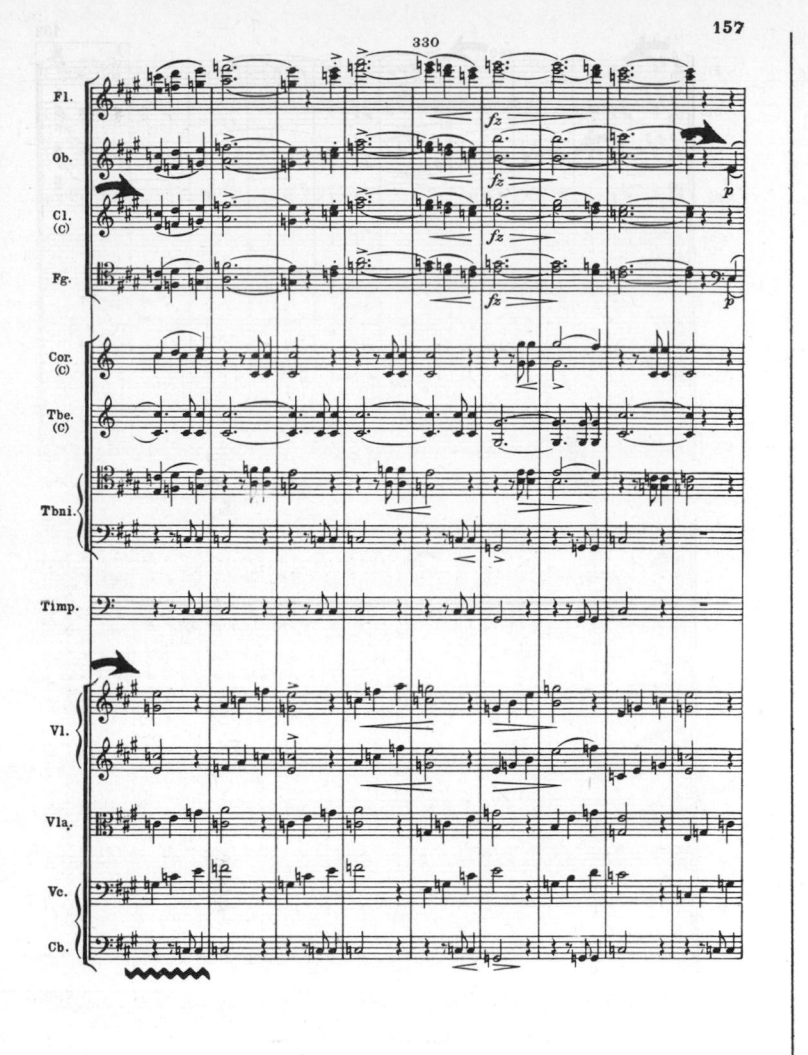

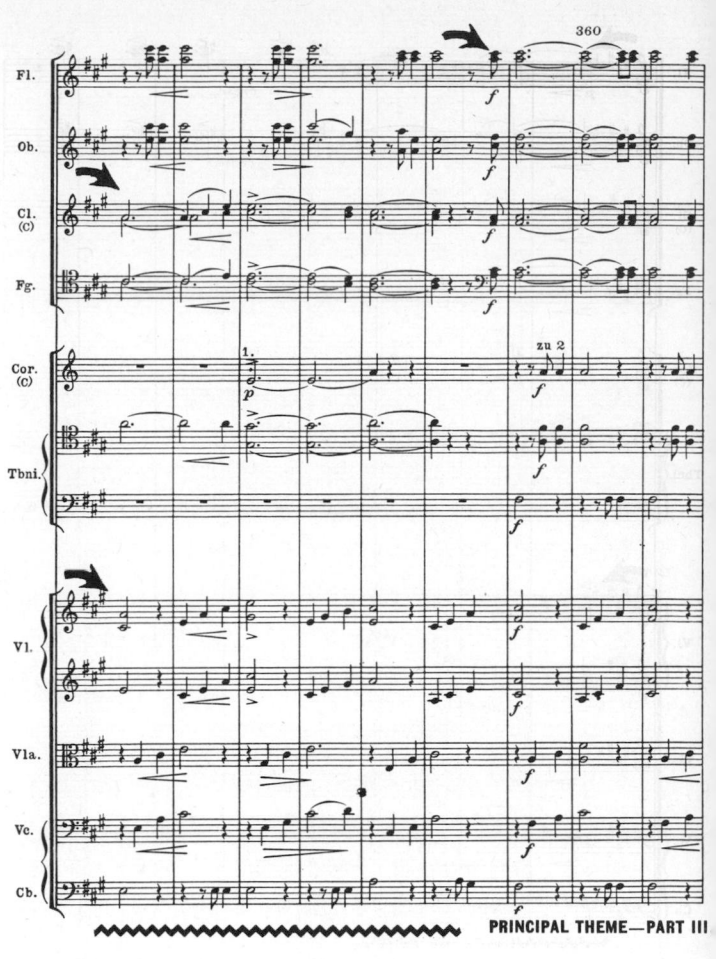

330
Fl.
Ob.
Cl. (C)
Fg.
Cor. (C)
Tbe. (C)
Tbni.
Timp.
Vl.
Vla.
Vc.
Cb.
fz
p

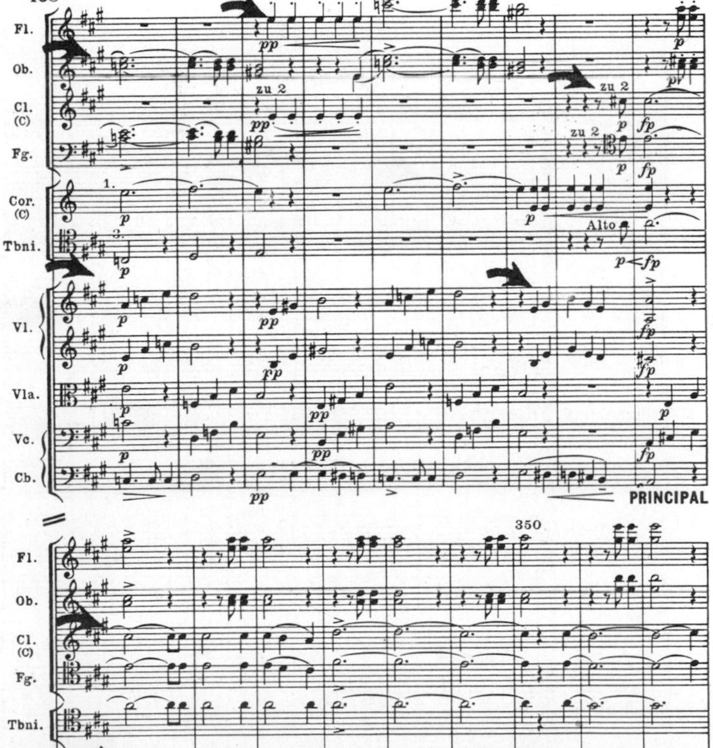
340
Fl.
Ob.
Cl. (C)
Fg.
Cor. (C)
Tbni.
Vl.
Vla.
Vc.
Cb.
zu 2
Alto
pp
p
fp
PRINCIPAL
350
THEME—PART III, 1st PERIOD

360
Fl.
Ob.
Cl. (C)
Fg.
Cor. (C)
Tbni.
Vl.
Vla.
Vc.
Cb.
zu 2
f
p
PRINCIPAL THEME—PART III

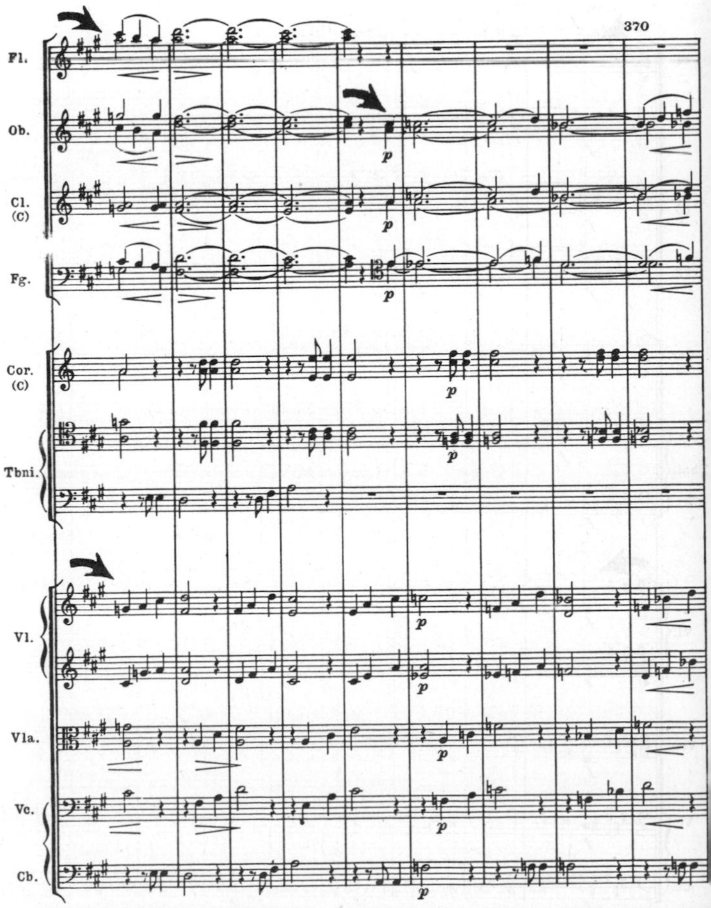
370
Fl.
Ob.
Cl. (C)
Fg.
Cor. (C)
Tbni.
Vl.
Vla.
Vc.
Cb.
p
2nd PERIOD

161

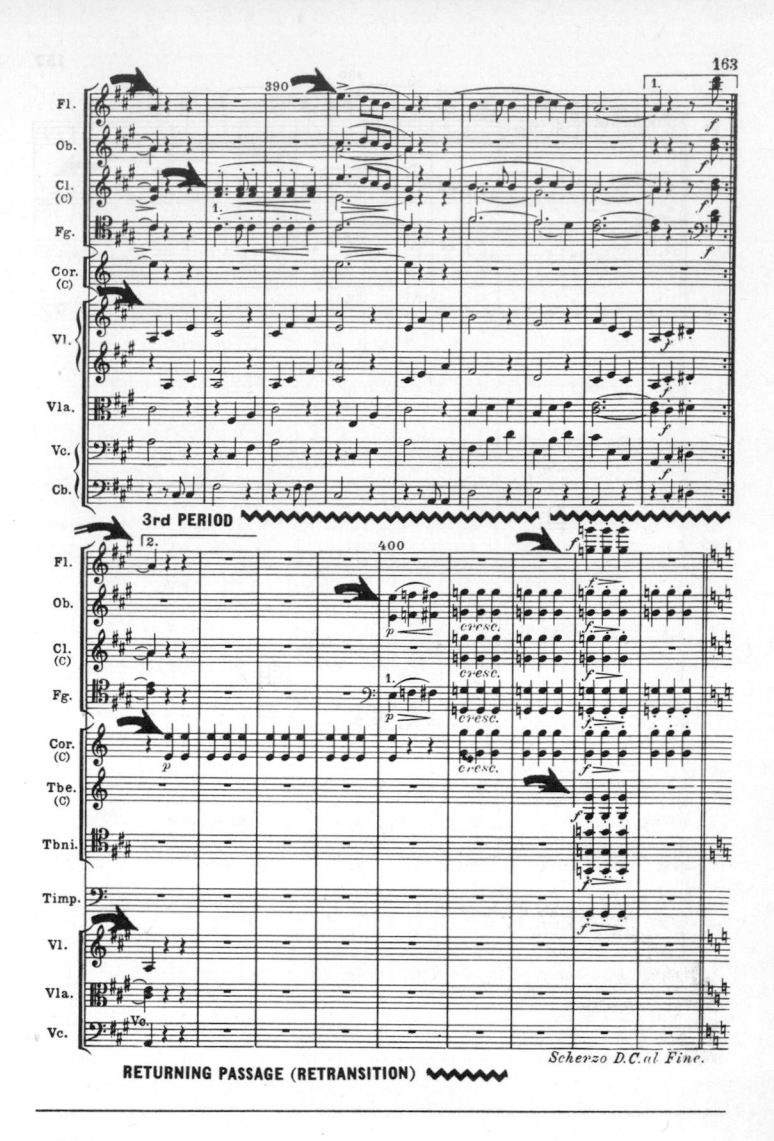

162

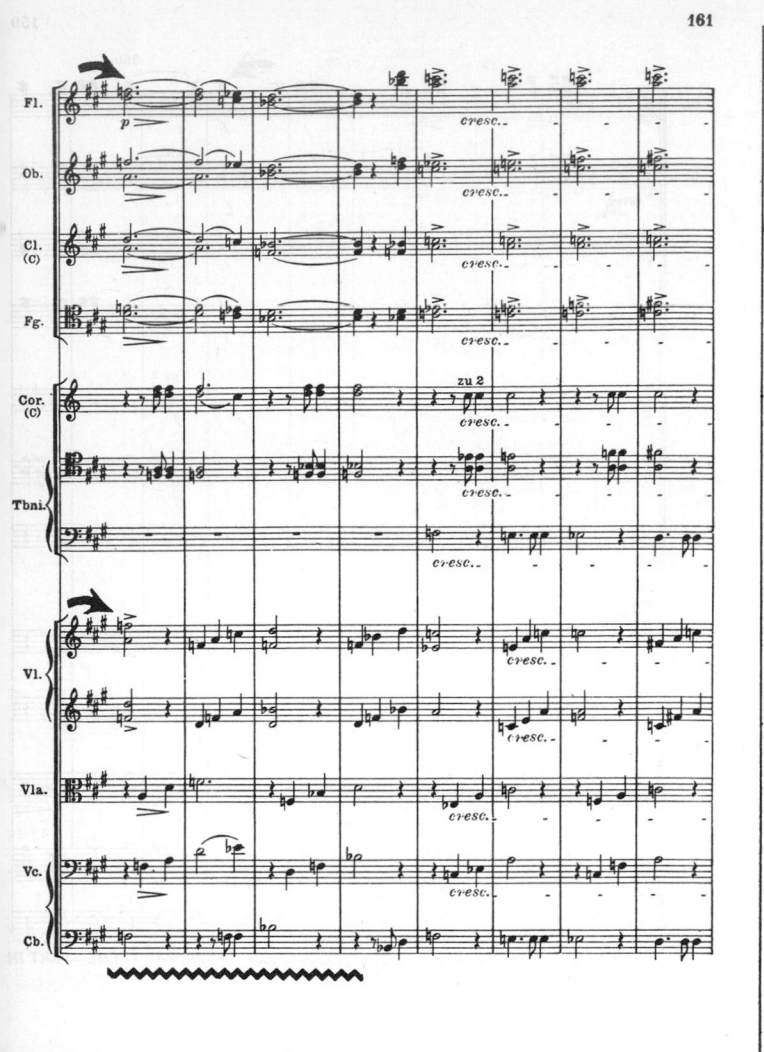

PRINCIPAL THEME—PART III.

163

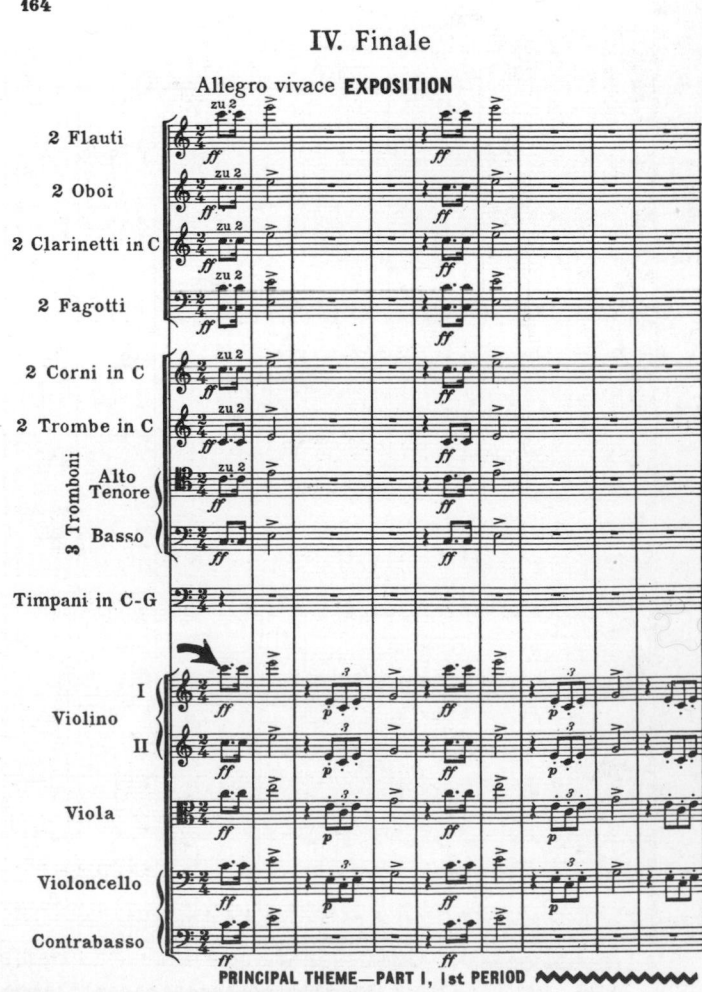

3rd PERIOD

RETURNING PASSAGE (RETRANSITION) 〰〰

Scherzo D.C. al Fine.

164

IV. Finale

Allegro vivace EXPOSITION

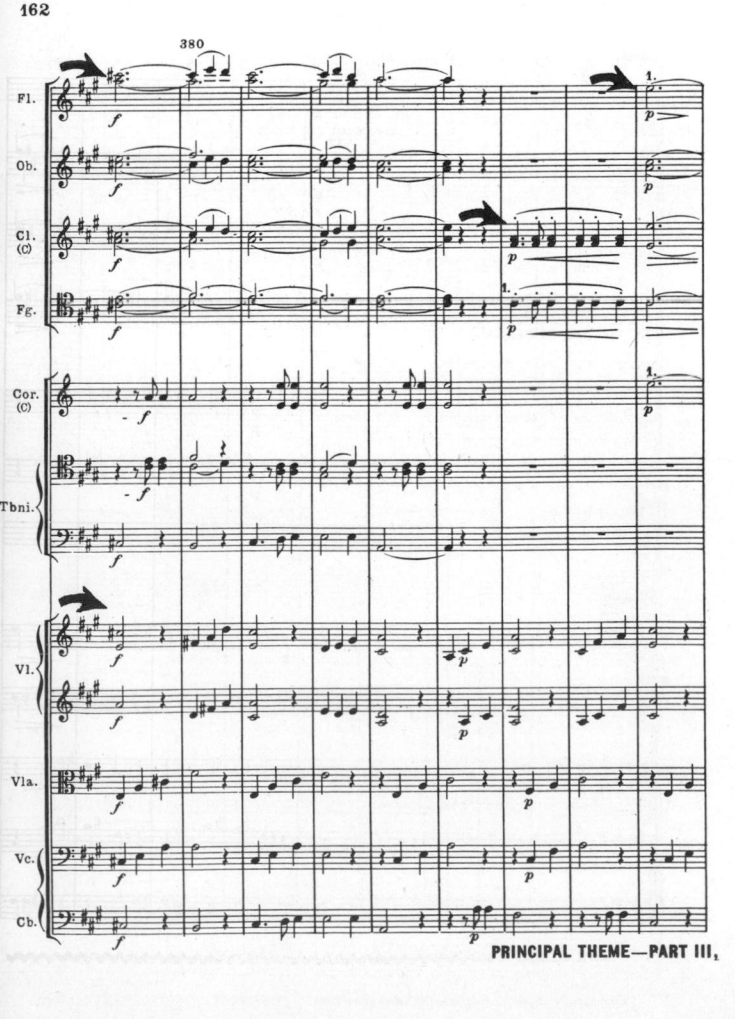

PRINCIPAL THEME—PART I, 1st PERIOD 〰〰〰

(293)

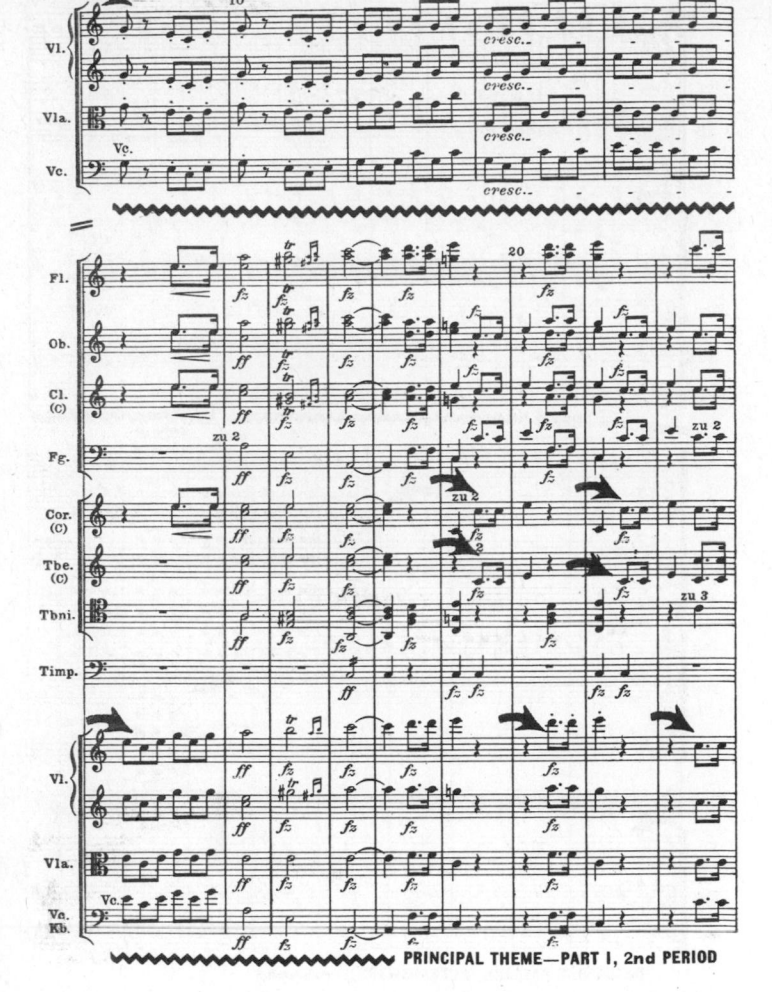

PRINCIPAL THEME—PART I, 2nd PERIOD

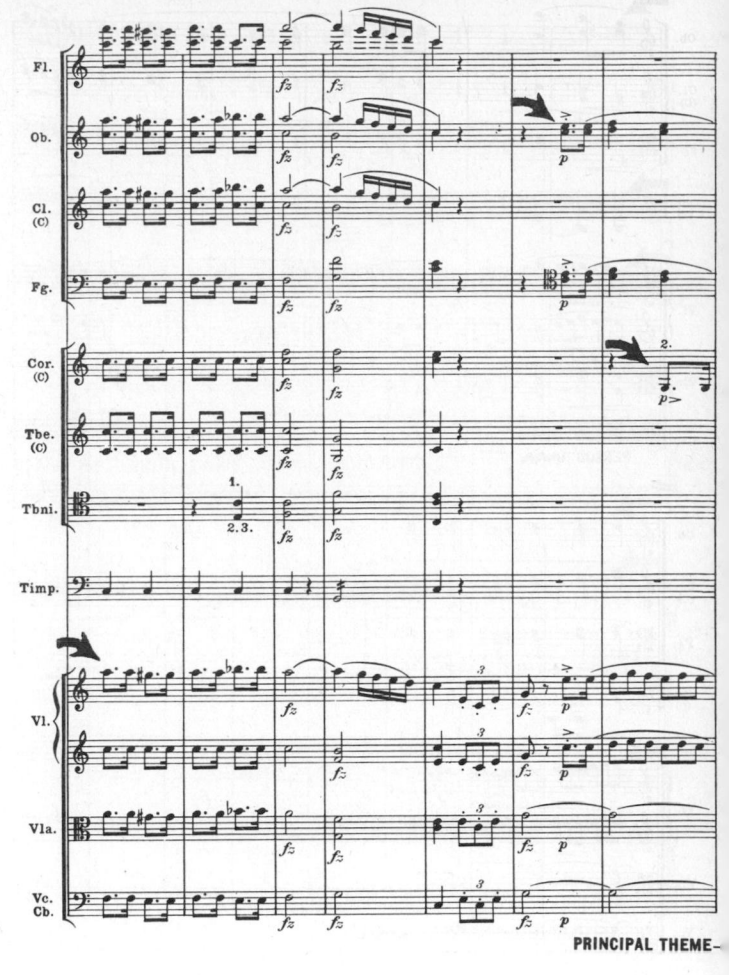

PRINCIPAL THEME—

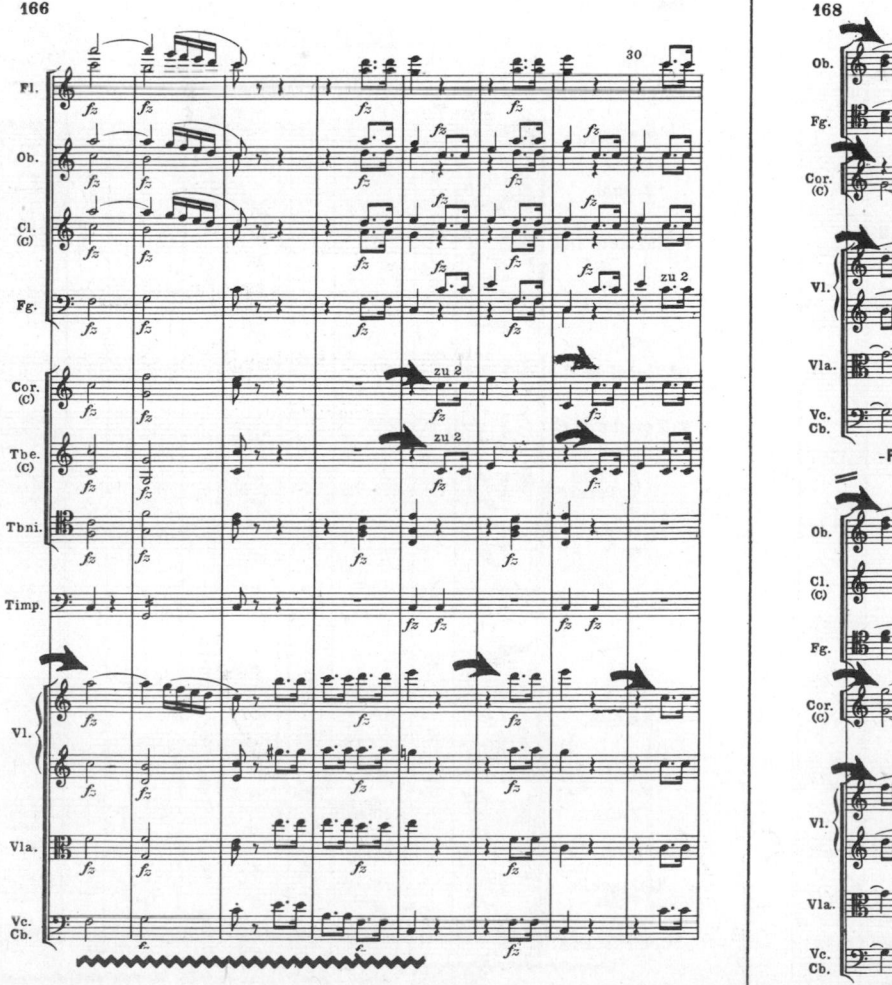

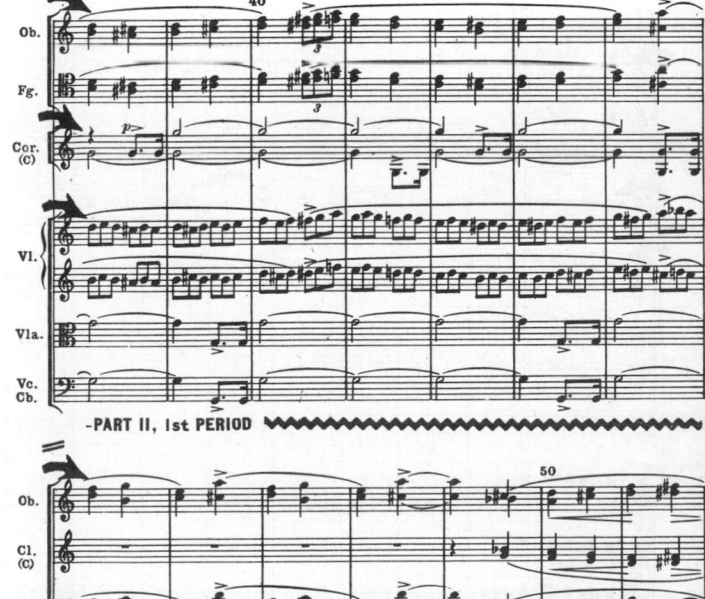

-PART II, 1st PERIOD

PRINCIPAL THEME—PART II, 2nd

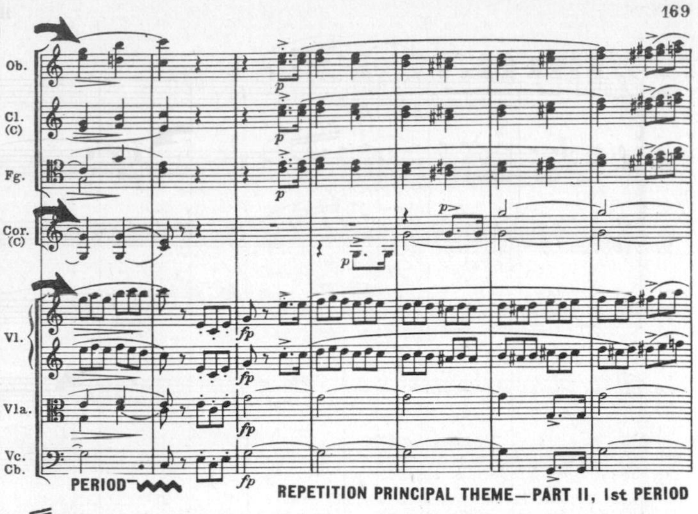
PERIOD
REPETITION PRINCIPAL THEME—PART II, 1st PERIOD

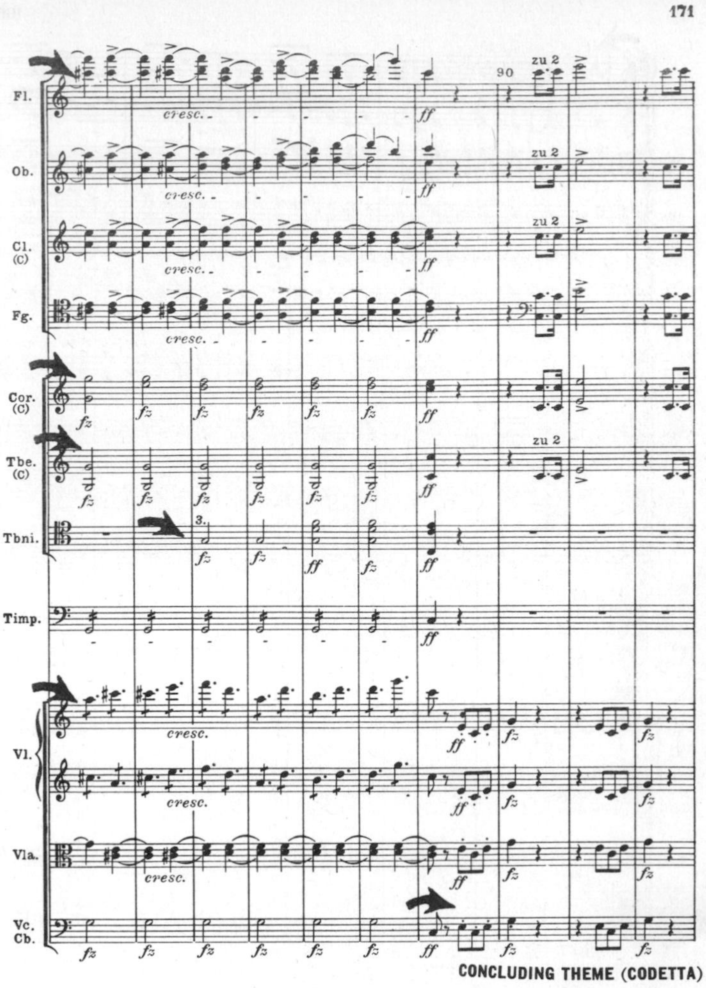
CONCLUDING THEME (CODETTA)

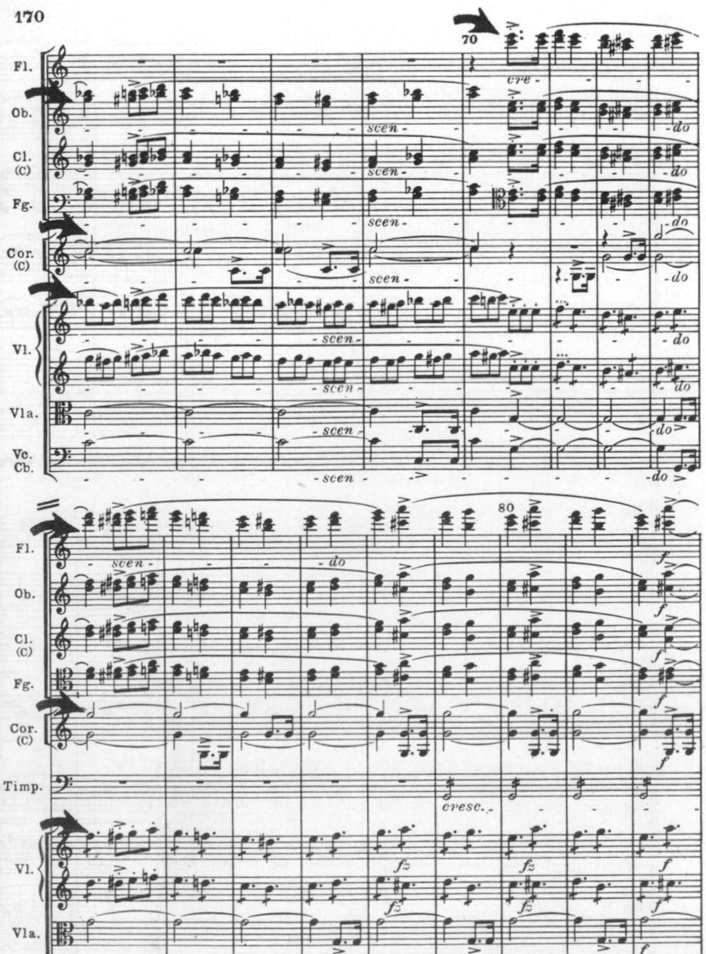

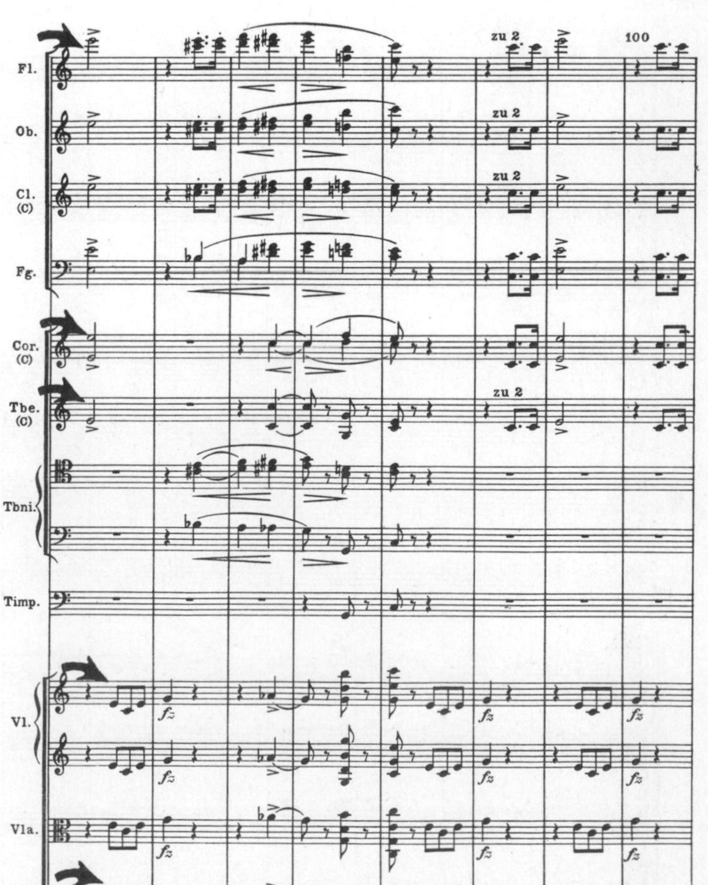

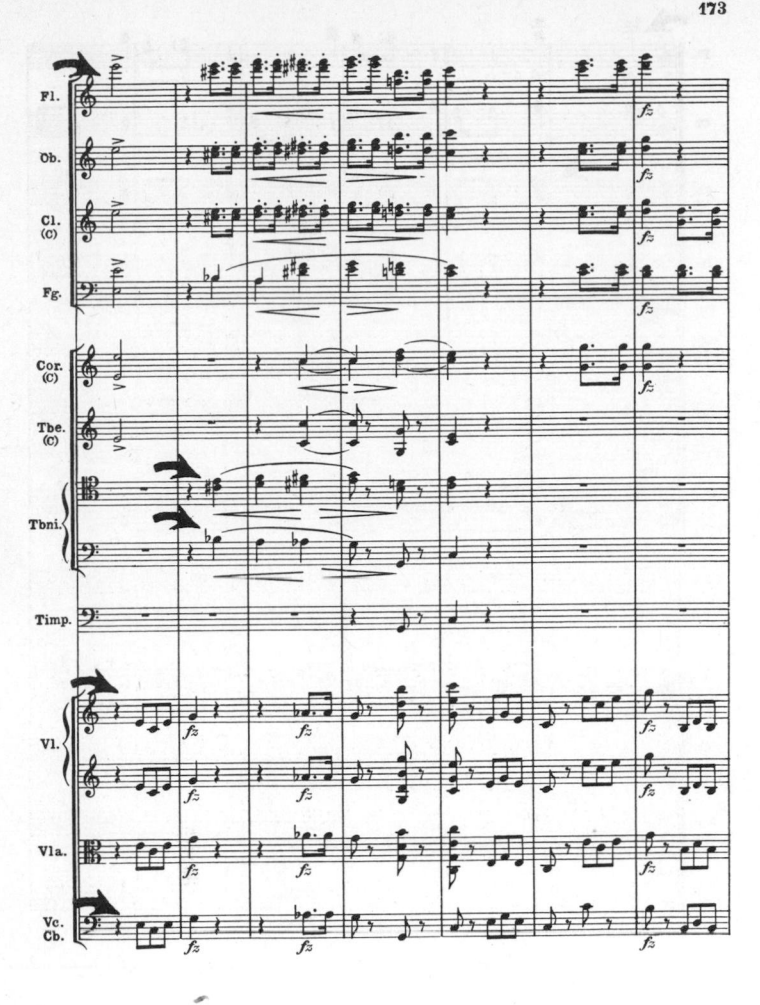

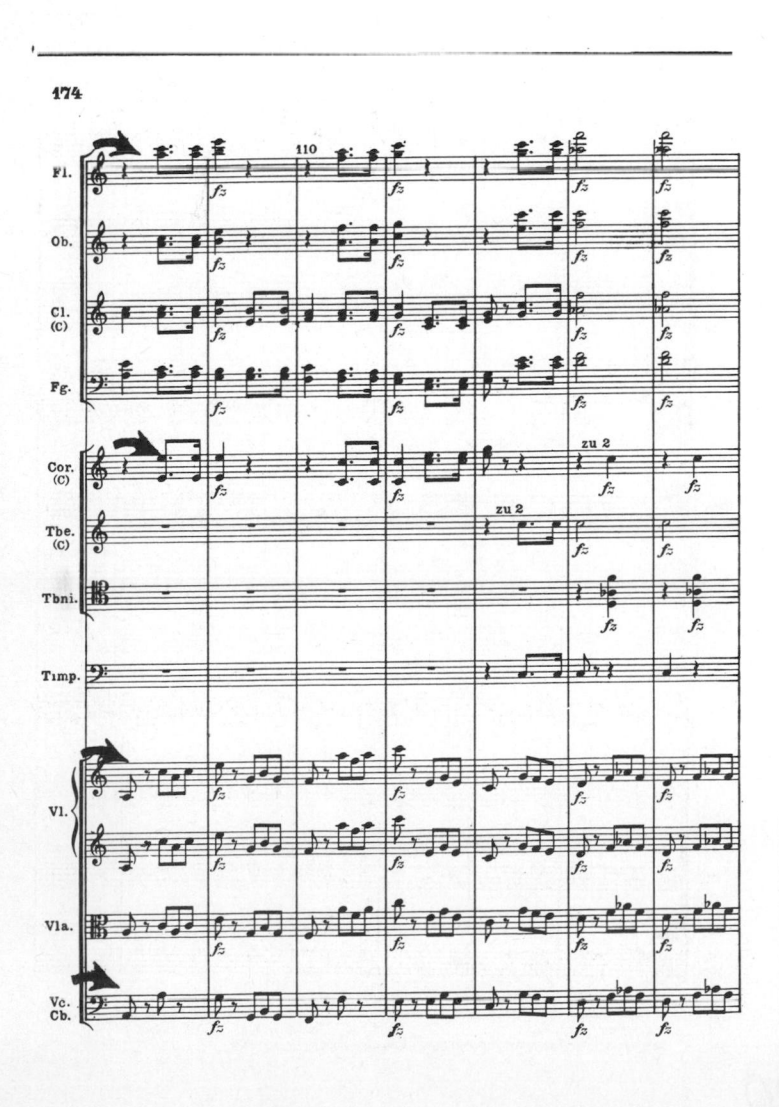

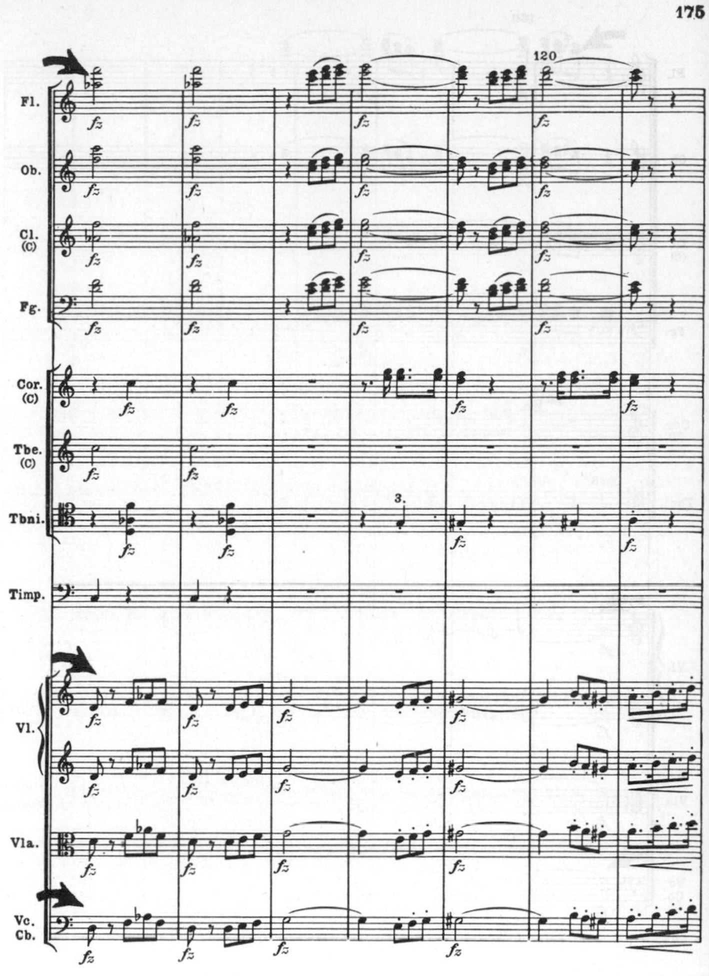

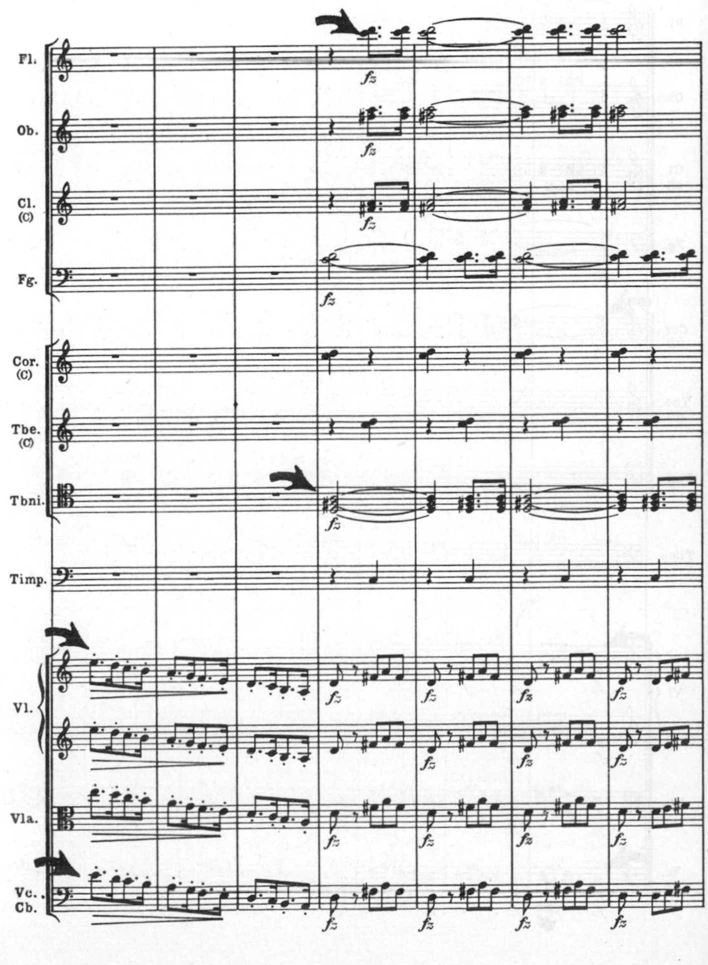

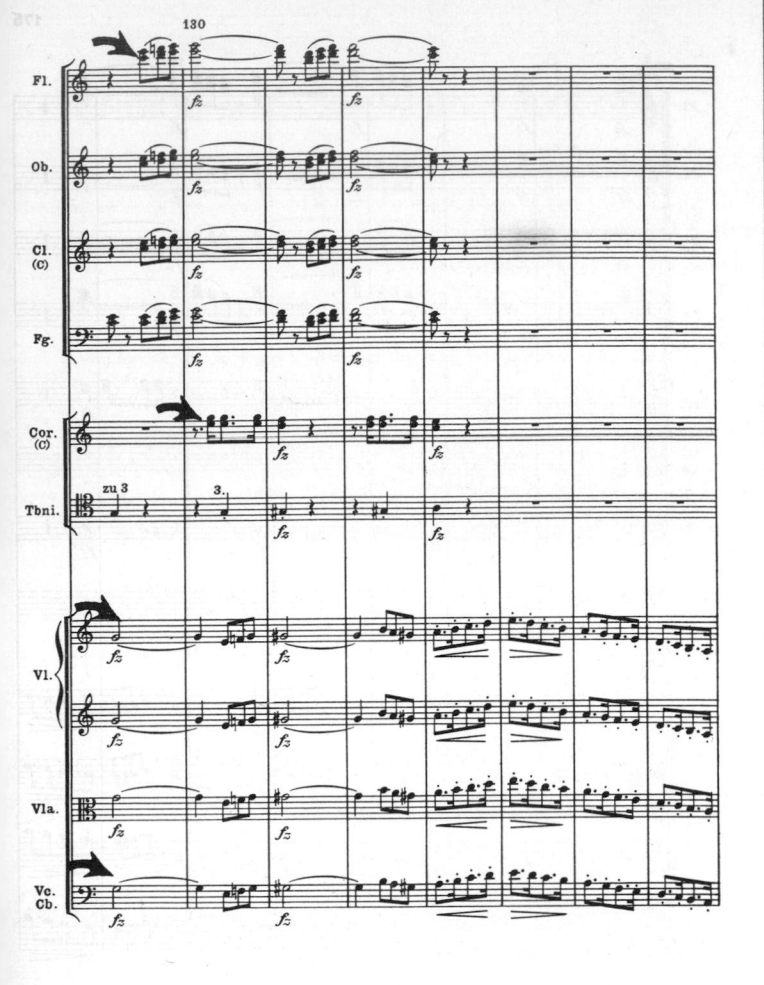

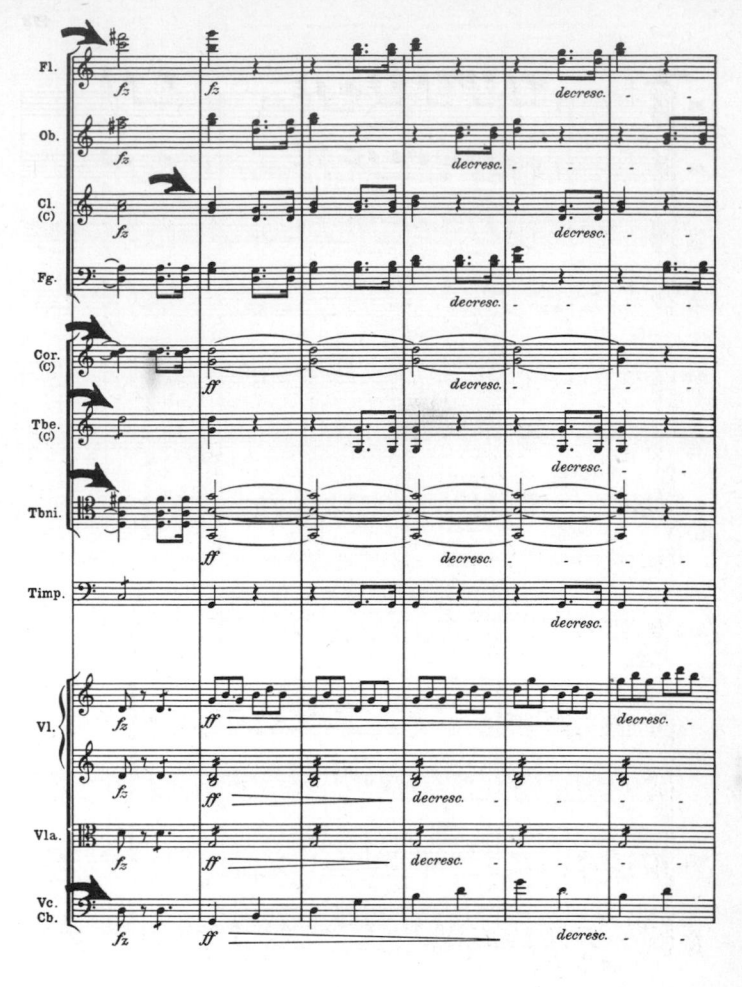

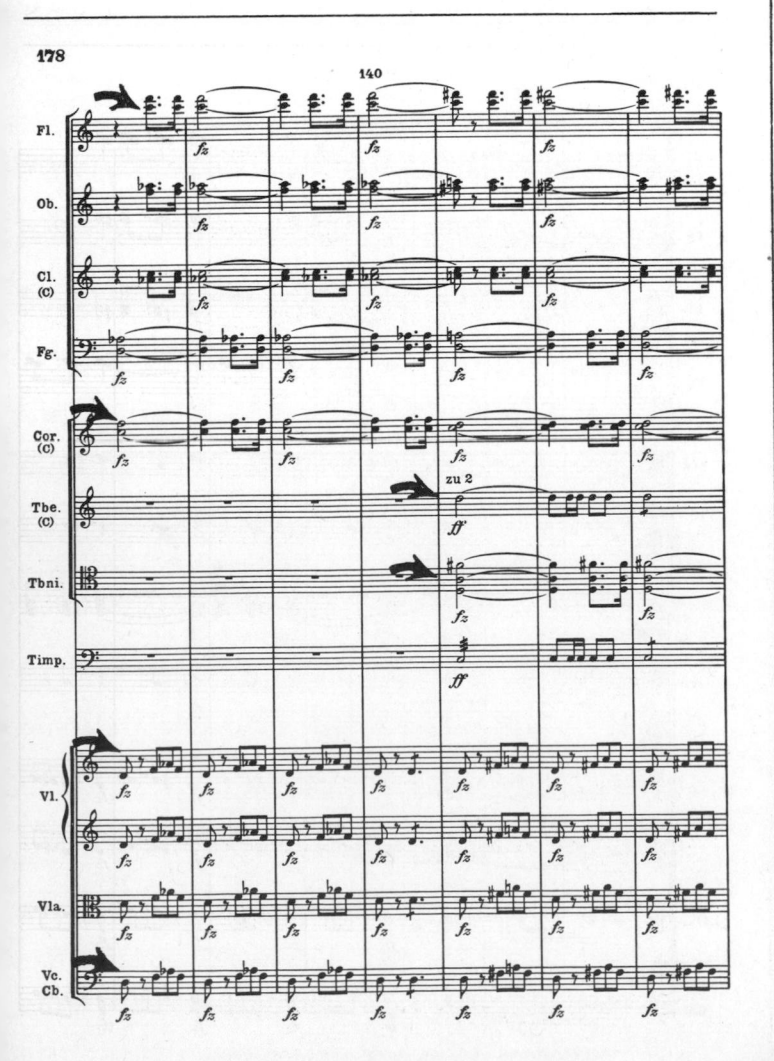

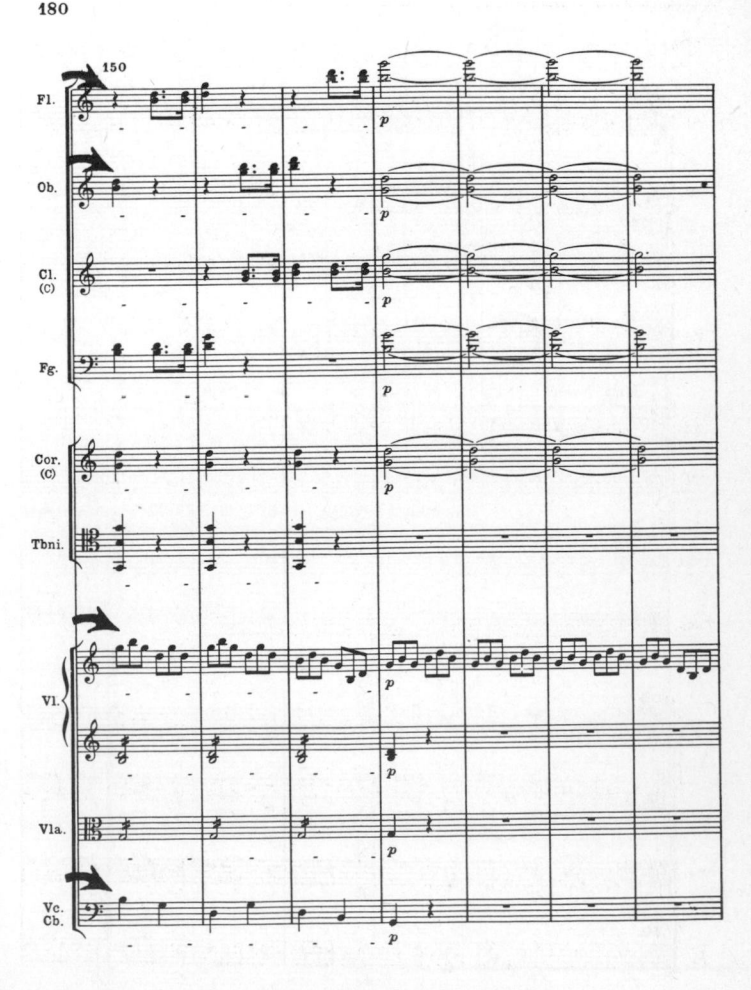

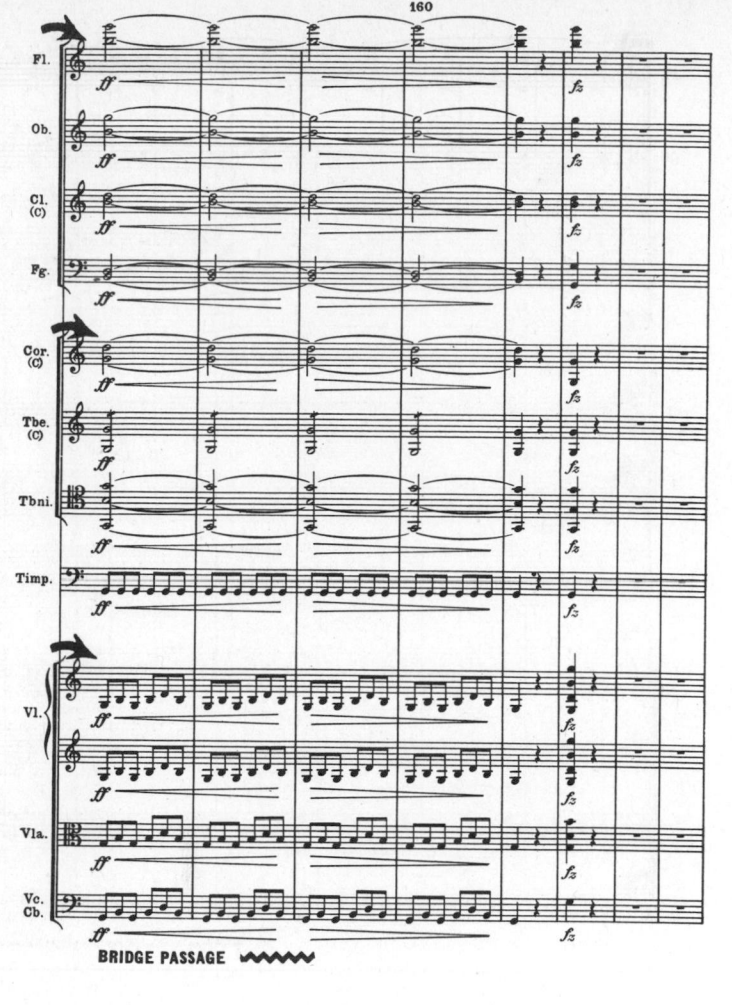

160

BRIDGE PASSAGE 〰〰

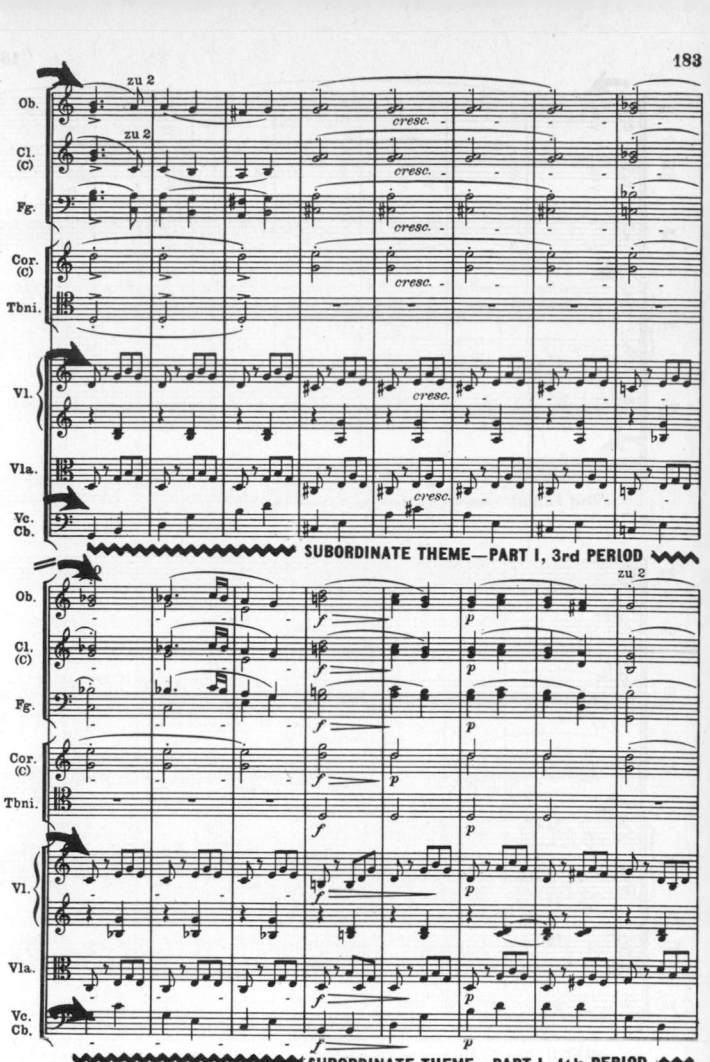

SUBORDINATE THEME—PART I, 3rd PERIOD 〰〰

SUBORDINATE THEME—PART I, 4th PERIOD 〰〰

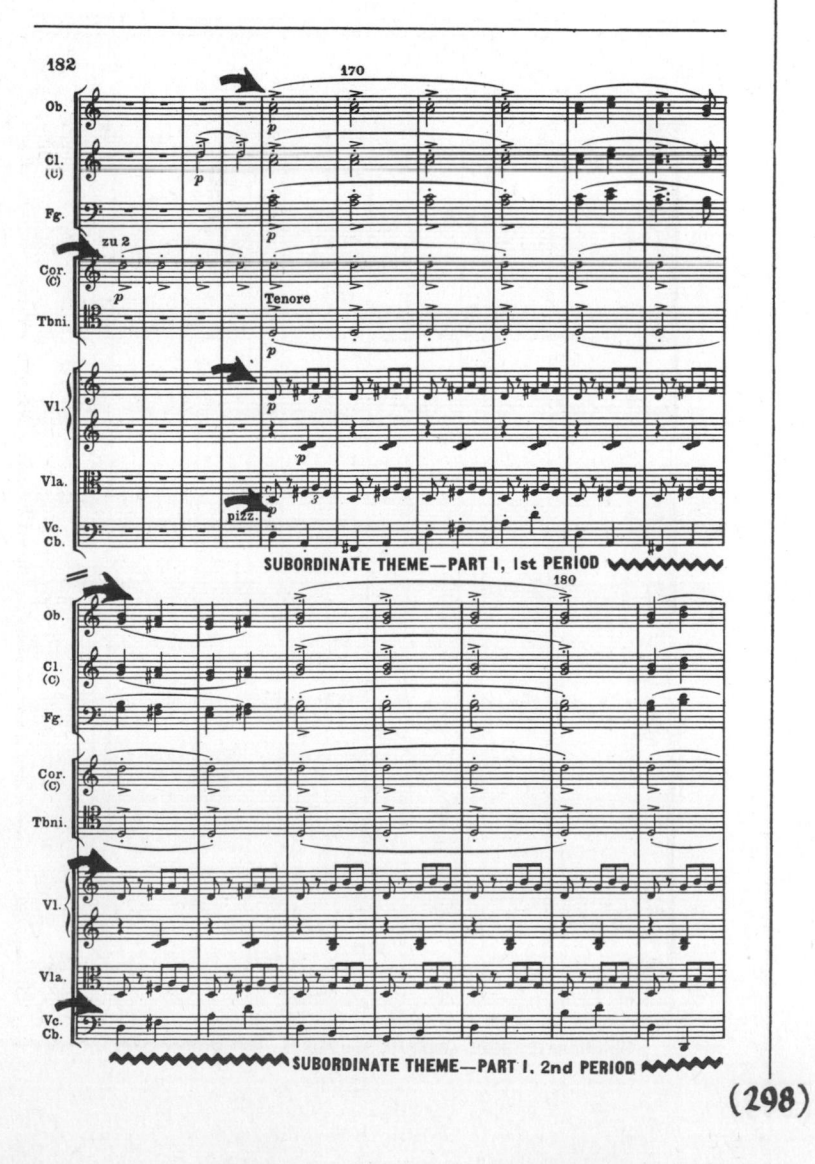

170

SUBORDINATE THEME—PART I, 1st PERIOD 〰〰

180

SUBORDINATE THEME—PART I, 2nd PERIOD 〰〰

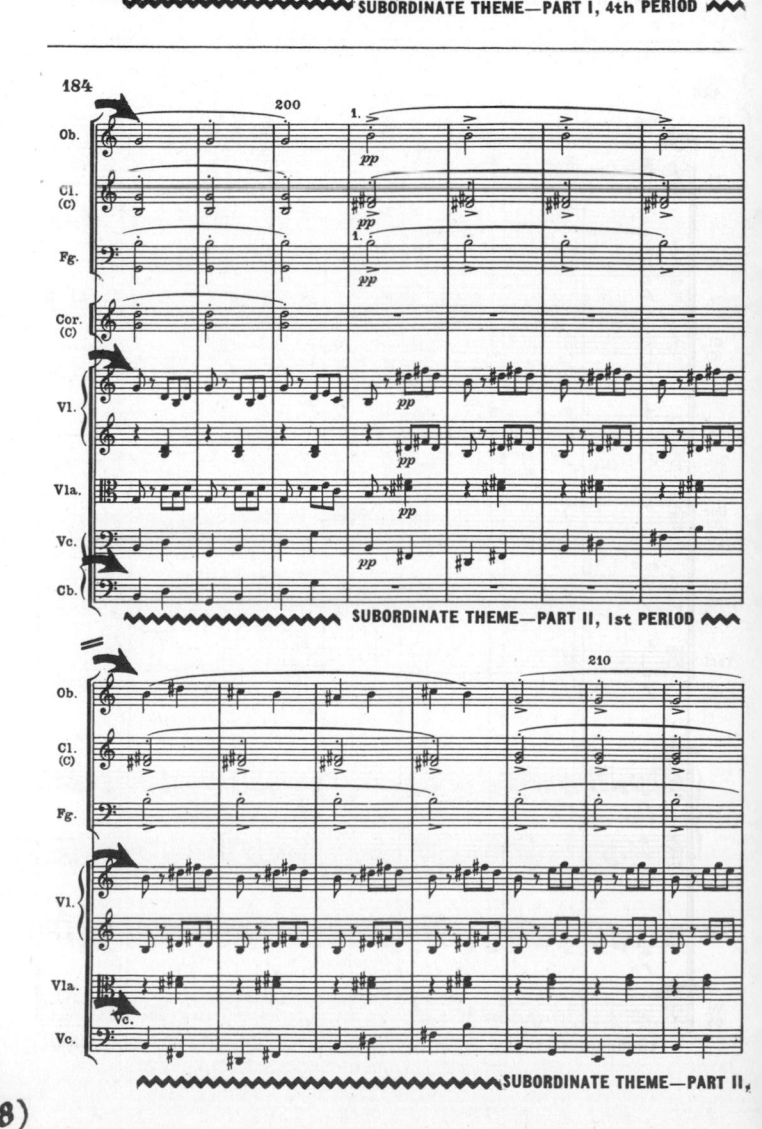

200

1.

SUBORDINATE THEME—PART II, 1st PERIOD 〰〰

210

SUBORDINATE THEME—PART II,

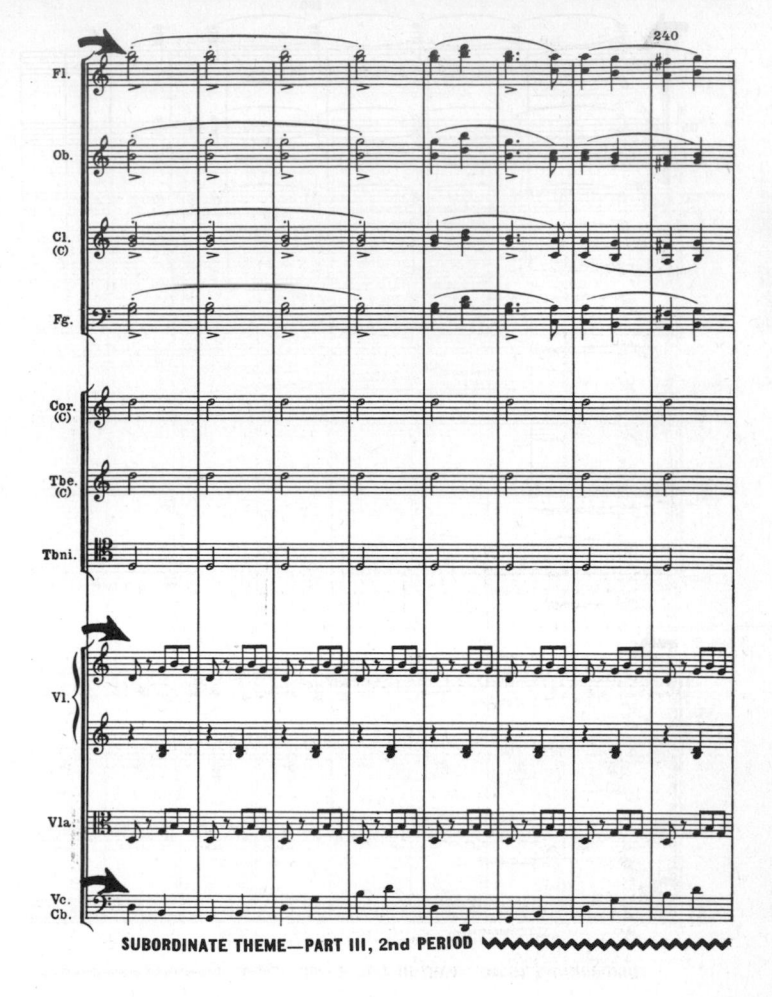

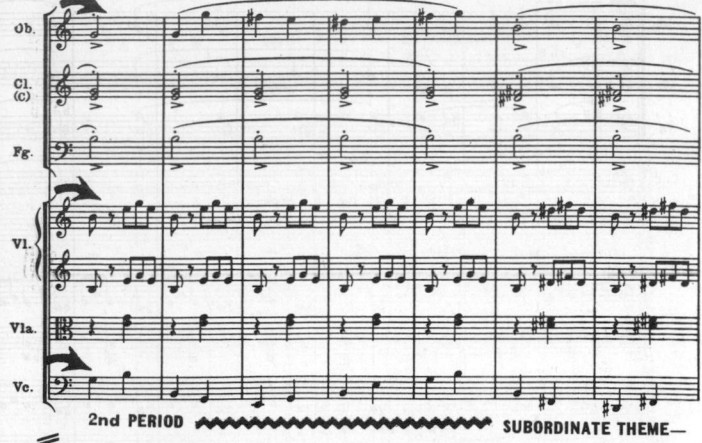

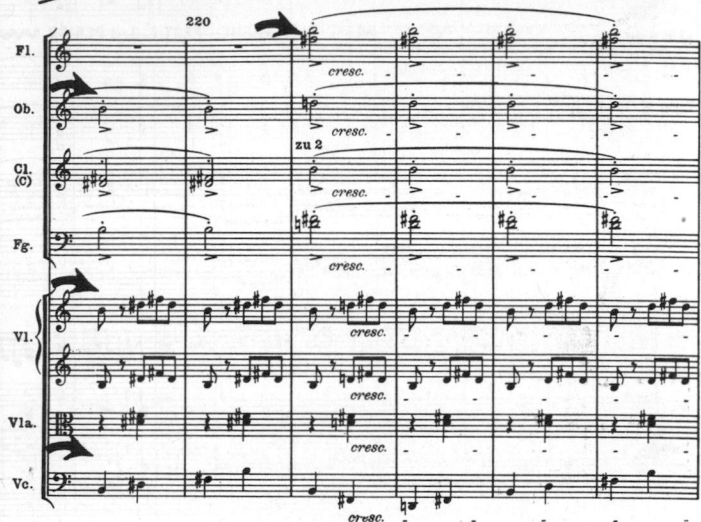

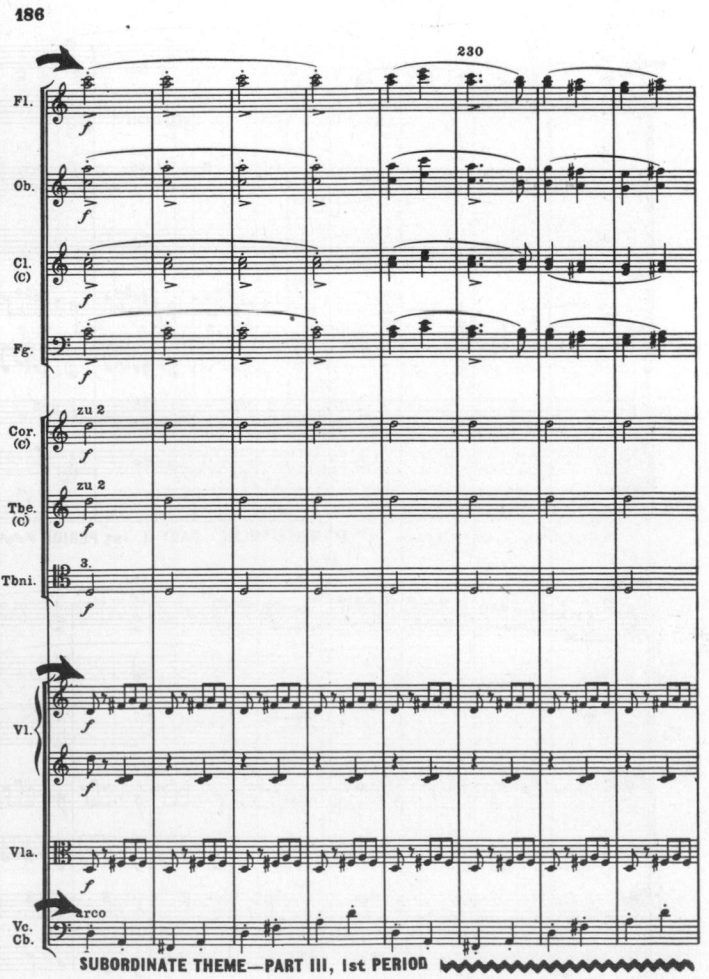

185

187

240

2nd PERIOD 〰〰〰〰〰〰〰〰〰〰〰〰 **SUBORDINATE THEME—**

220

cresc.

zu 2

cresc.

cresc.

cresc.

cresc.

cresc.

cresc.

PART II, 3rd PERIOD 〰〰〰〰〰〰〰〰〰〰〰〰〰

SUBORDINATE THEME—PART III, 2nd PERIOD 〰〰〰〰〰〰

186

188

230

zu 2

zu 2

3.

arco

SUBORDINATE THEME—PART III, 1st PERIOD 〰〰〰〰〰〰〰

cresc.

cresc.

cresc.

cresc.

cresc.

cresc.

cresc.

cresc.

SUBORDINATE THEME—PART III, 3rd PERIOD 〰〰〰〰〰〰

(299)

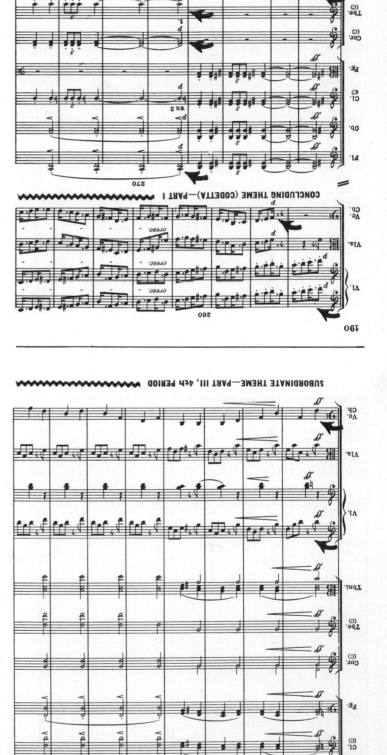

SUBORDINATE THEME—PART III, 4th PERIOD

CONCLUDING THEME (CODETTA)—PART I

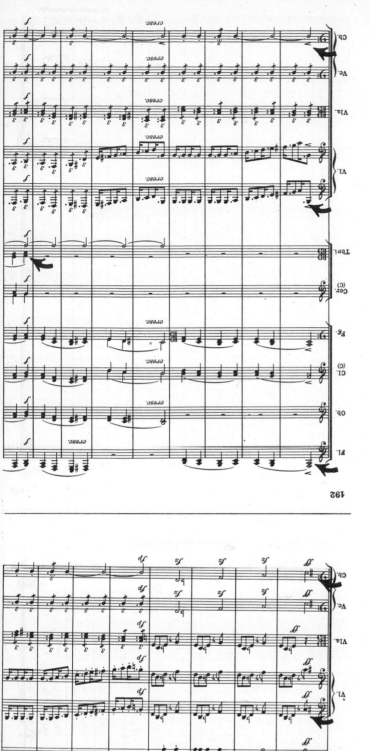

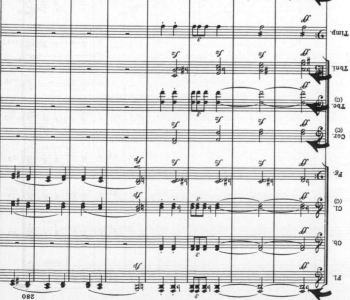

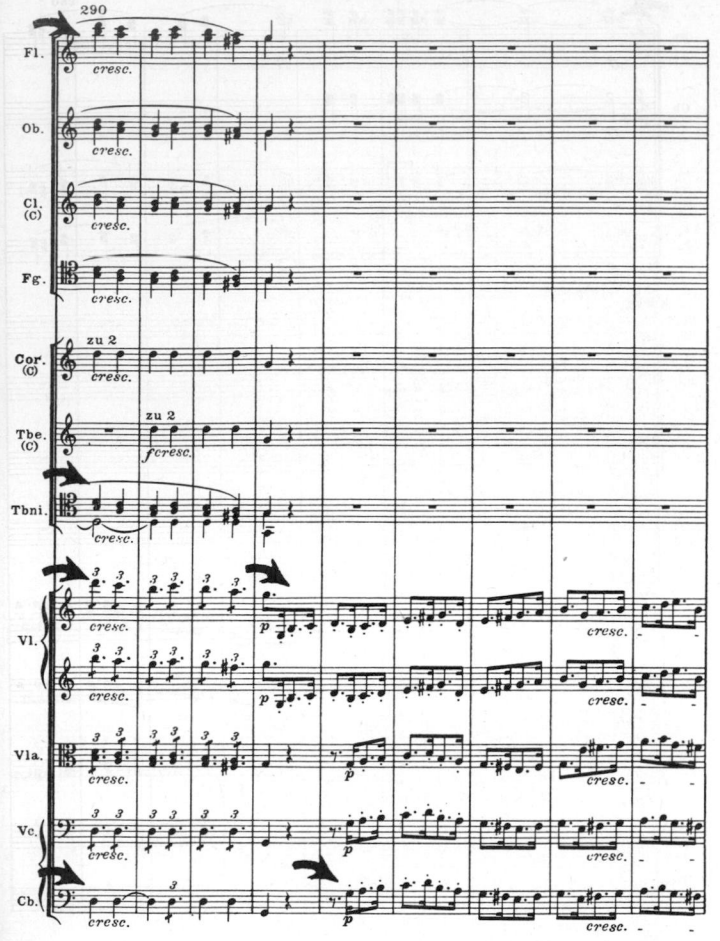

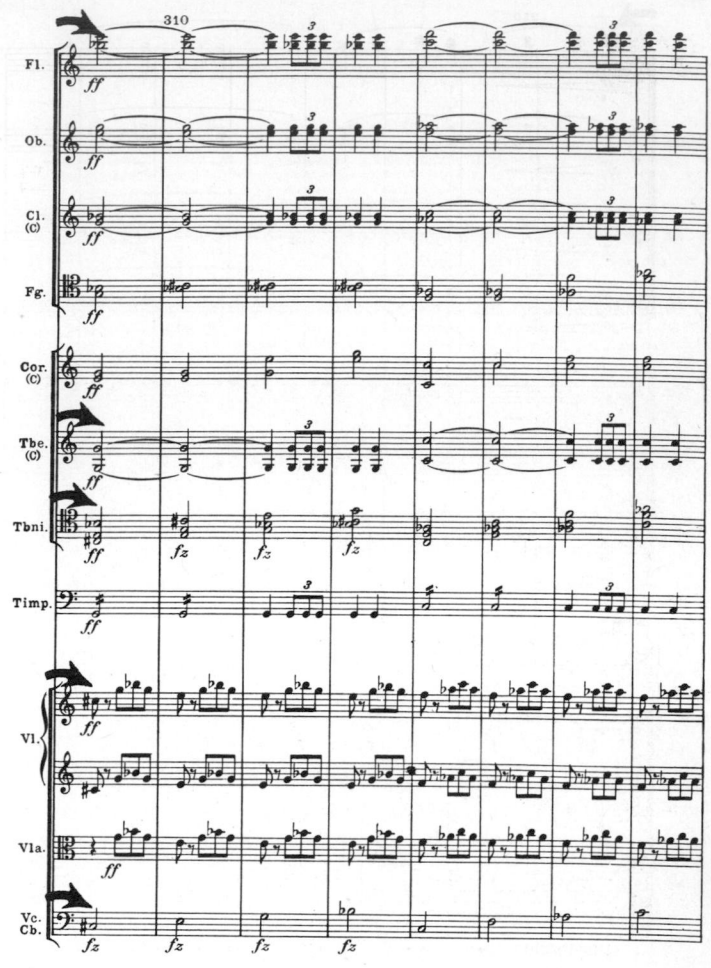

REPETITION CONCLUDING THEME (CODETTA)—PART I

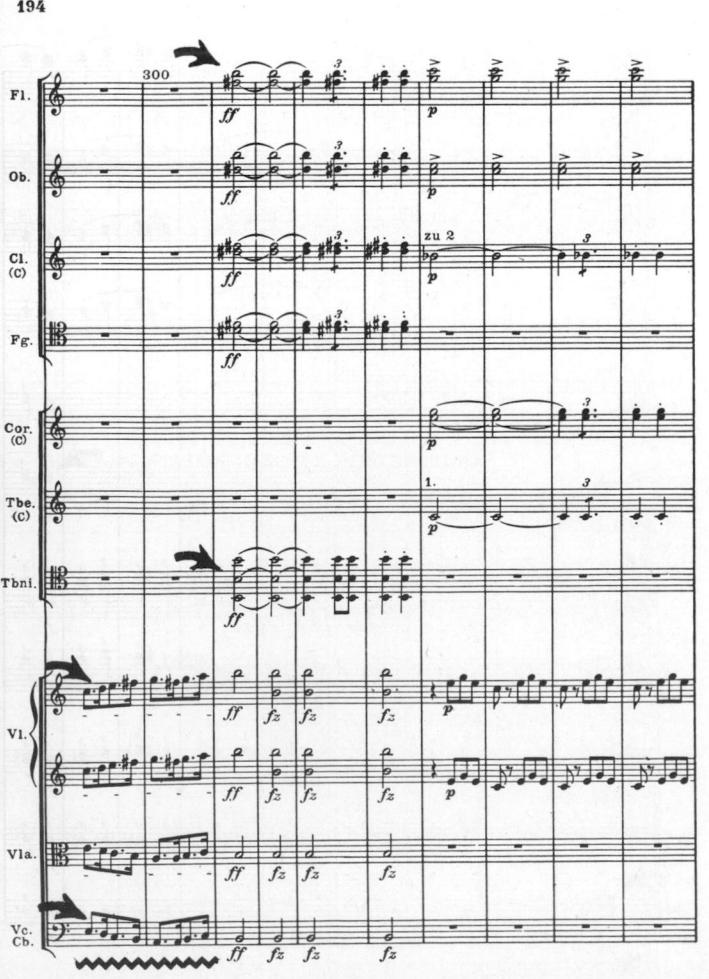

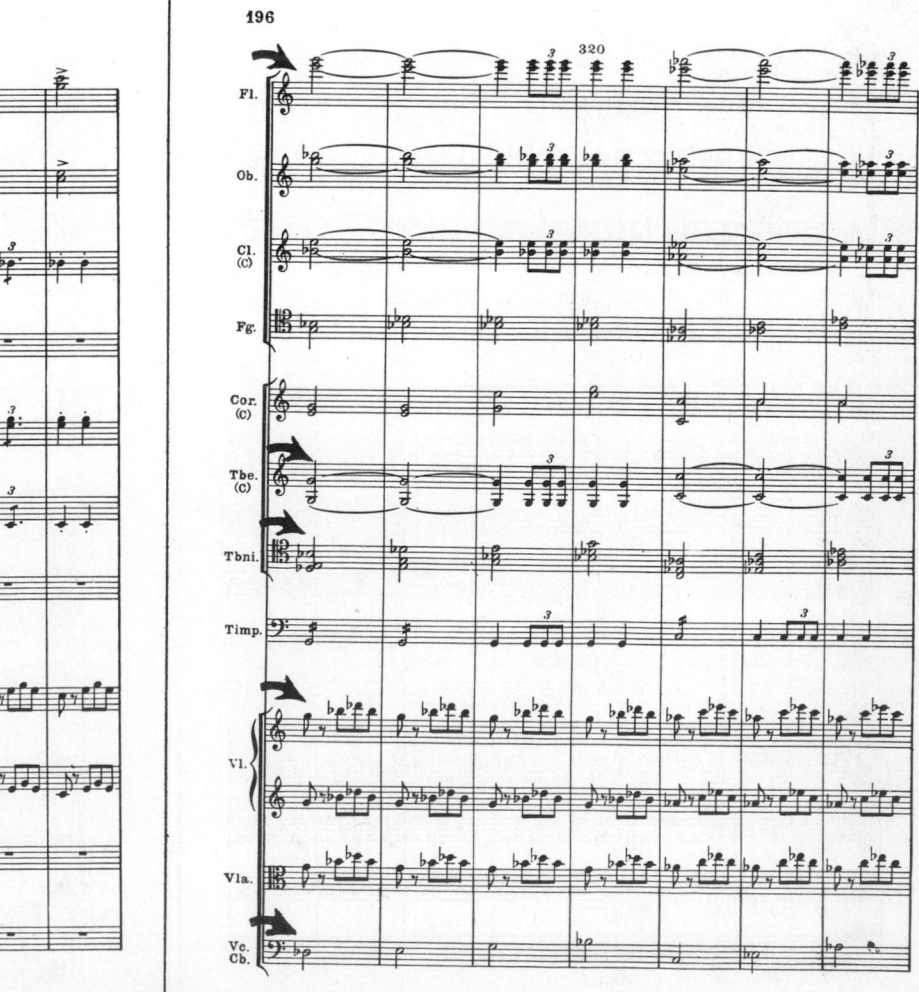

(301)

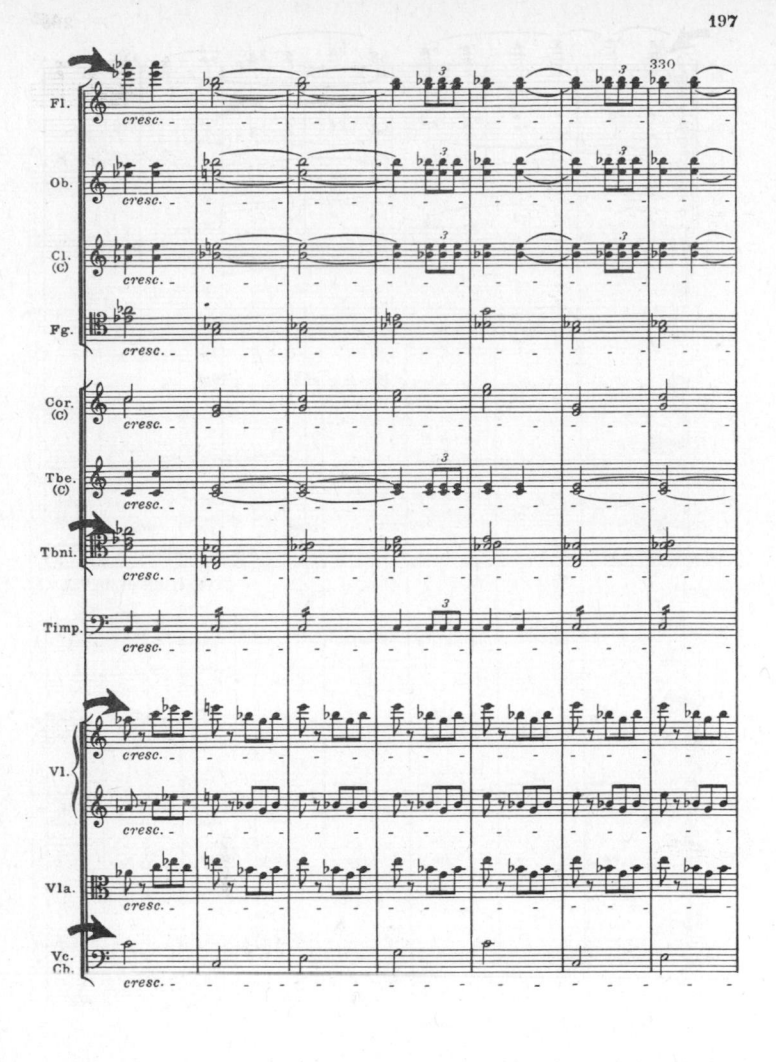

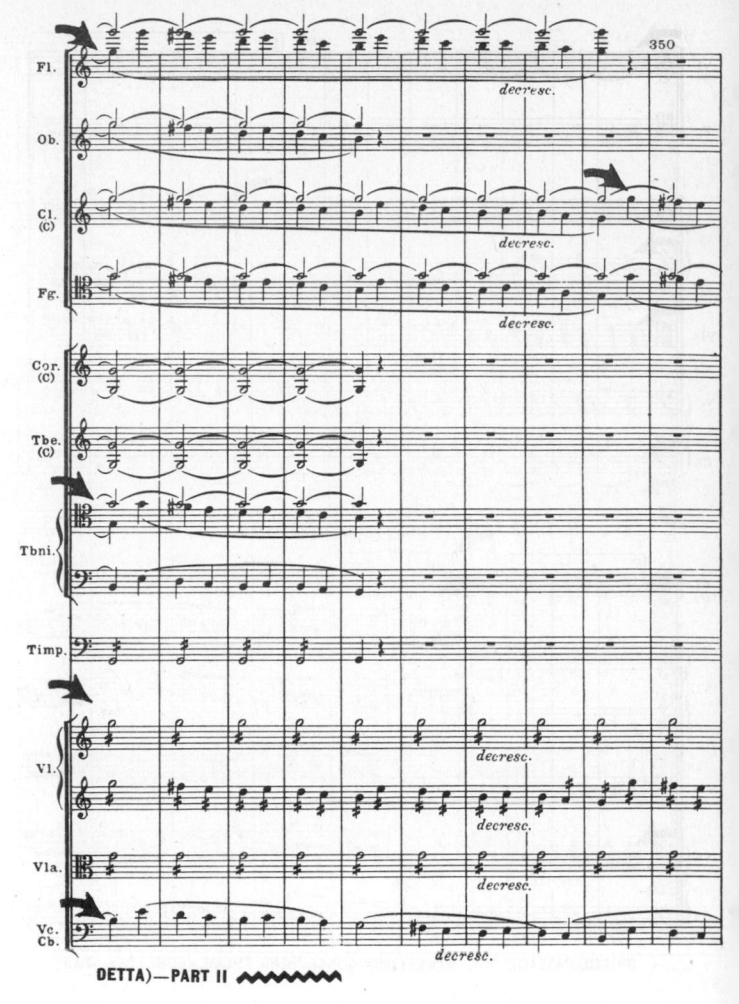

DETTA)—PART II ᗩᗩᗩᗩᗩᗩᗩ

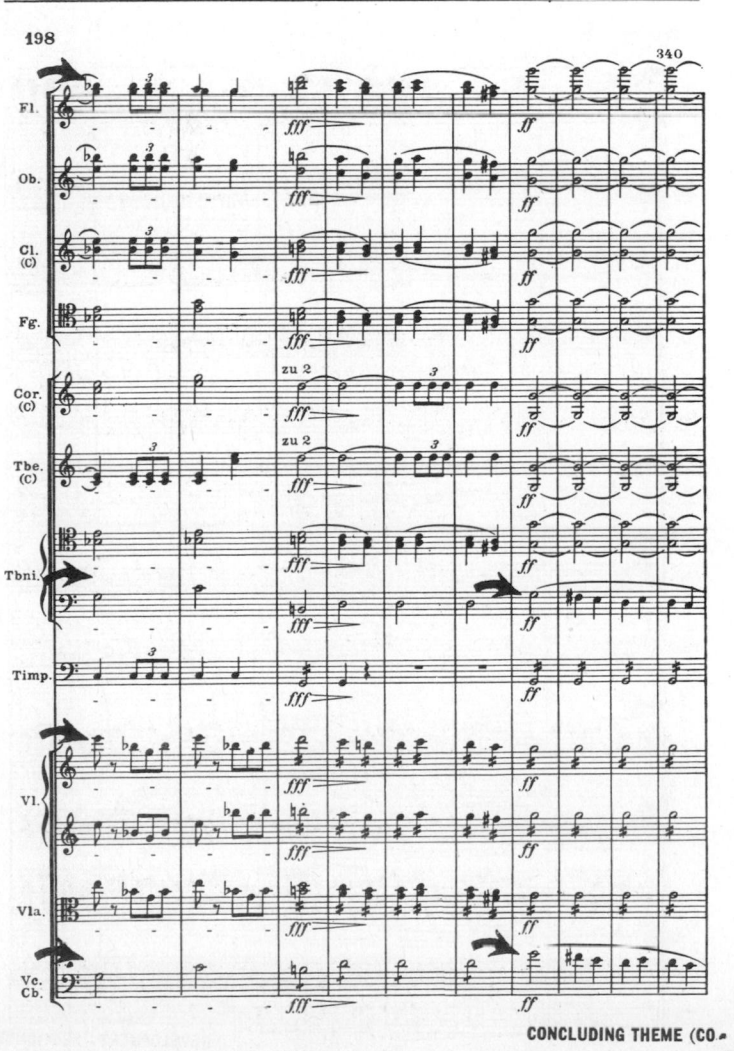

CONCLUDING THEME (CO-

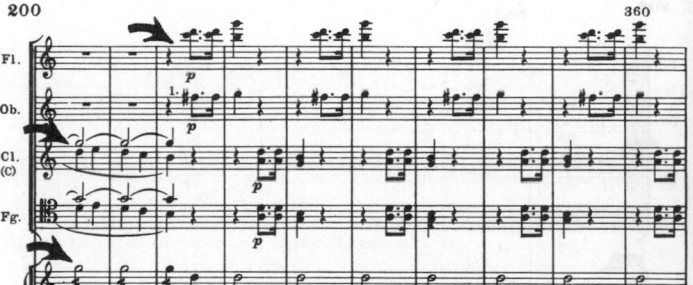

CONCLUDING THEME (CODETTA)—PART III ᗩᗩᗩᗩᗩᗩᗩᗩᗩᗩ

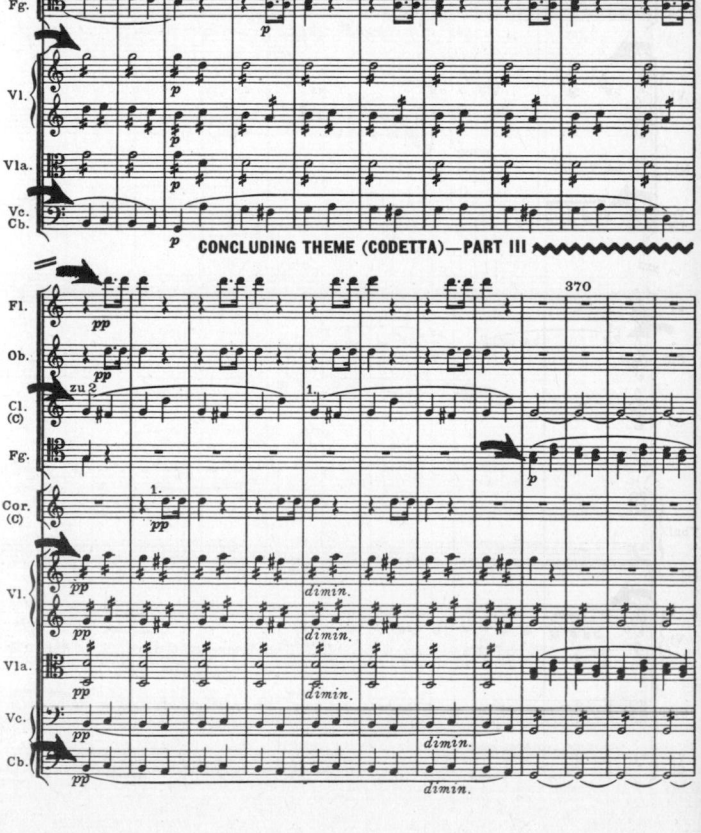

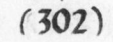

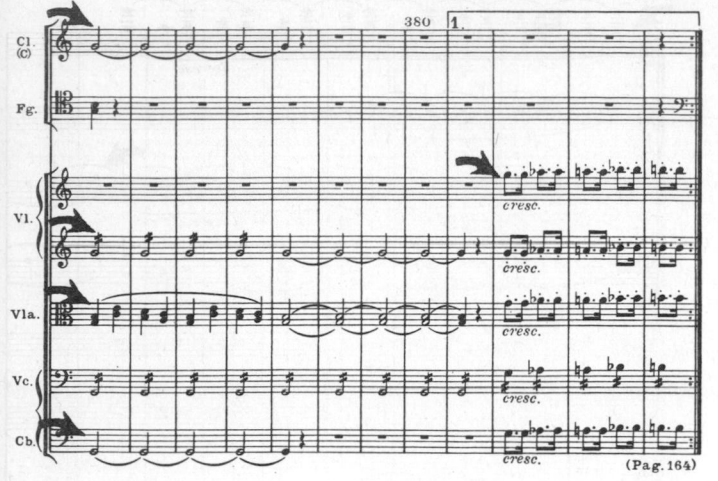

DEVELOPMENT

BRIDGE PASSAGE 〰 DEVELOPMENT—SECTION I 〰〰〰

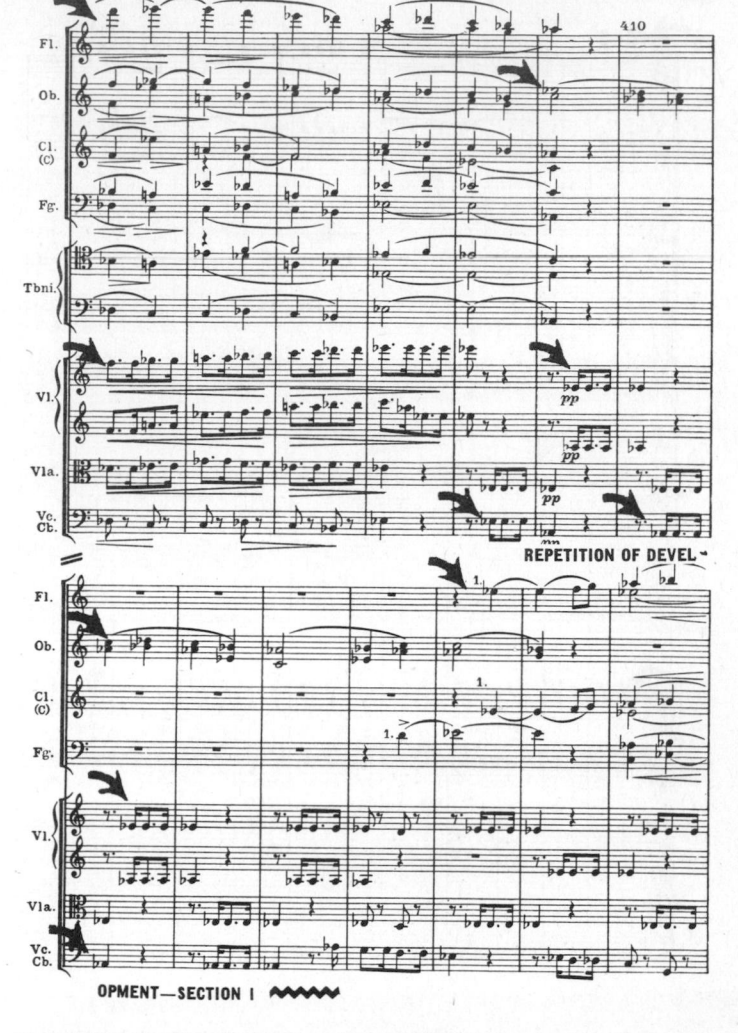

REPETITION OF DEVEL—

OPMENT—SECTION I 〰〰〰

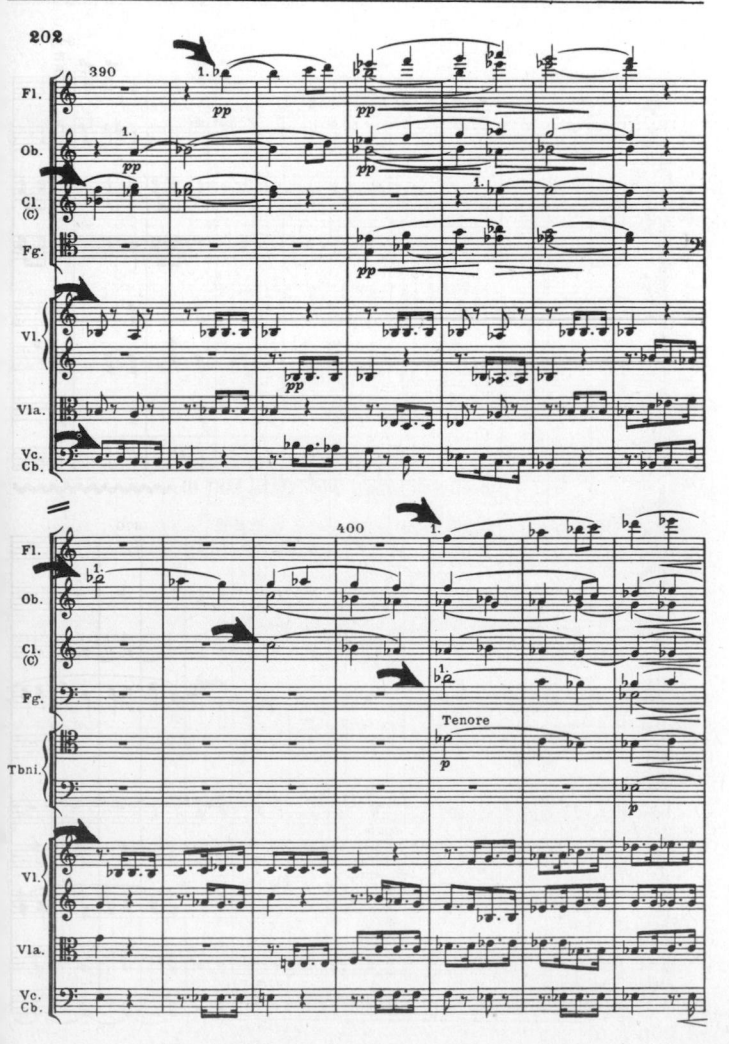

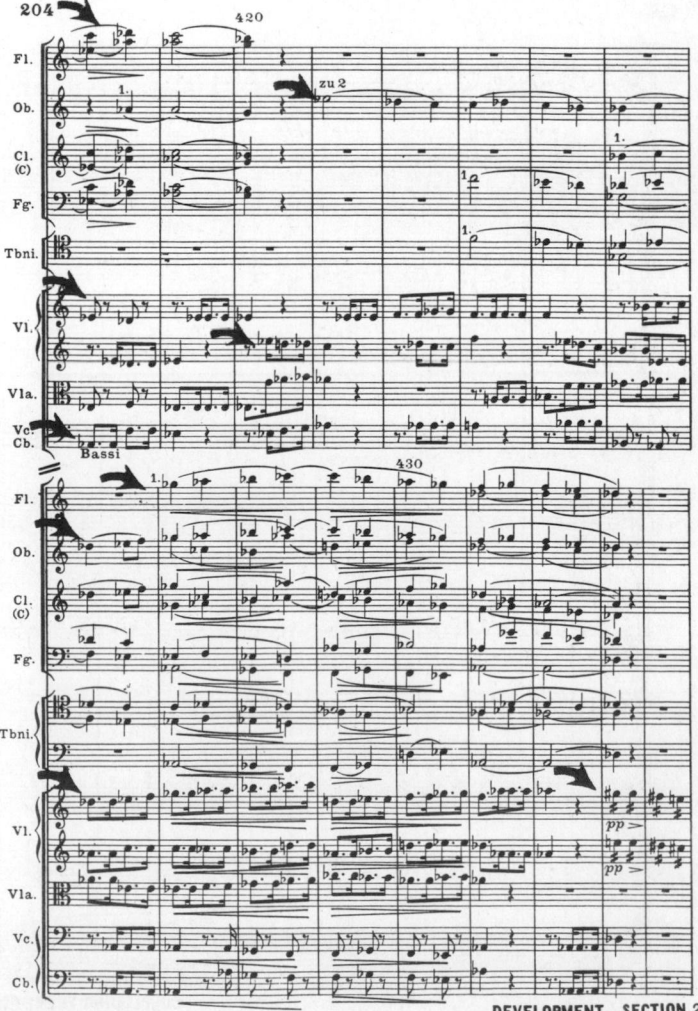

DEVELOPMENT—SECTION 2

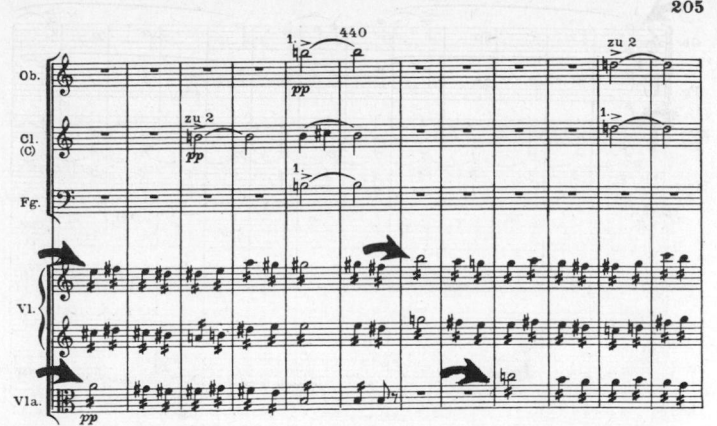

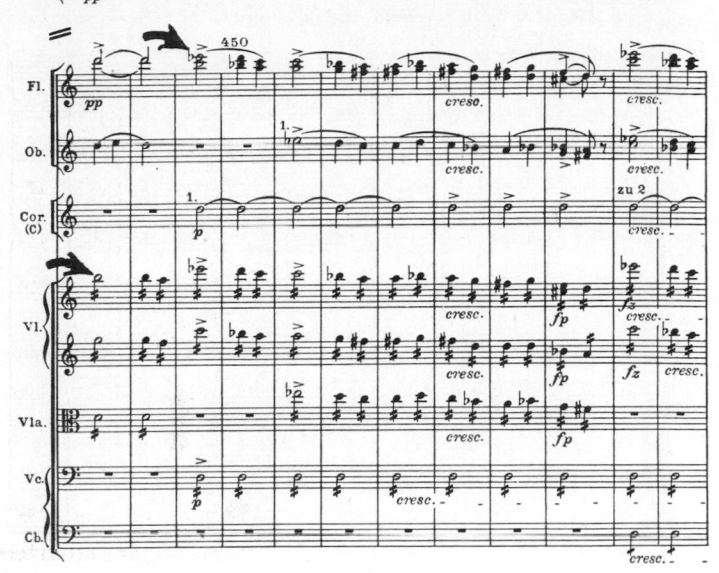

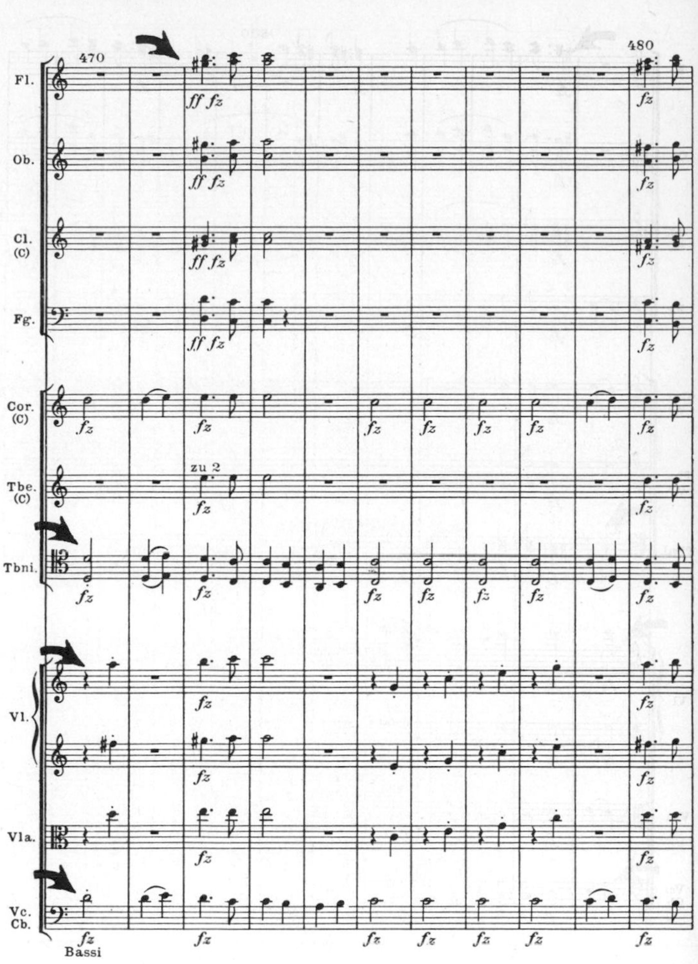

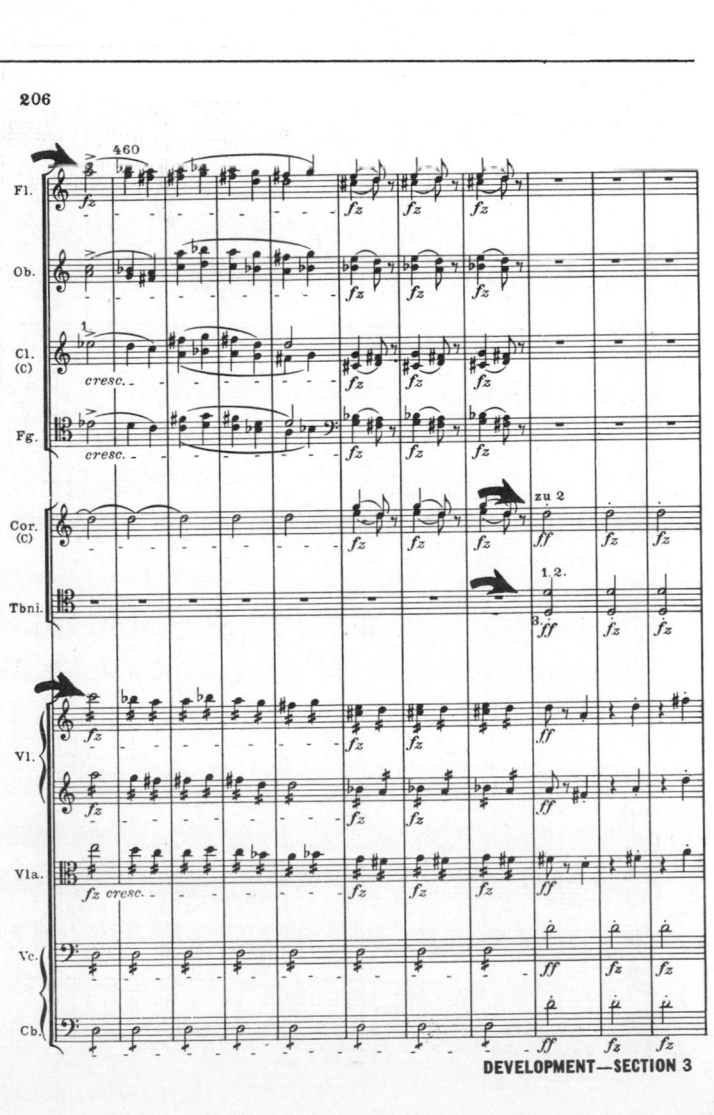

DEVELOPMENT—SECTION 3

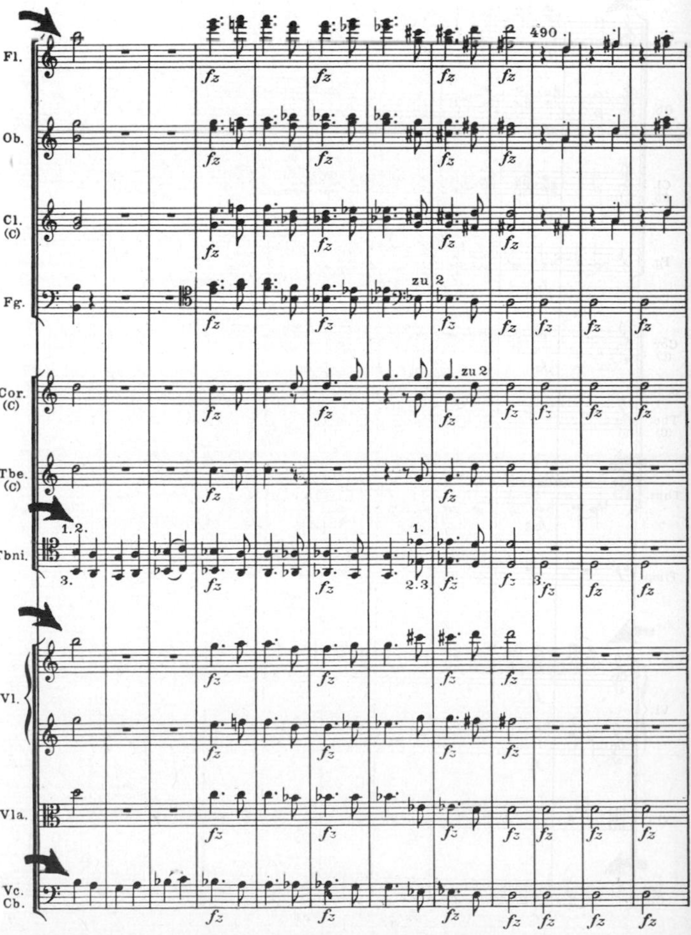

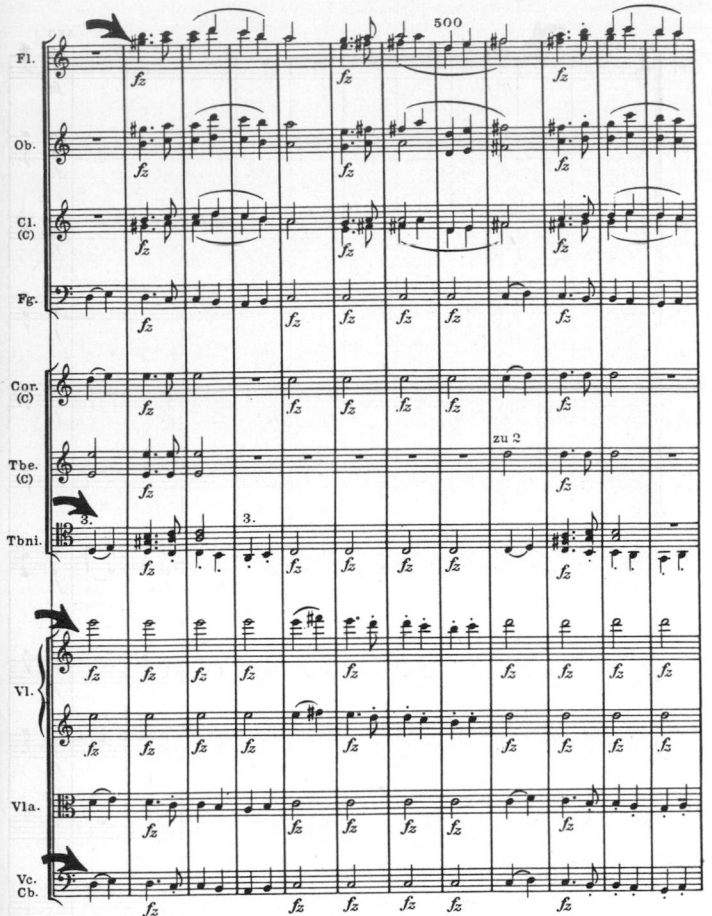

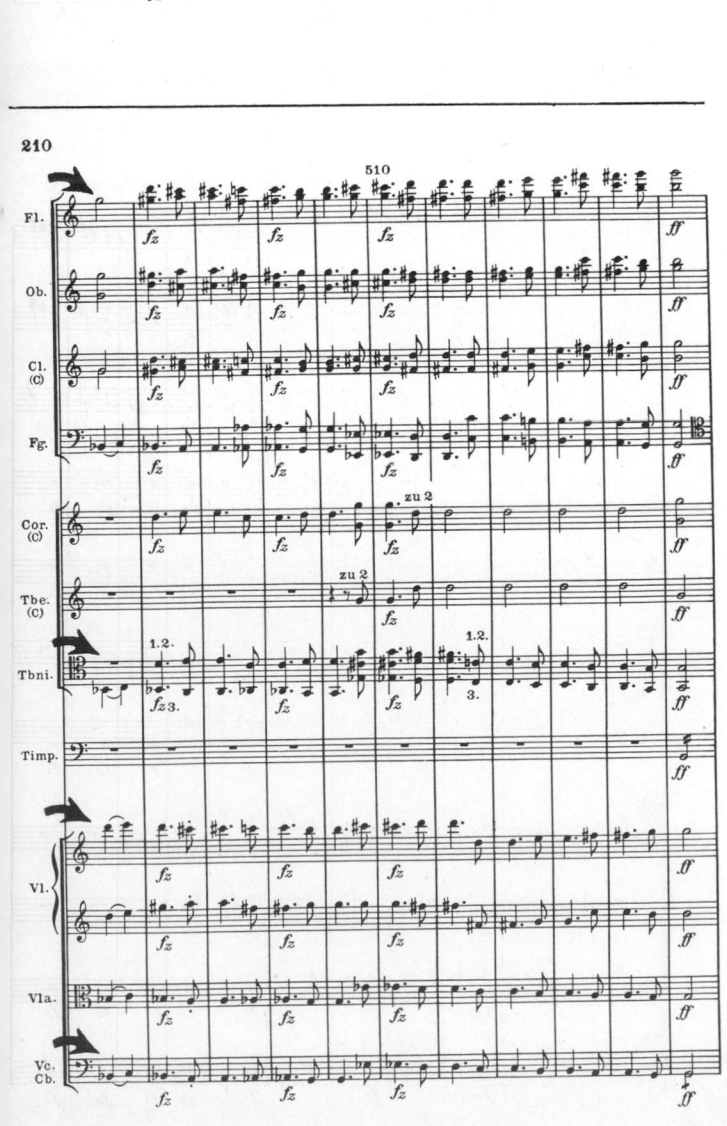

209
500
Fl.
Ob.
Cl. (C)
Fg.
Cor. (C)
Tbe. (C)
zu 2
Tbni.
Vl.
Vla.
Vc. Cb.

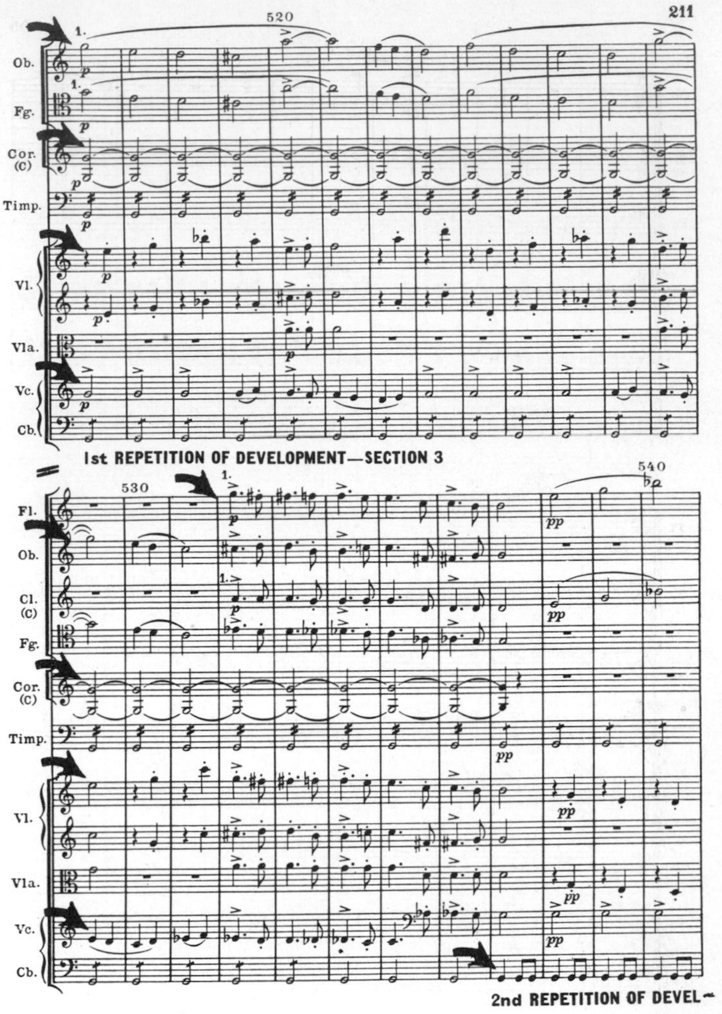

211
520
Ob.
Fg.
Cor. (C)
Timp.
Vl.
Vla.
Vc.
Cb.
1st REPETITION OF DEVELOPMENT—SECTION 3
530
540
2nd REPETITION OF DEVEL-

210
510
Fl.
Ob.
Cl. (C)
Fg.
Cor. (C)
zu 2
Tbe. (C)
Tbni.
Timp.
Vl.
Vla.
Vc. Cb.

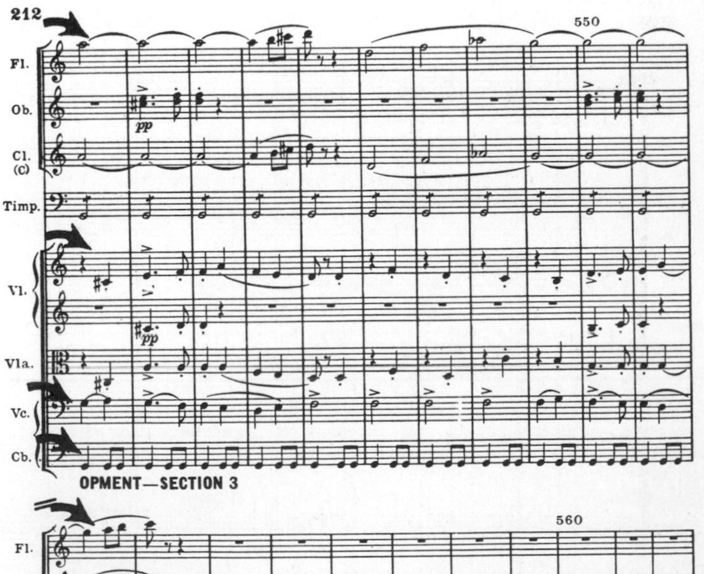

212
550
Fl.
Ob.
Cl. (C)
Timp.
Vl.
Vla.
Vc.
Cb.
OPMENT—SECTION 3
560
Cor. (C)

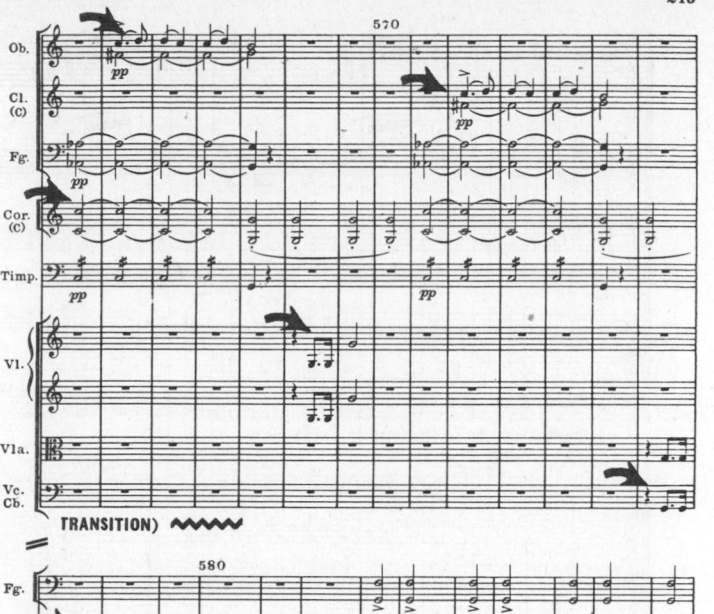

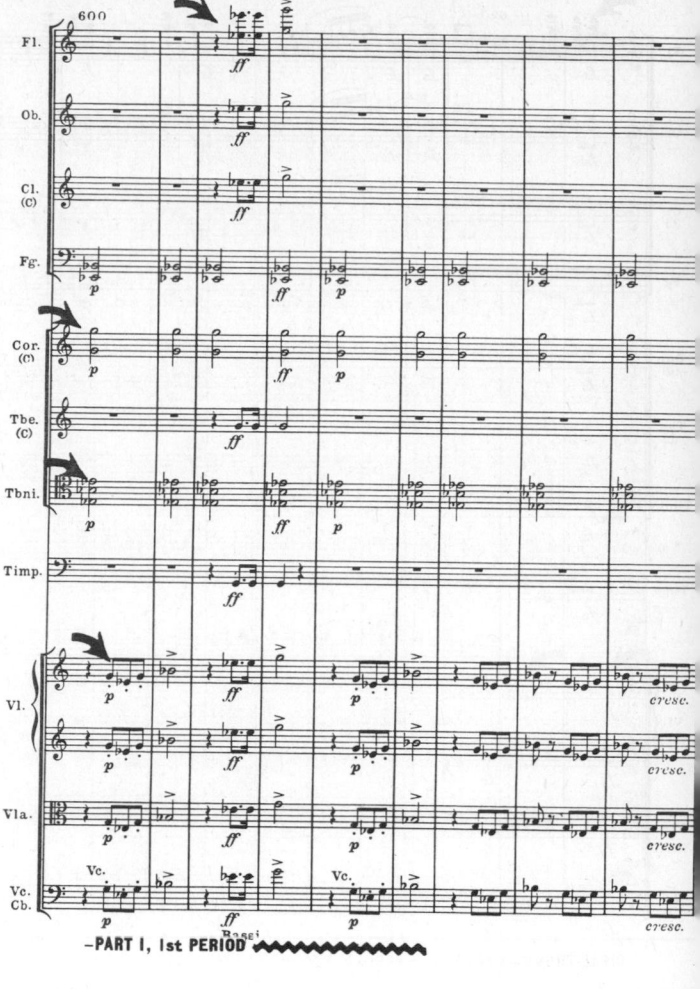

(TRANSITION)

RECAPITULATION

PART I, 1st PERIOD

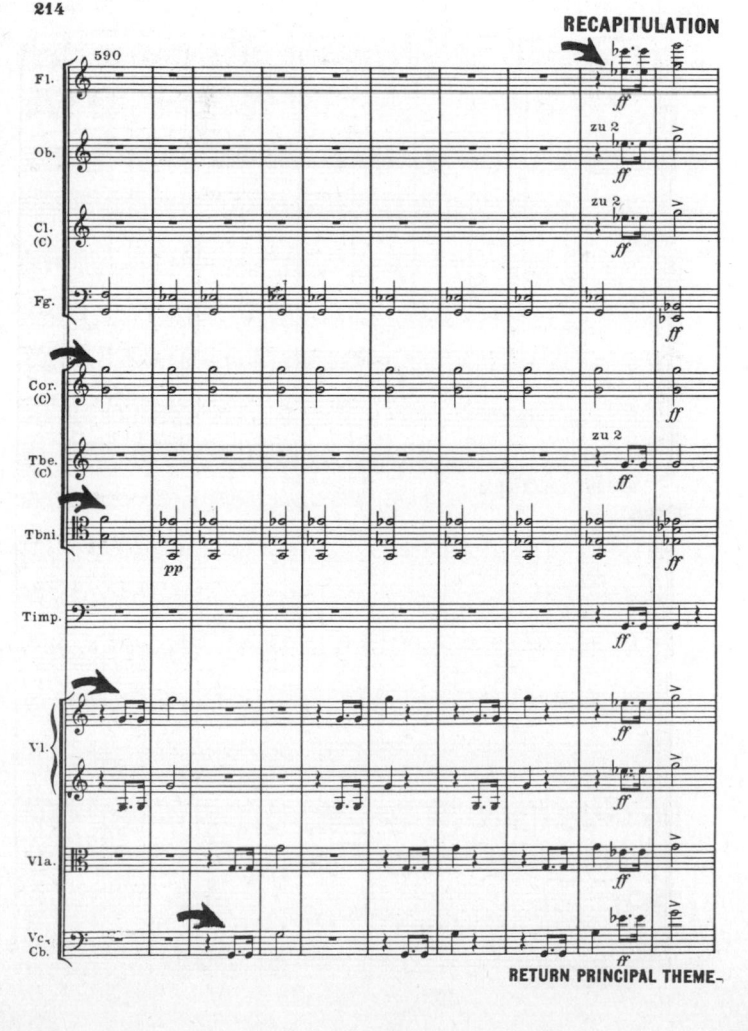

RETURN PRINCIPAL THEME

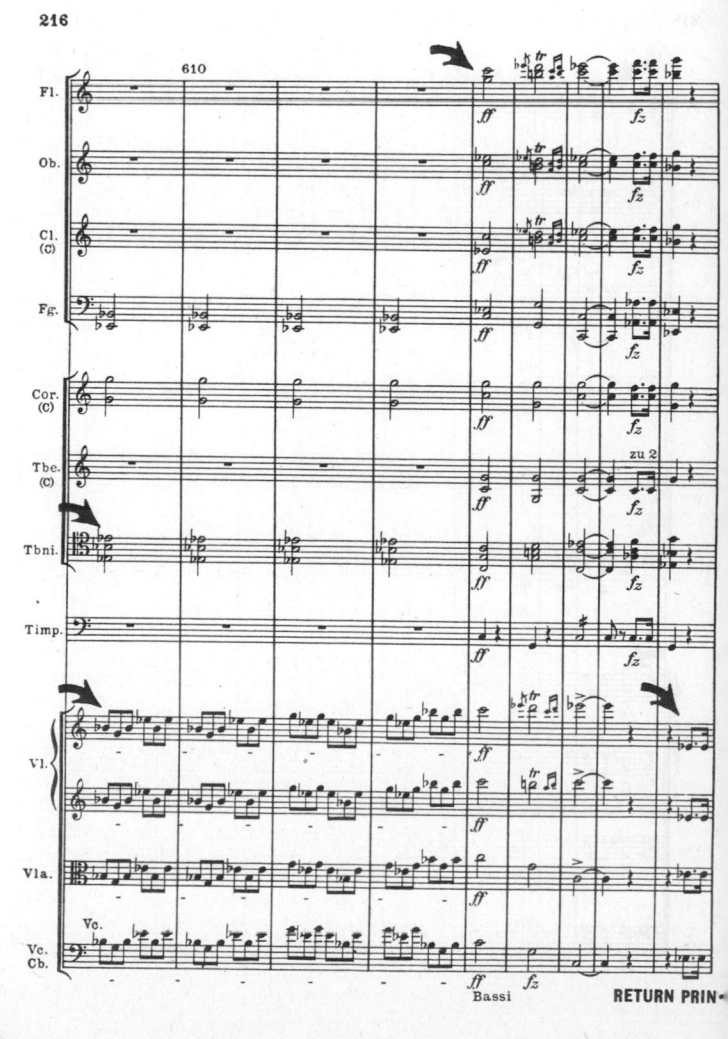

RETURN PRIN-

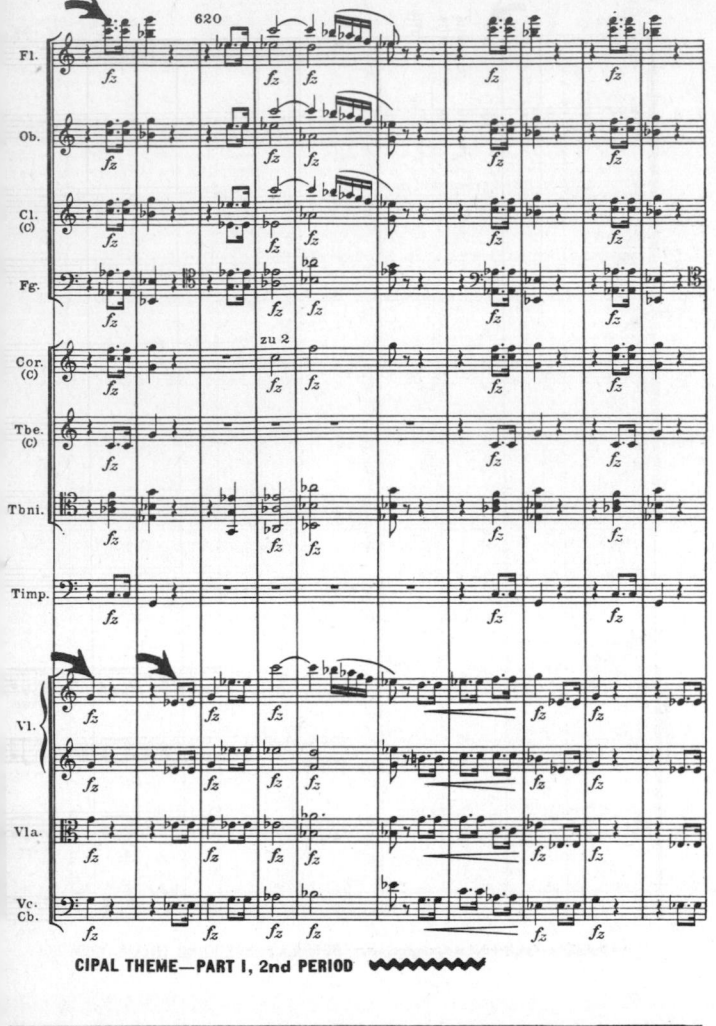

CIPAL THEME—PART I, 2nd PERIOD 〰〰〰〰

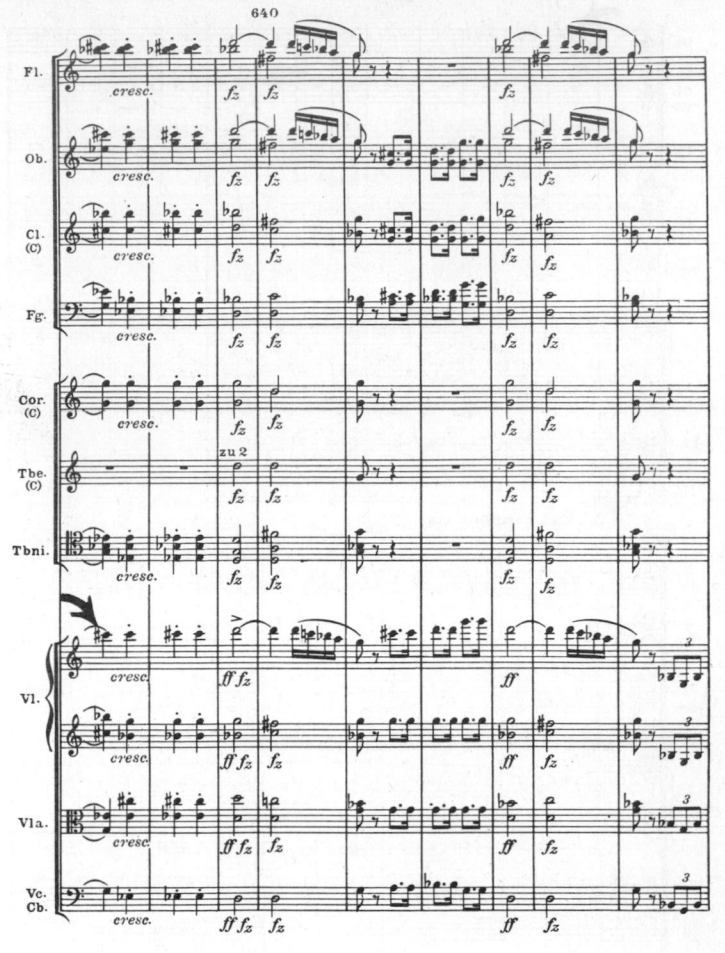

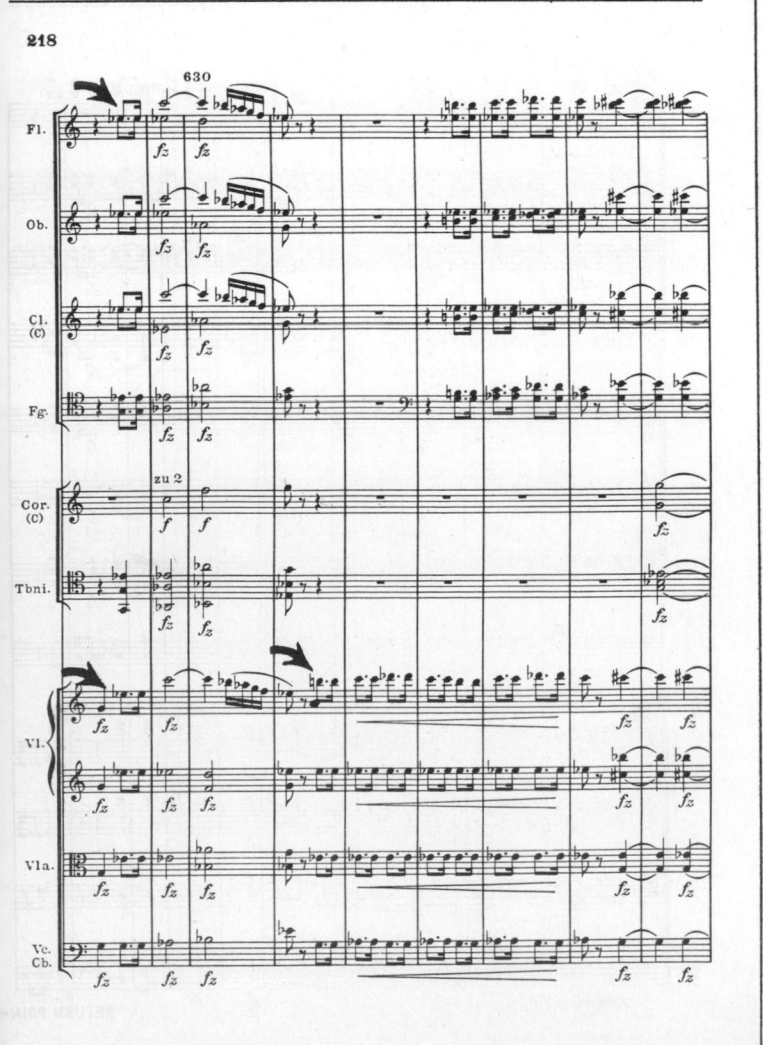

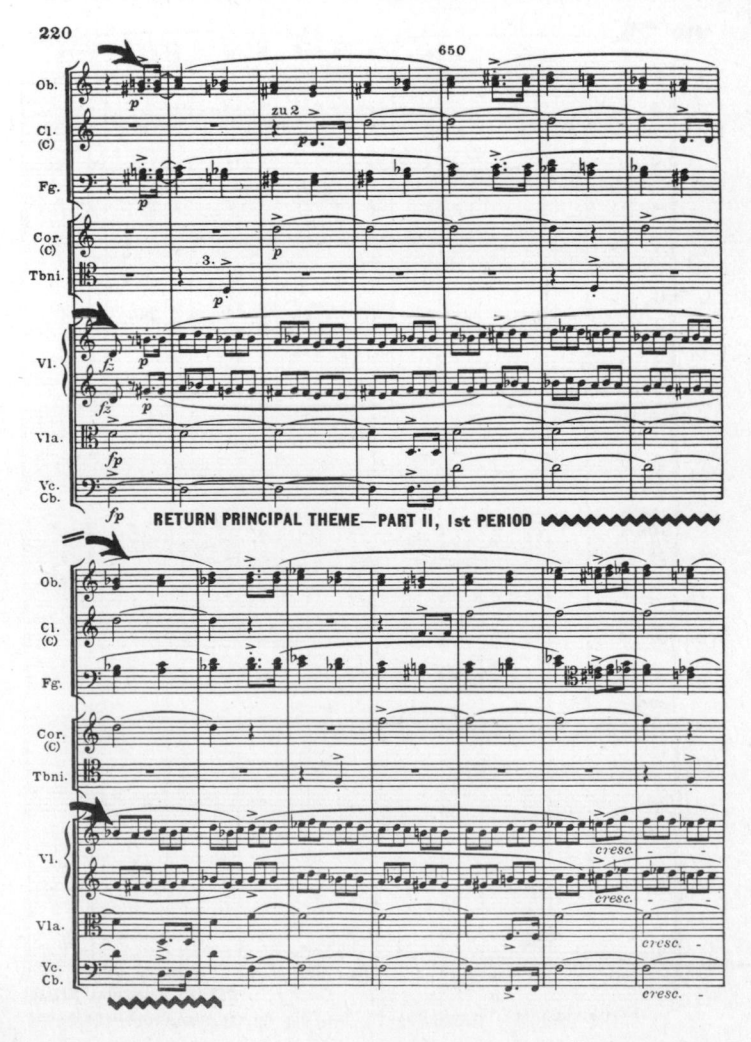

RETURN PRINCIPAL THEME—PART II, 1st PERIOD 〰〰〰〰

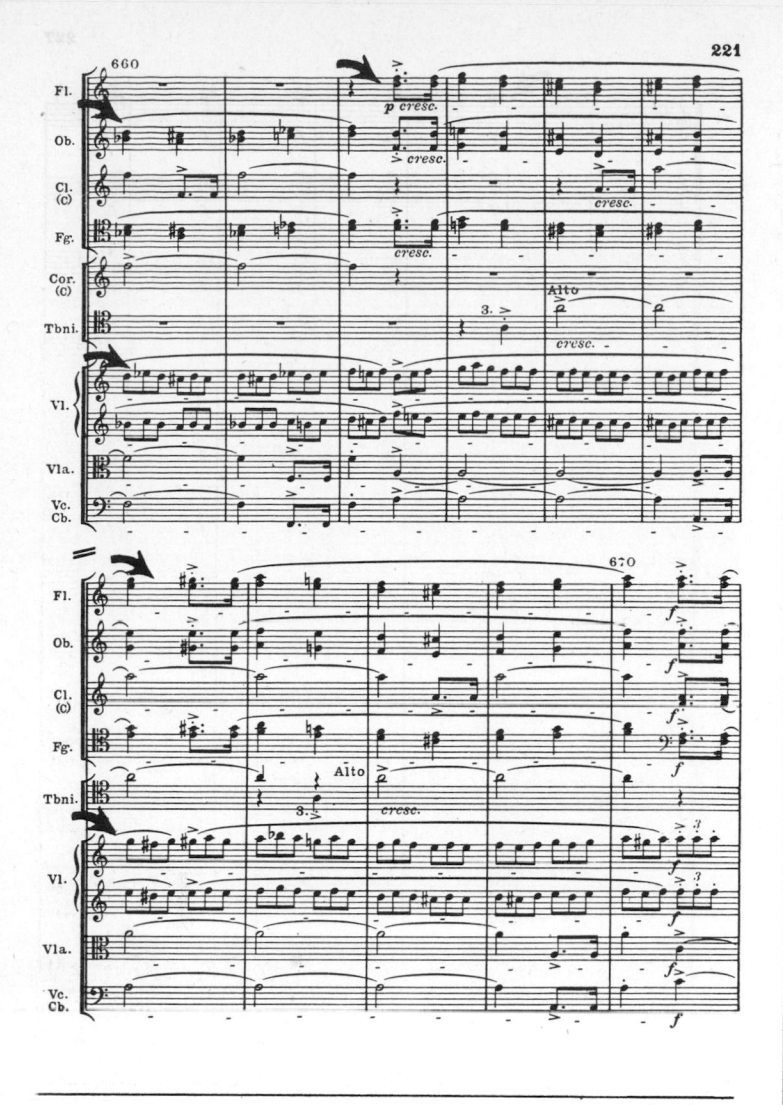

RETURN PRINCIPAL THEME—PART II, 2nd PERIOD

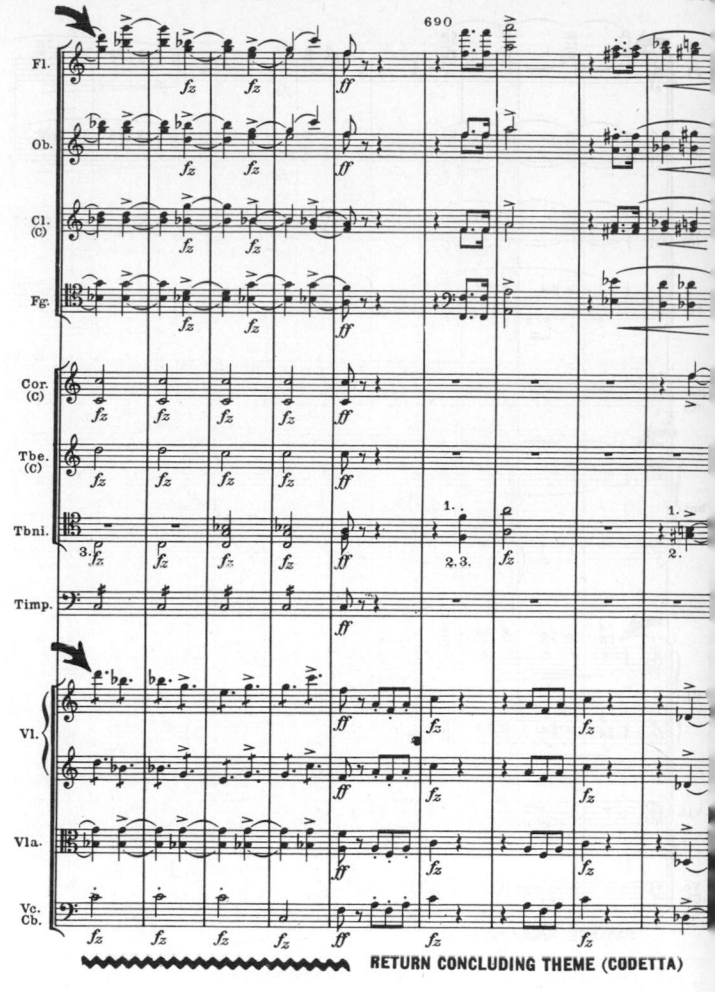

RETURN CONCLUDING THEME (CODETTA)

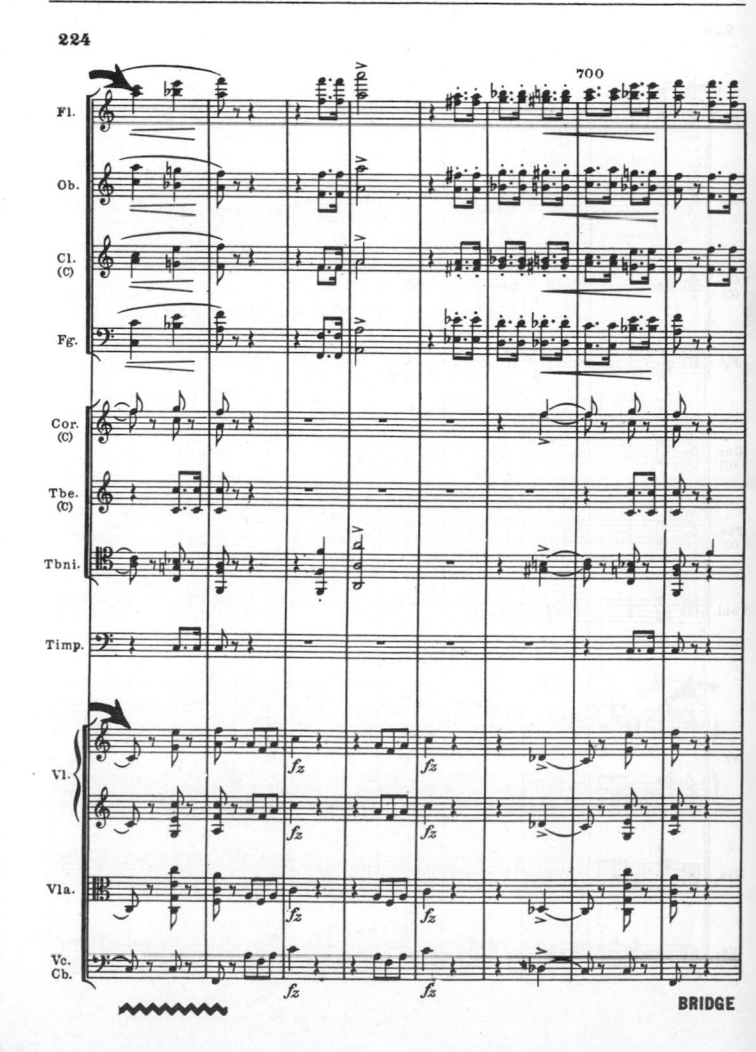

BRIDGE

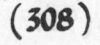

710
Fl.
Ob.
Cl. (C)
Fg.
Cor. (C)
Tbni.
Vl.
Vla.
Vc. Cb.
PASSAGE

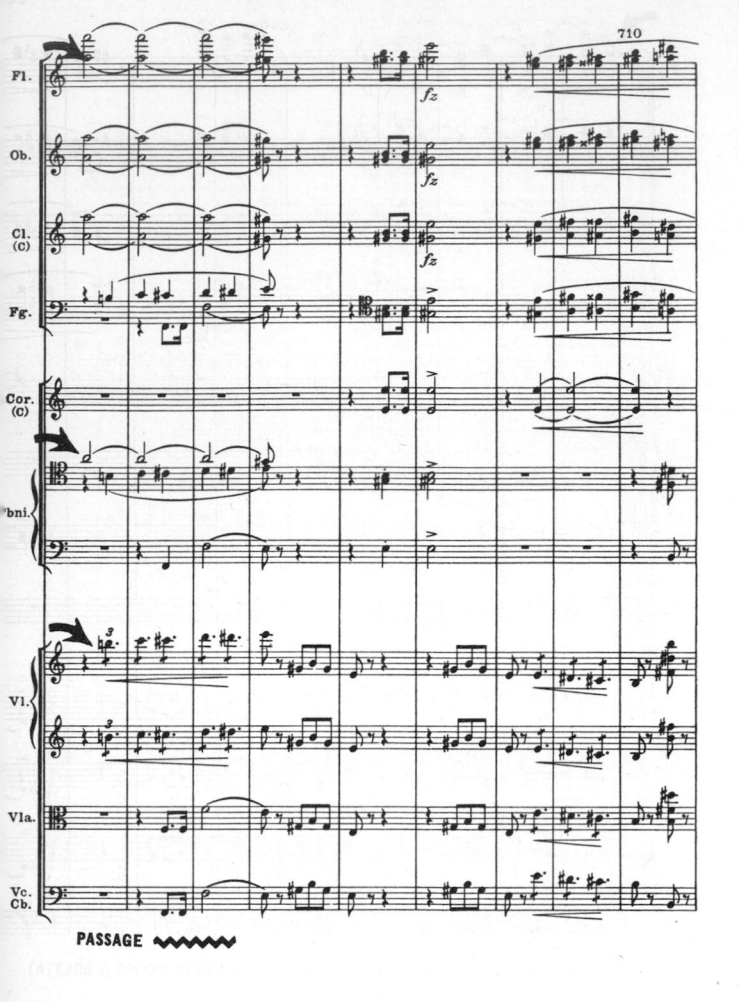

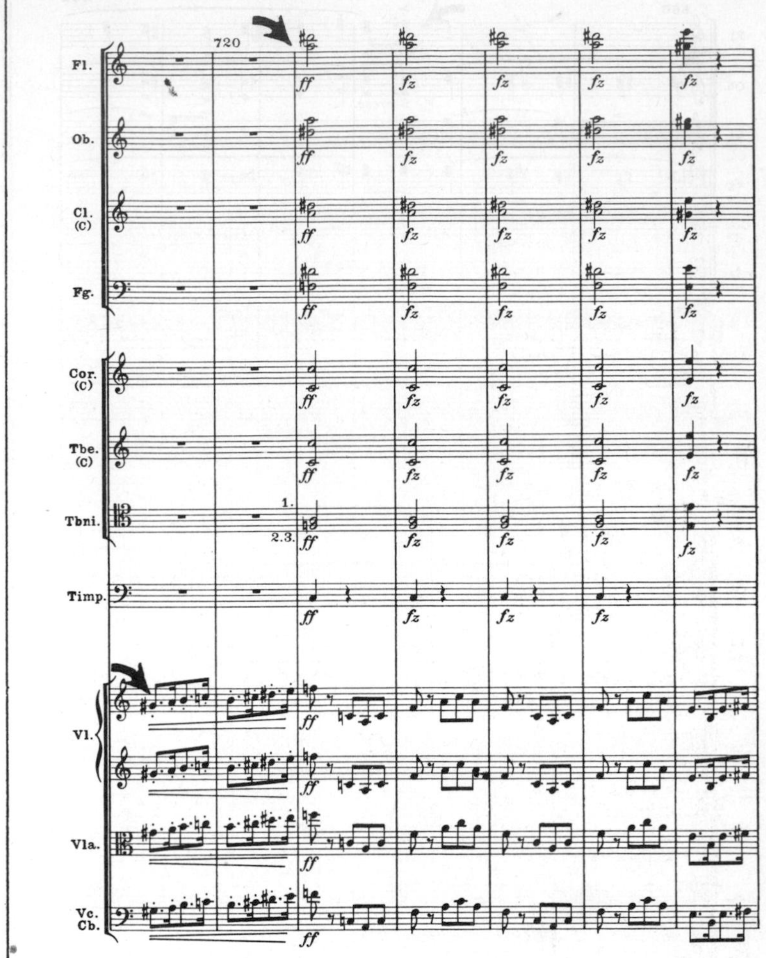
720
Fl.
Ob.
Cl. (C)
Fg.
Cor. (C)
Tbe. (C)
Tbni.
Timp.
Vl.
Vla.
Vc. Cb.

Fl.
Ob.
Cl. (C)
Fg.
Cor. (C)
Tbe. (C)
Tbni.
Vl.
Vla.
Vc. Cb.

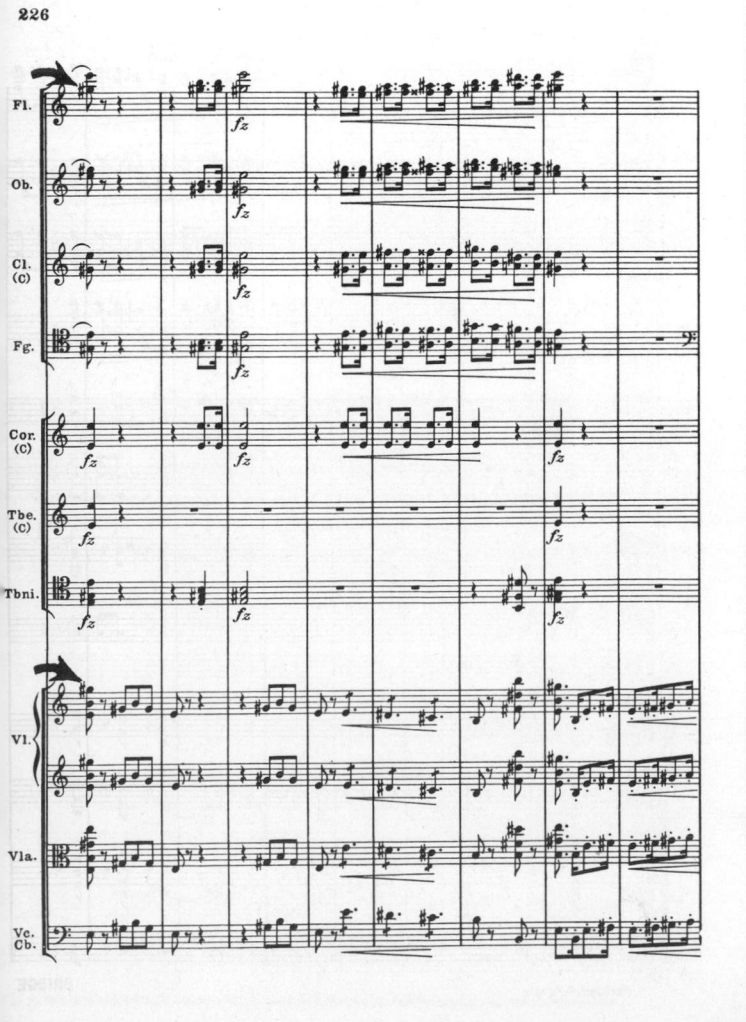

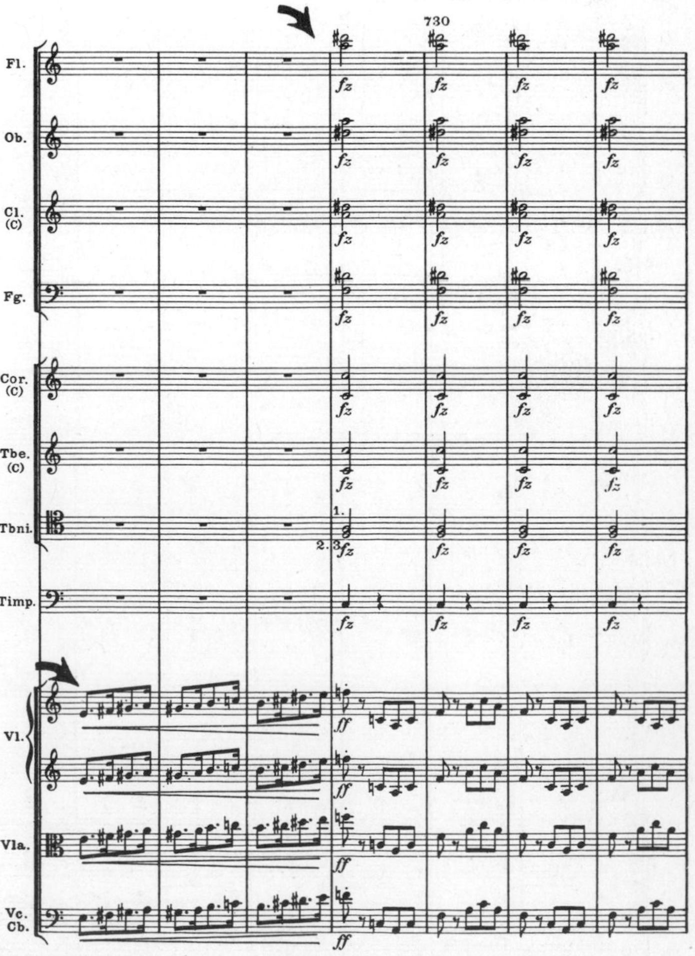
730
Fl.
Ob.
Cl. (C)
Fg.
Cor. (C)
Tbe. (C)
Tbni.
Timp.
Vl.
Vla.
Vc. Cb.

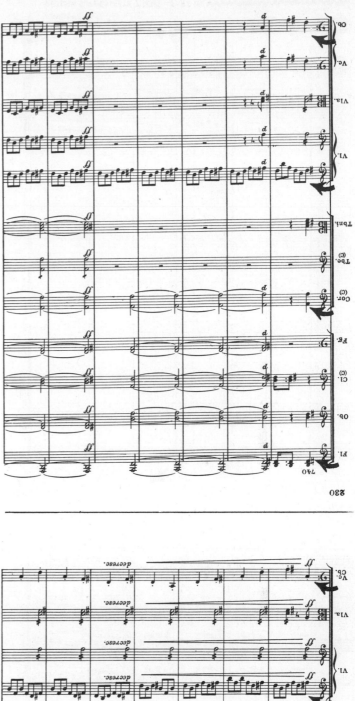
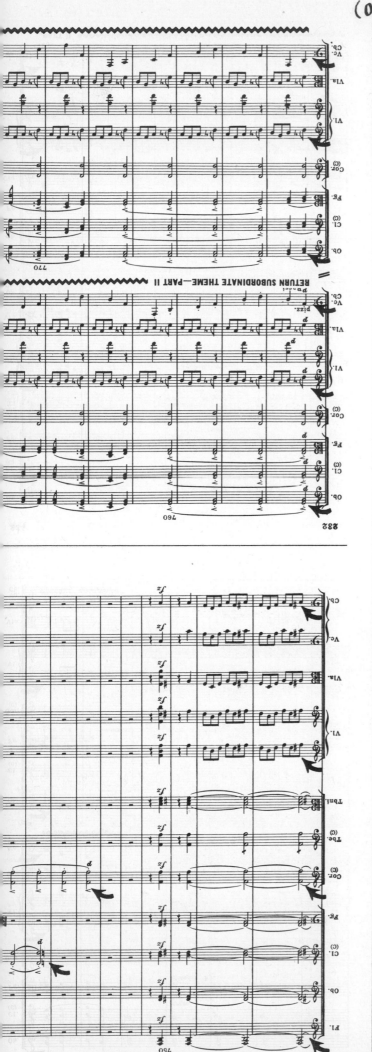
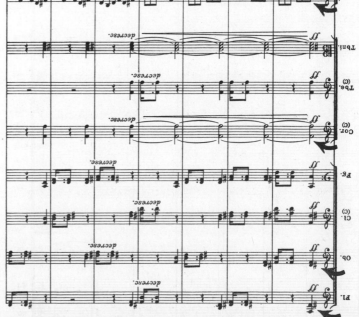

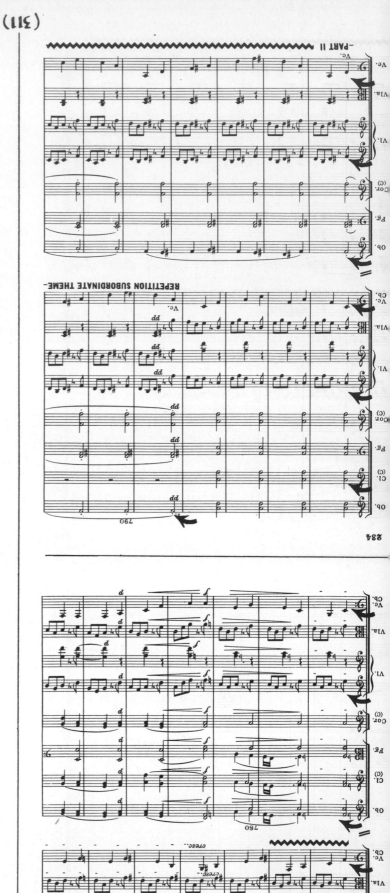
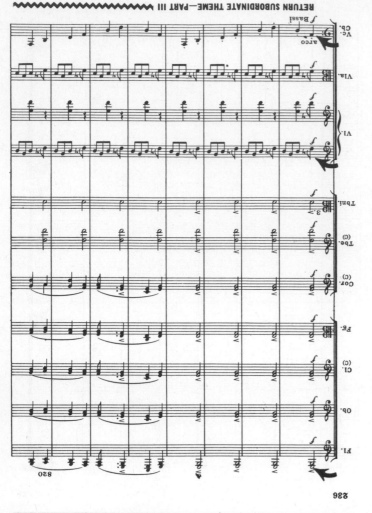
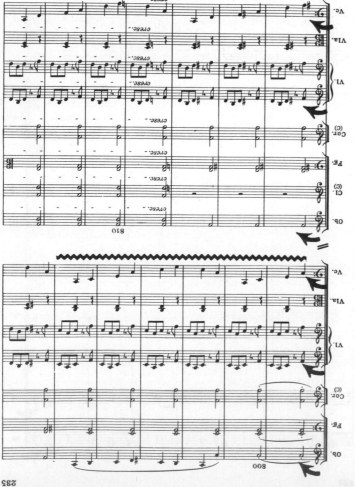

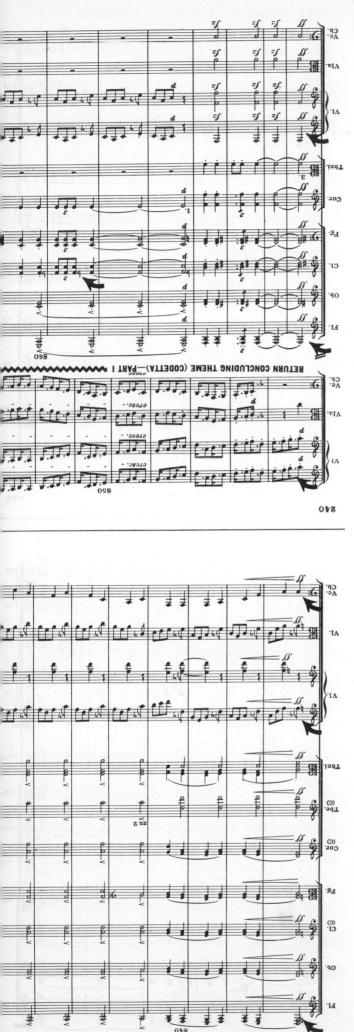
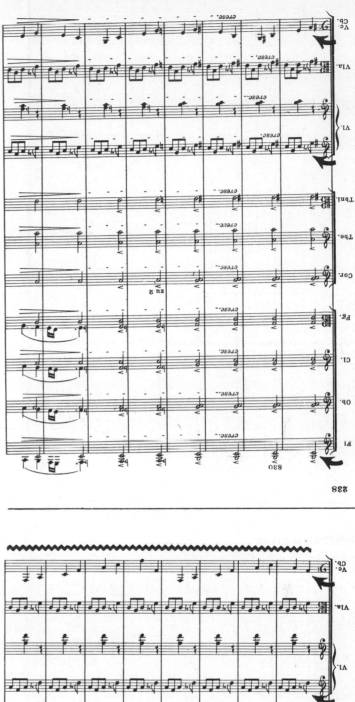
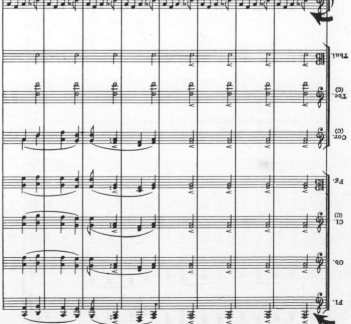

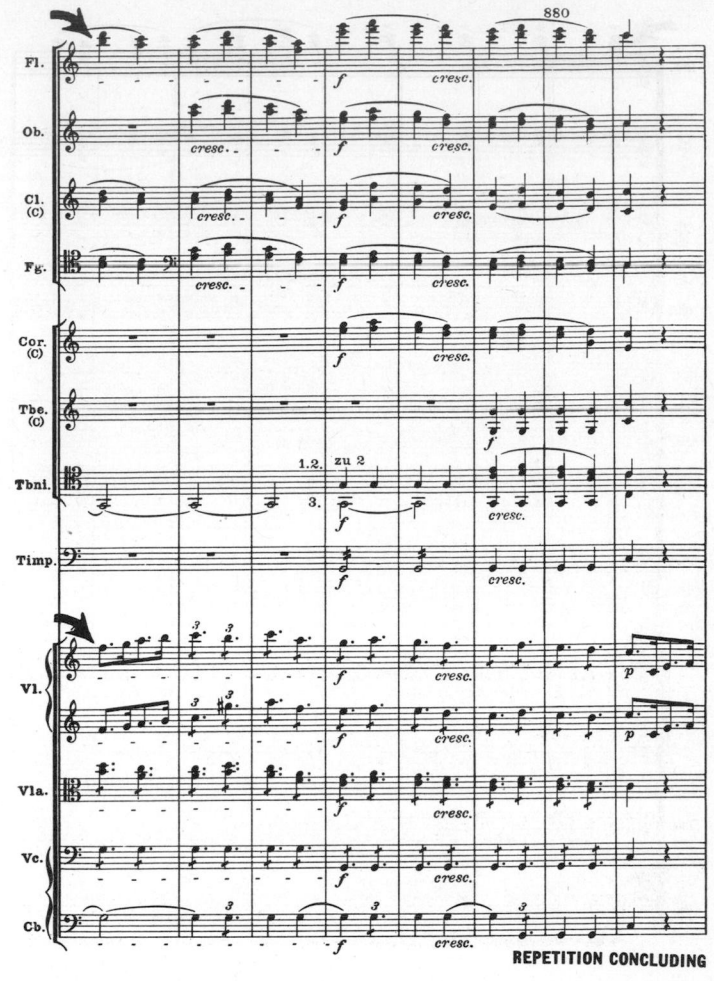

REPETITION CONCLUDING

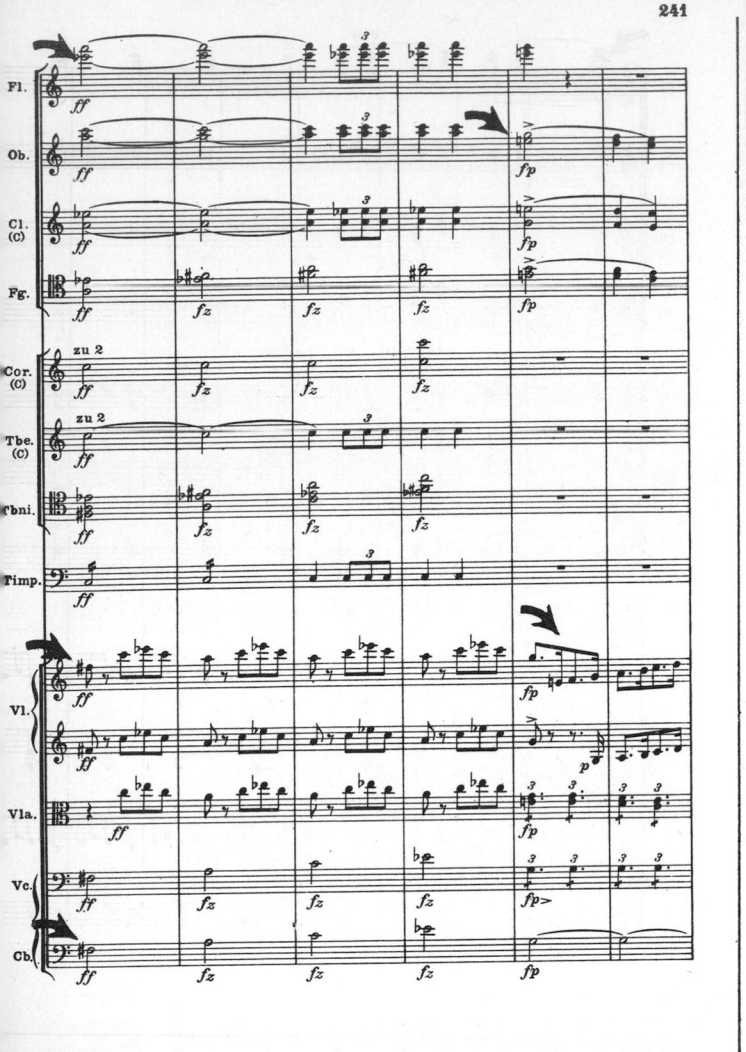

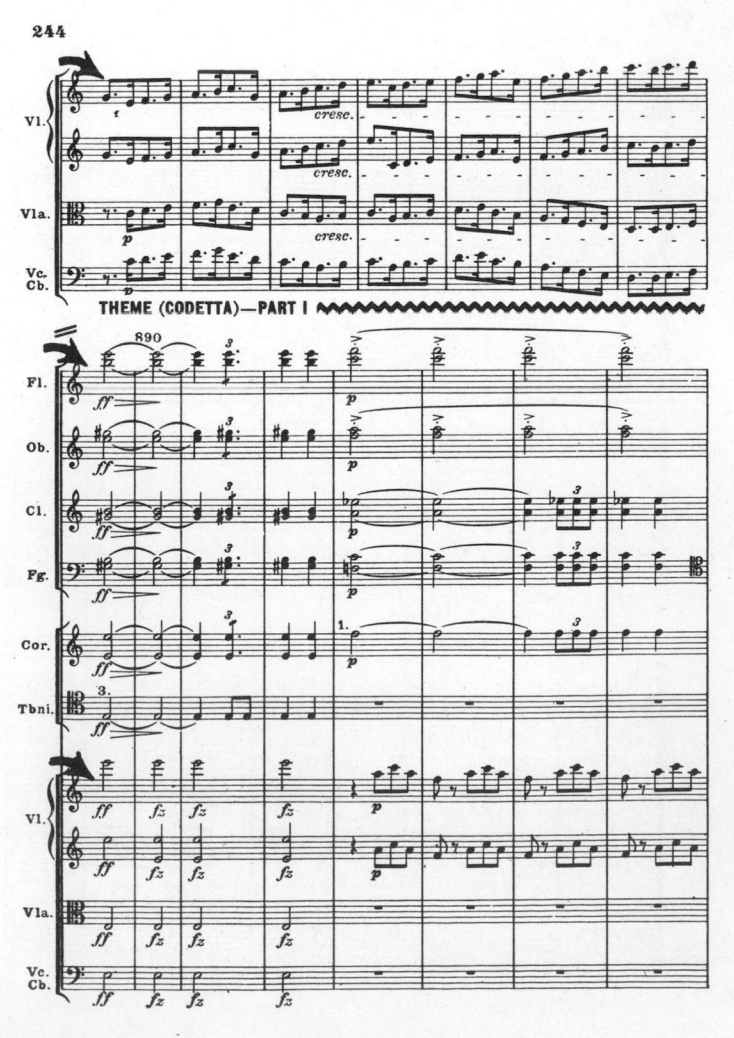

THEME (CODETTA)—PART I

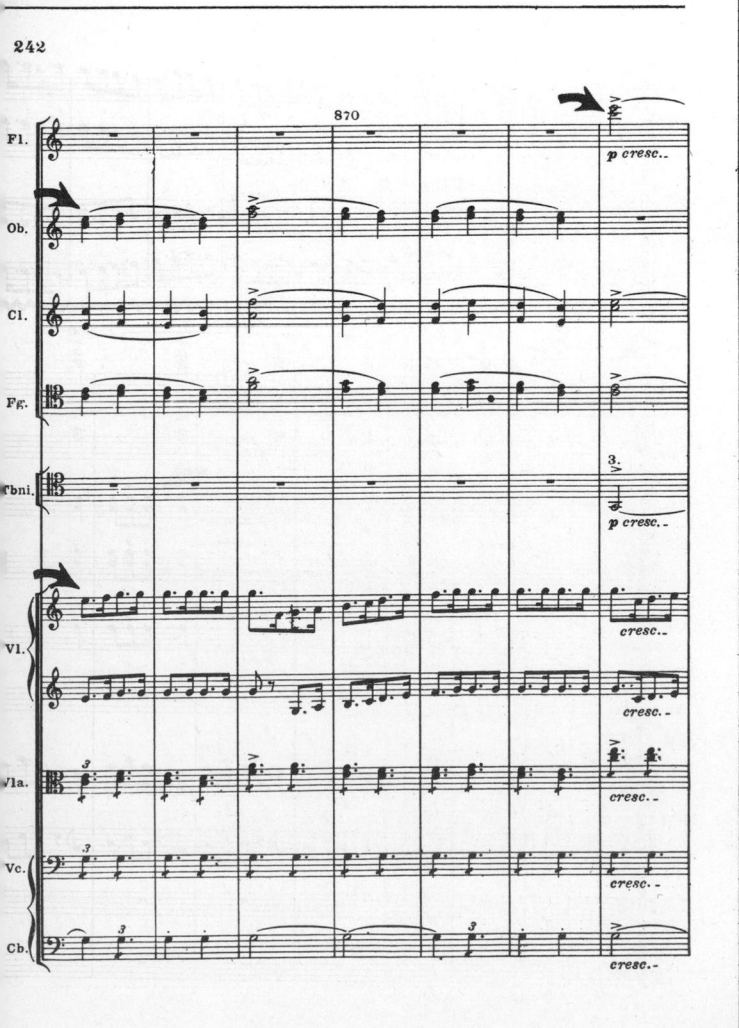

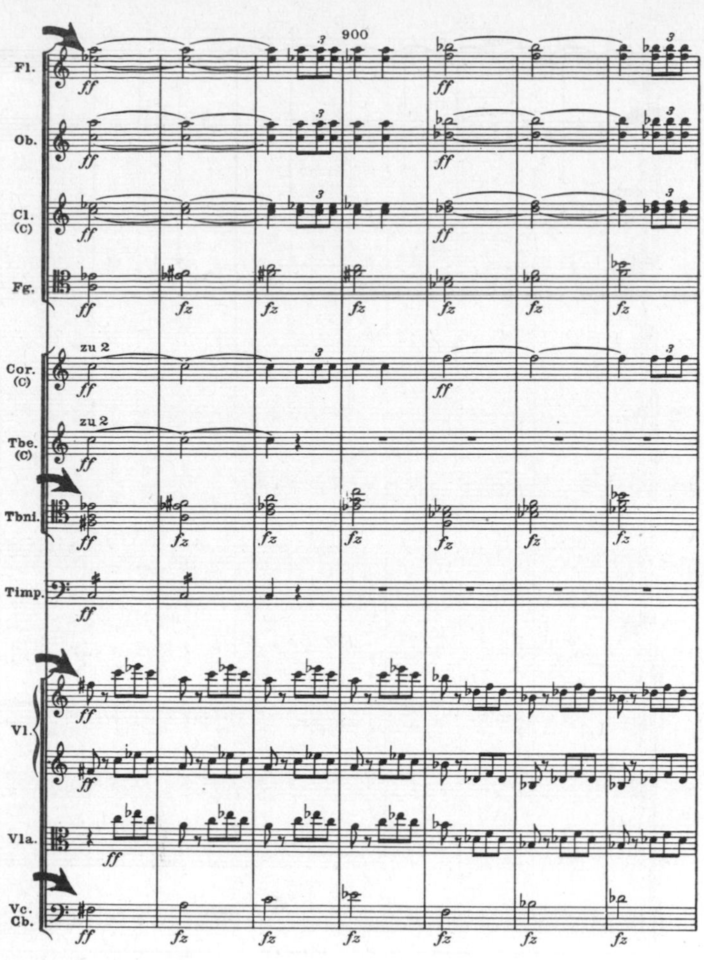

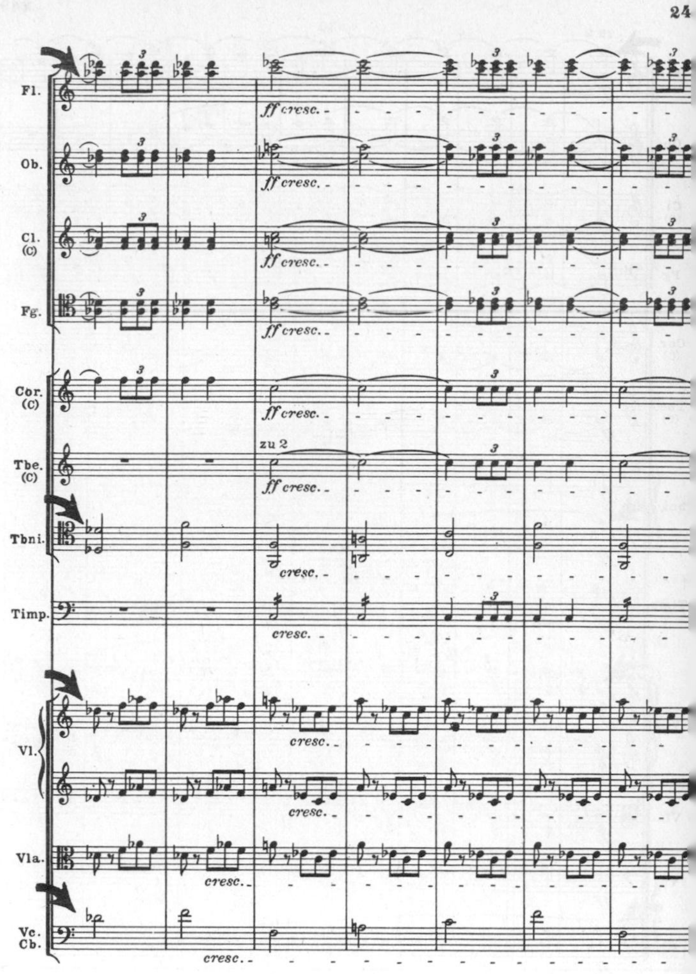

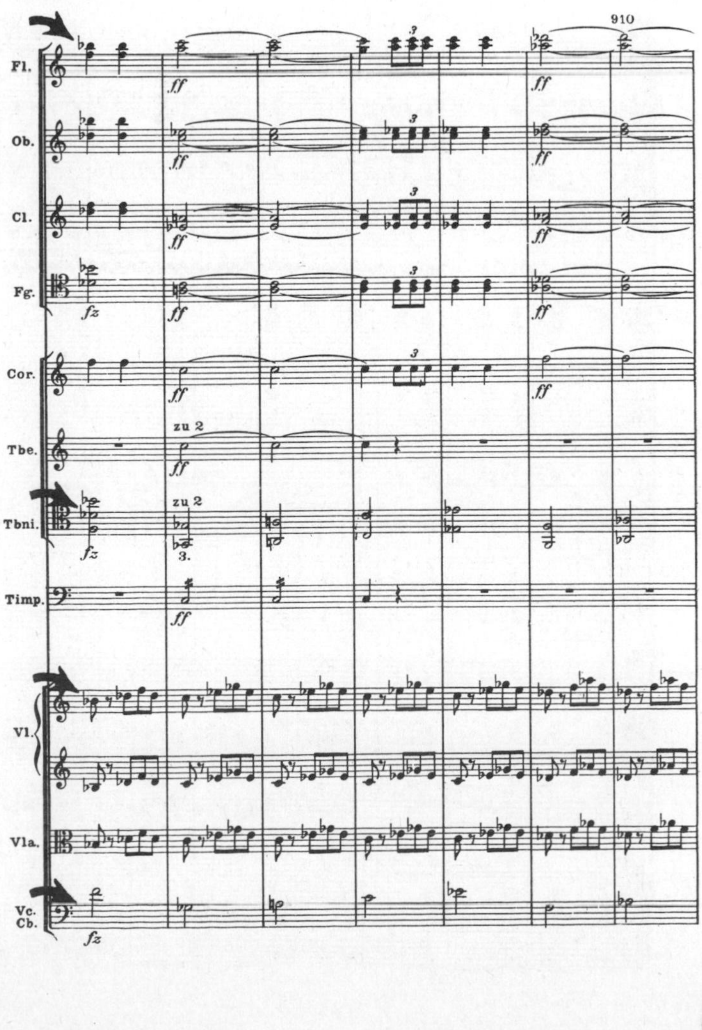

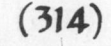

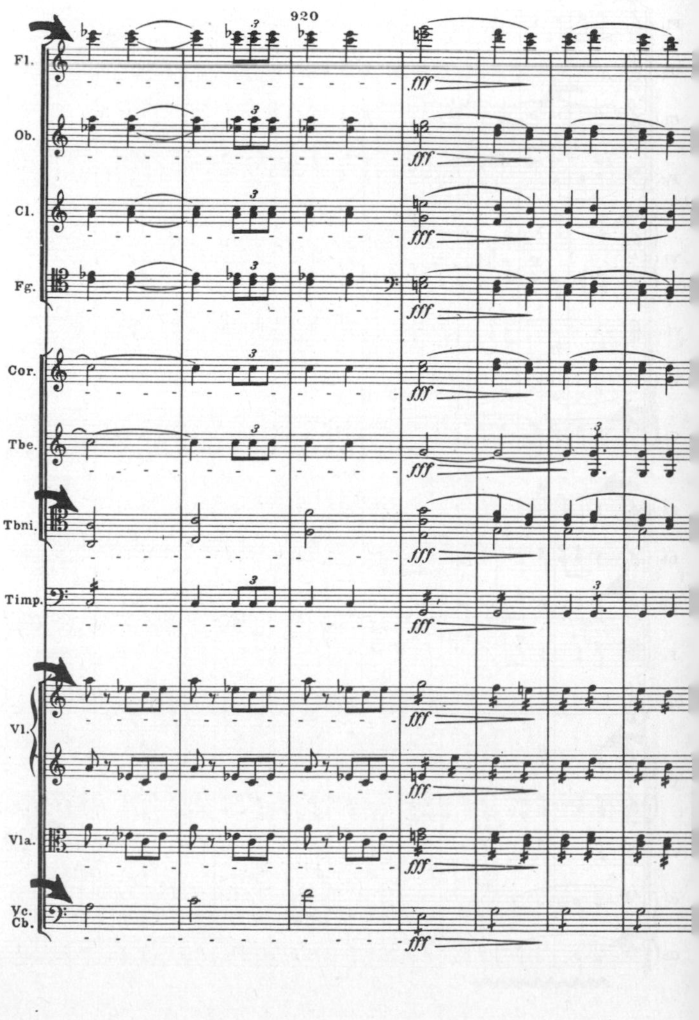

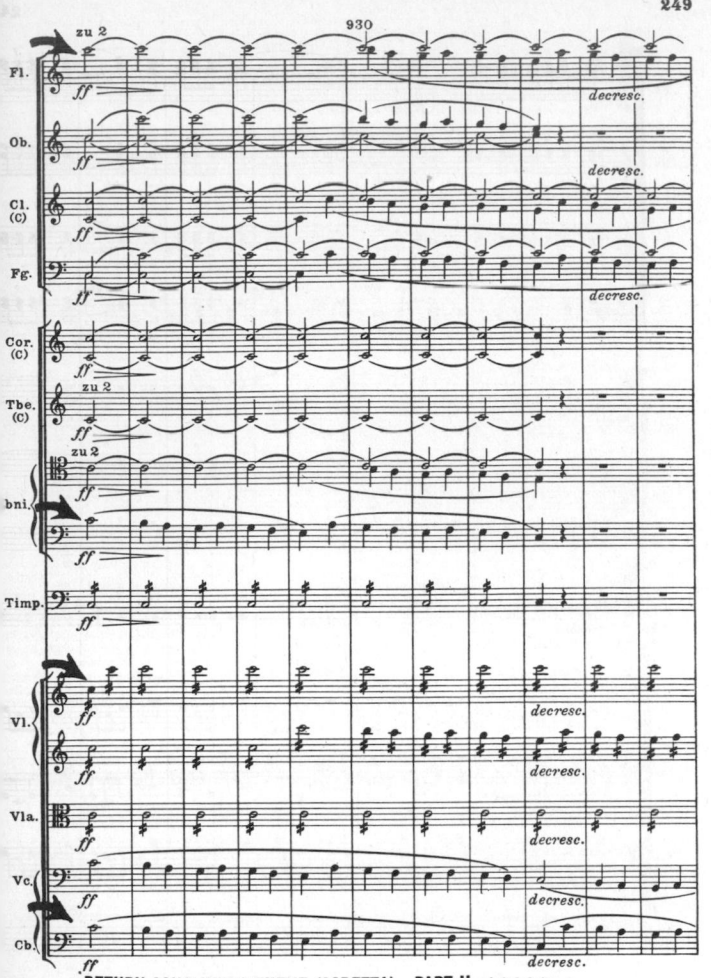

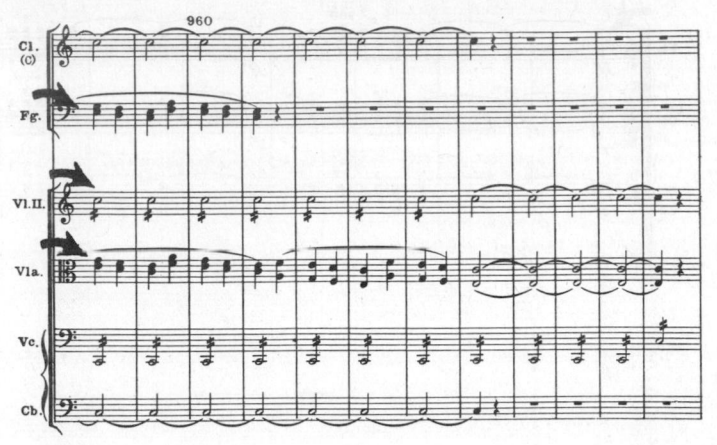

RETURN CONCLUDING THEME (CODETTA)—PART II 〰〰

CODA

CODA—SECTION I 〰〰

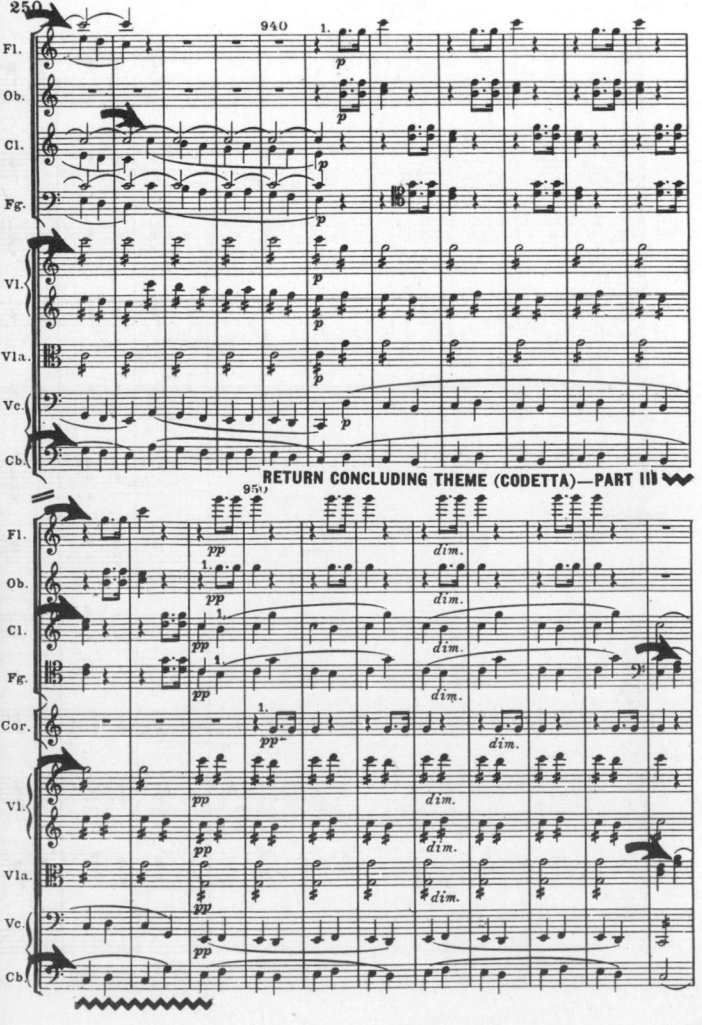

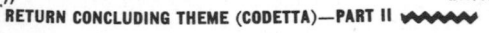

RETURN CONCLUDING THEME (CODETTA)—PART III 〰

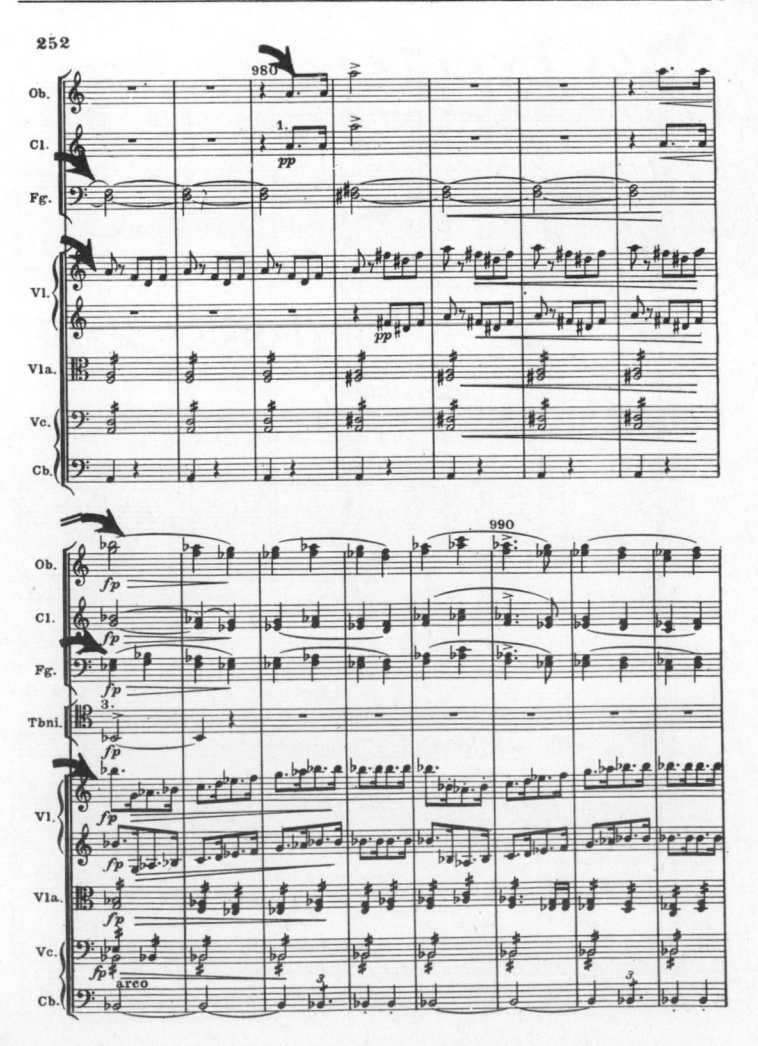

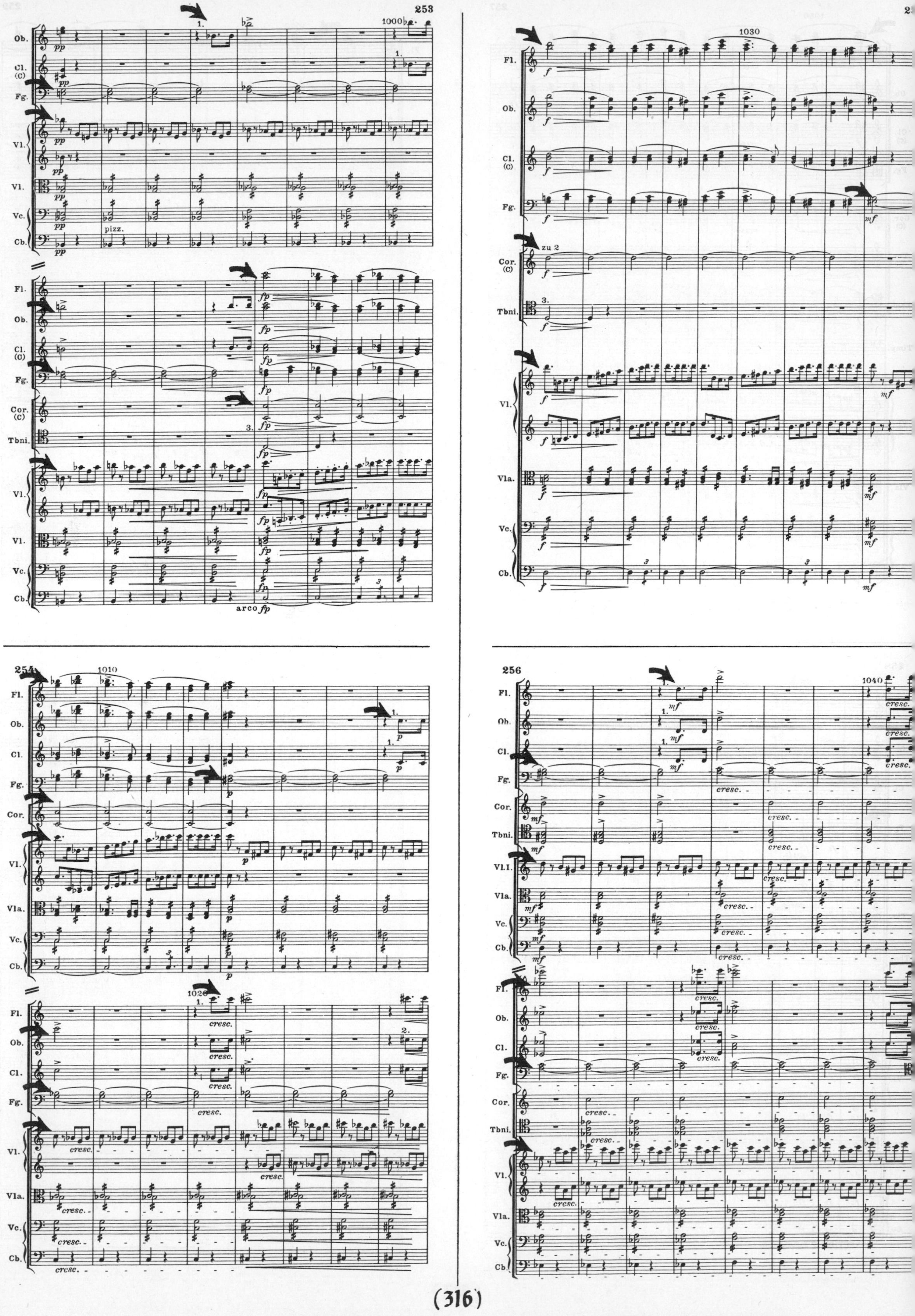
253
1000
1010
1020
1030
1040
254
256
Fl.
Ob.
Cl. (C)
Fg.
Cor. (C)
Tbni.
Vl.
Vl. I.
Vla.
Vc.
Cb.
zu 2
pizz.
arco
cresc.

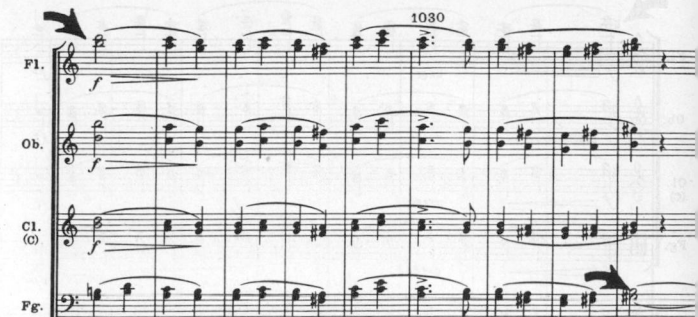

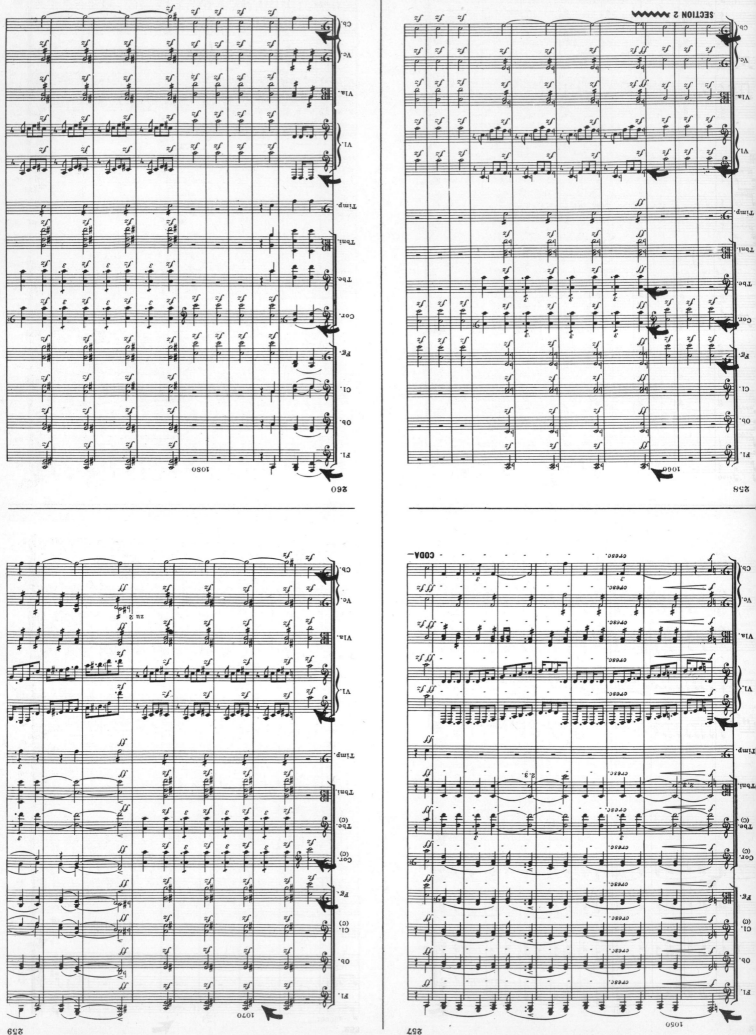

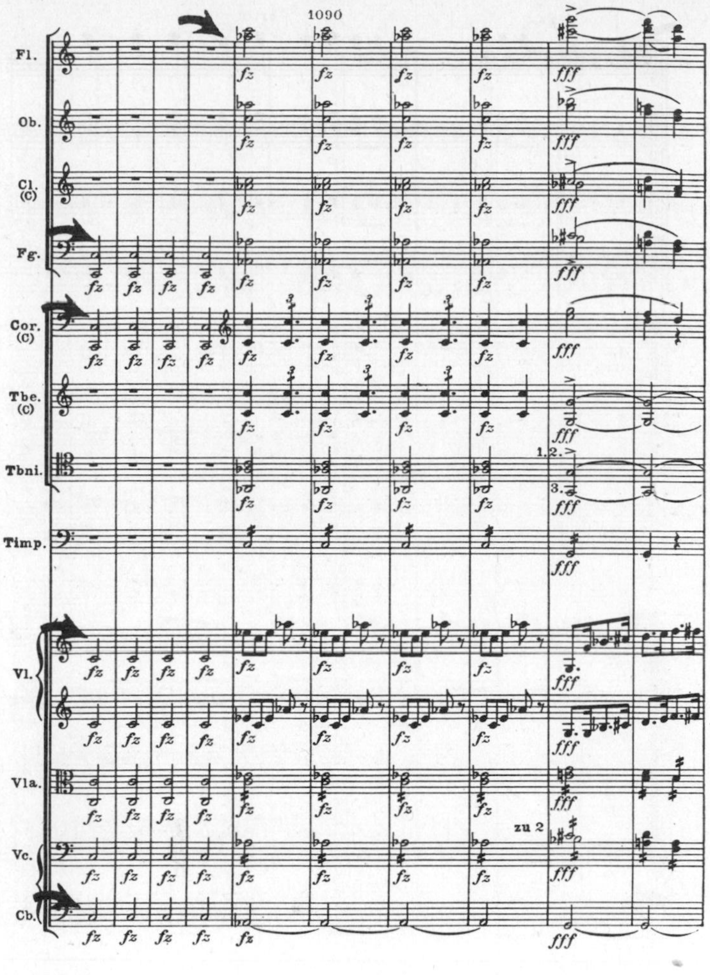

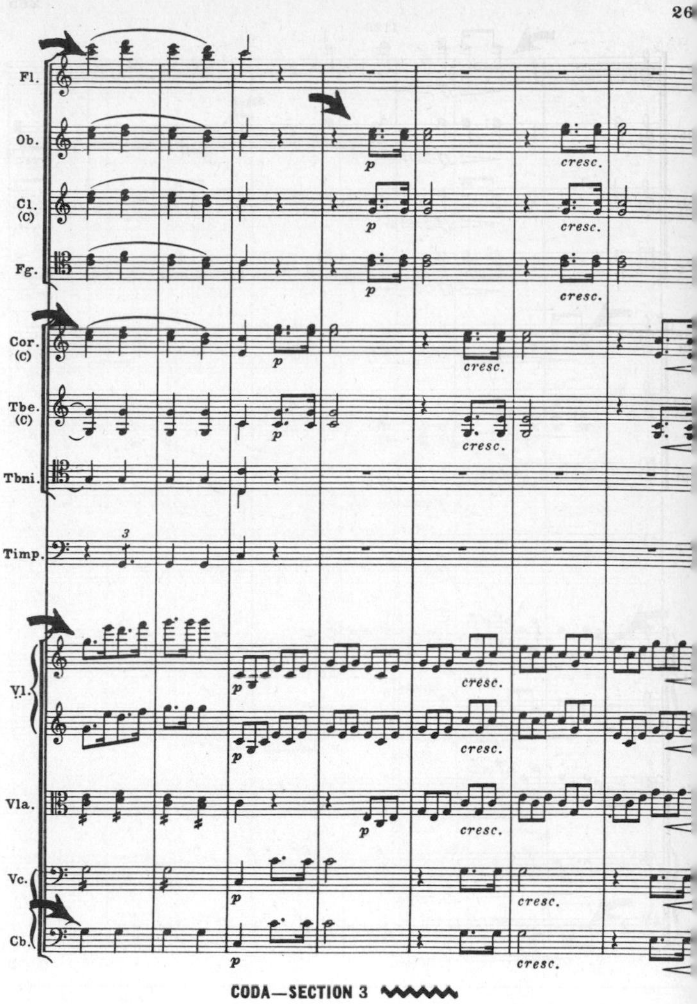

CODA—SECTION 3

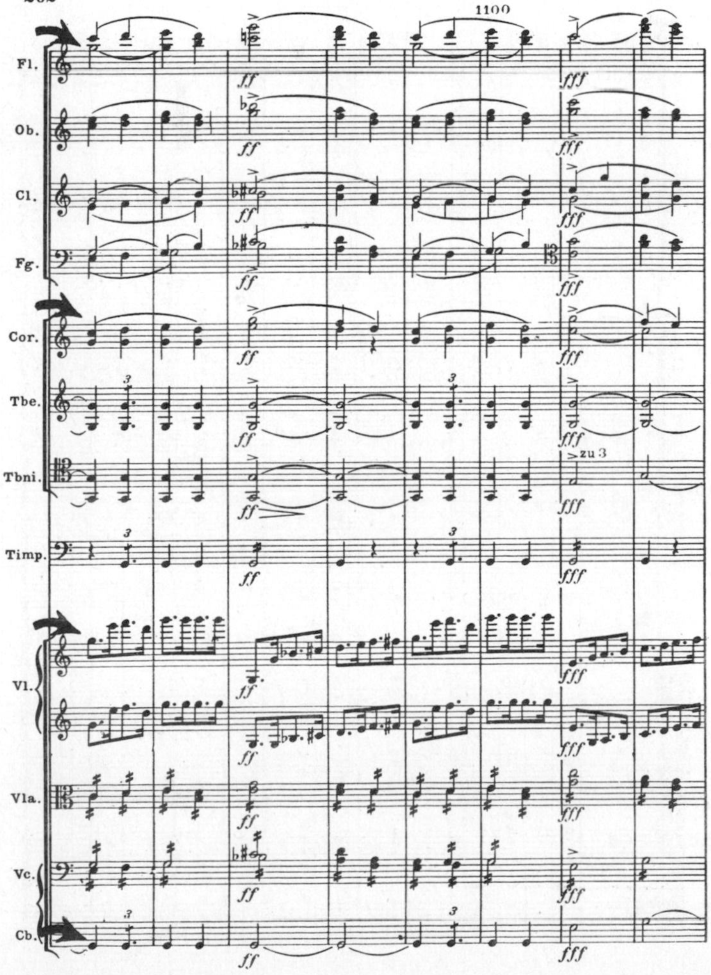

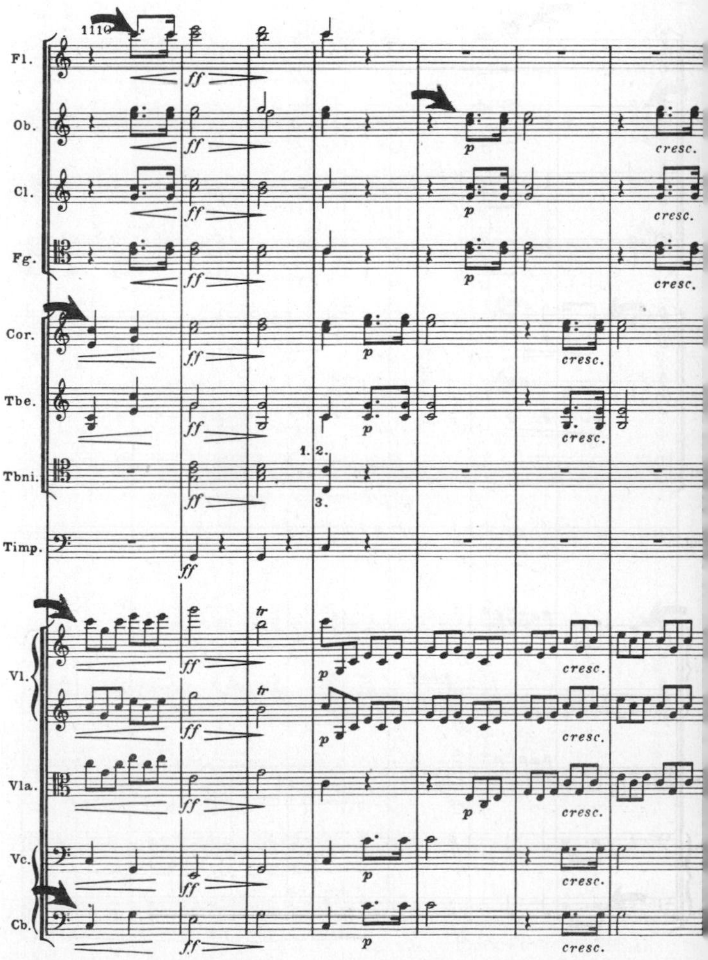

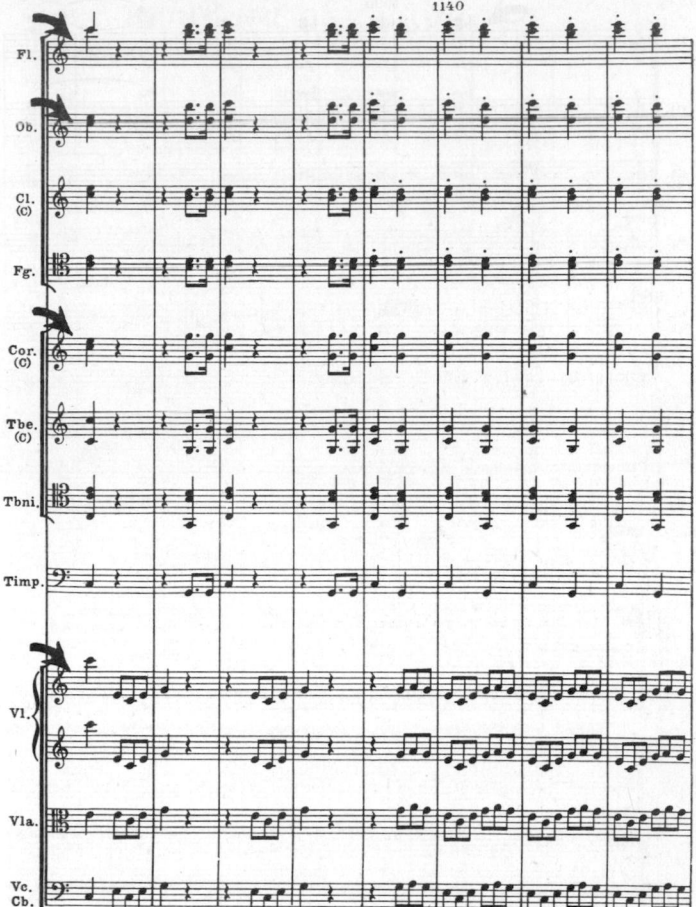

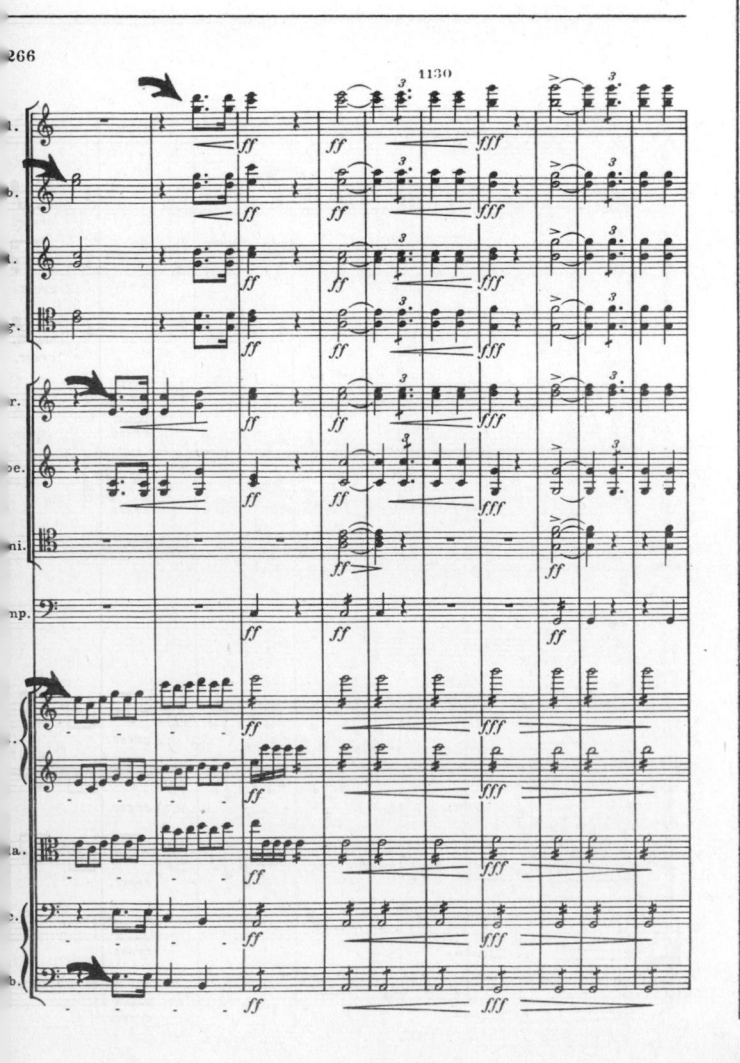

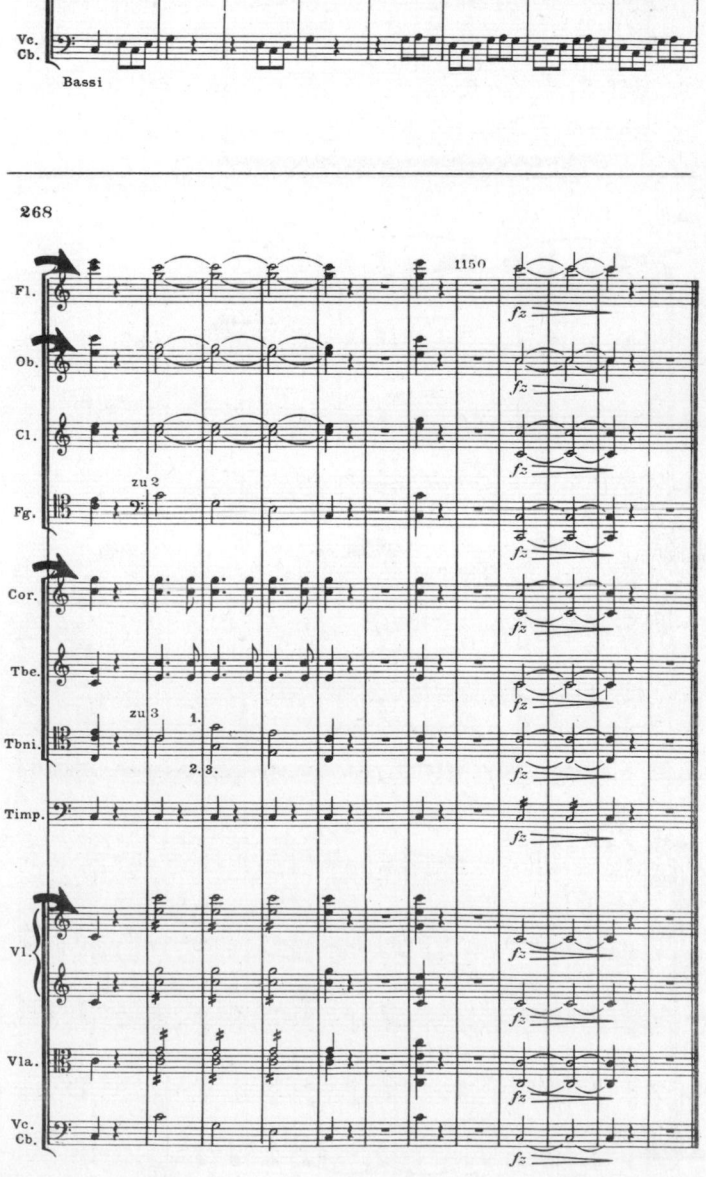

Symphony in Bb Major

Franz Schubert
(1797 - 1828)

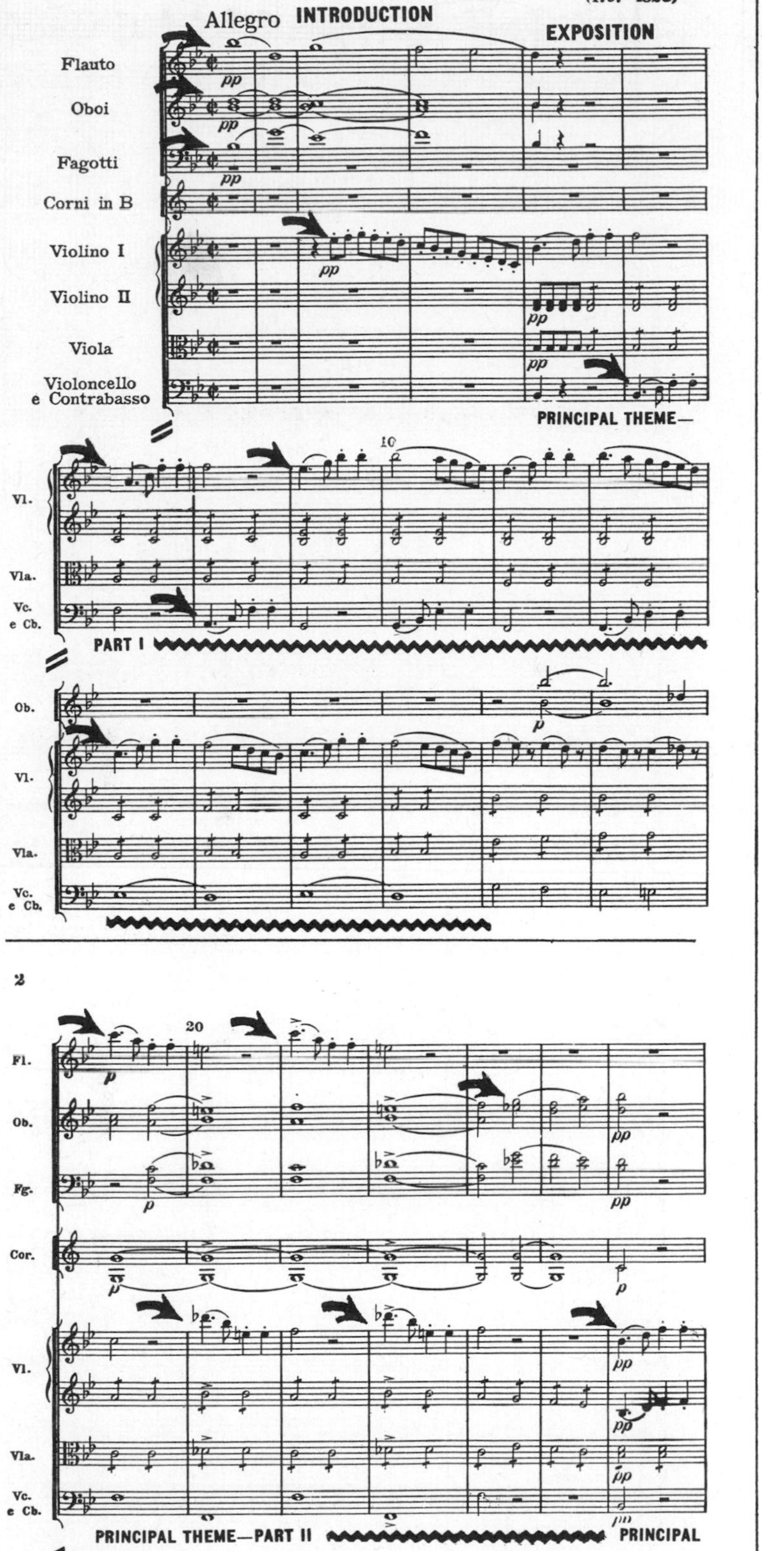

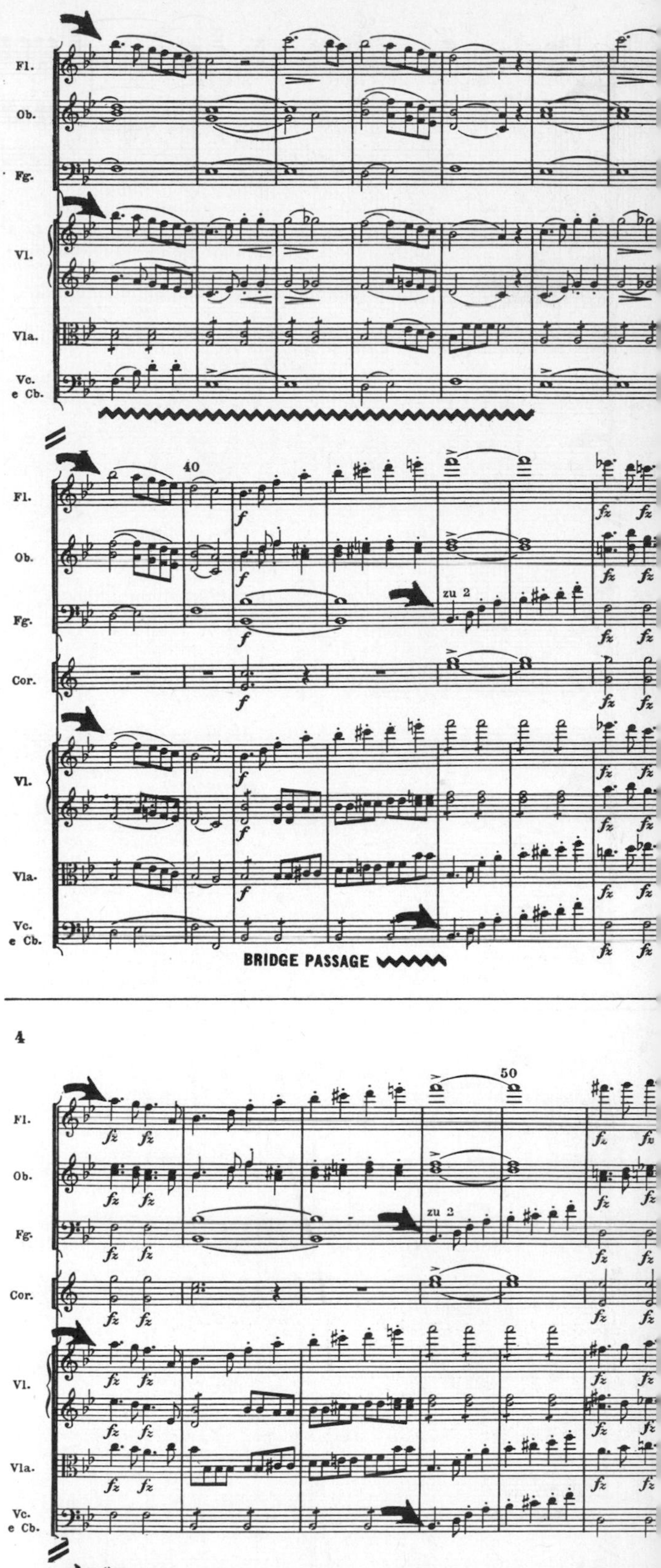

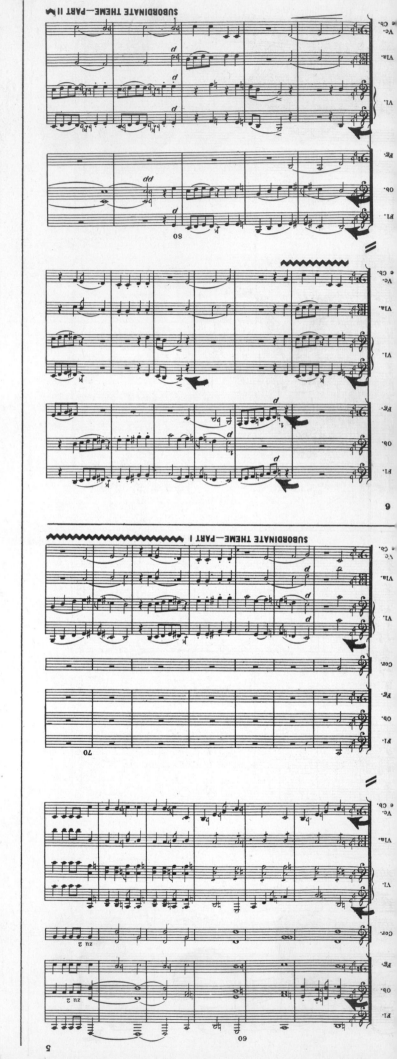
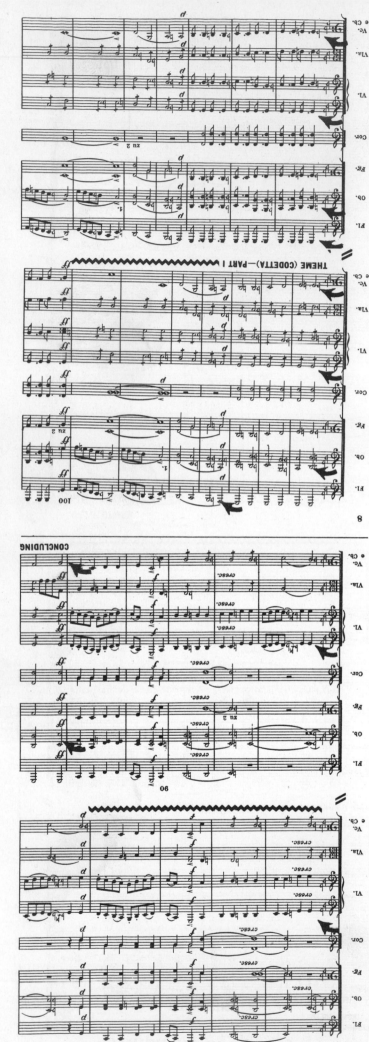

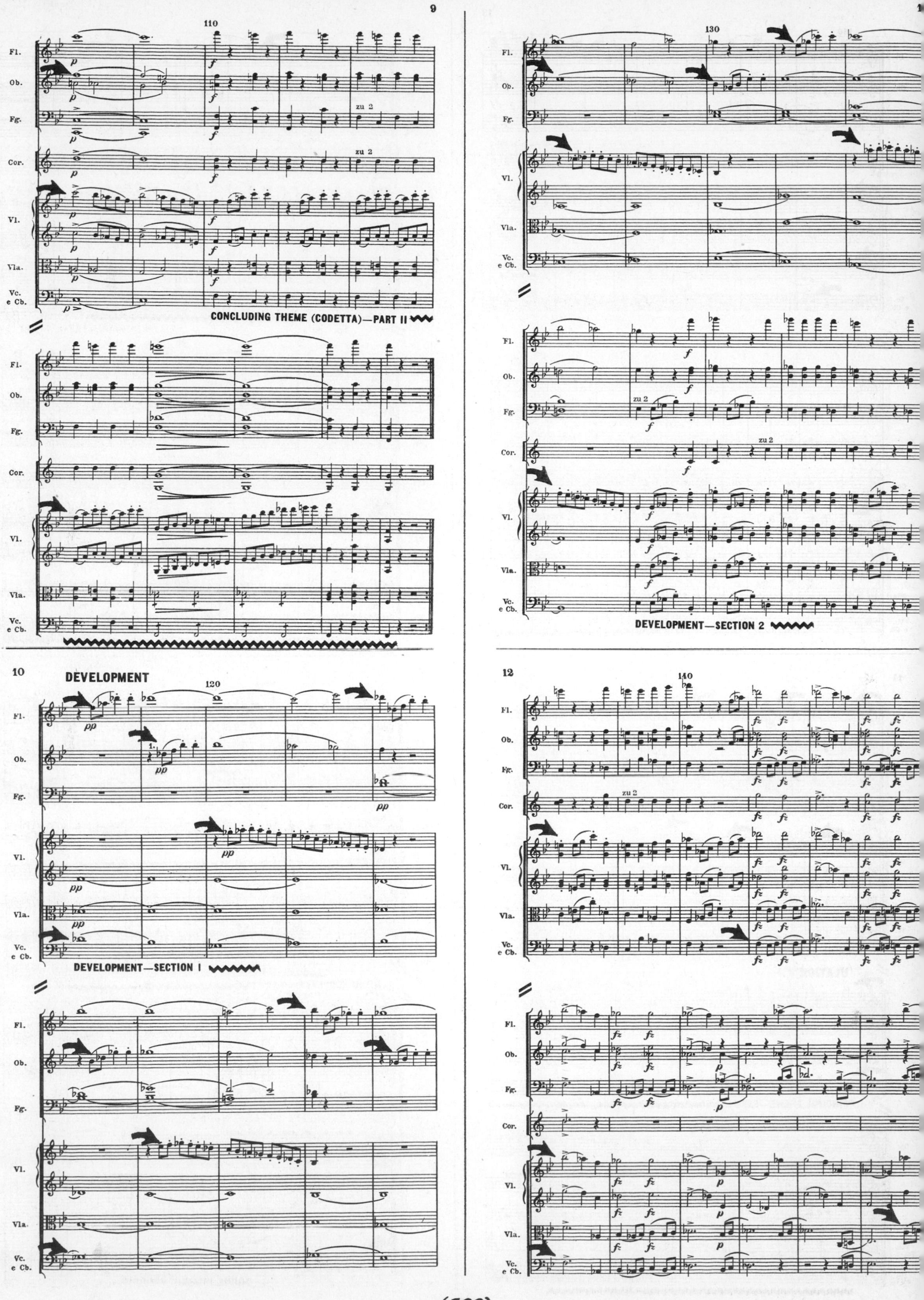
9
110
Fl.
Ob.
Fg.
Cor.
Vl.
Vla.
Vc. e Cb.
zu 2
CONCLUDING THEME (CODETTA)—PART II
10
DEVELOPMENT
120
1.
DEVELOPMENT—SECTION I
130
DEVELOPMENT—SECTION 2
12
140

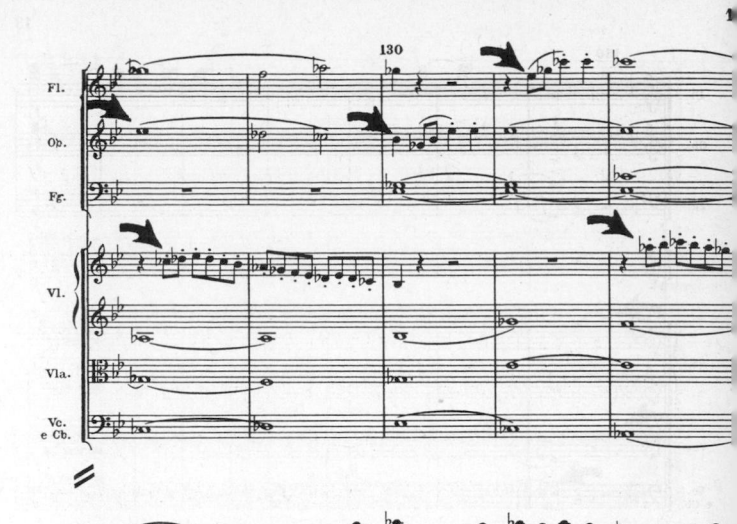

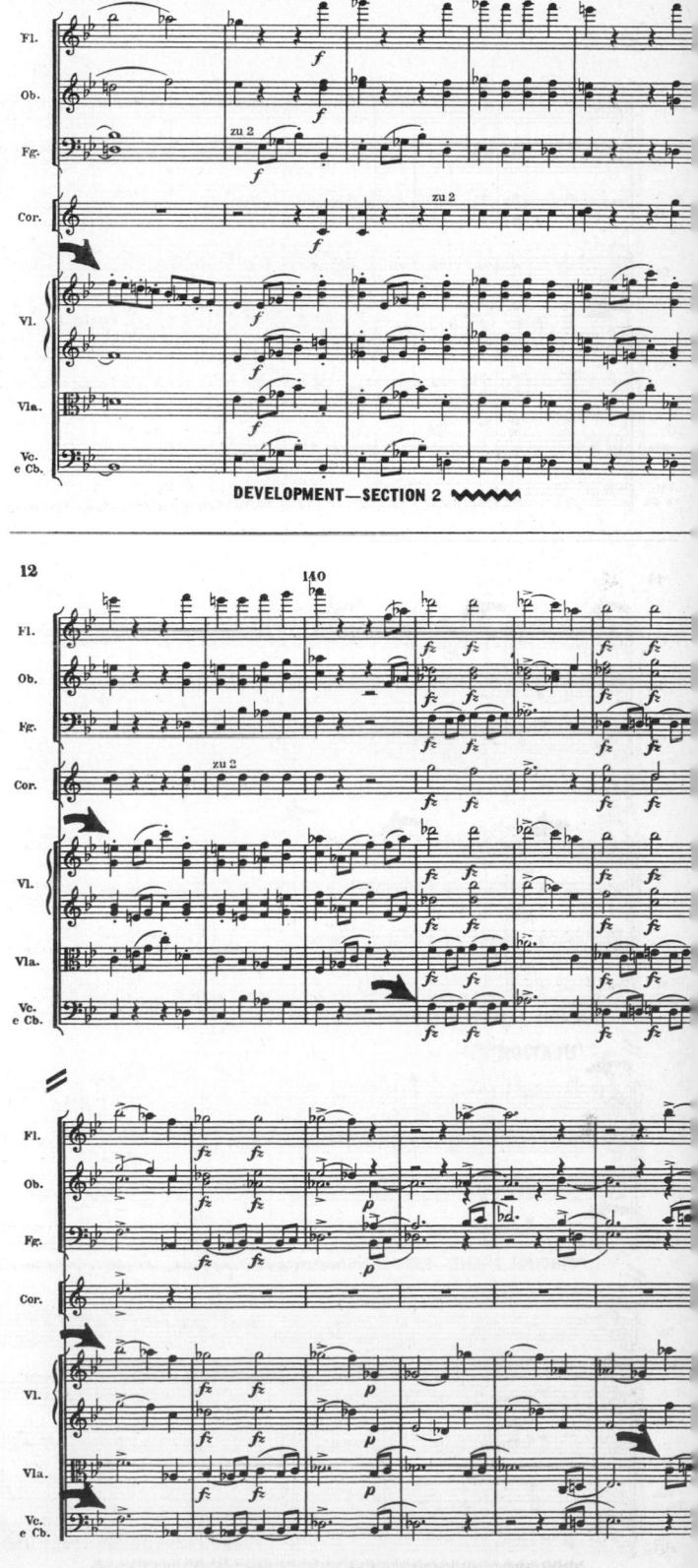

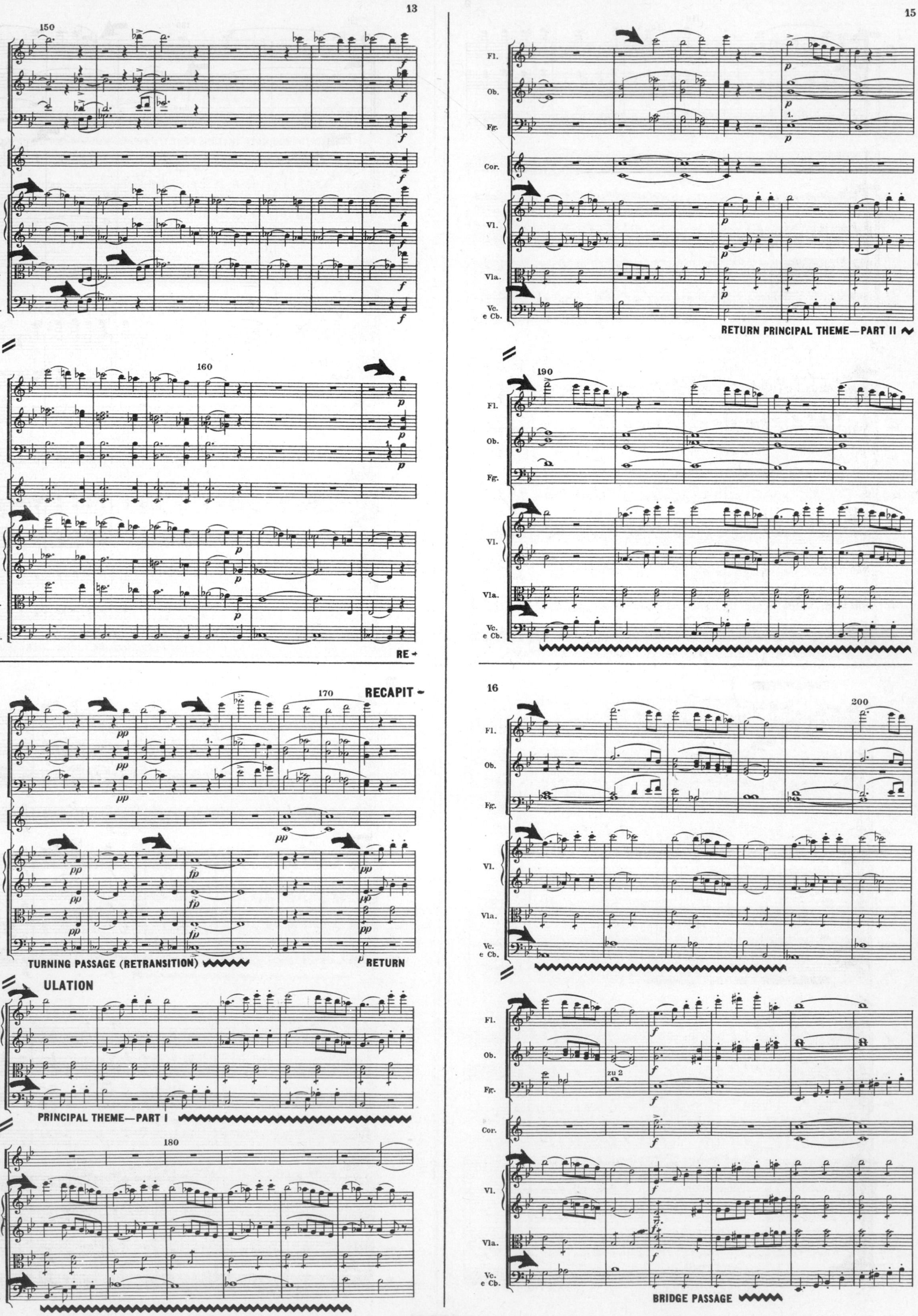

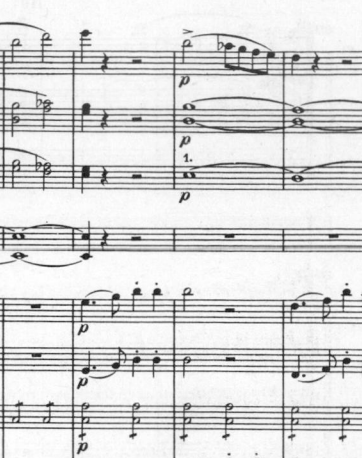

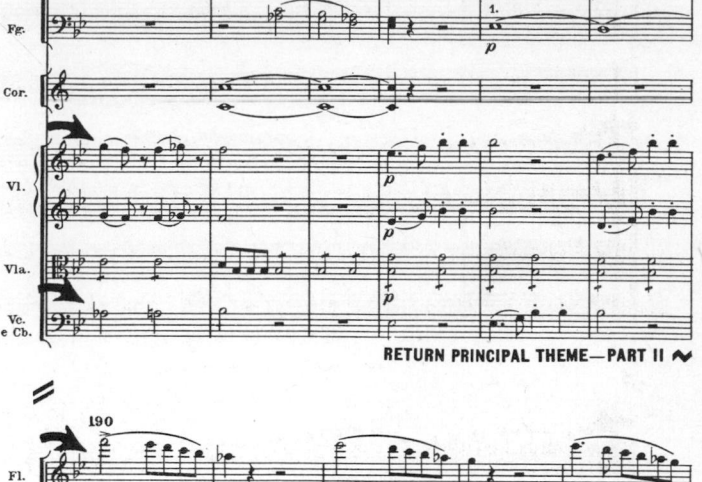

RETURN PRINCIPAL THEME—PART II

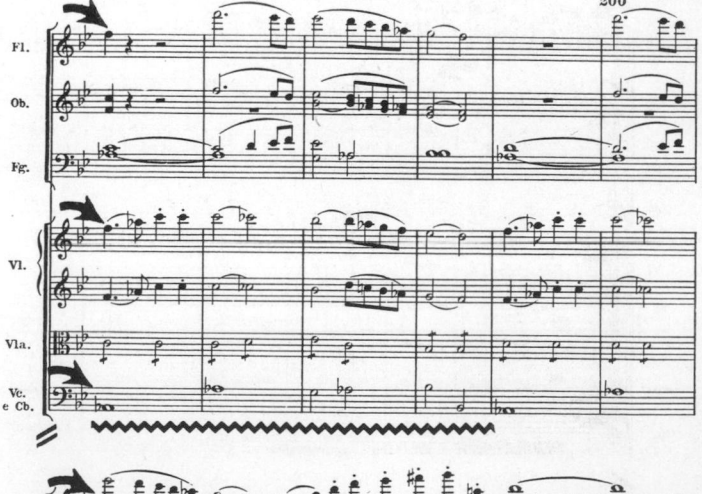

RE→

RECAPIT→

TURNING PASSAGE (RETRANSITION) ~~~~

RETURN

ULATION

PRINCIPAL THEME—PART I ~~~~

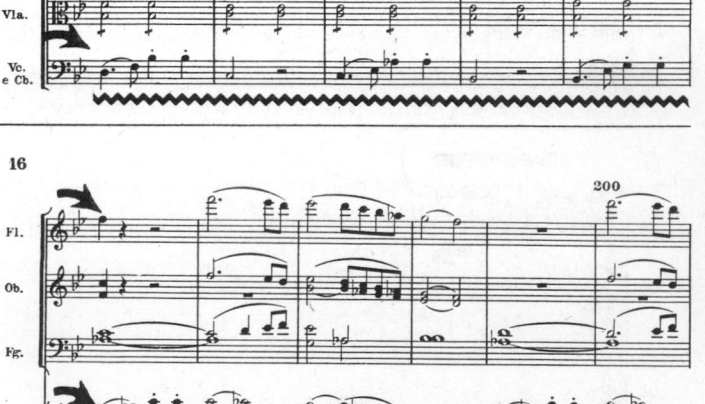

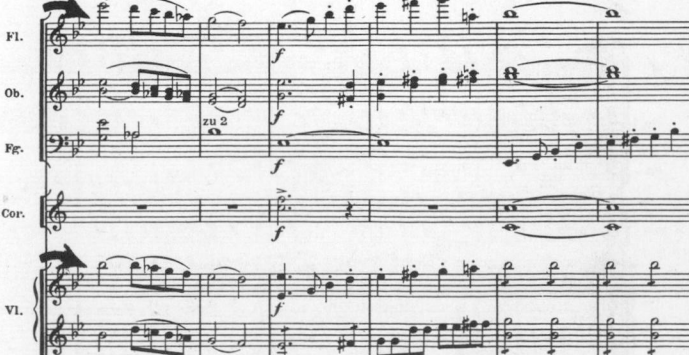

BRIDGE PASSAGE ~~~~

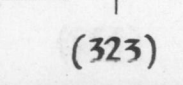

17
210
Fl.
Ob.
Fg.
Cor.
Vl.
Vla.
Vc. e Cb.
zu 2
18
220
230
fp
19
RETURN SUBORDINATE THEME—PART I
240
p
cresc.
RETURN SUBORDINATE THEME—PART II
20
250
f
260
ff
fz
RETURN CONCLUDING THEME (CO

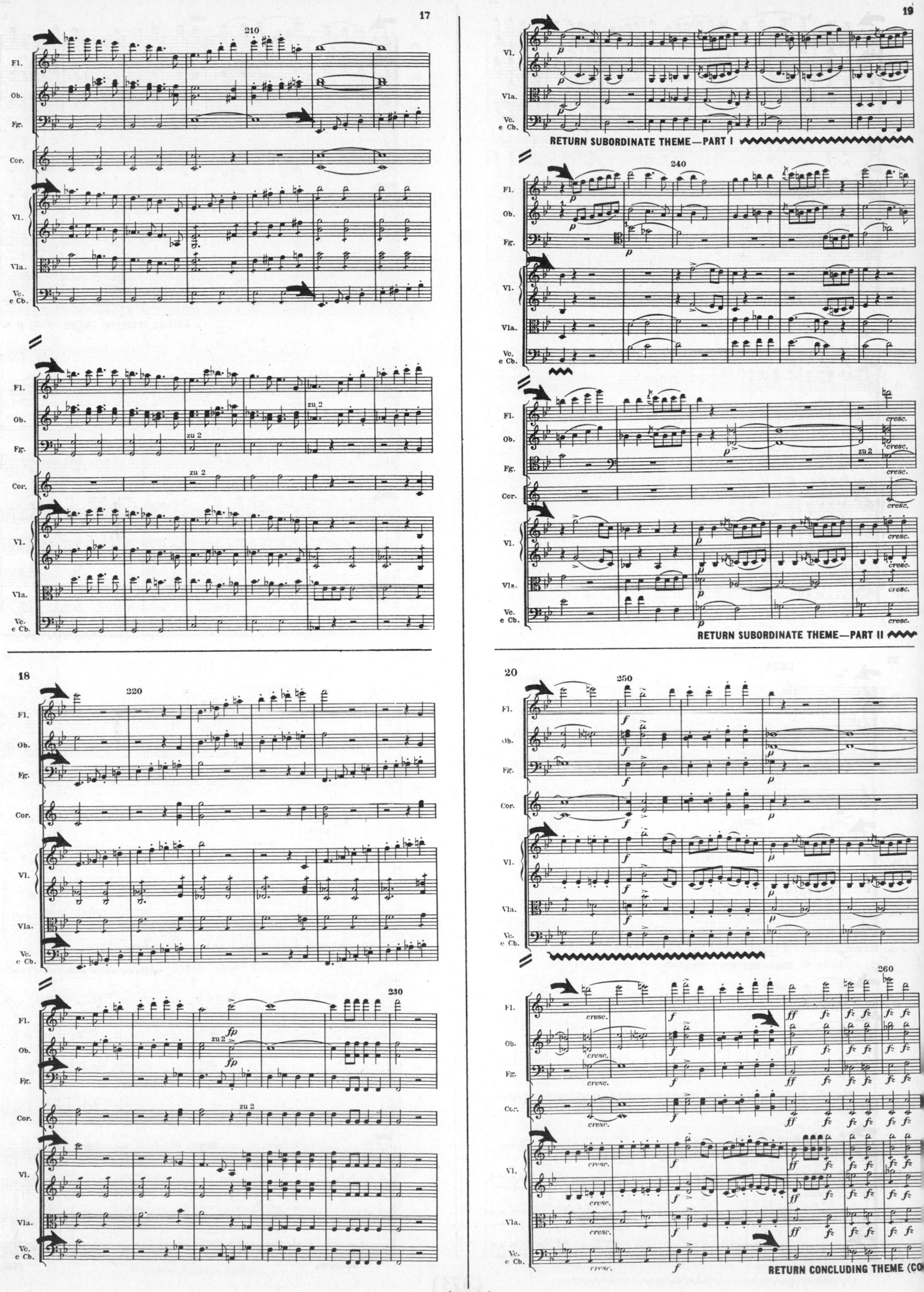

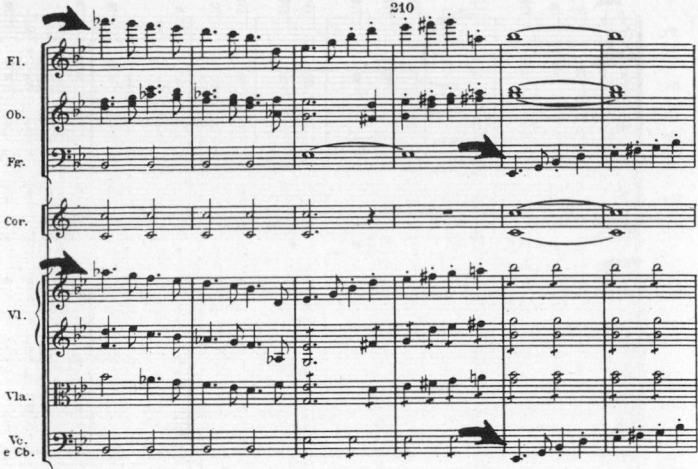

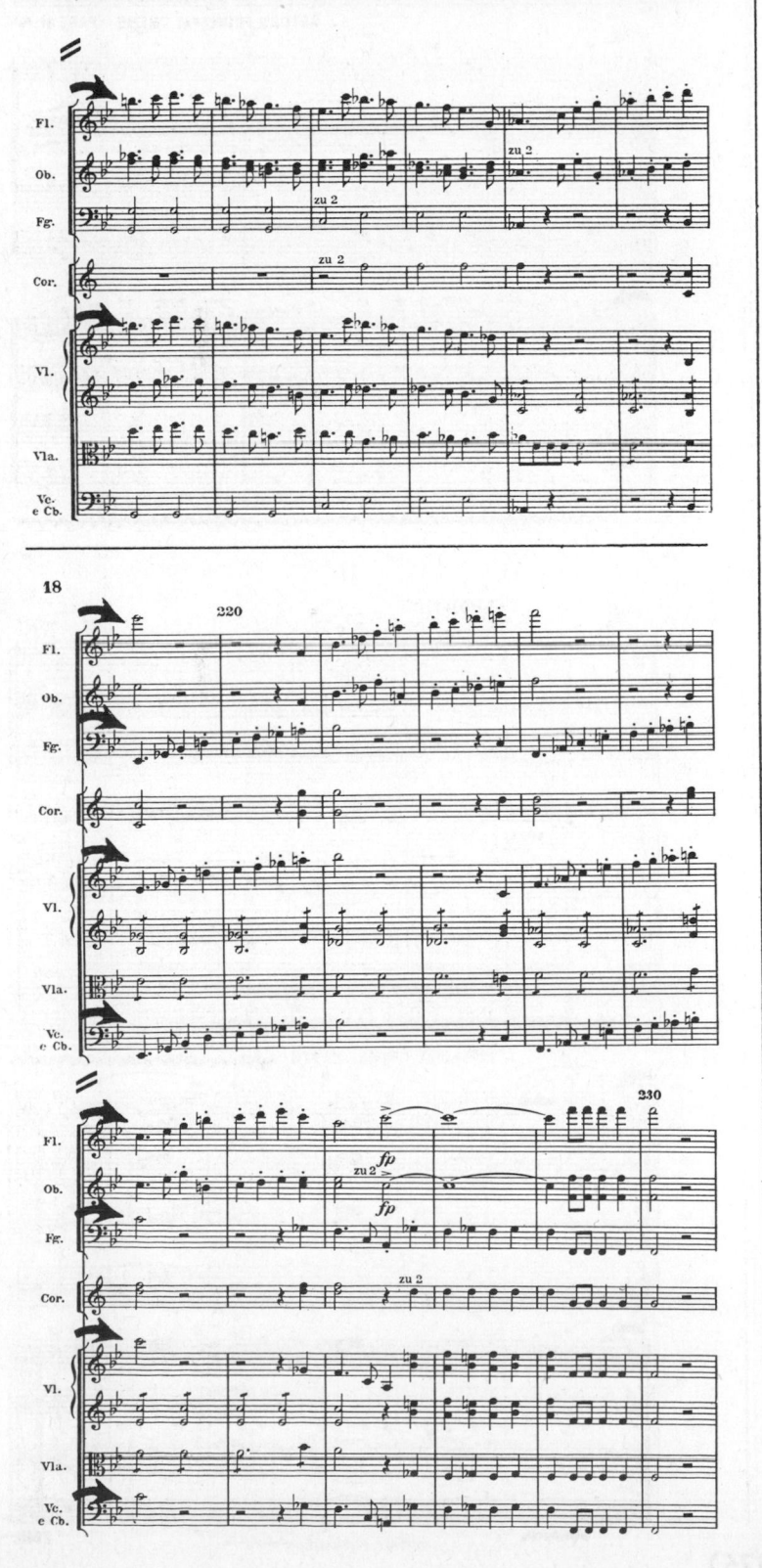

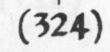

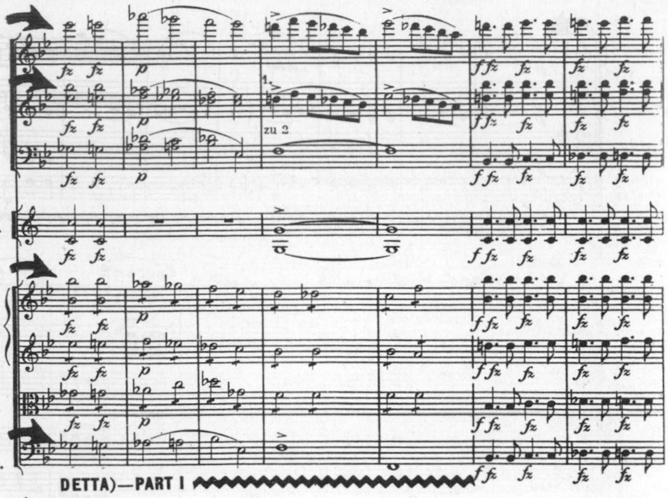

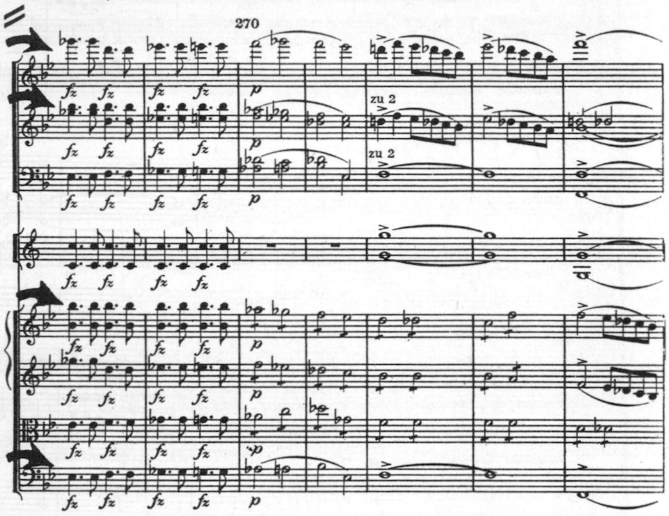

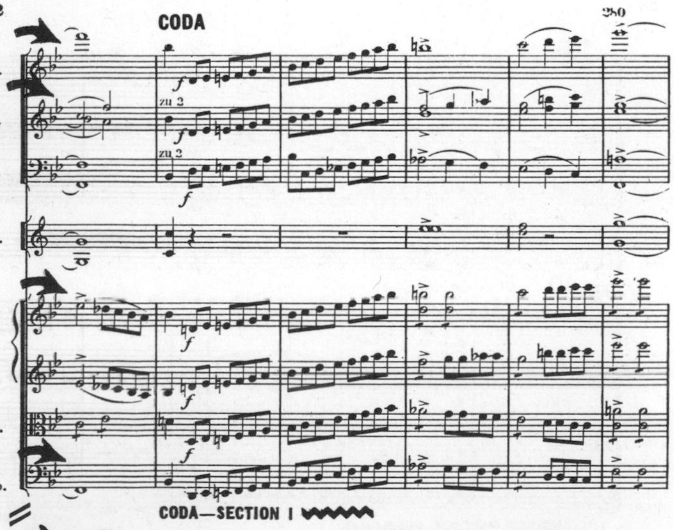

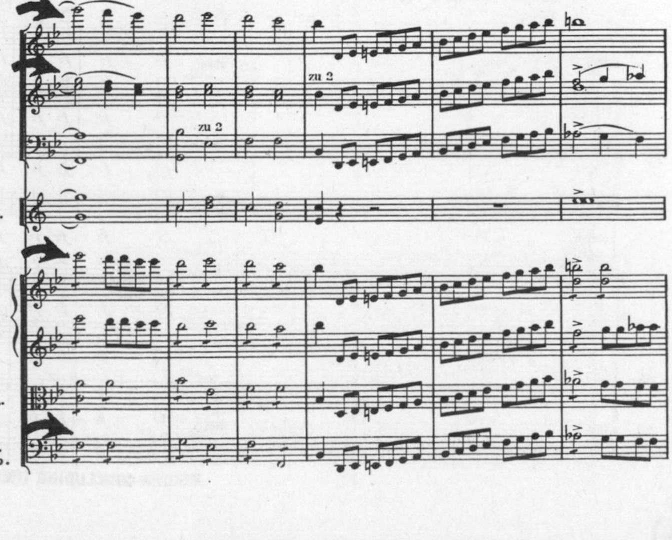

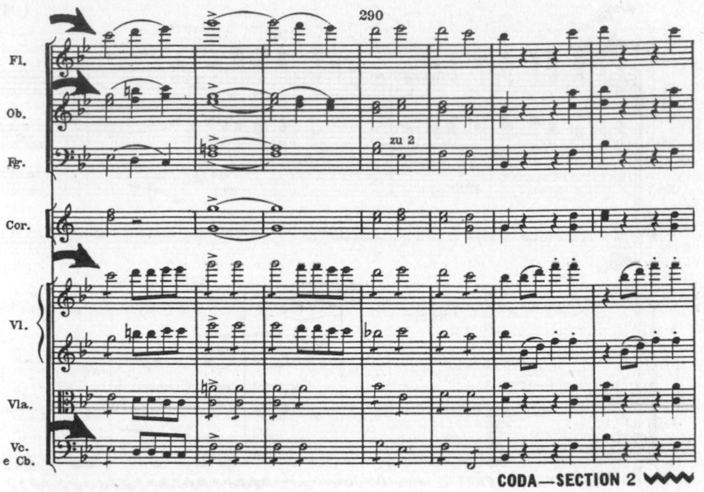

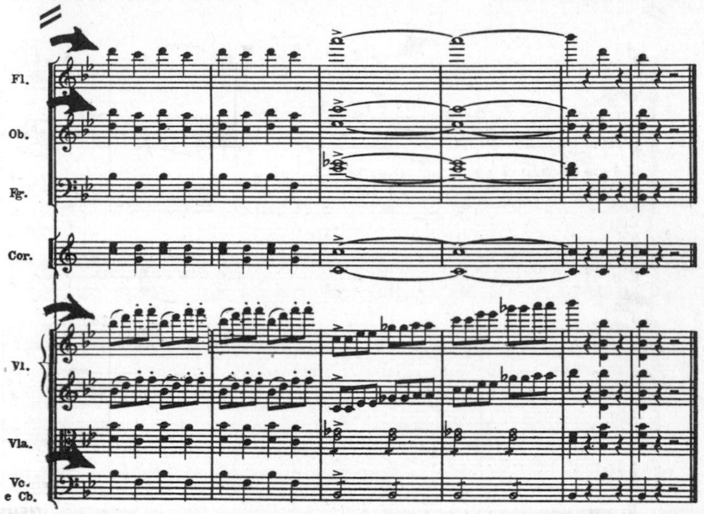

II

EXPOSITION

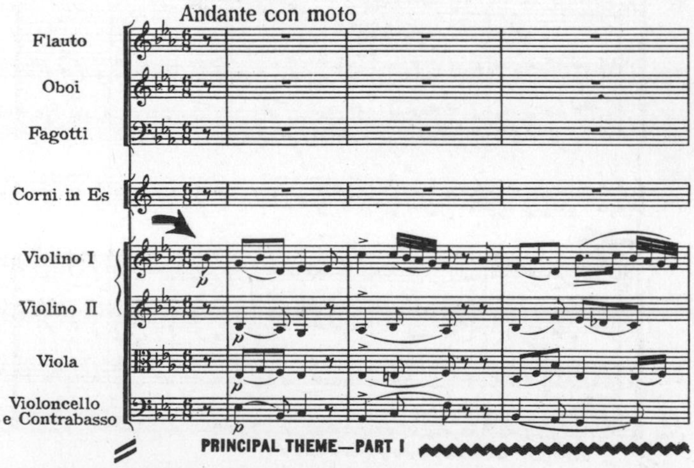

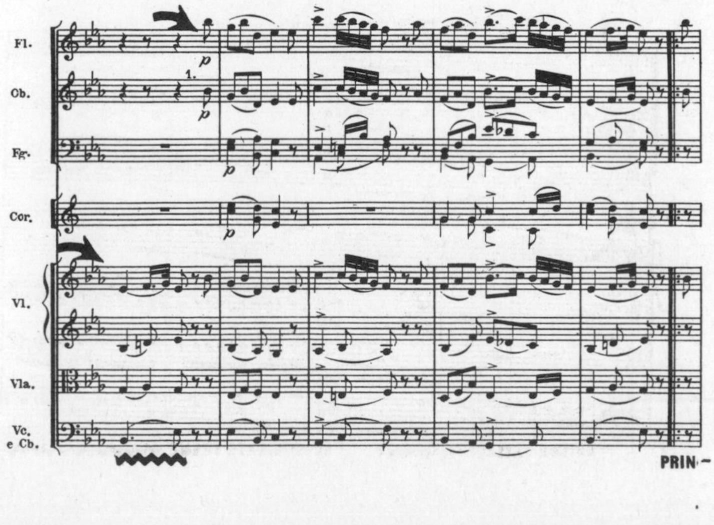

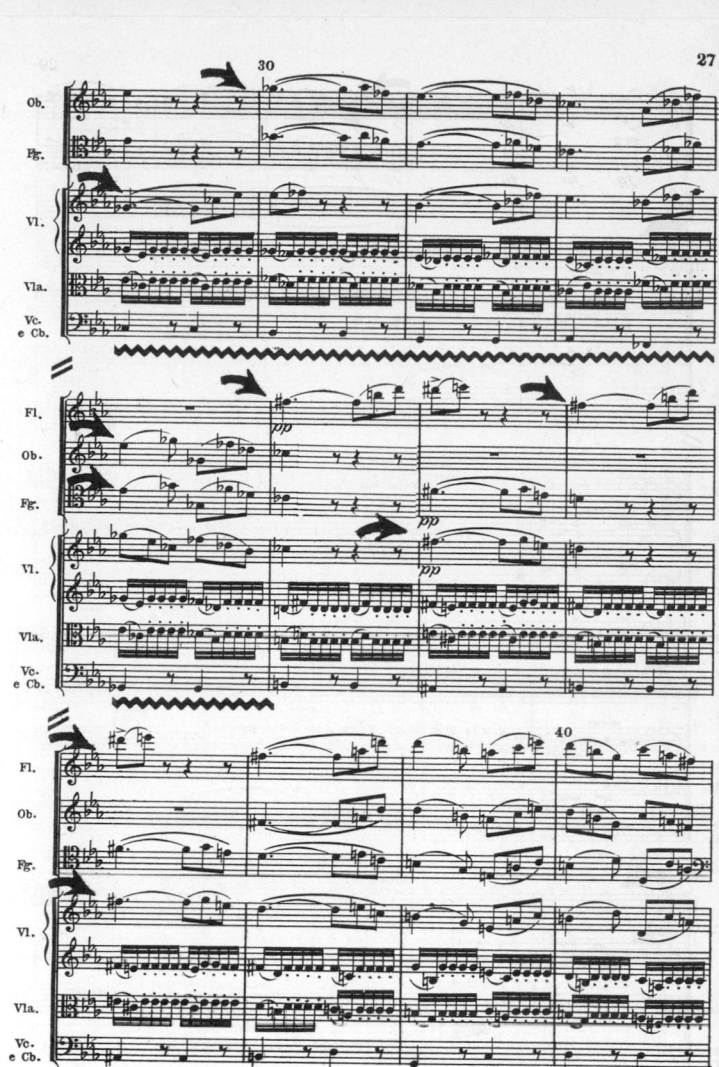

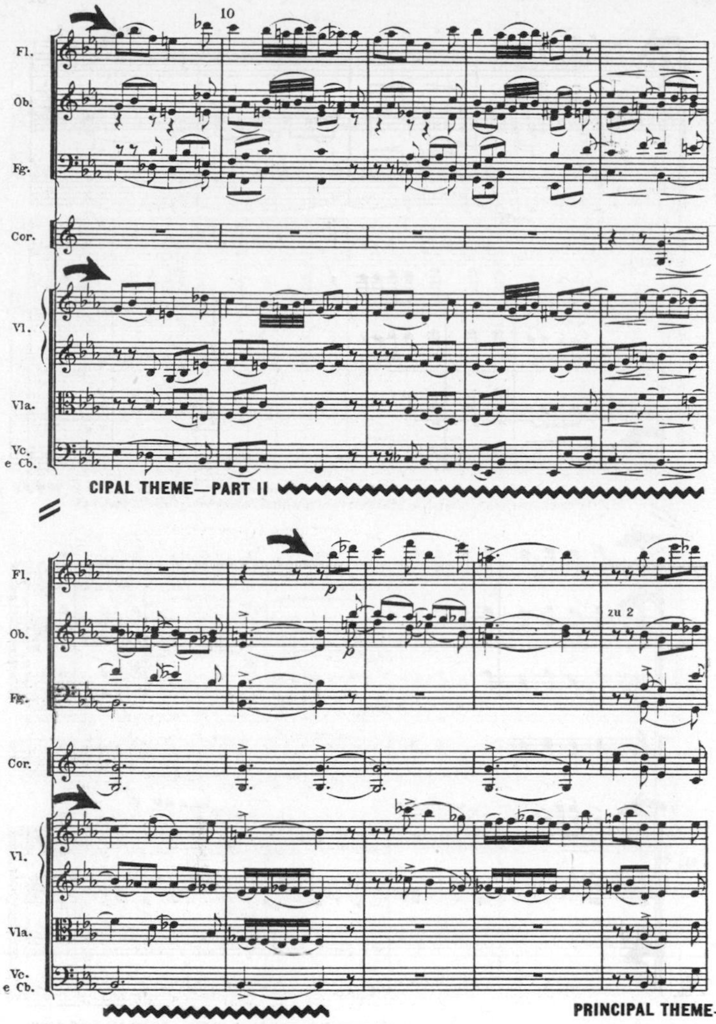
Fl.
Ob.
Fg.
Cor.
Vl.
Vla.
Vc. e Cb.
10
CIPAL THEME—PART II
zu 2
PRINCIPAL THEME—

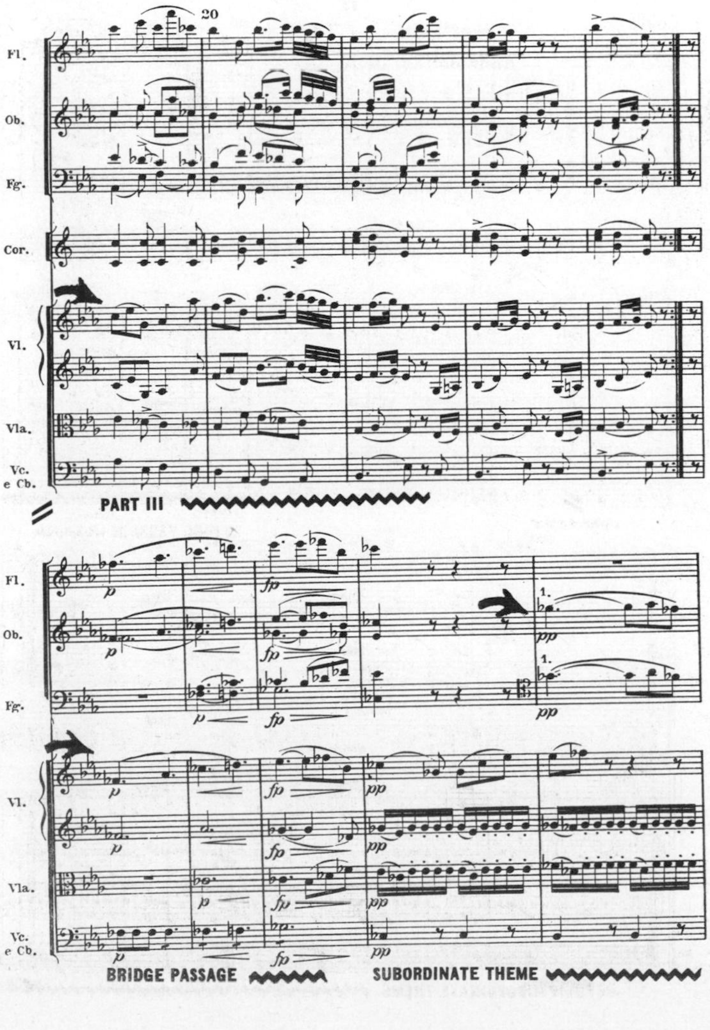
Fl.
Ob.
Fg.
Cor.
Vl.
Vla.
Vc. e Cb.
20
PART III
BRIDGE PASSAGE
SUBORDINATE THEME

Ob.
Fg.
Vl.
Vla.
Vc. e Cb.
30
Fl.
40

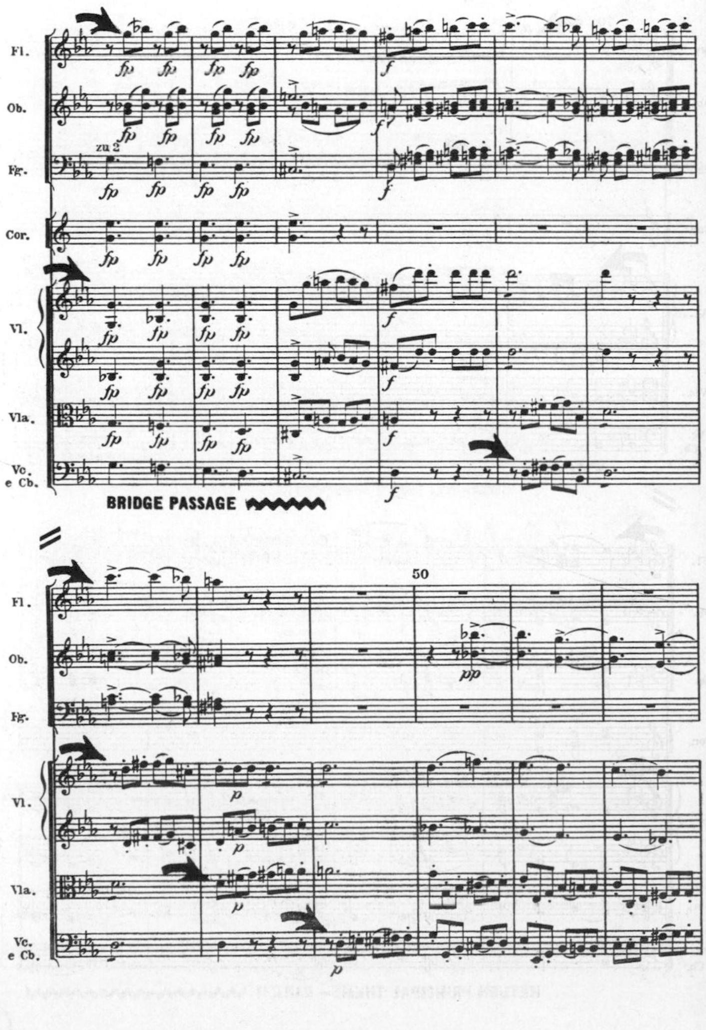
Fl.
Ob.
Fg.
Cor.
Vl.
Vla.
Vc. e Cb.
zu 2
BRIDGE PASSAGE
50

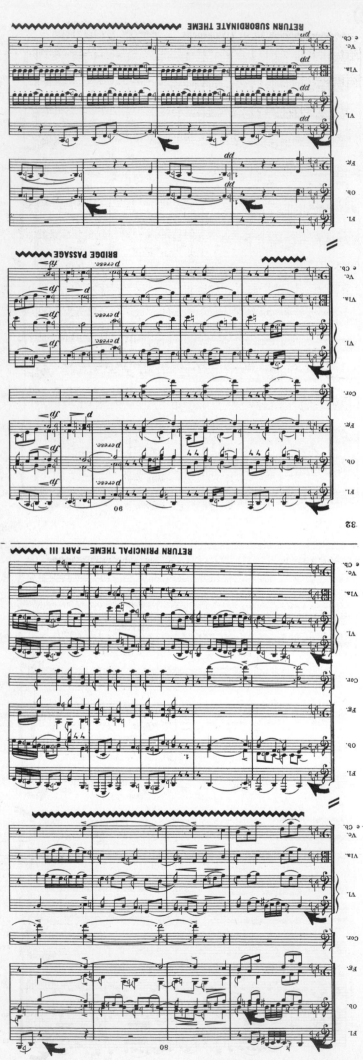

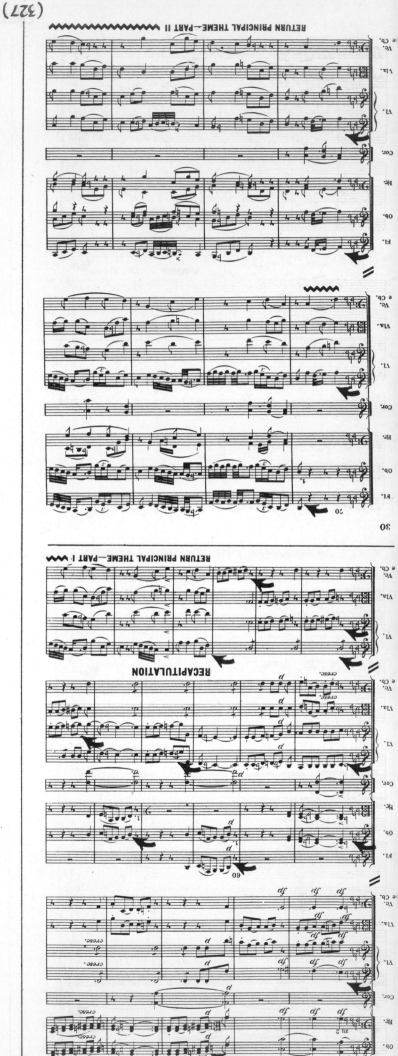

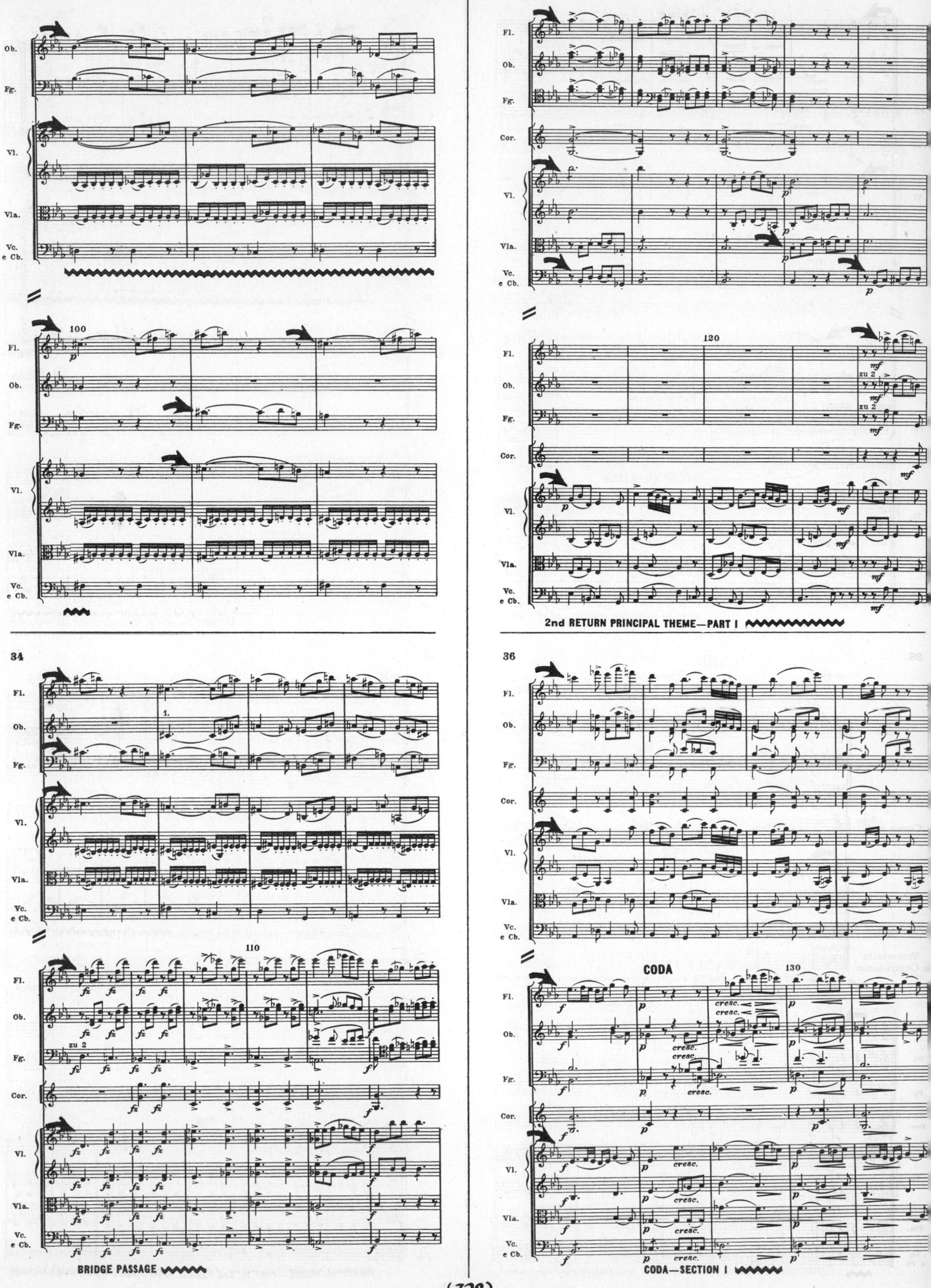

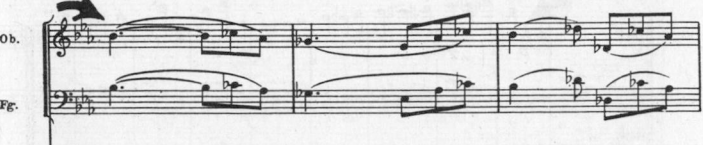

2nd RETURN PRINCIPAL THEME—PART I

34

36

BRIDGE PASSAGE

CODA

CODA—SECTION I

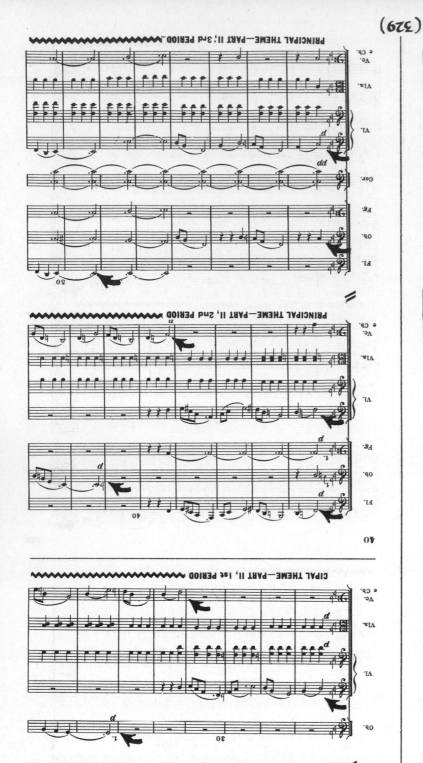
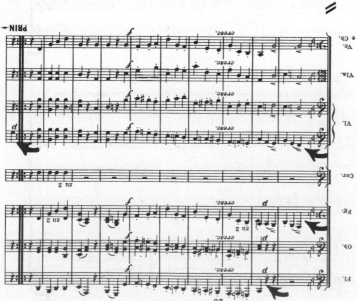
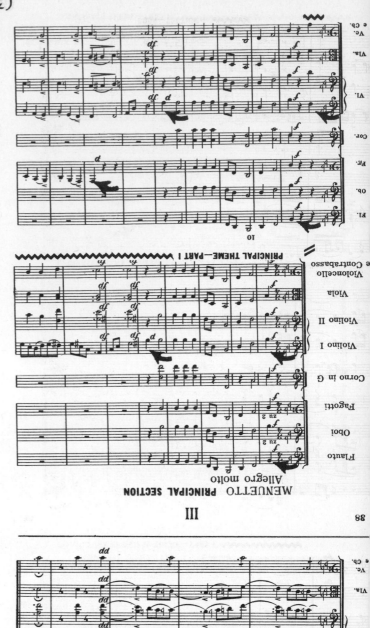
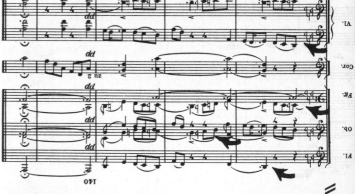
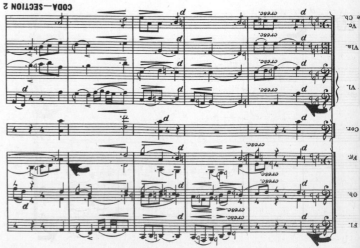

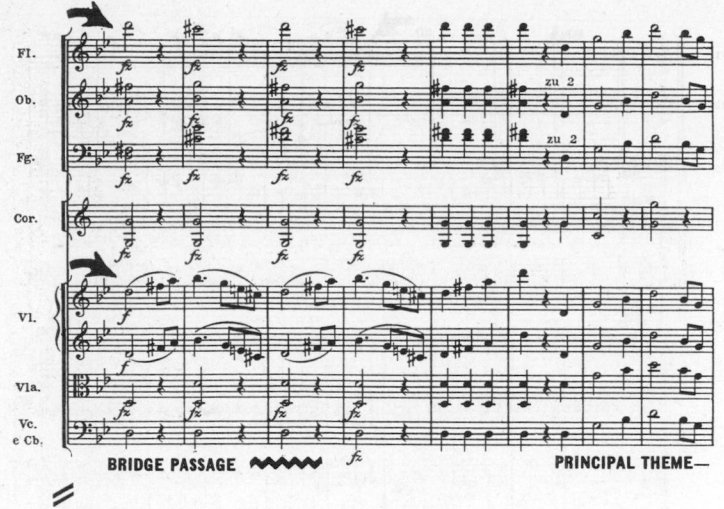

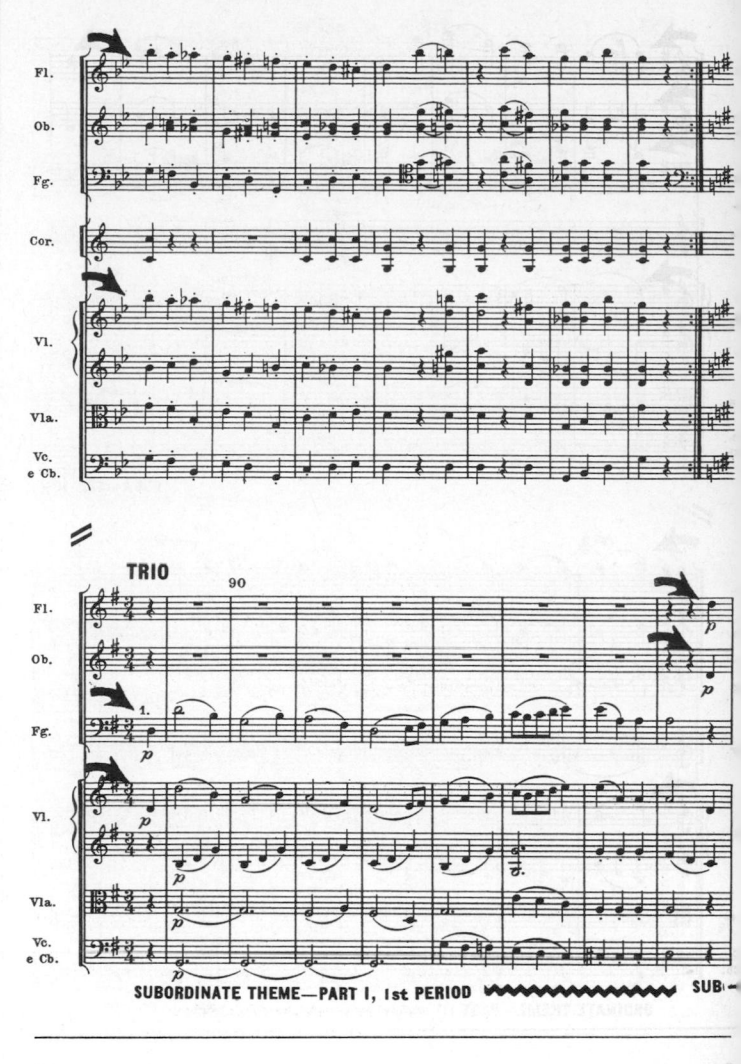

BRIDGE PASSAGE 〜〜〜〜 fz ... PRINCIPAL THEME—

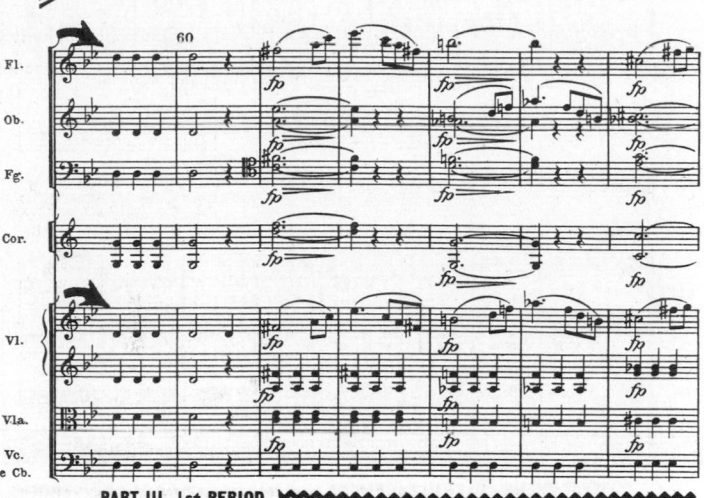

PART III, 1st PERIOD 〜〜〜〜〜〜〜〜〜〜〜〜〜〜

TRIO

SUBORDINATE THEME—PART I, 1st PERIOD 〜〜〜〜〜 SUB—

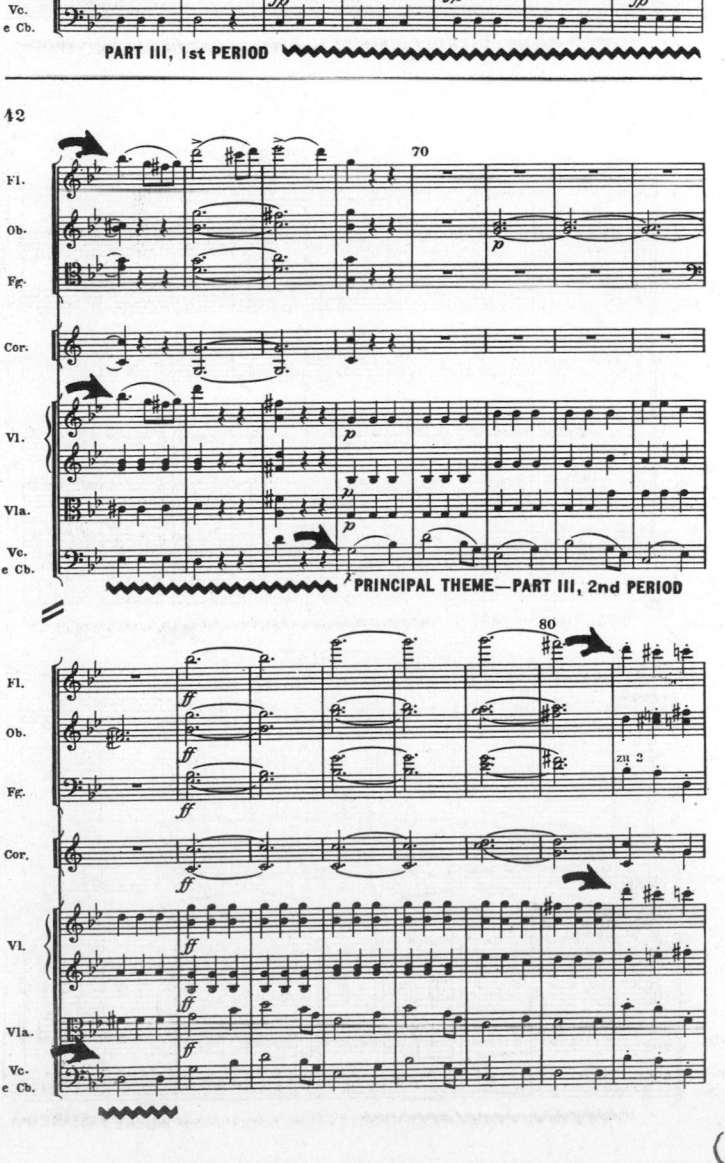

〜〜〜〜 PRINCIPAL THEME—PART III, 2nd PERIOD

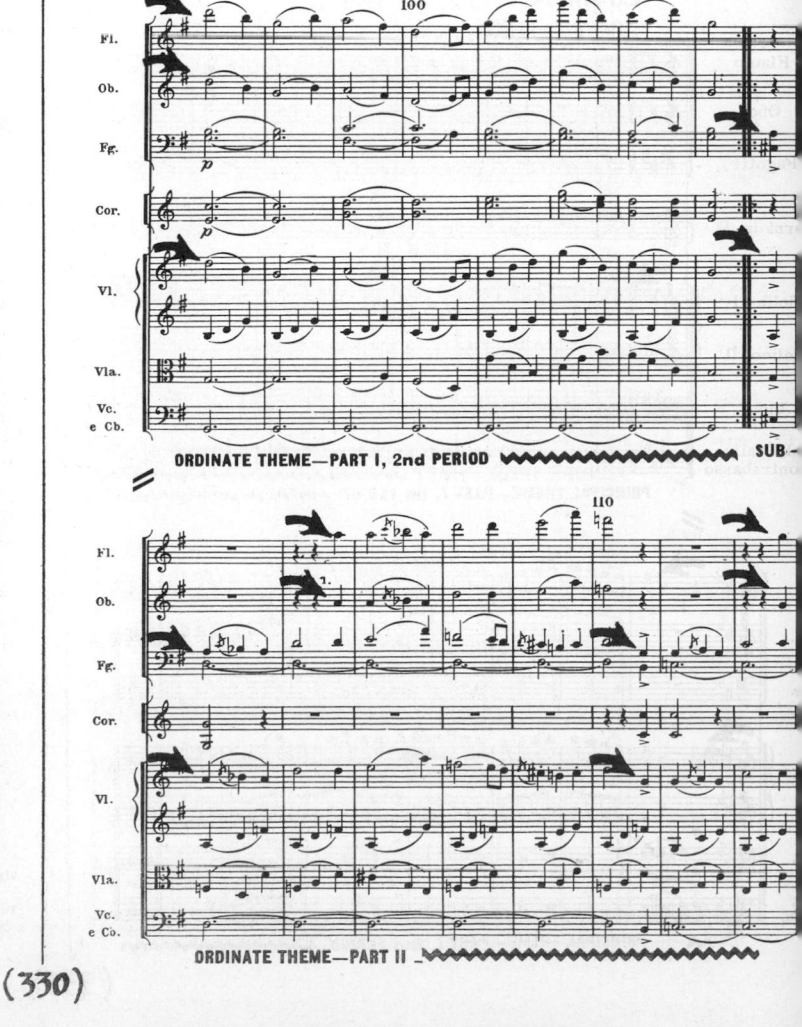

ORDINATE THEME—PART I, 2nd PERIOD 〜〜〜〜〜〜〜 SUB—

〜〜〜〜

ORDINATE THEME—PART II 〜〜〜〜

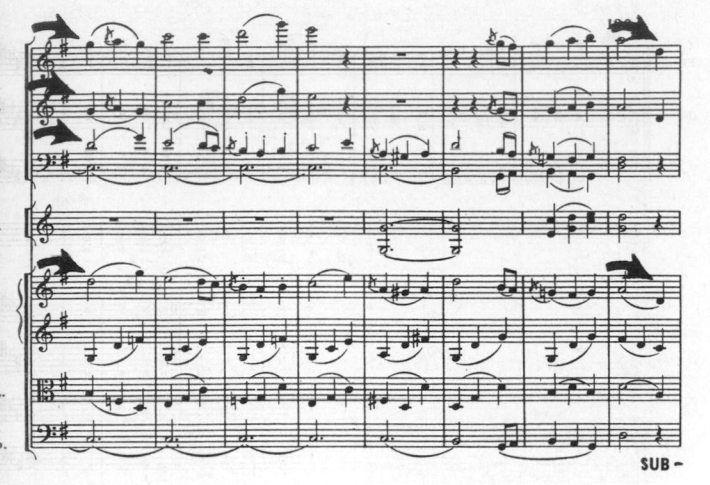

SUB -
ORDINATE THEME—PART III
Menuetto D. C.

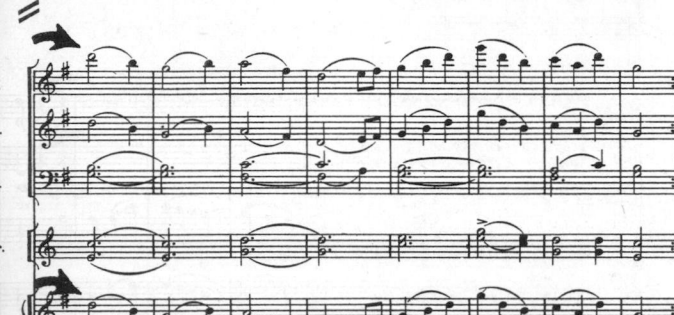

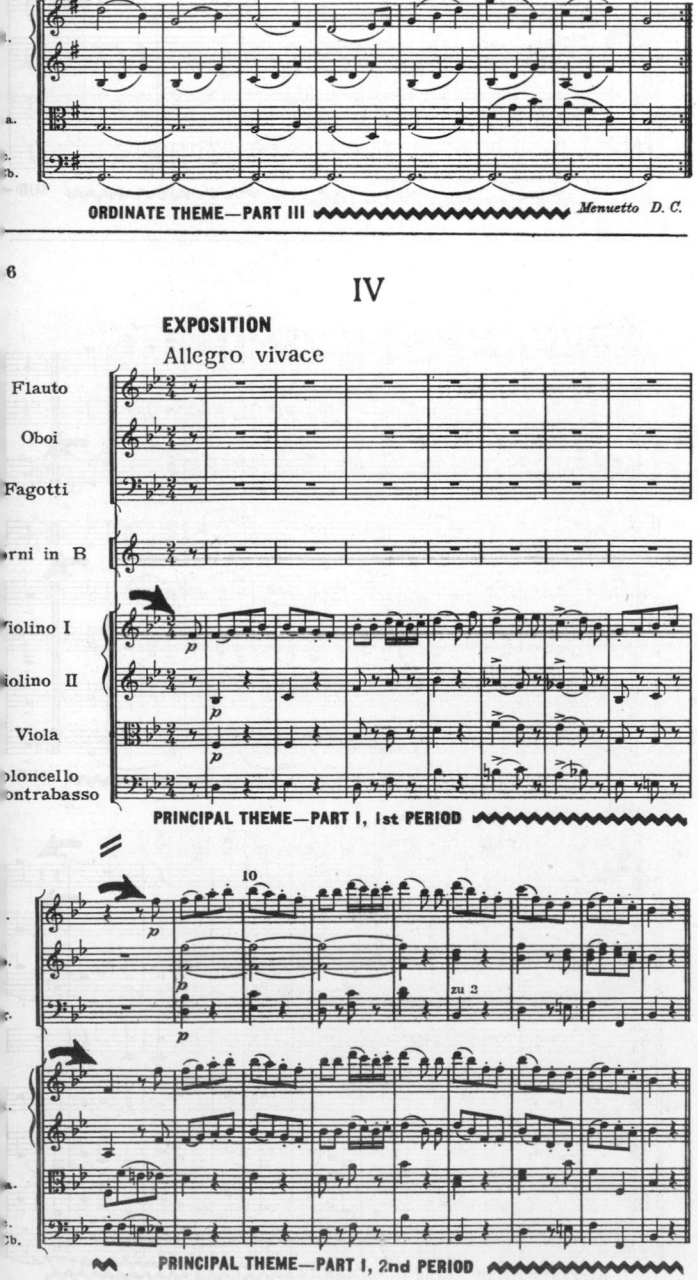

IV

EXPOSITION

Allegro vivace

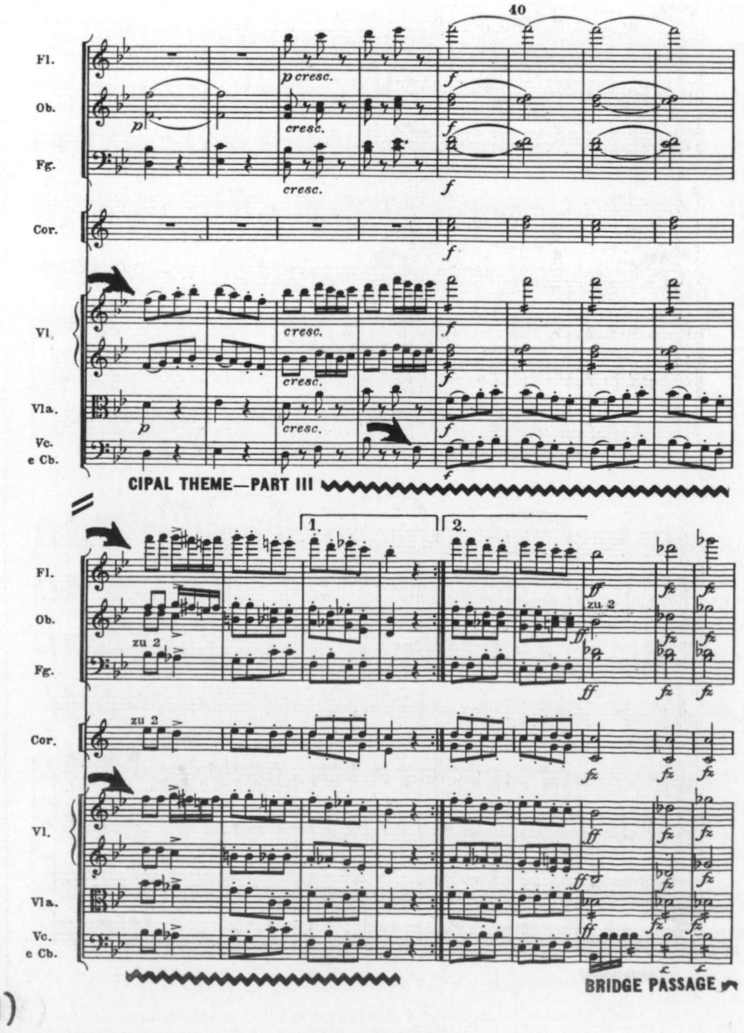

Flauto
Oboi
Fagotti
rni in B
Violino I
iolino II
Viola
loncello
ontrabasso
p
PRINCIPAL THEME—PART I, 1st PERIOD
10
zu 2
PRINCIPAL THEME—PART I, 2nd PERIOD

Fl.
Ob.
Fg.
Vl.
Vla.
Vc.
e Cb.
20
p
PRINCIPAL THEME—PART II, 1st PERIOD
30
Cor.
cresc.
f
zu 2
PRINCIPAL THEME—PART II, 2nd PERIOD
PRIN -

Fl.
Ob.
Fg.
Cor.
Vl.
Vla.
Vc.
e Cb.
40
p cresc.
cresc.
f
CIPAL THEME—PART III
1.
2.
zu 2
ff
fz
BRIDGE PASSAGE

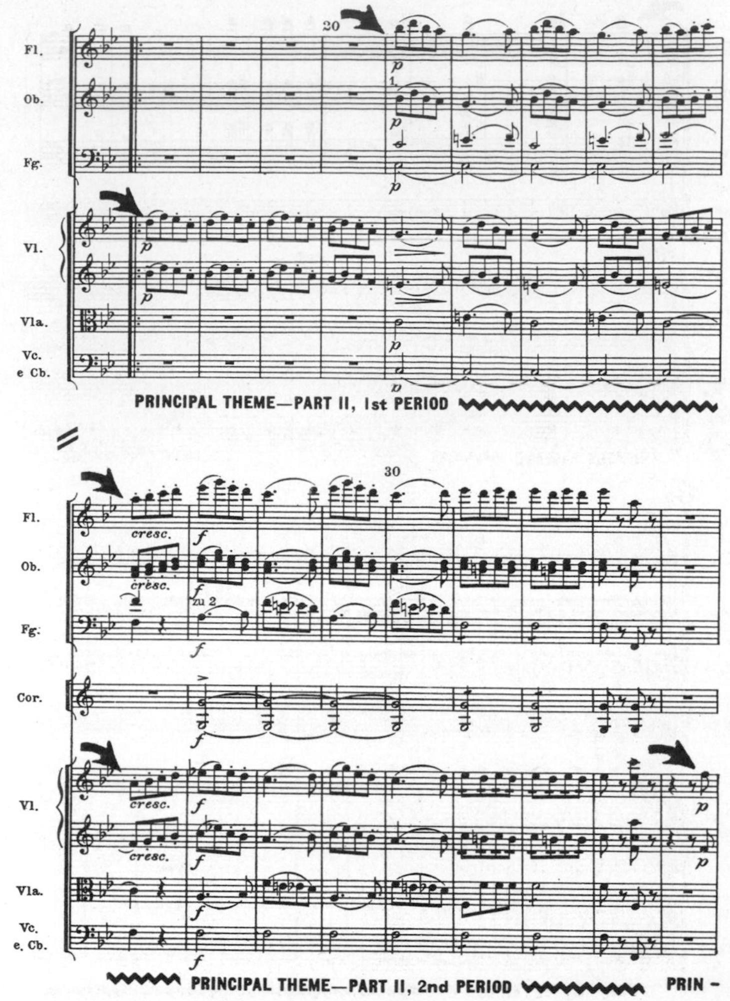

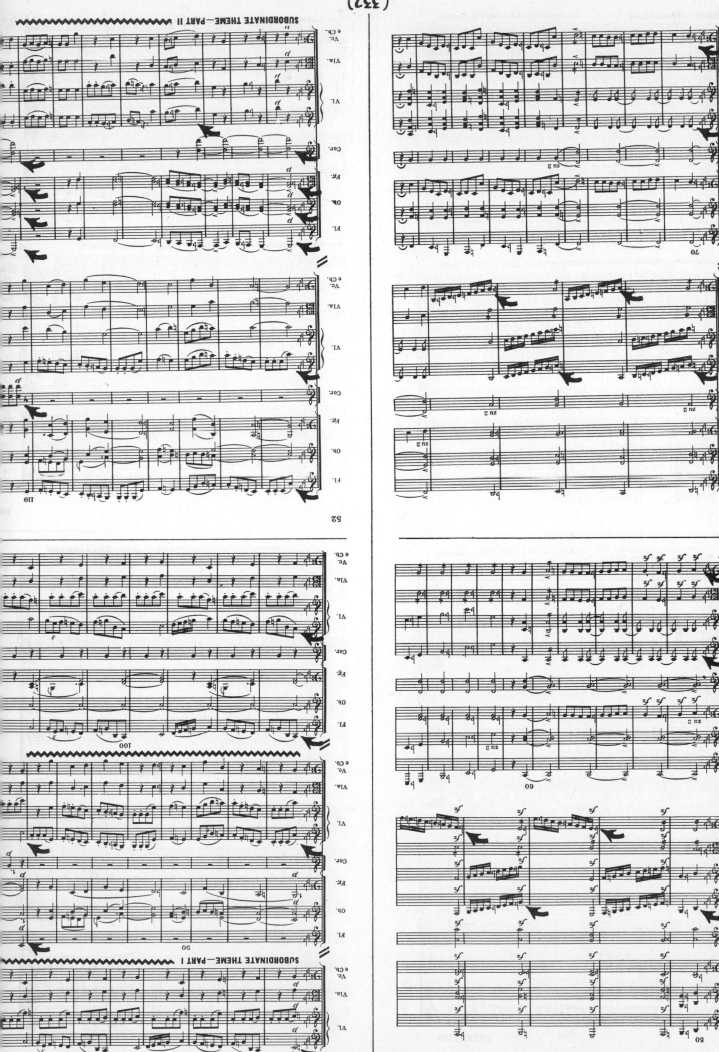

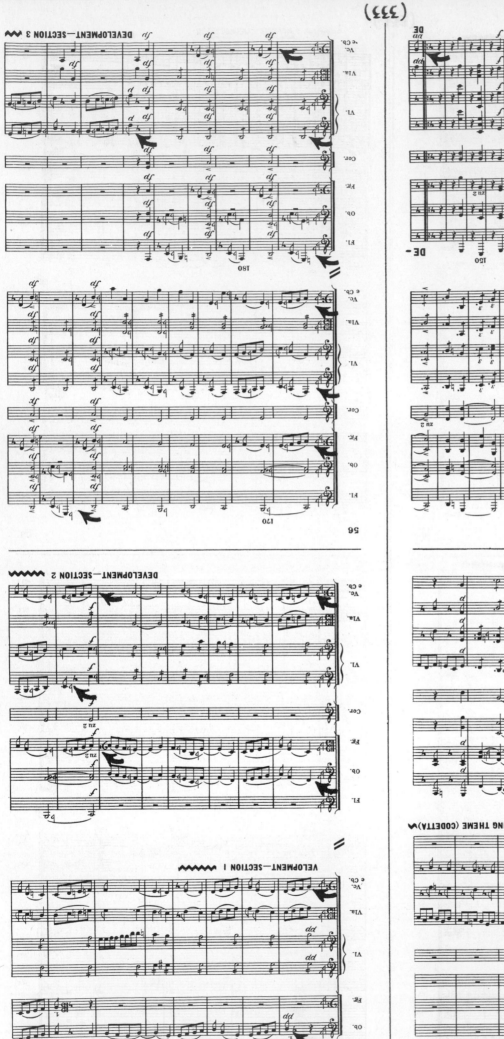
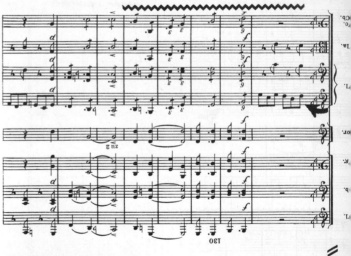

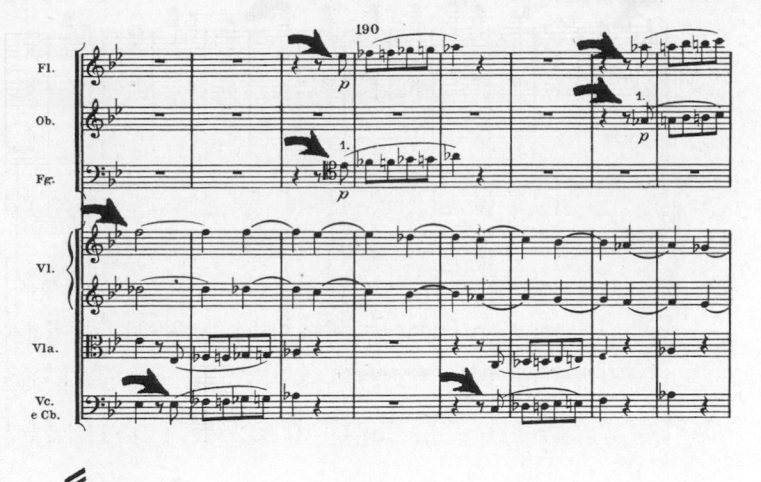

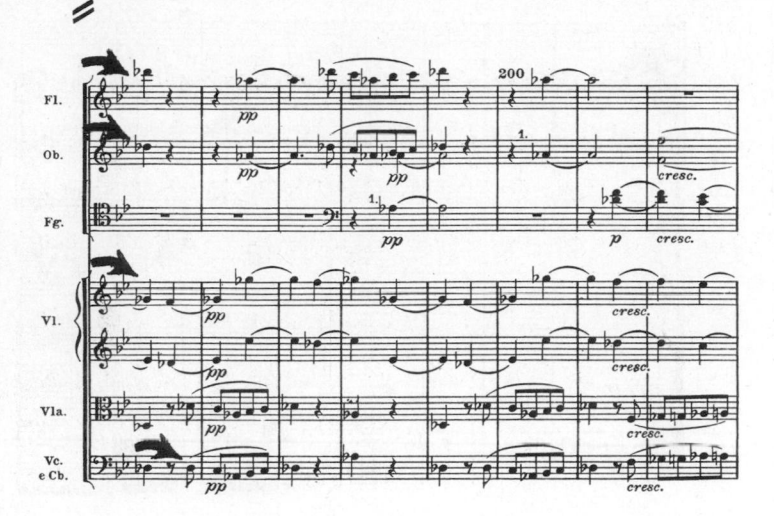

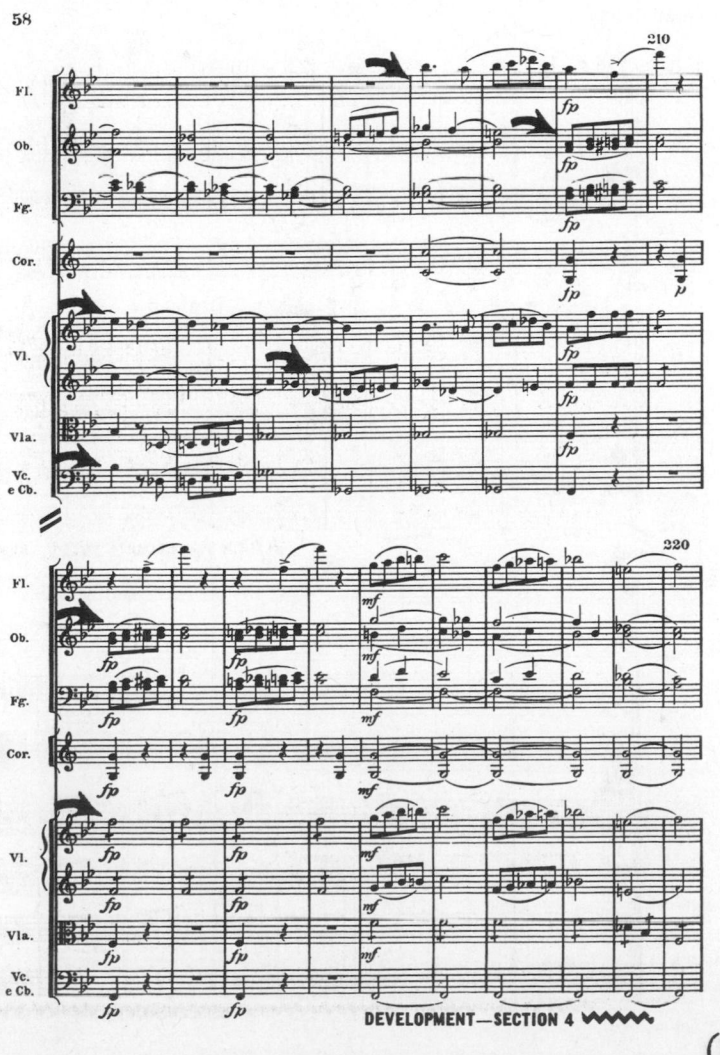

DEVELOPMENT—SECTION 4

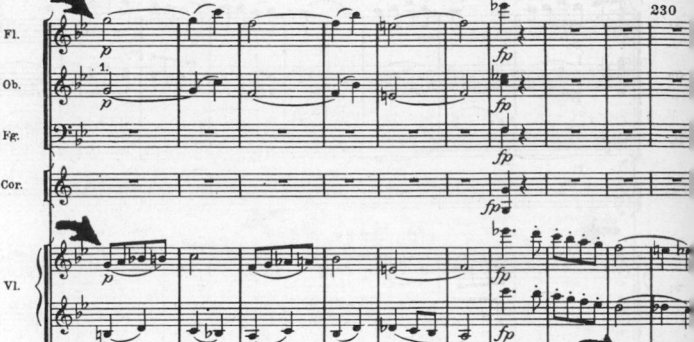

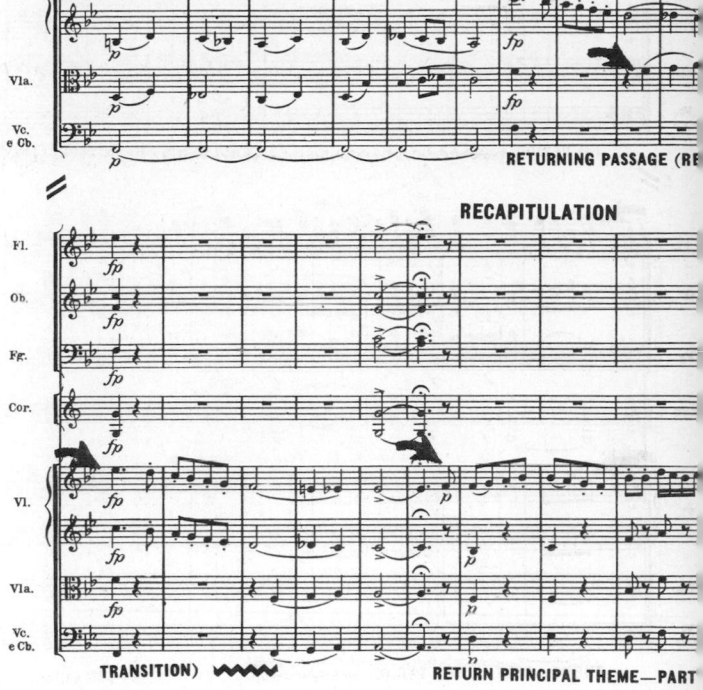

RETURNING PASSAGE (RE

RECAPITULATION

TRANSITION)   RETURN PRINCIPAL THEME—PART

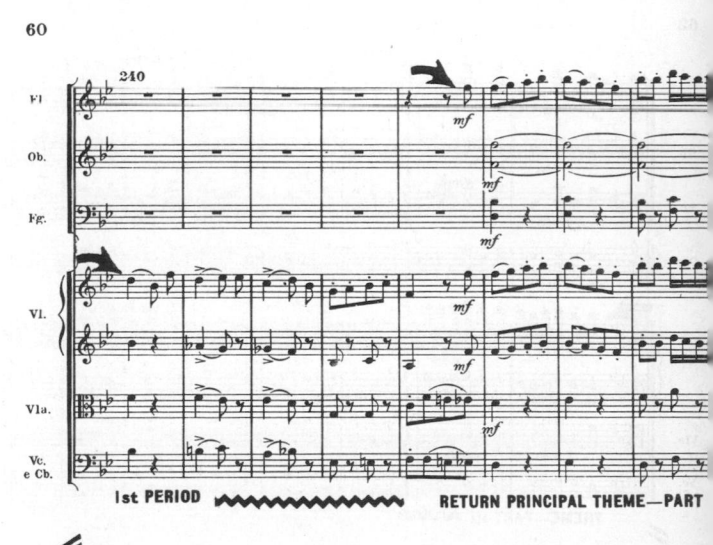

1st PERIOD   RETURN PRINCIPAL THEME—PART

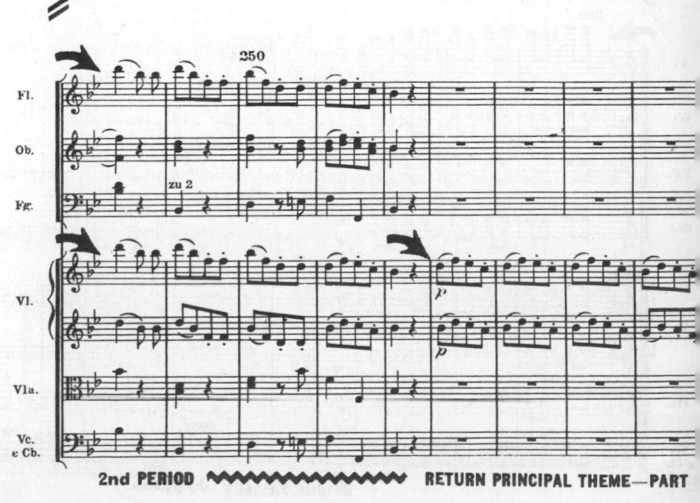

2nd PERIOD   RETURN PRINCIPAL THEME—PART

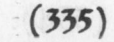

61

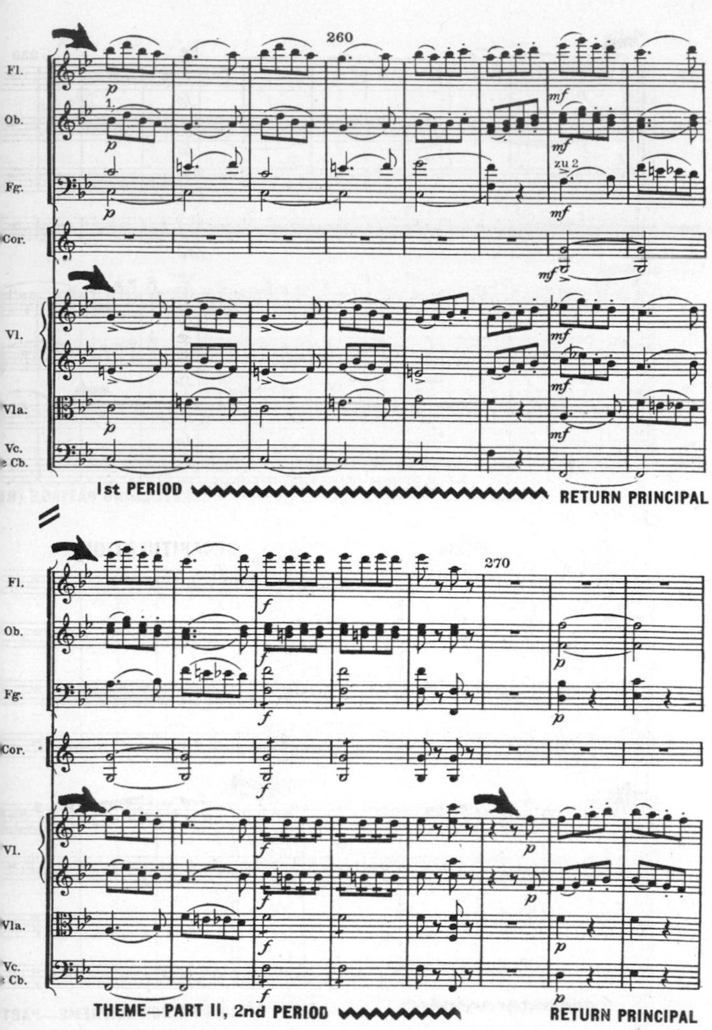

260

Fl.
Ob.
Fg.
Cor.
Vl.
Vla.
Vc. e Cb.

1st PERIOD 〜〜〜〜〜〜〜〜〜〜〜 RETURN PRINCIPAL

270

Fl.
Ob.
Fg.
Cor.
Vl.
Vla.
Vc. e Cb.

THEME—PART II, 2nd PERIOD 〜〜〜〜〜 RETURN PRINCIPAL

62

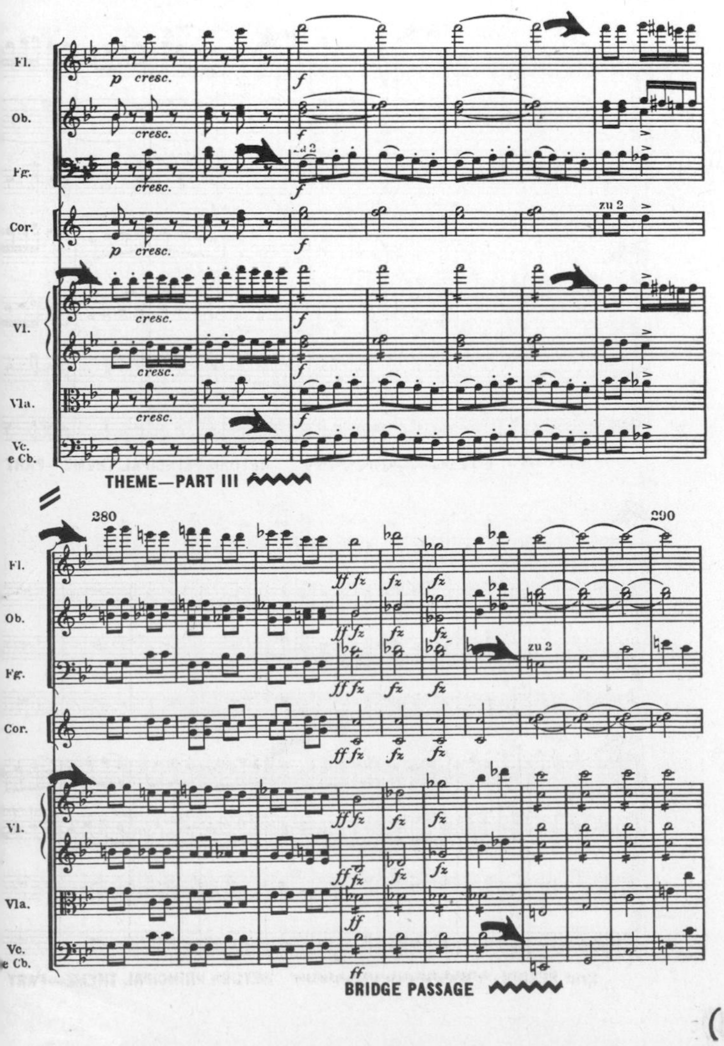

Fl.
Ob.
Fg.
Cor.
Vl.
Vla.
Vc. e Cb.

THEME—PART III 〜〜〜〜〜

280　　　　　　　　　　　　290

Fl.
Ob.
Fg.
Cor.
Vl.
Vla.
Vc. e Cb.

BRIDGE PASSAGE 〜〜〜〜〜

63

300

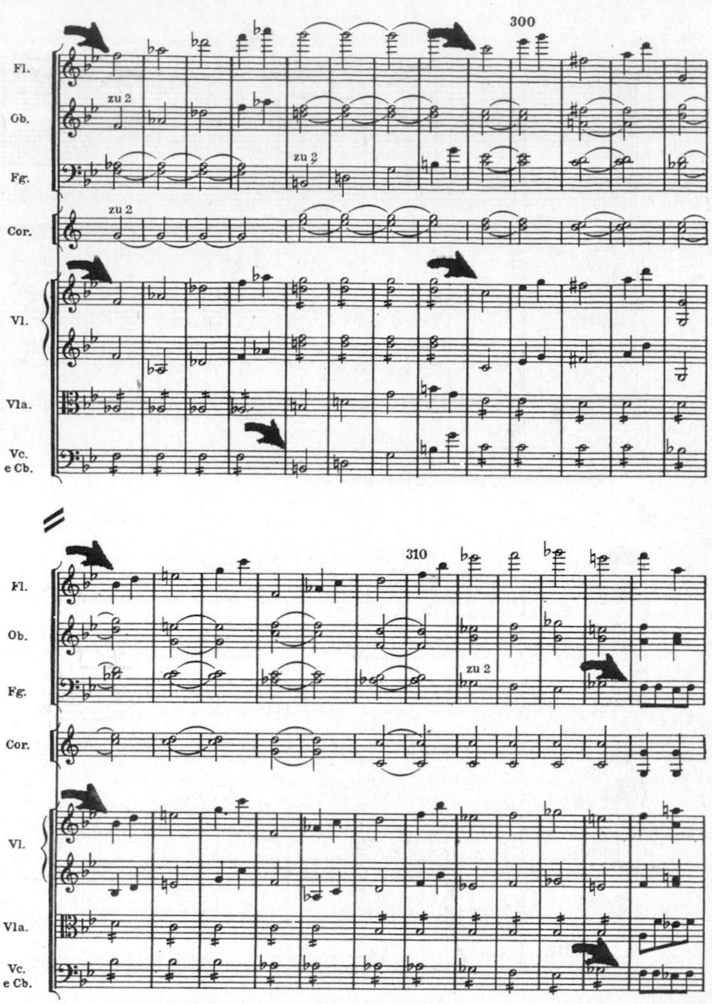

Fl.
Ob.
Fg.
Cor.
Vl.
Vla.
Vc. e Cb.

310

Fl.
Ob.
Fg.
Cor.
Vl.
Vla.
Vc. e Cb.

64

320

Fl.
Ob.
Fg.
Cor.
Vl.
Vla.
Vc. e Cb.

RETURN SUBORDINATE THEME—PART I

330

Ob.
Fg.
Vl.
Vla.
Vc. e Cb.

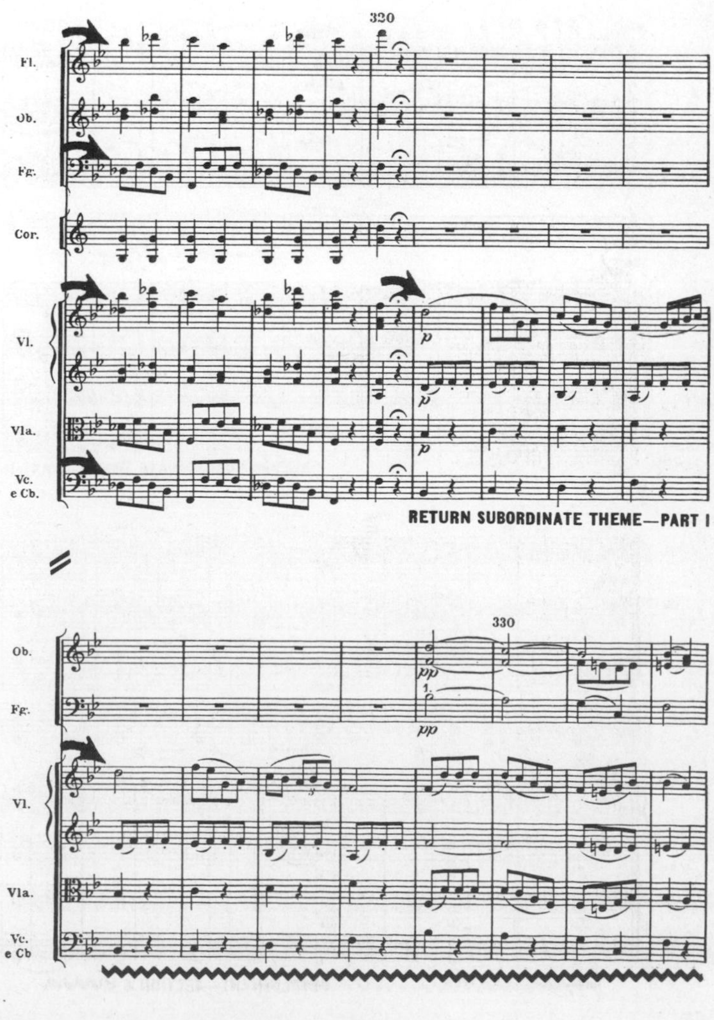

(335)

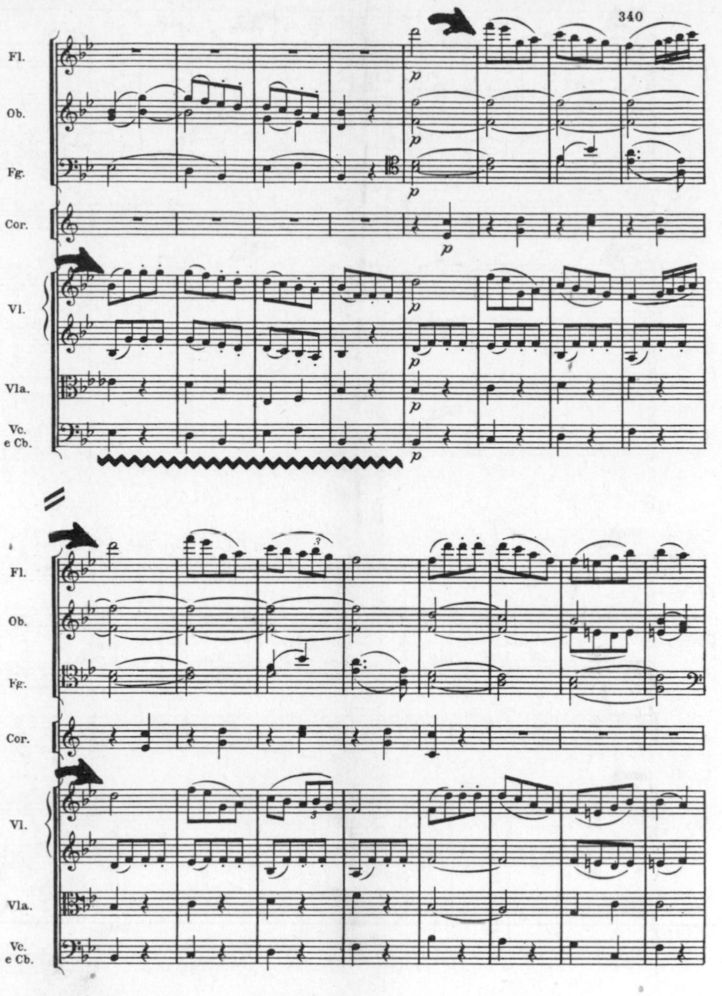
340
Fl.
Ob.
Fg.
Cor.
Vl.
Vla.
Vc. e Cb.

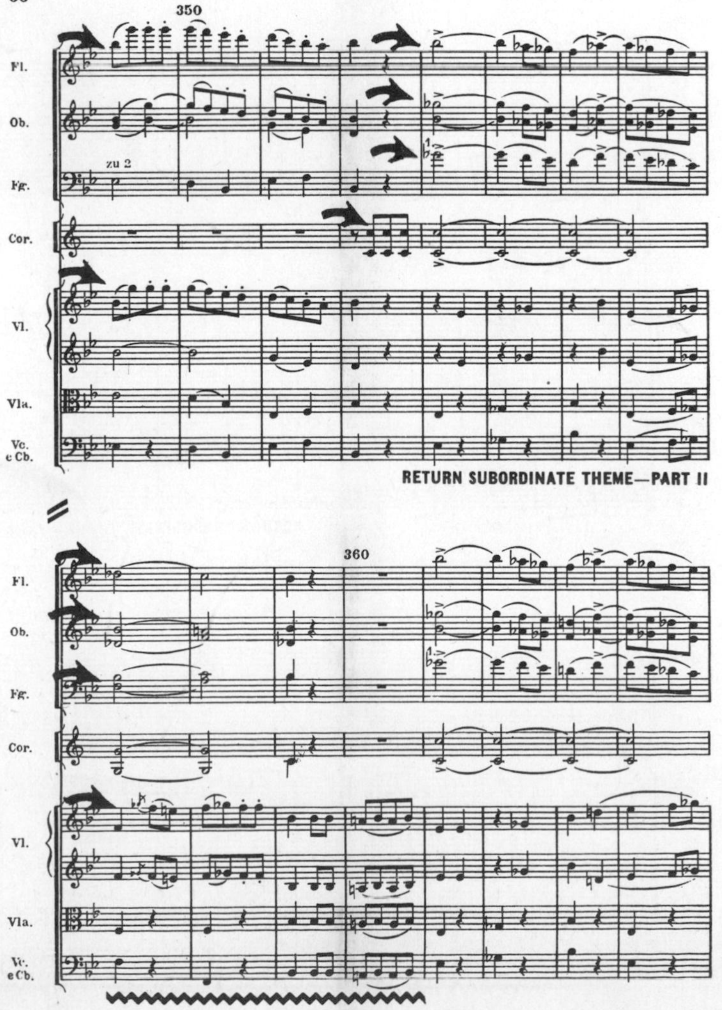
350
zu 2
Fl.
Ob.
Fg.
Cor.
Vl.
Vla.
Vc. e Cb.
RETURN SUBORDINATE THEME—PART II
360

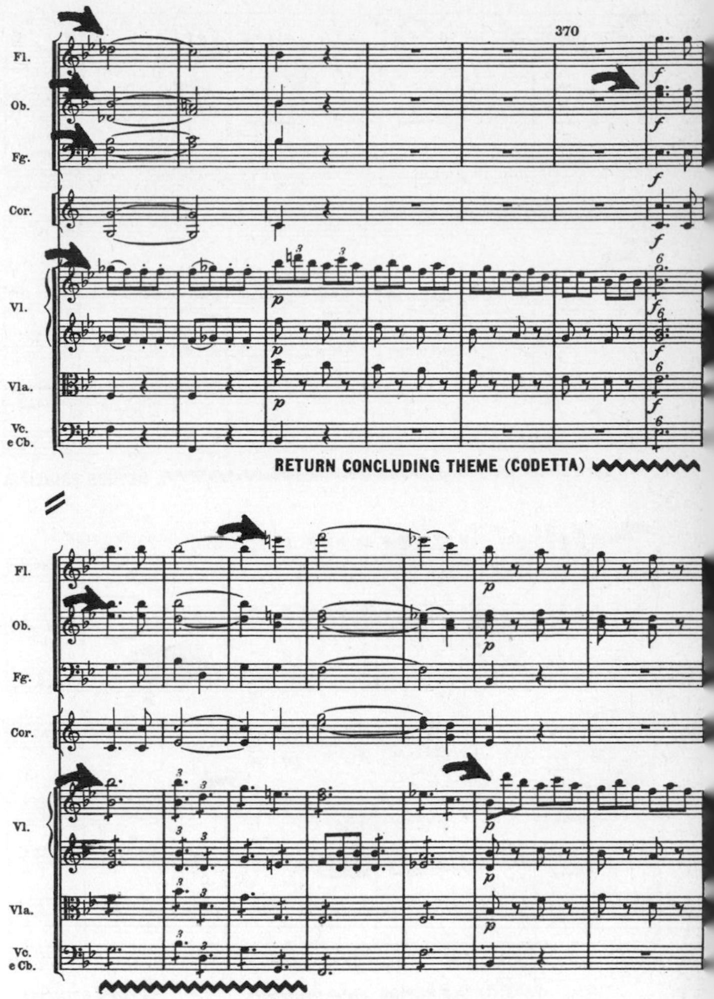
370
Fl.
Ob.
Fg.
Cor.
Vl.
Vla.
Vc. e Cb.
RETURN CONCLUDING THEME (CODETTA)

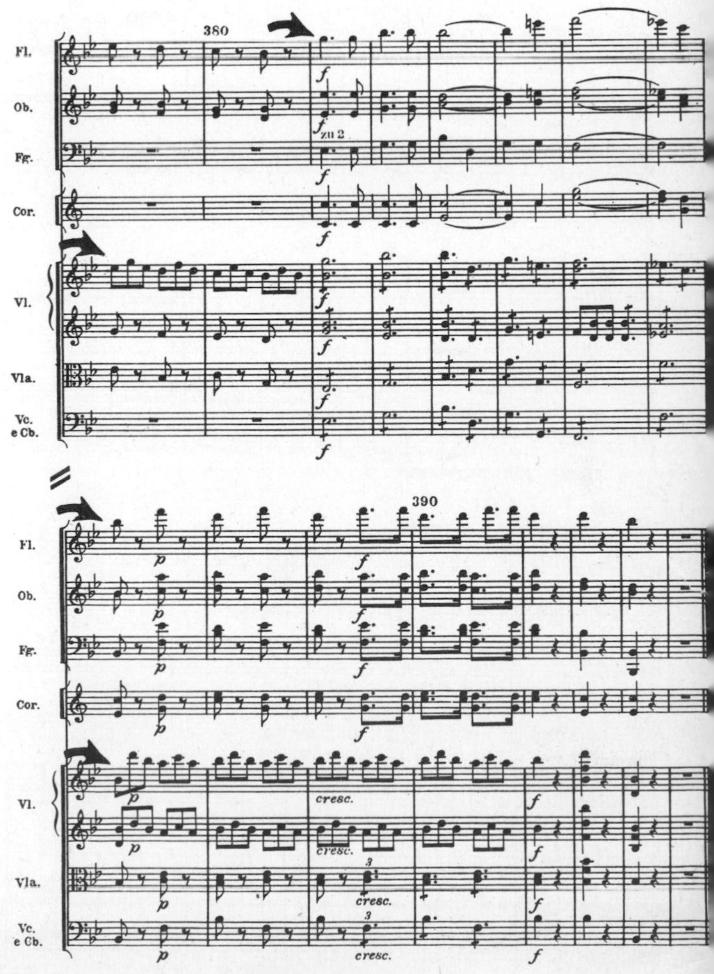
380
zu 2
Fl.
Ob.
Fg.
Cor.
Vl.
Vla.
Vc. e Cb.
390
cresc.

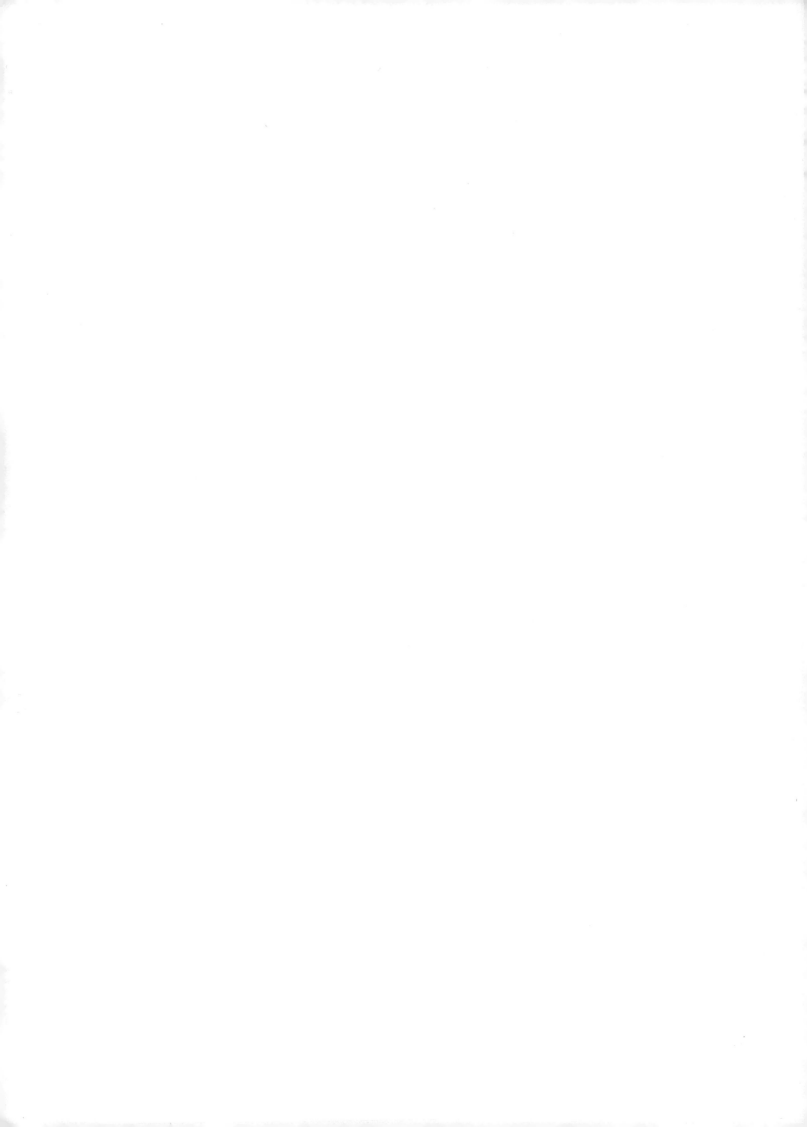